THE 'IDEAL'

DECIMAL COINAGE

RECKONER

Every Penny to £2 and every 5 pence thereafter to £9

Showing at a glance:—
the value of any number of articles from $\frac{1}{10}$ to 20,000;
also Tables of Percentage, Interest, Wages,
per Ton, Cwt., Kilo, Metric Conversion Tables, &c.

BY

R. M. G. INGLIS

———————

GALL & INGLIS (RECKONERS) LTD.
12 Newington Road, Edinburgh, 9
13 Henrietta Street, London, W.C. 2

85248 020 2

Made and Printed in Great Britain by
NEILL & CO. LTD., EDINBURGH
and
MARTINS LTD., BERWICK

PREFACE

This Reckoner is the Decimal Coinage equivalent of the Sterling Express Ready Reckoner of which over 3 million copies have been sold in the last 70 years.

Full explanations of its many uses for different bases of calculation are given on the next and succeeding pages.

CONTENTS

DECIMAL COINAGE RECKONER EXPLANATIONS

Fractions of a penny ($\frac{1}{4}$, $\frac{1}{2}$, $\frac{3}{4}$) are given solely to facilitate valuation of the penny up or down as may be desired, and for *true valuation* when addition of two or more values has to be made.

SECTION I.—READY RECKONER.

INVOICING.

(i) *At so much each per article or unit of weight or measurement.* Turn to the page headed by the Cost. The black columnar figures represent numbers of articles or units of weight or measurement; the light column figures represent the total cost.

Example. 121 articles @ 77 pence each = £93 17p.

121 Lbs./Cwts./Tons/Kilos/Feet/Yards/Sq. Ft./Sq. Yds. @ 77 pence per Lb. (or per any of the above or any unit of weight or measurement) = £93 17p.

(ii) *At per Lb.* Turn to the page headed by the required cost per lb.; the figures opposite the black columnar figures throughout the page represent the value of any number of lbs.; the figures in the "Sixteenths Box" at the foot of the page give oz. values. The equivalent rate per Cwt. and per Ton are those shown at 112 and 2240 respectively.

Example: 107 lbs.@ 77 pence per lb. = £82 39p.
13 ozs. @ 77 pence per lb. = 62½p.

(iii) *At per foot.* Turn to the page headed by the required cost per foot; the "Twelfths Box" at the foot of the page indicates the values for inches.

Example: 86 ft. @ 54 pence per foot = £46 44p.
11 inches @ 21½ pence per foot = 19¾p.

The cost per yard is the figure opposite black columnar figure 3, in this case £1 62p.

(iv) *Wages at per hour.* Turn to the page headed by the required rate per hour; hourly values are given by the figures opposite the black columnar figures. The "Twelfths Box" at the foot of the page gives 5 minute values, the "Twentieths Box" 3 minute values.

Example: 37 hrs. @ 93 pence per hr. = £34 41p
43 hrs. 40 min. = £40 61p
17 hrs. 33 min. = £16 32¼p.

At per week of so many hours. Turn to the page at which the required rate per week appears opposite the black marginal figures representing the basic number of hours per week. The figures on that page represent the values per hour. The "Twelfths Box" at the foot of the page gives 5 minute values, the "Twentieths Box" 3 minute values.

Example: 23 hrs. @ £30 80p per 40 hr. week.

£30 80p appears opposite black marginal figure 40 on page headed 77 pence.

$$23 \text{ hrs.} = £17 \ 71p$$
$$43 \text{ hrs. } 40 \text{ mins.} = £33 \ 62\tfrac{1}{4}p$$
$$17 \text{ hrs. } 33 \text{ mins.} = £13 \ 59\tfrac{1}{4}p$$

(v) *At per Ton.* (See also *per Ton and Cwt. Tables in Section IV.*) For prices per Ton below £2 use the Reckoner as (i) above; the black marginal figures represent the number of Tons.

Example: 44 Tons @ 63 pence per Ton = £27 72p.

The "Twentieths Box" at the foot of each page gives the Cwt. values.

13 Cwts. @ 63 pence per Ton = 41p.

For prices above £2 turn to the page which at the columnar black figure of 2240 shows the required (or nearest thereto) price per Ton. The black columnar figures represent the value for each Lb. at this rate. The page heading gives the cost per Lb.; the figure at black columnar figure 112 gives the cost per Cwt.

Examples: 73 Lbs. @ £481 60p per Ton.

£481 60p appears at 2240 on the page headed 21½p;
$$73 \text{ Lbs.} = £15 \ 69\tfrac{1}{2}p.$$

The cost per Lb. at this rate is 21½p; the cost per Cwt. is £24 8p.

(vi) *At per Cwt.* (See also *per Cwt. Tables in Section IV.*) For prices per Cwt. below £2 use the Reckoner as (i) above. The black columnar figures represent the number of Cwts.

Example: 76 Cwts. @ 37 pence per Cwt. = £28 12p.

The equivalent rate per Ton is that shown at columnar figure 20.

For prices per Cwt. above £2 turn to the page which at the black columnar figure of 112 shows the required (or nearest thereto) price per Cwt. The figures opposite the black columnar figures throughout the page represent the value for each Lb.; the page heading giving the cost per Lb.; the figure at 2240 giving the cost per Ton.

Example: 63 Lbs. @ £24 8p per Cwt.

£24 8p appears at 112 on the page headed 21½ pence;
thus 63 lbs. = £13 54½p.

WEIGHTS AND MEASURES.

Avoirdupois Weight is the British imperial weight.

The **Gallon**, in both Dry and Liquid measure, is 10 lb. of pure water at 62°F. (16⅔°C); it contains 277·463 cube inches (about 1/6th of a cube ft.), and is the cube of 6.52 ins.

The **Fluid Oz.** is 1 oz. Avoir. of water.

Avoirdupois Weight.

1 dram	(27¹¹⁄₃₂ grains)	1/16th oz.
16 drams	(437½ grains)	1 ounce
16 ounces	(7000 grains)	1 pound
14 pounds	(1/8th cwt.)	1 stone
28 pounds	(2 stones)	1 quarter
4 quarters	(112 lb. or 8 st.)	1 cwt.
20 cwt.	(2240 lb.)	1 'long' ton
1 short ton [U.S.] (2000 lb.)	0·893 ton
1 cental	(1/20th short ton)	100 lb.
1 metric ton (2204·6 lb.)	0·984 ton

Lineal Measure.

12 inches	.. ..	1 foot
3 feet	(36 inches)	1 yard
1760 yards	(5280 ft.)	1 statute mile
1 League, 3·356 miles; 1 Pace, 30 ins.;
1 Hand, 4 inches; 1 Mil, 1/1000th in.

Square or Land Measure.

144 square ins.	.. ..	1 sq. foot
9 sq. feet (1296 sq. ins.)	1 sq. yard

4840 sq. yards	.. ..	1 acre
640 acres	.. ..	1 sq. mile

Cubic or Solid Measure.

1728 cubic inches	..	1 cubic foot
27 cubic feet	..	1 cubic yard
40 cubic feet	..	1 shipping ton

Liquid and Dry Measure.

60 minims	..	1 fluid drachm
8 fluid drachms (480 min.)	1 fluid oz
8 ,, ounces ..	1 gill
4 gills	(20 fl. oz. or ⅛ gall.)	1 pint
2 pints	(40 fl. oz.)	1 quart
4 quarts	(160 fl. oz.)	1 gallon
2 gallons	(16 pints)	1 peck
4 pecks	(8 gallons)	1 bushel
8 bushels	(32 pecks)	1 quarter

Tablespoon, ½ fl. oz.; dessert, ¼ fl. oz.; teaspoon, ⅛ fluid oz.; tumbler, ½ pint; teacup, 3 oz. ; wineglass 2 oz.

U.S.A. liquid measures are ·8331, *the bushel and dry gallon* ·9688 *of British equivalent.*

Nautical Measure. 6 feet, 1 fathom ; 100 fathoms (600 feet), 1 cable ; 10 cables (6000 ft.), 1 sea mile (approx.), actual 6080 ft.=1.152 statute miles; 60 sea miles, 1 degree of latitude ; the knot (speeds only), and geographical mile = the sea mile.

Paper. 24 sheets, 1 quire ; 20 quires (480 sheets), 1 ream ; 21 quires, 1 504-sheet ream.

Timber. 165 cube feet = 1 Petrograd 'Standard.' 100 square feet = 1 square.

METRIC SYSTEM.
(*See also Tables, Section IV.*)

The **Metre** is 1/10-millionth of the surface-distance from the Equator to the Pole; the **gram**, a cube centimetre (millilitre); the **litre**, a cube decimetre, or 1000 cube centimetres, or 1 kilogram, of water at 39° F. The **are** is a square dekametre ; the **stere**, a cube metre (tonne, or kilolitre, or 1 million grams, of water)

Latin prefixes, deci-, centi-, milli- denote sub-divisions.

Greek prefixes, deka-, hekto-, kilo-, myria-, denote multiples.

*, †, ‡, §, show square and cube of length-measure with same sign.

Lineal :—	metres	Brit. equiv/ent
1 millimetre	₁₀₀₀	0·039 ins.
1 centimetre †	₁₀₀	0·394 ,,
1 decimetre †	₁₀	3·937 ,,
Metre*	1	39·370 ins.
1 dekametre §	10	32·808 feet
1 hektometre	100	328·084 ,,
1 kilometre	1000	1093·61 yds.
1 do. (abt ⅝ mile)		0·621 mile

Square :—	ares	Brit. equivalent
1 milliare	₁₀₀₀	1·076 sq.ft.
1 centiare*	₁₀₀	10·764 ,,
1 deciare	₁₀	107·639 ,,
Are §	1	119·599 sq.yds.
1 dekare	10	0·247 acre
1 hektare	100	2·4711 acres

Weight:—	grams	Brit. equivalent
1 milligram	₁₀₀₀	0·015 grain
1 centigram	₁₀₀	0·154 ,,
1 decigram	₁₀	1·543 ,,
Gram ‡ ..	1	15·432 grains
1 dekagram	10	5 drms. 18 grs
1 hektogram	100	3½ oz. 12 grs
1 kilogram †	1000	2 lb 3 oz 120 grs
1 myriagram	10,000	22 lb. 0⅜ oz.
1 Quintal	100,000	220·46 lbs.
1 **Tonne** or millier		0·984 ton, or
2204·622 lb. or 1·102 short tons.

Capacity:—	litres	Brit. equivalent
1 millilitre ‡	₁₀₀₀	16·9 minims
1 centilitre	₁₀₀	0·35 fluid oz
1 decilitre	₁₀	3·52 ,,
Litre† (1000 cc.)	1	·22 gall. (1·76 pts)
1 dekalitre	10	2 gall. 1·6 pts.
1 hektolitre	100	2¾ bush. (22 gls)
1 kilolitre*	1000	220·00 galls.

Cube :— 1 Stere* (cube metre) = 35·31 cube feet (metric ton, water); millistere† (·001 stere) = 61·02 c. in.

½ Pence ½ Pence

*Dozens.	£	P	Dozens.	£	P	Dozens	£	P	Dozens.	£	P		£	P
1	0	0½	51	0	25½	101	0	50½	152	0	76	310	1	55
2	0	1	52	0	26	102	0	51	154	0	77	320	1	60
3	0	1½	53	0	26½	103	0	51½	[13] 156	0	78	330	1	65
4	0	2	54	0	27	104	0	52	158	0	79	340	1	70
5	0	2½	55	0	27½	105	0	52½	160	0	80	350	1	75
6	0	3	56	0	28	106	0	53	162	0	81	360	1	80
7	0	3½	57	0	28½	107	0	53½	164	0	82	365	1	82½
8	0	4	58	0	29	[9] 108	0	54	166	0	83	370	1	85
9	0	4½	59	0	29½	109	0	54½	[14] 168	0	84	380	1	90
10	**0**	**5**	[5] **60**	**0**	**30**	**110**	**0**	**55**	170	0	85	390	1	95
*11	0	5½	61	0	30½	111	0	55½	172	0	86	400	2	0
* [1] 12	0	6	62	0	31	112	0	56	174	0	87	410	2	5
13	0	6½	63	0	31½	113	0	56½	175	0	87½	420	2	10
14	0	7	64	0	32	114	0	57	176	0	88	430	2	15
15	0	7½	65	0	32½	115	0	57½	178	0	89	440	2	20
16	0	8	66	0	33	116	0	58	[15] 180	0	90	450	2	25
17	0	8½	67	0	33½	117	0	58½	182	0	91	460	2	30
18	0	9	68	0	34	118	0	59	184	0	92	470	2	35
19	0	9½	69	0	34½	119	0	59½	186	0	93	480	2	40
20	**0**	**10**	**70**	**0**	**35**	**120**	**0**	**60**	188	0	94	490	2	45
21	0	10½	71	0	35½	121	0	60½	190	0	95	**500**	**2**	**50**
22	0	11	[6] 72	0	36	122	0	61	[18] 192	0	96	550	2	75
23	0	11½	73	0	36½	123	0	61½	194	0	97	600	3	00
[2] 24	0	12	74	0	37	124	0	62	196	0	98	650	3	25
25	0	12½	75	0	37½	125	0	62½	198	0	99	700	3	50
26	0	13	76	0	38	126	0	63	**200**	**1**	**0**	750	3	75
27	0	13½	77	0	38½	127	0	63½	[17] 204	1	2	800	4	0
28	0	14	78	0	39	128	0	64	205	1	2½	850	4	25
29	0	14½	79	0	39½	129	0	64½	210	1	5	900	4	50
30	**0**	**15**	**80**	**0**	**40**	**130**	**0**	**65**	215	1	7½	950	4	75
31	0	15½	81	0	40½	131	0	65½	[18] 216	1	8	**1000**	**5**	**0**
32	0	16	82	0	41	[11] 132	0	66	220	1	10	1016	5	8
33	0	16½	83	0	41½	133	0	66½	225	1	12½	1250	6	25
34	0	17	[7] 84	0	42	134	0	67	[19] 228	1	14	1500	7	50
35	0	17½	85	0	42½	135	0	67½	230	1	15	1728	8	64
[3] 36	0	18	86	0	43	136	0	68	235	1	17½	1750	8	75
37	0	18½	87	0	43½	137	0	68½	[20] 240	1	20	1760	8	80
38	0	19	88	0	44	138	0	69	245	1	22½	2000	10	0
39	0	19½	89	0	44½	139	0	69½	**250**	**1**	**25**	2240	11	20
40	**0**	**20**	**90**	**0**	**45**	**140**	**0**	**70**	255	1	27½	2500	12	50
41	0	20½	91	0	45½	141	0	70½	260	1	30	3000	15	0
42	0	21	92	0	46	142	0	71	265	1	32½	4000	20	0
43	0	21½	93	0	46½	143	0	71½	270	1	35	5000	25	0
44	0	22	94	0	47	[12] 144	0	72	275	1	37½	6000	30	0
45	0	22½	95	0	47½	145	0	72½	280	1	40	7000	35	0
46	0	23	[8] 96	0	48	146	0	73	285	1	42½	8000	40	0
47	0	23½	97	0	48½	147	0	73½	[24] 288	1	44	9000	45	0
[4] 48	0	24	98	0	49	148	0	74	290	1	45	10000	50	0
49	0	24½	99	0	49½	149	0	74½	295	1	47½	15000	75	0
50	**0**	**25**	**100**	**0**	**50**	**150**	**0**	**75**	**300**	**1**	**50**	20,000	100	0

Grosses.

	£	P
1.	0	72
2.	1	44
3.	2	16
4.	2	88
5.	3	60
6.	4	32
7.	5	4
8.	5	76
9.	6	48
10.	7	20
11.	7	92

Twelfths

		£	P
	1.		
⅙	2.	..	
	3.	0	0¼
⅓	4.	0	0¼
	5.	0	0¼
½	6.	0	0¼
	7.	0	0¼
⅔	8.	0	0¼
	9.	0	0½
⅚	10.	0	0½
	11.	0	0½

Twentieths

10ths		£	P	10ths		£	P
	1.	..			11.	0	0¼
·1	2.	..		·6	12.	0	0¼
	3.	..			13.	0	0¼
·2	4.	..		·7	14.	0	0¼
	5.	0	0¼		15.	0	0½
·3	6.	0	0¼	·8	16.	0	0½
	7.	0	0¼		17.	0	0½
·4	8.	0	0¼	·9	18.	0	0½
	9.	0	0¼		19.	0	0½
·5	10.	0	0¼		20.	0	0½

Sixteenths

		£	P			£	P
	1.	..			9.	0	0¼
⅛	2.	..		⅝	10.	0	0¼
	3.	..			11.	0	0¼
¼	4.	0	0¼	¾	12.	0	0½
	5.	0	0¼		13.	0	0½
⅜	6.	0	0¼	⅞	14.	0	0½
	7.	0	0¼		15.	0	0½
½	8.	0	0¼				

1 Pence

No.	£	P		No.	£	P		No.	£	P		No.	£	P		No.	£	P
1	0	1		51	0	51		101	1	1		152	1	52		310	3	10
2	0	2		52	0	52		102	1	2		154	1	54		320	3	20
*Dozens 3	0	3		Dozens 53	0	53		Dozens 103	1	3		¹³ 156	1	56		330	3	30
4	0	4		54	0	54		104	1	4		158	1	58		340	3	40
5	0	5		55	0	55		105	1	5		160	1	60		350	3	50
6	0	6		56	0	56		106	1	6		162	1	62		360	3	60
7	0	7		57	0	57		107	1	7		164	1	64		365	3	65
8	0	8		58	0	58		⁹ 108	1	8		166	1	66		370	3	70
9	0	9		59	0	59		109	1	9		¹⁴ 168	1	68		380	3	80
10	0	10		⁵ 60	0	60		110	1	10		170	1	70		390	3	90
*11	0	11		61	0	61		111	1	11		172	1	72		400	4	0
¹12	0	12		62	0	62		112	1	12		174	1	74		410	4	10
13	0	13		63	0	63		113	1	13		175	1	75		420	4	20
14	0	14		64	0	64		114	1	14		176	1	76		430	4	30
15	0	15		65	0	65		115	1	15		178	1	78		440	4	40
16	0	16		66	0	66		116	1	16		¹⁵ 180	1	80		450	4	50
17	0	17		67	0	67		117	1	17		182	1	82		460	4	60
18	0	18		68	0	68		118	1	18		184	1	84		470	4	70
19	0	19		69	0	69		119	1	19		186	1	86		480	4	80
20	0	20		70	0	70		120	1	20		188	1	88		490	4	90
21	0	21		71	0	71		121	1	21		190	1	90		500	5	0
22	0	22		⁶ 72	0	72		122	1	22		¹⁶ 192	1	92		550	5	50
23	0	23		73	0	73		123	1	23		194	1	94		600	6	0
²24	0	24		74	0	74		124	1	24		196	1	96		650	6	50
25	0	25		75	0	75		125	1	25		198	1	98		700	7	0
26	0	26		76	0	76		126	1	26		200	2	0		750	7	50
27	0	27		77	0	77		127	1	27		¹⁷ 204	2	4		800	8	0
28	0	28		78	0	78		128	1	28		205	2	5		850	8	50
29	0	29		79	0	79		129	1	29		210	2	10		900	9	0
30	0	30		80	0	80		130	1	30		215	2	15		950	9	50
31	0	31		81	0	81		131	1	31		¹⁸ 216	2	16		1000	10	0
32	0	32		82	0	82		132	1	32		220	2	20		1016	10	16
33	0	33		83	0	83		¹¹ 132	1	32		225	2	25		1250	12	50
34	0	34		⁷ 84	0	84		133	1	33		¹⁹ 228	2	28		1500	15	0
35	0	35		85	0	85		134	1	34		230	2	30		1728	17	28
³36	0	36		86	0	86		135	1	35		235	2	35		1750	17	50
37	0	37		87	0	87		136	1	36		²⁰ 240	2	40		1760	17	60
38	0	38		88	0	88		137	1	37		245	2	45		2000	20	0
39	0	39		89	0	89		138	1	38		250	2	50		2240	22	40
40	0	40		90	0	90		139	1	39		255	2	55		2500	25	0
41	0	41		91	0	91		140	1	40		260	2	60		3000	30	0
42	0	42		92	0	92		141	1	41		265	2	65		4000	40	0
43	0	43		93	0	93		142	1	42		270	2	70		5000	50	0
44	0	44		94	0	94		143	1	43		275	2	75		6000	60	0
45	0	45		95	0	95		¹²144	1	44		280	2	80		7000	70	0
46	0	46		⁸ 96	0	96		145	1	45		285	2	85		8000	80	0
47	0	47		97	0	97		146	1	46		²⁴ 288	2	88		9000	90	0
⁴48	0	48		98	0	98		147	1	47		290	2	90		10,000	100	0
49	0	49		99	0	99		148	1	48		295	2	95		15,000	150	0
50	0	50		100	1	0		149	1	49		300	3	0		20,000	200	0
								150	1	50								

Grosses			Twelfths			10ths / Twentieths				Sixteenths				
1.	1	44	1.	0	0	1.	..		11.	0	0½	1.	0	0¼	9.	0	0½
2.	2	88	½ 2.	0	0¼	·1 2.	0	0	·6 12.	0	0½	2.	0	0¼	10.	0	0½
3.	4	32	3.	0	0¼	3.	0	0¼	13.	0	0½	3.	0	0¼	11.	0	0¾
4.	5	76	¼ 4.	0	0½	·2 4.	0	0¼	·7 14.	0	0¾	4.	0	0¼	12.	0	0¾
5.	7	20	5.	0	0½	5.	0	0¼	15.	0	0¾	5.	0	0¼	13.	0	0¾
6.	8	64	⅙ 6.	0	0¾	·3 6.	0	0¼	·8 16.	0	0¾	6.	0	0¼	14.	0	1
7.	10	8	7.	0	0¾	7.	0	0½	17.	0	0¾	·6 6.	0	0¼	15.	0	1
8.	11	52	⅜ 8.	0	0¾	·4 8.	0	0½	·9 18.	0	1	7.	0	0½			
9.	12	96	9.	0	0¾	9.	0	0½	19.	0	1	·8 8.	0	0½			
10.	14	40	⁵⁄₁₂ 10.	0	0¾	·5 10.	0	0½	20.	0	1						
11.	15	84	11.	0	1												

Doz.		£	P	Doz.		£	P	Doz.		£	P	Doz.		£	P		£	P
	1	0	1½		51	0	76½		101	1	51½		152	2	28	310	4	65
	2	0	3		52	0	78		102	1	53		154	2	31	320	4	80
	3	0	4½		53	0	79½		103	1	54½	13	156	2	34	330	4	95
	4	0	6		54	0	81		104	1	56		158	2	37	340	5	10
	5	0	7½		55	0	82½		105	1	57½		160	2	40	350	5	25
*	6	0	9		56	0	84		106	1	59		162	2	43	360	5	40
	7	0	10½		57	0	85½		107	1	60½		164	2	46	365	5	47½
	8	0	12		58	0	87	9	108	1	62		166	2	49	370	5	55
	9	0	13½		59	0	88½		109	1	63½	14	168	2	52	380	5	70
	10	**0**	**15**	5	**60**	**0**	**90**		**110**	**1**	**65**		170	2	55	390	5	85
*	11	0	16½		61	0	91½		111	1	66½		172	2	58	400	6	0
1	12	0	18		62	0	93		112	1	68		174	2	61	410	6	15
	13	0	19½		63	0	94½		113	1	69½		175	2	62½	420	6	30
	14	0	21		64	0	96		114	1	71		176	2	64	430	6	45
	15	0	22½		65	0	97½		115	1	72½		178	2	67	440	6	60
	16	0	24		66	0	99		116	1	74	15	180	2	70	450	6	75
	17	0	25½		67	1	0½		117	1	75½		182	2	73	460	6	90
	18	0	27		68	1	2		118	1	77		184	2	76	470	7	5
	19	0	28½		69	1	3½		119	1	78½		186	2	79	480	7	20
	20	**0**	**30**		**70**	**1**	**5**		**120**	**1**	**80**		188	2	82	490	7	35
	21	0	31½		71	1	6½		121	1	81½		190	2	85	**500**	**7**	**50**
	22	0	33	6	72	1	8		122	1	83	16	192	2	88	550	8	25
	23	0	34½		73	1	9½		123	1	84½		194	2	91	600	9	0
2	24	0	36		74	1	11		124	1	86		196	2	94	650	9	75
	25	0	37½		75	1	12½		125	1	87½		198	2	97	700	10	50
	26	0	39		76	1	14		126	1	89		**200**	**3**	**0**	750	11	25
	27	0	40½		77	1	15½		127	1	90½	17	204	3	6	800	12	0
	28	0	42		78	1	17		128	1	92		205	3	7½	850	12	75
	29	0	43½		79	1	18½		129	1	93½		210	3	15	900	13	50
	30	**0**	**45**		**80**	**1**	**20**		**130**	**1**	**95**		215	3	22½	950	14	25
	31	0	46½		81	1	21½		131	1	96½	18	216	3	24	**1000**	**15**	**0**
	32	0	48		82	1	23	11	132	1	98		220	3	30	1016	15	24
	33	0	49½		83	1	24½		133	1	99½		225	3	37½	1250	18	75
	34	0	51	7	84	1	26		134	2	1	19	228	3	42	1500	22	50
	35	0	52½		85	1	27½		135	2	2½		230	3	45	1728	25	92
3	36	0	54		86	1	29		136	2	4		235	3	52½	1750	26	25
	37	0	55½		87	1	30½		137	2	5½	20	240	3	60	1760	26	40
	38	0	57		88	1	32		138	2	7		245	3	67½	2000	30	0
	39	0	58½		89	1	33½		139	2	8½		**250**	**3**	**75**	2240	33	60
	40	**0**	**60**		**90**	**1**	**35**		**140**	**2**	**10**		255	3	82½	2500	37	50
	41	0	61½		91	1	36½		141	2	11½		260	3	90	3000	45	0
	42	0	63		92	1	38		142	2	13		265	3	97½	4000	60	0
	43	0	64½		93	1	39½		143	2	14½		270	4	5	**5000**	**75**	**0**
	44	0	66		94	1	41	12	144	2	16		275	4	12½	6000	90	0
	45	0	67½		95	1	42½		145	2	17½		280	4	20	7000	105	0
	46	0	69	8	96	1	44		146	2	19		285	4	27½	8000	120	0
	47	0	70½		97	1	45½		147	2	20½	24	288	4	32	9000	135	0
4	48	0	72		98	1	47		148	2	22		290	4	35	10,000	150	0
	49	0	73½		99	1	48½		149	2	23½		295	4	42½	15,000	225	0
	50	**0**	**75**		**100**	**1**	**50**		**150**	**2**	**25**		**300**	**4**	**50**	20,000	300	0

Grosses

1.	2	16
2.	4	32
3.	6	48
4.	8	64
5.	10	80
6.	12	96
7.	15	12
8.	17	28
9.	19	44
10.	21	60
11.	23	76

Twelfths

	1.	0	0¼
⅙	2.	0	0¼
	3.	0	0½
⅓	4.	0	0½
	5.	0	0¾
½	6.	0	0¾
	7.	0	1
⅔	8.	0	1
	9.	0	1¼
⅚	10.	0	1¼
	11.	0	1½

Twentieths

10ths				10ths			
	1.	..			11.	0	0¾
·1	2.	0	0¼	·6	12.	0	1
	3.	0	0¼		13.	0	1
·2	4.	0	0¼	·7	14.	0	1
	5.	0	0½		15.	0	1¼
·3	6.	0	0½	·8	16.	0	1¼
	7.	0	0½		17.	0	1¼
·4	8.	0	0½	·9	18.	0	1¼
	9.	0	0¾		19.	0	1½
·5	10.	0	0¾		20.	0	1½

Sixteenths

	1.	..			9.	0	0¾
⅛	2.	0	0¼	⅝	10	0	1
	3.	0	0¼		11.	0	1
¼	4.	0	0½	¾	12.	0	1¼
	5.	0	0½		13.	0	1¼
⅜	6.	0	0½	⅞	14.	0	1¼
	7.	0	0¾		15.	0	1½
½	8.	0	0¾				

	£	P		£	P		£	P		£	P		£	P
1	0	2	51	1	2	101	2	2	152	3	4	310	6	20
2	0	4	52	1	4	102	2	4	154	3	8	320	6	40
3	0	6	53	1	6	103	2	6	[13] 156	3	12	330	6	60
4	0	8	54	1	8	104	2	8	158	3	16	340	6	80
5	0	10	55	1	10	105	2	10	160	3	20	350	7	0
*6	0	12	56	1	12	106	2	12	162	3	24	360	7	20
7	0	14	57	1	14	107	2	14	164	3	28	365	7	30
8	0	16	58	1	16	[9] 108	2	16	166	3	32	370	7	40
9	0	18	59	1	18	109	2	18	[14] 168	3	36	380	7	60
10	**0**	**20**	[5] **60**	**1**	**20**	**110**	**2**	**20**	170	3	40	390	7	80
*11	0	22	61	1	22	111	2	22	172	3	44	400	8	0
[1] 12	0	24	62	1	24	112	2	24	174	3	48	410	8	20
13	0	26	63	1	26	113	2	26	175	3	50	420	8	40
14	0	28	64	1	28	114	2	28	176	3	52	430	8	60
15	0	30	65	1	30	115	2	30	178	3	56	440	8	80
16	0	32	66	1	32	116	2	32	[15] 180	3	60	450	9	0
17	0	34	67	1	34	117	2	34	182	3	64	460	9	20
18	0	36	68	1	36	118	2	36	184	3	68	470	9	40
19	0	38	69	1	38	119	2	38	186	3	72	480	9	60
20	**0**	**40**	**70**	**1**	**40**	**120**	**2**	**40**	188	3	76	490	9	80
21	0	42	71	1	42	121	2	42	190	3	80	**500**	**10**	**0**
22	0	44	[6] 72	1	44	122	2	44	[16] 192	3	84	550	11	0
23	0	46	73	1	46	123	2	46	194	3	88	600	12	0
[2] 24	0	48	74	1	48	124	2	48	196	3	92	650	13	0
25	0	50	75	1	50	125	2	50	198	3	96	700	14	0
26	0	52	76	1	52	126	2	52	**200**	**4**	**0**	750	15	0
27	0	54	77	1	54	127	2	54	[17] 204	4	8	800	16	0
28	0	56	78	1	56	128	2	56	205	4	10	850	17	0
29	0	58	79	1	58	129	2	58	210	4	20	900	18	0
30	**0**	**60**	**80**	**1**	**60**	**130**	**2**	**60**	215	4	30	950	19	0
31	0	62	81	1	62	131	2	62	[18] 216	4	32	**1000**	**20**	**0**
32	0	64	82	1	64	[11] 132	2	64	220	4	40	1016	20	32
33	0	66	83	1	66	133	2	66	225	4	50	1250	25	0
34	0	68	[7] 84	1	68	134	2	68	[19] 228	4	56	1500	30	0
35	0	70	85	1	70	135	2	70	230	4	60	1728	34	56
[3] 36	0	72	86	1	72	136	2	72	235	4	70	1750	35	0
37	0	74	87	1	74	137	2	74	[20] 240	4	80	1760	35	20
38	0	76	88	1	76	138	2	76	245	4	90	2000	40	0
39	0	78	89	1	78	139	2	78	**250**	**5**	**0**	2240	44	80
40	**0**	**80**	**90**	**1**	**80**	**140**	**2**	**80**	255	5	10	2500	50	0
41	0	82	91	1	82	141	2	82	260	5	20	3000	60	0
42	0	84	92	1	84	142	2	84	265	5	30	4000	80	0
43	0	86	93	1	86	143	2	86	270	5	40	**5000**	**100**	**0**
44	0	88	94	1	88	[12] 144	2	88	275	5	50	6000	120	0
45	0	90	95	1	90	145	2	90	280	5	60	7000	140	0
46	0	92	[8] 96	1	92	146	2	92	285	5	70	8000	160	0
47	0	94	97	1	94	147	2	94	[24] 288	5	76	9000	180	0
[4] 48	0	96	98	1	96	148	2	96	290	5	80	10,000	200	0
49	0	98	99	1	98	149	2	98	295	5	90	15,000	300	0
50	**1**	**0**	**100**	**2**	**0**	**150**	**3**	**0**	**300**	**6**	**0**	20,000	400	0

Grosses

1.	2	88
2.	5	76
3.	8	64
4.	11	52
5.	14	40
6.	17	28
7.	20	16
8.	23	4
9.	25	92
10.	28	80
11.	31	68

Twelfths

	1.		0¼
⅙	2.	0	0¼
	3.	0	0½
⅓	4.	0	0¾
	5.	0	0¾
½	6.	0	1
	7.	0	1¼
⅔	8.	0	1¼
	9.	0	1½
⅚	10.	0	1¾
	11.	0	1¾

Twentieths

10ths							
	1.	..			11.	0	1
·1	2.	0	0¼	·6	12.	0	1¼
	3.	0	0¼		13.	0	1¼
·2	4.	0	0½	·7	14.	0	1½
	5.	0	0½		15.	0	1½
·3	6.	0	0½	·8	16.	0	1½
	7.	0	0¾		17.	0	1¾
·4	8.	0	0¾	·9	18.	0	1¾
	9.	0	1		19.	0	2
·5	10.	0	1		20.	0	2

Sixteenths

	1.	0	0¼		9.	0	1¼
⅛	2.	0	0¼	⅝	10.	0	1¼
	3.	0	0½		11.	0	1½
¼	4.	0	0½	¾	12.	0	1½
	5.	0	0¾		13.	0	1¾
⅜	6.	0	0¾	⅞	14.	0	1¾
	7.	0	1		15.	0	2
½	8.	0	1				

2½ Pence

2½ Pence

Dozens*	No.	£	P
	1	0	2½
	2	0	5
	3	0	7½
	4	0	10
	5	0	12½
	6	0	15
	7	0	17½
	8	0	20
	9	0	22½
	10	**0**	**25**
*	11	0	27½
1	12	0	30
	13	0	32½
	14	0	35
	15	0	37½
	16	0	40
	17	0	42½
	18	0	45
	19	0	47½
	20	**0**	**50**
	21	0	52½
	22	0	55
	23	0	57½
2	24	0	60
	25	0	62½
	26	0	65
	27	0	67½
	28	0	70
	29	0	72½
	30	**0**	**75**
	31	0	77½
	32	0	80
	33	0	82½
	34	0	85
	35	0	87½
3	36	0	90
	37	0	92½
	38	0	95
	39	0	97½
	40	**1**	**0**
	41	1	2½
	42	1	5
	43	1	7½
	44	1	10
	45	1	12½
	46	1	15
	47	1	17½
4	48	1	20
	49	1	22½
	50	**1**	**25**

Dozens	No.	£	P
	51	1	27½
	52	1	30
	53	1	32½
	54	1	35
	55	1	37½
	56	1	40
	57	1	42½
	58	1	45
	59	1	47½
5	**60**	**1**	**50**
	61	1	52½
	62	1	55
	63	1	57½
	64	1	60
	65	1	62½
	66	1	65
	67	1	67½
	68	1	70
	69	1	72½
	70	**1**	**75**
	71	1	77½
6	72	1	80
	73	1	82½
	74	1	85
	75	1	87½
	76	1	90
	77	1	92½
	78	1	95
	79	1	97½
	80	**2**	**0**
	81	2	2½
	82	2	5
	83	2	7½
7	84	2	10
	85	2	12½
	86	2	15½
	87	2	17½
	88	2	20
	89	2	22½
	90	**2**	**25**
	91	2	27½
	92	2	30
	93	2	32½
	94	2	35
	95	2	37½
8	96	2	40
	97	2	42½
	98	2	45
	99	2	47½
	100	**2**	**50**

Dozens	No.	£	P
	101	2	52½
	102	2	55
	103	2	57½
	104	2	60
	105	2	62½
	106	2	65
	107	2	67½
9	108	2	70
	109	2	72½
	110	**2**	**75**
	111	2	77½
	112	2	80
	113	2	82½
	114	2	85
	115	2	87½
	116	2	90
	117	2	92½
	118	2	95
	119	2	97½
	120	**3**	**0**
	121	3	2½
	122	3	5
	123	3	7½
	124	3	10
	125	3	12½
	126	3	15
	127	3	17½
	128	3	20
	129	3	22½
	130	**3**	**25**
	131	3	27½
11	132	3	30
	133	3	32½
	134	3	35
	135	3	37½
	136	3	40
	137	3	42½
	138	3	45
	139	3	47½
	140	**3**	**50**
	141	3	52½
	142	3	55
	143	3	57½
12	144	3	60
	145	3	62½
	146	3	65
	147	3	67½
	148	3	70
	149	3	72½
	150	**3**	**75**

Dozens	No.	£	P
	152	3	80
	154	3	85
13	156	3	90
	158	3	95
	160	4	0
	162	4	5
	164	4	10
	166	4	15
14	168	4	20
	170	4	25
	172	4	30
	174	4	35
	175	4	37½
	176	4	40
	178	4	45
15	180	4	50
	182	4	55
	184	4	60
	186	4	65
	188	4	70
	190	4	75
16	192	4	80
	194	4	85
	196	4	90
	198	4	95
	200	**5**	**0**
17	204	5	10
	205	5	12½
	210	5	25
	215	5	37½
18	216	5	40
	220	5	50
	225	5	62½
19	228	5	70
	230	5	75
	235	5	87½
20	240	6	0
	245	6	12½
	250	**6**	**25**
	255	6	37½
	260	6	50
	265	6	62½
	270	6	75
	275	6	87½
	280	7	0
	285	7	12½
24	288	7	20
	290	7	25
	295	7	37½
	300	**7**	**50**

No.	£	P
310	7	75
320	8	0
330	8	25
340	8	50
350	8	75
360	9	0
365	9	12½
370	9	25
380	9	50
390	9	75
400	10	0
410	10	25
420	10	50
430	10	75
440	11	0
450	11	25
460	11	50
470	11	75
480	12	0
490	12	25
500	**12**	**50**
550	13	75
600	15	0
650	16	25
700	17	50
750	18	75
800	20	0
850	21	25
900	22	50
950	23	75
1000	**25**	**0**
1016	25	40
1250	31	25
1500	37	50
1728	43	20
1750	43	75
1760	44	0
2000	50	0
2240	56	0
2500	62	50
3000	75	0
4000	100	0
5000	**125**	**0**
6000	150	0
7000	175	0
8000	200	0
9000	225	0
10,000	250	0
15,000	375	0
20,000	500	0

Grosses

1.	3	60
2.	7	20
3.	10	80
4.	14	40
5.	18	0
6.	21	60
7.	25	20
8.	28	80
9.	32	40
10.	36	0
11.	39	60

Twelfths

	1.	0	0¼
⅙	2.	0	0½
	3.	0	0¾
⅓	4.	0	0¾
	5.	0	1
½	6.	0	1¼
	7.	0	1½
⅔	8.	0	1¾
	9.	0	2
⅚	10.	0	2
	11.	0	2¼

Twentieths

10ths			
	1.	0	0¼
·1	2.	0	0¼
	3.	0	0½
·2	4.	0	0½
	5.	0	0¾
·3	6.	0	0¾
	7.	0	1
·4	8.	0	1
	9.	0	1¼
·5	10.	0	1¼
	11.	0	1½
·6	12.	0	1½
	13.	0	1¾
·7	14.	0	1¾
	15.	0	2
·8	16.	0	2
	17.	0	2¼
·9	18.	0	2¼
	19.	0	2½
	20.	0	2½

Sixteenths

	1.	0	0¼
⅛	2.	0	0¼
	3.	0	0½
¼	4.	0	0¾
	5.	0	0¾
⅜	6.	0	1
	7.	0	1
½	8.	0	1¼
	9.	0	1½
⅝	10.	0	1½
	11.	0	1¾
¾	12.	0	2
	13.	0	2
⅞	14.	0	2¼
	15.	0	2¼

3 Pence

*Dozens	No.	£	P	Dozens	No.	£	P	Dozens	No.	£	P	Dozens	No.	£	P	No.	£	P
	1	0	3		51	1	53		101	3	3		152	4	56	310	9	30
	2	0	6		52	1	56		102	3	6		154	4	62	320	9	60
	3	0	9		53	1	59		103	3	9	13	156	4	68	330	9	90
	4	0	12		54	1	62		104	3	12		158	4	74	340	10	20
	5	0	15		55	1	65		105	3	15		160	4	80	350	10	50
	6	0	18		56	1	68		106	3	18		162	4	86	360	10	80
	7	0	21		57	1	71		107	3	21		164	4	92	365	10	95
	8	0	24		58	1	74	9	108	3	24		166	4	98	370	11	10
	9	0	27		59	1	77		109	3	27	14	168	5	4	380	11	40
	10	**0**	**30**	5	**60**	**1**	**80**		**110**	**3**	**30**		170	5	10	390	11	70
	11	0	33		61	1	83		111	3	33		172	5	16	400	12	0
*1	12	0	36		62	1	86		112	3	36		174	5	22	410	12	30
	13	0	39		63	1	89		113	3	39		175	5	25	420	12	60
	14	0	42		64	1	92		114	3	42		176	5	28	430	12	90
	15	0	45		65	1	95		115	3	45		178	5	34	440	13	20
	16	0	48		66	1	98		116	3	48	15	180	5	40	450	13	50
	17	0	51		67	2	1		117	3	51		182	5	46	460	13	80
	18	0	54		68	2	4		118	3	54		184	5	52	470	14	10
	19	0	57		69	2	7		119	3	57		186	5	58	480	14	40
	20	**0**	**60**		**70**	**2**	**10**		**120**	**3**	**60**		188	5	64	490	14	70
	21	0	63		71	2	13		121	3	63		190	5	70	**500**	**15**	**0**
	22	0	66	6	72	2	16		122	3	66	16	192	5	76	550	16	50
	23	0	69		73	2	19		123	3	69		194	5	82	600	18	0
2	24	0	72		74	2	22		124	3	72		196	5	88	650	19	50
	25	0	75		75	2	25		125	3	75		198	5	94	700	21	0
	26	0	78		76	2	28		126	3	78		**200**	**6**	**0**	750	22	50
	27	0	81		77	2	31		127	3	81	17	204	6	12	800	24	0
	28	0	84		78	2	34		128	3	84		205	6	15	850	25	50
	29	0	87		79	2	37		129	3	87		210	6	30	900	27	0
	30	**0**	**90**		**80**	**2**	**40**		**130**	**3**	**90**		215	6	45	950	28	50
	31	0	93		81	2	43		131	3	93	18	216	6	48	**1000**	**30**	**0**
	32	0	96		82	2	46	11	132	3	96		220	6	60	1016	30	48
	33	0	99		83	2	49		133	3	99		225	6	75	1250	37	50
	34	1	2	7	84	2	52		134	4	2	19	228	6	84	1500	45	0
	35	1	5		85	2	55		135	4	5		230	6	90	1728	51	84
3	36	1	8		86	2	58		136	4	8		235	7	05	1750	52	50
	37	1	11		87	2	61		137	4	11	20	240	7	20	1760	52	80
	38	1	14		88	2	64		138	4	14		245	7	35	2000	60	0
	39	1	17		89	2	67		139	4	17		**250**	**7**	**50**	2240	67	20
	40	**1**	**20**		**90**	**2**	**70**		**140**	**4**	**20**		255	7	65	2500	75	0
	41	1	23		91	2	73		141	4	23		260	7	80	3000	90	0
	42	1	26		92	2	76		142	4	26		265	7	95	4000	120	0
	43	1	29		93	2	79		143	4	29		270	8	10	**5000**	**150**	**0**
	44	1	32		94	2	82	12	144	4	32		275	8	25	6000	180	0
	45	1	35		95	2	85		145	4	35		280	8	40	7000	210	0
	46	1	38	8	96	2	88		146	4	38		285	8	55	8000	240	0
	47	1	41		97	2	91		147	4	41	24	288	8	64	9000	270	0
4	48	1	44		98	2	94		148	4	44		290	8	70	10,000	300	0
	49	1	47		99	2	97		149	4	47		295	8	85	15,000	450	0
	50	**1**	**50**		**100**	**3**	**0**		**150**	**4**	**50**		**300**	**9**	**0**	20,000	600	0

Grosses

	£	P
1.	4	32
2.	8	64
3.	12	96
4.	17	28
5.	21	60
6.	25	92
7.	30	24
8.	34	56
9.	38	88
10.	43	20
11.	47	52

Twelfths

		£	P
	1.	0	0¼
⅙	2.	0	0½
	3.	0	0¾
⅓	4.	0	1
	5.	0	1¼
½	6.	0	1½
	7.	0	1¾
⅔	8.	0	2
	9.	0	2¼
⅚	10.	0	2½
	11.	0	2¾

Twentieths

10ths		£	P	10ths		£	P
	1.	0	0¼		11.	0	1¾
·1	2.	0	0¼	·6	12.	0	1¾
	3.	0	0½		13.	0	2
·2	4.	0	0½	·7	14.	0	2
	5.	0	0¾		15.	0	2¼
·3	6.	0	1	·8	16.	0	2½
	7.	0	1		17.	0	2½
·4	8.	0	1¼	·9	18.	0	2¾
	9.	0	1¼		19.	0	2¾
·5	10.	0	1½		20.	0	3

Sixteenths

		£	P			£	P
	1.	0	0¼		9.	0	1¾
⅛	2.	0	0½	⅝	10.	0	2
	3.	0	0½		11.	0	2
¼	4.	0	0¾	¾	12.	0	2¼
	5.	0	1		13.	0	2½
⅜	6.	0	1¼	⅞	14.	0	2¾
	7.	0	1¼		15.	0	2¾
½	8.	0	1½				

3½ Pence 3½ Pence

*Dozens	No.	£	P	Dozens	No.	£	P	Dozens	No.	£	P	Dozens	No.	£	P	No.	£	P
	1	0	3½		51	1	78½		101	3	53½		152	5	32	310	10	85
	2	0	7		52	1	82		102	3	57		154	5	39	320	11	20
	3	0	10½		53	1	85½		103	3	60½	13	156	5	46	330	11	55
	4	0	14		54	1	89		104	3	64		158	5	53	340	11	90
	5	0	17½		55	1	92½		105	3	67½		160	5	60	350	12	25
	6	0	21		56	1	96		106	3	71		162	5	67	360	12	60
	7	0	24½		57	1	99½		107	3	74½		164	5	74	365	12	77½
	8	0	28		58	2	3	9	108	3	78		166	5	81	370	12	95
	9	0	31½		59	2	6½		109	3	81½	14	168	5	88	380	13	30
	10	**0**	**35**	5	**60**	**2**	**10**		**110**	**3**	**85**		170	5	95	390	13	65
*	11	0	38½		61	2	13½		111	3	88½		172	6	2	400	14	0
1	12	0	42		62	2	17		112	3	92		174	6	9	410	14	35
	13	0	45½		63	2	20½		113	3	95½		175	6	12½	420	14	70
	14	0	49		64	2	24		114	3	99		176	6	16	430	15	5
	15	0	52½		65	2	27½		115	4	2½		178	6	23	440	15	40
	16	0	56		66	2	31		116	4	6	15	180	6	30	450	15	75
	17	0	59½		67	2	34½		117	4	9½		182	6	37	460	16	10
	18	0	63		68	2	38		118	4	13		184	6	44	470	16	45
	19	0	66½		69	2	41½		119	4	16½		186	6	51	480	16	80
	20	**0**	**70**		**70**	**2**	**45**		**120**	**4**	**20**		188	6	58	490	17	15
	21	0	73½		71	2	48½		121	4	23½		190	6	65	**500**	**17**	**50**
	22	0	77	6	72	2	52		122	4	27	16	192	6	72	550	19	25
	23	0	80½		73	2	55½		123	4	30½		194	6	79	600	21	0
2	24	0	84		74	2	59		124	4	34		196	6	86	650	22	75
	25	0	87½		75	2	62½		125	4	37½		198	6	93	700	24	50
	26	0	91		76	2	66		126	4	41		**200**	**7**	**0**	750	26	25
	27	0	94½		77	2	69½		127	4	44½	17	204	7	14	800	28	0
	28	0	98		78	2	73		128	4	48		205	7	17½	850	29	75
	29	1	1½		79	2	76½		129	4	51½		210	7	35	900	31	50
	30	**1**	**5**		**80**	**2**	**80**		**130**	**4**	**55**		215	7	52½	950	33	25
	31	1	8½		81	2	83½		131	4	58½	18	216	7	56	**1000**	**35**	**0**
	32	1	12		82	2	87	11	132	4	62		220	7	70	1016	35	56
	33	1	15½		83	2	90½		133	4	65½		225	7	87½	1250	43	75
	34	1	19	7	84	2	94		134	4	69	19	228	7	98	1500	52	50
	35	1	22½		85	2	97½		135	4	72½		230	8	5	1728	60	48
3	36	1	26		86	3	1		136	4	76		235	8	22½	1750	61	25
	37	1	29½		87	3	4½		137	4	79½	20	240	8	40	1760	61	60
	38	1	33		88	3	8		138	4	83		245	8	57½	2000	70	0
	39	1	36½		89	3	11½		139	4	86½		**250**	**8**	**75**	2240	78	40
	40	**1**	**40**		**90**	**3**	**15**		**140**	**4**	**90**		255	8	92½	2500	87	50
	41	1	43½		91	3	18½		141	4	93½		260	9	10	3000	105	0
	42	1	47		92	3	22		142	4	97		265	9	27½	4000	140	0
	43	1	50½		93	3	25½		143	5	0½		270	9	45	**5000**	**175**	**0**
	44	1	54		94	3	29	12	144	5	4		275	9	62½	6000	210	0
	45	1	57½		95	3	32½		145	5	7½		280	9	80	7000	245	0
	46	1	61	8	96	3	36		146	5	11		285	9	97½	8000	280	0
	47	1	64½		97	3	39½		147	5	14½	24	288	10	8	9000	315	0
4	48	1	68		98	3	43		148	5	18		290	10	15	10,000	350	0
	49	1	71½		99	3	46½		149	5	21½		295	10	32½	15,000	525	0
	50	**1**	**75**		**100**	**3**	**50**		**150**	**5**	**25**		**300**	**10**	**50**	20,000	700	0

Grosses

1.	5	4
2.	10	8
3.	15	12
4.	20	16
5.	25	20
6.	30	24
7.	35	28
8.	40	32
9.	45	36
10.	50	40
11.	55	44

Twelfths

	1.	0	0¼
⅙	2.	0	0½
	3.	0	1
⅓	4.	0	1¼
	5.	0	1½
½	6.	0	1¾
	7.	0	2
⅔	8.	0	2¼
	9.	0	2¾
⅚	10.	0	3
	11.	0	3¼

Twentieths

10ths							
	1.	0	0¼		11.	0	2
·1	2.	0	0¼	·6	12.	0	2
	3.	0	0½		13.	0	2¼
·2	4.	0	0¾	·7	14.	0	2½
	5.	0	1		15.	0	2¾
·3	6.	0	1	·8	16.	0	2¾
	7.	0	1¼		17.	0	3
·4	8.	0	1½	·9	18.	0	3¼
	9.	0	1½		19.	0	3¼
·5	10.	0	1¾		20.	0	3½

Sixteenths

	1.	0	0¼		9.	0	2
⅛	2.	0	0½	⅝	10	0	2¼
	3.	0	0¾		11.	0	2½
¼	4.	0	1	¾	12.	0	2¾
	5.	0	1		13.	0	2¾
⅜	6.	0	1¼	⅞	14.	0	3
	7.	0	1½		15.	0	3¼
½	8.	0	1¾				

*Dozens	£	P	Dozens	£	P	Dozens	£	P	Dozens	£	P		£	P
1	0	4	51	2	4	101	4	4	152	6	8	310	12	40
2	0	8	52	2	8	102	4	8	154	6	16	320	12	80
3	0	12	53	2	12	103	4	12	[13] 156	6	24	330	13	20
4	0	16	54	2	16	104	4	16	158	6	32	340	13	60
5	0	20	55	2	20	105	4	20	160	6	40	350	14	0
6	0	24	56	2	24	106	4	24	162	6	48	360	14	40
7	0	28	57	2	28	107	4	28	164	6	56	365	14	60
8	0	32	58	2	32	[9] 108	4	32	166	6	64	370	14	80
9	0	36	59	2	36	109	4	36	[14] 168	6	72	380	15	20
10	0	40	[5] **60**	2	40	**110**	4	40	170	6	80	390	15	60
11	0	44	61	2	44	111	4	44	172	6	88	400	16	0
[*1] 12	0	48	62	2	48	112	4	48	174	6	96	410	16	40
13	0	52	63	2	52	113	4	52	175	7	0	420	16	80
14	0	56	64	2	56	114	4	56	176	7	4	430	17	20
15	0	60	65	2	60	115	4	60	178	7	12	440	17	60
16	0	64	66	2	64	116	4	64	[15] 180	7	20	450	18	0
17	0	68	67	2	68	117	4	68	182	7	28	460	18	40
18	0	72	68	2	72	118	4	72	184	7	36	470	18	80
19	0	76	69	2	76	119	4	76	186	7	44	480	19	20
20	0	80	**70**	2	80	[10] **120**	4	80	188	7	52	490	19	60
21	0	84	71	2	84	121	4	84	190	7	60	**500**	20	00
22	0	88	[6] 72	2	88	122	4	88	[16] 192	7	68	550	22	0
23	0	92	73	2	92	123	4	92	194	7	76	600	24	0
[2] 24	0	96	74	2	96	124	4	96	196	7	84	650	26	0
25	1	0	75	3	0	125	5	0	198	7	92	700	28	0
26	1	4	76	3	4	126	5	4	**200**	8	0	750	30	0
27	1	8	77	3	8	127	5	8	[17] 204	8	16	800	32	0
28	1	12	78	3	12	128	5	12	205	8	20	850	34	0
29	1	16	79	3	16	129	5	16	210	8	40	900	36	0
30	1	20	**80**	3	20	**130**	5	20	215	8	60	950	38	0
31	1	24	81	3	24	131	5	24	[18] 216	8	64	**1000**	40	0
32	1	28	82	3	28	[11] 132	5	28	220	8	80	1016	40	64
33	1	32	83	3	32	133	5	32	225	9	0	1250	50	0
34	1	36	[7] 84	3	36	134	5	36	[19] 228	9	12	1500	60	0
35	1	40	85	3	40	135	5	40	230	9	20	1728	69	12
[3] 36	1	44	86	3	44	136	5	44	235	9	40	1750	70	0
37	1	48	87	3	48	137	5	48	[20] 240	9	60	1760	70	40
38	1	52	88	3	52	138	5	52	245	9	80	2000	80	0
39	1	56	89	3	56	139	5	56	**250**	10	0	2240	89	60
40	1	60	**90**	3	60	**140**	5	60	255	10	20	2500	100	0
41	1	64	91	3	64	141	5	64	260	10	40	3000	120	0
42	1	68	92	3	68	142	5	68	265	10	60	4000	160	0
43	1	72	93	3	72	143	5	72	270	10	80	**5000**	200	0
44	1	76	94	3	76	[12] 144	5	76	275	11	0	6000	240	0
45	1	80	95	3	80	145	5	80	280	11	20	7000	280	0
46	1	84	[8] 96	3	84	146	5	84	285	11	40	8000	320	0
47	1	88	97	3	88	147	5	88	[24] 288	11	52	9000	360	0
[4] 48	1	92	98	3	92	148	5	92	290	11	60	10,000	400	0
49	1	96	99	3	96	149	5	96	295	11	80	15,000	600	0
50	2	0	**100**	4	0	**150**	6	0	**300**	12	0	20,000	800	0

Grosses

1.	5	76
2.	11	52
3.	17	28
4.	23	04
5.	28	80
6.	34	56
7.	40	32
8.	46	08
9.	51	84
10.	57	60
11.	63	36

Twelfths

	1.	0	00$\frac{1}{4}$
$\frac{1}{6}$	2.	0	00$\frac{3}{4}$
	3.	0	01
$\frac{1}{3}$	4.	0	01$\frac{1}{4}$
	5.	0	01$\frac{3}{4}$
$\frac{1}{2}$	6.	0	02
	7.	0	02$\frac{1}{2}$
$\frac{2}{3}$	8.	0	02$\frac{3}{4}$
	9.	0	03
$\frac{5}{6}$	10.	0	03$\frac{1}{2}$
	11.	0	03$\frac{3}{4}$

Twentieths

10ths				10ths			
	1.	0	00$\frac{1}{4}$		11.	0	02$\frac{1}{4}$
·1	2.	0	00$\frac{1}{2}$	·6	12.	0	02$\frac{1}{2}$
	3.	0	00$\frac{1}{2}$		13.	0	02$\frac{1}{2}$
·2	4.	0	00$\frac{3}{4}$	·7	14.	0	02$\frac{3}{4}$
	5.	0	01		15.	0	03
·3	6.	0	01$\frac{1}{4}$	·8	16.	0	03$\frac{1}{4}$
	7.	0	01$\frac{1}{2}$		17.	0	03$\frac{1}{2}$
·4	8.	0	01$\frac{1}{2}$	·9	18.	0	03$\frac{1}{2}$
	9.	0	01$\frac{3}{4}$		19.	0	03$\frac{3}{4}$
·5	10.	0	02		20.	0	04

Sixteenths

	1.	0	00$\frac{1}{4}$		9.	0	02$\frac{1}{4}$
$\frac{1}{8}$	2.	0	00$\frac{1}{2}$	$\frac{5}{8}$	10.	0	02$\frac{1}{2}$
	3.	0	00$\frac{3}{4}$		11.	0	02$\frac{3}{4}$
$\frac{1}{4}$	4.	0	01	$\frac{3}{4}$	12.	0	03
	5.	0	01$\frac{1}{4}$		13.	0	03$\frac{1}{4}$
$\frac{3}{8}$	6.	0	01$\frac{1}{2}$	$\frac{7}{8}$	14.	0	03$\frac{1}{2}$
	7.	0	01$\frac{3}{4}$		15.	0	03$\frac{3}{4}$
$\frac{1}{2}$	8.	0	02				

4½ Pence

*Dozens		£	P	Dozens		£	P	Dozens		£	P	Dozens		£	P		£	P
	1	0	4½		51	2	29½		101	4	54½		152	6	84	310	13	95
	2	0	9		52	2	34		102	4	59		154	6	93	320	14	40
	3	0	13½		53	2	38½		103	4	63½	13	156	7	2	330	14	85
	4	0	18		54	2	43		104	4	68		158	7	11	340	15	30
	5	0	22½		55	2	47½		105	4	72½		160	7	20	350	15	75
	6	0	27		56	2	52		106	4	77		162	7	29	360	16	20
	7	0	31½		57	2	56½		107	4	81½		164	7	38	365	16	42½
	8	0	36		58	2	61	9	108	4	86		166	7	47	370	16	65
	9	0	40½		59	2	65½		109	4	90½	14	168	7	56	380	17	10
	10	**0**	**45**	5	**60**	**2**	**70**		**110**	**4**	**95**		170	7	65	390	17	55
*	11	0	49½		61	2	74½		111	4	99½		172	7	74	400	18	0
1	12	0	54		62	2	79		112	5	4		174	7	83	410	18	45
	13	0	58½		63	2	83½		113	5	8½		175	7	87½	420	18	90
	14	0	63		64	2	88		114	5	13		176	7	92	430	19	35
	15	0	67½		65	2	92½		115	5	17½		178	8	1	440	19	80
	16	0	72		66	2	97		116	5	22	15	180	8	10	450	20	25
	17	0	76½		67	3	1½		117	5	26½		182	8	19	460	20	70
	18	0	81		68	3	6		118	5	31		184	8	28	470	21	15
	19	0	85½		69	3	10½		119	5	35½		186	8	37	480	21	60
	20	**0**	**90**		**70**	**3**	**15**		**120**	**5**	**40**		188	8	46	490	22	5
	21	0	94½		71	3	19½		121	5	44½		190	8	55	**500**	**22**	**50**
	22	0	99	6	72	3	24		122	5	49	16	192	8	64	550	24	75
	23	1	3½		73	3	28½		123	5	53½		194	8	73	600	27	0
2	24	1	8		74	3	33		124	5	58		196	8	82	650	29	25
	25	1	12½		75	3	37½		125	5	62½		198	8	91	700	31	50
	26	1	17		76	3	42		126	5	67		**200**	**9**	**0**	750	33	75
	27	1	21½		77	3	46½		127	5	71½	17	204	9	18	800	36	0
	28	1	26		78	3	51		128	5	76		205	9	22½	850	38	25
	29	1	30½		79	3	55½		129	5	80½		210	9	45	900	40	50
	30	**1**	**35**		**80**	**3**	**60**		**130**	**5**	**85**		215	9	67½	950	42	75
	31	1	39½		81	3	64½		131	5	89½	18	216	9	72	**1000**	**45**	**0**
	32	1	44		82	3	69	11	132	5	94		220	9	90	1016	45	72
	33	1	48½		83	3	73½		133	5	98½		225	10	12½	1250	56	25
	34	1	53	7	84	3	78		134	6	3	19	228	10	26	1500	67	50
	35	1	57½		85	3	82½		135	6	7½		230	10	35	1728	77	76
3	36	1	62		86	3	87		136	6	12		235	10	57½	1750	78	75
	37	1	66½		87	3	91½		137	6	16½	20	240	10	80	1760	79	20
	38	1	71		88	3	96		138	6	21		245	11	2½	2000	90	0
	39	1	75½		89	4	0½		139	6	25½		**250**	**11**	**25**	2240	100	80
	40	**1**	**80**		**90**	**4**	**5**		**140**	**6**	**30**		255	11	47½	2500	112	50
	41	1	84½		91	4	9½		141	6	34½		260	11	70	3000	135	0
	42	1	89		92	4	14		142	6	39		265	11	92½	4000	180	0
	43	1	93½		93	4	18½		143	6	43½		270	12	15	**5000**	**225**	**0**
	44	1	98		94	4	23	12	144	6	48		275	12	37½	6000	270	0
	45	2	2½		95	4	27½		145	6	52½		280	12	60	7000	315	0
	46	2	7	8	96	4	32		146	6	57		285	12	82½	8000	360	0
	47	2	11½		97	4	36½		147	6	61½	24	288	12	96	9000	405	0
4	48	2	16		98	4	41		148	6	66		290	13	5	10,000	450	0
	49	2	20½		99	4	45½		149	6	70½		295	13	27½	15,000	675	0
	50	**2**	**25**		**100**	**4**	**50**		**150**	**6**	**75**		**300**	**13**	**50**	20,000	900	0

Grosses

1.	6	48
2.	12	96
3.	19	44
4.	25	92
5.	32	40
6.	38	88
7.	45	36
8.	51	84
9.	58	32
10.	64	80
11.	71	28

Twelfths

	1.	0	0½
⅙	2.	0	0¾
	3.	0	1¼
⅓	4.	0	1½
	5.	0	2
½	6.	0	2¼
	7.	0	2¾
⅔	8.	0	3
	9.	0	3½
⅚	10.	0	3¾
	11.	0	4¼

Twentieths

10ths				10ths			
	1.	0	0¼		11.	0	2½
·1	2.	0	0½	·6	12.	0	2¾
	3.	0	0¾		13.	0	3
·2	4.	0	1	·7	14.	0	3¼
	5.	0	1¼		15.	0	3½
·3	6.	0	1¼	·8	16.	0	3½
	7.	0	1½		17.	0	3¾
·4	8.	0	1¾	·9	18.	0	4
	9.	0	2		19.	0	4¼
·5	10.	0	2¼		20.	0	4½

Sixteenths

	1.	0	0¼		9.	0	2½
⅛	2.	0	0½	⅝	10	0	2¾
	3.	0	0¾		11.	0	3
¼	4.	0	1¼	¾	12.	0	3½
	5.	0	1½		13.	0	3¾
⅜	6.	0	1¾	⅞	14.	0	4
	7.	0	2		15.	0	4¼
½	8.	0	2¼				

	£	P		£	P		£	P		£	P		£	P
1	0	5	51	2	55	101	5	5	152	7	60	310	15	50
2	0	10	52	2	60	102	5	10	154	7	70	320	16	0
3	0	15	53	2	65	103	5	15	[13]156	7	80	330	16	50
*[Dozens]4	0	20	[Dozens]54	2	70	[Dozens]104	5	20	158	7	90	340	17	0
5	0	25	55	2	75	105	5	25	[Dozens]160	8	0	350	17	50
6	0	30	56	2	80	106	5	30	162	8	10	360	18	0
7	0	35	57	2	85	107	5	35	164	8	20	365	18	25
8	0	40	58	2	90	[9]108	5	40	166	8	30	370	18	50
9	0	45	59	2	95	109	5	45	[14]168	8	40	380	19	0
10	0	50	[5]60	3	0	110	5	50	170	8	50	390	19	50
11	0	55	61	3	5	111	5	55	172	8	60	400	20	0
[1]12	0	60	62	3	10	112	5	60	174	8	70	410	20	50
13	0	65	63	3	15	113	5	65	175	8	75	420	21	0
14	0	70	64	3	20	114	5	70	176	8	80	430	21	50
15	0	75	65	3	25	115	5	75	178	8	90	440	22	0
16	0	80	66	3	30	116	5	80	[15]180	9	0	450	22	50
17	0	85	67	3	35	117	5	85	182	9	10	460	23	0
18	0	90	68	3	40	118	5	90	184	9	20	470	23	50
19	0	95	69	3	45	119	5	95	186	9	30	480	24	0
20	1	0	70	3	50	120	6	0	188	9	40	490	24	50
21	1	5	71	3	55	121	6	5	190	9	50	500	25	0
22	1	10	[6]72	3	60	122	6	10	[16]192	9	60	550	27	50
23	1	15	73	3	65	123	6	15	194	9	70	600	30	0
[2]24	1	20	74	3	70	124	6	20	196	9	80	650	32	50
25	1	25	75	3	75	125	6	25	198	9	90	700	35	0
26	1	30	76	3	80	126	6	30	200	10	0	750	37	50
27	1	35	77	3	85	127	6	35	[17]204	10	20	800	40	0
28	1	40	78	3	90	128	6	40	205	10	25	850	42	50
29	1	45	79	3	95	129	6	45	210	10	50	900	45	0
30	1	50	80	4	0	130	6	50	215	10	75	950	47	50
31	1	55	81	4	5	131	6	55	[18]216	10	80	1000	50	0
32	1	60	82	4	10	[11]132	6	60	220	11	0	1016	50	80
33	1	65	83	4	15	133	6	65	225	11	25	1250	62	50
34	1	70	[7]84	4	20	134	6	70	[19]228	11	40	1500	75	0
35	1	75	85	4	25	135	6	75	230	11	50	1728	86	40
[3]36	1	80	86	4	30	136	6	80	235	11	75	1750	87	50
37	1	85	87	4	35	137	6	85	[20]240	12	0	1760	88	0
38	1	90	88	4	40	138	6	90	245	12	25	2000	100	0
39	1	95	89	4	45	139	6	95	250	12	50	2240	112	0
40	2	0	90	4	50	140	7	0	255	12	75	2500	125	0
41	2	5	91	4	55	141	7	5	260	13	0	3000	150	0
42	2	10	92	4	60	142	7	10	265	13	25	4000	200	0
43	2	15	93	4	65	143	7	15	270	13	50	5000	250	0
44	2	20	94	4	70	[12]144	7	20	275	13	75	6000	300	0
45	2	25	95	4	75	145	7	25	280	14	0	7000	350	0
46	2	30	[8]96	4	80	146	7	30	285	14	25	8000	400	0
47	2	35	97	4	85	147	7	35	[24]288	14	40	9000	450	0
[4]48	2	40	98	4	90	148	7	40	290	14	50	10000	500	0
49	2	45	99	4	95	149	7	45	295	14	75	15000	750	0
50	2	50	100	5	0	150	7	50	300	15	0	20000	1000	0

Grosses		Twelfths			Tenths / Twentieths			Sixteenths		
1.	7 20	1.	1. 0 0		1. 0 0½	11. 0 2¾		1. 0 0¼	9. 0 2¾
2.	14 40	⅛	2. 0 0½		2. 0 0½	12. 0 3		¹⁄₁₆ 2. 0 0½	10. 0 3¼
3.	21 60	¼	3. 0 1¼		3. 0 1	13. 0 3¼		3. 0 1	11. 0 3½
4.	28 80	⅜	4. 0 1½		4. 0 1½	14. 0 3½		¼ 4. 0 1¼	12. 0 3¾
5.	36 0		5. 0 2		5. 0 1½	15. 0 3¾		5. 0 1½	13. 0 4
6.	43 20	½	6. 0 2½		6. 0 2	16. 0 4		⅜ 6. 0 2	14. 0 4¼
7.	50 40		7. 0 3		7. 0 2½	17. 0 4¼		7. 0 2¼	14. 0 4½
8.	57 60	⅝	8. 0 3¼		8. 0 2½	18. 0 4½		½ 8. 0 2½	15. 0 4¾
9.	64 80		9. 0 3¾		9. 0 3	19. 0 4¾			
10.	72 0	¾	10. 0 4		10. 0 3½	20. 0 5			
11.	79 20		11. 0 4½						

No.	£ P	No.	£ P	No.	£ P	No.	£ P	No.	£ P
1	0 5½	51	2 80½	101	5 55½	152	8 36	310	17 5
2	0 11	52	2 86	102	5 61	154	8 47	320	17 60
3	0 16½	53	2 91½	103	5 66½	13 156	8 58	330	18 15
4	0 22	54	2 97	104	5 72	158	8 69	340	18 70
5	0 27½	55	3 2½	105	5 77½	160	8 80	350	19 25
6	0 33	56	3 8	106	5 83	162	8 91	360	19 80
7	0 38½	57	3 13½	107	5 88½	164	9 2	365	20 7½
8	0 44	58	3 19	9 108	5 94	166	9 13	370	20 35
9	0 49½	59	3 24½	109	5 99½	14 168	9 24	380	20 90
10	0 55	5 60	3 30	110	6 5	170	9 35	390	21 45
11	0 60½	61	3 35½	111	6 10½	172	9 46	400	22 0
12	0 66	62	3 41	112	6 16	174	9 57	410	22 55
13	0 71½	63	3 46½	113	6 21½	175	9 62½	420	23 10
14	0 77	64	3 52	114	6 27	176	9 68	430	23 65
15	0 82½	65	3 57½	115	6 32½	178	9 79	440	24 20
16	0 88	66	3 63	116	6 38	15 180	9 90	450	24 75
17	0 93½	67	3 68½	117	6 43½	182	10 1	460	25 30
18	0 99	68	3 74	118	6 49	184	10 12	470	25 85
19	1 4½	69	3 79½	119	6 54½	186	10 23	480	26 40
20	1 10	70	3 85	120	6 60	188	10 34	490	26 95
21	1 15½	71	3 90½	121	6 65½	190	10 45	500	27 50
22	1 21	6 72	3 96	122	6 71	16 192	10 56	550	30 25
23	1 26½	73	4 1½	123	6 76½	194	10 67	600	33 0
24	1 32	74	4 7	124	6 82	196	10 78	650	35 75
25	1 37½	75	4 12½	125	6 87½	198	10 89	700	38 50
26	1 43	76	4 18	126	6 93	200	11 0	750	41 25
27	1 48½	77	4 23½	127	6 98½	17 204	11 22	800	44 0
28	1 54	78	4 29	128	7 4	205	11 27½	850	46 75
29	1 59½	79	4 34½	129	7 9½	210	11 55	900	49 50
30	1 65	80	4 40	130	7 15	215	11 82½	950	52 25
31	1 70½	81	4 45½	131	7 20½	18 216	11 88	1000	55 0
32	1 76	82	4 51	11 132	7 26	220	12 10	1016	55 88
33	1 81½	83	4 56½	133	7 31½	225	12 37½	1250	68 75
34	1 87	7 84	4 62	134	7 37	19 228	12 54	1500	82 50
35	1 92½	85	4 67½	135	7 42½	230	12 65	1728	95 4
36	1 98	86	4 73	136	7 48	235	12 92½	1750	96 25
37	2 3½	87	4 78½	137	7 53½	20 240	13 20	1760	96 80
38	2 9	88	4 84	138	7 59	245	13 47½	2000	110 0
39	2 14½	89	4 89½	139	7 64½	250	13 75	2240	123 20
40	2 20	90	4 95	140	7 70	255	14 2½	2500	137 50
41	2 25½	91	5 0½	141	7 75½	260	14 30	3000	165 0
42	2 31	92	5 6	142	7 81	265	14 57½	4000	220 0
43	2 36½	93	5 11½	143	7 86½	270	14 85	5000	275 0
44	2 42	94	5 17	12 144	7 92	275	15 12½	6000	330 0
45	2 47½	95	5 22½	145	7 97½	280	15 40	7000	385 0
46	2 53	8 96	5 28	146	8 3	285	15 67½	8000	440 0
47	2 58½	97	5 33½	147	8 8½	24 288	15 84	9000	495 0
48	2 64	98	5 39	148	8 14	290	15 95	10,000	550 0
49	2 69½	99	5 44½	149	8 19½	295	16 22½	15,000	825 0
50	2 75	100	5 50	150	8 25	300	16 50	20,000	1100 0

Grosses		Twelfths		10ths	Twentieths				Sixteenths			
1.	7 92	1.	0 0½		1. 0 0¼		11. 0 3		1. 0 0¼		9. 0 3	
2.	15 84	2.	0 1		2. 0 0½		12. 0 3¼		2. 0 0½		10. 0 3¼	
3.	23 76	3.	0 1½	·1	3. 0 0¾	·6	13. 0 3½		3. 0 1		11. 0 3¾	
4.	31 68	4.	0 1¾		4. 0 1		14. 0 3¾		4. 0 1¼		12. 0 4¼	
5.	39 60	5.	0 2¼	·2	5. 0 1¼	·7	15. 0 4¼		5. 0 1¾		13. 0 4½	
6.	47 52	6.	0 2¾		6. 0 1½		16. 0 4½		6. 0 2		14. 0 4¾	
7.	55 44	7.	0 3¼	·3	7. 0 2	·8	17. 0 4¾		7. 0 2¼		15. 0 5¼	
8.	63 36	8.	0 3¾		8. 0 2¼	·9	18. 0 5		8. 0 2¾			
9.	71 28	9.	0 4¼	·4	9. 0 2½		19. 0 5¼					
10.	79 20	10.	0 4¾		10. 0 2¾		20. 0 5½					
11.	87 12	11.	0 5¼	·5								

Dozens		£	P	Dozens		£	P	Dozens		£	P	Dozens		£	P		£	P
	1	0	6		51	3	6		101	6	6		152	9	12	310	18	60
	2	0	12		52	3	12		102	6	12		154	9	24	320	19	20
	3	0	18		53	3	18		103	6	18	13	156	9	36	330	19	80
	4	0	24		54	3	24		104	6	24		158	9	48	340	20	40
	5	0	30		55	3	30		105	6	30		160	9	60	350	21	0
	6	0	36		56	3	36		106	6	36		162	9	72	360	21	60
	7	0	42		57	3	42		107	6	42		164	9	84	365	21	90
	8	0	48		58	3	48	9	108	6	48		166	9	96	370	22	20
	9	0	54		59	3	54		109	6	54	14	168	10	8	380	22	80
	10	**0**	**60**	5	**60**	**3**	**60**		**110**	**6**	**60**		170	10	20	390	23	40
	11	0	66		61	3	66		111	6	66		172	10	32	400	24	0
*1	12	0	72		62	3	72		112	6	72		174	10	44	410	24	60
	13	0	78		63	3	78		113	6	78		175	10	50	420	25	20
	14	0	84		64	3	84		114	6	84		176	10	56	430	25	80
	15	0	90		65	3	90		115	6	90		178	10	68	440	26	40
	16	0	96		66	3	96		116	6	96	15	180	10	80	450	27	00
	17	1	2		67	4	2		117	7	2		182	10	92	460	27	60
	18	1	8		68	4	8		118	7	8		184	11	4	470	28	20
	19	1	14		69	4	14		119	7	14		186	11	16	480	28	80
	20	**1**	**20**		**70**	**4**	**20**		**120**	**7**	**20**		188	11	28	490	29	40
	21	1	26		71	4	26		121	7	26		190	11	40	**500**	**30**	**0**
	22	1	32	6	72	4	32		122	7	32	16	192	11	52	550	33	0
	23	1	38		73	4	38		123	7	38		194	11	64	600	36	0
2	24	1	44		74	4	44		124	7	44		196	11	76	650	39	0
	25	1	50		75	4	50		125	7	50		198	11	88	700	42	0
	26	1	56		76	4	56		126	7	56		**200**	**12**	**0**	750	45	0
	27	1	62		77	4	62		127	7	62	17	204	12	24	800	48	0
	28	1	68		78	4	68		128	7	68		205	12	30	850	51	0
	29	1	74		79	4	74		129	7	74		210	12	60	900	54	0
	30	**1**	**80**		**80**	**4**	**80**		**130**	**7**	**80**		215	12	90	950	57	0
	31	1	86		81	4	86		131	7	86	18	216	12	96	**1000**	**60**	**0**
	32	1	92		82	4	92	11	132	7	92		220	13	20	1016	60	96
	33	1	98		83	4	98		133	7	98		225	13	50	1250	75	0
	34	2	4	7	84	5	4		134	8	4	19	228	13	68	1500	90	0
	35	2	10		85	5	10		135	8	10		230	13	80	1728	103	68
3	36	2	16		86	5	16		136	8	16		235	14	10	1750	105	0
	37	2	22		87	5	22		137	8	22	20	240	14	40	1760	105	60
	38	2	28		88	5	28		138	8	28		245	14	70	2000	120	0
	39	2	34		89	5	34		139	8	34		**250**	**15**	**0**	2240	134	40
	40	**2**	**40**		**90**	**5**	**40**		**140**	**8**	**40**		255	15	30	2500	150	0
	41	2	46		91	5	46		141	8	46		260	15	60	3000	180	0
	42	2	52		92	5	52		142	8	52		265	15	90	4000	240	0
	43	2	58		93	5	58		143	8	58		270	16	20	5000	300	0
	44	2	64		94	5	64	12	144	8	64		275	16	50	6000	360	0
	45	2	70		95	5	70		145	8	70		280	16	80	7000	420	0
	46	2	76	8	96	5	76		146	8	76		285	17	10	8000	480	0
	47	2	82		97	5	82		147	8	82	24	288	17	28	9000	540	0
4	48	2	88		98	5	88		148	8	88		290	17	40	10,000	600	0
	49	2	94		99	5	94		149	8	94		295	17	70	15,000	900	0
	50	**3**	**0**		**100**	**6**	**0**		**150**	**9**	**0**		**300**	**18**	**0**	20,000	1200	0

Grosses

1.	8	64
2.	17	28
3.	25	92
4.	34	56
5.	43	20
6.	51	84
7.	60	48
8.	69	12
9.	77	76
10.	86	40
11.	95	4

Twelfths

	1.	0	0½
⅙	2.	0	1
	3.	0	1½
⅓	4.	0	2
	5.	0	2½
½	6.	0	3
	7.	0	3½
⅔	8.	0	4
	9.	0	4½
⅚	10.	0	5
	11.	0	5½

Twentieths

10ths				10ths			
	1.	0	0¼		11.	0	3¼
·1	2.	0	0½	·6	12.	0	3½
	3.	0	1		13.	0	4
·2	4.	0	1¼	·7	14.	0	4¼
	5.	0	1½		15.	0	4½
·3	6.	0	1¾	·8	16.	0	4¾
	7.	0	2		17.	0	5
·4	8.	0	2½	·9	18.	0	5½
	9.	0	2¾		19.	0	5¾
·5	10.	0	3		20.	0	6

Sixteenths

	1.	0	0½		9.	0	3½
⅛	2.	0	0¾	⅝	10.	0	3¾
	3.	0	1¼		11.	0	4¼
¼	4.	0	1½	¾	12.	0	4½
	5.	0	2		13.	0	5
⅜	6.	0	2¼	⅞	14.	0	5¼
	7.	0	2¾		15.	0	5¾
½	8.	0	3				

No.	£ P	No.	£ P	No.	£ P	No.	£ P	No.	£ P
1	0 6½	51	3 31½	101	6 56½	152	9 88	310	20 15
2	0 13	52	3 38	102	6 63	154	10 1	320	20 80
3	0 19½	53	3 44½	103	6 69½	(13) 156	10 14	330	21 45
4	0 26	54	3 51	104	6 76	158	10 27	340	22 10
5	0 32½	55	3 57½	105	6 82½	160	10 40	350	22 75
6	0 39	56	3 64	106	6 89	162	10 53	360	23 40
7	0 45½	57	3 70½	107	6 95½	164	10 66	365	23 72½
8	0 52	58	3 77	(9) 108	7 2	166	10 79	370	24 5
9	0 58½	59	3 83½	109	7 8½	(14) 168	10 92	380	24 70
10	0 65	(5) **60**	3 90	**110**	7 15	170	11 5	390	25 35
(*)**11**	0 71½	61	3 96½	111	7 21½	172	11 18	400	26 0
(1)**12**	0 78	62	4 3	112	7 28	174	11 31	410	26 65
13	0 84½	63	4 9½	113	7 34½	175	11 37½	420	27 30
14	0 91	64	4 16	114	7 41	176	11 44	430	27 95
15	0 97½	65	4 22½	115	7 47½	178	11 57	440	28 60
16	1 4	66	4 29	116	7 54	(15) 180	11 70	450	29 25
17	1 10½	67	4 35½	117	7 60½	182	11 83	460	29 90
18	1 17	68	4 42	118	7 67	184	11 96	470	30 55
19	1 23½	69	4 48½	119	7 73½	186	12 9	480	31 20
20	1 30	70	4 55	**120**	7 80	188	12 22	490	31 85
21	1 36½	71	4 61½	121	7 86½	190	12 35	**500**	32 50
22	1 43	(6) 72	4 68	122	7 93	(16) 192	12 48	550	35 75
23	1 49½	73	4 74½	123	7 99½	194	12 61	600	39 0
(2)24	1 56	74	4 81	124	8 6	196	12 74	650	42 25
25	1 62½	75	4 87½	125	8 12½	198	12 87	700	45 50
26	1 69	76	4 94	126	8 19	**200**	13 0	750	48 75
27	1 75½	77	5 0½	127	8 25½	(17) 204	13 26	800	52 0
28	1 82	78	5 7	128	8 32	205	13 32½	850	55 25
29	1 88½	79	5 13½	129	8 38½	210	13 65	900	58 50
30	1 95	80	5 20	**130**	8 45	215	13 97½	950	61 75
31	2 1½	81	5 26½	131	8 51½	(18) 216	14 4	**1000**	65 0
32	2 8	82	5 33	(11) 132	8 58	220	14 30	1016	66 4
33	2 14½	83	5 39½	133	8 64½	225	14 62½	1250	81 25
34	2 21	(7) 84	5 46	134	8 71	(19) 228	14 82	1500	97 50
35	2 27½	85	5 52½	135	8 77½	230	14 95	1728	112 32
(3)36	2 34	86	5 59	136	8 84	235	15 27½	1750	113 75
37	2 40½	87	5 65½	137	8 90½	(20) 240	15 60	1760	114 40
38	2 47	88	5 72	138	8 97	245	15 92½	2000	130 0
39	2 53½	89	5 78½	139	9 3½	**250**	16 25	2240	145 60
40	2 60	90	5 85	**140**	9 10	255	16 57½	2500	162 50
41	2 66½	91	5 91½	141	9 16½	260	16 90	3000	195 0
42	2 73	92	5 98	142	9 23	265	17 22½	4000	260 0
43	2 79½	93	6 4½	143	9 29½	270	17 55	**5000**	325 0
44	2 86	94	6 11	(12) 144	9 36	275	17 87½	6000	390 0
45	2 92½	95	6 17½	145	9 42½	280	18 20	7000	455 0
46	2 99	(8) 96	6 24	146	9 49	285	18 52½	8000	520 0
47	3 5½	97	6 30½	147	9 55½	(24) 288	18 72	9000	585 0
(4)48	3 12	98	6 37	148	9 62	290	18 85	10,000	650 0
49	3 18½	99	6 43½	149	9 68½	295	19 17½	15,000	975 0
50	3 25	100	6 50	150	9 75	**300**	19 50	20,000	1300 0

Grosses		Twelfths		10ths	Twentieths				Sixteenths			
1.	9 36	1. 1 0	0½		1. 0	0¼	11. 0	3½	1. 0	0½	9. 0	3¾
2.	18 72	½2. 0	1	·1	2. 0	0¾	·6 12. 0	4	½2. 0	0¾	§10. 0	4
3.	28 8	3. 0	1½		3. 0	1	13. 0	4¼	3. 0	1¼	11. 0	4¼
4.	37 44	¼4. 0	2¼	·2	4. 0	1¼	·7 14. 0	4¾	¼4. 0	1½	12. 0	5
5.	46 80	5. 0	2¾		5. 0	1½	15. 0	5	5. 0	2	13. 0	5¼
6.	56 16	¼6. 0	3¼	·3	6. 0	2	·8 16. 0	5¼	⅜6. 0	2¼	¾14. 0	5¾
7.	65 52	7. 0	3¾		7. 0	2¼	17. 0	5½	7. 0	2¾	15. 0	6
8.	74 88	⅜8. 0	4¼	·4	8. 0	2½	·9 18. 0	5¾	½8. 0	3¼		
9.	84 24	9. 0	5		9. 0	3	19. 0	6¼				
10.	93 60	⅝10. 0	5½	·5	10. 0	3¼	·10 20. 0	6½				
11.	102 96	11. 0	6									

7 Pence 7 Pence

*Dozens		£	P	Dozens		£	P	Dozens		£	P	Dozens		£	P		£	P
	1	0	7		51	3	57		101	7	7		152	10	64	310	21	70
	2	0	14		52	3	64		102	7	14		154	10	78	320	22	40
	3	0	21		53	3	71		103	7	21	13	156	10	92	330	23	10
	4	0	28		54	3	78		104	7	28		158	11	6	340	23	80
	5	0	35		55	3	85		105	7	35		160	11	20	350	24	50
	6	0	42		56	3	92		106	7	42		162	11	34	360	25	20
	7	0	49		57	3	99		107	7	49		164	11	48	365	25	55
	8	0	56		58	4	6	9	108	7	56		166	11	62	370	25	90
	9	0	63		59	4	13		109	7	63	14	168	11	76	380	26	60
	10	**0**	**70**	5	**60**	**4**	**20**		**110**	**7**	**70**		170	11	90	390	27	30
*	11	0	77		61	4	27		111	7	77		172	12	4	400	28	0
1	12	0	84		62	4	34		112	7	84		174	12	18	410	28	70
	13	0	91		63	4	41		113	7	91		175	12	25	420	29	40
	14	0	98		64	4	48		114	7	98		176	12	32	430	30	10
	15	1	5		65	4	55		115	8	5		178	12	46	440	30	80
	16	1	12		66	4	62		116	8	12	15	180	12	60	450	31	50
	17	1	19		67	4	69		117	8	19		182	12	74	460	32	20
	18	1	26		68	4	76		118	8	26		184	12	88	470	32	90
	19	1	33		69	4	83		119	8	33		186	13	2	480	33	60
	20	**1**	**40**		**70**	**4**	**90**		**120**	**8**	**40**		188	13	16	490	34	30
	21	1	47		71	4	97		121	8	47		190	13	30	**500**	**35**	**0**
	22	1	54	6	72	5	4		122	8	54	16	192	13	44	550	38	50
	23	1	61		73	5	11		123	8	61		194	13	58	600	42	0
2	24	1	68		74	5	18		124	8	68		196	13	72	650	45	50
	25	1	75		75	5	25		125	8	75		198	13	86	700	49	0
	26	1	82		76	5	32		126	8	82		**200**	**14**	**0**	750	52	50
	27	1	89		77	5	39		127	8	89	17	204	14	28	800	56	0
	28	1	96		78	5	46		128	8	96		205	14	35	850	59	50
	29	2	3		79	5	53		129	9	3		210	14	70	900	63	0
	30	**2**	**10**		**80**	**5**	**60**		**130**	**9**	**10**		215	15	5	950	66	50
	31	2	17		81	5	67		131	9	17	18	216	15	12	**1000**	**70**	**0**
	32	2	24		82	5	74	11	132	9	24		220	15	40	1016	71	12
	33	2	31		83	5	81		133	9	31		225	15	75	1250	87	50
	34	2	38	7	84	5	88		134	9	38	19	228	15	96	1500	105	0
	35	2	45		85	5	95		135	9	45		230	16	10	1728	120	96
3	36	2	52		86	6	2		136	9	52		235	16	45	1750	122	50
	37	2	59		87	6	9		137	9	59	20	240	16	80	1760	123	20
	38	2	66		88	6	16		138	9	66		245	17	15	2000	140	0
	39	2	73		89	6	23		139	9	73		**250**	**17**	**50**	2240	156	80
	40	**2**	**80**		**90**	**6**	**30**		**140**	**9**	**80**		255	17	85	2500	175	0
	41	2	87		91	6	37		141	9	87		260	18	20	3000	210	0
	42	2	94		92	6	44		142	9	94		265	18	55	4000	280	0
	43	3	1		93	6	51		143	10	1		270	18	90	**5000**	**350**	**0**
	44	3	8		94	6	58	12	144	10	8		275	19	25	6000	420	0
	45	3	15		95	6	65		145	10	15		280	19	60	7000	490	0
	46	3	22	8	96	6	72		146	10	22		285	19	95	8000	560	0
	47	3	29		97	6	79		147	10	29	24	288	20	16	9000	630	0
4	48	3	36		98	6	86		148	10	36		290	20	30	10,000	700	0
	49	3	43		99	6	93		149	10	43		295	20	65	15,000	1050	0
	50	**3**	**50**		**100**	**7**	**0**		**150**	**10**	**50**		**300**	**21**	**0**	20,000	1400	0

Grosses				Twelfths			10ths	Twentieths			10ths	Twentieths		
1.	10	8		1.	0	0½		1.	0	0¼		11.	0	3¾
2.	20	16	⅙	2.	0	1¼	·1	2.	0	0¾	·6	12.	0	4¼
3.	30	24		3.	0	1¾		3.	0	1		13.	0	4½
4.	40	32	⅓	4.	0	2¼	·2	4.	0	1½	·7	14.	0	5
5.	50	40		5.	0	3		5.	0	1¾		15.	0	5¼
6.	60	48	½	6.	0	3½	·3	6.	0	2	·8	16.	0	5½
7.	70	56		7.	0	4		7.	0	2½		17.	0	6
8.	80	64	⅔	8.	0	4¾	·4	8.	0	2¾	·9	18.	0	6¼
9.	90	72		9.	0	5¼		9.	0	3¼		19.	0	6¾
10.	100	80	⅚	10.	0	5¾	·5	10.	0	3½		20.	0	7
11.	110	88		11.	0	6½								

Sixteenths							
	1.	0	0½		9.	0	4
⅛	2.	0	1	⅝	10.	0	4½
	3.	0	1¼		11.	0	4¾
¼	4.	0	1¾	¾	12.	0	5¼
	5.	0	2¼		13.	0	5¾
⅜	6.	0	2¾	⅞	14.	0	6¼
	7.	0	3		15.	0	6½
½	8.	0	3½				

Quantities are marked in the left margins with "Dozens" labels; round-dozen rows carry small dozen-number superscripts (12 = 1 doz, 24 = 2 doz, 36 = 3 doz, 48 = 4 doz, 60 = 5 doz, 72 = 6 doz, 84 = 7 doz, 96 = 8 doz, 108 = 9 doz, 120 = 10 doz, 132 = 11 doz, 144 = 12 doz = 1 gross).

No.	£	P	No.	£	P	No.	£	P
1	0	7½	51	3	82½	101	7	57½
2	0	15	52	3	90	102	7	65
3	0	22½	53	3	97½	103	7	72½
4	0	30	54	4	5	104	7	80
5	0	37½	55	4	12½	105	7	87½
6	0	45	56	4	20	106	7	95
7	0	52½	57	4	27½	107	8	2½
8	0	60	58	4	35	108	8	10
9	0	67½	59	4	42½	109	8	17½
10	0	75	60	4	50	110	8	25
11	0	82½	61	4	57½	111	8	32½
12	0	90	62	4	65	112	8	40
13	0	97½	63	4	72½	113	8	47½
14	1	5	64	4	80	114	8	55
15	1	12½	65	4	87½	115	8	62½
16	1	20	66	4	95	116	8	70
17	1	27½	67	5	2½	117	8	77½
18	1	35	68	5	10	118	8	85
19	1	42½	69	5	17½	119	8	92½
20	1	50	70	5	25	120	9	0
21	1	57½	71	5	32½	121	9	7½
22	1	65	72	5	40	122	9	15
23	1	72½	73	5	47½	123	9	22½
24	1	80	74	5	55	124	9	30
25	1	87½	75	5	62½	125	9	37½
26	1	95	76	5	70	126	9	45
27	2	2½	77	5	77½	127	9	52½
28	2	10	78	5	85	128	9	60
29	2	17½	79	5	92½	129	9	67½
30	2	25	80	6	0	130	9	75
31	2	32½	81	6	7½	131	9	82½
32	2	40	82	6	15	132	9	90
33	2	47½	83	6	22½	133	9	97½
34	2	55	84	6	30	134	10	5
35	2	62½	85	6	37½	135	10	12½
36	2	70	86	6	45	136	10	20
37	2	77½	87	6	52½	137	10	27½
38	2	85	88	6	60	138	10	35
39	2	92½	89	6	67½	139	10	42½
40	3	0	90	6	75	140	10	50
41	3	7½	91	6	82½	141	10	57½
42	3	15	92	6	90	142	10	65
43	3	22½	93	6	97½	143	10	72½
44	3	30	94	7	5	144	10	80
45	3	37½	95	7	12½	145	10	87½
46	3	45	96	7	20	146	10	95
47	3	52½	97	7	27½	147	11	2½
48	3	60	98	7	35	148	11	10
49	3	67½	99	7	42½	149	11	17½
50	3	75	100	7	50	150	11	25

No.	£	P	No.	£	P
152	11	40	310	23	25
154	11	55	320	24	0
156	11	70	330	24	75
158	11	85	340	25	50
160	12	0	350	26	25
162	12	15	360	27	0
164	12	30	365	27	37½
166	12	45	370	27	75
168	12	60	380	28	50
170	12	75	390	29	25
172	12	90	400	30	0
174	13	5	410	30	75
175	13	12½	420	31	50
176	13	20	430	32	25
178	13	35	440	33	0
180	13	50	450	33	75
182	13	65	460	34	50
184	13	80	470	35	25
186	13	95	480	36	0
188	14	10	490	36	75
190	14	25	500	37	50
192	14	40	550	41	25
194	14	55	600	45	0
196	14	70	650	48	75
198	14	85	700	52	50
200	15	0	750	56	25
204	15	30	800	60	0
205	15	37½	850	63	75
210	15	75	900	67	50
216	16	12½	950	71	25
220	16	50	1000	75	0
225	16	87½	1016	76	20
228	17	10	1250	93	75
230	17	25	1500	112	50
235	17	62½	1728	129	60
240	18	0	1750	131	25
245	18	37½	1760	132	0
250	18	75	2000	150	0
255	19	12½	2240	168	0
260	19	50	2500	187	50
265	19	87½	3000	225	0
270	20	25	4000	300	0
275	20	62½	5000	375	0
280	21	0	6000	450	0
285	21	37½	7000	525	0
288	21	60	8000	600	0
290	21	75	9000	675	0
295	22	12½	10,000	750	0
300	22	50	15,000	1125	0
			20,000	1500	0

Grosses			Twelfths			10ths Twentieths						Sixteenths					
1.	10	80	1.	0	0½		1.	0	0½	11.	0	4¼	1.	0	0½	9.	0	4¼
2.	21	60	⅙.	0	1¼	·1	2.	0	0¾	·6 12.	0	4½	⅛.	0	1	⅝.	0	4¾
3.	32	40	3.	0	2		3.	0	1	13.	0	5	3.	0	1½	11.	0	5¼
4.	43	20	⅓.	0	2½	·2	4.	0	1½	·7 14.	0	5¼	¼.	0	2	¾.	0	5½
5.	54	0	5.	0	3¼		5.	0	2	15.	0	5¾	5.	0	2½	13.	0	6
6.	64	80	⅙.	0	3¾	·3	6.	0	2¼	·8 16.	0	6¼	⅜.	0	2¾	⅞.	0	6
7.	75	60	7.	0	4½		7.	0	2½	17.	0	6½	7.	0	3¼	15.	0	7
8.	86	40	⅜.	0	5	·4	8.	0	3	·9 18.	0	6¾	½.	0	3¾			
9.	97	20	9.	0	5½		9.	0	3¼	19.	0	7¼						
10.	108	0	⅚10.	0	6¼	·5	10.	0	3¾	20.	0	7½						
11.	118	80	11.	0	7													

8 Pence

8 Pence

		£	P			£	P			£	P			£	P		£	P
	1	0	8		51	4	8		101	8	8		152	12	16	310	24	80
	2	0	16		52	4	16		102	8	16		154	12	32	320	25	60
Dozens	3	0	24	Dozens	53	4	24	Dozens	103	8	24	13	156	12	48	330	26	40
	4	0	32		54	4	32		104	8	32	Dozens	158	12	64	340	27	20
	5	0	40		55	4	40		105	8	40		160	12	80	350	28	0
*	6	0	48		56	4	48		106	8	48		162	12	96	360	28	80
	7	0	56		57	4	56		107	8	56		164	13	12	365	29	20
	8	0	64		58	4	64	9	108	8	64		166	13	28	370	29	60
	9	0	72		59	4	72		109	8	72	14	168	13	44	380	30	40
	10	**0**	**80**	5	**60**	**4**	**80**		**110**	**8**	**80**		170	13	60	390	31	20
*	11	0	88		61	4	88		111	8	88		172	13	76	400	32	0
1	12	0	96		62	4	96		112	8	96		174	13	92	410	32	80
	13	1	4		63	5	4		113	9	4		175	14	0	420	33	60
	14	1	12		64	5	12		114	9	12		176	14	8	430	34	40
	15	1	20		65	5	20		115	9	20		178	14	24	440	35	20
	16	1	28		66	5	28		116	9	28	15	180	14	40	450	36	0
	17	1	36		67	5	36		117	9	36		182	14	56	460	36	80
	18	1	44		68	5	44		118	9	44		184	14	72	470	37	60
	19	1	52		69	5	52		119	9	52		186	14	88	480	38	40
	20	**1**	**60**		**70**	**5**	**60**		**120**	**9**	**60**		188	15	4	490	39	20
	21	1	68		71	5	68		121	9	68		190	15	20	**500**	**40**	**0**
	22	1	76	6	72	5	76		122	9	76	16	192	15	36	550	44	0
	23	1	84		73	5	84		123	9	84		194	15	52	600	48	0
2	24	1	92		74	5	92		124	9	92		196	15	68	650	52	0
	25	2	0		75	6	0		125	10	0		198	15	84	700	56	0
	26	2	8		76	6	8		126	10	8		**200**	**16**	**0**	750	60	0
	27	2	16		77	6	16		127	10	16	17	204	16	32	800	64	0
	28	2	24		78	6	24		128	10	24		205	16	40	850	68	0
	29	2	32		79	6	32		129	10	32		210	16	80	900	72	0
	30	**2**	**40**		**80**	**6**	**40**		**130**	**10**	**40**		215	17	20	950	76	0
	31	2	48		81	6	48		131	10	48	18	216	17	28	**1000**	**80**	**0**
	32	2	56		82	6	56	11	132	10	56		220	17	60	1016	81	28
	33	2	64		83	6	64		133	10	64		225	18	0	1250	100	0
	34	2	72	7	84	6	72		134	10	72	19	228	18	24	1500	120	0
	35	2	80		85	6	80		135	10	80		230	18	40	1728	138	24
3	36	2	88		86	6	88		136	10	88		235	18	80	1750	140	0
	37	2	96		87	6	96		137	10	96	20	240	19	20	1760	140	80
	38	3	4		88	7	4		138	11	4		245	19	60	2000	160	0
	39	3	12		89	7	12		139	11	12		**250**	**20**	**0**	2240	179	20
	40	**3**	**20**		**90**	**7**	**20**		**140**	**11**	**20**		255	20	40	2500	200	0
	41	3	28		91	7	28		141	11	28		260	20	80	3000	240	0
	42	3	36		92	7	36		142	11	36		265	21	20	4000	320	0
	43	3	44		93	7	44		143	11	44		270	21	60	**5000**	**400**	**0**
	44	3	52		94	7	52	12	144	11	52		275	22	0	6000	480	0
	45	3	60		95	7	60		145	11	60		280	22	40	7000	560	0
	46	3	68	8	96	7	68		146	11	68		285	22	80	8000	640	0
	47	3	76		97	7	76		147	11	76	24	288	23	4	9000	720	0
4	48	3	84		98	7	84		148	11	84		290	23	20	10,000	800	0
	49	3	92		99	7	92		149	11	92		295	23	60	15,000	1200	0
	50	**4**	**0**		**100**	**8**	**0**		**150**	**12**	**0**		**300**	**24**	**0**	20,000	1600	0

Grosses

1.	11	52
2.	23	4
3.	34	56
4.	46	8
5.	57	60
6.	69	12
7.	80	64
8.	92	16
9.	103	68
10.	115	20
11.	126	72

Twelfths

	1.		0¾
⅙	2.	0	1¼
	3.	0	2
⅓	4.	0	2¾
	5.	0	3¼
½	6.	0	4
	7.	0	4¾
⅔	8.	0	5¼
	9.	0	6
⅚	10.	0	6¾
	11.	0	7¼

Twentieths

10ths				10ths			
	1.	0	0½		11.	0	4½
·1	2.	0	0¾	·6	12.	0	4¾
	3.	0	1¼		13.	0	5¼
·2	4.	0	1½	·7	14.	0	5½
	5.	0	2		15.	0	6
·3	6.	0	2½	·8	16.	0	6½
	7.	0	2¾		17.	0	6¾
·4	8.	0	3¼	·9	18.	0	7¼
	9.	0	3½		19.	0	7½
·5	10.	0	4		20.	0	8

Sixteenths

	1.	0	0½		9.	0	4½
⅛	2.	0	1	⅝	10.	0	5
	3.	0	1½		11.	0	5½
¼	4.	0	2	¾	12.	0	6
	5.	0	2½		13.	0	6½
⅜	6.	0	3	⅞	14.	0	7
	7.	0	3½		15.	0	7½
½	8.	0	4				

8½ Pence   8½ Pence

No.	£ P	No.	£ P	No.	£ P	No.	£ P	No.	£ P
1	0 8½	51	4 33½	101	8 58½	152	12 92	310	26 35
2	0 17	52	4 42	102	8 67	154	13 9	320	27 20
3	0 25½	53	4 50½	103	8 75½	13 156	13 26	330	28 5
4	0 34	54	4 59	104	8 84	158	13 43	340	28 90
5	0 42½	55	4 67½	105	8 92½	160	13 60	350	29 75
*6	0 51	56	4 76	106	9 1	162	13 77	360	30 60
7	0 59½	57	4 84½	107	9 9½	164	13 94	365	31 2½
8	0 68	58	4 93	8 108	9 18	166	14 11	370	31 45
9	0 76½	59	5 1½	109	9 26½	14 168	14 28	380	32 30
10	0 85	60	5 10	110	9 35	170	14 45	390	33 15
11	0 93½	61	5 18½	111	9 43½	172	14 62	400	34 0
12	1 2	62	5 27	112	9 52	174	14 79	410	34 85
13	1 10½	63	5 35½	113	9 60½	175	14 87½	420	35 70
14	1 19	64	5 44	114	9 69	176	14 96	430	36 55
15	1 27½	65	5 52½	115	9 77½	178	15 13	440	37 40
16	1 36	66	5 61	116	9 86	15 180	15 30	450	38 25
17	1 44½	67	5 69½	117	9 94½	182	15 47	460	39 10
18	1 53	68	5 78	118	10 3	184	15 64	470	39 95
19	1 61½	69	5 86½	119	10 11½	186	15 81	480	40 80
20	1 70	70	5 95	120	10 20	188	15 98	490	41 65
21	1 78½	71	6 3½	121	10 28½	190	16 15	500	42 50
22	1 87	72	6 12	122	10 37	16 192	16 32	550	46 75
23	1 95½	73	6 20½	123	10 45½	194	16 49	600	51 0
24	2 4	74	6 29	124	10 54	196	16 66	650	55 25
25	2 12½	75	6 37½	125	10 62½	198	16 83	700	59 50
26	2 21	76	6 46	126	10 71	200	17 0	750	63 75
27	2 29½	77	6 54½	127	10 79½	17 204	17 34	800	68 0
28	2 38	78	6 63	128	10 88	205	17 42½	850	72 25
29	2 46½	79	6 71½	129	10 96½	210	17 85	900	76 50
30	2 55	80	6 80	130	11 5	215	18 27½	950	80 75
31	2 63½	81	6 88½	131	11 13½	18 216	18 36	1000	85 0
32	2 72	82	6 97	132	11 22	220	18 70	1016	86 36
33	2 80½	83	7 5½	133	11 30½	225	19 12½	1250	106 25
34	2 89	84	7 14	134	11 39	19 228	19 38	1500	127 50
35	2 97½	85	7 22½	135	11 47½	230	19 55	1728	146 88
36	3 6	86	7 31	136	11 56	235	19 97½	1750	148 75
37	3 14½	87	7 39½	137	11 64½	20 240	20 40	1760	149 60
38	3 23	88	7 48	138	11 73	245	20 82½	2000	170 0
39	3 31½	89	7 56½	139	11 81½	250	21 25	2240	190 40
40	3 40	90	7 65	140	11 90	255	21 67½	2500	212 50
41	3 48½	91	7 73½	141	11 98½	260	22 10	3000	255 0
42	3 57	92	7 82	142	12 7	265	22 52½	4000	340 0
43	3 65½	93	7 90½	143	12 15½	270	22 95	5000	425 0
44	3 74	94	7 99	144	12 24	275	23 37½	6000	510 0
45	3 82½	95	8 7½	145	12 32½	280	23 80	7000	595 0
46	3 91	96	8 16	146	12 41	285	24 22½	8000	680 0
47	3 99½	97	8 24½	147	12 49½	24 290	24 65	9000	765 0
48	4 8	98	8 33	148	12 58	295	25 7½	10,000	850 0
49	4 16½	99	8 41½	149	12 66½	300	25 50	15,000	1275 0
50	4 25	100	8 50	150	12 75			20,000	1700 0

Grosses			Twelfths			10ths	Twentieths					Sixteenths			
1.	12	24	½ 1.	0	0½		1.	0	0½	11.	0	4¾	1.	0	0½	9.	0	4¾
2.	24	48	½ 2.	0	1½	·1	2.	0	1	12.	0	5	2.	0	1	10.	0	5¼
3.	36	72	3.	0	2¼	2	3.	0	1½	13.	0	5½	3.	0	1½	11.	0	5¾
4.	48	96	¼ 4.	0	2¾	·2	4.	0	2	14.	0	6	4.	0	2¼	12.	0	6
5.	61	20	5.	0	3½	3	5.	0	2½	15.	0	6½	5.	0	2¾	13.	0	7
6.	73	44	¾ 6.	0	4¼	·3	6.	0	3	16.	0	6¾	6.	0	3¼	14.	0	7¼
7.	85	68	7.	0	5	4	7.	0	3½	17.	0	7¼	7.	0	3¾	15.	0	8
8.	97	92	¼ 8.	0	5¾	·4	8.	0	4	18.	0	7¾	8.	0	4½			
9.	110	16	9.	0	6½	9	9.	0	4½	19.	0	8						
10	122	40	½10.	0	7	·5	10.	0	4¼	20.	0	8½						
11	134	64	11.	0	7¾													

Dozens	No.	£	p	Dozens	No.	£	p	Dozens	No.	£	p	Dozens	No.	£	p	No.	£	p
	1	0	9		51	4	59		101	9	9		152	13	68	310	27	90
	2	0	18		52	4	68		102	9	18		154	13	86	320	28	80
	3	0	27		53	4	77		103	9	27	13	156	14	4	330	29	70
	4	0	36		54	4	86		104	9	36		158	14	22	340	30	60
	5	0	45		55	4	95		105	9	45		160	14	40	350	31	50
	6	0	54		56	5	4		106	9	54		162	14	58	360	32	40
	7	0	63		57	5	13		107	9	63		164	14	76	365	32	85
	8	0	72		58	5	22	9	108	9	72		166	14	94	370	33	30
	9	0	81		59	5	31		109	9	81	14	168	15	12	380	34	20
	10	**0**	**90**	5	**60**	5	40		**110**	**9**	**90**		170	15	30	390	35	10
	11	0	99		61	5	49		111	9	99		172	15	48	400	36	0
*1	12	1	8		62	5	58		112	10	8		174	15	66	410	36	90
	13	1	17		63	5	67		113	10	17		175	15	75	420	37	80
	14	1	26		64	5	76		114	10	26		176	15	84	430	38	70
	15	1	35		65	5	85		115	10	35		178	16	2	440	39	60
	16	1	44		66	5	94		116	10	44	15	180	16	20	450	40	50
	17	1	53		67	6	3		117	10	53		182	16	38	460	41	40
	18	1	62		68	6	12		118	10	62		184	16	56	470	42	30
	19	1	71		69	6	21		119	10	71		186	16	74	480	43	20
	20	1	80		**70**	6	30	10	**120**	10	80		188	16	92	490	44	10
	21	1	89		71	6	39		121	10	89		190	17	10	**500**	45	0
	22	1	98	6	72	6	48		122	10	98	16	192	17	28	550	49	50
	23	2	7		73	6	57		123	11	7		194	17	46	600	54	0
2	24	2	16		74	6	66		124	11	16		196	17	64	650	58	50
	25	2	25		75	6	75		125	11	25		198	17	82	700	63	0
	26	2	34		76	6	84		126	11	34		**200**	18	0	750	67	50
	27	2	43		77	6	93		127	11	43	17	204	18	36	800	72	0
	28	2	52		78	7	2		128	11	52		205	18	45	850	76	50
	29	2	61		79	7	11		129	11	61		210	18	90	900	81	0
	30	2	70		**80**	7	20		**130**	11	70		215	19	35	950	85	50
	31	2	79		81	7	29		131	11	79	18	216	19	44	**1000**	**90**	**0**
	32	2	88		82	7	38	11	132	11	88		220	19	80	1016	91	44
	33	2	97		83	7	47		133	11	97		225	20	25	1250	112	50
	34	3	6	7	84	7	56		134	12	6	19	228	20	52	1500	135	0
	35	3	15		85	7	65		135	12	15		230	20	70	1728	155	52
3	36	3	24		86	7	74		136	12	24		235	21	15	1750	157	50
	37	3	33		87	7	83		137	12	33	20	240	21	60	1760	158	40
	38	3	42		88	7	92		138	12	42		245	22	5	2000	180	0
	39	3	51		89	8	1		139	12	51		**250**	**22**	**50**	2240	201	60
	40	3	60		**90**	8	10		**140**	12	60		255	22	95	2500	225	0
	41	3	69		91	8	19		141	12	69		260	23	40	3000	270	0
	42	3	78		92	8	28		142	12	78		265	23	85	4000	360	0
	43	3	87		93	8	37		143	12	87		270	24	30	**5000**	450	0
	44	3	96		94	8	46	12	144	12	96		275	24	75	6000	540	0
	45	4	5		95	8	55		145	13	5		280	25	20	7000	630	0
	46	4	14	8	96	8	64		146	13	14		285	25	65	8000	720	0
	47	4	23		97	8	73		147	13	23	24	288	25	92	9000	810	0
4	48	4	32		98	8	82		148	13	32		290	26	10	10,000	900	0
	49	4	41		99	8	91		149	13	41		295	26	55	15,000	1350	0
	50	4	50		**100**	9	0		**150**	13	50		**300**	27	0	20,000	1800	0

*Dozens

Grosses	£	p		Twelfths	£	p	10ths	Twentieths	£	p	10ths	Twentieths	£	p		Sixteenths	£	p		Sixteenths	£	p
1.	12	96		1.	0	0¾		1.	0	0½		11.	0	5		1.	0	0½		9.	0	5
2.	25	92	⅙	2.	0	1½	·1	2.	0	1	·6	12.	0	5½	⅛	2.	0	1¼	⅝	10.	0	5⅝
3.	38	88		3.	0	2¼		3.	0	1¼		13.	0	5¾		3.	0	1¾		11.	0	6¼
4.	51	84	⅓	4.	0	3	·2	4.	0	1¾	·7	14.	0	6¼	¼	4.	0	2¼	¾	12.	0	6¾
5.	64	80		5.	0	3¾		5.	0	2¼		15.	0	6¾		5.	0	2¾		13.	0	7¼
6.	77	76	½	6.	0	4½	·3	6.	0	2¾	·8	16.	0	7¼	⅜	6.	0	3½	⅞	14.	0	8
7.	90	72		7.	0	5¼		7.	0	3¼		17.	0	7¾		7.	0	4		15.	0	8½
8.	103	68	⅔	8.	0	6	·4	8.	0	3½	·9	18.	0	8	½	8.	0	4½				
9.	116	64		9.	0	6¾		9.	0	4		19.	0	8½								
10.	129	60	⅚	10.	0	7½	·5	10.	0	4½		20.	0	9								
11.	142	56		11.	0	8¼																

9½ Pence

	£	P		£	P		£	P		£	P		£	P
1	0	9½	51	4	84½	101	9	59½	152	14	44	310	29	45
2	0	19	52	4	94	102	9	69	154	14	63	320	30	40
3	0	28½	53	5	3½	103	9	78½	[13] 156	14	82	330	31	35
4	0	38	54	5	13	104	9	88	158	15	1	340	32	30
5	0	47½	55	5	22½	105	9	97½	160	15	20	350	33	25
6	0	57	56	5	32	106	10	7	162	15	39	360	34	20
7	0	66½	57	5	41½	107	10	16½	164	15	58	365	34	67½
8	0	76	58	5	51	[9] 108	10	26	166	15	77	370	35	15
9	0	85½	59	5	60½	109	10	35½	[14] 168	15	96	380	36	10
10	0	95	[5] **60**	5	70	**110**	10	45	170	16	15	390	37	5
[*] 11	1	4½	61	5	79½	111	10	54½	172	16	34	400	38	0
[1] 12	1	14	62	5	89	112	10	64	174	16	53	410	38	95
13	1	23½	63	5	98½	113	10	73½	175	16	62½	420	39	90
14	1	33	64	6	8	114	10	83	176	16	72	430	40	85
15	1	42½	65	6	17½	115	10	92½	178	16	91	440	41	80
16	1	52	66	6	27	116	11	2	[15] 180	17	10	450	42	75
17	1	61½	67	6	36½	117	11	11½	182	17	29	460	43	70
18	1	71	68	6	46	118	11	21	184	17	48	470	44	65
19	1	80½	69	6	55½	119	11	30½	186	17	67	480	45	60
20	1	90	**70**	6	65	**120**	11	40	188	17	86	490	46	55
21	1	99½	71	6	74½	121	11	49½	190	18	5	**500**	47	50
22	2	9	[6] 72	6	84	122	11	59	[16] 192	18	24	550	52	25
23	2	18½	73	6	93½	123	11	68½	194	18	43	600	57	0
[2] 24	2	28	74	7	3	124	11	78	196	18	62	650	61	75
25	2	37½	75	7	12½	125	11	87½	198	18	81	700	66	50
26	2	47	76	7	22	126	11	97	**200**	19	0	750	71	25
27	2	56½	77	7	31½	127	12	6½	[17] 204	19	38	800	76	0
28	2	66	78	7	41	128	12	16	205	19	47½	850	80	75
29	2	75½	79	7	50½	129	12	25½	210	19	95	900	85	50
30	2	85	**80**	7	60	**130**	12	35	215	20	42½	950	90	25
31	2	94½	81	7	69½	131	12	44½	[18] 216	20	52	**1000**	95	0
32	3	4	82	7	79	[11] 132	12	54	220	20	90	1016	96	52
33	3	13½	83	7	88½	133	12	63½	225	21	37½	1250	118	75
34	3	23	[7] 84	7	98	134	12	73	[19] 228	21	66	1500	142	50
35	3	32½	85	8	7½	135	12	82½	230	21	85	1728	164	16
[3] 36	3	42	86	8	17	136	12	92	235	22	32½	1750	166	25
37	3	51½	87	8	26½	137	13	1½	[20] 240	22	80	1760	167	20
38	3	61	88	8	36	138	13	11	245	23	27½	2000	190	0
39	3	70½	89	8	45½	139	13	20½	**250**	23	75	2240	212	80
40	3	80	**90**	8	55	**140**	13	30	255	24	22½	2500	237	50
41	3	89½	91	8	64½	141	13	39½	260	24	70	3000	285	0
42	3	99	92	8	74	142	13	49	265	25	17½	4000	380	0
43	4	8½	93	8	83½	143	13	58½	270	25	65	**5000**	475	0
44	4	18	94	8	93	[12] 144	13	68	275	26	12½	6000	570	0
45	4	27½	95	9	2½	145	13	77½	280	26	60	7000	665	0
46	4	37	[8] 96	9	12	146	13	87	285	27	7½	8000	760	0
47	4	46½	97	9	21½	147	13	96½	[24] 288	27	36	9000	855	0
[4] 48	4	56	98	9	31	148	14	6	290	27	55	10,000	950	0
49	4	65½	99	9	40½	149	14	15½	295	28	2½	15,000	1425	0
50	4	75	**100**	9	50	**150**	14	25	**300**	28	50	20,000	1900	0

*Dozens

Grosses

1.	13	68
2.	27	36
3.	41	04
4.	54	72
5.	68	40
6.	82	8
7.	95	76
8.	109	44
9.	123	12
10.	136	80
11.	150	48

Twelfths

1.	0	0¾
⅙ 2.	0	1½
3.	0	2½
⅓ 4.	0	3¼
5.	0	4
½ 6.	0	4¾
7.	0	5½
⅔ 8.	0	6¼
9.	0	7¼
⅚ 10.	0	8
11.	0	8¾

Twentieths (10ths)

1.	0	0½	11.	0	5¼
·1 2.	0	1	·6 12.	0	5¾
3.	0	1½	13.	0	6¼
·2 4.	0	2	·7 14.	0	6¾
5.	0	2½	15.	0	7¼
·3 6.	0	2¾	·8 16.	0	7½
7.	0	3¼	17.	0	8
·4 8.	0	3¾	·9 18.	0	8½
9.	0	4¼	19.	0	9
·5 10.	0	4¾	20.	0	9½

Sixteenths

1.	0	0½	9.	0	5¼
⅛ 2.	0	1¼	⅝ 10.	0	6
3.	0	1¾	11.	0	6½
¼ 4.	0	2½	¾ 12.	0	7¼
5.	0	3	13.	0	7¾
⅜ 6.	0	3½	⅞ 14.	0	8¼
7.	0	4¼	15.	0	9
½ 8.	0	4¾			

*Dozens	No.	£	P
	1	0	10
	2	0	20
	3	0	30
	4	0	40
	5	0	50
	6	0	60
	7	0	70
	8	0	80
	9	0	90
	10	1	0
	11	1	10
1	12	1	20
	13	1	30
	14	1	40
	15	1	50
	16	1	60
	17	1	70
	18	1	80
	19	1	90
	20	2	0
	21	2	10
	22	2	20
	23	2	30
2	24	2	40
	25	2	50
	26	2	60
	27	2	70
	28	2	80
	29	2	90
	30	3	0
	31	3	10
	32	3	20
	33	3	30
	34	3	40
	35	3	50
3	36	3	60
	37	3	70
	38	3	80
	39	3	90
	40	4	0
	41	4	10
	42	4	20
	43	4	30
	44	4	40
	45	4	50
	46	4	60
	47	4	70
4	48	4	80
	49	4	90
	50	5	0

Dozens	No.	£	P
	51	5	10
	52	5	20
	53	5	30
	54	5	40
	55	5	50
	56	5	60
	57	5	70
	58	5	80
	59	5	90
5	**60**	6	0
	61	6	10
	62	6	20
	63	6	30
	64	6	40
	65	6	50
	66	6	60
	67	6	70
	68	6	80
	69	6	90
	70	7	0
	71	7	10
6	72	7	20
	73	7	30
	74	7	40
	75	7	50
	76	7	60
	77	7	70
	78	7	80
	79	7	90
	80	8	0
	81	8	10
	82	8	20
	83	8	30
7	84	8	40
	85	8	50
	86	8	60
	87	8	70
	88	8	80
	89	8	90
	90	9	0
	91	9	10
	92	9	20
	93	9	30
	94	9	40
	95	9	50
8	96	9	60
	97	9	70
	98	9	80
	99	9	90
	100	10	0

Dozens	No.	£	P
	101	10	10
	102	10	20
	103	10	30
	104	10	40
	105	10	50
	106	10	60
	107	10	70
9	108	10	80
	109	10	90
	110	11	0
	111	11	10
	112	11	20
	113	11	30
	114	11	40
	115	11	50
	116	11	60
	117	11	70
	118	11	80
	119	11	90
	120	12	0
	121	12	10
	122	12	20
	123	12	30
	124	12	40
	125	12	50
	126	12	60
	127	12	70
	128	12	80
	129	12	90
	130	13	0
	131	13	10
11	132	13	20
	133	13	30
	134	13	40
	135	13	50
	136	13	60
	137	13	70
	138	13	80
	139	13	90
	140	14	0
	141	14	10
	142	14	20
	143	14	30
12	144	14	40
	145	14	50
	146	14	60
	147	14	70
	148	14	80
	149	14	90
	150	15	0

Dozens	No.	£	P
	152	15	20
	154	15	40
13	156	15	60
	158	15	80
	160	16	0
	162	16	20
	164	16	40
	166	16	60
14	168	16	80
	170	17	0
	172	17	20
	174	17	40
	175	17	50
	176	17	60
	178	17	80
15	180	18	0
	182	18	20
	184	18	40
	186	18	60
	188	18	80
	190	19	0
16	192	19	20
	194	19	40
	196	19	60
	198	19	80
	200	20	0
17	204	20	40
	205	20	50
	210	21	0
	215	21	50
18	216	21	60
	220	22	0
	225	22	50
19	228	22	80
	230	23	0
	235	23	50
20	240	24	0
	245	24	50
	250	25	0
	255	25	50
	260	26	0
	265	26	50
	270	27	0
	275	27	50
	280	28	0
	285	28	50
24	288	28	80
	290	29	0
	295	29	50
	300	30	0

No.	£	P
310	31	0
320	32	0
330	33	0
340	34	0
350	35	0
360	36	0
365	36	50
370	37	0
380	38	0
390	39	0
400	40	0
410	41	0
420	42	0
430	43	0
440	44	0
450	45	0
460	46	0
470	47	0
480	48	0
490	49	0
500	50	0
550	55	0
600	60	0
650	65	0
700	70	0
750	75	0
800	80	0
850	85	0
900	90	0
950	95	0
1000	100	0
1016	101	60
1250	125	0
1500	150	0
1728	172	80
1750	175	0
1760	176	0
2000	200	0
2240	224	0
2500	250	0
3000	300	0
4000	400	0
5000	500	0
6000	600	0
7000	700	0
8000	800	0
9000	900	0
10,000	1000	0
15,000	1500	0
20,000	2000	0

Grosses

No.	£	P
1.	14	40
2.	28	80
3.	43	20
4.	57	60
5.	72	0
6.	86	40
7.	100	80
8.	115	20
9.	129	60
10.	144	0
11.	158	40

Twelfths

	No.	£	P
	1.	0	0¾
⅙	2.	0	1¾
	3.	0	2½
⅓	4.	0	3¼
	5.	0	4¼
½	6.	0	5
	7.	0	5¾
⅔	8.	0	6¾
	9.	0	7½
⅚	10.	0	8¼
	11.	0	9¼

Twentieths

10ths	No.	£	P	10ths	No.	£	P
	1.	0	0½		11.	0	5½
·1	2.	0	1	·6	12.	0	6
	3.	0	1½		13.	0	6½
·2	4.	0	2	·7	14.	0	7
	5.	0	2½		15.	0	7½
·3	6.	0	3	·8	16.	0	8
	7.	0	3½		17.	0	8½
·4	8.	0	4	·9	18.	0	9
	9.	0	4½		19.	0	9½
·5	10.	0	5		20.	0	10

Sixteenths

	No.	£	P		No.	£	P
	1.	0	0¾		9.	0	5¾
⅛	2.	0	1¼	⅝	10.	0	6¼
	3.	0	2		11.	0	7
¼	4.	0	2½	¾	12.	0	7½
	5.	0	3¼		13.	0	8¼
⅜	6.	0	3¾	⅞	14.	0	8¾
	7.	0	4½		15.	0	9½
½	8.	0	5				

	£ P		£ P		£ P		£ P		£ P
1	0 10½	51	5 35½	101	10 60½	152	15 96	310	32 55
2	0 21	52	5 46	102	10 71	154	16 17	320	33 60
3	0 31½	53	5 56½	103	10 81½	[13] 156	16 38	330	34 65
4	0 42	54	5 67	104	10 92	158	16 59	340	35 70
5	0 52½	55	5 77½	105	11 2½	160	16 80	350	36 75
6	0 63	56	5 88	106	11 13	162	17 1	360	37 80
7	0 73½	57	5 98½	107	11 23½	164	17 22	365	38 32½
8	0 84	58	6 9	[9] 108	11 34	166	17 43	370	38 85
9	0 94½	59	6 19½	109	11 44½	[14] 168	17 64	380	39 90
10	1 5	[5] **60**	6 30	**110**	11 55	170	17 85	390	40 95
*11	1 15½	61	6 40½	111	11 65½	172	18 6	400	42 0
[1] 12	1 26	62	6 51	112	11 76	174	18 27	410	43 5
13	1 36½	63	6 61½	113	11 86½	175	18 37½	420	44 10
14	1 47	64	6 72	114	11 97	176	18 48	430	45 15
15	1 57½	65	6 82½	115	12 7½	178	18 69	440	46 20
16	1 68	66	6 93	116	12 18	[15] 180	18 90	450	47 25
17	1 78½	67	7 3½	117	12 28½	182	19 11	460	48 30
18	1 89	68	7 14	118	12 39	184	19 32	470	49 35
19	1 99½	69	7 24½	119	12 49½	186	19 53	480	50 40
20	2 10	**70**	7 35	**120**	12 60	188	19 74	490	51 45
21	2 20½	71	7 45½	121	12 70½	190	19 95	**500**	52 50
22	2 31	[6] 72	7 56	122	12 81	[16] 192	20 16	550	57 75
23	2 41½	73	7 66½	123	12 91½	194	20 37	600	63 0
[2] 24	2 52	74	7 77	124	13 2	196	20 58	650	68 25
25	2 62½	75	7 87½	125	13 12½	198	20 79	700	73 50
26	2 73	76	7 98	126	13 23	**200**	21 0	750	78 75
27	2 83½	77	8 8½	127	13 33½	[17] 204	21 42	800	84 0
28	2 94	78	8 19	128	13 44	205	21 52½	850	89 25
29	3 4½	79	8 29½	129	13 54½	210	22 5	900	94 50
30	3 15	**80**	8 40	**130**	13 65	215	22 57½	950	99 75
31	3 25½	81	8 50½	131	13 75½	[18] 216	22 68	**1000**	105 0
32	3 36	82	8 61	[11] 132	13 86	220	23 10	1016	106 68
33	3 46½	83	8 71½	133	13 96½	225	23 62½	1250	131 25
34	3 57	[7] 84	8 82	134	14 7	[19] 228	23 94	1500	157 50
35	3 67½	85	8 92½	135	14 17½	230	24 15	1728	181 44
[3] 36	3 78	86	9 3	136	14 28	235	24 67½	1750	183 75
37	3 88½	87	9 13½	137	14 38½	[20] 240	25 20	1760	184 80
38	3 99	88	9 24	138	14 49	245	25 72½	2000	210 0
39	4 9½	89	9 34½	139	14 59½	**250**	26 25	2240	235 20
40	4 20	**90**	9 45	**140**	14 70	255	26 77½	2500	262 50
41	4 30½	91	9 55½	141	14 80½	260	27 30	3000	315 0
42	4 41	92	9 66	142	14 91	265	27 82½	4000	420 0
43	4 51½	93	9 76½	143	15 1½	270	28 35	5000	525 0
44	4 62	94	9 87	[12] 144	15 12	275	28 87½	6000	630 0
45	4 72½	95	9 97½	145	15 22½	280	29 40	7000	735 0
46	4 83	[8] 96	10 8	146	15 33	285	29 92½	8000	840 0
47	4 93½	97	10 18½	147	15 43½	[24] 288	30 24	9000	945 0
[4] 48	5 4	98	10 29	148	15 54	290	30 45	10000	1050 0
49	5 14½	99	10 39½	149	15 64½	295	30 97½	15000	1575 0
50	5 25	**100**	10 50	**150**	15 75	**300**	31 50	20000	2100 0

*Dozens.

Grosses.

1.	15	12
2.	30	24
3.	45	36
4.	60	48
5.	75	60
6.	90	72
7.	105	84
8.	120	96
9.	136	8
10.	151	20
11.	166	32

Twelfths

1.	0	1
⅙ 2.	0	1¾
3.	0	2¾
⅓ 4.	0	3½
5.	0	4½
½ 6.	0	5¼
7.	0	6¼
⅔ 8.	0	7
9.	0	8
⅚ 10.	0	8¾
11.	0	9¾

Twentieths (10ths)

10ths			10ths		
	1.	0 0½		11.	0 5¾
·1	2.	0 1	·6	12.	0 6¼
	3.	0 1½		13.	0 6¾
·2	4.	0 2	·7	14.	0 7¼
	5.	0 2¾		15.	0 8
·3	6.	0 3¼	·8	16.	0 8½
	7.	0 3¾		17.	0 9
·4	8.	0 4¼	·9	18.	0 9½
	9.	0 4¾		19.	0 10
·5	10.	0 5¼		20.	0 10½

Sixteenths

1.	0 0¾	9.	0 6
⅛ 2.	0 1¼	⅝ 10.	0 6½
3.	0 2	11.	0 7¼
¼ 4.	0 2¾	¾ 12.	0 8
5.	0 3¼	13.	0 8½
⅜ 6.	0 4	⅞ 14.	0 9¼
7.	0 4½	15.	0 9¾
½ 8.	0 5¼		

No.	£ P	No.	£ P	No.	£ P	No.	£ P	No.	£ P
1	0 11	51	5 61	101	11 11	152	16 72	310	34 10
2	0 22	52	5 72	102	11 22	154	16 94	320	35 20
3	0 33	53	5 83	103	11 33	¹³156	17 16	330	36 30
4	0 44	54	5 94	104	11 44	158	17 38	340	37 40
5	0 55	55	6 5	105	11 55	160	17 60	350	38 50
6	0 66	56	6 16	106	11 66	162	17 82	360	39 60
7	0 77	57	6 27	107	11 77	164	18 4	365	40 15
8	0 88	58	6 38	⁹108	11 88	166	18 26	370	40 70
9	0 99	59	6 49	109	11 99	¹⁴168	18 48	380	41 80
10	1 10	⁵60	6 60	110	12 10	170	18 70	390	42 90
*11	1 21	61	6 71	111	12 21	172	18 92	400	44 0
¹12	1 32	62	6 82	112	12 32	174	19 14	410	45 10
13	1 43	63	6 93	113	12 43	175	19 25	420	46 20
14	1 54	64	7 4	114	12 54	176	19 36	430	47 30
15	1 65	65	7 15	115	12 65	178	19 58	440	48 40
16	1 76	66	7 26	116	12 76	¹⁵180	19 80	450	49 50
17	1 87	67	7 37	117	12 87	182	20 2	460	50 60
18	1 98	68	7 48	118	12 98	184	20 24	470	51 70
19	2 9	69	7 59	119	13 9	186	20 46	480	52 80
20	2 20	70	7 70	¹⁰120	13 20	188	20 68	490	53 90
21	2 31	71	7 81	121	13 31	190	20 90	500	55 0
22	2 42	⁶72	7 92	122	13 42	¹⁶192	21 12	550	60 50
23	2 53	73	8 3	123	13 53	194	21 34	600	66 0
²24	2 64	74	8 14	124	13 64	196	21 56	650	71 50
25	2 75	75	8 25	125	13 75	198	21 78	700	77 0
26	2 86	76	8 36	126	13 86	200	22 0	750	82 50
27	2 97	77	8 47	127	13 97	¹⁷204	22 44	800	88 0
28	3 8	78	8 58	128	14 8	205	22 55	850	93 50
29	3 19	79	8 69	129	14 19	210	23 10	900	99 0
30	3 30	80	8 80	130	14 30	215	23 65	950	104 50
31	3 41	81	8 91	131	14 41	¹⁸216	23 76	1000	110 0
32	3 52	82	9 2	¹¹132	14 52	220	24 20	1016	111 76
33	3 63	83	9 13	133	14 63	225	24 75	1250	137 50
34	3 74	⁷84	9 24	134	14 74	¹⁹228	25 8	1500	165 0
35	3 85	85	9 35	135	14 85	230	25 30	1728	190 8
³36	3 96	86	9 46	136	14 96	235	25 85	1750	192 50
37	4 7	87	9 57	137	15 7	²⁰240	26 40	1760	193 60
38	4 18	88	9 68	138	15 18	245	26 95	2000	220 0
39	4 29	89	9 79	139	15 29	250	27 50	2240	246 40
40	4 40	90	9 90	140	15 40	255	28 5	2500	275 0
41	4 51	91	10 1	141	15 51	260	28 60	3000	330 0
42	4 62	92	10 12	142	15 62	265	29 15	4000	440 0
43	4 73	93	10 23	143	15 73	270	29 70	5000	550 0
44	4 84	94	10 34	¹²144	15 84	275	30 25	6000	660 0
45	4 95	95	10 45	145	15 95	280	30 80	7000	770 0
46	5 6	⁸96	10 56	146	16 6	285	31 35	8000	880 0
47	5 17	97	10 67	147	16 17	²⁴288	31 68	9000	990 0
⁴48	5 28	98	10 78	148	16 28	290	31 90	10,000	1100 0
49	5 39	99	10 89	149	16 39	295	32 45	15,000	1650 0
50	5 50	100	11 0	150	16 50	300	33 0	20,000	2200 0

Grosses		Twelfths			10ths	Twentieths				Sixteenths			
1.	15 84		1.	0 1		1.	0 0½	11.	0 6		1.	0 0¾	9. 0 6¼
2.	31 68	⅙	2.	0 1¾	·1	2.	0 1	·6 12.	0 6½	⅛	2.	0 1½	10. 0 7
3.	47 52	¼	3.	0 2¾		3.	0 1½	13.	0 7		3.	0 2	11. 0 7½
4.	63 36	⅓	4.	0 3¾	·2	4.	0 2¼	·7 14.	0 7¾	¼	4.	0 2¾	12. 0 8¼
5.	79 20		5.	0 4½		5.	0 2¾	15.	0 8¼		5.	0 3½	13. 0 9
6.	95 4	½	6.	0 5½	·3	6.	0 3½	·8 16.	0 8¾	⅜	6.	0 4¼	14. 0 9¾
7.	110 88		7.	0 6½		7.	0 3¾	17.	0 9¼		7.	0 4¾	15. 0 10¼
8.	126 72	⅔	8.	0 7¼	·4	8.	0 4½	·9 18.	0 10	½	8.	0 5½	
9.	142 56		9.	0 8¼		9.	0 5	19.	0 10½				
10.	158 40	⅚	10.	0 9¼	·5	10.	0 5½	20.	0 11				
11.	174 24		11.	0 10									

Columns: Quantity | £   P

Qty	£ P	Qty	£ P	Qty	£ P	Qty	£ P	Qty	£ P
1	0 11½	51	5 86½	101	11 61½	152	17 48	310	35 65
2	0 23	52	5 98	102	11 73	154	17 71	320	36 80
3	0 34½	53	6 9½	103	11 84½	[13]156	17 94	330	37 95
4	0 46	54	6 21	104	11 96	158	18 17	340	39 10
5	0 57½	55	6 32½	105	12 7½	160	18 40	350	40 25
*6	0 69	56	6 44	106	12 19	162	18 63	360	41 40
7	0 80½	57	6 55½	107	12 30½	164	18 86	365	41 97½
8	0 92	58	6 67	[9]108	12 42	166	19 9	370	42 55
9	1 3½	59	6 78½	109	12 53½	[14]168	19 32	380	43 70
10	1 15	[5]60	6 90	110	12 65	170	19 55	390	44 85
*11	1 26½	61	7 1½	111	12 76½	172	19 78	400	46 0
[1]12	1 38	62	7 13	112	12 88	174	20 1	410	47 15
13	1 49½	63	7 24½	113	12 99½	175	20 12½	420	48 30
14	1 61	64	7 36	114	13 11	176	20 24	430	49 45
15	1 72½	65	7 47½	115	13 22½	178	20 47	440	50 60
16	1 84	66	7 59	116	13 34	[15]180	20 70	450	51 75
17	1 95½	67	7 70½	117	13 45½	182	20 93	460	52 90
18	2 7	68	7 82	118	13 57	184	21 16	470	54 5
19	2 18½	69	7 93½	119	13 68½	186	21 39	480	55 20
20	2 30	70	8 5	120	13 80	188	21 62	490	56 35
21	2 41½	71	8 16½	121	13 91½	190	21 85	500	57 50
22	2 53	[6]72	8 28	122	14 3	[16]192	22 8	550	63 25
23	2 64½	73	8 39½	123	14 14½	194	22 31	600	69 0
[2]24	2 76	74	8 51	124	14 26	196	22 54	650	74 75
25	2 87½	75	8 62½	125	14 37½	198	22 77	700	80 50
26	2 99	76	8 74	126	14 49	200	23 0	750	86 25
27	3 10½	77	8 85½	127	14 60½	[17]204	23 46	800	92 0
28	3 22	78	8 97	128	14 72	205	23 57½	850	97 75
29	3 33½	79	9 8½	129	14 83½	210	24 15	900	103 50
30	3 45	80	9 20	130	14 95	215	24 72½	950	109 25
31	3 56½	81	9 31½	131	15 6½	[18]216	24 84	1000	115 0
32	3 68	82	9 43	[11]132	15 18	220	25 30	1016	116 84
33	3 79½	83	9 54½	133	15 29½	225	25 87½	1250	143 75
34	3 91	[7]84	9 66	134	15 41	[19]228	26 22	1500	172 50
35	4 2½	85	9 77½	135	15 52½	230	26 45	1728	198 72
*36	4 14	86	9 89	136	15 64	235	27 2½	1750	201 25
37	4 25½	87	10 0½	137	15 75½	[20]240	27 60	1760	202 40
38	4 37	88	10 12	138	15 87	245	28 17½	2000	230 0
39	4 48½	89	10 23½	139	15 98½	250	28 75	2240	257 60
40	4 60	90	10 35	140	16 10	255	29 32½	2500	287 50
41	4 71½	91	10 46½	141	16 21½	260	29 90	3000	345 0
42	4 83	92	10 58	142	16 33	265	30 47½	4000	460 0
43	4 94½	93	10 69½	143	16 44½	270	31 5	5000	575 0
44	5 6	94	10 81	[12]144	16 56	275	31 62½	6000	690 0
45	5 17½	95	10 92½	145	16 67½	280	32 20	7000	805 0
46	5 29	[8]96	11 4	146	16 79	285	32 77½	8000	920 0
47	5 40½	97	11 15½	147	16 90½	[24]288	33 12	9000	1035 0
*48	5 52	98	11 27	148	17 2	290	33 35	10,000	1150 0
49	5 63½	99	11 38½	149	17 13½	295	33 92½	15,000	1725 0
50	5 75	100	11 50	150	17 25	300	34 50	20,000	2300 0

(margin label: *Dozens*)

Grosses	£ P	Twelfths	£ P	10ths / Twentieths	£ P		£ P	Sixteenths	£ P		£ P
1.	16 56	1.	0 1	1.	0 0½	11.	0 6¼	1.	0 0½	9.	0 6½
2.	33 12	2.	0 2	2.	0 0¾	12.	0 7	2.	0 1½	10.	0 7¼
3.	49 68	3.	0 3½	3.	0 1½	13.	0 7½	3.	0 2	11.	0 8
4.	66 24	4.	0 3¾	4.	0 2¼	14.	0 8	4.	0 3	12.	0 8½
5.	82 80	5.	0 5¼	5.	0 3	15.	0 8½	5.	0 3½	13.	0 9¼
6.	99 36	6.	0 5¾	6.	0 3½	16.	0 9¼	6.	0 4½	14.	0 10
7.	115 92	7.	0 6¾	7.	0 4	17.	0 9¾	7.	0 5	14.	0 10
8.	132 48	8.	0 7½	8.	0 4¾	18.	0 10¼	8.	0 5¾	15.	0 10½
9.	149 4	9.	0 8¼	9.	0 5½	19.	0 11				
10.	165 60	10.	0 9¼	10.	0 5¾	20.	0 11½				
11.	182 16	11.	0 10½								

*Dozens	£	P	Dozens	£	P	Dozens	£	P	Dozens	£	P		£	P
1	0	12	51	6	12	101	12	12	152	18	24	310	37	20
2	0	24	52	6	24	102	12	24	154	18	48	320	38	40
3	0	36	53	6	36	103	12	36	[13] 156	18	72	330	39	60
4	0	48	54	6	48	104	12	48	158	18	96	340	40	80
5	0	60	55	6	60	105	12	60	160	19	20	350	42	00
6	0	72	56	6	72	106	12	72	162	19	44	360	43	20
7	0	84	57	6	84	107	12	84	164	19	68	365	43	80
8	0	96	58	6	96	[9] 108	12	96	166	19	92	370	44	40
9	1	8	59	7	8	109	13	8	[14] 168	20	16	380	45	60
10	1	20	[5] **60**	7	20	**110**	13	20	170	20	40	390	46	80
11	1	32	61	7	32	111	13	32	172	20	64	400	48	0
[1] 12	1	44	62	7	44	112	13	44	174	20	88	410	49	20
13	1	56	63	7	56	113	13	56	175	21	0	420	50	40
14	1	68	64	7	68	114	13	68	176	21	12	430	51	60
15	1	80	65	7	80	115	13	80	178	21	36	440	52	80
16	1	92	66	7	92	116	13	92	[15] 180	21	60	450	54	0
17	2	4	67	8	4	117	14	4	182	21	84	460	55	20
18	2	16	68	8	16	118	14	16	184	22	8	470	56	40
19	2	28	69	8	28	119	14	28	186	22	32	480	57	60
20	2	40	**70**	8	40	**120**	14	40	188	22	56	490	58	80
21	2	52	71	8	52	121	14	52	190	22	80	500	60	0
22	2	64	[6] 72	8	64	122	14	64	[16] 192	23	4	550	66	0
23	2	76	73	8	76	123	14	76	194	23	28	600	72	0
[2] 24	2	88	74	8	88	124	14	88	196	23	52	650	78	0
25	3	0	75	9	0	125	15	0	198	23	76	700	84	0
26	3	12	76	9	12	126	15	12	**200**	24	0	750	90	0
27	3	24	77	9	24	127	15	24	[17] 204	24	48	800	96	0
28	3	36	78	9	36	128	15	36	205	24	60	850	102	0
29	3	48	79	9	48	129	15	48	210	25	20	900	108	0
30	3	60	**80**	9	60	**130**	15	60	215	25	80	950	114	0
31	3	72	81	9	72	131	15	72	[18] 216	25	92	1000	120	0
32	3	84	82	9	84	[11] 132	15	84	220	26	40	1016	121	92
33	3	96	83	9	96	133	15	96	225	27	0	1250	150	0
34	4	8	[7] 84	10	8	134	16	8	[19] 228	27	36	1500	180	0
35	4	20	85	10	20	135	16	20	230	27	60	1728	207	36
[3] 36	4	32	86	10	32	136	16	32	235	28	20	1750	210	0
37	4	44	87	10	44	137	16	44	[20] 240	28	80	1760	211	20
38	4	56	88	10	56	138	16	56	245	29	40	2000	240	0
39	4	68	89	10	68	139	16	68	**250**	30	0	2240	268	80
40	4	80	**90**	10	80	**140**	16	80	255	30	60	2500	300	0
41	4	92	91	10	92	141	16	92	260	31	20	3000	360	0
42	5	4	92	11	4	142	17	4	265	31	80	4000	480	0
43	5	16	93	11	16	143	17	16	270	32	40	5000	600	0
44	5	28	94	11	28	[12] 144	17	28	275	33	00	6000	720	0
45	5	40	95	11	40	145	17	40	280	33	60	7000	840	0
46	5	52	[8] 96	11	52	146	17	52	285	34	20	8000	960	0
47	5	64	97	11	64	147	17	64	[24] 288	34	56	9000	1080	0
[4] 48	5	76	98	11	76	148	17	76	290	34	80	10,000	1200	0
49	5	88	99	11	88	149	17	88	295	35	40	15,000	1800	0
50	6	0	**100**	12	0	**150**	18	0	**300**	36	0	20,000	2400	0

Grosses

1.	17	28
2.	34	56
3.	51	84
4.	69	12
5.	86	40
6.	103	68
7.	120	96
8.	138	24
9.	155	52
10.	172	80
11.	190	8

Twelfths

	1.	0	1
⅙	2.	0	2
	3.	0	3
⅓	4.	0	4
	5.	0	5
½	6.	0	6
	7.	0	7
⅔	8.	0	8
	9.	0	9
⅚	10.	0	10
	11.	0	11

Twentieths

10ths				10ths			
	1.	0	0½		11.	0	6½
·1	2.	0	1¼	·6	12.	0	7¼
	3.	0	1¾		13.	0	7¾
·2	4.	0	2½	·7	14.	0	8½
	5.	0	3		15.	0	9
·3	6.	0	3½	·8	16.	0	9½
	7.	0	4¼		17.	0	10¼
·4	8.	0	4¾	·9	18.	0	10¾
	9.	0	5½		19.	0	11½
·5	10.	0	6		20.	0	12

Sixteenths

	1.	0	0¾		9.	0	6¾
⅛	2.	0	1½	⅝	10.	0	7½
	3.	0	2¼		11.	0	8¼
¼	4.	0	3	¾	12.	0	9
	5.	0	3¾		13.	0	9¾
⅜	6.	0	4½	⅞	14.	0	10½
	7.	0	5¼		15.	0	11¼
½	8.	0	6				

*Dozens		£	P	Dozens		£	P	Dozens		£	P	Dozens		£	P		£	P
	1	0	12½		51	6	37½		101	12	62½		152	19	0	310	38	75
	2	0	25		52	6	50		102	12	75		154	19	25	320	40	0
	3	0	37½		53	6	62½		103	12	87½	13	156	19	50	330	41	25
	4	0	50		54	6	75		104	13	0		158	19	75	340	42	50
	5	0	62½		55	6	87½		105	13	12½		160	20	0	350	43	75
	6	0	75		56	7	0		106	13	25		162	20	25	360	45	0
	7	0	87½		57	7	12½		107	13	37½		164	20	50	365	45	62½
	8	1	0		58	7	25	9	108	13	50		166	20	75	370	46	25
	9	1	12½		59	7	37½		109	13	62½	14	168	21	0	380	47	50
	10	1	25	5	**60**	7	50		**110**	13	75		170	21	25	390	48	75
*	11	1	37½		61	7	62½		111	13	87½		172	21	50	400	50	0
1	12	1	50		62	7	75		112	14	0		174	21	75	410	51	25
	13	1	62½		63	7	87½		113	14	12½		175	21	87½	420	52	50
	14	1	75		64	8	0		114	14	25		176	22	0	430	53	75
	15	1	87½		65	8	12½		115	14	37½		178	22	25	440	55	0
	16	2	0		66	8	25		116	14	50	15	180	22	50	450	56	25
	17	2	12½		67	8	37½		117	14	62½		182	22	75	460	57	50
	18	2	25		68	8	50		118	14	75		184	23	0	470	58	75
	19	2	37½		69	8	62½		119	14	87½		186	23	25	480	60	0
	20	2	50		**70**	8	75		**120**	15	0		188	23	50	490	61	25
	21	2	62½		71	8	87½		121	15	12½		190	23	75	**500**	62	50
	22	2	75	6	72	9	0		122	15	25	16	192	24	0	550	68	75
	23	2	87½		73	9	12½		123	15	37½		194	24	25	600	75	0
2	24	3	0		74	9	25		124	15	50		196	24	50	650	81	25
	25	3	12½		75	9	37½		125	15	62½		198	24	75	700	87	50
	26	3	25		76	9	50		126	15	75		**200**	25	0	750	93	75
	27	3	37½		77	9	62½		127	15	87½	17	204	25	50	800	100	0
	28	3	50		78	9	75		128	16	0		205	25	62½	850	106	25
	29	3	62½		79	9	87½		129	16	12½		210	26	25	900	112	50
	30	3	75		**80**	10	0		**130**	16	25		215	26	87½	950	118	75
	31	3	87½		81	10	12½		131	16	37½	18	216	27	0	**1000**	125	0
	32	4	0		82	10	25	11	132	16	50		220	27	50	1016	127	0
	33	4	12½		83	10	37½		133	16	62½		225	28	12½	1250	156	25
	34	4	25	7	84	10	50		134	16	75	19	228	28	50	1500	187	50
	35	4	37½		85	10	62½		135	16	87½		230	28	75	1728	216	0
3	36	4	50		86	10	75		136	17	0		235	29	37½	1750	218	75
	37	4	62½		87	10	87½		137	17	12½	20	240	30	0	1760	220	0
	38	4	75		88	11	0		138	17	25		245	30	62½	2000	250	0
	39	4	87½		89	11	12½		139	17	37½		**250**	31	25	2240	280	0
	40	5	0		**90**	11	25		**140**	17	50		255	31	87½	2500	312	50
	41	5	12½		91	11	37½		141	17	62½		260	32	50	3000	375	0
	42	5	25		92	11	50		142	17	75		265	33	12½	4000	500	0
	43	5	37½		93	11	62½		143	17	87½		270	33	75	**5000**	625	0
	44	5	50		94	11	75	12	144	18	0		275	34	37½	6000	750	0
	45	5	62½		95	11	87½		145	18	12½		280	35	0	7000	875	0
	46	5	75	8	96	12	0		146	18	25		285	35	62½	8000	1000	0
	47	5	87½		97	12	12½		147	18	37½	24	288	36	0	9000	1125	0
4	48	6	0		98	12	25		148	18	50		290	36	25	10,000	1250	0
	49	6	12½		99	12	37½		149	18	62½		295	36	87½	15,000	1875	0
	50	6	25		**100**	12	50		**150**	18	75		**300**	37	50	20,000	2500	0

Grosses

1.	18	0
2.	36	0
3.	54	0
4.	72	0
5.	90	0
6.	108	0
7.	126	0
8.	144	0
9.	162	0
10.	180	0
11.	198	0

Twelfths

	1.	0	1
⅙	2.	0	2
	3.	0	3¼
⅓	4.	0	4¼
	5.	0	5¼
½	6.	0	6¼
	7.	0	7¼
⅔	8.	0	8¼
	9.	0	9½
⅚	10.	0	10½
	11.	0	11½

Twentieths

10ths				10ths			
	1.	0	0¾		11.	0	7
·1	2.	0	1¼	·6	12.	0	7½
	3.	0	2		13.	0	8¼
·2	4.	0	2½	·7	14.	0	8¾
	5.	0	3¼		15.	0	9½
·3	6.	0	3¾	·8	16.	0	10
	7.	0	4½		17.	0	10¾
·4	8.	0	5	·9	18.	0	11¼
	9.	0	5¾		19.	0	12
·5	10.	0	6¼		20.	0	12½

Sixteenths

	1.	0	0¾		9.	0	7
⅛	2.	0	1½	⅝	10.	0	7¾
	3.	0	2¼		11.	0	8½
¼	4.	0	3¼	¾	12.	0	9½
	5.	0	4		13.	0	10¼
⅜	6.	0	4¾	⅞	14.	0	11
	7.	0	5½		15.	0	11¾
½	8.	0	6¼				

	£	P		£	P		£	P		£	P		£	P
1	0	13	51	6	63	101	13	13	152	19	76	310	40	30
2	0	26	52	6	76	102	13	26	154	20	2	320	41	60
3	0	39	53	6	89	103	13	39	156	20	28	330	42	90
4	0	52	54	7	2	104	13	52	158	20	54	340	44	20
5	0	65	55	7	15	105	13	65	160	20	80	350	45	50
6	0	78	56	7	28	106	13	78	162	21	6	360	46	80
7	0	91	57	7	41	107	13	91	164	21	32	365	47	45
8	1	4	58	7	54	108	14	4	166	21	58	370	48	10
9	1	17	59	7	67	109	14	17	168	21	84	380	49	40
10	1	30	60	7	80	110	14	30	170	22	10	390	50	70
11	1	43	61	7	93	111	14	43	172	22	36	400	52	0
12	1	56	62	8	6	112	14	56	174	22	62	410	53	30
13	1	69	63	8	19	113	14	69	175	22	75	420	54	60
14	1	82	64	8	32	114	14	82	176	22	88	430	55	90
15	1	95	65	8	45	115	14	95	178	23	14	440	57	20
16	2	8	66	8	58	116	15	8	180	23	40	450	58	50
17	2	21	67	8	71	117	15	21	182	23	66	460	59	80
18	2	34	68	8	84	118	15	34	184	23	92	470	61	10
19	2	47	69	8	97	119	15	47	186	24	18	480	62	40
20	2	60	70	9	10	120	15	60	188	24	44	490	63	70
21	2	73	71	9	23	121	15	73	190	24	70	500	65	0
22	2	86	72	9	36	122	15	86	192	24	96	550	71	50
23	2	99	73	9	49	123	15	99	194	25	22	600	78	0
24	3	12	74	9	62	124	16	12	196	25	48	650	84	50
25	3	25	75	9	75	125	16	25	198	25	74	700	91	0
26	3	38	76	9	88	126	16	38	200	26	0	750	97	50
27	3	51	77	10	1	127	16	51	204	26	52	800	104	0
28	3	64	78	10	14	128	16	64	205	26	65	850	110	50
29	3	77	79	10	27	129	16	77	210	27	30	900	117	0
30	3	90	80	10	40	130	16	90	215	27	95	950	123	50
31	4	3	81	10	53	131	17	3	216	28	8	1000	130	0
32	4	16	82	10	66	132	17	16	220	28	60	1016	132	8
33	4	29	83	10	79	133	17	29	225	29	25	1250	162	50
34	4	42	84	10	92	134	17	42	228	29	64	1500	195	0
35	4	55	85	11	5	135	17	55	230	29	90	1728	224	64
36	4	68	86	11	18	136	17	68	235	30	55	1750	227	50
37	4	81	87	11	31	137	17	81	240	31	20	1760	228	80
38	4	94	88	11	44	138	17	94	245	31	85	2000	260	0
39	5	7	89	11	57	139	18	7	250	32	50	2240	291	20
40	5	20	90	11	70	140	18	20	255	33	15	2500	325	0
41	5	33	91	11	83	141	18	33	260	33	80	3000	390	0
42	5	46	92	11	96	142	18	46	265	34	45	4000	520	0
43	5	59	93	12	9	143	18	59	270	35	10	5000	650	0
44	5	72	94	12	22	144	18	72	275	35	75	6000	780	0
45	5	85	95	12	35	145	18	85	280	36	40	7000	910	0
46	5	98	96	12	48	146	18	98	285	37	5	8000	1040	0
47	6	11	97	12	61	147	19	11	288	37	44	9000	1170	0
48	6	24	98	12	74	148	19	24	290	37	70	10,000	1300	0
49	6	37	99	12	87	149	19	37	295	38	35	15,000	1950	0
50	6	50	100	13	0	150	19	50	300	39	0	20,000	2600	0

Grosses			Twelfths			10ths / Twentieths						Sixteenths					
1.	18	72	1/12 1.	0	1		1.	0	0½		11.	0	7½	1.	0	0¾	9.	0	7½
2.	37	44	1/6 2.	0	2¼	·1	2.	0	1¼	·6	12.	0	7¾	1/2 2.	0	1¾	5/8 10.	0	8¼
3.	56	16	1/4 3.	0	3¼		3.	0	1¾		13.	0	8½	3.	0	2½	11.	0	9
4.	74	88	1/3 4.	0	4¼	·2	4.	0	2½	·7	14.	0	9	1/4 4.	0	3¼	3/4 12.	0	9¾
5.	93	60	5.	0	5¼		5.	0	3¼		15.	0	9¾	5.	0	4	13.	0	10½
6.	112	32	1/2 6.	0	6¼	·3	6.	0	4	·8	16.	0	10½	3/8 6.	0	5	7/8 14.	0	11¼
7.	131	4	7.	0	7¼		7.	0	4½		17.	0	11	7.	0	5¾	15.	0	12¼
8.	149	76	2/3 8.	0	8¼	·4	8.	0	5¼	·9	18.	0	11¾	1/2 8.	0	6½			
9.	168	48	9.	0	9¼		9.	0	5¾		19.	0	12¼						
10.	187	20	5/6 10.	0	10¼	·5	10.	0	6½		20.	0	13						
11.	205	92	11.	0	12														

*Dozens.	£	P	Dozens.	£	P	Dozens	£	P	Dozens.	£	P		£	P
1	0	13½	51	6	88½	101	13	63½	152	20	52	310	41	85
2	0	27	52	7	2	102	13	77	154	20	79	320	43	20
3	0	40½	53	7	15½	103	13	90½	[13] 156	21	6	330	44	55
4	0	54	54	7	29	104	14	4	158	21	33	340	45	90
5	0	67½	55	7	42½	105	14	17½	160	21	60	350	47	25
6	0	81	56	7	56	106	14	31	162	21	87	360	48	60
7	0	94½	57	7	69½	107	14	44½	164	22	14	365	49	27½
8	1	8	58	7	83	[9] 108	14	58	166	22	41	370	49	95
9	1	21½	59	7	96½	109	14	71½	[14] 168	22	68	380	51	30
10	1	35	[5] **60**	8	10	**110**	14	85	170	22	95	390	52	65
11	1	48½	61	8	23½	111	14	98½	172	23	22	400	54	00
*[1] 12	1	62	62	8	37	112	15	12	174	23	49	410	55	35
13	1	75½	63	8	50½	113	15	25½	175	23	62½	420	56	70
14	1	89	64	8	64	114	15	39	176	23	76	430	58	05
15	2	2½	65	8	77½	115	15	52½	178	24	3	440	59	40
16	2	16	66	8	91	116	15	66	[15] 180	24	30	450	60	75
17	2	29½	67	9	4½	117	15	79½	182	24	57	460	62	10
18	2	43	68	9	18	118	15	93	184	24	84	470	63	45
19	2	56½	69	9	31½	119	16	6½	186	25	11	480	64	80
20	2	70	**70**	9	45	**120**	16	20	188	25	38	490	66	15
21	2	83½	71	9	58½	121	16	33½	190	25	65	**500**	67	50
22	2	97	[6] 72	9	72	122	16	47	[16] 192	25	92	550	74	25
23	3	10½	73	9	85½	123	16	60½	194	26	19	600	81	0
[2] 24	3	24	74	9	99	124	16	74	196	26	46	650	87	75
25	3	37½	75	10	12½	125	16	87½	198	26	73	700	94	50
26	3	51	76	10	26	126	17	1	**200**	27	0	750	101	25
27	3	64½	77	10	39½	127	17	14½	[17] 204	27	54	800	108	0
28	3	78	78	10	53	128	17	28	205	27	67½	850	114	75
29	3	91½	79	10	66½	129	17	41½	210	28	35	900	121	50
30	4	5	**80**	10	80	**130**	17	55	215	29	2½	950	128	25
31	4	18½	81	10	93½	131	17	68½	[18] 216	29	16	**1000**	135	0
32	4	32	82	11	7	[11] 132	17	82	220	29	70	1016	137	16
33	4	45½	83	11	20½	133	17	95½	225	30	37½	1250	168	75
34	4	59	[7] 84	11	34	134	18	9	[19] 228	30	78	1500	202	50
35	4	72½	85	11	47½	135	18	22½	230	31	5	1728	233	28
[3] 36	4	86	86	11	61	136	18	36	235	31	72½	1750	236	25
37	4	99½	87	11	74½	137	18	49½	[20] 240	32	40	1760	237	60
38	5	13	88	11	88	138	18	63	245	33	7½	2000	270	0
39	5	26½	89	12	1½	139	18	76½	**250**	33	75	2240	302	40
40	5	40	**90**	12	15	**140**	18	90	255	34	42½	2500	337	50
41	5	53½	91	12	28½	141	19	3½	260	35	10	3000	405	0
42	5	67	92	12	42	142	19	17	265	35	77½	4000	540	0
43	5	80½	93	12	55½	143	19	30½	270	36	45	5000	675	0
44	5	94	94	12	69	[12] 144	19	44	275	37	12½	6000	810	0
45	6	7½	95	12	82½	145	19	57½	280	37	80	7000	945	0
46	6	21	[8] 96	12	96	146	19	71	285	38	47½	8000	1080	0
47	6	34½	97	13	9½	147	19	84½	[24] 288	38	88	9000	1215	0
[4] 48	6	48	98	13	23	148	19	98	290	39	15	10000	1350	0
49	6	61½	99	13	36½	149	20	11½	295	39	82½	15000	2025	0
50	6	75	**100**	13	50	**150**	20	25	**300**	40	50	20000	2700	0

Grosses.

1.	19	44
2.	38	88
3.	58	32
4.	77	76
5.	97	20
6.	116	64
7.	136	08
8.	155	52
9.	174	96
10.	194	40
11.	213	84

Twelfths

1.	0	1¼
⅙ 2.	0	2¼
3.	0	3½
¼ 4.	0	4½
5.	0	5¾
½ 6.	0	6¾
7.	0	8
⅔ 8.	0	9
9.	0	10¼
⅚ 10.	0	11¼
11.	0	12½

Twentieths

10ths				10ths			
	1.	0	0¾		11.	0	7½
·1	2.	0	1¼	·6	12.	0	8
	3.	0	2		13.	0	8¾
·2	4.	0	2¾	·7	14.	0	9½
	5.	0	3½		15.	0	10¼
·3	6.	0	4	·8	16.	0	10¾
	7.	0	4¾		17.	0	11½
·4	8.	0	5½	·9	18.	0	12¼
	9.	0	6		19.	0	12¾
·5	10.	0	5¾		20.	0	13½

Sixteenths

1.	0	0¾	9.	0	7½
⅛ 2.	0	1¾	⅝ 10.	0	8½
3.	0	2½	11.	0	9¼
¼ 4.	0	3½	¾ 12.	0	10¼
5.	0	4¼	13.	0	11
⅜ 6.	0	5	⅞ 14.	0	11¾
7.	0	6	15.	0	12¾
½ 8.	0	6¾			

Qty	£	P	Qty	£	P	Qty	£	P	Qty	£	P	Qty	£	P
1	0	14	51	7	14	101	14	14	152	21	28	310	43	40
2	0	28	52	7	28	102	14	28	154	21	56	320	44	80
3	0	42	53	7	42	103	14	42	[13] 156	21	84	330	46	20
4	0	56	54	7	56	104	14	56	158	22	12	340	47	60
5	0	70	55	7	70	105	14	70	160	22	40	350	49	0
*6	0	84	56	7	84	106	14	84	162	22	68	360	50	40
7	0	98	57	7	98	107	14	98	164	22	96	365	51	10
8	1	12	58	8	12	[9] 108	15	12	166	23	24	370	51	80
9	1	26	59	8	26	109	15	26	[14] 168	23	52	380	53	20
10	**1**	**40**	[5] **60**	**8**	**40**	**110**	**15**	**40**	170	23	80	390	54	60
*11	1	54	61	8	54	111	15	54	172	24	8	400	56	0
[1] 12	1	68	62	8	68	112	15	68	174	24	36	410	57	40
13	1	82	63	8	82	113	15	82	175	24	50	420	58	80
14	1	96	64	8	96	114	15	96	176	24	64	430	60	20
15	2	10	65	9	10	115	16	10	178	24	92	440	61	60
16	2	24	66	9	24	116	16	24	[15] 180	25	20	450	63	0
17	2	38	67	9	38	117	16	38	182	25	48	460	64	40
18	2	52	68	9	52	118	16	52	184	25	76	470	65	80
19	2	66	69	9	66	119	16	66	186	26	4	480	67	20
20	**2**	**80**	**70**	**9**	**80**	**120**	**16**	**80**	188	26	32	490	68	60
21	2	94	71	9	94	121	16	94	190	26	60	**500**	**70**	**0**
22	3	8	[6] 72	10	8	122	17	8	[16] 192	26	88	550	77	0
23	3	22	73	10	22	123	17	22	194	27	16	600	84	0
[2] 24	3	36	74	10	36	124	17	36	196	27	44	650	91	0
25	3	50	75	10	50	125	17	50	198	27	72	700	98	0
26	3	64	76	10	64	126	17	64	**200**	**28**	**0**	750	105	0
27	3	78	77	10	78	127	17	78	[17] 204	28	56	800	112	0
28	3	92	78	10	92	128	17	92	205	28	70	850	119	0
29	4	6	79	11	6	129	18	6	210	29	40	900	126	0
30	**4**	**20**	**80**	**11**	**20**	**130**	**18**	**20**	215	30	10	950	133	0
31	4	34	81	11	34	131	18	34	[18] 216	30	24	**1000**	**140**	**0**
32	4	48	82	11	48	[11] 132	18	48	220	30	80	1016	142	24
33	4	62	83	11	62	133	18	62	225	31	50	1250	175	0
34	4	76	[7] 84	11	76	134	18	76	[19] 228	31	92	1500	210	0
35	4	90	85	11	90	135	18	90	230	32	20	1728	241	92
[3] 36	5	4	86	12	4	136	19	4	235	32	90	1750	245	0
37	5	18	87	12	18	137	19	18	[20] 240	33	60	1760	246	40
38	5	32	88	12	32	138	19	32	245	34	30	2000	280	0
39	5	46	89	12	46	139	19	46	**250**	**35**	**0**	2240	313	60
40	**5**	**60**	**90**	**12**	**60**	**140**	**19**	**60**	255	35	70	2500	350	0
41	5	74	91	12	74	141	19	74	260	36	40	3000	420	0
42	5	88	92	12	88	142	19	88	265	37	10	4000	560	0
43	6	2	93	13	2	143	20	2	270	37	80	**5000**	**700**	**0**
44	6	16	94	13	16	[12] 144	20	16	275	38	50	6000	840	0
45	6	30	95	13	30	145	20	30	280	39	20	7000	980	0
46	6	44	[8] 96	13	44	146	20	44	285	39	90	8000	1120	0
47	6	58	97	13	58	147	20	58	[24] 288	40	32	9000	1260	0
[4] 48	6	72	98	13	72	148	20	72	290	40	60	10,000	1400	0
49	6	86	99	13	86	149	20	86	295	41	30	15,000	2100	0
50	**7**	**0**	**100**	**14**	**0**	**150**	**21**	**0**	**300**	**42**	**0**	20,000	2800	0

(Dozens)

Grosses

1.	20	16
2.	40	32
3.	60	48
4.	80	64
5.	100	80
6.	120	96
7.	141	12
8.	161	28
9.	181	44
10.	201	60
11.	221	76

Twelfths

	1.		1¼
⅙	2.	0	2¼
	3.	0	3½
⅓	4.	0	4¾
	5.	0	5¾
½	6.	0	7
	7.	0	8¼
⅔	8.	0	9¼
	9.	0	10½
⅚	10.	0	11¾
	11.	0	12¾

Twentieths

10ths				10ths			
	1.	0	0¾		11.	0	7¾
·1	2.	0	1½	·6	12.	0	8½
	3.	0	2		13.	0	9
·2	4.	0	2¾	·7	14.	0	9¾
	5.	0	3½		15.	0	10½
·3	6.	0	4¼	·8	16.	0	11¼
	7.	0	5		17.	0	12
·4	8.	0	5½	·9	18.	0	12½
	9.	0	6¼		19.	0	13¼
·5	10.	0	7		20.	0	14

Sixteenths

	1.	0	1		9.	0	8
⅛	2.	0	1¾	⅝	10.	0	8¾
	3.	0	2¾		11.	0	9¾
¼	4.	0	3½	¾	12.	0	10½
	5.	0	4⅓		13.	0	11½
⅜	6.	0	5¼	⅞	14.	0	12¼
	7.	0	6¼		15.	0	13¼
½	8.	0	7				

	£ P		£ P		£ P		£ P		£ P		£ P
1	0 14½	51	7 39½	101	14 64½	152	22 4	310	44 95		
2	0 29	52	7 54	102	14 79	154	22 33	320	46 40		
3	0 43½	53	7 68½	103	14 93½	13 156	22 62	330	47 85		
4	0 58	54	7 83	104	15 8	158	22 91	340	49 30		
5	0 72½	55	7 97½	105	15 22½	160	23 20	350	50 75		
6	0 87	56	8 12	106	15 37	162	23 49	360	52 20		
7	1 1½	57	8 26½	107	15 51½	164	23 78	365	52 92½		
8	1 16	58	8 41	9 108	15 66	166	24 7	370	53 65		
9	1 30½	59	8 55½	109	15 80½	14 168	24 36	380	55 10		
10	1 45	5 60	8 70	110	15 95	170	24 65	390	56 55		
11	1 59½	61	8 84½	111	16 9½	172	24 94	400	58 0		
12	1 74	62	8 99	112	16 24	174	25 23	410	59 45		
13	1 88½	63	9 13½	113	16 38½	175	25 37½	420	60 90		
14	2 3	64	9 28	114	16 53	176	25 52	430	62 35		
15	2 17½	65	9 42½	115	16 67½	178	25 81	440	63 80		
16	2 32	66	9 57	116	16 82	15 180	26 10	450	65 25		
17	2 46½	67	9 71½	117	16 96½	182	26 39	460	66 70		
18	2 61	68	9 86	118	17 11	184	26 68	470	68 15		
19	2 75½	69	10 0½	119	17 25½	186	26 97	480	69 60		
20	2 90	70	10 15	120	17 40	188	27 26	490	71 5		
21	3 4½	71	10 29½	121	17 54½	190	27 55	500	72 50		
22	3 19	6 72	10 44	122	17 69	16 192	27 84	550	79 75		
23	3 33½	73	10 58½	123	17 83½	194	28 13	600	87 0		
24	3 48	74	10 73	124	17 98	196	28 42	650	94 25		
25	3 62½	75	10 87½	125	18 12½	198	28 71	700	101 50		
26	3 77	76	11 2	126	18 27	200	29 0	750	108 75		
27	3 91½	77	11 16½	127	18 41½	17 204	29 58	800	116 0		
28	4 6	78	11 31	128	18 56	205	29 72½	850	123 25		
29	4 20½	79	11 45½	129	18 70½	210	30 45	900	130 50		
30	4 35	80	11 60	130	18 85	215	31 17½	950	137 75		
31	4 49½	81	11 74½	131	18 99½	18 216	31 32	1000	145 0		
32	4 64	82	11 89	11 132	19 14	220	31 90	1016	147 32		
33	4 78½	83	12 3½	133	19 28½	225	32 62½	1250	181 25		
34	4 93	7 84	12 18	134	19 43	19 228	33 6	1500	217 50		
35	5 7½	85	12 32½	135	19 57½	230	33 35	1728	250 56		
36	5 22	86	12 47	136	19 72	235	34 7½	1750	253 75		
37	5 36½	87	12 61½	137	19 86½	20 240	34 80	1760	255 20		
38	5 51	88	12 76	138	20 1	245	35 52½	2000	290 0		
39	5 65½	89	12 90½	139	20 15½	250	36 25	2240	324 80		
40	5 80	90	13 5	140	20 30	255	36 97½	2500	362 50		
41	5 94½	91	13 19½	141	20 44½	260	37 70	3000	435 0		
42	6 9	92	13 34	142	20 59	265	38 42½	4000	580 0		
43	6 23½	93	13 48½	143	20 73½	270	39 15	5000	725 0		
44	6 38	94	13 63	12 144	20 88	275	39 87½	6000	870 0		
45	6 52½	95	13 77½	145	21 2½	280	40 60	7000	1015 0		
46	6 67	8 96	13 92	146	21 17	285	41 32½	8000	1160 0		
47	6 81½	97	14 6½	147	21 31½	24 288	41 76	9000	1305 0		
48	6 96	98	14 21	148	21 46	290	42 5	10,000	1450 0		
49	7 10½	99	14 35½	149	21 60½	295	42 77½	15,000	2175 0		
50	7 25	100	14 50	150	21 75	300	43 50	20,000	2900 0		

Grosses		Twelfths			10ths	Twentieths				Sixteenths			
1.	20 88	1.	0 1¼			1.	0¾	11.	0 8	1.		9.	0 8¼
2.	41 76	½2.	0 2½		·1	2.	0 1½	·6 12.	0 8¾	2.	0 1¾	10.	0 9
3.	62 64	3.	0 3¾			3.	0 2¼	13.	0 9½	½2.	0 1¾	11.	0 10
4.	83 52	¼4.	0 4½		·2	4.	0 3	·7 14.	0 10¼	3.	0 2¾	¼12.	0 11
5.	104 40	5.	0 6			5.	0 3¾	15.	0 11	¼4.	0 3¾	½12.	0 11
6.	125 28	½6.	0 7¼		·3	6.	0 4½	·8 16.	0 11¾	5.	0 4½	13.	0 11¾
7.	146 16	7.	0 8½			7.	0 5	17.	0 12½	½6.	0 5½	¾14.	0 12¾
8.	167 4	¾8.	0 9¾		·4	8.	0 6¼	·9 18.	0 13	7.	0 6¼	15.	0 13¼
9.	187 92	9.	0 11			9.	0 6¾	19.	0 13¾	¾8.	0 7¼		
10.	208 80	½10.	0 12		·5	10.	0 7½	20.	0 14½				
11.	229 68	11.	0 13¼										

15 Pence

15 Pence

*Dozens	£	P	Dozens	£	P	Dozens	£	P	Dozens	£	P		£	P
1	0	15	51	7	65	101	15	15	152	22	80	310	46	50
2	0	30	52	7	80	102	15	30	154	23	10	320	48	0
3	0	45	53	7	95	103	15	45	[13] 156	23	40	330	49	50
4	0	60	54	8	10	104	15	60	158	23	70	340	51	0
5	0	75	55	8	25	105	15	75	160	24	0	350	52	50
6	0	90	56	8	40	106	15	90	162	24	30	360	54	0
7	1	5	57	8	55	107	16	5	164	24	60	365	54	75
8	1	20	58	8	70	[9] 108	16	20	166	24	90	370	55	50
9	1	35	59	8	85	109	16	35	[14] 168	25	20	380	57	0
10	1	50	[5] **60**	9	0	**110**	16	50	170	25	50	390	58	50
*11	1	65	61	9	15	111	16	65	172	25	80	400	60	0
[1] 12	1	80	62	9	30	112	16	80	174	26	10	410	61	50
13	1	95	63	9	45	113	16	95	175	26	25	420	63	0
14	2	10	64	9	60	114	17	10	176	26	40	430	64	50
15	2	25	65	9	75	115	17	25	178	26	70	440	66	0
16	2	40	66	9	90	116	17	40	[15] 180	27	0	450	67	50
17	2	55	67	10	5	117	17	55	182	27	30	460	69	0
18	2	70	68	10	20	118	17	70	184	27	60	470	70	50
19	2	85	69	10	35	119	17	85	186	27	90	480	72	0
20	3	0	**70**	10	50	**120**	18	0	188	28	20	490	73	50
21	3	15	71	10	65	121	18	15	190	28	50	**500**	75	0
22	3	30	[6] 72	10	80	122	18	30	[16] 192	28	80	550	82	50
23	3	45	73	10	95	123	18	45	194	29	10	600	90	0
[2] 24	3	60	74	11	10	124	18	60	196	29	40	650	97	50
25	3	75	75	11	25	125	18	75	198	29	70	700	105	0
26	3	90	76	11	40	126	18	90	**200**	30	0	750	112	50
27	4	5	77	11	55	127	19	5	[17] 204	30	60	800	120	0
28	4	20	78	11	70	128	19	20	205	30	75	850	127	50
29	4	35	79	11	85	129	19	35	210	31	50	900	135	0
30	4	50	**80**	12	0	**130**	19	50	215	32	25	950	142	50
31	4	65	81	12	15	131	19	65	[18] 216	32	40	**1000**	150	0
32	4	80	82	12	30	[11] 132	19	80	220	33	0	1016	152	40
33	4	95	83	12	45	133	19	95	225	33	75	1250	187	50
34	5	10	[7] 84	12	60	134	20	10	[19] 228	34	20	1500	225	0
35	5	25	85	12	75	135	20	25	230	34	50	1728	259	20
[3] 36	5	40	86	12	90	136	20	40	235	35	25	1750	262	50
37	5	55	87	13	5	137	20	55	[20] 240	36	0	1760	264	0
38	5	70	88	13	20	138	20	70	245	36	75	2000	300	0
39	5	85	89	13	35	139	20	85	**250**	37	50	2240	336	0
40	6	0	**90**	13	50	**140**	21	0	255	38	25	2500	375	0
41	6	15	91	13	65	141	21	15	260	39	0	3000	450	0
42	6	30	92	13	80	142	21	30	265	39	75	4000	600	0
43	6	45	93	13	95	143	21	45	270	40	50	5000	750	0
44	6	60	94	14	10	[12] 144	21	60	275	41	25	6000	900	0
45	6	75	95	14	25	145	21	75	280	42	0	7000	1050	0
46	6	90	[8] 96	14	40	146	21	90	285	42	75	8000	1200	0
47	7	5	97	14	55	147	22	5	[24] 288	43	20	9000	1350	0
[4] 48	7	20	98	14	70	148	22	20	290	43	50	10,000	1500	0
49	7	35	99	14	85	149	22	35	295	44	25	15,000	2250	0
50	7	50	**100**	15	0	**150**	22	50	**300**	45	0	20,000	3000	0

Grosses

1.	21	60
2.	43	20
3.	64	80
4.	86	40
5.	108	0
6.	129	60
7.	151	20
8.	172	80
9.	194	40
10.	216	0
11.	237	60

Twelfths

	1.	0	1¼
⅙	2.	0	2½
	3.	0	3¾
⅓	4.	0	5
	5.	0	6¼
½	6.	0	7½
	7.	0	8¾
⅔	8.	0	10
	9.	0	11¼
⅚	10.	0	12½
	11.	0	13¾

Twentieths

10ths				10ths			
	1.	0	0¾		11.	0	8¼
·1	2.	0	1½	·6	12.	0	9
	3.	0	2¼		13.	0	9¾
·2	4.	0	3	·7	14.	0	10½
	5.	0	3¾		15.	0	11¼
·3	6.	0	4½	·8	16.	0	12
	7.	0	5¼		17.	0	12¾
·4	8.	0	6	·9	18.	0	13½
	9.	0	6¾		19.	0	14¼
·5	10.	0	7½		20.	0	15

Sixteenths

	1.	0	1		9.	0	8½
⅛	2.	0	2	⅝	10.	0	9½
	3.	0	2¾		11.	0	10¼
¼	4.	0	3¾	¾	12.	0	11¼
	5.	0	4¾		13.	0	12¼
⅜	6.	0	5¾	⅞	14.	0	13¼
	7.	0	6½		15.	0	14
½	8.	0	7½				

15½ Pence

15½ Pence

*Dozens.

	£	P		£	P		£	P		£	P		£	P
1	0	15½	51	7	90½	101	15	65½	152	23	56	310	48	5
2	0	31	52	8	6	102	15	81	154	23	87	320	49	60
3	0	46½	53	8	21½	103	15	96½	[13] 156	24	18	330	51	15
4	0	62	54	8	37	104	16	12	158	24	49	340	52	70
5	0	77½	55	8	52½	105	16	27½	160	24	80	350	54	25
6	0	93	56	8	68	106	16	43	162	25	11	360	55	80
7	1	8½	57	8	83½	107	16	58½	164	25	42	365	56	57½
8	1	24	58	8	99	[9] 108	16	74	166	25	73	370	57	35
9	1	39½	59	9	14½	109	16	89½	[14] 168	26	4	380	58	90
10	1	55	[5] **60**	9	30	**110**	17	5	170	26	35	390	60	45
*11	1	70½	61	9	45½	111	17	20½	172	26	66	400	62	0
[1] 12	1	86	62	9	61	112	17	36	174	26	97	410	63	55
13	2	1½	63	9	76½	113	17	51½	175	27	12½	420	65	10
14	2	17	64	9	92	114	17	67	176	27	28	430	66	65
15	2	32½	65	10	7½	115	17	82½	178	27	59	440	68	20
16	2	48	66	10	23	116	17	98	[15] 180	27	90	450	69	75
17	2	63½	67	10	38½	117	18	13½	182	28	21	460	71	30
18	2	79	68	10	54	118	18	29	184	28	52	470	72	85
19	2	94½	69	10	69½	119	18	44½	186	28	83	480	74	40
20	3	10	**70**	10	85	**120**	18	60	188	29	14	490	75	95
21	3	25½	71	11	0½	121	18	75½	190	29	45	**500**	77	50
22	3	41	[6] 72	11	16	122	18	91	[16] 192	29	76	550	85	25
23	3	56½	73	11	31½	123	19	6½	194	30	7	600	93	0
[2] 24	3	72	74	11	47	124	19	22	196	30	38	650	100	75
25	3	87½	75	11	62½	125	19	37½	198	30	69	700	108	50
26	4	3	76	11	78	126	19	53	**200**	31	0	750	116	25
27	4	18½	77	11	93½	127	19	68½	[17] 204	31	62	800	124	0
28	4	34	78	12	9	128	19	84	205	31	77½	850	131	75
29	4	49½	79	12	24½	129	19	99½	210	32	55	900	139	50
30	4	65	**80**	12	40	**130**	20	15	215	33	32½	950	147	25
31	4	80½	81	12	55½	131	20	30½	[18] 216	33	48	**1000**	155	0
32	4	96	82	12	71	[11] 132	20	46	220	34	10	1016	157	48
33	5	11½	83	12	86½	133	20	61½	225	34	87½	1250	193	75
34	5	27	[7] 84	13	2	134	20	77	[19] 228	35	34	1500	232	50
35	5	42½	85	13	17½	135	20	92½	230	35	65	1728	267	84
[3] 36	5	58	86	13	33	136	21	8	235	36	42½	1750	271	25
37	5	73½	87	13	48½	137	21	23½	[20] 240	37	20	1760	272	80
38	5	89	88	13	64	138	21	39	245	37	97½	2000	310	0
39	6	4½	89	13	79½	139	21	54½	**250**	38	75	2240	347	20
40	6	20	**90**	13	95	**140**	21	70	255	39	52½	2500	387	50
41	6	35½	91	14	10½	141	21	85½	260	40	30	3000	465	0
42	6	51	92	14	26	142	22	1	265	41	7½	4000	620	0
43	6	66½	93	14	41½	143	22	16½	270	41	85	5000	775	0
44	6	82	94	14	57	[12] 144	22	32	275	42	62½	6000	930	0
45	6	97½	95	14	72½	145	22	47½	280	43	40	7000	1085	0
46	7	13	[8] 96	14	88	146	22	63	285	44	17½	8000	1240	0
47	7	28½	97	15	3½	147	22	78½	[24] 288	44	64	9000	1395	0
[4] 48	7	44	98	15	19	148	22	94	290	44	95	10000	1550	0
49	7	59½	99	15	34½	149	23	9½	295	45	72½	15000	2325	0
50	7	75	**100**	15	50	**150**	23	25	**300**	46	50	20000	3100	0

Grosses.

1.	22	32
2.	44	64
3.	66	96
4.	89	28
5.	111	60
6.	133	92
7.	156	24
8.	178	56
9.	200	88
10.	223	20
11.	245	52

Twelfths

	1.	0	1¼
⅙	2.	0	2½
	3.	0	4
⅓	4.	0	5¼
	5.	0	6½
½	6.	0	7¾
	7.	0	9
⅔	8.	0	10¼
	9.	0	11¾
⅚	10.	0	13
	11.	0	14¼

Twentieths

10ths				10ths			
	1.	0	0¾		11.	0	8½
·1	2.	0	1½	·6	12.	0	9¼
	3.	0	2¼		13.	0	10
·2	4.	0	3	·7	14.	0	10¾
	5.	0	4		15.	0	11¾
·3	6.	0	4¾	·8	16.	0	12½
	7.	0	5½		17.	0	13¼
·4	8.	0	6¼	·9	18.	0	14
	9.	0	7		19.	0	14¾
·5	10.	0	7¾		20.	0	15½

Sixteenths

	1.	0	1		9.	0	8¾
⅛	2.	0	2	⅝	10.	0	9¾
	3.	0	3		11.	0	10¾
¼	4.	0	4	¾	12.	0	11¾
	5.	0	4¾		13.	0	12½
⅜	6.	0	5¾	⅞	14.	0	13½
	7.	0	6¾		15.	0	14½
½	8.	0	7¾				

16 Pence

16 Pence

*Dozens		£	P	Dozens		£	P	Dozens		£	P	Dozens		£	P		£	P
	1	0	16		51	8	16		101	16	16		152	24	32	310	49	60
	2	0	32		52	8	32		102	16	32		154	24	64	320	51	20
	3	0	48		53	8	48		103	16	48	13	156	24	96	330	52	80
	4	0	64		54	8	64		104	16	64		158	25	28	340	54	40
	5	0	80		55	8	80		105	16	80		160	25	60	350	56	0
	6	0	96		56	8	96		106	16	96		162	25	92	360	57	60
	7	1	12		57	9	12		107	17	12		164	26	24	365	58	40
	8	1	28		58	9	28	9	108	17	28		166	26	56	370	59	20
	9	1	44		59	9	44		109	17	44	14	168	26	88	380	60	80
	10	1	60	5	**60**	9	60		**110**	17	60		170	27	20	390	62	40
*	11	1	76		61	9	76		111	17	76		172	27	52	400	64	0
1	12	1	92		62	9	92		112	17	92		174	27	84	410	65	60
	13	2	8		63	10	8		113	18	8		175	28	0	420	67	20
	14	2	24		64	10	24		114	18	24		176	28	16	430	68	80
	15	2	40		65	10	40		115	18	40		178	28	48	440	70	40
	16	2	56		66	10	56		116	18	56	15	180	28	80	450	72	00
	17	2	72		67	10	72		117	18	72		182	29	12	460	73	60
	18	2	88		68	10	88		118	18	88		184	29	44	470	75	20
	19	3	4		69	11	4		119	19	4		186	29	76	480	76	80
	20	3	20		**70**	11	20		**120**	19	20		188	30	8	490	78	40
	21	3	36		71	11	36		121	19	36		190	30	40	**500**	80	0
	22	3	52	6	72	11	52		122	19	52	16	192	30	72	550	88	0
	23	3	68		73	11	68		123	19	68		194	31	4	600	96	0
2	24	3	84		74	11	84		124	19	84		196	31	36	650	104	0
	25	4	0		75	12	0		125	20	0		198	31	68	700	112	0
	26	4	16		76	12	16		126	20	16		**200**	32	0	750	120	0
	27	4	32		77	12	32		127	20	32	17	204	32	64	800	128	0
	28	4	48		78	12	48		128	20	48		205	32	80	850	136	0
	29	4	64		79	12	64		129	20	64		210	33	60	900	144	0
	30	4	80		**80**	12	80		**130**	20	80		215	34	40	950	152	0
	31	4	96		81	12	96		131	20	96	18	216	34	56	**1000**	160	0
	32	5	12		82	13	12	11	132	21	12		220	35	20	1016	162	56
	33	5	28		83	13	28		133	21	28		225	36	0	1250	200	0
	34	5	44	7	84	13	44		134	21	44	19	228	36	48	1500	240	0
	35	5	60		85	13	60		135	21	60		230	36	80	1728	276	48
3	36	5	76		86	13	76		136	21	76		235	37	60	1750	280	0
	37	5	92		87	13	92		137	21	92	20	240	38	40	1760	281	60
	38	6	8		88	14	8		138	22	8		245	39	20	2000	320	0
	39	6	24		89	14	24		139	22	24		**250**	40	0	2240	358	40
	40	6	40		**90**	14	40		**140**	22	40		255	40	80	2500	400	0
	41	6	56		91	14	56		141	22	56		260	41	60	3000	480	0
	42	6	72		92	14	72		142	22	72		265	42	40	4000	640	0
	43	6	88		93	14	88		143	22	88		270	43	20	5000	800	0
	44	7	4		94	15	4	12	144	23	4		275	44	0	6000	960	0
	45	7	20		95	15	20		145	23	20		280	44	80	7000	1120	0
	46	7	36	8	96	15	36		146	23	36		285	45	60	8000	1280	0
	47	7	52		97	15	52		147	23	52	24	288	46	8	9000	1440	0
4	48	7	68		98	15	68		148	23	68		290	46	40	10,000	1600	0
	49	7	84		99	15	84		149	23	84		295	47	20	15,000	2400	0
	50	8	0		**100**	16	0		**150**	24	0		**300**	48	0	20,000	3200	0

Grosses

1.	23	4
2.	46	8
3.	69	12
4.	92	16
5.	115	20
6.	138	24
7.	161	28
8.	184	32
9.	207	36
10.	230	40
11.	253	44

Twelfths

	1.	0	1¼
⅙	2.	0	2¾
	3.	0	4
⅓	4.	0	5¼
	5.	0	6¾
½	6.	0	8
	7.	0	9¼
⅔	8.	0	10¾
	9.	0	12
⅚	10.	0	13¼
	11.	0	14¾

Twentieths

10ths				10ths			
	1.	0	0¾		11.	0	8¾
·1	2.	0	1½	·6	12.	0	9½
	3.	0	2½		13.	0	10½
·2	4.	0	3¼	·7	14.	0	11¼
	5.	0	4		15.	0	12
·3	6.	0	4¾	·8	16.	0	12¾
	7.	0	5½		17.	0	13½
·4	8.	0	6½	·9	18.	0	14½
	9.	0	7¼		19.	0	15¼
·5	10.	0	8		20.	0	16

Sixteenths

	1.	0	1		9.	0	9
⅛	2.	0	2	⅝	10.	0	10
	3.	0	3		11.	0	11
¼	4.	0	4	¾	12.	0	12
	5.	0	5		13.	0	13
⅜	6.	0	6	⅞	14.	0	14
	7.	0	7		15.	0	15
½	8.	0	8				

Doz.	No.	£	P	Doz.	No.	£	P	Doz.	No.	£	P	Doz.	No.	£	P	No.	£	P
	1	0	16½		51	8	41½		101	16	66½		152	25	8	310	51	15
	2	0	33		52	8	58		102	16	83		154	25	41	320	52	80
	3	0	49½		53	8	74½		103	16	99½	13	156	25	74	330	54	45
	4	0	66		54	8	91		104	17	16		158	26	7	340	56	10
	5	0	82½		55	9	7½		105	17	32½		160	26	40	350	57	75
	6	0	99		56	9	24		106	17	49		162	26	73	360	59	40
	7	1	15½		57	9	40½		107	17	65½		164	27	6	365	60	22½
	8	1	32		58	9	57	9	108	17	82		166	27	39	370	61	5
	9	1	48½		59	9	73½		109	17	98½	14	168	27	72	380	62	70
	10	1	65	5	**60**	9	90		**110**	18	15		170	28	5	390	64	35
*	11	1	81½		61	10	6½		111	18	31½		172	28	38	400	66	0
1	12	1	98		62	10	23		112	18	48		174	28	71	410	67	65
	13	2	14½		63	10	39½		113	18	64½		175	28	87½	420	69	30
	14	2	31		64	10	56		114	18	81		176	29	4	430	70	95
	15	2	47½		65	10	72½		115	18	97½		178	29	37	440	72	60
	16	2	64		66	10	89		116	19	14	15	180	29	70	450	74	25
	17	2	80½		67	11	5½		117	19	30½		182	30	3	460	75	90
	18	2	97		68	11	22		118	19	47		184	30	36	470	77	55
	19	3	13½		69	11	38½		119	19	63½		186	30	69	480	79	20
	20	3	30		**70**	11	55		**120**	19	80		188	31	2	490	80	85
	21	3	46½		71	11	71½		121	19	96½		190	31	35	**500**	82	50
	22	3	63	6	72	11	88		122	20	13	16	192	31	68	550	90	75
	23	3	79½		73	12	4½		123	20	29½		194	32	1	600	99	0
2	24	3	96		74	12	21		124	20	46		196	32	34	650	107	25
	25	4	12½		75	12	37½		125	20	62½		198	32	67	700	115	50
	26	4	29		76	12	54		126	20	79		**200**	33	0	750	123	75
	27	4	45½		77	12	70½		127	20	95½	17	204	33	66	800	132	0
	28	4	62		78	12	87		128	21	12		205	33	82½	850	140	25
	29	4	78½		79	13	3½		129	21	28½		210	34	65	900	148	50
	30	4	95		**80**	13	20		**130**	21	45		215	35	47½	950	156	75
	31	5	11½		81	13	36½		131	21	61½	18	216	35	64	**1000**	165	0
	32	5	28		82	13	53	11	132	21	78		220	36	30	1016	167	64
	33	5	44½		83	13	69½		133	21	94½		225	37	12½	1250	206	25
	34	5	61	7	84	13	86		134	22	11	19	228	37	62	1500	247	50
	35	5	77½		85	14	2½		135	22	27½		230	37	95	1728	285	12
3	36	5	94		86	14	19		136	22	44		235	38	77½	1750	288	75
	37	6	10½		87	14	35½		137	22	60½	20	240	39	60	1760	290	40
	38	6	27		88	14	52		138	22	77		245	40	42½	2000	330	0
	39	6	43½		89	14	68½		139	22	93½		**250**	41	25	2240	369	60
	40	6	60		**90**	14	85		**140**	23	10		255	42	7½	2500	412	50
	41	6	76½		91	15	1½		141	23	26½		260	42	90	3000	495	0
	42	6	93		92	15	18		142	23	43		265	43	72½	4000	660	0
	43	7	9½		93	15	34½		143	23	59½		270	44	55	**5000**	825	0
	44	7	26		94	15	51	12	144	23	76		275	45	37½	6000	990	0
	45	7	42½		95	15	67½		145	23	92½		280	46	20	7000	1155	0
	46	7	59	8	96	15	84		146	24	9		285	47	2½	8000	1320	0
	47	7	75½		97	16	0½		147	24	25½	24	288	47	52	9000	1485	0
4	48	7	92		98	16	17		148	24	42		290	47	85	10000	1650	0
	49	8	8½		99	16	33½		149	24	58½		295	48	67½	15000	2475	0
	50	8	25		**100**	16	50		**150**	24	75		**300**	49	50	20000	3300	0

Grosses

1.	23	76
2.	47	52
3.	71	28
4.	95	4
5.	118	80
6.	142	56
7.	166	32
8.	190	08
9.	213	84
10.	237	60
11.	261	36

Twelfths

	1.	0	1½
⅙	2.	0	2¾
	3.	0	4¼
⅓	4.	0	5½
	5.	0	7
½	6.	0	8¼
	7.	0	9¾
⅔	8.	0	11
	9.	0	12½
⅚	10.	0	13¾
	11.	0	15¼

Twentieths

10ths				10ths			
	1.		0¾		11.	0	9
·1	2.	0	1¾	·6	12.	0	10
	3.	0	2½		13.	0	10¾
·2	4.	0	3¼	·7	14.	0	11½
	5.	0	4¼		15.	0	12½
·3	6.	0	5	·8	16.	0	13¼
	7.	0	5¾		17.	0	14
·4	8.	0	6½	·9	18.	0	14¾
	9.	0	7½		19.	0	15¾
·5	10.	0	8¼		20.	0	16½

Sixteenths

	1.		1		9.	0	9¼
⅛	2.	0	2	⅝	10	0	10¼
	3.	0	3		11.	0	11¼
¼	4.	0	4¼	¾	12.	0	12¼
	5.	0	5¼		13.	0	13½
⅜	6.	0	6¼	⅞	14.	0	14¼
	7.	0	7¼		15.	0	15½
½	8.	0	8¼				

	£	P
1	0	17
2	0	34
3	0	51
*Dozens 4	0	68
5	0	85
6	1	2
7	1	19
8	1	36
9	1	53
10	1	70
11	1	87
¹12	2	4
13	2	21
14	2	38
15	2	55
16	2	72
17	2	89
18	3	6
19	3	23
20	3	40
21	3	57
22	3	74
23	3	91
²24	4	8
25	4	25
26	4	42
27	4	59
28	4	76
29	4	93
30	5	10
31	5	27
32	5	44
33	5	61
34	5	78
35	5	95
³36	6	12
37	6	29
38	6	46
39	6	63
40	6	80
41	6	97
42	7	14
43	7	31
44	7	48
45	7	65
46	7	82
47	7	99
⁴48	8	16
49	8	33
50	8	50

	£	P
51	8	67
52	8	84
53	9	1
Dozens 54	9	18
55	9	35
56	9	52
57	9	69
58	9	86
59	10	3
⁵60	10	20
61	10	37
62	10	54
63	10	71
64	10	88
65	11	5
66	11	22
67	11	39
68	11	56
69	11	73
70	11	90
71	12	7
⁶72	12	24
73	12	41
74	12	58
75	12	75
76	12	92
77	13	9
78	13	26
79	13	43
80	13	60
81	13	77
82	13	94
83	14	11
⁷84	14	28
85	14	45
86	14	62
87	14	79
88	14	96
89	15	13
90	15	30
91	15	47
92	15	64
93	15	81
94	15	98
95	16	15
⁸96	16	32
97	16	49
98	16	66
99	16	83
100	17	0

	£	P
101	17	17
102	17	34
103	17	51
Dozens 104	17	68
105	17	85
106	18	2
107	18	19
⁹108	18	36
109	18	53
110	18	70
111	18	87
112	19	4
113	19	21
114	19	38
115	19	55
116	19	72
117	19	89
118	20	6
119	20	23
¹⁰120	20	40
121	20	57
122	20	74
123	20	91
124	21	8
125	21	25
126	21	42
127	21	59
128	21	76
129	21	93
130	22	10
131	22	27
¹¹132	22	44
133	22	61
134	22	78
135	22	95
136	23	12
137	23	29
138	23	46
139	23	63
140	23	80
141	23	97
142	24	14
143	24	31
¹²144	24	48
145	24	65
146	24	82
147	24	99
148	25	16
149	25	33
150	25	50

	£	P
152	25	84
154	26	18
¹³156	26	52
158	26	86
160	27	20
162	27	54
164	27	88
166	28	22
¹⁴168	28	56
170	28	90
172	29	24
174	29	58
175	29	75
176	29	92
178	30	26
¹⁵180	30	60
182	30	94
184	31	28
186	31	62
188	31	96
190	32	30
¹⁶192	32	64
194	32	98
196	33	32
198	33	66
200	34	0
¹⁷204	34	68
205	34	85
210	35	70
215	36	55
¹⁸216	36	72
220	37	40
225	38	25
¹⁹228	38	76
230	39	10
235	39	95
²⁰240	40	80
245	41	65
250	42	50
255	43	35
260	44	20
265	45	5
270	45	90
275	46	75
280	47	60
285	48	45
²⁴290	49	30
295	50	15
300	51	0

	£	P
310	52	70
320	54	40
330	56	10
340	57	80
350	59	50
360	61	20
365	62	5
370	62	90
380	64	60
390	66	30
400	68	0
410	69	70
420	71	40
430	73	10
440	74	80
450	76	50
460	78	20
470	79	90
480	81	60
490	83	30
500	85	0
550	93	50
600	102	0
650	110	50
700	119	0
750	127	50
800	136	0
850	144	50
900	153	0
950	161	50
1000	170	0
1016	172	72
1250	212	50
1500	255	0
1728	293	76
1750	297	50
1760	299	50
2000	340	0
2240	380	80
2500	425	0
3000	510	0
4000	680	0
5000	850	0
6000	1020	0
7000	1190	0
8000	1360	0
9000	1530	0
10,000	1700	0
15,000	2550	0
20,000	3400	0

Grosses		Twelfths			Twentieths				Sixteenths		
1. 24 48			1. 0 1½		1. 0 0½	11. 0 9½			1. 0 1		9. 0 9½
2. 48 96		⅙ 2. 0 2¾		·1 2. 0 1¾	·6 12. 0 10¼			⅛ 2. 0 2¼		⅝10. 0 10½
3. 73 44		⅓ 3. 0 4¼		3. 0 2½	13. 0 11			3. 0 3½		11. 0 11½
4. 97 92		½ 4. 0 5¾		·2 4. 0 3½	·7 14. 0 12			¼ 4. 0 4½		¾12. 0 12½
5. 122 40		5. 0 7		5. 0 4¼	15. 0 12¾			5. 0 5½		13. 0 13¾
6. 146 88		⅔ 6. 0 8½		·3 6. 0 5	·8 16. 0 13¾			⅜ 6. 0 6¾		⅞14. 0 15
7. 171 36		7. 0 10		7. 0 6	17. 0 14½			7. 0 7½		15. 0 16
8. 195 84		⅔ 8. 0 11¼		·4 8. 0 6¾	·9 18. 0 15½			½ 8. 0 8½		
9. 220 32		9. 0 12¾		9. 0 7½	19. 0 16¼					
10. 244 80		⅚10. 0 14¼		·5 10. 0 8½	20. 0 17					
11. 269 28		11. 0 15½								

No.	£ P	No.	£ P	No.	£ P	No.	£ P	No.	£ P
1	0 17½	51	8 92½	101	17 67½	152	26 60	310	54 25
2	0 35	52	9 10	102	17 85	154	26 95	320	56 0
3	0 52½	53	9 27½	103	18 2½	156	27 30	330	57 75
4	0 70	54	9 45	104	18 20	158	27 65	340	59 50
5	0 87½	55	9 62½	105	18 37½	160	28 0	350	61 25
6	1 5	56	9 80	106	18 55	162	28 35	360	63 0
7	1 22½	57	9 97½	107	18 72½	164	28 70	365	63 87½
8	1 40	58	10 15	108	18 90	166	29 5	370	64 75
9	1 57½	59	10 32½	109	19 7½	168	29 40	380	66 50
10	1 75	60	10 50	110	19 25	170	29 75	390	68 25
11	1 92½	61	10 67½	111	19 42½	172	30 10	400	70 0
12	2 10	62	10 85	112	19 60	174	30 45	410	71 75
13	2 27½	63	11 2½	113	19 77½	175	30 62½	420	73 50
14	2 45	64	11 20	114	19 95	176	30 80	430	75 25
15	2 62½	65	11 37½	115	20 12½	178	31 15	440	77 0
16	2 80	66	11 55	116	20 30	180	31 50	450	78 75
17	2 97½	67	11 72½	117	20 47½	182	31 85	460	80 50
18	3 15	68	11 90	118	20 65	184	32 20	470	82 25
19	3 32½	69	12 7½	119	20 82½	186	32 55	480	84 0
20	3 50	70	12 25	120	21 0	188	32 90	490	85 75
21	3 67½	71	12 42½	121	21 17½	190	33 25	500	87 50
22	3 85	72	12 60	122	21 35	192	33 60	550	96 25
23	4 2½	73	12 77½	123	21 52½	194	33 95	600	105 0
24	4 20	74	12 95	124	21 70	196	34 30	650	113 75
25	4 37½	75	13 12½	125	21 87½	198	34 65	700	122 50
26	4 55	76	13 30	126	22 5	200	35 0	750	131 25
27	4 72½	77	13 47½	127	22 22½	204	35 70	800	140 0
28	4 90	78	13 65	128	22 40	205	35 87½	850	148 75
29	5 7½	79	13 82½	129	22 57½	210	36 75	900	157 50
30	5 25	80	14 0	130	22 75	215	37 62½	950	166 25
31	5 42½	81	14 17½	131	22 92½	216	37 80	1000	175 0
32	5 60	82	14 35	132	23 10	220	38 50	1016	177 80
33	5 77½	83	14 52½	133	23 27½	225	39 37½	1250	218 75
34	5 95	84	14 70	134	23 45	228	39 90	1500	262 50
35	6 12½	85	14 87½	135	23 62½	230	40 25	1728	302 40
36	6 30	86	15 5	136	23 80	235	41 12½	1750	306 25
37	6 47½	87	15 22½	137	23 97½	240	42 0	1760	308 0
38	6 65	88	15 40	138	24 15	245	42 87½	2000	350 0
39	6 82½	89	15 57½	139	24 32½	250	43 75	2240	392 0
40	7 0	90	15 75	140	24 50	255	44 62½	2500	437 50
41	7 17½	91	15 92½	141	24 67½	260	45 50	3000	525 0
42	7 35	92	16 10	142	24 85	265	46 37½	4000	700 0
43	7 52½	93	16 27½	143	25 2½	270	47 25	5000	875 0
44	7 70	94	16 45	144	25 20	275	48 12½	6000	1050 0
45	7 87½	95	16 62½	145	25 37½	280	49 0	7000	1225 0
46	8 5	96	16 80	146	25 55	285	49 87½	8000	1400 0
47	8 22½	97	16 97½	147	25 72½	288	50 40	9000	1575 0
48	8 40	98	17 15	148	25 90	290	50 75	10000	1750 0
49	8 57½	99	17 32½	149	26 7½	295	51 62½	15000	2625 0
50	8 75	100	17 50	150	26 25	300	52 50	20,000	3500 0

Grosses.		Twelfths.		10ths	Twentieths.			Sixteenths.	
1.	25 20	1.	0 1½		1. 0 1		11. 0 9¾	1. 0 1	9. 0 9¾
2.	50 40	2.	0 3		2. 0 1½		12. 0 10¼	2. 0 2¼	10. 0 11
3.	75 60	3.	0 4½		3. 0 2½		13. 0 11½	3. 0 3¼	11. 0 12
4.	100 80	4.	0 5¼		4. 0 3½		14. 0 12½	4. 0 4¼	12. 0 13¼
5.	126 0	5.	0 7½		5. 0 4½		15. 0 13½	5. 0 5½	13. 0 14¼
6.	151 20	6.	0 8½		6. 0 5¼		16. 0 14	6. 0 6½	14. 0 15¼
7.	176 40	7.	0 10½		7. 0 6		17. 0 15	7. 0 7½	15. 0 16½
8.	201 60	8.	0 11½		8. 0 7		18. 0 15½	8. 0 8¾	
9.	226 80	9.	0 13½		9. 0 8		19. 0 16½		
10.	252 0	10.	0 14½		10. 0 8¾		20. 0 17½		
11.	277 20	11.	0 16						

*Dozens	£	P	Dozens	£	P	Dozens	£	P	Dozens	£	P		£	P
1	0	18	51	9	18	101	18	18	152	27	36	310	55	80
2	0	36	52	9	36	102	18	36	154	27	72	320	57	60
3	0	54	53	9	54	103	18	54	[13] 156	28	8	330	59	40
4	0	72	54	9	72	104	18	72	158	28	44	340	61	20
5	0	90	55	9	90	105	18	90	160	28	80	350	63	00
6	1	8	56	10	8	106	19	8	162	29	16	360	64	80
7	1	26	57	10	26	107	19	26	164	29	52	365	65	70
8	1	44	58	10	44	[9] 108	19	44	166	29	88	370	66	60
9	1	62	59	10	62	109	19	62	[14] 168	30	24	380	68	40
10	1	80	[5] **60**	10	80	**110**	19	80	170	30	60	390	70	20
11	1	98	61	10	98	111	19	98	172	30	96	400	72	0
[1] 12	2	16	62	11	16	112	20	16	174	31	32	410	73	80
13	2	34	63	11	34	113	20	34	175	31	50	420	75	60
14	2	52	64	11	52	114	20	52	176	31	68	430	77	40
15	2	70	65	11	70	115	20	70	178	32	4	440	79	20
16	2	88	66	11	88	116	20	88	[15] 180	32	40	450	81	0
17	3	6	67	12	6	117	21	6	182	32	76	460	82	80
18	3	24	68	12	24	118	21	24	184	33	12	470	84	60
19	3	42	69	12	42	119	21	42	186	33	48	480	86	40
20	3	60	**70**	12	60	**120**	21	60	188	33	84	490	88	20
21	3	78	71	12	78	121	21	78	190	34	20	500	90	0
22	3	96	[6] 72	12	96	122	21	96	[16] 192	34	56	550	99	0
23	4	14	73	13	14	123	22	14	194	34	92	600	108	0
[2] 24	4	32	74	13	32	124	22	32	196	35	28	650	117	0
25	4	50	75	13	50	125	22	50	198	35	64	700	126	0
26	4	68	76	13	68	126	22	68	**200**	36	0	750	135	0
27	4	86	77	13	86	127	22	86	[17] 204	36	72	800	144	0
28	5	4	78	14	4	128	23	4	205	36	90	850	153	0
29	5	22	79	14	22	129	23	22	210	37	80	900	162	0
30	5	40	**80**	14	40	**130**	23	40	215	38	70	950	171	0
31	5	58	81	14	58	131	23	58	[18] 216	38	88	1000	180	0
32	5	76	82	14	76	[11] 132	23	76	220	39	60	1016	182	88
33	5	94	83	14	94	133	23	94	225	40	50	1250	225	0
34	6	12	[7] 84	15	12	134	24	12	[19] 228	41	4	1500	270	0
35	6	30	85	15	30	135	24	30	230	41	40	1728	311	4
[3] 36	6	48	86	15	48	136	24	48	235	42	30	1750	315	0
37	6	66	87	15	66	137	24	66	[20] 240	43	20	1760	316	80
38	6	84	88	15	84	138	24	84	245	44	10	2000	360	0
39	7	2	89	16	2	139	25	2	**250**	45	0	2240	403	20
40	7	20	**90**	16	20	**140**	25	20	255	45	90	2500	450	0
41	7	38	91	16	38	141	25	38	260	46	80	3000	540	0
42	7	56	92	16	56	142	25	56	265	47	70	4000	720	0
43	7	74	93	16	74	143	25	74	270	48	60	5000	900	0
44	7	92	94	16	92	[12] 144	25	92	275	49	50	6000	1080	0
45	8	10	95	17	10	145	26	10	280	50	40	7000	1260	0
46	8	28	[8] 96	17	28	146	26	28	285	51	30	8000	1440	0
47	8	46	97	17	46	147	26	46	[24] 288	51	84	9000	1620	0
[4] 48	8	64	98	17	64	148	26	64	290	52	20	10,000	1800	0
49	8	82	99	17	82	149	26	82	295	53	10	15,000	2700	0
50	9	0	**100**	18	0	**150**	27	0	**300**	54	0	20,000	3600	0

Grosses

1.	25	92
2.	51	84
3.	77	76
4.	103	68
5.	129	60
6.	155	52
7.	181	44
8.	207	36
9.	233	28
10.	259	20
11.	285	12

Twelfths

	1.	0	1½
⅙	2.	0	3
	3.	0	4½
⅓	4.	0	6
	5.	0	7½
½	6.	0	9
	7.	0	10½
⅔	8.	0	12
	9.	0	13½
⅚	10.	0	15
	11.	0	16½

Twentieths

10ths				10ths			
	1.	0	1		11.	0	10
·1	2.	0	1¾	·6	12.	0	10¾
	3.	0	2¾		13.	0	11¾
·2	4.	0	3½	·7	14.	0	12½
	5.	0	4½		15.	0	13½
·3	6.	0	5½	·8	16.	0	14½
	7.	0	6¼		17.	0	15¼
·4	8.	0	7¼	·9	18.	0	16¼
	9.	0	8		19.	0	17
·5	10.	0	9		20.	0	18

Sixteenths

	1.	0	1¼		9.	0	10¼
⅛	2.	0	2¼	⅝	10.	0	11¼
	3.	0	3½		11.	0	12½
¼	4.	0	4½	¾	12.	0	13½
	5.	0	5¾		13.	0	14¾
⅜	6.	0	6¾	⅞	14.	0	15¾
	7.	0	8		15.	0	17
½	8.	0	9				

18½ Pence 18½ Pence

*Dozens	No.	£	P	Dozens	No.	£	P	Dozens	No.	£	P	Dozens	No.	£	P	No.	£	P
	1	0	18½		51	9	43½		101	18	68½		152	28	12	310	57	35
	2	0	37		52	9	62		102	18	87		154	28	49	320	59	20
	3	0	55½		53	9	80½		103	19	5½	13	156	28	86	330	61	5
	4	0	74		54	9	99		104	19	24		158	29	23	340	62	90
	5	0	92½		55	10	17½		105	19	42½		160	29	60	350	64	75
	6	1	11		56	10	36		106	19	61		162	29	97	360	66	60
	7	1	29½		57	10	54½		107	19	79½		164	30	34	365	67	52½
	8	1	48		58	10	73	9	108	19	98		166	30	71	370	68	45
	9	1	66½		59	10	91½		109	20	16½	14	168	31	8	380	70	30
	10	1	85	5	**60**	11	10		**110**	20	35		170	31	45	390	72	15
	11	2	3½		61	11	28½		111	20	53½		172	31	82	400	74	0
*1	12	2	22		62	11	47		112	20	72		174	32	19	410	75	85
	13	2	40½		63	11	65½		113	20	90½		175	32	37½	420	77	70
	14	2	59		64	11	84		114	21	9		176	32	56	430	79	55
	15	2	77½		65	12	2½		115	21	27½		178	32	93	440	81	40
	16	2	96		66	12	21		116	21	46	15	180	33	30	450	83	25
	17	3	14½		67	12	39½		117	21	64½		182	33	67	460	85	10
	18	3	33		68	12	58		118	21	83		184	34	4	470	86	95
	19	3	51½		69	12	76½		119	22	1½		186	34	41	480	88	80
	20	3	70		**70**	12	95		**120**	22	20		188	34	78	490	90	65
	21	3	88½		71	13	13½		121	22	38½		190	35	15	**500**	92	50
	22	4	7	6	72	13	32		122	22	57	16	192	35	52	550	101	75
	23	4	25½		73	13	50½		123	22	75½		194	35	89	600	111	0
2	24	4	44		74	13	69		124	22	94		196	36	26	650	120	25
	25	4	62½		75	13	87½		125	23	12½		198	36	63	700	129	50
	26	4	81		76	14	6		126	23	31		**200**	37	0	750	138	75
	27	4	99½		77	14	24½		127	23	49½	17	204	37	74	800	148	0
	28	5	18		78	14	43		128	23	68		205	37	92½	850	157	25
	29	5	36½		79	14	61½		129	23	86½		210	38	85	900	166	50
	30	5	55		**80**	14	80		**130**	24	5		215	39	77½	950	175	75
	31	5	73½		81	14	98½		131	24	23½	18	216	39	96	**1000**	185	0
	32	5	92		82	15	17	11	132	24	42		220	40	70	1016	187	96
	33	6	10½		83	15	35½		133	24	60½		225	41	62½	1250	231	25
	34	6	29	7	84	15	54		134	24	79	19	228	42	18	1500	277	50
	35	6	47½		85	15	72½		135	24	97½		230	42	55	1728	319	68
3	36	6	66		86	15	91		136	25	16		235	43	47½	1750	323	75
	37	6	84½		87	16	9½		137	25	34½	20	240	44	40	1760	325	60
	38	7	3		88	16	28		138	25	53		245	45	32½	2000	370	0
	39	7	21½		89	16	46½		139	25	71½		**250**	46	25	2240	414	40
	40	7	40		**90**	16	65		**140**	25	90		255	47	17½	2500	462	50
	41	7	58½		91	16	83½		141	26	8½		260	48	10	3000	555	0
	42	7	77		92	17	2		142	26	27		265	49	2½	4000	740	0
	43	7	95½		93	17	20½		143	26	45½		270	49	95	**5000**	925	0
	44	8	14		94	17	39	12	144	26	64		275	50	87½	6000	1110	0
	45	8	32½		95	17	57½		145	26	82½		280	51	80	7000	1295	0
	46	8	51	8	96	17	76		146	27	1		285	52	72½	8000	1480	0
	47	8	69½		97	17	94½		147	27	19½	24	288	53	28	9000	1665	0
4	48	8	88		98	18	13		148	27	38		290	53	65	10000	1850	0
	49	9	6½		99	18	31½		149	27	56½		295	54	57½	15000	2775	0
	50	9	25		**100**	18	50		**150**	27	75		**300**	55	50	20000	3700	0

Grosses

1.	26	64
2.	53	28
3.	79	92
4.	106	56
5.	133	20
6.	159	84
7.	186	48
8.	213	12
9.	239	76
10.	266	40
11.	293	04

Twelfths

	1.	0	1½
⅙	2.	0	3
	3.	0	4¾
⅓	4.	0	6¼
	5.	0	7¾
½	6.	0	9¼
	7.	0	10¾
⅔	8.	0	12¼
	9.	0	14
⅚	10.	0	15½
	11.	0	17

Twentieths (10ths)

10ths				10ths			
	1.		1		11.	0	10¼
·1	2.	0	1¾	·6	12.	0	11
	3.	0	2¾		13.	0	12
·2	4.	0	3¾	·7	14.	0	13
	5.	0	4¾		15.	0	14
·3	6.	0	5½	·8	16.	0	14¾
	7.	0	6½		17.	0	15¾
·4	8.	0	7½	·9	18.	0	16¾
	9.	0	8¼		19.	0	17½
·5	10.	0	9¼		20.	0	18½

Sixteenths

	1.		1¼		9.	0	10½
⅛	2.	0	2¼	⅝	10	0	11½
	3.	0	3½		11.	0	12¾
¼	4.	0	4¾	¾	12.	0	14
	5.	0	5¾		13.	0	15
⅜	6.	0	7	⅞	14.	0	16¼
	7.	0	8		15.	0	17½
½	8.	0	9¼				

Doz.	No.	£	P	Doz.	No.	£	P	Doz.	No.	£	P	Doz.	No.	£	P	No.	£	P
	1	0	19		51	9	69		101	19	19		152	28	88	310	58	90
	2	0	38		52	9	88		102	19	38		154	29	26	320	60	80
	3	0	57		53	10	7		103	19	57	13	156	29	64	330	62	70
	4	0	76		54	10	26		104	19	76		158	30	2	340	64	60
	5	0	95		55	10	45		105	19	95		160	30	40	350	66	50
*	6	1	14		56	10	64		106	20	14		162	30	78	360	68	40
	7	1	33		57	10	83		107	20	33		164	31	16	365	69	35
	8	1	52		58	11	2	9	108	20	52		166	31	54	370	70	30
	9	1	71		59	11	21		109	20	71	14	168	31	92	380	72	20
	10	1	90	5	**60**	11	40		**110**	20	90		170	32	30	390	74	10
*	11	2	9		61	11	59		111	21	9		172	32	68	400	76	0
1	12	2	28		62	11	78		112	21	28		174	33	6	410	77	90
	13	2	47		63	11	97		113	21	47		175	33	25	420	79	80
	14	2	66		64	12	16		114	21	66		176	33	44	430	81	70
	15	2	85		65	12	35		115	21	85		178	33	82	440	83	60
	16	3	4		66	12	54		116	22	4	15	180	34	20	450	85	50
	17	3	23		67	12	73		117	22	23		182	34	58	460	87	40
	18	3	42		68	12	92		118	22	42		184	34	96	470	89	30
	19	3	61		69	13	11		119	22	61		186	35	34	480	91	20
	20	3	80		**70**	13	30		**120**	22	80		188	35	72	490	93	10
	21	3	99		71	13	49		121	22	99		190	36	10	**500**	95	0
	22	4	18	6	72	13	68		122	23	18	16	192	36	48	550	104	50
	23	4	37		73	13	87		123	23	37		194	36	86	600	114	0
2	24	4	56		74	14	6		124	23	56		196	37	24	650	123	50
	25	4	75		75	14	25		125	23	75		198	37	62	700	133	0
	26	4	94		76	14	44		126	23	94		**200**	38	0	750	142	50
	27	5	13		77	14	63		127	24	13	17	204	38	76	800	152	0
	28	5	32		78	14	82		128	24	32		205	38	95	850	161	50
	29	5	51		79	15	1		129	24	51		210	39	90	900	171	0
	30	5	70		**80**	15	20		**130**	24	70		215	40	85	950	180	50
	31	5	89		81	15	39		131	24	89	18	216	41	4	**1000**	190	0
	32	6	8		82	15	58	11	132	25	8		220	41	80	1016	193	4
	33	6	27		83	15	77		133	25	27		225	42	75	1250	237	50
	34	6	46	7	84	15	96		134	25	46	19	228	43	32	1500	285	0
	35	6	65		85	16	15		135	25	65		230	43	70	1728	328	32
3	36	6	84		86	16	34		136	25	84		235	44	65	1750	332	50
	37	7	3		87	16	53		137	26	3	20	240	45	60	1760	334	40
	38	7	22		88	16	72		138	26	22		245	46	55	2000	380	0
	39	7	41		89	16	91		139	26	41		**250**	47	50	2240	425	60
	40	7	60		**90**	17	10		**140**	26	60		255	48	45	2500	475	0
	41	7	79		91	17	29		141	26	79		260	49	40	3000	570	0
	42	7	98		92	17	48		142	26	98		265	50	35	4000	760	0
	43	8	17		93	17	67		143	27	17		270	51	30	**5000**	950	0
	44	8	36		94	17	86	12	144	27	36		275	52	25	6000	1140	0
	45	8	55		95	18	5		145	27	55		280	53	20	7000	1330	0
	46	8	74	8	96	18	24		146	27	74		285	54	15	8000	1520	0
	47	8	93		97	18	43		147	27	93	24	288	54	72	9000	1710	0
4	48	9	12		98	18	62		148	28	12		290	55	10	10,000	1900	0
	49	9	31		99	18	81		149	28	31		295	56	5	15,000	2850	0
	50	9	50		**100**	19	0		**150**	28	50		**300**	57	0	20,000	3800	0

(Dozens.)

Grosses.		
1.	27	36
2.	54	72
3.	82	8
4.	109	44
5.	136	80
6.	164	16
7.	191	52
8.	218	88
9.	246	24
10.	273	60
11.	300	96

Twelfths			
	1.	0	1½
⅙	2.	0	3¼
	3.	0	4¾
⅓	4.	0	6¼
	5.	0	8
½	6.	0	9½
	7.	0	11
⅔	8.	0	12¾
	9.	0	14¼
⅚	10.	0	15¾
	11.	0	17½

10ths	Twentieths			10ths			
	1.	0	1		11.	0	10½
·1	2.	0	2	·6	12.	0	11½
	3.	0	2¾		13.	0	12¼
·2	4.	0	3¾	·7	14.	0	13¼
	5.	0	4¾		15.	0	14¼
·3	6.	0	5¾	8	16.	0	15¼
	7.	0	6¾		17.	0	16¼
·4	8.	0	7½	·9	18.	0	17
	9.	0	8½		19.	0	18
·5	10.	0	9½		20.	0	19

Sixteenths							
	1.	0	1¼		9.	0	10¾
⅛	2.	0	2½	⅝	10.	0	12
	3.	0	3½		11.	0	13
¼	4.	0	4¾	¾	12.	0	14¼
	5.	0	6		13.	0	15½
⅜	6.	0	7¼	⅞	14.	0	16¾
	7.	0	8¼		15.	0	17¾
½	8.	0	9½				

No.	£	P	No.	£	P	No.	£	P	No.	£	P	No.	£	P
1	0	19½	51	9	94½	101	19	69½	152	29	64	310	60	45
2	0	39	52	10	14	102	19	89	154	30	3	320	62	40
3	0	58½	53	10	33½	103	20	8½	13)156	30	42	330	64	35
4	0	78	54	10	53	104	20	28	158	30	81	340	66	30
5	0	97½	55	10	72½	105	20	47½	160	31	20	350	68	25
*6	1	17	56	10	92	106	20	67	162	31	59	360	70	20
7	1	36½	57	11	11½	107	20	86½	164	31	98	365	71	17½
8	1	56	58	11	31	108	21	6	166	32	37	370	72	15
9	1	75½	59	11	50½	109	21	25½	14)168	32	76	380	74	10
10	1	95	60	11	70	110	21	45	170	33	15	390	76	5
*11	2	14½	61	11	89½	111	21	64½	172	33	54	400	78	0
12	2	34	62	12	9	112	21	84	174	33	93	410	79	95
13	2	53½	63	12	28½	113	22	3½	175	34	12½	420	81	90
14	2	73	64	12	48	114	22	23	176	34	32	430	83	85
15	2	92½	65	12	67½	115	22	42½	178	34	71	440	85	80
16	3	12	66	12	87	116	22	62	15)180	35	10	450	87	75
17	3	31½	67	13	6½	117	22	81½	182	35	49	460	89	70
18	3	51	68	13	26	118	23	1	184	35	88	470	91	65
19	3	70½	69	13	45½	119	23	20½	186	36	27	480	93	60
20	3	90	70	13	65	120	23	40	188	36	66	490	95	55
21	4	9½	71	13	84½	121	23	59½	190	37	5	500	97	50
22	4	29	6)72	14	4	122	23	79	16)192	37	44	550	107	25
23	4	48½	73	14	23½	123	23	98½	194	37	83	600	117	0
24	4	68	74	14	43	124	24	18	196	38	22	650	126	75
25	4	87½	75	14	62½	125	24	37½	198	38	61	700	136	50
26	5	7	76	14	82	126	24	57	200	39	0	750	146	25
27	5	26½	77	15	1½	127	24	76½	17)204	39	78	800	156	0
28	5	46	78	15	21	128	24	96	205	39	97½	850	165	75
29	5	65½	79	15	40½	129	25	15½	210	40	95	900	175	50
30	5	85	80	15	60	130	25	35	215	41	92½	950	185	25
31	6	4½	81	15	79½	131	25	54½	18)216	42	12	1000	195	0
32	6	24	82	15	99	11)132	25	74	220	42	90	1016	198	12
33	6	43½	83	16	18½	133	25	93½	225	43	87½	1250	243	75
34	6	63	7)84	16	38	134	26	13	19)228	44	46	1500	292	50
35	6	82½	85	16	57½	135	26	32½	230	44	85	1728	336	96
$36	7	2	86	16	77	136	26	52	235	45	82½	1750	341	25
37	7	21½	87	16	96½	137	26	71½	20)240	46	80	1760	343	20
38	7	41	88	17	16	138	26	91	245	47	77½	2000	390	0
39	7	60½	89	17	35½	139	27	10½	250	48	75	2240	436	80
40	7	80	90	17	55	140	27	30	255	49	72½	2500	487	50
41	7	99½	91	17	74½	141	27	49½	260	50	70	3000	585	0
42	8	19	92	17	94	142	27	69	265	51	67½	4000	780	0
43	8	38½	93	18	13½	143	27	88½	270	52	65	5000	975	0
44	8	58	94	18	33	12)144	28	8	275	53	62½	6000	1170	0
45	8	77½	95	18	52½	145	28	27½	280	54	60	7000	1365	0
46	8	97	8)96	18	72	146	28	47	285	55	57½	8000	1560	0
47	9	16½	97	18	91½	147	28	66½	24)288	56	16	9000	1755	0
*48	9	36	98	19	11	148	28	86	290	56	55	10000	1950	0
49	9	55½	99	19	30½	149	29	5½	295	57	52½	15000	2925	0
50	9	75	100	19	50	150	29	25	300	58	50	20000	3900	0

Grosses.			Twelfths.			10ths	Twentieths				Sixteenths			
1.	28	8	1.	0	1½		1. 0	1	11. 0	10½	1. 0	1½	9. 0	11
2.	56	16	½2.	0	3¼	·1	2. 0	2	12. 0	11½	½10. 0	12½		
3.	84	24	3.	0	5		3. 0	3	13. 0	12½	3. 0	3¼	11. 0	13½
4.	112	32	¼4.	0	6½	·2	4. 0	4	·7 14. 0	13¾	¼4. 0	5		
5.	140	40	5.	0	8¼		5. 0	5	15. 0	14¾	5. 0	6		
6.	168	48	⅙6.	0	9¾	·3	6. 0	5½	·8 16. 0	15½	⅜6. 0	7½	12. 0	14½
7.	196	56	7.	0	11½		7. 0	6½	17. 0	16½	7. 0	8½	13. 0	15½
8.	224	64	¾8.	0	13	·4	8. 0	7½	·9 18. 0	17½	⅞8. 0	9¾	¾14. 0	17
9.	252	72	9.	0	14½		9. 0	8½	19. 0	18½				
10.	280	80	⅚10.	0	16¼	·5	10. 0	9½	20. 0	19½			15. 0	18½
11.	308	88	11.	0	18									

Dozens.	No.	£	P	Dozens.	No.	£	P	Dozens.	No.	£	P	Doz.	No.	£	P	No.	£	P
	1	0	20		51	10	20		101	20	20		152	30	40	310	62	0
	2	0	40		52	10	40		102	20	40		154	30	80	320	64	0
	3	0	60		53	10	60		103	20	60	13	156	31	20	330	66	0
	4	0	80		54	10	80		104	20	80		158	31	60	340	68	0
	5	1	0		55	11	0		105	21	0		160	32	0	350	70	0
*	6	1	20		56	11	20		106	21	20		162	32	40	360	72	0
	7	1	40		57	11	40		107	21	40		164	32	80	365	73	0
	8	1	60		58	11	60	9	108	21	60		166	33	20	370	74	0
	9	1	80		59	11	80		109	21	80	14	168	33	60	380	76	0
	10	2	0	5	**60**	12	0		**110**	22	0		170	34	0	390	78	0
*	11	2	20		61	12	20		111	22	20		172	34	40	400	80	0
1	12	2	40		62	12	40		112	22	40		174	34	80	410	82	0
	13	2	60		63	12	60		113	22	60		175	35	0	420	84	0
	14	2	80		64	12	80		114	22	80		176	35	20	430	86	0
	15	3	0		65	13	0		115	23	0		178	35	60	440	88	0
	16	3	20		66	13	20		116	23	20	15	180	36	0	450	90	0
	17	3	40		67	13	40		117	23	40		182	36	40	460	92	0
	18	3	60		68	13	60		118	23	60		184	36	80	470	94	0
	19	3	80		69	13	80		119	23	80		186	37	20	480	96	0
	20	4	0		**70**	14	0		**120**	24	0		188	37	60	490	98	0
	21	4	20		71	14	20		121	24	20		190	38	0	**500**	100	0
	22	4	40	6	72	14	40		122	24	40	16	192	38	40	550	110	0
	23	4	60		73	14	60		123	24	60		194	38	80	600	120	0
2	24	4	80		74	14	80		124	24	80		196	39	20	650	130	0
	25	5	0		75	15	0		125	25	0		198	39	60	700	140	0
	26	5	20		76	15	20		126	25	20		**200**	40	0	750	150	0
	27	5	40		77	15	40		127	25	40	17	204	40	80	800	160	0
	28	5	60		78	15	60		128	25	60		205	41	0	850	170	0
	29	5	80		79	15	80		129	25	80		210	42	0	900	180	0
	30	6	0		**80**	16	0		**130**	26	0		215	43	0	950	190	0
	31	6	20		81	16	20		131	26	20	18	216	43	20	**1000**	200	0
	32	6	40		82	16	40	11	132	26	40		220	44	0	1016	203	20
	33	6	60		83	16	60		133	26	60		225	45	0	1250	250	0
	34	6	80	7	84	16	80		134	26	80	19	228	45	60	1500	300	0
	35	7	0		85	17	0		135	27	0		230	46	0	1728	345	60
3	36	7	20		86	17	20		136	27	20		235	47	0	1750	350	0
	37	7	40		87	17	40		137	27	40	20	240	48	0	1760	352	0
	38	7	60		88	17	60		138	27	60		245	49	0	2000	400	0
	39	7	80		89	17	80		139	27	80		**250**	50	0	2240	448	0
	40	8	0		**90**	18	0		**140**	28	0		255	51	0	2500	500	0
	41	8	20		91	18	20		141	28	20		260	52	0	3000	600	0
	42	8	40		92	18	40		142	28	40		265	53	0	4000	800	0
	43	8	60		93	18	60		143	28	60		270	54	0	**5000**	1000	0
	44	8	80		94	18	80	12	144	28	80		275	55	0	6000	1200	0
	45	9	0		95	19	0		145	29	0		280	56	0	7000	1400	0
	46	9	20	8	96	19	20		146	29	20		285	57	0	8000	1600	0
	47	9	40		97	19	40		147	29	40	24	288	57	60	9000	1800	0
4	48	9	60		98	19	60		148	29	60		290	58	0	10,000	2000	0
	49	9	80		99	19	80		149	29	80		295	59	0	15,000	3000	0
	50	10	0		**100**	20	0		**150**	30	0		**300**	60	0	20,000	4000	0

Grosses.

1.	28	80
2.	57	60
3.	86	40
4.	115	20
5.	144	0
6.	172	80
7.	201	60
8.	230	40
9.	259	20
10.	288	0
11.	316	80

Twelfths

	1.	0	1¾
⅙	2.	0	3¼
	3.	0	5
⅓	4.	0	6¾
	5.	0	8¼
½	6.	0	10
	7.	0	11¾
⅔	8.	0	13¼
	9.	0	15
⅚	10.	0	16¾
	11.	0	18¼

Twentieths

10ths						
	1.	0	1		11.	0	11
·1	2.	0	2	·6	12.	0	12
	3.	0	3		13.	0	13
·2	4.	0	4	·7	14.	0	14
	5.	0	5		15.	0	15
·3	6.	0	6	·8	16.	0	16
	7.	0	7		17.	0	17
·4	8.	0	8	·9	18.	0	18
	9.	0	9		19.	0	19
·5	10.	0	10		20.	0	20

Sixteenths

	1.	0	1¼		9.	0	11¼
⅛	2.	0	2½	⅝	10.	0	12½
	3.	0	3¾		11.	0	13¾
¼	4.	0	5	¾	12.	0	15
	5.	0	6¼		13.	0	16¼
⅜	6.	0	7½	⅞	14.	0	17½
	7.	0	8¾		15.	0	18¾
½	8.	0	10				

	£	P		£	P		£	P		£	P		£	P
1	0	20½	51	10	45½	101	20	70½	152	31	16	310	63	55
2	0	41	52	10	66	102	20	91	154	31	57	320	65	60
3	0	61½	53	10	86½	103	21	11½	13 156	31	98	330	67	65
4	0	82	54	11	7	104	21	32	158	32	39	340	69	70
5	1	2½	55	11	27½	105	21	52½	160	32	80	350	71	75
*6	1	23	56	11	48	106	21	73	162	33	21	360	73	80
7	1	43½	57	11	68½	107	21	93½	164	33	62	365	74	82½
8	1	64	58	11	89	9 108	22	14	166	34	3	370	75	85
9	1	84½	59	12	9½	109	22	34½	14 168	34	44	380	77	90
10	2	5	5 60	12	30	110	22	55	170	34	85	390	79	95
*11	2	25½	61	12	50½	111	22	75½	172	35	26	400	82	0
1 12	2	46	62	12	71	112	22	96	174	35	67	410	84	5
13	2	66½	63	12	91½	113	23	16½	175	35	87½	420	86	10
14	2	87	64	13	12	114	23	37	176	36	8	430	88	15
15	3	7½	65	13	32½	115	23	57½	178	36	49	440	90	20
16	3	28	66	13	53	116	23	78	15 180	36	90	450	92	25
17	3	48½	67	13	73½	117	23	98½	182	37	31	460	94	30
18	3	69	68	13	94	118	24	19	184	37	72	470	96	35
19	3	89½	69	14	14½	119	24	39½	186	38	13	480	98	40
20	4	10	70	14	35	120	24	60	188	38	54	490	100	45
21	4	30½	71	14	55½	121	24	80½	190	38	95	500	102	50
22	4	51	6 72	14	76	122	25	1	16 192	39	36	550	112	75
23	4	71½	73	14	96½	123	25	21½	194	39	77	600	123	0
2 24	4	92	74	15	17	124	25	42	196	40	18	650	133	25
25	5	12½	75	15	37½	125	25	62½	198	40	59	700	143	50
26	5	33	76	15	58	126	25	83	200	41	0	750	153	75
27	5	53½	77	15	78½	127	26	3½	17 204	41	82	800	164	0
28	5	74	78	15	99	128	26	24	205	42	2½	850	174	25
29	5	94½	79	16	19½	129	26	44½	210	43	5	900	184	50
30	6	15	80	16	40	130	26	65	215	44	7½	950	194	75
31	6	35½	81	16	60½	131	26	85½	18 216	44	28	1000	205	0
32	6	56	82	16	81	11 132	27	6	220	45	10	1016	208	28
33	6	76½	83	17	1½	133	27	26½	225	46	12½	1250	256	25
34	6	97	7 84	17	22	134	27	47	19 228	46	74	1500	307	50
35	7	17½	85	17	42½	135	27	67½	230	47	15	1728	354	24
3 36	7	38	86	17	63	136	27	88	235	48	17½	1750	358	75
37	7	58½	87	17	83½	137	28	8½	20 240	49	20	1760	360	80
38	7	79	88	18	4	138	28	29	245	50	22½	2000	410	0
39	7	99½	89	18	24½	139	28	49½	250	51	25	2240	459	20
40	8	20	90	18	45	140	28	70	255	52	27½	2500	512	50
41	8	40½	91	18	65½	141	28	90½	260	53	30	3000	615	0
42	8	61	92	18	86	142	29	11	265	54	32½	4000	820	0
43	8	81½	93	19	6½	143	29	31½	270	55	35	5000	1025	0
44	9	2	94	19	27	12 144	29	52	275	56	37½	6000	1230	0
45	9	22½	95	19	47½	145	29	72½	280	57	40	7000	1435	0
46	9	43	8 96	19	68	146	29	93	285	58	42½	8000	1640	0
47	9	63½	97	19	88½	147	30	13½	24 288	59	4	9000	1845	0
4 48	9	84	98	20	9	148	30	34	290	59	45	10000	2050	0
49	10	4½	99	20	29½	149	30	54½	295	60	47½	15000	3075	0
50	10	25	100	20	50	150	30	75	300	61	50	20000	4100	0

Grosses			Twelfths			10ths	Twentieths						Sixteenths		
1.	29	52	1.	0	1¾		1. 0 1			11. 0 11½			1. 0 1¼		9. 0 11¼
2.	59	04	½2.	0	3½	·1	2. 0 2		·6	12. 0 12½			½2. 0 2¼		§10. 0 12¼
3.	88	56	3.	0	5¼		3. 0 3			13. 0 13½			3. 0 3½		11. 0 14
4.	118	08	¼4.	0	6¾	·2	4. 0 4		·7	14. 0 14½			¼4. 0 5¼		¾12. 0 15¼
5.	147	60	5.	0	8½		5. 0 5½			15. 0 15½			5. 0 6½		13. 0 16¾
6.	177	12	¾6.	0	10¼	·3	6. 0 6½		·8	16. 0 16½			⅜6. 0 7½		14. 0 18
7.	206	64	7.	0	12		7. 0 7½			17. 0 17½			7. 0 9		
8.	236	16	⅞8.	0	13¾	·4	8. 0 8½		·9	18. 0 18½			½8. 0 10¼		13. 0 16¾
9.	265	68	9.	0	15¼		9. 0 9½			19. 0 19½			7. 0 9		⅞14. 0 18
10.	295	20	⅝10.	0	17	·5	10. 0 10½			20. 0 20½			⅜8. 0 10¼		15. 0 19¼
11.	324	72	11.	0	18¾										

	£ P		£ P		£ P		£ P		£ P
1	0 21	51	10 71	101	21 21	152	31 92	310	65 10
2	0 42	52	10 92	102	21 42	154	32 34	320	67 20
*Dozens 3	0 63	53	11 13	103	21 63	13 156	32 76	330	69 30
4	0 84	Dozens 54	11 34	Dozens 104	21 84	158	33 18	340	71 40
5	1 5	55	11 55	105	22 5	160	33 60	350	73 50
6	1 26	56	11 76	106	22 26	162	34 2	360	75 60
7	1 47	57	11 97	107	22 47	Dozens 164	34 44	365	76 65
8	1 68	58	12 18	⁹108	22 68	166	34 86	370	77 70
9	1 89	59	12 39	109	22 89	14 168	35 28	380	79 80
10	2 10	⁵60	12 60	110	23 10	170	35 70	390	81 90
*11	2 31	61	12 81	111	23 31	172	36 12	400	84 0
¹12	2 52	62	13 2	112	23 52	174	36 54	410	86 10
13	2 73	63	13 23	113	23 73	175	36 75	420	88 20
14	2 94	64	13 44	114	23 94	176	36 96	430	90 30
15	3 15	65	13 65	115	24 15	178	37 38	440	92 40
16	3 36	66	13 86	116	24 36	15 180	37 80	450	94 50
17	3 57	67	14 7	117	24 57	182	38 22	460	96 60
18	3 78	68	14 28	118	24 78	184	38 64	470	98 70
19	3 99	69	14 49	119	24 99	186	39 6	480	100 80
20	4 20	70	14 70	120	25 20	188	39 48	490	102 90
21	4 41	71	14 91	121	25 41	190	39 90	500	105 0
22	4 62	⁶72	15 12	122	25 62	16 192	40 32	550	115 50
23	4 83	73	15 33	123	25 83	194	40 74	600	126 0
²24	5 4	74	15 54	124	26 4	196	41 16	650	136 50
25	5 25	75	15 75	125	26 25	198	41 58	700	147 0
26	5 46	76	15 96	126	26 46	200	42 0	750	157 50
27	5 67	77	16 17	127	26 67	17 204	42 84	800	168 0
28	5 88	78	16 38	128	26 88	205	43 5	850	178 50
29	6 9	79	16 59	129	27 9	210	44 10	900	189 0
30	6 30	80	16 80	130	27 30	215	45 15	950	199 50
31	6 51	81	17 1	131	27 51	18 216	45 36	1000	210 0
32	6 72	82	17 22	¹¹132	27 72	220	46 20	1016	213 36
33	6 93	83	17 43	133	27 93	225	47 25	1250	262 50
34	7 14	⁷84	17 64	134	28 14	19 228	47 88	1500	315 0
35	7 35	85	17 85	135	28 35	230	48 30	1728	362 88
³36	7 56	86	18 6	136	28 56	235	49 35	1750	367 50
37	7 77	87	18 27	137	28 77	20 240	50 40	1760	369 60
38	7 98	88	18 48	138	28 98	245	51 45	2000	420 0
39	8 19	89	18 69	139	29 19	250	52 50	2240	479 40
40	8 40	90	18 90	140	29 40	255	53 55	2500	525 0
41	8 61	91	19 11	141	29 61	260	54 60	3000	630 0
42	8 82	92	19 32	142	29 82	265	55 65	4000	840 0
43	9 3	93	19 53	143	30 3	270	56 70	5000	1050 0
44	9 24	94	19 74	¹²144	30 24	275	57 75	6000	1260 0
45	9 45	95	19 95	145	30 45	280	58 80	7000	1470 0
46	9 66	⁸96	20 16	146	30 66	285	59 85	8000	1680 0
47	9 87	97	20 37	147	30 87	24 288	60 48	9000	1890 0
⁴48	10 8	98	20 58	148	31 8	290	60 90	10,000	2100 0
49	10 29	99	20 79	149	31 29	295	61 95	15,000	3150 0
50	10 50	100	21 0	150	31 50	300	63 0	20,000	4200 0

Grosses		Twelfths		10ths	Twentieths		Sixteenths		
1.	30 24	1/12.	0 1¾		1. 0 1	11. 0 11½	1. 0 1¼	9. 0 11¾
2.	60 48	⅙ 2.	0 3½	·1	2. 0 2	·6 12. 0 12½	⅛2. 0 2¾	⅝10. 0 13¼
3.	90 72	3.	0 5¼		3. 0 3½	13. 0 13½	3. 0 4	11. 0 14½
4.	120 96	¼ 4.	0 7	·2	4. 0 4½	·7 14. 0 14½	¼4. 0 5¼	¾12. 0 15¾
5.	151 20	5.	0 8¾		5. 0 5½	15. 0 15¾	5. 0 6½	13. 0 17
6.	181 44	⅙.	0 10½	·3	6. 0 6½	·8 16. 0 16½	⅜6. 0 8	⅞14. 0 18½
7.	211 68	7.	0 12¼		7. 0 7½	17. 0 17½	7. 0 9¼	15. 0 19¾
8.	241 92	⅜ 8.	0 14	·4	8. 0 8½	·9 18. 0 19	½8. 0 10½	
9.	272 16	9.	0 15¾		9. 0 9½	19. 0 20		
10.	302 40	⁵10.	0 17½	·5	10. 0 10½	20. 0 21		
11.	332 64	11.	0 19¼					

*Dozens	£	P	Dozens	£	P	Dozens	£	P	Dozens	£	P		£	P
1	0	21½	51	10	96½	101	21	71½	152	32	68	310	66	65
2	0	43	52	11	18	102	21	93	154	33	11	320	68	80
3	0	64½	53	11	39½	103	22	14½	[13] 156	33	54	330	70	95
4	0	86	54	11	61	104	22	36	158	33	97	340	73	10
5	1	7½	55	11	82½	105	22	57½	160	34	40	350	75	25
6	1	29	56	12	4	106	22	79	162	34	83	360	77	40
7	1	50½	57	12	25½	107	23	0½	164	35	26	365	78	47½
8	1	72	58	12	47	[9] 108	23	22	166	35	69	370	79	55
9	1	93½	59	12	68½	109	23	43½	[14] 168	36	12	380	81	70
10	2	15	[5] **60**	12	90	**110**	23	65	170	36	55	390	83	85
*11	2	36½	61	13	11½	111	23	86½	172	36	98	400	86	0
[1] 12	2	58	62	13	33	112	24	8	174	37	41	410	88	15
13	2	79½	63	13	54½	113	24	29½	175	37	62½	420	90	30
14	3	1	64	13	76	114	24	51	176	37	84	430	92	45
15	3	22½	65	13	97½	115	24	72½	178	38	27	440	94	60
16	3	44	66	14	19	116	24	94	[15] 180	38	70	450	96	75
17	3	65½	67	14	40½	117	25	15½	182	39	13	460	98	90
18	3	87	68	14	62	118	25	37	184	39	56	470	101	5
19	4	8½	69	14	83½	119	25	58½	186	39	99	480	103	20
20	4	30	**70**	15	5	**120**	25	80	188	40	42	490	105	35
21	4	51½	71	15	26½	121	26	1½	190	40	85	**500**	107	50
22	4	73	[6] 72	15	48	122	26	23	[16] 192	41	28	550	118	25
23	4	94½	73	15	69½	123	26	44½	194	41	71	600	129	0
[2] 24	5	16	74	15	91	124	26	66	196	42	14	650	139	75
25	5	37½	75	16	12½	125	26	87½	198	42	57	700	150	50
26	5	59	76	16	34	126	27	9	**200**	43	0	750	161	25
27	5	80½	77	16	55½	127	27	30½	[17] 204	43	86	800	172	0
28	6	2	78	16	77	128	27	52	205	44	7½	850	182	75
29	6	23½	79	16	98½	129	27	73½	210	45	15	900	193	50
30	6	45	**80**	17	20	**130**	27	95	215	46	22½	950	204	25
31	6	66½	81	17	41½	131	28	16½	[18] 216	46	44	**1000**	215	0
32	6	88	82	17	63	[11] 132	28	38	220	47	30	1016	218	44
33	7	9½	83	17	84½	133	28	59½	225	48	37½	1250	268	75
34	7	31	[7] 84	18	6	134	28	81	[19] 228	49	2	1500	322	50
35	7	52½	85	18	27½	135	29	2½	230	49	45	1728	371	52
[3] 36	7	74	86	18	49	136	29	24	235	50	52½	1750	376	25
37	7	95½	87	18	70½	137	29	45½	[20] 240	51	60	1760	378	40
38	8	17	88	18	92	138	29	67	245	52	67½	2000	430	0
39	8	38½	89	19	13½	139	29	88½	**250**	53	75	2240	481	60
40	8	60	**90**	19	35	**140**	30	10	255	54	82½	2500	537	50
41	8	81½	91	19	56½	141	30	31½	260	55	90	3000	645	0
42	9	3	92	19	78	142	30	53	265	56	97½	4000	860	0
43	9	24½	93	19	99½	143	30	74½	270	58	5	5000	1075	0
44	9	46	94	20	21	[12] 144	30	96	275	59	12½	6000	1290	0
45	9	67½	95	20	42½	145	31	17½	280	60	20	7000	1505	0
46	9	89	[8] 96	20	64	146	31	39	285	61	27½	8000	1720	0
47	10	10½	97	20	85½	147	31	60½	[24] 288	61	92	9000	1935	0
[4] 48	10	32	98	21	7	148	31	82	290	62	35	10000	2150	0
49	10	53½	99	21	28½	149	32	3½	295	63	42½	15000	3225	0
50	10	75	**100**	21	50	**150**	32	25	**300**	64	50	20000	4300	0

Grosses.

1.	30	96
2.	61	92
3.	92	88
4.	123	84
5.	154	80
6.	185	76
7.	216	72
8.	247	68
9.	278	64
10.	309	60
11.	340	56

Twelfths

1.	0	1¾
⅙ 2.	0	3½
3.	0	5½
⅓ 4.	0	7¼
5.	0	9
½ 6.	0	10¾
7.	0	12½
⅔ 8.	0	14¼
9.	0	16¼
⅚ 10.	0	18
11.	0	19¾

10ths / **Twentieths**

10ths				10ths			
	1.	0	1		11.	0	11¾
·1	2.	0	2¼	·6	12.	0	13
	3.	0	3¼		13.	0	14
·2	4.	0	4¼	·7	14.	0	15
	5.	0	5½		15.	0	16¼
·3	6.	0	6½	·8	16.	0	17¼
	7.	0	7½		17.	0	18¼
·4	8.	0	8½	·9	18.	0	19¼
	9.	0	9¾		19.	0	20½
·5	10.	0	10¾		20.	0	21½

Sixteenths

1.	0	1¼	9.	0	12
⅛ 2.	0	2¾	⅝ 10.	0	13½
3.	0	4	11.	0	14¾
¼ 4.	0	5½	¾ 12.	0	16¼
5.	0	6¾	13.	0	17½
⅜ 6.	0	8	⅞ 14.	0	18¾
7.	0	9½	15.	0	20¼
½ 8.	0	10¾			

 22 Pence

	£	P		£	P		£	P		£	P		£	P
1	0	22	51	11	22	101	22	22	152	33	44	310	68	20
2	0	44	52	11	44	102	22	44	154	33	88	320	70	40
3	0	66	53	11	66	103	22	66	[13] 156	34	32	330	72	60
4	0	88	54	11	88	104	22	88	158	34	76	340	74	80
5	1	10	55	12	10	105	23	10	160	35	20	350	77	0
*6	1	32	56	12	32	106	23	32	162	35	64	360	79	20
7	1	54	57	12	54	107	23	54	164	36	8	365	80	30
8	1	76	58	12	76	[9] 108	23	76	166	36	52	370	81	40
9	1	98	59	12	98	109	23	98	[14] 168	36	96	380	83	60
10	2	20	[5] **60**	13	20	**110**	24	20	170	37	40	390	85	80
*11	2	42	61	13	42	111	24	42	172	37	84	400	88	0
[1] 12	2	64	62	13	64	112	24	64	174	38	28	410	90	20
13	2	86	63	13	86	113	24	86	175	38	50	420	92	40
14	3	8	64	14	8	114	25	8	176	38	72	430	94	60
15	3	30	65	14	30	115	25	30	178	39	16	440	96	80
16	3	52	66	14	52	116	25	52	[15] 180	39	60	450	99	0
17	3	74	67	14	74	117	25	74	182	40	4	460	101	20
18	3	96	68	14	96	118	25	96	184	40	48	470	103	40
19	4	18	69	15	18	119	26	18	186	40	92	480	105	60
20	4	40	**70**	15	40	**120**	26	40	188	41	36	490	107	80
21	4	62	71	15	62	121	26	62	190	41	80	**500**	110	0
22	4	84	[6] 72	15	84	122	26	84	[16] 192	42	24	550	121	0
23	5	6	73	16	6	123	27	6	194	42	68	600	132	0
[2] 24	5	28	74	16	28	124	27	28	196	43	12	650	143	0
25	5	50	75	16	50	125	27	50	198	43	56	700	154	0
26	5	72	76	16	72	126	27	72	**200**	44	0	750	165	0
27	5	94	77	16	94	127	27	94	[17] 204	44	88	800	176	0
28	6	16	78	17	16	128	28	16	205	45	10	850	187	0
29	6	38	79	17	38	129	28	38	210	46	20	900	198	0
30	6	60	**80**	17	60	**130**	28	60	215	47	30	950	209	0
31	6	82	81	17	82	131	28	82	[18] 216	47	52	**1000**	220	0
32	7	4	82	18	4	[11] 132	29	4	220	48	40	1016	223	52
33	7	26	83	18	26	133	29	26	225	49	50	1250	275	0
34	7	48	[7] 84	18	48	134	29	48	[19] 228	50	16	1500	330	0
35	7	70	85	18	70	135	29	70	230	50	60	1728	380	16
[3] 36	7	92	86	18	92	136	29	92	235	51	70	1750	385	0
37	8	14	87	19	14	137	30	14	[20] 240	52	80	1760	387	20
38	8	36	88	19	36	138	30	36	245	53	90	2000	440	0
39	8	58	89	19	58	139	30	58	**250**	55	0	2240	492	80
40	8	80	**90**	19	80	**140**	30	80	255	56	10	2500	550	0
41	9	2	91	20	2	141	31	2	260	57	20	3000	660	0
42	9	24	92	20	24	142	31	24	265	58	30	4000	880	0
43	9	46	93	20	46	143	31	46	270	59	40	**5000**	1100	0
44	9	68	94	20	68	[12] 144	31	68	275	60	50	6000	1320	0
45	9	90	95	20	90	145	31	90	280	61	60	7000	1540	0
46	10	12	[8] 96	21	12	146	32	12	285	62	70	8000	1760	0
47	10	34	97	21	34	147	32	34	[24] 288	63	36	9000	1980	0
[4] 48	10	56	98	21	56	148	32	56	290	63	80	10,000	2200	0
49	10	78	99	21	78	149	32	78	295	64	90	15,000	3300	0
50	11	0	**100**	22	0	**150**	33	0	**300**	66	0	20,000	4400	0

(Dozens)

Grosses

1.	31	68
2.	63	36
3.	95	04
4.	126	72
5.	158	40
6.	190	08
7.	221	76
8.	253	44
9.	285	12
10.	316	80
11.	348	48

Twelfths

	1.		1¾
⅙	2.	0	3¾
	3.	0	5½
⅓	4.	0	7¼
	5.	0	9¼
½	6.	0	11
	7.	0	12¾
⅔	8.	0	14¾
	9.	0	16½
⅚	10.	0	18¼
	11.	0	20¼

Twentieths

10ths				10ths			
	1.	0	1		11.	0	12
·1	2.	0	2¼	·6	12.	0	13¼
	3.	0	3¼		13.	0	14¼
·2	4.	0	4½	7	14.	0	15½
	5.	0	5½		15.	0	16½
·3	6.	0	6½	·8	16.	0	17½
	7.	0	7¾		17.	0	18¾
·4	8.	0	8¾	·9	18.	0	19¾
	9.	0	10		19.	0	21
·5	10.	0	11		20.	0	22

Sixteenths

	1.	0	1½		9.	0	12½
⅛	2.	0	2¾	⅝	10.	0	13¾
	3.	0	4¼		11.	0	15¼
¼	4.	0	5½	¾	12.	0	16½
	5.	0	7		13.	0	18
⅜	6.	0	8¼	⅞	14.	0	19¼
	7.	0	9¾		15.	0	20¾
½	8.	0	11				

*Dozens.	£	P	Dozens.	£	P	Dozens	£	P	Dozens.	£	P		£	P
1	0	22½	51	11	47½	101	22	72½	152	34	20	310	69	75
2	0	45	52	11	70	102	22	95	154	34	65	320	72	0
3	0	67½	53	11	92½	103	23	17½	[13]156	35	10	330	74	25
4	0	90	54	12	15	104	23	40	158	35	55	340	76	50
5	1	12½	55	12	37½	105	23	62½	160	36	0	350	78	75
6	1	35	56	12	60	106	23	85	162	36	45	360	81	0
7	1	57½	57	12	82½	107	24	7½	164	36	90	365	82	12½
8	1	80	58	13	5	[9]108	24	30	166	37	35	370	83	25
9	2	2½	59	13	27½	109	24	52½	[14]168	37	80	380	85	50
10	2	25	[5]**60**	13	50	**110**	24	75	170	38	25	390	87	75
*11	2	47½	61	13	72½	111	24	97½	172	38	70	400	90	00
[1]12	2	70	62	13	95	112	25	20	174	39	15	410	92	25
13	2	92½	63	14	17½	113	25	42½	175	39	37½	420	94	50
14	3	15	64	14	40	114	25	65	176	39	60	430	96	75
15	3	37½	65	14	62½	115	25	87½	178	40	5	440	99	00
16	3	60	66	14	85	116	26	10	[15]180	40	50	450	101	25
17	3	82½	67	15	7½	117	26	32½	182	40	95	460	103	50
18	4	5	68	15	30	118	26	55	184	41	40	470	105	75
19	4	27½	69	15	52½	119	26	77½	186	41	85	480	108	00
20	4	50	**70**	15	75	**120**	27	0	188	42	30	490	110	25
21	4	72½	71	15	97½	121	27	22½	190	42	75	**500**	112	50
22	4	95	[6]72	16	20	122	27	45	[16]192	43	20	550	123	75
23	5	17½	73	16	42½	123	27	67½	194	43	65	600	135	0
[2]24	5	40	74	16	65	124	27	90	196	44	10	650	146	25
25	5	62½	75	16	87½	125	28	12½	198	44	55	700	157	50
26	5	85	76	17	10	126	28	35	**200**	45	0	750	168	75
27	6	7½	77	17	32½	127	28	57½	[17]204	45	90	800	180	0
28	6	30	78	17	55	128	28	80	205	46	12½	850	191	25
29	6	52½	79	17	77½	129	29	2½	210	47	25	900	202	50
30	6	75	**80**	18	0	**130**	29	25	215	48	37½	950	213	75
31	6	97½	81	18	22½	131	29	47½	[18]216	48	60	**1000**	225	0
32	7	20	82	18	45	[11]132	29	70	220	49	50	1016	228	60
33	7	42½	83	18	67½	133	29	92½	225	50	62½	1250	281	25
34	7	65	[7]84	18	90	134	30	15	[19]228	51	30	1500	337	50
35	7	87½	85	19	12½	135	30	37½	230	51	75	1728	388	80
[3]36	8	10	86	19	35	136	30	60	235	52	87½	1750	393	75
37	8	32½	87	19	57½	137	30	82½	[20]240	54	0	1760	396	0
38	8	55	88	19	80	138	31	5	245	55	12½	2000	450	0
39	8	77½	89	20	2½	139	31	27½	**250**	56	25	2240	504	0
40	9	0	**90**	20	25	**140**	31	50	255	57	37½	2500	562	50
41	9	22½	91	20	47½	141	31	72½	260	58	50	3000	675	0
42	9	45	92	20	70	142	31	95	265	59	62½	4000	900	0
43	9	67½	93	20	92½	143	32	17½	270	60	75	5000	1125	0
44	9	90	94	21	15	[12]144	32	40	275	61	87½	6000	1350	0
45	10	12½	95	21	37½	145	32	62½	280	63	0	7000	1575	0
46	10	35	[8]96	21	60	146	32	85	285	64	12½	8000	1800	0
47	10	57½	97	21	82½	147	33	7½	[24]288	64	80	9000	2025	0
[4]48	10	80	98	22	5	148	33	30	290	65	25	10000	2250	0
49	11	2½	99	22	27½	149	33	52½	295	66	37½	15000	3375	0
50	11	25	**100**	22	50	**150**	33	75	**300**	67	50	20000	4500	0

Grosses.			Twelfths			10ths	Twentieths			10ths				Sixteenths					
1.	32	40	1.	0	2		1.	0	1¼		11.	0	12½	1.	0	1½	9.	0	12¾
2.	64	80	⅙2.	0	3¾	·1	2.	0	2¼	·6	12.	0	13½	⅛2.	0	2¾	⅝10.	0	14
3.	97	20	3.	0	5¾		3.	0	3½		13.	0	14¾	3.	0	4¼	11.	0	15½
4.	129	60	⅓4.	0	7½	·2	4.	0	4½	·7	14.	0	15¾	¼4.	0	5¾	¾12.	0	17
5.	162	0	5.	0	9½		5.	0	5¾		15.	0	17	5.	0	7	13.	0	18¼
6.	194	40	½6.	0	11¼	·3	6.	0	6¾	·8	16.	0	18	⅜6.	0	8½	⅞14.	0	19¾
7.	226	80	7.	0	13¼		7.	0	8		17.	0	19¼	7.	0	9¾	15.	0	21
8.	259	20	⅔8.	0	15	·4	8.	0	9	·9	18.	0	20¼	½8.	0	11¼			
9.	291	60	9.	0	17		9.	0	10¼		19.	0	21½						
10.	324	0	⅚10.	0	18¾	·5	10.	0	11¼		20.	0	22½						
11.	356	40	11.	0	20¾														

		£	P			£	P			£	P			£	P		£	P
	1	0	23		51	11	73		101	23	23		152	34	96	310	71	30
	2	0	46		52	11	96		102	23	46		154	35	42	320	73	60
Dozens.	3	0	69	Dozens.	53	12	19	Dozens.	103	23	69	13	156	35	88	330	75	90
	4	0	92		54	12	42		104	23	92		158	36	34	340	78	20
	5	1	15		55	12	65		105	24	15	Doz.	160	36	80	350	80	50
*	6	1	38		56	12	88		106	24	38		162	37	26	360	82	80
	7	1	61		57	13	11		107	24	61		164	37	72	365	83	95
	8	1	84		58	13	34	9	108	24	84		166	38	18	370	85	10
	9	2	7		59	13	57		109	25	7	14	168	38	64	380	87	40
	10	2	30	5	**60**	13	80		**110**	25	30		170	39	10	390	89	70
*	11	2	53		61	14	3		111	25	53		172	39	56	400	92	0
1	12	2	76		62	14	26		112	25	76		174	40	2	410	94	30
	13	2	99		63	14	49		113	25	99		175	40	25	420	96	60
	14	3	22		64	14	72		114	26	22		176	40	48	430	98	90
	15	3	45		65	14	95		115	26	45		178	40	94	440	101	20
	16	3	68		66	15	18		116	26	68	15	180	41	40	450	103	50
	17	3	91		67	15	41		117	26	91		182	41	86	460	105	80
	18	4	14		68	15	64		118	27	14		184	42	32	470	108	10
	19	4	37		69	15	87		119	27	37		186	42	78	480	110	40
	20	4	60		**70**	16	10		**120**	27	60		188	43	24	490	112	70
	21	4	83		71	16	33		121	27	83		190	43	70	**500**	115	0
	22	5	6	6	72	16	56		122	28	6	16	192	44	16	550	126	50
	23	5	29		73	16	79		123	28	29		194	44	62	600	138	0
2	24	5	52		74	17	2		124	28	52		196	45	8	650	149	50
	25	5	75		75	17	25		125	28	75		198	45	54	700	161	0
	26	5	98		76	17	48		126	28	98		**200**	46	0	750	172	50
	27	6	21		77	17	71		127	29	21	17	204	46	92	800	184	0
	28	6	44		78	17	94		128	29	44		205	47	15	850	195	50
	29	6	67		79	18	17		129	29	67		210	48	30	900	207	0
	30	6	90		**80**	18	40		**130**	29	90		215	49	45	950	218	50
	31	7	13		81	18	63		131	30	13	18	216	49	68	**1000**	230	0
	32	7	36		82	18	86	11	132	30	36		220	50	60	1016	233	68
	33	7	59		83	19	9		133	30	59		225	51	75	1250	287	50
	34	7	82	7	84	19	32		134	30	82	19	228	52	44	1500	345	0
	35	8	5		85	19	55		135	31	5		230	52	90	1728	397	44
3	36	8	28		86	19	78		136	31	28		235	54	5	1750	402	50
	37	8	51		87	20	1		137	31	51	20	240	55	20	1760	404	80
	38	8	74		88	20	24		138	31	74		245	56	35	2000	460	0
	39	8	97		89	20	47		139	31	97		**250**	57	50	2240	515	20
	40	9	20		**90**	20	70		**140**	32	20		255	58	65	2500	575	0
	41	9	43		91	20	93		141	32	43		260	59	80	3000	690	0
	42	9	66		92	21	16		142	32	66		265	60	95	4000	920	0
	43	9	89		93	21	39		143	32	89		270	62	10	**5000**	1150	0
	44	10	12		94	21	62	12	144	33	12		275	63	25	6000	1380	0
	45	10	35		95	21	85		145	33	35		280	64	40	7000	1610	0
	46	10	58	8	96	22	8		146	33	58		285	65	55	8000	1840	0
	47	10	81		97	22	31		147	33	81	24	288	66	24	9000	2070	0
4	48	11	4		98	22	54		148	34	4		290	66	70	10,000	2300	0
	49	11	27		99	22	77		149	34	27		295	67	85	15,000	3450	0
	50	11	50		**100**	23	0		**150**	34	50		**300**	69	0	20,000	4600	0

Grosses.

1.	33	12
2.	66	24
3.	99	36
4.	132	48
5.	165	60
6.	198	72
7.	231	84
8.	264	96
9.	298	8
10.	331	20
11.	364	32

Twelfths

	1.	0	2
1/6	2.	0	3¾
	3.	0	5¾
1/3	4.	0	7¾
	5.	0	9½
1/2	6.	0	11½
	7.	0	13½
2/3	8.	0	15¼
	9.	0	17¼
5/6	10.	0	19¼
	11.	0	21

Twentieths (10ths)

	1.	0	1¼		11.	0	12¾
·1	2.	0	2¼	·6	12.	0	13¾
	3.	0	3½		13.	0	15
·2	4.	0	4½	·7	14.	0	16
	5.	0	5¾		15.	0	17¼
·3	6.	0	7	·8	16.	0	18½
	7.	0	8		17.	0	19½
·4	8.	0	9¼	·9	18.	0	20¾
	9.	0	10¼		19.	0	21¾
·5	10.	0	11½		20.	0	23

Sixteenths

	1.	0	1½		9.	0	13
1/8	2.	0	3	5/8	10.	0	14½
	3.	0	4¼		11.	0	15¾
1/4	4.	0	5¾	3/4	12.	0	17¼
	5.	0	7¼		13.	0	18¾
3/8	6.	0	8¾	7/8	14.	0	20¼
	7.	0	10		15.	0	21½
1/2	8.	0	11½				

	£ P		£ P		£ P		£ P		£ P
1	0 23½	51	11 98½	101	23 73½	152	35 72	310	72 85
2	0 47	52	12 22	102	23 97	154	36 19	320	75 20
3	0 70½	53	12 45½	103	24 20½	156	36 66	330	77 55
4	0 94	54	12 69	104	24 44	158	37 13	340	79 90
*5	1 17½	55	12 92½	105	24 67½	160	37 60	350	82 25
*6	1 41	56	13 16	106	24 91	162	38 7	360	84 60
7	1 64½	57	13 39½	107	25 14½	164	38 54	365	85 77½
8	1 88	58	13 63	108	25 38	166	39 1	370	86 95
9	2 11½	59	13 86½	109	25 61½	168	39 48	380	89 30
10	2 35	60	14 10	110	25 85	170	39 95	390	91 65
*11	2 58½	61	14 33½	111	26 8½	172	40 42	400	94 0
†12	2 82	62	14 57	112	26 32	174	40 89	410	96 35
13	3 5½	63	14 80½	113	26 55½	175	41 12½	420	98 70
14	3 29	64	15 4	114	26 79	176	41 36	430	101 5
15	3 52½	65	15 27½	115	27 2½	178	41 83	440	103 40
16	3 76	66	15 51	116	27 26	180	42 30	450	105 75
17	3 99½	67	15 74½	117	27 49½	182	42 77	460	108 10
18	4 23	68	15 98	118	27 73	184	43 24	470	110 45
19	4 46½	69	16 21½	119	27 96½	186	43 71	480	112 80
20	4 70	70	16 45	120	28 20	188	44 18	490	115 15
21	4 93½	71	16 68½	121	28 43½	190	44 65	500	117 50
22	5 17	72	16 92	122	28 67	192	45 12	550	129 25
23	5 40½	73	17 15½	123	28 90½	194	45 59	600	141 0
*24	5 64	74	17 39	124	29 14	196	46 6	650	152 75
25	5 87½	75	17 62½	125	29 37½	198	46 53	700	164 50
26	6 11	76	17 86	126	29 61	200	47 0	750	176 25
27	6 34½	77	18 9½	127	29 84½	204	47 94	800	188 0
28	6 58	78	18 33	128	30 8	205	48 17½	850	199 75
29	6 81½	79	18 56½	129	30 31½	210	49 35	900	211 50
30	7 5	80	18 80	130	30 55	215	50 52½	950	223 25
31	7 28½	81	19 3½	131	30 78½	216	50 76	1000	235 0
32	7 52	82	19 27	132	31 2	220	51 70	1016	238 76
33	7 75½	83	19 50½	133	31 25½	225	52 87½	1250	293 75
34	7 99	84	19 74	134	31 49	228	53 58	1500	352 50
35	8 22½	85	19 97½	135	31 72½	230	54 5	1728	406 8
*36	8 46	86	20 21	136	31 96	235	55 22½	1750	411 25
37	8 69½	87	20 44½	137	32 19½	240	56 40	1760	413 60
38	8 93	88	20 68	138	32 43	245	57 57½	2000	470 0
39	9 16½	89	20 91½	139	32 66½	250	58 75	2240	526 40
40	9 40	90	21 15	140	32 90	255	59 92½	2500	587 50
41	9 63½	91	21 38½	141	33 13½	260	61 10	3000	705 0
42	9 87	92	21 62	142	33 37	265	62 27½	4000	940 0
43	10 10½	93	21 85½	143	33 60½	270	63 45	5000	1175 0
44	10 34	94	22 9	144	33 84	275	64 62½	6000	1410 0
45	10 57½	95	22 32½	145	34 7½	280	65 80	7000	1645 0
46	10 81	96	22 56	146	34 31	285	66 97½	8000	1880 0
47	11 4½	97	22 79½	147	34 54½	288	67 68	9000	2115 0
*48	11 28	98	23 3	148	34 78	290	68 15	10000	2350 0
49	11 51½	99	23 26½	149	35 1½	295	69 32½	15000	3525 0
50	11 75	100	23 50	150	35 25	300	70 50	20000	4700 0

Grosses		Twelfths		10ths	Twentieths			Sixteenths			
1.	33 84	1.	1 0 2					1.0	1½	9.0	13½
2.	67 68	½2.	2 0 4		1.0	1½	11.0	13	½2.0	3	§10.0	14½
3.	101 52	3.	3 0 6	·1	2.0	2½	12.0	14	3.0	4½	11.0	16½
4.	135 36	¼4.	4 0 7½		3.0	3½	13.0	15½	¼4.0	6	½12.0	17½
5.	169 20	5.	5 0 9½	·2	4.0	4½	14.0	16½	5.0	7½	13.0	19
6.	203 04	½6.	6 0 11½		5.0	6	15.0	17½	½6.0	8½	§14.0	20½
7.	236 88	7.	7 0 13½	·3	6.0	7½	16.0	18½	7.0	10½	15.0	22
8.	270 72	¾8.	8 0 15½		7.0	8½	17.0	20	¾8.0	11½		
9.	304 56	9.	9 0 17½	·4	8.0	9½	18.0	21½				
10.	338 40	½10.	10 0 19½		9.0	10½	19.0	22½				
11.	372 24	11.	11 0 21½	·5	10.0	11½	20.0	23½				

24 Pence

*Dozens	No.	£	P	Dozens	No.	£	P	Dozens	No.	£	P	Dozens	No.	£	P	No.	£	P
	1	0	24		51	12	24		101	24	24		152	36	48	310	74	40
	2	0	48		52	12	48		102	24	48		154	36	96	320	76	80
	3	0	72		53	12	72		103	24	72	13	156	37	44	330	79	20
	4	0	96		54	12	96		104	24	96		158	37	92	340	81	60
	5	1	20		55	13	20		105	25	20		160	38	40	350	84	0
	6	1	44		56	13	44		106	25	44		162	38	88	360	86	40
	7	1	68		57	13	68		107	25	68		164	39	36	365	87	60
	8	1	92		58	13	92	9	108	25	92		166	39	84	370	88	80
	9	2	16		59	14	16		109	26	16	14	168	40	32	380	91	20
	10	2	40	5	**60**	14	40		**110**	26	40		170	40	80	390	93	60
	11	2	64		61	14	64		111	26	64		172	41	28	400	96	0
*1	12	2	88		62	14	88		112	26	88		174	41	76	410	98	40
	13	3	12		63	15	12		113	27	12		175	42	0	420	100	80
	14	3	36		64	15	36		114	27	36		176	42	24	430	103	20
	15	3	60		65	15	60		115	27	60		178	42	72	440	105	60
	16	3	84		66	15	84		116	27	84	15	180	43	20	450	108	0
	17	4	8		67	16	8		117	28	8		182	43	68	460	110	40
	18	4	32		68	16	32		118	28	32		184	44	16	470	112	80
	19	4	56		69	16	56		119	28	56		186	44	64	480	115	20
	20	4	80		**70**	16	80	10	**120**	28	80		188	45	12	490	117	60
	21	5	4		71	17	4		121	29	4		190	45	60	**500**	120	0
	22	5	28	6	72	17	28		122	29	28	16	192	46	8	550	132	0
	23	5	52		73	17	52		123	29	52		194	46	56	600	144	0
2	24	5	76		74	17	76		124	29	76		196	47	4	650	156	0
	25	6	0		75	18	0		125	30	0		198	47	52	700	168	0
	26	6	24		76	18	24		126	30	24		**200**	48	0	750	180	0
	27	6	48		77	18	48		127	30	48	17	204	48	96	800	192	0
	28	6	72		78	18	72		128	30	72		205	49	20	850	204	0
	29	6	96		79	18	96		129	30	96		210	50	40	900	216	0
	30	7	20		**80**	19	20		**130**	31	20		215	51	60	950	228	0
	31	7	44		81	19	44		131	31	44	18	216	51	84	**1000**	240	0
	32	7	68		82	19	68	11	132	31	68		220	52	80	1016	243	84
	33	7	92		83	19	92		133	31	92		225	54	0	1250	300	0
	34	8	16	7	84	20	16		134	32	16	19	228	54	72	1500	360	0
	35	8	40		85	20	40		135	32	40		230	55	20	1728	414	72
3	36	8	64		86	20	64		136	32	64		235	56	40	1750	420	0
	37	8	88		87	20	88		137	32	88	20	240	57	60	1760	422	40
	38	9	12		88	21	12		138	33	12		245	58	80	2000	480	0
	39	9	36		89	21	36		139	33	36		**250**	60	0	2240	537	60
	40	9	60		**90**	21	60		**140**	33	60		255	61	20	2500	600	0
	41	9	84		91	21	84		141	33	84		260	62	40	3000	720	0
	42	10	8		92	22	8		142	34	8		265	63	60	4000	960	0
	43	10	32		93	22	32		143	34	32		270	64	80	**5000**	1200	0
	44	10	56		94	22	56	12	144	34	56		275	66	0	6000	1440	0
	45	10	80		95	22	80		145	34	80		280	67	20	7000	1680	0
	46	11	4	8	96	23	4		146	35	4		285	68	40	8000	1920	0
	47	11	28		97	23	28		147	35	28	24	288	69	12	9000	2160	0
4	48	11	52		98	23	52		148	35	52		290	69	60	10,000	2400	0
	49	11	76		99	23	76		149	35	76		295	70	80	15,000	3600	0
	50	12	0		**100**	24	0		**150**	36	0		**300**	72	0	20,000	4800	0

Grosses

1.	34	56
2.	69	12
3.	103	68
4.	138	24
5.	172	80
6.	207	36
7.	241	92
8.	276	48
9.	311	04
10.	345	60
11.	380	16

Twelfths

	1.	0	2
1/6	2.	0	4
	3.	0	6
1/3	4.	0	8
	5.	0	10
1/2	6.	0	12
	7.	0	14
2/3	8.	0	16
	9.	0	18
5/6	10.	0	20
	11.	0	22

Twentieths

10ths				10ths			
	1.	0	1¼		11.	0	13¼
·1	2.	0	2½	·6	12.	0	14½
	3.	0	3½		13.	0	15½
·2	4.	0	4¾	·7	14.	0	16¾
	5.	0	6		15.	0	18
·3	6.	0	7¼	·8	16.	0	19¼
	7.	0	8½		17.	0	20½
·4	8.	0	9½	·9	18.	0	21½
	9.	0	10¾		19.	0	22¾
·5	10.	0	12		20.	0	24

Sixteenths

	1.	0	1½		9.	0	13½
1/8	2.	0	3	5/8	10.	0	15
	3.	0	4½		11.	0	16½
1/4	4.	0	6	3/4	12.	0	18
	5.	0	7½		13.	0	19½
3/8	6.	0	9	7/8	14.	0	21
	7.	0	10½		15.	0	22½
1/2	8.	0	12				

	£ P		£ P		£ P		£ P		£ P
1	0 24½	51	12 49½	101	24 74½	152	37 24	310	75 95
2	0 49	52	12 74	102	24 99	154	37 73	320	78 40
3	0 73½	53	12 98½	103	25 23½	¹³156	38 22	330	80 85
4	0 98	54	13 23	104	25 48	158	38 71	340	83 30
*5	1 22½	55	13 47½	105	25 72½	160	39 20	350	85 75
6	1 47	56	13 72	106	25 97	162	39 69	360	88 20
7	1 71½	57	13 96½	107	26 21½	164	40 18	365	89 42½
8	1 96	58	14 21	⁹108	26 46	166	40 67	370	90 65
9	2 20½	59	14 45½	109	26 70½	¹⁴168	41 16	380	93 10
10	2 45	⁵60	14 70	110	26 95	170	41 65	390	95 55
*11	2 69½	61	14 94½	111	27 19½	172	42 14	400	98 0
†12	2 94	62	15 19	112	27 44	174	42 63	410	100 45
13	3 18½	63	15 43½	113	27 68½	175	42 87½	420	102 90
14	3 43	64	15 68	114	27 93	176	43 12	430	105 35
15	3 67½	65	15 92½	115	28 17½	178	43 61	440	107 80
16	3 92	66	16 17	116	28 42	¹⁵180	44 10	450	110 25
17	4 16½	67	16 41½	117	28 66½	182	44 59	460	112 70
18	4 41	68	16 66	118	28 91	184	45 8	470	115 15
19	4 65½	69	16 90½	119	29 15½	186	45 57	480	117 60
20	4 90	70	17 15	120	29 40	188	46 6	490	120 5
21	5 14½	71	17 39½	121	29 64½	190	46 55	500	122 50
22	5 39	⁶72	17 64	122	29 89	¹⁶192	47 4	550	134 75
23	5 63½	73	17 88½	123	30 13½	194	47 53	600	147 0
†24	5 88	74	18 13	124	30 38	196	48 2	650	159 25
25	6 12½	75	18 37½	125	30 62½	198	48 51	700	171 50
26	6 37	76	18 62	126	30 87	200	49 0	750	183 75
27	6 61½	77	18 86½	127	31 11½	¹⁷204	49 98	800	196 0
28	6 86	78	19 11	128	31 36	205	50 22½	850	208 25
29	7 10½	79	19 35½	129	31 60½	210	51 45	900	220 50
30	7 35	80	19 60	130	31 85	215	52 67½	950	232 75
31	7 59½	81	19 84½	131	32 9½	¹⁸216	52 92	1000	245 0
32	7 84	82	20 9	¹¹132	32 34	220	53 90	1016	248 92
33	8 8½	83	20 33½	133	32 58½	225	55 12½	1250	306 25
34	8 33	⁷84	20 58	134	32 83	¹⁹228	55 86	1500	367 50
35	8 57½	85	20 82½	135	33 7½	230	56 35	1728	423 36
†36	8 82	86	21 7	136	33 32	235	57 57½	1750	428 75
37	9 6½	87	21 31½	137	33 56½	²⁰240	58 80	1760	431 20
38	9 31	88	21 56	138	33 81	245	60 2½	2000	490 0
39	9 55½	89	21 80½	139	34 5½	250	61 25	2240	548 80
40	9 80	90	22 5	140	34 30	255	62 47½	2500	612 50
41	10 4½	91	22 29½	141	34 54½	260	63 70	3000	735 0
42	10 29	92	22 54	142	34 79	265	64 92½	4000	980 0
43	10 53½	93	22 78½	143	35 3½	270	66 15	5000	1225 0
44	10 78	94	23 3	¹²144	35 28	275	67 37½	6000	1470 0
45	11 2½	95	23 27½	145	35 52½	280	68 60	7000	1715 0
46	11 27	⁸96	23 52	146	35 77	285	69 82½	8000	1960 0
47	11 51½	97	23 76½	147	36 1½	²⁴288	70 56	9000	2205 0
†48	11 76	98	24 1	148	36 26	290	71 5	10000	2450 0
49	12 0½	99	24 25½	149	36 50½	295	72 27½	15000	3675 0
50	12 25	100	24 50	150	36 75	300	73 50	20000	4900 0

Grosses		Twelfths		10ths	Twentieths		Sixteenths	
1. 35 28		1. 0 2			1. 0 1½	11. 0 13½	1. 0 1½	9. 0 13¾
2. 70 56		½2. 0 4		·1 2. 0 2½	·6 12. 0 14¾	½2. 0 3	⅝10. 0 15¼
3. 105 84		3. 0 6½		3. 0 3¾	13. 0 16	3. 0 4½	11. 0 16¾
4. 141 12		¼4. 0 8½		·2 4. 0 5	·7 14. 0 17¼	¼4. 0 6¼	¾12. 0 18¼
5. 176 40		5. 0 10½		5. 0 6¼	15. 0 18½	5. 0 7¾	13. 0 20
6. 211 68		½6. 0 12½		·3 6. 0 7½	·8 16. 0 19¾	⅜6. 0 9¼	⅞14. 0 21½
7. 246 96		7. 0 14½		7. 0 8¾	17. 0 20¼	7. 0 10¾	15. 0 23
8. 282 24		¾8. 0 16½		·4 8. 0 10	·9 18. 0 22	½8. 0 12¼	
9. 317 52		9. 0 18½		9. 0 11	19. 0 23½		
10. 352 80		½10. 0 20½		·5 10. 0 12¼	20. 0 24½		
11. 388 8		11. 0 22½					

	£	P		£	P		£	P		£	P		£	P
1	0	25	51	12	75	101	25	25	152	38	0	310	77	50
2	0	50	52	13	0	102	25	50	154	38	50	320	80	0
3	0	75	53	13	25	103	25	75	¹³156	39	0	330	82	50
*Dozens 4	1	0	54	13	50	Dozens 104	26	0	158	39	50	340	85	0
5	1	25	55	13	75	105	26	25	160	40	0	350	87	50
6	1	50	56	14	0	106	26	50	162	40	50	360	90	0
7	1	75	57	14	25	107	26	75	164	41	0	365	91	25
8	2	0	58	14	50	⁹108	27	0	166	41	50	370	92	50
9	2	25	59	14	75	109	27	25	¹⁴168	42	0	380	95	0
10	2	50	⁵60	15	0	110	27	50	170	42	50	390	97	50
11	2	75	61	15	25	111	27	75	172	43	0	400	100	0
¹12	3	0	62	15	50	112	28	0	174	43	50	410	102	50
13	3	25	63	15	75	113	28	25	175	43	75	420	105	0
14	3	50	64	16	0	114	28	50	176	44	0	430	107	50
15	3	75	65	16	25	115	28	75	178	44	50	440	110	0
16	4	0	66	16	50	116	29	0	¹⁵180	45	0	450	112	50
17	4	25	67	16	75	117	29	25	182	45	50	460	115	0
18	4	50	68	17	0	118	29	50	184	46	0	470	117	50
19	4	75	69	17	25	119	29	75	186	46	50	480	120	0
20	5	0	70	17	50	120	30	0	188	47	0	490	122	50
21	5	25	71	17	75	121	30	25	190	47	50	500	125	0
22	5	50	⁶72	18	0	122	30	50	¹⁶192	48	0	550	137	50
23	5	75	73	18	25	123	30	75	194	48	50	600	150	0
²24	6	0	74	18	50	124	31	0	196	49	0	650	162	50
25	6	25	75	18	75	125	31	25	198	49	50	700	175	0
26	6	50	76	19	0	126	31	50	200	50	0	750	187	50
27	6	75	77	19	25	127	31	75	¹⁷204	51	0	800	200	0
28	7	0	78	19	50	128	32	0	205	51	25	850	212	50
29	7	25	79	19	75	129	32	25	210	52	50	900	225	0
30	7	50	80	20	0	130	32	50	215	53	75	950	237	50
31	7	75	81	20	25	131	32	75	¹⁸216	54	0	1000	250	0
32	8	0	82	20	50	¹¹132	33	0	220	55	0	1016	254	0
33	8	25	83	20	75	133	33	25	225	56	25	1250	312	50
34	8	50	⁷84	21	0	134	33	50	¹⁹228	57	0	1500	375	0
35	8	75	85	21	25	135	33	75	230	57	50	1728	432	0
³36	9	0	86	21	50	136	34	0	235	58	75	1750	437	50
37	9	25	87	21	75	137	34	25	²⁰240	60	0	1760	440	0
38	9	50	88	22	0	138	34	50	245	61	25	2000	500	0
39	9	75	89	22	25	139	34	75	250	62	50	2240	560	0
40	10	0	90	22	50	140	35	0	255	63	75	2500	625	0
41	10	25	91	22	75	141	35	25	260	65	0	3000	750	0
42	10	50	92	23	0	142	35	50	265	66	25	4000	1000	0
43	10	75	93	23	25	143	35	75	270	67	50	5000	1250	0
44	11	0	94	23	50	¹²144	36	0	275	68	75	6000	1500	0
45	11	25	95	23	75	145	36	25	280	70	0	7000	1750	0
46	11	50	⁸96	24	0	146	36	50	285	71	25	8000	2000	0
47	11	75	97	24	25	147	36	75	²⁴288	72	0	9000	2250	0
⁴48	12	0	98	24	50	148	37	0	290	72	50	10,000	2500	0
49	12	25	99	24	75	149	37	25	295	73	75	15,000	3750	0
50	12	50	100	25	0	150	37	50	300	75	0	20,000	5000	0

Grosses			Twelfths			10ths	Twentieths				Sixteenths		
1.	36	0		1.	0 2		1.	0 1¼	11.	0 13¾	1.	0 1½	9. 0 14
2.	72	0	⅓ 2.	0 4½		·1 2.	0 2½	·6 12.	0 15	¹⁄₁₆ 2.	0 3¼	10. 0 15¾
3.	108	0	3.	0 6¼		3.	0 3¾	13.	0 16¼	3.	0 4¾	11. 0 17¼
4.	144	0	¼ 4.	0 8¼		·2 4.	0 5	·7 14.	0 17½	¼ 4.	0 6¼	¹²⁄₁₆ 12. 0 18¾
5.	180	0	5.	0 10½		5.	0 6¼	15.	0 18¾	5.	0 7¾	13. 0 20¼
6.	216	0	⅙ 6.	0 12½		·3 6.	0 7½	·8 16.	0 20	⁶⁄₁₆ 6.	0 9½	14. 0 22
7.	252	0	7.	0 14½		7.	0 8¾	17.	0 21¼	7.	0 11	15. 0 23¾
8.	288	0	⅜ 8.	0 16½		·4 8.	0 10	·9 18.	0 22½	⁸⁄₁₆ 8.	0 12½	
9.	324	0	9.	0 18¾		9.	0 11¼	19.	0 23¾			
10.	360	0	⁵⁄₁₂ 10.	0 20¾		·5 10.	0 12½	20.	0 25			
11.	396	0	11.	0 23								

Dozens		£	P	Dozens		£	P	Dozens		£	P	Dozens		£	P		£	P
	1	0	26		51	13	26		101	26	26		152	39	52	310	80	60
	2	0	52		52	13	52		102	26	52		154	40	4	320	83	20
	3	0	78		53	13	78		103	26	78	13	156	40	56	330	85	80
	4	1	4		54	14	4		104	27	4		158	41	8	340	88	40
	5	1	30		55	14	30		105	27	30		160	41	60	350	91	0
*	6	1	56		56	14	56		106	27	56		162	42	12	360	93	60
	7	1	82		57	14	82		107	27	82		164	42	64	365	94	90
	8	2	8		58	15	8	9	108	28	8		166	43	16	370	96	20
	9	2	34		59	15	34		109	28	34	14	168	43	68	380	98	80
	10	2	60	5	60	15	60		110	28	60		170	44	20	390	101	40
*	11	2	86		61	15	86		111	28	86		172	44	72	400	104	0
1	12	3	12		62	16	12		112	29	12		174	45	24	410	106	60
	13	3	38		63	16	38		113	29	38		175	45	50	420	109	20
	14	3	64		64	16	64		114	29	64		176	45	76	430	111	80
	15	3	90		65	16	90		115	29	90		178	46	28	440	114	40
	16	4	16		66	17	16		116	30	16	15	180	46	80	450	117	0
	17	4	42		67	17	42		117	30	42		182	47	32	460	119	60
	18	4	68		68	17	68		118	30	68		184	47	84	470	122	20
	19	4	94		69	17	94		119	30	94		186	48	36	480	124	80
	20	5	20		70	18	20		120	31	20		188	48	88	490	127	40
	21	5	46		71	18	46		121	31	46		190	49	40	500	130	0
	22	5	72	6	72	18	72		122	31	72	16	192	49	92	550	143	0
	23	5	98		73	18	98		123	31	98		194	50	44	600	156	0
2	24	6	24		74	19	24		124	32	24		196	50	96	650	169	0
	25	6	50		75	19	50		125	32	50		198	51	48	700	182	0
	26	6	76		76	19	76		126	32	76		200	52	0	750	195	0
	27	7	2		77	20	2		127	33	2	17	204	53	4	800	208	0
	28	7	28		78	20	28		128	33	28		205	53	30	850	221	0
	29	7	54		79	20	54		129	33	54		210	54	60	900	234	0
	30	7	80		80	20	80		130	33	80		215	55	90	950	247	0
	31	8	6		81	21	6		131	34	6	18	216	56	16	1000	260	0
	32	8	32		82	21	32	11	132	34	32		220	57	20	1016	264	16
	33	8	58		83	21	58		133	34	58		225	58	50	1250	325	0
	34	8	84	7	84	21	84		134	34	84	19	228	59	28	1500	390	0
	35	9	10		85	22	10		135	35	10		230	59	80	1728	449	28
3	36	9	36		86	22	36		136	35	36		235	61	10	1750	455	0
	37	9	62		87	22	62		137	35	62	20	240	62	40	1760	457	60
	38	9	88		88	22	88		138	35	88		245	63	70	2000	520	0
	39	10	14		89	23	14		139	36	14		250	65	0	2240	582	40
	40	10	40		90	23	40		140	36	40		255	66	30	2500	650	0
	41	10	66		91	23	66		141	36	66		260	67	60	3000	780	0
	42	10	92		92	23	92		142	36	92		265	68	90	4000	1040	0
	43	11	18		93	24	18		143	37	18		270	70	20	5000	1300	0
	44	11	44		94	24	44	12	144	37	44		275	71	50	6000	1560	0
	45	11	70		95	24	70		145	37	70		280	72	80	7000	1820	0
	46	11	96	8	96	24	96		146	37	96		285	74	10	8000	2080	0
	47	12	22		97	25	22		147	38	22	24	288	74	88	9000	2340	0
4	48	12	48		98	25	48		148	38	48		290	75	40	10,000	2600	0
	49	12	74		99	25	74		149	38	74		295	76	70	15,000	3900	0
	50	13	0		100	26	0		150	39	0		300	78	0	20,000	5200	0

Grosses				Twelfths			10ths	Twentieths			10ths	Twentieths				Sixteenths				Sixteenths		
1.	37	44		1.		2¼		1.	0	1¼		11.	0	14¼		1.	0	1¾		9.	0	14¾
2.	74	88	1/6	2.	0	4¼	·1	2.	0	2½	·6	12.	0	16½	1/8	2.	0	3¼	5/8	10.	0	16¼
3.	112	32		3.	0	6½		3.	0	4		13.	0	17		3.	0	5		11.	0	18
4.	149	76	1/3	4.	0	8¾	·2	4.	0	5¼	·7	14.	0	18¼	1/4	4.	0	6½	3/4	12.	0	19½
5.	187	20		5.	0	10¾		5.	0	6½		15.	0	19½		5.	0	8¼		13.	0	21¼
6.	224	64	1/2	6.	0	13	·3	6.	0	7¾	·8	16.	0	20¾	3/8	6.	0	9¾	7/8	14.	0	22¾
7.	262	8		7.	0	15¼		7.	0	9		17.	0	22		7.	0	11½		15.	0	24½
8.	299	52	2/3	8.	0	17¼	·4	8.	0	10½	·9	18.	0	23½	1/2	8.	0	13				
9.	336	96		9.	0	19½		9.	0	11¾		19.	0	24¾								
10.	374	40	5/6	10.	0	21¾	·5	10.	0	13		20.	0	26								
11.	411	84		11.	0	23¾																

*Dozens	£	P	Dozens	£	P	Dozens	£	P	Dozens	£	P		£	P
1	0	27	51	13	77	101	27	27	152	41	4	310	83	70
2	0	54	52	14	4	102	27	54	154	41	58	320	86	40
3	0	81	53	14	31	103	27	81	[13] 156	42	12	330	89	10
4	1	8	54	14	58	104	28	8	158	42	66	340	91	80
5	1	35	55	14	85	105	28	35	160	43	20	350	94	50
6	1	62	56	15	12	106	28	62	162	43	74	360	97	20
7	1	89	57	15	39	107	28	89	164	44	28	365	98	55
8	2	16	58	15	66	[9] 108	29	16	166	44	82	370	99	90
9	2	43	59	15	93	109	29	43	[14] 168	45	36	380	102	60
10	2	70	[5] **60**	16	20	**110**	29	70	170	45	90	390	105	30
*11	2	97	61	16	47	111	29	97	172	46	44	400	108	0
[1] 12	3	24	62	16	74	112	30	24	174	46	98	410	110	70
13	3	51	63	17	1	113	30	51	175	47	25	420	113	40
14	3	78	64	17	28	114	30	78	176	47	52	430	116	10
15	4	5	65	17	55	115	31	5	178	48	6	440	118	80
16	4	32	66	17	82	116	31	32	[15] 180	48	60	450	121	50
17	4	59	67	18	9	117	31	59	182	49	14	460	124	20
18	4	86	68	18	36	118	31	86	184	49	68	470	126	90
19	5	13	69	18	63	119	32	13	186	50	22	480	129	60
20	5	40	**70**	18	90	**120**	32	40	188	50	76	490	132	30
21	5	67	71	19	17	121	32	67	190	51	30	**500**	135	0
22	5	94	[6] 72	19	44	122	32	94	[16] 192	51	84	550	148	50
23	6	21	73	19	71	123	33	21	194	52	38	600	162	0
[2] 24	6	48	74	19	98	124	33	48	196	52	92	650	175	50
25	6	75	75	20	25	125	33	75	198	53	46	700	189	0
26	7	2	76	20	52	126	34	2	**200**	54	0	750	202	50
27	7	29	77	20	79	127	34	29	[17] 204	55	8	800	216	0
28	7	56	78	21	6	128	34	56	205	55	35	850	229	50
29	7	83	79	21	33	129	34	83	210	56	70	900	243	0
30	8	10	**80**	21	60	**130**	35	10	215	58	5	950	256	50
31	8	37	81	21	87	131	35	37	[18] 216	58	32	**1000**	270	0
32	8	64	82	22	14	[11] 132	35	64	220	59	40	1016	274	32
33	8	91	83	22	41	133	35	91	225	60	75	1250	337	50
34	9	18	[7] 84	22	68	134	36	18	[19] 228	61	56	1500	405	0
35	9	45	85	22	95	135	36	45	230	62	10	1728	466	56
[3] 36	9	72	86	23	22	136	36	72	235	63	45	1750	472	50
37	9	99	87	23	49	137	36	99	[20] 240	64	80	1760	475	20
38	10	26	88	23	76	138	37	26	245	66	15	2000	540	0
39	10	53	89	24	3	139	37	53	**250**	67	50	2240	604	80
40	10	80	**90**	24	30	**140**	37	80	255	68	85	2500	675	0
41	11	7	91	24	57	141	38	7	260	70	20	3000	810	0
42	11	34	92	24	84	142	38	34	265	71	55	4000	1080	0
43	11	61	93	25	11	143	38	61	270	72	90	**5000**	1350	0
44	11	88	94	25	38	[12] 144	38	88	275	74	25	6000	1620	0
45	12	15	95	25	65	145	39	15	280	75	60	7000	1890	0
46	12	42	[8] 96	25	92	146	39	42	285	76	95	8000	2160	0
47	12	69	97	26	19	147	39	69	[24] 288	77	76	9000	2430	0
[4] 48	12	96	98	26	46	148	39	96	290	78	30	10,000	2700	0
49	13	23	99	26	73	149	40	23	295	79	65	15,000	4050	0
50	13	50	**100**	27	0	**150**	40	50	**300**	81	0	20,000	5400	0

Grosses

1.	38	88
2.	77	76
3.	116	64
4.	155	52
5.	194	40
6.	233	28
7.	272	16
8.	311	4
9.	349	92
10.	388	80
11.	427	68

Twelfths

	1.	0	2¼
1/6	2.	0	4½
	3.	0	6¾
1/3	4.	0	9
	5.	0	11¼
1/2	6.	0	13½
	7.	0	15¾
2/3	8.	0	18
	9.	0	20¼
5/6	10.	0	22½
	11.	0	24¾

Twentieths

10ths				10ths			
	1.	0	1¼		11.	0	14¾
·1	2.	0	2¾	·6	12.	0	16¼
	3.	0	4		13.	0	17½
·2	4.	0	5½	·7	14.	0	19
	5.	0	6¾		15.	0	20¼
·3	6.	0	8	·8	16.	0	21½
	7.	0	9½		17.	0	23
·4	8.	0	10¾	·9	18.	0	24¼
	9.	0	12¼		19.	0	25¾
·5	10.	0	13½		20.	0	27

Sixteenths

	1.	0	1¾		9.	0	15¼
1/8	2.	0	3½	5/8	10.	0	17
	3.	0	5		11.	0	18½
1/4	4.	0	6¾	3/4	12.	0	20¼
	5.	0	8½		13.	0	22
3/8	6.	0	10¼	7/8	14.	0	23¾
	7.	0	11¾		15.	0	25¼
1/2	8.	0	13½				

 27½ Pence

	£	P		£	P		£	P		£	P		£	P
1	0	27½	51	14	2½	101	27	77½	152	41	80	310	85	25
2	0	55	52	14	30	102	28	5	154	42	35	320	88	0
3	0	82½	53	14	57½	103	28	32½	[13] 156	42	90	330	90	75
4	1	10	54	14	85	104	28	60	158	43	45	340	93	50
5	1	37½	55	15	12½	105	28	87½	160	44	0	350	96	25
6	1	65	56	15	40	106	29	15	162	44	55	360	99	0
7	1	92½	57	15	67½	107	29	42½	164	45	10	365	100	37½
8	2	20	58	15	95	[9] 108	29	70	166	45	65	370	101	75
9	2	47½	59	16	22½	109	29	97½	[14] 168	46	20	380	104	50
10	2	75	[5] **60**	16	50	**110**	30	25	170	46	75	390	107	25
11	3	2½	61	16	77½	111	30	52½	172	47	30	400	110	0
[*1] 12	3	30	62	17	5	112	30	80	174	47	85	410	112	75
13	3	57½	63	17	32½	113	31	7½	175	48	12½	420	115	50
14	3	85	64	17	60	114	31	35	176	48	40	430	118	25
15	4	12½	65	17	87½	115	31	62½	178	48	95	440	121	00
16	4	40	66	18	15	116	31	90	[15] 180	49	50	450	123	75
17	4	67½	67	18	42½	117	32	17½	182	50	5	460	126	50
18	4	95	68	18	70	118	32	45	184	50	60	470	129	25
19	5	22½	69	18	97½	119	32	72½	186	51	15	480	132	00
20	5	50	**70**	19	25	**120**	33	0	188	51	70	490	134	75
21	5	77½	71	19	52½	121	33	27½	190	52	25	**500**	137	50
22	6	5	[6] 72	19	80	122	33	55	[16] 192	52	80	550	151	25
23	6	32½	73	20	7½	123	33	82½	194	53	35	600	165	0
[2] 24	6	60	74	20	35	124	34	10	196	53	90	650	178	75
25	6	87½	75	20	62½	125	34	37½	198	54	45	700	192	50
26	7	15	76	20	90	126	34	65	**200**	55	0	750	206	25
27	7	42½	77	21	17½	127	34	92½	[17] 204	56	10	800	220	0
28	7	70	78	21	45	128	35	20	205	56	37½	850	233	75
29	7	97½	79	21	72½	129	35	47½	210	57	75	900	247	50
30	8	25	**80**	22	0	**130**	35	75	215	59	12½	950	261	25
31	8	52½	81	22	27½	131	36	2½	[18] 216	59	40	**1000**	275	0
32	8	80	82	22	55	[11] 132	36	30	220	60	50	1016	279	40
33	9	7½	83	22	82½	133	36	57½	225	61	87½	1250	343	75
34	9	35	[7] 84	23	10	134	36	85	[19] 228	62	70	1500	412	50
35	9	62½	85	23	37½	135	37	12½	230	63	25	1728	475	20
[3] 36	9	90	86	23	65	136	37	40	235	64	62½	1750	481	25
37	10	17½	87	23	92½	137	37	67½	[20] 240	66	0	1760	484	0
38	10	45	88	24	20	138	37	95	245	67	37½	2000	550	0
39	10	72½	89	24	47½	139	38	22½	**250**	68	75	2240	616	0
40	11	0	**90**	24	75	**140**	38	50	255	70	12½	2500	687	50
41	11	27½	91	25	2½	141	38	77½	260	71	50	3000	825	0
42	11	55	92	25	30	142	39	5	265	72	87½	4000	1100	0
43	11	82½	93	25	57½	143	39	32½	270	74	25	5000	1375	0
44	12	10	94	25	85	[12] 144	39	60	275	75	62½	6000	1650	0
45	12	37½	95	26	12½	145	39	87½	280	77	0	7000	1925	0
46	12	65	[8] 96	26	40	146	40	15	285	78	37½	8000	2200	0
47	12	92½	97	26	67½	147	40	42½	[24] 288	79	20	9000	2475	0
[4] 48	13	20	98	26	95	148	40	70	290	79	75	10000	2750	0
49	13	47½	99	27	22½	149	40	97½	295	81	12½	15000	4125	0
50	13	75	**100**	27	50	**150**	41	25	**300**	82	50	20000	5500	0

(*Dozens — marked in the margin beside 12, 24, 36 … 288)

Grosses.

1.	39	60
2.	79	20
3.	118	80
4.	158	40
5.	198	0
6.	237	60
7.	277	20
8.	316	80
9.	356	40
10.	396	0
11.	435	60

Twelfths

	1.	0	2¼
⅙	2.	0	4½
	3.	0	7
⅓	4.	0	9¼
	5.	0	11½
½	6.	0	13¾
	7.	0	16
⅔	8.	0	18¼
	9.	0	20¾
⅚	10.	0	23
	11.	0	25¼

Twentieths

10ths				10ths			
	1.	0	1½		11.	0	15¼
·1	2.	0	2¾	·6	12.	0	16½
	3.	0	4¼		13.	0	18
·2	4.	0	5½	·7	14.	0	19¼
	5.	0	7		15.	0	20¾
·3	6.	0	8¼	·8	16.	0	22
	7.	0	9¾		17.	0	23½
·4	8.	0	11	·9	18.	0	24¾
	9.	0	12½		19.	0	26¼
·5	10.	0	13¾		20.	0	27½

Sixteenths

	1.	0	1¾		9.	0	15½
⅛	2.	0	3½	⅝	10.	0	17¼
	3.	0	5¼		11.	0	19
¼	4.	0	7	¾	12.	0	20¾
	5.	0	8½		13.	0	22¼
⅜	6.	0	10¼	⅞	14.	0	24
	7.	0	12		15.	0	25¾
½	8.	0	13¾				

 28 Pence

*Dozens		£	p	Dozens		£	p	Dozens		£	p	Dozens		£	p		£	p
	1	0	28		51	14	28		101	28	28		152	42	56	310	86	80
	2	0	56		52	14	56		102	28	56		154	43	12	320	89	60
	3	0	84		53	14	84		103	28	84	13	156	43	68	330	92	40
	4	1	12		54	15	12		104	29	12		158	44	24	340	95	20
	5	1	40		55	15	40		105	29	40		160	44	80	350	98	0
	6	1	68		56	15	68		106	29	68		162	45	36	360	100	80
	7	1	96		57	15	96		107	29	96		164	45	92	365	102	20
	8	2	24		58	16	24	9	108	30	24		166	46	48	370	103	60
	9	2	52		59	16	52		109	30	52	14	168	47	4	380	106	40
	10	2	80	5	**60**	16	80		**110**	30	80		170	47	60	390	109	20
*	11	3	8		61	17	8		111	31	8		172	48	16	400	112	0
1	12	3	36		62	17	36		112	31	36		174	48	72	410	114	80
	13	3	64		63	17	64		113	31	64		175	49	0	420	117	60
	14	3	92		64	17	92		114	31	92		176	49	28	430	120	40
	15	4	20		65	18	20		115	32	20		178	49	84	440	123	20
	16	4	48		66	18	48		116	32	48	15	180	50	40	450	126	0
	17	4	76		67	18	76		117	32	76		182	50	96	460	128	80
	18	5	4		68	19	4		118	33	4		184	51	52	470	131	60
	19	5	32		69	19	32		119	33	32		186	52	8	480	134	40
	20	5	60		**70**	19	60	10	**120**	33	60		188	52	64	490	137	20
	21	5	88		71	19	88		121	33	88		190	53	20	**500**	140	0
	22	6	16	6	72	20	16		122	34	16	16	192	53	76	550	154	0
	23	6	44		73	20	44		123	34	44		194	54	32	600	168	0
2	24	6	72		74	20	72		124	34	72		196	54	88	650	182	0
	25	7	0		75	21	0		125	35	0		198	55	44	700	196	0
	26	7	28		76	21	28		126	35	28		**200**	56	0	750	210	0
	27	7	56		77	21	56		127	35	56	17	204	57	12	800	224	0
	28	7	84		78	21	84		128	35	84		205	57	40	850	238	0
	29	8	12		79	22	12		129	36	12		210	58	80	900	252	0
	30	8	40		**80**	22	40		**130**	36	40		215	60	20	950	266	0
	31	8	68		81	22	68		131	36	68	18	216	60	48	**1000**	280	0
	32	8	96		82	22	96	11	132	36	96		220	61	60	1016	284	48
	33	9	24		83	23	24		133	37	24		225	63	0	1250	350	0
	34	9	52	7	84	23	52		134	37	52	19	228	63	84	1500	420	0
	35	9	80		85	23	80		135	37	80		230	64	40	1728	483	84
3	36	10	8		86	24	8		136	38	8		235	65	80	1750	490	0
	37	10	36		87	24	36		137	38	36	20	240	67	20	1760	492	80
	38	10	64		88	24	64		138	38	64		245	68	60	2000	560	0
	39	10	92		89	24	92		139	38	92		**250**	70	0	2240	627	20
	40	11	20		**90**	25	20		**140**	39	20		255	71	40	2500	700	0
	41	11	48		91	25	48		141	39	48		260	72	80	3000	840	0
	42	11	76		92	25	76		142	39	76		265	74	20	4000	1120	0
	43	12	4		93	26	4		143	40	4		270	75	60	**5000**	1400	0
	44	12	32		94	26	32	12	144	40	32		275	77	0	6000	1680	0
	45	12	60		95	26	60		145	40	60		280	78	40	7000	1960	0
	46	12	88	8	96	26	88		146	40	88		285	79	80	8000	2240	0
	47	13	16		97	27	16		147	41	16	24	288	80	64	9000	2520	0
4	48	13	44		98	27	44		148	41	44		290	81	20	10,000	2800	0
	49	13	72		99	27	72		149	41	72		295	82	60	15,000	4200	0
	50	14	0		**100**	28	0		**150**	42	0		**300**	84	0	20,000	5600	0

Grosses

1.	40	32
2.	80	64
3.	120	96
4.	161	28
5.	201	60
6.	241	92
7.	282	24
8.	322	56
9.	362	88
10.	403	20
11.	443	52

Twelfths

	1.	0	2¼
⅙	2.	0	4¾
	3.	0	7
⅓	4.	0	9¼
	5.	0	11¾
½	6.	0	14
	7.	0	16¼
⅔	8.	0	18¾
	9.	0	21
⅚	10.	0	23¼
	11.	0	25¾

Twentieths

10ths				10ths			
	1.	0	1½		11.	0	15½
·1	2.	0	2¾	·6	12.	0	16¾
	3.	0	4¼		13.	0	18¼
·2	4.	0	5½	·7	14.	0	19½
	5.	0	7		15.	0	21
·3	6.	0	8½	·8	16.	0	22½
	7.	0	9¾		17.	0	23¾
·4	8.	0	11¼	·9	18.	0	25¼
	9.	0	12½		19.	0	26½
·5	10.	0	14		20.	0	28

Sixteenths

	1.	0	1¾		9.	0	15¾
⅛	2.	0	3½	⅝	10.	0	17½
	3.	0	5¼		11.	0	19¼
¼	4.	0	7	¾	12.	0	21
	5.	0	8¾		13.	0	22¾
⅜	6.	0	10½	⅞	14.	0	24½
	7.	0	12¼		15.	0	26¼
½	8.	0	14				

	£	P		£	P		£	P		£	P		£	P
1	0	29	51	14	79	101	29	29	152	44	8	310	89	90
2	0	58	52	15	8	102	29	58	154	44	66	320	92	80
3	0	87	53	15	37	103	29	87	13 156	45	24	330	95	70
4	1	16	54	15	66	104	30	16	158	45	82	340	98	60
5	1	45	55	15	95	105	30	45	160	46	40	350	101	50
6	1	74	56	16	24	106	30	74	162	46	98	360	104	40
7	2	3	57	16	53	107	31	3	164	47	56	365	105	85
8	2	32	58	16	82	108	31	32	166	48	14	370	107	30
9	2	61	59	17	11	109	31	61	14 168	48	72	380	110	20
10	2	90	60	17	40	110	31	90	170	49	30	390	113	10
11	3	19	61	17	69	111	32	19	172	49	88	400	116	0
12	3	48	62	17	98	112	32	48	174	50	46	410	118	90
13	3	77	63	18	27	113	32	77	175	50	75	420	121	80
14	4	6	64	18	56	114	33	6	176	51	4	430	124	70
15	4	35	65	18	85	115	33	35	178	51	62	440	127	60
16	4	64	66	19	14	116	33	64	15 180	52	20	450	130	50
17	4	93	67	19	43	117	33	93	182	52	78	460	133	40
18	5	22	68	19	72	118	34	22	184	53	36	470	136	30
19	5	51	69	20	1	119	34	51	186	53	94	480	139	20
20	5	80	70	20	30	120	34	80	188	54	52	490	142	10
21	6	9	71	20	59	121	35	9	190	55	10	500	145	0
22	6	38	72	20	88	122	35	38	16 192	55	68	550	159	50
23	6	67	73	21	17	123	35	67	194	56	26	600	174	0
24	6	96	74	21	46	124	35	96	196	56	84	650	188	50
25	7	25	75	21	75	125	36	25	198	57	42	700	203	0
26	7	54	76	22	4	126	36	54	200	58	0	750	217	50
27	7	83	77	22	33	127	36	83	17 204	59	16	800	232	0
28	8	12	78	22	62	128	37	12	205	59	45	850	246	50
29	8	41	79	22	91	129	37	41	210	60	90	900	261	0
30	8	70	80	23	20	130	37	70	215	62	35	950	275	50
31	8	99	81	23	49	131	37	99	18 216	62	64	1000	290	0
32	9	28	82	23	78	132	38	28	220	63	80	1016	294	64
33	9	57	83	24	7	133	38	57	225	65	25	1250	362	50
34	9	86	84	24	36	134	38	86	19 228	66	12	1500	435	0
35	10	15	85	24	65	135	39	15	230	66	70	1728	501	12
36	10	44	86	24	94	136	39	44	235	68	15	1750	507	50
37	10	73	87	25	23	137	39	73	20 240	69	60	1760	510	40
38	11	2	88	25	52	138	40	2	245	71	5	2000	580	0
39	11	31	89	25	81	139	40	31	250	72	50	2240	649	60
40	11	60	90	26	10	140	40	60	255	73	95	2500	725	0
41	11	89	91	26	39	141	40	89	260	75	40	3000	870	0
42	12	18	92	26	68	142	41	18	265	76	85	4000	1160	0
43	12	47	93	26	97	143	41	47	270	78	30	5000	1450	0
44	12	76	94	27	26	144	41	76	275	79	75	6000	1740	0
45	13	5	95	27	55	145	42	5	280	81	20	7000	2030	0
46	13	34	96	27	84	146	42	34	285	82	65	8000	2320	0
47	13	63	97	28	13	147	42	63	24 288	83	52	9000	2610	0
48	13	92	98	28	42	148	42	92	290	84	10	10,000	2900	0
49	14	21	99	28	71	149	43	21	295	85	55	15,000	4350	0
50	14	50	100	29	0	150	43	50	300	87	0	20,000	5800	0

Grosses			Twelfths			Twentieths						Sixteenths				
1.	41	76	1.	0	2½				1. 0	1½		11. 0	16	1. 0	1¾	9. 0	16¼
2.	83	52	1/6 2.	0	4¾	1	2. 0	3	6 12. 0	17½		1/2 2. 0	3½	1/10. 0	18½
3.	125	28	3.	0	7¼		3. 0	4¼	13. 0	18½		3. 0	5½	11. 0	20
4.	167	4	1/4 4.	0	9½	2	4. 0	5½	7 14. 0	20¼		1/4 4. 0	7	1/12. 0	21½
5.	208	80	5.	0	12		5. 0	7¼	15. 0	21½		5. 0	9	13. 0	23½
6.	250	56	1/6 6.	0	14½	3	6. 0	8½	8 16. 0	23¼		1/6 6. 0	11	7/14. 0	25¼
7.	292	32	7.	0	17		7. 0	10¼	17. 0	24½		7. 0	12½	15. 0	27¼
8.	334	8	3/8 8.	0	19½	4	8. 0	11½	9 18. 0	26		1/8 8. 0	14½		
9.	375	84	9.	0	21½		9. 0	13	19. 0	27½					
10.	417	60	5/10.	0	24¼	5 10. 0	14½	20. 0	29					
11.	459	36	11.	0	26½									

No.	£ P	No.	£ P	No.	£ P	No.	£ P	No.	£ P
1	0 30	51	15 30	101	30 30	152	45 60	310	93 0
2	0 60	52	15 60	102	30 60	154	46 20	320	96 0
3	0 90	53	15 90	103	30 90	156	46 80	330	99 0
4	1 20	54	16 20	104	31 20	158	47 40	340	102 0
5	1 50	55	16 50	105	31 50	160	48 0	350	105 0
6	1 80	56	16 80	106	31 80	162	48 60	360	108 0
7	2 10	57	17 10	107	32 10	164	49 20	365	109 50
8	2 40	58	17 40	108	32 40	166	49 80	370	111 0
9	2 70	59	17 70	109	32 70	168	50 40	380	114 0
10	3 0	60	18 0	110	33 0	170	51 0	390	117 0
11	3 30	61	18 30	111	33 30	172	51 60	400	120 0
12	3 60	62	18 60	112	33 60	174	52 20	410	123 0
13	3 90	63	18 90	113	33 90	176	52 80	420	126 0
14	4 20	64	19 20	114	34 20	178	53 40	430	129 0
15	4 50	65	19 50	115	34 50	180	54 0	440	132 0
16	4 80	66	19 80	116	34 80	182	54 60	450	135 0
17	5 10	67	20 10	117	35 10	184	55 20	460	138 0
18	5 40	68	20 40	118	35 40	186	55 80	470	141 0
19	5 70	69	20 70	119	35 70	188	56 40	480	144 0
20	6 0	70	21 0	120	36 0	190	57 0	490	147 0
21	6 30	71	21 30	121	36 30	192	57 60	500	150 0
22	6 60	72	21 60	122	36 60	194	58 20	550	165 0
23	6 90	73	21 90	123	36 90	196	58 80	600	180 0
24	7 20	74	22 20	124	37 20	198	59 40	650	195 0
25	7 50	75	22 50	125	37 50	200	60 0	700	210 0
26	7 80	76	22 80	126	37 80	204	61 20	750	225 0
27	8 10	77	23 10	127	38 10	205	61 50	800	240 0
28	8 40	78	23 40	128	38 40	210	63 0	850	255 0
29	8 70	79	23 70	129	38 70	215	64 50	900	270 0
30	9 0	80	24 0	130	39 0	216	64 80	950	285 0
31	9 30	81	24 30	131	39 30	220	66 0	1000	300 0
32	9 60	82	24 60	132	39 60	225	67 50	1016	304 80
33	9 90	83	24 90	133	39 90	228	68 40	1250	375 0
34	10 20	84	25 20	134	40 20	230	69 0	1500	450 0
35	10 50	85	25 50	135	40 50	235	70 50	1728	518 40
36	10 80	86	25 80	136	40 80	240	72 0	1750	525 0
37	11 10	87	26 10	137	41 10	245	73 50	1760	528 0
38	11 40	88	26 40	138	41 40	250	75 0	2000	600 0
39	11 70	89	26 70	139	41 70	255	76 50	2240	672 0
40	12 0	90	27 0	140	42 0	260	78 0	2500	750 0
41	12 30	91	27 30	141	42 30	265	79 50	3000	900 0
42	12 60	92	27 60	142	42 60	270	81 0	4000	1200 0
43	12 90	93	27 90	143	42 90	275	82 50	5000	1500 0
44	13 20	94	28 20	144	43 20	280	84 0	6000	1800 0
45	13 50	95	28 50	145	43 50	288	86 40	7000	2100 0
46	13 80	96	28 80	146	43 80	290	87 0	8000	2400 0
47	14 10	97	29 10	147	44 10	295	88 50	9000	2700 0
48	14 40	98	29 40	148	44 40	300	90 0	10,000	3000 0
49	14 70	99	29 70	149	44 70			15,000	4500 0
50	15 0	100	30 0	150	45 0			20,000	6000 0

Grosses		Twelfths		16ths	Twentieths		Sixteenths	
1.	43 20	½12 1.	0 2½		1. 0 1½	11. 0 16½	1. 0 2	9. 0 17
2.	86 40	½ 2.	0 5	·1	2. 0 3	12. 0 18	½ 2. 0 3¾	½10. 0 18¾
3.	129 60	3.	0 7½		3. 0 4½	13. 0 19½	3. 0 5¾	11. 0 20¾
4.	172 80	¾ 4.	0 10	·2	4. 0 6	14. 0 21	¼ 4. 0 7½	½12. 0 22½
5.	216 0	5.	0 12½		5. 0 7½	15. 0 22½	5. 0 9¼	13. 0 24¼
6.	259 20	⅙ 6.	0 15	·3	6. 0 9	16. 0 24	½ 6. 0 11¼	½14. 0 26¼
7.	302 40	7.	0 17½		7. 0 10½	17. 0 25½	7. 0 13¼	15. 0 28¼
8.	345 60	⅔ 8.	0 20	·4	8. 0 12	18. 0 27	½ 8. 0 15	
9.	388 80	9.	0 22½		9. 0 13½	19. 0 28½		
10.	432 0	⅚10.	0 25	·5	10. 0 15	20. 0 30		
11.	475 20	11.	0 27½					

	£	P
1	0	31
2	0	62
3	0	93
4	1	24
5	1	55
*6	1	86
7	2	17
8	2	48
9	2	79
10	3	10
*11	3	41
¹12	3	72
13	4	3
14	4	34
15	4	65
16	4	96
17	5	27
18	5	58
19	5	89
20	6	20
21	6	51
22	6	82
23	7	13
²24	7	44
25	7	75
26	8	6
27	8	37
28	8	68
29	8	99
30	9	30
31	9	61
32	9	92
33	10	23
34	10	54
35	10	85
³36	11	16
37	11	47
38	11	78
39	12	9
40	12	40
41	12	71
42	13	2
43	13	33
44	13	64
45	13	95
46	14	26
47	14	57
⁴48	14	88
49	15	19
50	15	50

	£	P
51	15	81
52	16	12
53	16	43
54	16	74
55	17	5
56	17	36
57	17	67
58	17	98
59	18	29
⁵60	18	60
61	18	91
62	19	22
63	19	53
64	19	84
65	20	15
66	20	46
67	20	77
68	21	8
69	21	39
70	21	70
71	22	1
⁶72	22	32
73	22	63
74	22	94
75	23	25
76	23	56
77	23	87
78	24	18
79	24	49
80	24	80
81	25	11
82	25	42
83	25	73
⁷84	26	4
85	26	35
86	26	66
87	26	97
88	27	28
89	27	59
90	27	90
91	28	21
92	28	52
93	28	83
94	29	14
95	29	45
⁸96	29	76
97	30	7
98	30	38
99	30	69
100	31	0

	£	P
101	31	31
102	31	62
103	31	93
104	32	24
105	32	55
106	32	86
107	33	17
⁹108	33	48
109	33	79
110	34	10
111	34	41
112	34	72
113	35	3
114	35	34
115	35	65
116	35	96
117	36	27
118	36	58
119	36	89
120	37	20
121	37	51
122	37	82
123	38	13
124	38	44
125	38	75
126	39	6
127	39	37
128	39	68
129	39	99
130	40	30
131	40	61
¹¹132	40	92
133	41	23
134	41	54
135	41	85
136	42	16
137	42	47
138	42	78
139	43	9
140	43	40
141	43	71
142	44	2
143	44	33
¹²144	44	64
145	44	95
146	45	26
147	45	57
148	45	88
149	46	19
150	46	50

	£	P
152	47	12
154	47	74
¹³156	48	36
158	48	98
160	49	60
162	50	22
164	50	84
166	51	46
168	52	8
170	52	70
172	53	32
174	53	94
175	54	25
176	54	56
178	55	18
¹⁵180	55	80
182	56	42
184	57	4
186	57	66
188	58	28
190	58	90
¹⁶192	59	52
194	60	14
196	60	76
198	61	38
200	62	0
¹⁷204	63	24
205	63	55
210	65	10
215	66	65
¹⁸216	66	96
220	68	20
225	69	75
¹⁹228	70	68
230	71	30
235	72	85
²⁰240	74	40
245	75	95
250	77	50
255	79	5
260	80	60
265	82	15
270	83	70
275	85	25
280	86	80
285	88	35
²⁴288	89	28
290	89	90
295	91	45
300	93	0

	£	P
310	96	10
320	99	20
330	102	30
340	105	40
350	108	50
360	111	60
365	113	15
370	114	70
380	117	80
390	120	90
400	124	0
410	127	10
420	130	20
430	133	30
440	136	40
450	139	50
460	142	60
470	145	70
480	148	80
490	151	90
500	155	0
550	170	50
600	186	0
650	201	50
700	217	0
750	232	50
800	248	0
850	263	50
900	279	0
950	294	50
1000	310	0
1016	314	96
1250	387	50
1500	465	0
1728	535	68
1750	542	50
1760	545	60
2000	620	0
2240	694	40
2500	775	0
3000	930	0
4000	1240	0
5000	1550	0
6000	1860	0
7000	2170	0
8000	2480	0
9000	2790	0
10,000	3100	0
15,000	4650	0
20,000	6200	0

Grosses.			Twelfths			Twentieths			Sixteenths		
1.	44	64	1.	0	2½	1.	0	1½	1.	0	2
2.	89	28	⅙ 2.	0	5¼	2.	0	3	½ 2.	0	4
3.	133	92	3.	0	7¾	3.	0	4½	3.	0	5¾
4.	178	56	¼ 4.	0	10¼	4.	0	6¼	¼ 4.	0	7¾
5.	223	20	5.	0	13	5.	0	7¾	5.	0	9½
6.	267	84	⅙ 6.	0	15½	6.	0	9¼	½ 6.	0	11½
7.	312	48	7.	0	18	7.	0	10½	7.	0	13½
8.	357	12	⅜ 8.	0	20½	8.	0	12½	½ 8.	0	15¼
9.	401	76	9.	0	23¼	9.	0	14	9.	0	17½
10.	446	40	⁵⁄₁₂ 10.	0	25¾	10.	0	15½	10.	0	19½
11.	491	4	11.	0	28¼	11.	0	17	11.	0	21½
						12.	0	18½	12.	0	23½
						13.	0	20¼	13.	0	25¼
						14.	0	21¾	14.	0	27½
						15.	0	23¼	15.	0	29
						16.	0	24½			
						17.	0	26¼			
						18.	0	28			
						19.	0	29½			
						20.	0	31			

Dozens	£	P	Dozens	£	P	Dozens	£	P	Dozens	£	P		£	P
1	0	32	51	16	32	101	32	32	152	48	64	310	99	20
2	0	64	52	16	64	102	32	64	154	49	28	320	102	40
3	0	96	53	16	96	103	32	96	13 156	49	92	330	105	60
4	1	28	54	17	28	104	33	28	158	50	56	340	108	80
5	1	60	55	17	60	105	33	60	160	51	20	350	112	0
*6	1	92	56	17	92	106	33	92	162	51	84	360	115	20
7	2	24	57	18	24	107	34	24	164	52	48	365	116	80
8	2	56	58	18	56	9 108	34	56	166	53	12	370	118	40
9	2	88	59	18	88	109	34	88	14 168	53	76	380	121	60
10	3	20	5 60	19	20	110	35	20	170	54	40	390	124	80
*11	3	52	61	19	52	111	35	52	172	55	4	400	128	0
1 12	3	84	62	19	84	112	35	84	174	55	68	410	131	20
13	4	16	63	20	16	113	36	16	175	56	0	420	134	40
14	4	48	64	20	48	114	36	48	176	56	32	430	137	60
15	4	80	65	20	80	115	36	80	178	56	96	440	140	80
16	5	12	66	21	12	116	37	12	15 180	57	60	450	144	0
17	5	44	67	21	44	117	37	44	182	58	24	460	147	20
18	5	76	68	21	76	118	37	76	184	58	88	470	150	40
19	6	8	69	22	8	119	38	8	186	59	52	480	153	60
20	6	40	70	22	40	120	38	40	188	60	16	490	156	80
21	6	72	71	22	72	121	38	72	190	60	80	500	160	0
22	7	4	6 72	23	4	122	39	4	16 192	61	44	550	176	0
23	7	36	73	23	36	123	39	36	194	62	8	600	192	0
2 24	7	68	74	23	68	124	39	68	196	62	72	650	208	0
25	8	0	75	24	0	125	40	0	198	63	36	700	224	0
26	8	32	76	24	32	126	40	32	200	64	0	750	240	0
27	8	64	77	24	64	127	40	64	17 204	65	28	800	256	0
28	8	96	78	24	96	128	40	96	205	65	60	850	272	0
29	9	28	79	25	28	129	41	28	210	67	20	900	288	0
30	9	60	80	25	60	130	41	60	215	68	80	950	304	0
31	9	92	81	25	92	131	41	92	18 216	69	12	1000	320	0
32	10	24	82	26	24	11 132	42	24	220	70	40	1016	325	12
33	10	56	83	26	56	133	42	56	225	72	0	1250	400	0
34	10	88	7 84	26	88	134	42	88	19 228	72	96	1500	480	0
35	11	20	85	27	20	135	43	20	230	73	60	1728	552	96
3 36	11	52	86	27	52	136	43	52	235	75	20	1750	560	0
37	11	84	87	27	84	137	43	84	20 240	76	80	1760	563	20
38	12	16	88	28	16	138	44	16	245	78	40	2000	640	0
39	12	48	89	28	48	139	44	48	250	80	0	2240	716	80
40	12	80	90	28	80	140	44	80	255	81	60	2500	800	0
41	13	12	91	29	12	141	45	12	260	83	20	3000	960	0
42	13	44	92	29	44	142	45	44	265	84	80	4000	1280	0
43	13	76	93	29	76	143	45	76	270	86	40	5000	1600	0
44	14	8	94	30	8	12 144	46	8	275	88	0	6000	1920	0
45	14	40	95	30	40	145	46	40	280	89	60	7000	2240	0
46	14	72	8 96	30	72	146	46	72	285	91	20	8000	2560	0
47	15	4	97	31	4	147	47	4	24 288	92	16	9000	2880	0
4 48	15	36	98	31	36	148	47	36	290	92	80	10,000	3200	0
49	15	68	99	31	68	149	47	68	295	94	40	15,000	4800	0
50	16	0	100	32	0	150	48	0	300	96	0	20,000	6400	0

Grosses

1.	46	8
2.	92	16
3.	138	24
4.	184	32
5.	230	40
6.	276	48
7.	322	56
8.	368	64
9.	414	72
10.	460	80
11.	506	88

Twelfths

	1.		2¾
⅙	2.	0	5¼
	3.	0	8
⅓	4.	0	10¾
	5.	0	13¼
½	6.	0	16
	7.	0	18¾
⅔	8.	0	21¼
	9.	0	24
⅚	10.	0	26¾
	11.	0	29¼

Twentieths

10ths				10ths			
	1.	0	1½		11.	0	17½
·1	2.	0	3¼	·6	12.	0	19¼
	3.	0	4¾		13.	0	20¾
·2	4.	0	6½	·7	14.	0	22½
	5.	0	8		15.	0	24
·3	6.	0	9½	·8	16.	0	25½
	7.	0	11¼		17.	0	27¼
·4	8.	0	12¾	·9	18.	0	28¾
	9.	0	14½		19.	0	30½
·5	10.	0	16		20.	0	32

Sixteenths

	1.	0	2		9.	0	18
⅛	2.	0	4	⅝	10.	0	20
	3.	0	6		11.	0	22
¼	4.	0	8	¾	12.	0	24
	5.	0	10		13.	0	26
⅜	6.	0	12	⅞	14.	0	28
	7.	0	14		15.	0	30
½	8.	0	16				

*Dozens.

	£	P		£	P		£	P		£	P		£	P
1	0	32½	51	16	57½	101	32	82½	152	49	40	310	100	75
2	0	65	52	16	90	102	33	15	154	50	5	320	104	0
3	0	97½	53	17	22½	103	33	47½	[13] 156	50	70	330	107	25
4	1	30	54	17	55	104	33	80	158	51	35	340	110	50
5	1	62½	55	17	87½	105	34	12½	160	52	0	350	113	75
6	1	95	56	18	20	106	34	45	162	52	65	360	117	0
7	2	27½	57	18	52½	107	34	77½	164	53	30	365	118	62½
8	2	60	58	18	85	[9] 108	35	10	166	53	95	370	120	25
9	2	92½	59	19	17½	109	35	42½	[14] 168	54	60	380	123	50
10	3	25	[5] **60**	19	50	**110**	35	75	170	55	25	390	126	75
*11	3	57½	61	19	82½	111	36	7½	172	55	90	400	130	0
[1] 12	3	90	62	20	15	112	36	40	174	56	55	410	133	25
13	4	22½	63	20	47½	113	36	72½	175	56	87½	420	136	50
14	4	55	64	20	80	114	37	5	176	57	20	430	139	75
15	4	87½	65	21	12½	115	37	37½	178	57	85	440	143	0
16	5	20	66	21	45	116	37	70	[15] 180	58	50	450	146	25
17	5	52½	67	21	77½	117	38	2½	182	59	15	460	149	50
18	5	85	68	22	10	118	38	35	184	59	80	470	152	75
19	6	17½	69	22	42½	119	38	67½	186	60	45	480	156	0
20	6	50	**70**	22	75	**120**	39	0	188	61	10	490	159	25
21	6	82½	71	23	7½	121	39	32½	190	61	75	**500**	162	50
22	7	15	[6] 72	23	40	122	39	65	[16] 192	62	40	550	178	75
23	7	47½	73	23	72½	123	39	97½	194	63	5	600	195	0
[2] 24	7	80	74	24	5	124	40	30	196	63	70	650	211	25
25	8	12½	75	24	37½	125	40	62½	198	64	35	700	227	50
26	8	45	76	24	70	126	40	95	**200**	65	0	750	243	75
27	8	77½	77	25	2½	127	41	27½	[17] 204	66	30	800	260	0
28	9	10	78	25	35	128	41	60	205	66	62½	850	276	25
29	9	42½	79	25	67½	129	41	92½	210	68	25	900	292	50
30	9	75	**80**	26	0	**130**	42	25	215	69	87½	950	308	75
31	10	7½	81	26	32½	131	42	57½	[18] 216	70	20	**1000**	325	0
32	10	40	82	26	65	[11] 132	42	90	220	71	50	1016	330	20
33	10	72½	83	26	97½	133	43	22½	225	73	12½	1250	406	25
34	11	5	[7] 84	27	30	134	43	55	[19] 228	74	10	1500	487	50
35	11	37½	85	27	62½	135	43	87½	230	74	75	1728	561	60
[3] 36	11	70	86	27	95	136	44	20	235	76	37½	1750	568	75
37	12	2½	87	28	27½	137	44	52½	[20] 240	78	0	1760	572	0
38	12	35	88	28	60	138	44	85	245	79	62½	2000	650	0
39	12	67½	89	28	92½	139	45	17½	**250**	81	25	2240	728	0
40	13	0	**90**	29	25	**140**	45	50	255	82	87½	2500	812	50
41	13	32½	91	29	57½	141	45	82½	260	84	50	3000	975	0
42	13	65	92	29	90	142	46	15	265	86	12½	4000	1300	0
43	13	97½	93	30	22½	143	46	47½	270	87	75	5000	1625	0
44	14	30	94	30	55	[12] 144	46	80	275	89	37½	6000	1950	0
45	14	62½	95	30	87½	145	47	12½	280	91	0	7000	2275	0
46	14	95	[8] 96	31	20	146	47	45	285	92	62½	8000	2600	0
47	15	27½	97	31	52½	147	47	77½	[24] 288	93	60	9000	2925	0
[4] 48	15	60	98	31	85	148	48	10	290	94	25	10000	3250	0
49	15	92½	99	32	17½	149	48	42½	295	95	87½	15000	4875	0
50	16	25	**100**	32	50	**150**	48	75	**300**	97	50	20000	6500	0

Grosses.

	£	P
1.	46	80
2.	93	60
3.	140	40
4.	187	20
5.	234	0
6.	280	80
7.	327	60
8.	374	40
9.	421	20
10.	468	0
11.	514	80

Twelfths

		£	P
	1.	0	2¾
⅙	2.	0	5½
	3.	0	8¼
⅓	4.	0	10¾
	5.	0	13½
½	6.	0	16¼
	7.	0	19
⅔	8.	0	21¾
	9.	0	24½
⅚	10.	0	27
	11.	0	29¾

Twentieths

10ths		£	P	10ths		£	P
	1.	0	1¾		11.	0	18
·1	2.	0	3¼	·6	12.	0	19½
	3.	0	5		13.	0	21¼
·2	4.	0	6½	·7	14.	0	22¾
	5.	0	8¼		15.	0	24½
·3	6.	0	9¾	·8	16.	0	26
	7.	0	11½		17.	0	27¾
·4	8.	0	13	·9	18.	0	29¼
	9.	0	14¾		19.	0	31
·5	10.	0	16¼		20.	0	32½

Sixteenths

		£	P			£	P
	1.	0	2		9.	0	18¼
⅛	2.	0	4	⅝	10.	0	20¼
	3.	0	6		11.	0	22¼
¼	4.	0	8¼	¾	12.	0	24½
	5.	0	10¼		13.	0	26½
⅜	6.	0	12¼	⅞	14.	0	28½
	7.	0	14¼		15.	0	30½
½	8.	0	16¼				

*Dozens		£	P
	1	0	33
	2	0	66
	3	0	99
	4	1	32
	5	1	65
	6	1	98
	7	2	31
	8	2	64
	9	2	97
	10	3	30
	11	3	63
1	12	3	96
	13	4	29
	14	4	62
	15	4	95
	16	5	28
	17	5	61
	18	5	94
	19	6	27
	20	6	60
	21	6	93
	22	7	26
	23	7	59
2	24	7	92
	25	8	25
	26	8	58
	27	8	91
	28	9	24
	29	9	57
	30	9	90
	31	10	23
	32	10	56
	33	10	89
	34	11	22
	35	11	55
3	36	11	88
	37	12	21
	38	12	54
	39	12	87
	40	13	20
	41	13	53
	42	13	86
	43	14	19
	44	14	52
	45	14	85
	46	15	18
	47	15	51
4	48	15	84
	49	16	17
	50	16	50

Dozens		£	P
	51	16	83
	52	17	16
	53	17	49
	54	17	82
	55	18	15
	56	18	48
	57	18	81
	58	19	14
	59	19	47
5	**60**	19	80
	61	20	13
	62	20	46
	63	20	79
	64	21	12
	65	21	45
	66	21	78
	67	22	11
	68	22	44
	69	22	77
	70	23	10
	71	23	43
6	72	23	76
	73	24	09
	74	24	42
	75	24	75
	76	25	08
	77	25	41
	78	25	74
	79	26	07
	80	26	40
	81	26	73
	82	27	06
	83	27	39
7	84	27	72
	85	28	05
	86	28	38
	87	28	71
	88	29	04
	89	29	37
	90	29	70
	91	30	03
	92	30	36
	93	30	69
	94	31	02
	95	31	35
8	96	31	68
	97	32	01
	98	32	34
	99	32	67
	100	33	00

Dozens		£	P
	101	33	33
	102	33	66
	103	33	99
	104	34	32
	105	34	65
	106	34	98
	107	35	31
9	108	35	64
	109	35	97
	110	36	30
	111	36	63
	112	36	96
	113	37	29
	114	37	62
	115	37	95
	116	38	28
	117	38	61
	118	38	94
	119	39	27
	120	39	60
	121	39	93
	122	40	26
	123	40	59
	124	40	92
	125	41	25
	126	41	58
	127	41	91
	128	42	24
	129	42	57
	130	42	90
	131	43	23
11	132	43	56
	133	43	89
	134	44	22
	135	44	55
	136	44	88
	137	45	21
	138	45	54
	139	45	87
	140	46	20
	141	46	53
	142	46	86
	143	47	19
12	144	47	52
	145	47	85
	146	48	18
	147	48	51
	148	48	84
	149	49	17
	150	49	50

Dozens		£	P
	152	50	16
	154	50	82
13	156	51	48
	158	52	14
	160	52	80
	162	53	46
	164	54	12
	166	54	78
14	168	55	44
	170	56	10
	172	56	76
	174	57	42
	175	57	75
	176	58	8
	178	58	74
15	180	59	40
	182	60	6
	184	60	72
	186	61	38
	188	62	4
	190	62	70
16	192	63	36
	194	64	2
	196	64	68
	198	65	34
	200	66	0
17	204	67	32
	205	67	65
	210	69	30
	215	70	95
18	216	71	28
	220	72	60
	225	74	25
19	228	75	24
	230	75	90
	235	77	55
20	240	79	20
	245	80	85
	250	82	50
	255	84	15
	260	85	80
	265	87	45
	270	89	10
	275	90	75
	280	92	40
	285	94	5
24	288	95	4
	290	95	70
	295	97	35
	300	99	0

	£	P
310	102	30
320	105	60
330	108	90
340	112	20
350	115	50
360	118	8
365	120	45
370	122	10
380	125	40
390	128	70
400	132	0
410	135	30
420	138	60
430	141	90
440	145	20
450	148	50
460	151	80
470	155	10
480	158	40
490	161	70
500	165	0
550	181	50
600	198	0
650	214	50
700	231	0
750	247	50
800	264	0
850	280	50
900	297	0
950	313	50
1000	330	0
1016	335	28
1250	412	50
1500	495	0
1728	570	24
1750	577	50
1760	580	80
2000	660	0
2240	739	20
2500	825	0
3000	990	0
4000	1320	0
5000	1650	0
6000	1980	0
7000	2310	0
8000	2640	0
9000	2970	0
10,000	3300	0
15,000	4950	0
20,000	6600	0

Grosses

	£	P
1.	47	52
2.	95	4
3.	142	56
4.	190	8
5.	237	60
6.	285	12
7.	332	64
8.	380	16
9.	427	68
10.	475	20
11.	522	72

Twelfths

		£	P
	1.	0	2¾
⅙	2.	0	5½
	3.	0	8¼
⅓	4.	0	11
	5.	0	13¾
½	6.	0	16½
	7.	0	19¼
⅔	8.	0	22
	9.	0	24¾
⅚	10.	0	27½
	11.	0	30¼

Twentieths

10ths		£	P			£	P
	1.	0	1¾		11.	0	18¼
·1	2.	0	3¼	·6	12.	0	19¾
	3.	0	5		13.	0	21½
·2	4.	0	6½	·7	14.	0	23
	5.	0	8¼		15.	0	24¾
·3	6.	0	10	·8	16.	0	26½
	7.	0	11½		17.	0	28
·4	8.	0	13¼	·9	18.	0	29¾
	9.	0	14¾		19.	0	31¼
·5	10.	0	16½		20.	0	33

Sixteenths

		£	P			£	P
	1.	0	2		9.	0	18½
⅛	2.	0	4¼	⅝	10.	0	20¾
	3.	0	6¼		11.	0	22¾
¼	4.	0	8¼	¾	12.	0	24¾
	5.	0	10¼		13.	0	26¾
⅜	6.	0	12½	⅞	14.	0	29
	7.	0	14½		15.	0	31
½	8.	0	16½				

No.	£	P
1	0	34
2	0	68
3	1	2
4	1	36
5	1	70
6	2	4
7	2	38
8	2	72
9	3	6
10	3	40
11	3	74
12	4	8
13	4	42
14	4	76
15	5	10
16	5	44
17	5	78
18	6	12
19	6	46
20	6	80
21	7	14
22	7	48
23	7	82
24	8	16
25	8	50
26	8	84
27	9	18
28	9	52
29	9	86
30	10	20
31	10	54
32	10	88
33	11	22
34	11	56
35	11	90
36	12	24
37	12	58
38	12	92
39	13	26
40	13	60
41	13	94
42	14	28
43	14	62
44	14	96
45	15	30
46	15	64
47	15	98
48	16	32
49	16	66
50	17	0

No.	£	P
51	17	34
52	17	68
53	18	2
54	18	36
55	18	70
56	19	4
57	19	38
58	19	72
59	20	6
60	20	40
61	20	74
62	21	8
63	21	42
64	21	76
65	22	10
66	22	44
67	22	78
68	23	12
69	23	46
70	23	80
71	24	14
72	24	48
73	24	82
74	25	16
75	25	50
76	25	84
77	26	18
78	26	52
79	26	86
80	27	20
81	27	54
82	27	88
83	28	22
84	28	56
85	28	90
86	29	24
87	29	58
88	29	92
89	30	26
90	30	60
91	30	94
92	31	28
93	31	62
94	31	96
95	32	30
96	32	64
97	32	98
98	33	32
99	33	66
100	34	0

No.	£	P
101	34	34
102	34	68
103	35	2
104	35	36
105	35	70
106	36	4
107	36	38
108	36	72
109	37	6
110	37	40
111	37	74
112	38	8
113	38	42
114	38	76
115	39	10
116	39	44
117	39	78
118	40	12
119	40	46
120	40	80
121	41	14
122	41	48
123	41	82
124	42	16
125	42	50
126	42	84
127	43	18
128	43	52
129	43	86
130	44	20
131	44	54
132	44	88
133	45	22
134	45	56
135	45	90
136	46	24
137	46	58
138	46	92
139	47	26
140	47	60
141	47	94
142	48	28
143	48	62
144	48	96
145	49	30
146	49	64
147	49	98
148	50	32
149	50	66
150	51	0

No.	£	P
152	51	68
154	52	36
156	53	4
158	53	72
160	54	40
162	55	8
164	55	76
166	56	44
168	57	12
170	57	80
172	58	48
174	59	16
175	59	50
176	59	84
178	60	52
180	61	20
182	61	88
184	62	56
186	63	24
188	63	92
190	64	60
192	65	28
194	65	96
196	66	64
198	67	32
200	68	0
204	69	36
205	69	70
210	71	40
215	73	10
216	73	44
220	74	80
225	76	50
228	77	52
230	78	20
235	79	90
240	81	60
245	83	30
250	85	0
255	86	70
260	88	40
265	90	10
270	91	80
275	93	50
280	95	20
285	96	90
288	97	92
290	98	60
295	100	30
300	102	0

No.	£	P
310	105	40
320	108	80
330	112	20
340	115	60
350	119	0
360	122	40
365	124	10
370	125	80
380	129	20
390	132	60
400	136	0
410	139	40
420	142	80
430	146	20
440	149	60
450	153	0
460	156	40
470	159	80
480	163	20
490	166	60
500	170	0
550	187	0
600	204	0
650	221	0
700	238	0
750	255	0
800	272	0
850	289	0
900	306	0
950	323	0
1000	340	0
1016	345	44
1250	425	0
1500	510	0
1728	587	52
1750	595	0
1760	598	40
2000	680	0
2240	761	60
2500	850	0
3000	1020	0
4000	1360	0
5000	1700	0
6000	2040	0
7000	2380	0
8000	2720	0
9000	3060	0
10,000	3400	0
15,000	5100	0
20,000	6800	0

Grosses			Twelfths			Twentieths				Sixteenths		
1.	48	96	1.	0	2¾	1.	0	1¾	11. 0 18¼	1.	0	2⅛	9. 0 19⅛
2.	97	92	⅙ 2.	0	5⅔	2.	0	3¼	12. 0 20½	⅛ 2.	0	4¼	10. 0 21¼
3.	146	88	3.	0	8½	3.	0	5	13. 0 22	3.	0	6⅜	11. 0 23⅜
4.	195	84	⅓ 4.	0	11⅓	4.	0	6½	14. 0 23¾	¼ 4.	0	8½	12. 0 25½
5.	244	80	5.	0	14¼	5.	0	8½	15. 0 25¼	5.	0	10⅝	13. 0 27⅝
6.	293	76	½ 6.	0	17	6.	0	10¼	16. 0 27¼	⅜ 6.	0	12¾	14. 0 29¾
7.	342	72	7.	0	19¾	7.	0	12	17. 0 29	7.	0	15	15. 0 32
8.	391	68	⅔ 8.	0	22⅔	8.	0	13½	18. 0 30½	½ 8.	0	17	
9.	440	64	9.	0	25½	9.	0	15¼	19. 0 32½				
10.	489	60	10.	0	28⅓	10.	0	17	20. 0 34				
11.	538	56	11.	0	31¼								

	£	P		£	P		£	P		£	P		£	P
1	0	35	51	17	85	101	35	35	152	53	20	310	108	50
2	0	70	52	18	20	102	35	70	154	53	90	320	112	0
3	1	5	53	18	55	103	36	5	13 156	54	60	330	115	50
*Dozens 4	1	40	Dozens 54	18	90	Dozens 104	36	40	Dozens 158	55	30	340	119	0
5	1	75	55	19	25	105	36	75	160	56	0	350	122	50
6	2	10	56	19	60	106	37	10	162	56	70	360	126	0
7	2	45	57	19	95	107	37	45	164	57	40	365	127	75
8	2	80	58	20	30	9 108	37	80	166	58	10	370	129	50
9	3	15	59	20	65	109	38	15	14 168	58	80	380	133	0
10	3	50	5 60	21	0	110	38	50	170	59	50	390	136	50
*11	3	85	61	21	35	111	38	85	172	60	20	400	140	0
1 12	4	20	62	21	70	112	39	20	174	60	90	410	143	50
13	4	55	63	22	5	113	39	55	175	61	25	420	147	0
14	4	90	64	22	40	114	39	90	176	61	60	430	150	50
15	5	25	65	22	75	115	40	25	178	62	30	440	154	0
16	5	60	66	23	10	116	40	60	15 180	63	0	450	157	50
17	5	95	67	23	45	117	40	95	182	63	70	460	161	0
18	6	30	68	23	80	118	41	30	184	64	40	470	164	50
19	6	65	69	24	15	119	41	65	186	65	10	480	168	0
20	7	0	70	24	50	120	42	0	188	65	80	490	171	50
21	7	35	71	24	85	121	42	35	190	66	50	500	175	0
22	7	70	6 72	25	20	122	42	70	16 192	67	20	550	192	50
23	8	5	73	25	55	123	43	5	194	67	90	600	210	0
2 24	8	40	74	25	90	124	43	40	196	68	60	650	227	50
25	8	75	75	26	25	125	43	75	198	69	30	700	245	0
26	9	10	76	26	60	126	44	10	200	70	0	750	262	50
27	9	45	77	26	95	127	44	45	17 204	71	40	800	280	0
28	9	80	78	27	30	128	44	80	205	71	75	850	297	50
29	10	15	79	27	65	129	45	15	210	73	50	900	315	0
30	10	50	80	28	0	130	45	50	215	75	25	950	332	50
31	10	85	81	28	35	131	45	85	18 216	75	60	1000	350	0
32	11	20	82	28	70	11 132	46	20	220	77	0	1016	355	60
33	11	55	83	29	5	133	46	55	225	78	75	1250	437	50
34	11	90	7 84	29	40	134	46	90	19 228	79	80	1500	525	0
35	12	25	85	29	75	135	47	25	230	80	50	1728	604	80
3 36	12	60	86	30	10	136	47	60	235	82	25	1750	612	50
37	12	95	87	30	45	137	47	95	20 240	84	0	1760	616	0
38	13	30	88	30	80	138	48	30	245	85	75	2000	700	0
39	13	65	89	31	15	139	48	65	250	87	50	2240	784	0
40	14	0	90	31	50	140	49	0	255	89	25	2500	875	0
41	14	35	91	31	85	141	49	35	260	91	0	3000	1050	0
42	14	70	92	32	20	142	49	70	265	92	75	4000	1400	0
43	15	5	93	32	55	143	50	5	270	94	50	5000	1750	0
44	15	40	94	32	90	12 144	50	40	275	96	25	6000	2100	0
45	15	75	95	33	25	145	50	75	280	98	0	7000	2450	0
46	16	10	8 96	33	60	146	51	10	285	99	75	8000	2800	0
47	16	45	97	33	95	147	51	45	24 288	100	80	9000	3150	0
4 48	16	80	98	34	30	148	51	80	290	101	50	10,000	3500	0
49	17	15	99	34	65	149	52	15	295	103	25	15,000	5250	0
50	17	50	100	35	0	150	52	50	300	105	0	20,000	7000	0

Grosses			Twelfths			Twentieths						Sixteenths		
1.	50	40	1.	0	3	1.	0	1¾	11.	0	19¼	1.	0	2¼
2.	100	80	⅙ 2.	0	5¾	x 2.	0	3½	6 12.	0	21	½ 2.	0	4½
3.	151	20	⅓ 3.	0	8¾	3.	0	5¼	13.	0	22¾	3.	0	6¾
4.	201	60	¼ 4.	0	11¼	7 4.	0	7	14.	0	24½	¼ 4.	0	8¾
5.	252	0	5.	0	14¼	5.	0	8¾	15.	0	26¼	5.	0	11
6.	302	40	⅖ 6.	0	17¼	3 6.	0	10½	16.	0	28	½ 6.	0	13¼
7.	352	80	7.	0	20¼	7.	0	12¼	17.	0	29¾	7.	0	15½
8.	403	20	⅔ 8.	0	23¼	4 8.	0	14	9 18.	0	31½	7 14.	0	30½
9.	453	60	9.	0	26¼	9.	0	15¾	10 19.	0	33¼	13.	0	28½
10.	504	0	⅚10.	0	29¼	5 10.	0	17½	20.	0	35	½ 8.	0	17¾
11.	554	40	11.	0	32							15.	0	32¾

*Dozens

	£	P		£	P		£	P		£	P		£	P
1	0	36	51	18	36	101	36	36	152	54	72	310	111	60
2	0	72	52	18	72	102	36	72	154	55	44	320	115	20
3	1	8	53	19	8	103	37	8	[13] 156	56	16	330	118	80
4	1	44	54	19	44	104	37	44	158	56	88	340	122	40
5	1	80	55	19	80	105	37	80	160	57	60	350	126	0
6	2	16	56	20	16	106	38	16	162	58	32	360	129	60
7	2	52	57	20	52	107	38	52	164	59	4	365	131	40
8	2	88	58	20	88	[9] 108	38	88	166	59	76	370	133	20
9	3	24	59	21	24	109	39	24	[14] 168	60	48	380	136	80
10	3	60	[5] 60	21	60	110	39	60	170	61	20	390	140	40
11	3	96	61	21	96	111	39	96	172	61	92	400	144	0
[1] 12	4	32	62	22	32	112	40	32	174	62	64	410	147	60
13	4	68	63	22	68	113	40	68	175	63	0	420	151	20
14	5	4	64	23	4	114	41	4	176	63	36	430	154	80
15	5	40	65	23	40	115	41	40	178	64	8	440	158	40
16	5	76	66	23	76	116	41	76	[15] 180	64	80	450	162	0
17	6	12	67	24	12	117	42	12	182	65	52	460	165	60
18	6	48	68	24	48	118	42	48	184	66	24	470	169	20
19	6	84	69	24	84	119	42	84	186	66	96	480	172	80
20	7	20	70	25	20	120	43	20	188	67	68	490	176	40
21	7	56	71	25	56	121	43	56	190	68	40	500	180	0
22	7	92	[6] 72	25	92	122	43	92	[16] 192	69	12	550	198	0
23	8	28	73	26	28	123	44	28	194	69	84	600	216	0
[2] 24	8	64	74	26	64	124	44	64	196	70	56	650	234	0
25	9	0	75	27	0	125	45	0	198	71	28	700	252	0
26	9	36	76	27	36	126	45	36	200	72	0	750	270	0
27	9	72	77	27	72	127	45	72	[17] 204	73	44	800	288	0
28	10	8	78	28	8	128	46	8	205	73	80	850	306	0
29	10	44	79	28	44	129	46	44	210	75	60	900	324	0
30	10	80	80	28	80	130	46	80	215	77	40	950	342	0
31	11	16	81	29	16	131	47	16	[18] 216	77	76	1000	360	0
32	11	52	82	29	52	[11] 132	47	52	220	79	20	1016	365	76
33	11	88	83	29	88	133	47	88	225	81	0	1250	450	0
34	12	24	[7] 84	30	24	134	48	24	[19] 228	82	8	1500	540	0
35	12	60	85	30	60	135	48	60	230	82	80	1728	622	8
[3] 36	12	96	86	30	96	136	48	96	235	84	60	1750	630	0
37	13	32	87	31	32	137	49	32	[20] 240	86	40	1760	633	60
38	13	68	88	31	68	138	49	68	245	88	20	2000	720	0
39	14	4	89	32	4	139	50	4	250	90	0	2240	806	40
40	14	40	90	32	40	140	50	40	255	91	80	2500	900	0
41	14	76	91	32	76	141	50	76	260	93	60	3000	1080	0
42	15	12	92	33	12	142	51	12	265	95	40	4000	1440	0
43	15	48	93	33	48	143	51	48	270	97	20	5000	1800	0
44	15	84	94	33	84	[12] 144	51	84	275	99	0	6000	2160	0
45	16	20	95	34	20	145	52	20	280	100	80	7000	2520	0
46	16	56	[8] 96	34	56	146	52	56	285	102	60	8000	2880	0
47	16	92	97	34	92	147	52	92	[24] 288	103	68	9000	3240	0
[4] 48	17	28	98	35	28	148	53	28	290	104	40	10,000	3600	0
49	17	64	99	35	64	149	53	64	295	106	20	15,000	5400	0
50	18	0	100	36	0	150	54	0	300	108	0	20,000	7200	0

Grosses

1.	51	84
2.	103	68
3.	155	52
4.	207	36
5.	259	20
6.	311	4
7.	362	88
8.	414	72
9.	466	56
10.	518	40
11.	570	24

Twelfths

	1.	0	3
1/6	2.	0	6
	3.	0	9
1/3	4.	0	12
	5.	0	15
1/2	6.	0	18
	7.	0	21
2/3	8.	0	24
	9.	0	27
5/6	10.	0	30
	11.	0	33

Twentieths

10ths				10ths			
	1.	0	1¾		11.	0	19¾
·1	2.	0	3½	·6	12.	0	21½
	3.	0	5½		13.	0	23½
·2	4.	0	7¼	·7	14.	0	25¼
	5.	0	9		15.	0	27
·3	6.	0	10¾	·8	16.	0	28¾
	7.	0	12½		17.	0	30½
·4	8.	0	14½	·9	18.	0	32½
	9.	0	16¼		19.	0	34¼
·5	10.	0	18		20.	0	36

Sixteenths

	1.	0	2¼		9.	0	20¼
1/8	2.	0	4½	5/8	10.	0	22½
	3.	0	6¾		11.	0	24¾
1/4	4.	0	9	3/4	12.	0	27
	5.	0	11¼		13.	0	29¼
3/8	6.	0	13½	7/8	14.	0	31½
	7.	0	15¾		15.	0	33¾
1/2	8.	0	18				

	£	P		£	P		£	P		£	P		£	P
1	0	37	51	18	87	101	37	37	152	56	24	310	114	70
2	0	74	52	19	24	102	37	74	154	56	98	320	118	40
3	1	11	53	19	61	103	38	11	[13] 156	57	72	330	122	10
4	1	48	54	19	98	104	38	48	158	58	46	340	125	80
5	1	85	55	20	35	105	38	85	160	59	20	350	129	50
* 6	2	22	56	20	72	106	39	22	162	59	94	360	133	20
7	2	59	57	21	9	107	39	59	164	60	68	365	135	5
8	2	96	58	21	46	[9] 108	39	96	166	61	42	370	136	90
9	3	33	59	21	83	109	40	33	[14] 168	62	16	380	140	60
10	3	70	[5] **60**	22	20	**110**	40	70	170	62	90	390	144	30
* 11	4	7	61	22	57	111	41	7	172	63	64	400	148	0
[1] 12	4	44	62	22	94	112	41	44	174	64	38	410	151	70
13	4	81	63	23	31	113	41	81	175	64	75	420	155	40
14	5	18	64	23	68	114	42	18	176	65	12	430	159	10
15	5	55	65	24	5	115	42	55	178	65	86	440	162	80
16	5	92	66	24	42	116	42	92	[15] 180	66	60	450	166	50
17	6	29	67	24	79	117	43	29	182	67	34	460	170	20
18	6	66	68	25	16	118	43	66	184	68	8	470	173	90
19	7	3	69	25	53	119	44	3	186	68	82	480	177	60
20	7	40	**70**	25	90	**120**	44	40	188	69	56	490	181	30
21	7	77	71	26	27	121	44	77	190	70	30	**500**	185	0
22	8	14	[6] 72	26	64	122	45	14	[16] 192	71	4	550	203	50
23	8	51	73	27	1	123	45	51	194	71	78	600	222	0
[2] 24	8	88	74	27	38	124	45	88	196	72	52	650	240	50
25	9	25	75	27	75	125	46	25	198	73	26	700	259	0
26	9	62	76	28	12	126	46	62	**200**	74	0	750	277	50
27	9	99	77	28	49	127	46	99	[17] 204	75	48	800	296	0
28	10	36	78	28	86	128	47	36	205	75	85	850	314	50
29	10	73	79	29	23	129	47	73	210	77	70	900	333	0
30	11	10	**80**	29	60	**130**	48	10	215	79	55	950	351	50
31	11	47	81	29	97	131	48	47	[18] 216	79	92	**1000**	370	0
32	11	84	82	30	34	[11] 132	48	84	220	81	40	1016	375	92
33	12	21	83	30	71	133	49	21	225	83	25	1250	462	50
34	12	58	[7] 84	31	8	134	49	58	[19] 228	84	36	1500	555	0
35	12	95	85	31	45	135	49	95	230	85	10	1728	639	36
[3] 36	13	32	86	31	82	136	50	32	235	86	95	1750	647	50
37	13	69	87	32	19	137	50	69	[20] 240	88	80	1760	651	20
38	14	6	88	32	56	138	51	6	245	90	65	2000	740	0
39	14	43	89	32	93	139	51	43	**250**	92	50	2240	828	80
40	14	80	**90**	33	30	**140**	51	80	255	94	35	2500	925	0
41	15	17	91	33	67	141	52	17	260	96	20	3000	1110	0
42	15	54	92	34	4	142	52	54	265	98	5	4000	1480	0
43	15	91	93	34	41	143	52	91	270	99	90	**5000**	1850	0
44	16	28	94	34	78	[12] 144	53	28	275	101	75	6000	2220	0
45	16	65	95	35	15	145	53	65	280	103	60	7000	2590	0
46	17	2	[8] 96	35	52	146	54	2	285	105	45	8000	2960	0
47	17	39	97	35	89	147	54	39	[24] 288	106	56	9000	3330	0
[4] 48	17	76	98	36	26	148	54	76	290	107	30	10,000	3700	0
49	18	13	99	36	63	149	55	13	295	109	15	15,000	5550	0
50	18	50	**100**	37	0	**150**	55	50	**300**	111	0	20,000	7400	0

(* Dozens. — Dozens. — Dozens. — Doz.)

Grosses.

1.	53	28
2.	106	56
3.	159	84
4.	213	12
5.	266	40
6.	319	68
7.	372	96
8.	426	24
9.	479	52
10.	532	80
11.	586	8

Twelfths

	1.	0	3
⅙	2.	0	6¼
	3.	0	9¼
⅓	4.	0	12¼
	5.	0	15½
½	6.	0	18½
	7.	0	21½
⅔	8.	0	24¾
	9.	0	27¾
⅚	10.	0	30¾
	11.	0	34

Twentieths

10ths							
	1.	0	1¾		11.	0	20¼
·1	2.	0	3¾	·6	12.	0	22¼
	3.	0	5½		13.	0	24
·2	4.	0	7½	·7	14.	0	26
	5.	0	9¼		15.	0	27¾
·3	6.	0	11	·8	16.	0	29½
	7.	0	13		17.	0	31½
·4	8.	0	14¾	·9	18.	0	33¼
	9.	0	16½		19.	0	35¼
·5	10.	0	18½		20.	0	37

Sixteenths

	1.	0	2¼		9.	0	20¾
⅛	2.	0	4¾	⅝	10.	0	23¼
	3.	0	7		11.	0	25½
¼	4.	0	9¼	¾	12.	0	27¾
	5.	0	11½		13.	0	30
⅜	6.	0	14	⅞	14.	0	32½
	7.	0	16¼		15.	0	34¾
½	8.	0	18½				

No.	£	P
1	0	37½
2	0	75
3	1	12½
4	1	50
5	1	87½
6	2	25
7	2	62½
8	3	0
9	3	37½
10	3	75
11	4	12½
12	4	50
13	4	87½
14	5	25
15	5	62½
16	6	0
17	6	37½
18	6	75
19	7	12½
20	7	50
21	7	87½
22	8	25
23	8	62½
24	9	0
25	9	37½
26	9	75
27	10	12½
28	10	50
29	10	87½
30	11	25
31	11	62½
32	12	0
33	12	37½
34	12	75
35	13	12½
36	13	50
37	13	87½
38	14	25
39	14	62½
40	15	0
41	15	37½
42	15	75
43	16	12½
44	16	50
45	16	87½
46	17	25
47	17	62½
48	18	0
49	18	37½
50	18	75

No.	£	P
51	19	12½
52	19	50
53	19	87½
54	20	25
55	20	62½
56	21	0
57	21	37½
58	21	75
59	22	12½
60	22	50
61	22	87½
62	23	25
63	23	62½
64	24	0
65	24	37½
66	24	75
67	25	12½
68	25	50
69	25	87½
70	26	25
71	26	62½
72	27	0
73	27	37½
74	27	75
75	28	12½
76	28	50
77	28	87½
78	29	25
79	29	62½
80	30	0
81	30	37½
82	30	75
83	31	12½
84	31	50
85	31	87½
86	32	25
87	32	62½
88	33	0
89	33	37½
90	33	75
91	34	12½
92	34	50
93	34	87½
94	35	25
95	35	62½
96	36	0
97	36	37½
98	36	75
99	37	12½
100	37	50

No.	£	P
101	37	87½
102	38	25
103	38	62½
104	39	0
105	39	37½
106	39	75
107	40	12½
108	40	50
109	40	87½
110	41	25
111	41	62½
112	42	0
113	42	37½
114	42	75
115	43	12½
116	43	50
117	43	87½
118	44	25
119	44	62½
120	45	0
121	45	37½
122	45	75
123	46	12½
124	46	50
125	46	87½
126	47	25
127	47	62½
128	48	0
129	48	37½
130	48	75
131	49	12½
132	49	50
133	49	87½
134	50	25
135	50	62½
136	51	0
137	51	37½
138	51	75
139	52	12½
140	52	50
141	52	87½
142	53	25
143	53	62½
144	54	0
145	54	37½
146	54	75
147	55	12½
148	55	50
149	55	87½
150	56	25

No.	£	P
152	57	0
154	57	75
156	58	50
158	59	25
160	60	0
162	60	75
164	61	50
166	62	25
168	63	0
170	63	75
172	64	50
174	65	25
175	65	62½
176	66	0
178	66	75
180	67	50
182	68	25
184	69	0
186	69	75
188	70	50
190	71	25
192	72	0
194	72	75
196	73	50
198	74	25
200	75	0
204	76	50
205	76	87½
210	78	75
215	80	62½
216	81	0
220	82	50
225	84	37½
230	86	25
235	88	12½
240	90	0
245	91	87½
250	93	75
255	95	62½
260	97	50
265	99	37½
270	101	25
275	103	12½
280	105	0
285	106	87½
288	108	0
290	108	75
295	110	62½
300	112	50

No.	£	P
310	116	25
320	120	0
330	123	75
340	127	50
350	131	25
360	135	0
365	136	87½
370	138	75
380	142	50
390	146	25
400	150	0
410	153	75
420	157	50
430	161	25
440	165	0
450	168	75
460	172	50
470	176	25
480	180	0
490	183	75
500	187	50
550	206	25
600	225	0
650	243	75
700	262	50
750	281	25
800	300	0
850	318	75
900	337	50
950	356	25
1000	375	0
1016	381	0
1250	468	75
1500	562	50
1728	648	0
1750	656	25
1760	660	0
2000	750	0
2240	840	0
2500	937	50
3000	1125	0
4000	1500	0
5000	1875	0
6000	2250	0
7000	2625	0
8000	3000	0
9000	3375	0
10000	3750	0
15000	5625	0
20000	7500	0

*Dozens.

Grosses.	£		Twelfths	£		10th Twentieths	£			£		Sixteenths	£			£	
1.	54	0	1.	0	3½	1.	0	2	11.	0	20½	1.	0	2¼	9.	0	21
2.	108	0	½.	0	6¼	2.	0	3¾	12.	0	22¼	½2.	0	4½	½10.	0	23¼
3.	162	0	3.	0	9½	3.	0	5¾	13.	0	24¼	3.	0	7	11.	0	25½
4.	216	0	⅓4.	0	12½	4.	0	7½	14.	0	26¼	¼4.	0	9½	½12.	0	28¼
5.	270	0	5.	0	15½	5.	0	9½	15.	0	28	5.	0	11¾	13.	0	30½
6.	324	0	½6.	0	18½	6.	0	11¼	16.	0	30	¾6.	0	14	13.	0	30½
7.	378	0	7.	0	22	7.	0	13¼	17.	0	32	7.	0	16½	¾14.	0	32½
8.	432	0	8.	0	25	8.	0	15	18.	0	33¾	⅛8.	0	18¾	15.	0	35½
9.	486	0	9.	0	28½	9.	0	17	19.	0	35½						
10.	540	0	⅚10.	0	31½	10.	0	18¾	20.	0	37½						
11.	594	0	11.	0	34½												

Dozens	£	p	Dozens	£	p	Dozens	£	p	Dozens	£	p		£	p
1	0	38	51	19	38	101	38	38	152	57	76	310	117	80
2	0	76	52	19	76	102	38	76	154	58	52	320	121	60
3	1	14	53	20	14	103	39	14	[13] 156	59	28	330	125	40
4	1	52	54	20	52	104	39	52	158	60	4	340	129	20
5	1	90	55	20	90	105	39	90	160	60	80	350	133	0
*6	2	28	56	21	28	106	40	28	162	61	56	360	136	80
7	2	66	57	21	66	107	40	66	164	62	32	365	138	70
8	3	4	58	22	4	[9] 108	41	4	166	63	8	370	140	60
9	3	42	59	22	42	109	41	42	[14] 168	63	84	380	144	40
10	3	80	[5] **60**	22	80	**110**	41	80	170	64	60	390	148	20
*11	4	18	61	23	18	111	42	18	172	65	36	400	152	0
[1] 12	4	56	62	23	56	112	42	56	174	66	12	410	155	80
13	4	94	63	23	94	113	42	94	175	66	50	420	159	60
14	5	32	64	24	32	114	43	32	176	66	88	430	163	40
15	5	70	65	24	70	115	43	70	178	67	64	440	167	20
16	6	8	66	25	8	116	44	8	[15] 180	68	40	450	171	0
17	6	46	67	25	46	117	44	46	182	69	16	460	174	80
18	6	84	68	25	84	118	44	84	184	69	92	470	178	60
19	7	22	69	26	22	119	45	22	186	70	68	480	182	40
20	7	60	**70**	26	60	**120**	45	60	188	71	44	490	186	20
21	7	98	71	26	98	121	45	98	190	72	20	**500**	190	0
22	8	36	[6] 72	27	36	122	46	36	[16] 192	72	96	550	209	0
23	8	74	73	27	74	123	46	74	194	73	72	600	228	0
[2] 24	9	12	74	28	12	124	47	12	196	74	48	650	247	0
25	9	50	75	28	50	125	47	50	198	75	24	700	266	0
26	9	88	76	28	88	126	47	88	**200**	76	0	750	285	0
27	10	26	77	29	26	127	48	26	[17] 204	77	52	800	304	0
28	10	64	78	29	64	128	48	64	205	77	90	850	323	0
29	11	2	79	30	2	129	49	2	210	79	80	900	342	0
30	11	40	**80**	30	40	**130**	49	40	215	81	70	950	361	0
31	11	78	81	30	78	131	49	78	[18] 216	82	8	**1000**	380	0
32	12	16	82	31	16	[11] 132	50	16	220	83	60	1016	386	8
33	12	54	83	31	54	133	50	54	225	85	50	1250	475	0
34	12	92	[7] 84	31	92	134	50	92	[19] 228	86	64	1500	570	0
35	13	30	85	32	30	135	51	30	230	87	40	1728	656	64
[3] 36	13	68	86	32	68	136	51	68	235	89	30	1750	665	0
37	14	6	87	33	6	137	52	6	[20] 240	91	20	1760	668	80
38	14	44	88	33	44	138	52	44	245	93	10	2000	760	0
39	14	82	89	33	82	139	52	82	**250**	95	0	2240	851	20
40	15	20	**90**	34	20	**140**	53	20	255	96	90	2500	950	0
41	15	58	91	34	58	141	53	58	260	98	80	3000	1140	0
42	15	96	92	34	96	142	53	96	265	100	70	4000	1520	0
43	16	34	93	35	34	143	54	34	270	102	60	**5000**	1900	0
44	16	72	94	35	72	[12] 144	54	72	275	104	50	6000	2280	0
45	17	10	95	36	10	145	55	10	280	106	40	7000	2660	0
46	17	48	[8] 96	36	48	146	55	48	285	108	30	8000	3040	0
47	17	86	97	36	86	147	55	86	[24] 288	109	44	9000	3420	0
[4] 48	18	24	98	37	24	148	56	24	290	110	20	10,000	3800	0
49	18	62	99	37	62	149	56	62	295	112	10	15,000	5700	0
50	19	0	**100**	38	0	**150**	57	0	**300**	114	0	20,000	7600	0

Grosses

1.	54	72
2.	109	44
3.	164	16
4.	218	88
5.	273	60
6.	328	32
7.	383	4
8.	437	76
9.	492	48
10.	547	20
11.	601	92

Twelfths

	1.		3¼
⅙	2.	0	6¼
	3.	0	9½
⅓	4.	0	12¾
	5.	0	15¾
½	6.	0	19
	7.	0	22¼
⅔	8.	0	25¼
	9.	0	28½
⅚	10.	0	31¾
	11.	0	34¾

Twentieths

10ths		U	0	10ths			
	1.	0	2		11.	0	21
·1	2.	0	3¾	·6	12.	0	22¾
	3.	0	5¾		13.	0	24¾
·2	4.	0	7½	·7	14.	0	26½
	5.	0	9½		15.	0	28½
·3	6.	0	11½	·8	16.	0	30½
	7.	0	13¼		17.	0	32¼
·4	8.	0	15¼	·9	18.	0	34¼
	9.	0	17		19.	0	36
·5	10.	0	19		20.	0	38

Sixteenths

	1.	0	2½		9.	0	21½
⅛	2.	0	4¾	⅝	10.	0	23¾
	3.	0	7¼		11.	0	26¼
¼	4.	0	9½	¾	12.	0	28½
	5.	0	12		13.	0	31
⅜	6.	0	14¼	⅞	14.	0	33¼
	7.	0	16¾		15.	0	35¾
½	8.	0	19				

*Dozens	£	p	Dozens	£	p	Dozens	£	p	Dozens	£	p		£	p
1	0	39	51	19	89	101	39	39	152	59	28	310	120	90
2	0	78	52	20	28	102	39	78	154	60	6	320	124	80
3	1	17	53	20	67	103	40	17	[13] 156	60	84	330	128	70
4	1	56	54	21	6	104	40	56	158	61	62	340	132	60
5	1	95	55	21	45	105	40	95	160	62	40	350	136	50
6	2	34	56	21	84	106	41	34	162	63	18	360	140	40
7	2	73	57	22	23	107	41	73	164	63	96	365	142	35
8	3	12	58	22	62	[9] 108	42	12	166	64	74	370	144	30
9	3	51	59	23	1	109	42	51	[14] 168	65	52	380	148	20
10	3	90	[5] **60**	23	40	**110**	42	90	170	66	30	390	152	10
11	4	29	61	23	79	111	43	29	172	67	8	400	156	0
[*1] 12	4	68	62	24	18	112	43	68	174	67	86	410	159	90
13	5	7	63	24	57	113	44	7	175	68	25	420	163	80
14	5	46	64	24	96	114	44	46	176	68	64	430	167	70
15	5	85	65	25	35	115	44	85	178	69	42	440	171	60
16	6	24	66	25	74	116	45	24	[15] 180	70	20	450	175	50
17	6	63	67	26	13	117	45	63	182	70	98	460	179	40
18	7	2	68	26	52	118	46	2	184	71	76	470	183	30
19	7	41	69	26	91	119	46	41	186	72	54	480	187	20
20	7	80	**70**	27	30	**120**	46	80	188	73	32	490	191	10
21	8	19	71	27	69	121	47	19	190	74	10	**500**	195	0
22	8	58	[6] 72	28	8	122	47	58	[16] 192	74	88	550	214	50
23	8	97	73	28	47	123	47	97	194	75	66	600	234	0
[2] 24	9	36	74	28	86	124	48	36	196	76	44	650	253	50
25	9	75	75	29	25	125	48	75	198	77	22	700	273	0
26	10	14	76	29	64	126	49	14	**200**	78	0	750	292	50
27	10	53	77	30	3	127	49	53	[17] 204	79	56	800	312	0
28	10	92	78	30	42	128	49	92	205	79	95	850	331	50
29	11	31	79	30	81	129	50	31	210	81	90	900	351	0
30	11	70	**80**	31	20	**130**	50	70	215	83	85	950	370	50
31	12	9	81	31	59	131	51	9	[18] 216	84	24	**1000**	390	0
32	12	48	82	31	98	[11] 132	51	48	220	85	80	1016	396	24
33	12	87	83	32	37	133	51	87	225	87	75	1250	487	50
34	13	26	[7] 84	32	76	134	52	26	[19] 228	88	92	1500	585	0
35	13	65	85	33	15	135	52	65	230	89	70	1728	673	92
[3] 36	14	4	86	33	54	136	53	4	235	91	65	1750	682	50
37	14	43	87	33	93	137	53	43	[20] 240	93	60	1760	686	40
38	14	82	88	34	32	138	53	82	245	95	55	2000	780	0
39	15	21	89	34	71	139	54	21	**250**	97	50	2240	873	60
40	15	60	**90**	35	10	**140**	54	60	255	99	45	2500	975	0
41	15	99	91	35	49	141	54	99	260	101	40	3000	1170	0
42	16	38	92	35	88	142	55	38	265	103	35	4000	1560	0
43	16	77	93	36	27	143	55	77	270	105	30	**5000**	1950	0
44	17	16	94	36	66	[12] 144	56	16	275	107	25	6000	2340	0
45	17	55	95	37	5	145	56	55	280	109	20	7000	2730	0
46	17	94	[8] 96	37	44	146	56	94	285	111	15	8000	3120	0
47	18	33	97	37	83	147	57	33	[24] 288	112	32	9000	3510	0
[4] 48	18	72	98	38	22	148	57	72	290	113	10	10,000	3900	0
49	19	11	99	38	61	149	58	11	295	115	5	15,000	5850	0
50	19	50	**100**	39	0	**150**	58	50	**300**	117	0	20,000	7800	0

Grosses

	£	p
1.	56	16
2.	112	32
3.	168	48
4.	224	64
5.	280	80
6.	336	96
7.	393	12
8.	449	28
9.	505	44
10.	561	60
11.	617	76

Twelfths

		£	p
	1.	0	3¼
⅙	2.	0	6½
	3.	0	9¾
⅓	4.	0	13
	5.	0	16¼
½	6.	0	19½
	7.	0	22¾
⅔	8.	0	26
	9.	0	29¼
⅚	10.	0	32½
	11.	0	35¾

Twentieths

10ths		£	p	10ths		£	p
	1.	0	2		11.	0	21½
·1	2.	0	4	·6	12.	0	23½
	3.	0	5¾		13.	0	25¼
·2	4.	0	7¾	·7	14.	0	27¼
	5.	0	9¾		15.	0	29¼
·3	6.	0	11¾	·8	16.	0	31¼
	7.	0	13¾		17.	0	33¼
·4	8.	0	15½	·9	18.	0	35
	9.	0	17½		19.	0	37
·5	10.	0	19½		20.	0	39

Sixteenths

		£	p			£	p
	1.	0	2½		9.	0	22
⅛	2.	0	5	⅝	10.	0	24½
	3.	0	7¼		11.	0	26¾
¼	4.	0	9¾	¾	12.	0	29¼
	5.	0	12¼		13.	0	31¾
⅜	6.	0	14¾	⅞	14.	0	34¼
	7.	0	17		15.	0	36½
½	8.	0	19½				

	£	P		£	P		£	P		£	P		£	P
1	0	40	51	20	40	101	40	40	152	60	80	310	124	0
2	0	80	52	20	80	102	40	80	154	61	60	320	128	0
3	1	20	53	21	20	103	41	20	13 156	62	40	330	132	0
4	1	60	54	21	60	104	41	60	158	63	20	340	136	0
5	2	0	55	22	0	105	42	0	160	64	0	350	140	0
6	2	40	56	22	40	106	42	40	162	64	80	360	144	0
7	2	80	57	22	80	107	42	80	164	65	60	365	146	0
8	3	20	58	23	20	108	43	20	166	66	40	370	148	0
9	3	60	59	23	60	109	43	60	14 168	67	20	380	152	0
10	4	0	60	24	0	110	44	0	170	68	0	390	156	0
11	4	40	61	24	40	111	44	40	172	68	80	400	160	0
12	4	80	62	24	80	112	44	80	174	69	60	410	164	0
13	5	20	63	25	20	113	45	20	175	70	0	420	168	0
14	5	60	64	25	60	114	45	60	176	70	40	430	172	0
15	6	0	65	26	0	115	46	0	178	71	20	440	176	0
16	6	40	66	26	40	116	46	40	15 180	72	0	450	180	0
17	6	80	67	26	80	117	46	80	182	72	80	460	184	0
18	7	20	68	27	20	118	47	20	184	73	60	470	188	0
19	7	60	69	27	60	119	47	60	186	74	40	480	192	0
20	8	0	70	28	0	120	48	0	188	75	20	490	196	0
21	8	40	71	28	40	121	48	40	190	76	0	500	200	0
22	8	80	72	28	80	122	48	80	16 192	76	80	550	220	0
23	9	20	73	29	20	123	49	20	194	77	60	600	240	0
24	9	60	74	29	60	124	49	60	196	78	40	650	260	0
25	10	0	75	30	0	125	50	0	198	79	20	700	280	0
26	10	40	76	30	40	126	50	40	200	80	0	750	300	0
27	10	80	77	30	80	127	50	80	17 204	81	60	800	320	0
28	11	20	78	31	20	128	51	20	205	82	0	850	340	0
29	11	60	79	31	60	129	51	60	210	84	0	900	360	0
30	12	0	80	32	0	130	52	0	215	86	0	950	380	0
31	12	40	81	32	40	131	52	40	18 216	86	40	1000	400	0
32	12	80	82	32	80	132	52	80	220	88	0	1016	406	40
33	13	20	83	33	20	133	53	20	225	90	0	1250	500	0
34	13	60	84	33	60	134	53	60	19 228	91	20	1500	600	0
35	14	0	85	34	0	135	54	0	230	92	0	1728	691	20
36	14	40	86	34	40	136	54	40	235	94	0	1750	700	0
37	14	80	87	34	80	137	54	80	20 240	96	0	1760	704	0
38	15	20	88	35	20	138	55	20	245	98	0	2000	800	0
39	15	60	89	35	60	139	55	60	250	100	0	2240	896	0
40	16	0	90	36	0	140	56	0	255	102	0	2500	1000	0
41	16	40	91	36	40	141	56	40	260	104	0	3000	1200	0
42	16	80	92	36	80	142	56	80	265	106	0	4000	1600	0
43	17	20	93	37	20	143	57	20	270	108	0	5000	2000	0
44	17	60	94	37	60	144	57	60	275	110	0	6000	2400	0
45	18	0	95	38	0	145	58	0	280	112	0	7000	2800	0
46	18	40	96	38	40	146	58	40	285	114	0	8000	3200	0
47	18	80	97	38	80	147	58	80	24 288	115	20	9000	3600	0
48	19	20	98	39	20	148	59	20	290	116	0	10,000	4000	0
49	19	60	99	39	60	149	59	60	295	118	0	15,000	6000	0
50	20	0	100	40	0	150	60	0	300	120	0	20,000	8000	0

Grosses			Twelfths			10ths	Twentieths				Sixteenths				
1.	57	60	1.	0	3⅓						1.	0	2½	9.	0 22½
2.	115	20	⅓2.	0	6⅔		·1.	0 2	11.	0 22	2.	0	5	10.	0 25
3.	172	80	3.	0	10	·1	2.	0 4	·6 12.	0 24	3.	0	7½	11.	0 27½
4.	230	40	⅓4.	0	13⅓		3.	0 6	13.	0 26	4.	0	10	12.	0 30
5.	288	0	5.	0	16⅔	·2	4.	0 8	·7 14.	0 28	5.	0	12½	13.	0 32½
6.	345	60	⅓6.	0	20		5.	0 10	15.	0 30	6.	0	15	14.	0 35
7.	403	20	7.	0	23⅓	·3	6.	0 12	·8 16.	0 32	7.	0	17½	15.	0 37½
8.	460	80	⅔8.	0	26⅔		7.	0 14	17.	0 34	8.	0	20		
9.	518	40	9.	0	30	·4	8.	0 16	·9 18.	0 36					
10.	576	0	⅓10.	0	33⅓		9.	0 18	19.	0 38					
11.	633	60	11.	0	36⅔	·5	10.	0 20	20.	0 40					

	£	P		£	P		£	P		£	P		£	P
1	0	41	51	20	91	101	41	41	152	62	32	310	127	10
2	0	82	52	21	32	102	41	82	154	63	14	320	131	20
3	1	23	53	21	73	103	42	23	[13] 156	63	96	330	135	30
4	1	64	54	22	14	104	42	64	158	64	78	340	139	40
5	2	5	55	22	55	105	43	5	160	65	60	350	143	50
6	2	46	56	22	96	106	43	46	162	66	42	360	147	60
7	2	87	57	23	37	107	43	87	164	67	24	365	149	65
8	3	28	58	23	78	[9] 108	44	28	166	68	6	370	151	70
9	3	69	59	24	19	109	44	69	[14] 168	68	88	380	155	80
10	4	10	[5] **60**	24	60	**110**	45	10	170	69	70	390	159	90
11	4	51	61	25	1	111	45	51	172	70	52	400	164	0
[1] 12	4	92	62	25	42	112	45	92	174	71	34	410	168	10
13	5	33	63	25	83	113	46	33	175	71	75	420	172	20
14	5	74	64	26	24	114	46	74	176	72	16	430	176	30
15	6	15	65	26	65	115	47	15	178	72	98	440	180	40
16	6	56	66	27	6	116	47	56	[15] 180	73	80	450	184	50
17	6	97	67	27	47	117	47	97	182	74	62	460	188	60
18	7	38	68	27	88	118	48	38	184	75	44	470	192	70
19	7	79	69	28	29	119	48	79	186	76	26	480	196	80
20	8	20	**70**	28	70	**120**	49	20	188	77	8	490	200	90
21	8	61	71	29	11	121	49	61	190	77	90	**500**	205	0
22	9	2	[6] 72	29	52	122	50	2	[16] 192	78	72	550	225	50
23	9	43	73	29	93	123	50	43	194	79	54	600	246	0
[2] 24	9	84	74	30	34	124	50	84	196	80	36	650	266	50
25	10	25	75	30	75	125	51	25	198	81	18	700	287	0
26	10	66	76	31	16	126	51	66	**200**	82	0	750	307	50
27	11	7	77	31	57	127	52	7	[17] 204	83	64	800	328	0
28	11	48	78	31	98	128	52	48	205	84	5	850	348	50
29	11	89	79	32	39	129	52	89	210	86	10	900	369	0
30	12	30	**80**	32	80	**130**	53	30	215	88	15	950	389	50
31	12	71	81	33	21	131	53	71	[18] 216	88	56	**1000**	410	0
32	13	12	82	33	62	[11] 132	54	12	220	90	20	1016	416	56
33	13	53	83	34	3	133	54	53	225	92	25	1250	512	50
34	13	94	[7] 84	34	44	134	54	94	[19] 228	93	48	1500	615	0
35	14	35	85	34	85	135	55	35	230	94	30	1728	708	48
[3] 36	14	76	86	35	26	136	55	76	235	96	35	1750	717	50
37	15	17	87	35	67	137	56	17	[20] 240	98	40	1760	721	60
38	15	58	88	36	8	138	56	58	245	100	45	2000	820	0
39	15	99	89	36	49	139	56	99	**250**	102	50	2240	918	40
40	16	40	**90**	36	90	**140**	57	40	255	104	55	2500	1025	0
41	16	81	91	37	31	141	57	81	260	106	60	3000	1230	0
42	17	22	92	37	72	142	58	22	265	108	65	4000	1640	0
43	17	63	93	38	13	143	58	63	270	110	70	**5000**	2050	0
44	18	4	94	38	54	[12] 144	59	4	275	112	75	6000	2460	0
45	18	45	95	38	95	145	59	45	280	114	80	7000	2870	0
46	18	86	[8] 96	39	36	146	59	86	285	116	85	8000	3280	0
47	19	27	97	39	77	147	60	27	[24] 288	118	8	9000	3690	0
[4] 48	19	68	98	40	18	148	60	68	290	118	90	10,000	4100	0
49	20	9	99	40	59	149	61	9	295	120	95	15,000	6150	0
50	20	50	**100**	41	0	**150**	61	50	**300**	123	0	20,000	8200	0

Grosses.

1.	59	4
2.	118	8
3.	177	12
4.	236	16
5.	295	20
6.	354	24
7.	413	28
8.	472	32
9.	531	36
10.	590	40
11.	649	44

Twelfths

	1.	0	3½
⅙	2.	0	6¾
	3.	0	10¼
⅓	4.	0	13¾
	5.	0	17
½	6.	0	20½
	7.	0	24
⅔	8.	0	27¼
	9.	0	30¾
⅚	10.	0	34¼
	11.	0	37½

Twentieths (10ths)

	1.	0	2		11.	0	22½
·1	2.	0	4	·6	12.	0	24½
	3.	0	6¼		13.	0	26¾
·2	4.	0	8¼	·7	14.	0	28¾
	5.	0	10¼		15.	0	30¾
·3	6.	0	12¼	·8	16.	0	32¾
	7.	0	14¼		17.	0	34¾
·4	8.	0	16½	·9	18.	0	37
	9.	0	18½		19.	0	39
·5	10.	0	20½		20.	0	41

Sixteenths

	1.	0	2½		9.	0	23
⅛	2.	0	5¼	⅝	10.	0	25¾
	3.	0	7¾		11.	0	28¼
¼	4.	0	10¼	¾	12.	0	30¾
	5.	0	12¾		13.	0	33¼
⅜	6.	0	15½	⅞	14.	0	36
	7.	0	18		15.	0	38½
½	8.	0	20½				

Dozens	£	p	Dozens	£	p	Dozens	£	p	Dozens	£	p		£	p
1	0	42	51	21	42	101	42	42	152	63	84	310	130	20
2	0	84	52	21	84	102	42	84	154	64	68	320	134	40
3	1	26	53	22	26	103	43	26	[13] 156	65	52	330	138	60
4	1	68	54	22	68	104	43	68	158	66	36	340	142	80
5	2	10	55	23	10	105	44	10	160	67	20	350	147	0
6	2	52	56	23	52	106	44	52	162	68	4	360	151	20
7	2	94	57	23	94	107	44	94	164	68	88	365	153	30
8	3	36	58	24	36	[9] 108	45	36	166	69	72	370	155	40
9	3	78	59	24	78	109	45	78	[14] 168	70	56	380	159	60
10	4	20	[5] **60**	25	20	**110**	46	20	170	71	40	390	163	80
*11	4	62	61	25	62	111	46	62	172	72	24	400	168	0
[1] 12	5	4	62	26	4	112	47	4	174	73	8	410	172	20
13	5	46	63	26	46	113	47	46	175	73	50	420	176	40
14	5	88	64	26	88	114	47	88	176	73	92	430	180	60
15	6	30	65	27	30	115	48	30	178	74	76	440	184	80
16	6	72	66	27	72	116	48	72	[15] 180	75	60	450	189	0
17	7	14	67	28	14	117	49	14	182	76	44	460	193	20
18	7	56	68	28	56	118	49	56	184	77	28	470	197	40
19	7	98	69	28	98	119	49	98	186	78	12	480	201	60
20	8	40	**70**	29	40	[10] **120**	50	40	188	78	96	490	205	80
21	8	82	71	29	82	121	50	82	190	79	80	**500**	210	0
22	9	24	[6] 72	30	24	122	51	24	[16] 192	80	64	550	231	0
23	9	66	73	30	66	123	51	66	194	81	48	600	252	0
[2] 24	10	8	74	31	8	124	52	8	196	82	32	650	273	0
25	10	50	75	31	50	125	52	50	198	83	16	700	294	0
26	10	92	76	31	92	126	52	92	**200**	84	0	750	315	0
27	11	34	77	32	34	127	53	34	[17] 204	85	68	800	336	0
28	11	76	78	32	76	128	53	76	205	86	10	850	357	0
29	12	18	79	33	18	129	54	18	210	88	20	900	378	0
30	12	60	**80**	33	60	**130**	54	60	215	90	30	950	399	0
31	13	2	81	34	2	131	55	2	[18] 216	90	72	**1000**	420	0
32	13	44	82	34	44	[11] 132	55	44	220	92	40	1016	426	72
33	13	86	83	34	86	133	55	86	225	94	50	1250	525	0
34	14	28	[7] 84	35	28	134	56	28	[19] 228	95	76	1500	630	0
35	14	70	85	35	70	135	56	70	230	96	60	1728	725	76
[3] 36	15	12	86	36	12	136	57	12	235	98	70	1750	735	0
37	15	54	87	36	54	137	57	54	[20] 240	100	80	1760	739	20
38	15	96	88	36	96	138	57	96	245	102	90	2000	840	0
39	16	38	89	37	38	139	58	38	**250**	105	0	2240	940	80
40	16	80	**90**	37	80	**140**	58	80	255	107	10	2500	1050	0
41	17	22	91	38	22	141	59	22	260	109	20	3000	1260	0
42	17	64	92	38	64	142	59	64	265	111	30	4000	1680	0
43	18	6	93	39	6	143	60	6	270	113	40	**5000**	2100	0
44	18	48	94	39	48	[12] 144	60	48	275	115	50	6000	2520	0
45	18	90	95	39	90	145	60	90	280	117	60	7000	2940	0
46	19	32	[8] 96	40	32	146	61	32	285	119	70	8000	3360	0
47	19	74	97	40	74	147	61	74	[24] 288	120	96	9000	3780	0
[4] 48	20	16	98	41	16	148	62	16	290	121	80	10,000	4200	0
49	20	58	99	41	58	149	62	58	295	123	90	15,000	6300	0
50	21	0	**100**	42	0	**150**	63	0	**300**	126	0	20,000	8400	0

Grosses

1.	60	48
2.	120	96
3.	181	44
4.	241	92
5.	302	40
6.	362	88
7.	423	36
8.	483	84
9.	544	32
10.	604	80
11.	665	28

Twelfths

	1.	0	3½
⅙	2.	0	7
	3.	0	10½
⅓	4.	0	14
	5.	0	17½
½	6.	0	21
	7.	0	24½
⅔	8.	0	28
	9.	0	31½
⅚	10.	0	35
	11.	0	38½

Twentieths

10ths				10ths			
	1.	0	2		11.	0	23
·1	2.	0	4¼	·6	12.	0	25¼
	3.	0	6¼		13.	0	27¼
·2	4.	0	8½	·7	14.	0	29½
	5.	0	10½		15.	0	31½
·3	6.	0	12½	·8	16.	0	33½
	7.	0	14¾		17.	0	35¾
·4	8.	0	16¾	·9	18.	0	37¾
	9.	0	19		19.	0	40
·5	10.	0	21		20.	0	42

Sixteenths

	1.	0	2¾		9.	0	23¾
⅛	2.	0	5¼	⅝	10.	0	26¼
	3.	0	8		11.	0	29
¼	4.	0	10½	¾	12.	0	31½
	5.	0	13¼		13.	0	34¼
⅜	6.	0	15¾	⅞	14.	0	36¾
	7.	0	18½		15.	0	39½
½	8.	0	21				

*Dozens.

	£	P		£	P		£	P		£	P		£	P
1	0	42½	51	21	67½	101	42	92½	152	64	60	310	131	75
2	0	85	52	22	10	102	43	35	154	65	45	320	136	0
3	1	27½	53	22	52½	103	43	77½	[13] 156	66	30	330	140	25
4	1	70	54	22	95	104	44	20	158	67	15	340	144	50
5	2	12½	55	23	37½	105	44	62½	160	68	0	350	148	75
6	2	55	56	23	80	106	45	5	162	68	85	360	153	0
7	2	97½	57	24	22½	107	45	47½	164	69	70	365	155	12½
8	3	40	58	24	65	[9] 108	45	90	166	70	55	370	157	25
9	3	82½	59	25	7½	109	46	32½	[14] 168	71	40	380	161	50
10	4	25	[5] **60**	25	50	**110**	46	75	170	72	25	390	165	75
*11	4	67½	61	25	92½	111	47	17½	172	73	10	400	170	0
[1] 12	5	10	62	26	35	112	47	60	174	73	95	410	174	25
13	5	52½	63	26	77½	113	48	2½	175	74	37½	420	178	50
14	5	95	64	27	20	114	48	45	176	74	80	430	182	75
15	6	37½	65	27	62½	115	48	87½	178	75	65	440	187	0
16	6	80	66	28	5	116	49	30	[15] 180	76	50	450	191	25
17	7	22½	67	28	47½	117	49	72½	182	77	35	460	195	50
18	7	65	68	28	90	118	50	15	184	78	20	470	199	75
19	8	7½	69	29	32½	119	50	57½	186	79	5	480	204	0
20	8	50	**70**	29	75	**120**	51	0	188	79	90	490	208	25
21	8	92½	71	30	17½	121	51	42½	190	80	75	**500**	212	50
22	9	35	[6] 72	30	60	122	51	85	[16] 192	81	60	550	233	75
23	9	77½	73	31	2½	123	52	27½	194	82	45	600	255	0
[2] 24	10	20	74	31	45	124	52	70	196	83	30	650	276	25
25	10	62½	75	31	87½	125	53	12½	198	84	15	700	297	50
26	11	5	76	32	30	126	53	55	**200**	85	0	750	318	75
27	11	47½	77	32	72½	127	53	97½	[17] 204	86	70	800	340	0
28	11	90	78	33	15	128	54	40	205	87	12½	850	361	25
29	12	32½	79	33	57½	129	54	82½	210	89	25	900	382	50
30	12	75	**80**	34	0	**130**	55	25	215	91	37½	950	403	75
31	13	17½	81	34	42½	131	55	67½	[18] 216	91	80	**1000**	425	0
32	13	60	82	34	85	[11] 132	56	10	220	93	50	1016	431	80
33	14	2½	83	35	27½	133	56	52½	225	95	62½	1250	531	25
34	14	45	[7] 84	35	70	134	56	95	[19] 228	96	90	1500	637	50
35	14	87½	85	36	12½	135	57	37½	230	97	75	1728	734	40
[3] 36	15	30	86	36	55	136	57	80	235	99	87½	1750	743	75
37	15	72½	87	36	97½	137	58	22½	[20] 240	102	0	1760	748	0
38	16	15	88	37	40	138	58	65	245	104	12½	2000	850	0
39	16	57½	89	37	82½	139	59	7½	**250**	106	25	2240	952	0
40	17	0	**90**	38	25	**140**	59	50	255	108	37½	2500	1062	50
41	17	42½	91	38	67½	141	59	92½	260	110	50	3000	1275	0
42	17	85	92	39	10	142	60	35	265	112	62½	4000	1700	0
43	18	27½	93	39	52½	143	60	77½	270	114	75	5000	2125	0
44	18	70	94	39	95	[12] 144	61	20	275	116	87½	6000	2550	0
45	19	12½	95	40	37½	145	61	62½	280	119	0	7000	2975	0
46	19	55	[8] 96	40	80	146	62	5	285	121	12½	8000	3400	0
47	19	97½	97	41	22½	147	62	47½	[24] 288	122	40	9000	3825	0
[4] 48	20	40	98	41	65	148	62	90	290	123	25	10000	4250	0
49	20	82½	99	42	7½	149	63	32½	295	125	37½	15000	6375	0
50	21	25	**100**	42	50	**150**	63	75	**300**	127	50	20000	8500	0

Grosses.

1.	61	20
2.	122	40
3.	183	60
4.	244	80
5.	306	0
6.	367	20
7.	428	40
8.	489	60
9.	550	80
10.	612	00
11.	673	20

Twelfths

	1.	0	3½
⅙	2.	0	7
	3.	0	10¾
⅓	4.	0	14¼
	5.	0	17¾
½	6.	0	21¼
	7.	0	24¾
⅔	8.	0	28¼
	9.	0	32
⅚	10.	0	35½
	11.	0	39

Twentieths

10ths				10ths			
	1.	0	2¼		11.	0	23½
·1	2.	0	4¼	·6	12.	0	25½
	3.	0	6½		13.	0	27¾
·2	4.	0	8½	·7	14.	0	29¾
	5.	0	10¾		15.	0	32
·3	6.	0	12¾	·8	16.	0	34
	7.	0	15		17.	0	36¼
·4	8.	0	17	·9	18.	0	38¼
	9.	0	19¼		19.	0	40½
·5	10.	0	21¼		20.	0	42½

Sixteenths

	1.	0	2¾		9.	0	24
⅛	2.	0	5¼	⅝	10.	0	26½
	3.	0	8		11.	0	29¼
¼	4.	0	10¾	¾	12.	0	32
	5.	0	13¼		13.	0	34½
⅜	6.	0	16	⅞	14.	0	37¼
	7.	0	18½		15.	0	39¾
½	8.	0	21¼				

*Dozens		£	P	Dozens		£	P	Dozens		£	P	Dozens		£	P		£	P
	1	0	43		51	21	93		101	43	43		152	65	36	310	133	30
	2	0	86		52	22	36		102	43	86		154	66	22	320	137	60
	3	1	29		53	22	79		103	44	29	13	156	67	8	330	141	90
	4	1	72		54	23	22		104	44	72		158	67	94	340	146	20
	5	2	15		55	23	65		105	45	15		160	68	80	350	150	50
	6	2	58		56	24	8		106	45	58		162	69	66	360	154	80
	7	3	1		57	24	51		107	46	1		164	70	52	365	156	95
	8	3	44		58	24	94	9	108	46	44		166	71	38	370	159	10
	9	3	87		59	25	37		109	46	87	14	168	72	24	380	163	40
	10	4	30	5	**60**	25	80		**110**	47	30		170	73	10	390	167	70
	11	4	73		61	26	23		111	47	73		172	73	96	400	172	0
1	12	5	16		62	26	66		112	48	16		174	74	82	410	176	30
	13	5	59		63	27	9		113	48	59		175	75	25	420	180	60
	14	6	2		64	27	52		114	49	2		176	75	68	430	184	90
	15	6	45		65	27	95		115	49	45		178	76	54	440	189	20
	16	6	88		66	28	38		116	49	88	15	180	77	40	450	193	50
	17	7	31		67	28	81		117	50	31		182	78	26	460	197	80
	18	7	74		68	29	24		118	50	74		184	79	12	470	202	10
	19	8	17		69	29	67		119	51	17		186	79	98	480	206	40
	20	8	60		**70**	30	10		**120**	51	60		188	80	84	490	210	70
	21	9	3		71	30	53		121	52	3		190	81	70	500	215	0
	22	9	46	6	72	30	96		122	52	46	16	192	82	56	550	236	50
	23	9	89		73	31	39		123	52	89		194	83	42	600	258	0
2	24	10	32		74	31	82		124	53	32		196	84	28	650	279	50
	25	10	75		75	32	25		125	53	75		198	85	14	700	301	0
	26	11	18		76	32	68		126	54	18		**200**	86	0	750	322	50
	27	11	61		77	33	11		127	54	61	17	204	87	72	800	344	0
	28	12	4		78	33	54		128	55	4		205	88	15	850	365	50
	29	12	47		79	33	97		129	55	47		210	90	30	900	387	0
	30	12	90		**80**	34	40		**130**	55	90		215	92	45	950	408	50
	31	13	33		81	34	83		131	56	33	18	216	92	88	1000	430	0
	32	13	76		82	35	26	11	132	56	76		220	94	60	1016	436	88
	33	14	19		83	35	69		133	57	19		225	96	75	1250	537	50
	34	14	62	7	84	36	12		134	57	62	19	228	98	4	1500	645	0
	35	15	5		85	36	55		135	58	5		230	98	90	1728	743	4
3	36	15	48		86	36	98		136	58	48		235	101	5	1750	752	50
	37	15	91		87	37	41		137	58	91	20	240	103	20	1760	756	80
	38	16	34		88	37	84		138	59	34		245	105	35	2000	860	0
	39	16	77		89	38	27		139	59	77		**250**	107	50	2240	963	20
	40	17	20		**90**	38	70		**140**	60	20		255	109	65	2500	1075	0
	41	17	63		91	39	13		141	60	63		260	111	80	3000	1290	0
	42	18	6		92	39	56		142	61	6		265	113	95	4000	1720	0
	43	18	49		93	39	99		143	61	49		270	116	10	5000	2150	0
	44	18	92		94	40	42	12	144	61	92		275	118	25	6000	2580	0
	45	19	35		95	40	85		145	62	35		280	120	40	7000	3010	0
	46	19	78	8	96	41	28		146	62	78		285	122	55	8000	3440	0
	47	20	21		97	41	71		147	63	21	24	288	123	84	9000	3870	0
4	48	20	64		98	42	14		148	63	64		290	124	70	10,000	4300	0
	49	21	7		99	42	57		149	64	7		295	126	85	15,000	6450	0
	50	21	50		**100**	43	0		**150**	64	50		**300**	129	0	20,000	8600	0

Grosses

1.	61	92
2.	123	84
3.	185	76
4.	247	68
5.	309	60
6.	371	52
7.	433	44
8.	495	36
9.	557	28
10.	619	20
11.	681	12

Twelfths

	1.	0	3½
⅙	2.	0	7¼
	3.	0	10¾
⅓	4.	0	14¼
	5.	0	18
½	6.	0	21½
	7.	0	25
⅔	8.	0	28¾
	9.	0	32¼
⅚	10.	0	35¾
	11.	0	39½

Twentieths

10ths				10ths			
	1.	0	2¼		11.	0	23¾
·1	2.	0	4¼	·6	12.	0	25¾
	3.	0	6½		13.	0	28
·2	4.	0	8½	·7	14.	0	30
	5.	0	10¾		15.	0	32¼
·3	6.	0	13	·8	16.	0	34½
	7.	0	15		17.	0	36½
·4	8.	0	17¼	·9	18.	0	38¾
	9.	0	19¼		19.	0	40¾
·5	10.	0	21½		20.	0	43

Sixteenths

	1.	0	2¾		9.	0	24¼
⅛	2.	0	5½	⅝	10.	0	27
	3.	0	8		11.	0	29½
¼	4.	0	10¾	¾	12.	0	32¼
	5.	0	13½		13.	0	35
⅜	6.	0	16¼	⅞	14.	0	37¾
	7.	0	18¾		15.	0	40¼
½	8.	0	21½				

*Dozens		£	P
	1	0	44
	2	0	88
	3	1	32
	4	1	76
	5	2	20
	6	2	64
	7	3	8
	8	3	52
	9	3	96
	10	4	40
*	11	4	84
1	12	5	28
	13	5	72
	14	6	16
	15	6	60
	16	7	4
	17	7	48
	18	7	92
	19	8	36
	20	8	80
	21	9	24
	22	9	68
	23	10	12
2	24	10	56
	25	11	0
	26	11	44
	27	11	88
	28	12	32
	29	12	76
	30	13	20
	31	13	64
	32	14	8
	33	14	52
	34	14	96
	35	15	40
3	36	15	84
	37	16	28
	38	16	72
	39	17	16
	40	17	60
	41	18	4
	42	18	48
	43	18	92
	44	19	36
	45	19	80
	46	20	24
	47	20	68
4	48	21	12
	49	21	56
	50	22	0

Dozens		£	P
	51	22	44
	52	22	88
	53	23	32
	54	23	76
	55	24	20
	56	24	64
	57	25	8
	58	25	52
	59	25	96
5	**60**	26	40
	61	26	84
	62	27	28
	63	27	72
	64	28	16
	65	28	60
	66	29	4
	67	29	48
	68	29	92
	69	30	36
	70	30	80
	71	31	24
6	72	31	68
	73	32	12
	74	32	56
	75	33	0
	76	33	44
	77	33	88
	78	34	32
	79	34	76
	80	35	20
	81	35	64
	82	36	8
	83	36	52
7	84	36	96
	85	37	40
	86	37	84
	87	38	28
	88	38	72
	89	39	16
	90	39	60
	91	40	4
	92	40	48
	93	40	92
	94	41	36
	95	41	80
8	96	42	24
	97	42	68
	98	43	12
	99	43	56
	100	44	0

Dozens		£	P
	101	44	44
	102	44	88
	103	45	32
	104	45	76
	105	46	20
	106	46	64
	107	47	8
9	108	47	52
	109	47	96
	110	48	40
	111	48	84
	112	49	28
	113	49	72
	114	50	16
	115	50	60
	116	51	4
	117	51	48
	118	51	92
	119	52	36
	120	52	80
	121	53	24
	122	53	68
	123	54	12
	124	54	56
	125	55	0
	126	55	44
	127	55	88
	128	56	32
	129	56	76
	130	57	20
	131	57	64
11	132	58	8
	133	58	52
	134	58	96
	135	59	40
	136	59	84
	137	60	28
	138	60	72
	139	61	16
	140	61	60
	141	62	4
	142	62	48
	143	62	92
12	144	63	36
	145	63	80
	146	64	24
	147	64	68
	148	65	12
	149	65	56
	150	66	0

Dozens		£	P
	152	66	88
	154	67	76
13	156	68	64
	158	69	52
	160	70	40
	162	71	28
	164	72	16
	166	73	4
14	168	73	92
	170	74	80
	172	75	68
	174	76	56
	175	77	0
	176	77	44
	178	78	32
15	180	79	20
	182	80	8
	184	80	96
	186	81	84
	188	82	72
	190	83	60
16	192	84	48
	194	85	36
	196	86	24
	198	87	12
	200	88	0
17	204	89	76
	205	90	20
	210	92	40
	215	94	60
18	216	95	4
	220	96	80
	225	99	0
19	228	100	32
	230	101	20
	235	103	40
20	240	105	60
	245	107	80
	250	110	0
	255	112	20
	260	114	40
	265	116	60
	270	118	80
	275	121	0
	280	123	20
	285	125	40
24	288	126	72
	290	127	60
	295	129	80
	300	132	0

	£	P
310	136	40
320	140	80
330	145	20
340	149	60
350	154	0
360	158	40
365	160	60
370	162	80
380	167	20
390	171	60
400	176	0
410	180	40
420	184	80
430	189	20
440	193	60
450	198	0
460	202	40
470	206	80
480	211	20
490	215	60
500	220	0
550	242	0
600	264	0
650	286	0
700	308	0
750	330	0
800	352	0
850	374	0
900	396	0
950	418	0
1000	440	0
1016	447	4
1250	550	0
1500	660	0
1728	760	32
1750	770	0
1760	774	40
2000	880	0
2240	985	60
2500	1100	0
3000	1320	0
4000	1760	0
5000	2200	0
6000	2640	0
7000	3080	0
8000	3520	0
9000	3960	0
10,000	4400	0
15,000	6600	0
20,000	8800	0

Grosses

1.	63	36
2.	126	72
3.	190	8
4.	253	44
5.	316	80
6.	380	16
7.	443	52
8.	506	88
9.	570	24
10.	633	60
11.	696	96

Twelfths

	1.	0	3¾
⅙	2.	0	7¼
	3.	0	11
⅓	4.	0	14¾
	5.	0	18¼
½	6.	0	22
	7.	0	25¾
⅔	8.	0	29¼
	9.	0	33
⅚	10.	0	36¾
	11.	0	40¼

Twentieths

10ths			
	1.	0	2¼
·1	2.	0	4½
	3.	0	6½
·2	4.	0	8¾
	5.	0	11
·3	6.	0	13¼
	7.	0	15½
·4	8.	0	17½
	9.	0	19¾
·5	10.	0	22
	11.	0	24¼
·6	12.	0	26½
	13.	0	28½
·7	14.	0	30¾
	15.	0	33
·8	16.	0	35¼
	17.	0	37½
·9	18.	0	39½
	19.	0	41¾
	20.	0	44

Sixteenths

	1.	0	2¾
⅛	2.	0	5½
	3.	0	8¼
¼	4.	0	11
	5.	0	13¾
⅜	6.	0	16½
	7.	0	19¼
½	8.	0	22
	9.	0	24¾
⅝	10.	0	27½
	11.	0	30¼
¾	12.	0	33
	13.	0	35¾
⅞	14.	0	38½
	15.	0	41¼

Qty	£ P	Qty	£ P	Qty	£ P	Qty	£ P	Qty	£ P
1	0 45	51	22 95	101	45 45	152	68 40	310	139 50
2	0 90	52	23 40	102	45 90	154	69 30	320	144 0
3	1 35	53	23 85	103	46 35	[13] 156	70 20	330	148 50
4	1 80	54	24 30	104	46 80	158	71 10	340	153 0
5	2 25	55	24 75	105	47 25	160	72 0	350	157 50
6	2 70	56	25 20	106	47 70	162	72 90	360	162 0
7	3 15	57	25 65	107	48 15	164	73 80	365	164 25
8	3 60	58	26 10	[9] 108	48 60	166	74 70	370	166 50
9	4 5	59	26 55	109	49 5	[14] 168	75 60	380	171 0
10	4 50	[5] 60	27 0	110	49 50	170	76 50	390	175 50
11	4 95	61	27 45	111	49 95	172	77 40	400	180 0
[1] 12	5 40	62	27 90	112	50 40	174	78 30	410	184 50
13	5 85	63	28 35	113	50 85	175	78 75	420	189 0
14	6 30	64	28 80	114	51 30	176	79 20	430	193 50
15	6 75	65	29 25	115	51 75	178	80 10	440	198 0
16	7 20	66	29 70	116	52 20	[15] 180	81 0	450	202 50
17	7 65	67	30 15	117	52 65	182	81 90	460	207 0
18	8 10	68	30 60	118	53 10	184	82 80	470	211 50
19	8 55	69	31 5	119	53 55	186	83 70	480	216 0
20	9 0	70	31 50	120	54 0	188	84 60	490	220 50
21	9 45	71	31 95	121	54 45	190	85 50	500	225 0
22	9 90	[6] 72	32 40	122	54 90	[16] 192	86 40	550	247 50
23	10 35	73	32 85	123	55 35	194	87 30	600	270 0
[2] 24	10 80	74	33 30	124	55 80	196	88 20	650	292 50
25	11 25	75	33 75	125	56 25	198	89 10	700	315 0
26	11 70	76	34 20	126	56 70	200	90 0	750	337 50
27	12 15	77	34 65	127	57 15	[17] 204	91 80	800	360 0
28	12 60	78	35 10	128	57 60	205	92 25	850	382 50
29	13 5	79	35 55	129	58 5	210	94 50	900	405 0
30	13 50	80	36 0	130	58 50	215	96 75	950	427 50
31	13 95	81	36 45	131	58 95	[18] 216	97 20	1000	450 0
32	14 40	82	36 90	132	59 40	220	99 0	1016	457 20
33	14 85	83	37 35	133	59 85	225	101 25	1250	562 50
34	15 30	[7] 84	37 80	134	60 30	[19] 228	102 60	1500	675 0
35	15 75	85	38 25	135	60 75	230	103 50	1728	777 60
36	16 20	86	38 70	136	61 20	235	105 75	1750	787 50
37	16 65	87	39 15	137	61 65	[20] 240	108 0	1760	792 0
38	17 10	88	39 60	138	62 10	245	110 25	2000	900 0
39	17 55	89	40 5	139	62 55	250	112 50	2240	1008 0
40	18 0	90	40 50	140	63 0	255	114 75	2500	1125 0
41	18 45	91	40 95	141	63 45	260	117 0	3000	1350 0
42	18 90	92	41 40	142	63 90	265	119 25	4000	1800 0
43	19 35	93	41 85	143	64 35	270	121 50	5000	2250 0
44	19 80	94	42 30	[12] 144	64 80	275	123 75	6000	2700 0
45	20 25	95	42 75	145	65 25	280	126 0	7000	3150 0
46	20 70	[8] 96	43 20	146	65 70	285	128 25	8000	3600 0
47	21 15	97	43 65	147	66 15	[24] 288	129 60	9000	4050 0
48	21 60	98	44 10	148	66 60	290	130 50	10,000	4500 0
49	22 5	99	44 55	149	67 5	295	132 75	15,000	6750 0
50	22 50	100	45 0	150	67 50	300	135 0	20,000	9000 0

Grosses		Twelfths		10ths	Twentieths		Sixteenths	
1.	64 80	1. 0 3¾		1. 0 2¼	11. 0 24¾		1. 0 2¼	9. 0 25¼
2.	129 60	⅛ 2. 0 7½		·2. 0 4½	·6 12. 0 27		½ 2. 0 5½	§10. 0 28¼
3.	194 40	¼ 3. 0 11¼		3. 0 6¾	13. 0 29¼		3. 0 8	11. 0 31
4.	259 20	⅓ 4. 0 15		·2 4. 0 9	·7 14. 0 31½		¼ 4. 0 11¼	¾12. 0 33¾
5.	324 0	5. 0 18¾		5. 0 11¼	15. 0 33¾		5. 0 14	13. 0 36¼
6.	388 80	½ 6. 0 22½		·3 6. 0 13½	·8 16. 0 36		½ 6. 0 17	¼14. 0 39½
7.	453 60	7. 0 26¼		7. 0 15¾	17. 0 38¼		7. 0 19¼	¾14. 0 39¼
8.	518 40	⅔ 8. 0 30		·4 8. 0 18	·9 18. 0 40½		8. 0 22¼	15. 0 42¼
9.	583 20	9. 0 33¾		9. 0 20¼	19. 0 42¾			
10.	648 0	⅚10. 0 37½		·5 10. 0 22½	20. 0 45			
11.	712 80	11. 0 41¼						

No.	£	P	No.	£	P	No.	£	P
1	0	46	51	23	46	101	46	46
2	0	92	52	23	92	102	46	92
3	1	38	53	24	38	103	47	38
4	1	84	54	24	84	104	47	84
5	2	30	55	25	30	105	48	30
*6	2	76	56	25	76	106	48	76
7	3	22	57	26	22	107	49	22
8	3	68	58	26	68	108	49	68
9	4	14	59	27	14	109	50	14
10	4	60	60	27	60	110	50	60
11	5	6	61	28	6	111	51	6
12	5	52	62	28	52	112	51	52
13	5	98	63	28	98	113	51	98
14	6	44	64	29	44	114	52	44
15	6	90	65	29	90	115	52	90
16	7	36	66	30	36	116	53	36
17	7	82	67	30	82	117	53	82
18	8	28	68	31	28	118	54	28
19	8	74	69	31	74	119	54	74
20	9	20	70	32	20	120	55	20
21	9	66	71	32	66	121	55	66
22	10	12	72	33	12	122	56	12
23	10	58	73	33	58	123	56	58
24	11	4	74	34	4	124	57	4
25	11	50	75	34	50	125	57	50
26	11	96	76	34	96	126	57	96
27	12	42	77	35	42	127	58	42
28	12	88	78	35	88	128	58	88
29	13	34	79	36	34	129	59	34
30	13	80	80	36	80	130	59	80
31	14	26	81	37	26	131	60	26
32	14	72	82	37	72	132	60	72
33	15	18	83	38	18	133	61	18
34	15	64	84	38	64	134	61	64
35	16	10	85	39	10	135	62	10
36	16	56	86	39	56	136	62	56
37	17	2	87	40	2	137	63	2
38	17	48	88	40	48	138	63	48
39	17	94	89	40	94	139	63	94
40	18	40	90	41	40	140	64	40
41	18	86	91	41	86	141	64	86
42	19	32	92	42	32	142	65	32
43	19	78	93	42	78	143	65	78
44	20	24	94	43	24	144	66	24
45	20	70	95	43	70	145	66	70
46	21	16	96	44	16	146	67	16
47	21	62	97	44	62	147	67	62
48	22	8	98	45	8	148	68	8
49	22	54	99	45	54	149	68	54
50	23	0	100	46	0	150	69	0

No.	£	P	No.	£	P
152	69	92	310	142	60
154	70	84	320	147	20
156	71	76	330	151	80
158	72	68	340	156	40
160	73	60	350	161	0
162	74	52	360	165	60
164	75	44	365	167	90
166	76	36	370	170	20
168	77	28	380	174	80
170	78	20	390	179	40
172	79	12	400	184	0
174	80	4	410	188	60
175	80	50	420	193	20
176	80	96	430	197	80
178	81	88	440	202	40
180	82	80	450	207	0
182	83	72	460	211	60
184	84	64	470	216	20
186	85	56	480	220	80
188	86	48	490	225	40
190	87	40	500	230	0
192	88	32	550	253	0
194	89	24	600	276	0
196	90	16	650	299	0
198	91	8	700	322	0
200	92	0	750	345	0
204	93	84	800	368	0
205	94	30	850	391	0
210	96	60	900	414	0
215	98	90	950	437	0
216	99	36	1000	460	0
220	101	20	1016	467	36
225	103	50	1250	575	0
228	104	88	1500	690	0
230	105	80	1728	794	88
235	108	10	1750	805	0
240	110	40	1760	809	60
245	112	70	2000	920	0
250	115	0	2240	1030	40
255	117	30	2500	1150	0
260	119	60	3000	1380	0
265	121	90	4000	1840	0
270	124	20	5000	2300	0
275	126	50	6000	2760	0
280	128	80	7000	3220	0
288	132	48	8000	3680	0
290	133	40	9000	4140	0
295	135	70	10,000	4600	0
300	138	0	15,000	6900	0
			20,000	9200	0

Grosses			Twelfths			10ths Twentieths			Sixteenths		
1.	66	24	1.		3¾	1. 0 2¼	11. 0 25¼		1. 0 3	9. 0 26	
2.	132	48	½ 2.	0	7½	2. 0 4½	12. 0 27½		½ 2. 0 5¼	10. 0 28¾	
3.	198	72	3.	0	11¼	3. 0 7	13. 0 30		3. 0 8¾	11. 0 31½	
4.	264	96	¼ 4.	0	15¼	4. 0 9¼	14. 0 32½		¼ 4. 0 11½	12. 0 34½	
5.	331	20	5.	0	19¼	5. 0 11½	15. 0 34½		5. 0 14¼	13. 0 37½	
6.	397	44	⅙ 6.	0	23	6. 0 13¾	16. 0 36½		⅜ 6. 0 17¼	14. 0 40½	
7.	463	68	7.	0	26¾	7. 0 16	17. 0 39		7. 0 20¼	15. 0 43½	
8.	529	92	⅓ 8.	0	30¾	8. 0 18¼	18. 0 41½		½ 8. 0 23		
9.	596	16	9.	0	34½	9. 0 20¼	19. 0 43½				
10.	662	40	⅚ 10.	0	38¼	10. 0 23	20. 0 46				
11.	728	64	11.	0	42½						

47 Pence

*Dozens	£	P	Dozens	£	P	Dozens	£	P	Dozens	£	P		£	P
1	0	47	51	23	97	101	47	47	152	71	44	310	145	70
2	0	94	52	24	44	102	47	94	154	72	38	320	150	40
3	1	41	53	24	91	103	48	41	[13] 156	73	32	330	155	10
4	1	88	54	25	38	104	48	88	158	74	26	340	159	80
5	2	35	55	25	85	105	49	35	160	75	20	350	164	50
6	2	82	56	26	32	106	49	82	162	76	14	360	169	20
7	3	29	57	26	79	107	50	29	164	77	8	365	171	55
8	3	76	58	27	26	[9] 108	50	76	166	78	2	370	173	90
9	4	23	59	27	73	109	51	23	[14] 168	78	96	380	178	60
10	4	70	[5] **60**	28	20	**110**	51	70	170	79	90	390	183	30
11	5	17	61	28	67	111	52	17	172	80	84	400	188	0
[1] 12	5	64	62	29	14	112	52	64	174	81	78	410	192	70
13	6	11	63	29	61	113	53	11	175	82	25	420	197	40
14	6	58	64	30	8	114	53	58	176	82	72	430	202	10
15	7	5	65	30	55	115	54	5	178	83	66	440	206	80
16	7	52	66	31	2	116	54	52	[15] 180	84	60	450	211	50
17	7	99	67	31	49	117	54	99	182	85	54	460	216	20
18	8	46	68	31	96	118	55	46	184	86	48	470	220	90
19	8	93	69	32	43	119	55	93	186	87	42	480	225	60
20	9	40	**70**	32	90	**120**	56	40	188	88	36	490	230	30
21	9	87	71	33	37	121	56	87	190	89	30	500	235	0
22	10	34	[6] 72	33	84	122	57	34	[16] 192	90	24	550	258	50
23	10	81	73	34	31	123	57	81	194	91	18	600	282	0
[2] 24	11	28	74	34	78	124	58	28	196	92	12	650	305	50
25	11	75	75	35	25	125	58	75	198	93	6	700	329	0
26	12	22	76	35	72	126	59	22	**200**	94	0	750	352	50
27	12	69	77	36	19	127	59	69	[17] 204	95	88	800	376	0
28	13	16	78	36	66	128	60	16	205	96	35	850	399	50
29	13	63	79	37	13	129	60	63	210	98	70	900	423	0
30	14	10	**80**	37	60	**130**	61	10	215	101	5	950	446	50
31	14	57	81	38	7	131	61	57	[18] 216	101	52	1000	470	0
32	15	4	82	38	54	[11] 132	62	4	220	103	40	1016	477	52
33	15	51	83	39	1	133	62	51	225	105	75	1250	587	50
34	15	98	[7] 84	39	48	134	62	98	[19] 228	107	16	1500	705	0
35	16	45	85	39	95	135	63	45	230	108	10	1728	812	16
[3] 36	16	92	86	40	42	136	63	92	235	110	45	1750	822	50
37	17	39	87	40	89	137	64	39	[20] 240	112	80	1760	827	20
38	17	86	88	41	36	138	64	86	245	115	15	2000	940	0
39	18	33	89	41	83	139	65	33	**250**	117	50	2240	1052	80
40	18	80	**90**	42	30	**140**	65	80	255	119	85	2500	1175	0
41	19	27	91	42	77	141	66	27	260	122	20	3000	1410	0
42	19	74	92	43	24	142	66	74	265	124	55	4000	1880	0
43	20	21	93	43	71	143	67	21	270	126	90	5000	2350	0
44	20	68	94	44	18	[12] 144	67	68	275	129	25	6000	2820	0
45	21	15	95	44	65	145	68	15	280	131	60	7000	3290	0
46	21	62	[8] 96	45	12	146	68	62	285	133	95	8000	3760	0
47	22	9	97	45	59	147	69	9	[24] 288	135	36	9000	4230	0
[4] 48	22	56	98	46	6	148	69	56	290	136	30	10,000	4700	0
49	23	3	99	46	53	149	70	3	295	138	65	15,000	7050	0
50	23	50	**100**	47	0	**150**	70	50	**300**	141	0	20,000	9400	0

Grosses	£	P
1.	67	68
2.	135	36
3.	203	04
4.	270	72
5.	338	40
6.	406	08
7.	473	76
8.	541	44
9.	609	12
10.	676	80
11.	744	48

	Twelfths	£	P
	1.	0	4
⅙	2.	0	7¾
	3.	0	11¾
⅓	4.	0	15¾
	5.	0	19½
½	6.	0	23½
	7.	0	27½
⅔	8.	0	31¼
	9.	0	35¼
⅚	10.	0	39¼
	11.	0	43

10ths	Twentieths	£	P	10ths	Twentieths	£	P
	1.	0	2¼		11.	0	25¾
·1	2.	0	4¾	·6	12.	0	28¼
	3.	0	7		13.	0	30½
·2	4.	0	9½	·7	14.	0	33
	5.	0	11¾		15.	0	35¼
·3	6.	0	14	·8	16.	0	37½
	7.	0	16½		17.	0	40
·4	8.	0	18¾	·9	18.	0	42¼
	9.	0	21¼		19.	0	44¾
·5	10.	0	23½		20.	0	47

Sixteenths	£	P	Sixteenths	£	P
1.	0	3	9.	0	26½
⅛ 2.	0	6	⅝ 10.	0	29½
3.	0	8¾	11.	0	32¼
¼ 4.	0	11¾	¾ 12.	0	35¼
5.	0	14¾	13.	0	38¼
⅜ 6.	0	17¾	⅞ 14.	0	41¼
7.	0	20½	15.	0	44
½ 8.	0	23½			

No.	£	P
1	0	48
2	0	96
3	1	44
4	1	92
5	2	40
6	2	88
7	3	36
8	3	84
9	4	32
10	4	80
*11	5	28
*12	5	76
13	6	24
14	6	72
15	7	20
16	7	68
17	8	16
18	8	64
19	9	12
20	9	60
21	10	8
22	10	56
23	11	4
*24	11	52
25	12	0
26	12	48
27	12	96
28	13	44
29	13	92
30	14	40
31	14	88
32	15	36
33	15	84
34	16	32
35	16	80
*36	17	28
37	17	76
38	18	24
39	18	72
40	19	20
41	19	68
42	20	16
43	20	64
44	21	12
45	21	60
46	22	8
47	22	56
*48	23	4
49	23	52
50	24	0

No.	£	P
51	24	48
52	24	96
53	25	44
54	25	92
55	26	40
56	26	88
57	27	36
58	27	84
59	28	32
5·60	28	80
61	29	28
62	29	76
63	30	24
64	30	72
65	31	20
66	31	68
67	32	16
68	32	64
69	33	12
70	33	60
71	34	8
6·72	34	56
73	35	4
74	35	52
75	36	0
76	36	48
77	36	96
78	37	44
79	37	92
80	38	40
81	38	88
82	39	36
83	39	84
7·84	40	32
85	40	80
86	41	28
87	41	76
88	42	24
89	42	72
90	43	20
91	43	68
92	44	16
93	44	64
94	45	12
95	45	60
8·96	46	8
97	46	56
98	47	4
99	47	52
100	48	0

No.	£	P
101	48	48
102	48	96
103	49	44
104	49	92
105	50	40
106	50	88
107	51	36
9·108	51	84
109	52	32
110	52	80
111	53	28
112	53	76
113	54	24
114	54	72
115	55	20
116	55	68
117	56	16
118	56	64
119	57	12
10·120	57	60
121	58	8
122	58	56
123	59	4
124	59	52
125	60	0
126	60	48
127	60	96
128	61	44
129	61	92
130	62	40
131	62	88
11·132	63	36
133	63	84
134	64	32
135	64	80
136	65	28
137	65	76
138	66	24
139	66	72
140	67	20
141	67	68
142	68	16
143	68	64
12·144	69	12
145	69	60
146	70	8
147	70	56
148	71	4
149	71	52
150	72	0

No.	£	P
152	72	96
154	73	92
13·156	74	88
158	75	84
160	76	80
162	77	76
164	78	72
166	79	68
14·168	80	64
170	81	60
172	82	56
174	83	52
175	84	0
176	84	48
178	85	44
15·180	86	40
182	87	36
184	88	32
186	89	28
188	90	24
190	91	20
16·192	92	16
194	93	12
196	94	8
198	95	4
200	96	0
17·204	97	92
205	98	40
210	100	80
215	103	20
18·216	103	68
220	105	60
225	108	0
19·228	109	44
230	110	40
235	112	80
20·240	115	20
245	117	60
250	120	0
255	122	40
260	124	80
265	127	20
270	129	60
275	132	0
280	134	40
285	136	80
24·288	138	24
290	139	20
295	141	60
300	144	0

No.	£	P
310	148	80
320	153	60
330	158	40
340	163	20
350	168	0
360	172	80
365	175	20
370	177	60
380	182	40
390	187	20
400	192	0
410	196	80
420	201	60
430	206	40
440	211	20
450	216	0
460	220	80
470	225	60
480	230	40
490	235	20
500	240	0
550	264	0
600	288	0
650	312	0
700	336	0
750	360	0
800	384	0
850	408	0
900	432	0
950	456	0
1000	480	0
1016	487	68
1250	600	0
1500	720	0
1728	829	44
1750	840	0
1760	844	80
2000	960	0
2240	1075	20
2500	1200	0
3000	1440	0
4000	1920	0
5000	2400	0
6000	2880	0
7000	3360	0
8000	3840	0
9000	4320	0
10,000	4800	0
15,000	7200	0
20,000	9600	0

Grosses			Twelfths			Twentieths			Sixteenths		
1.	69	12	1/12 1.	0	4	1.	0	2⅖	11.	0	26⅖	1.	0	3
2.	138	24	⅙ 2.	0	8	2.	0	4⅘	12.	0	28⅘	⅛ 2.	0	6
3.	207	36	3.	0	12	3.	0	7⅕	13.	0	31⅕	3.	0	9
4.	276	48	¼ 4.	0	16	4.	0	9⅗	14.	0	33⅗	¼ 4.	0	12
5.	345	60	5.	0	20	5.	0	12	15.	0	36	5.	0	15
6.	414	72	½ 6.	0	24	6.	0	14⅖	16.	0	38⅖	⅜ 6.	0	18
7.	483	84	7.	0	28	7.	0	16⅘	17.	0	40⅘	7.	0	21
8.	552	96	⅔ 8.	0	32	8.	0	19⅕	18.	0	43⅕	½ 8.	0	24
9.	622	08	9.	0	36	9.	0	21⅗	19.	0	45⅗	9.	0	27
10.	691	20	⅚ 10.	0	40	10.	0	24	20.	0	48	⅝ 10.	0	30
11.	760	32	11.	0	44							11.	0	33
												¾ 12.	0	36
												13.	0	39
												⅞ 14.	0	42
												15.	0	45

Dozens	No.	£	p	Dozens	No.	£	p	Dozens	No.	£	p	Dozens	No.	£	p
	1	0	49		51	24	99		101	49	49		152	74	48
	2	0	98		52	25	48		102	49	98		154	75	46
	3	1	47		53	25	97		103	50	47	13	156	76	44
	4	1	96		54	26	46		104	50	96		158	77	42
	5	2	45		55	26	95		105	51	45		160	78	40
	6	2	94		56	27	44		106	51	94		162	79	38
	7	3	43		57	27	93		107	52	43		164	80	36
	8	3	92		58	28	42	9	108	52	92		166	81	34
	9	4	41		59	28	91		109	53	41	14	168	82	32
	10	4	90	5	**60**	29	40		**110**	53	90		170	83	30
	*11	5	39		61	29	89		111	54	39		172	84	28
1	12	5	88		62	30	38		112	54	88		174	85	26
	13	6	37		63	30	87		113	55	37		175	85	75
	14	6	86		64	31	36		114	55	86		176	86	24
	15	7	35		65	31	85		115	56	35		178	87	22
	16	7	84		66	32	34		116	56	84	15	180	88	20
	17	8	33		67	32	83		117	57	33		182	89	18
	18	8	82		68	33	32		118	57	82		184	90	16
	19	9	31		69	33	81		119	58	31		186	91	14
	20	9	80		**70**	34	30		**120**	58	80		188	92	12
	21	10	29		71	34	79		121	59	29		190	93	10
	22	10	78	6	72	35	28		122	59	78	16	192	94	8
	23	11	27		73	35	77		123	60	27		194	95	6
2	24	11	76		74	36	26		124	60	76		196	96	4
	25	12	25		75	36	75		125	61	25		198	97	2
	26	12	74		76	37	24		126	61	74		**200**	98	0
	27	13	23		77	37	73		127	62	23	17	204	99	96
	28	13	72		78	38	22		128	62	72		205	100	45
	29	14	21		79	38	71		129	63	21		210	102	90
	30	14	70		**80**	39	20		**130**	63	70		215	105	35
	31	15	19		81	39	69		131	64	19	18	216	105	84
	32	15	68		82	40	18	11	132	64	68		220	107	80
	33	16	17		83	40	67		133	65	17		225	110	25
	34	16	66	7	84	41	16		134	65	66	19	228	111	72
	35	17	15		85	41	65		135	66	15		230	112	70
3	36	17	64		86	42	14		136	66	64		235	115	15
	37	18	13		87	42	63		137	67	13	20	240	117	60
	38	18	62		88	43	12		138	67	62		245	120	5
	39	19	11		89	43	61		139	68	11		**250**	122	50
	40	19	60		**90**	44	10		**140**	68	60		255	124	95
	41	20	9		91	44	59		141	69	9		260	127	40
	42	20	58		92	45	8		142	69	58		265	129	85
	43	21	7		93	45	57		143	70	7		270	132	30
	44	21	56		94	46	6	12	144	70	56		275	134	75
	45	22	5		95	46	55		145	71	5		280	137	20
	46	22	54	8	96	47	4		146	71	54		285	139	65
	47	23	3		97	47	53		147	72	3	24	288	141	12
4	48	23	52		98	48	2		148	72	52		290	142	10
	49	24	1		99	48	51		149	73	1		295	144	55
	50	24	50		**100**	49	0		**150**	73	50		**300**	147	0

No.	£	p
310	151	90
320	156	80
330	161	70
340	166	60
350	171	50
360	176	40
365	178	85
370	181	30
380	186	20
390	191	10
400	196	0
410	200	90
420	205	80
430	210	70
440	215	60
450	220	50
460	225	40
470	230	30
480	235	20
490	240	10
500	245	0
550	269	50
600	294	0
650	318	50
700	343	0
750	367	50
800	392	0
850	416	50
900	441	0
950	465	50
1000	490	0
1016	497	84
1250	612	50
1500	735	0
1728	846	72
1750	857	50
1760	862	40
2000	980	0
2240	1097	60
2500	1225	0
3000	1470	0
4000	1960	0
5000	2450	0
6000	2940	0
7000	3430	0
8000	3920	0
9000	4410	0
10,000	4900	0
15,000	7350	0
20,000	9800	0

Grosses

1.	70	56
2.	141	12
3.	211	68
4.	282	24
5.	352	80
6.	423	36
7.	493	92
8.	564	48
9.	635	4
10.	705	60
11.	776	16

Twelfths

	1.	0	4
1/6	2.	0	8¼
	3.	0	12¼
1/3	4.	0	16¼
	5.	0	20½
1/2	6.	0	24½
	7.	0	28½
2/3	8.	0	32¾
	9.	0	36¾
5/6	10.	0	40¾
	11.	0	45

Twentieths

10ths				10ths			
	1.	0	2½		11.	0	27
·1	2.	0	5	·6	12.	0	29½
	3.	0	7¼		13.	0	31¾
·2	4.	0	9¾	·7	14.	0	34¼
	5.	0	12¼		15.	0	36¾
·3	6.	0	14¾	·8	16.	0	39¼
	7.	0	17¼		17.	0	41¾
·4	8.	0	19½	·9	18.	0	44
	9.	0	22		19.	0	46½
·5	10.	0	24½		20.	0	49

Sixteenths

	1.	0	3		9.	0	27½
1/8	2.	0	6¼	5/8	10.	0	30¾
	3.	0	9¼		11.	0	33¾
1/4	4.	0	12¼	3/4	12.	0	36¾
	5.	0	15¼		13.	0	39¾
3/8	6.	0	18½	7/8	14.	0	43
	7.	0	21½		15.	0	46
1/2	8.	0	24½				

	£	P		£	P		£	P		£	P		£	P
1	0	50	51	25	50	101	50	50	152	76	0	310	155	0
2	1	0	52	26	0	102	51	0	154	77	0	320	160	0
3	1	50	53	26	50	103	51	50	13 156	78	0	330	165	0
4	2	0	54	27	0	104	52	0	158	79	0	340	170	0
5	2	50	55	27	50	105	52	50	160	80	0	350	175	0
6	3	0	56	28	0	106	53	0	162	81	0	360	180	0
7	3	50	57	28	50	107	53	50	164	82	0	365	182	50
8	4	0	58	29	0	108	54	0	166	83	0	370	185	0
9	4	50	59	29	50	109	54	50	14 168	84	0	380	190	0
10	5	0	60	30	0	110	55	0	170	85	0	390	195	0
11	5	50	61	30	50	111	55	50	172	86	0	400	200	0
12	6	0	62	31	0	112	56	0	174	87	0	410	205	0
13	6	50	63	31	50	113	56	50	175	87	50	420	210	0
14	7	0	64	32	0	114	57	0	176	88	0	430	215	0
15	7	50	65	32	50	115	57	50	178	89	0	440	220	0
16	8	0	66	33	0	116	58	0	15 180	90	0	450	225	0
17	8	50	67	33	50	117	58	50	182	91	0	460	230	0
18	9	0	68	34	0	118	59	0	184	92	0	470	235	0
19	9	50	69	34	50	119	59	50	186	93	0	480	240	0
20	10	0	70	35	0	120	60	0	188	94	0	490	245	0
21	10	50	71	35	50	121	60	50	190	95	0	**500**	250	0
22	11	0	72	36	0	122	61	0	16 192	96	0	550	275	0
23	11	50	73	36	50	123	61	50	194	97	0	600	300	0
24	12	0	74	37	0	124	62	0	196	98	0	650	325	0
25	12	50	75	37	50	125	62	50	198	99	0	700	350	0
26	13	0	76	38	0	126	63	0	200	100	0	750	375	0
27	13	50	77	38	50	127	63	50	17 204	102	0	800	400	0
28	14	0	78	39	0	128	64	0	205	102	50	850	425	0
29	14	50	79	39	50	129	64	50	210	105	0	900	450	0
30	15	0	80	40	0	130	65	0	215	107	50	950	475	0
31	15	50	81	40	50	131	65	50	18 216	108	0	**1000**	500	0
32	16	0	82	41	0	132	66	0	220	110	0	1016	508	0
33	16	50	83	41	50	133	66	50	225	112	50	1250	625	0
34	17	0	84	42	0	134	67	0	19 228	114	0	1500	750	0
35	17	50	85	42	50	135	67	50	230	115	0	1728	864	0
36	18	0	86	43	0	136	68	0	235	117	50	1750	875	0
37	18	50	87	43	50	137	68	50	20 240	120	0	1760	880	0
38	19	0	88	44	0	138	69	0	245	122	50	2000	1000	0
39	19	50	89	44	50	139	69	50	250	125	0	2240	1120	0
40	20	0	90	45	0	140	70	0	255	127	50	2500	1250	0
41	20	50	91	45	50	141	70	50	260	130	0	3000	1500	0
42	21	0	92	46	0	142	71	0	265	132	50	4000	2000	0
43	21	50	93	46	50	143	71	50	270	135	0	**5000**	2500	0
44	22	0	94	47	0	144	72	0	275	137	50	6000	3000	0
45	22	50	95	47	50	145	72	50	280	140	0	7000	3500	0
46	23	0	96	48	0	146	73	0	285	142	50	8000	4000	0
47	23	50	97	48	50	147	73	50	24 288	144	0	9000	4500	0
48	24	0	98	49	0	148	74	0	290	145	0	10000	5000	0
49	24	50	99	49	50	149	74	50	295	147	50	15000	7500	0
50	25	0	100	50	0	150	75	0	300	150	0	20000	10000	0

*Left margin of first column marked **Dozens** (at 12, 24, 36, 48); second, third and fourth columns also marked **Dozens**.*

Grosses			Twelfths			Twentieths						Sixteenths					
1.	72	0	1.	0	4½							1.	0	3½	9.	0	28½
2.	144	0	½ 2.	0	8½	1.	0	2½	11.	0	27½	⅛ 2.	0	6	½ 10.	0	31½
3.	216	0	3.	0	12½	·1 2.	0	5	·6 12.	0	30	3.	0	9½	11.	0	34½
4.	288	0	¼ 4.	0	16½	3.	0	7½	13.	0	32½	¼ 4.	0	12½	¾ 12.	0	37½
5.	360	0	5.	0	20½	·2 4.	0	10	·7 14.	0	35	5.	0	15½	13.	0	40½
6.	432	0	¾ 6.	0	25	5.	0	12½	15.	0	37½	⅜ 6.	0	18½	⅞ 14.	0	43½
7.	504	0	7.	0	29½	·3 6.	0	15	·8 16.	0	40	7.	0	22	15.	0	47
8.	576	0	⅜ 8.	0	33½	7.	0	17½	17.	0	42½	½ 8.	0	25			
9.	648	0	9.	0	37½	·4 8.	0	20	·9 18.	0	45						
10.	720	0	⅝ 10.	0	41½	9.	0	22½	19.	0	47½						
11.	792	0	11.	0	45½	·5 10.	0	25	20.	0	50						

The Twentieths column has a "10ths" label at its head.

No.	£	P	No.	£	P	No.	£	P
1	0	51	51	26	1	101	51	51
2	1	2	52	26	52	102	52	2
3	1	53	53	27	3	103	52	53
4	2	4	54	27	54	104	53	4
5	2	55	55	28	5	105	53	55
6	3	6	56	28	56	106	54	6
7	3	57	57	29	7	107	54	57
8	4	8	58	29	58	[9] 108	55	8
9	4	59	59	30	9	109	55	59
10	5	10	[5] **60**	30	60	**110**	56	10
* 11	5	61	61	31	11	111	56	61
[1] 12	6	12	62	31	62	112	57	12
13	6	63	63	32	13	113	57	63
14	7	14	64	32	64	114	58	14
15	7	65	65	33	15	115	58	65
16	8	16	66	33	66	116	59	16
17	8	67	67	34	17	117	59	67
18	9	18	68	34	68	118	60	18
19	9	69	69	35	19	119	60	69
20	10	20	**70**	35	70	**120**	61	20
21	10	71	71	36	21	121	61	71
22	11	22	[6] 72	36	72	122	62	22
23	11	73	73	37	23	123	62	73
[2] 24	12	24	74	37	74	124	63	24
25	12	75	75	38	25	125	63	75
26	13	26	76	38	76	126	64	26
27	13	77	77	39	27	127	64	77
28	14	28	78	39	78	128	65	28
29	14	79	79	40	29	129	65	79
30	15	30	**80**	40	80	**130**	66	30
31	15	81	81	41	31	131	66	81
32	16	32	82	41	82	[11] 132	67	32
33	16	83	83	42	33	133	67	83
34	17	34	[7] 84	42	84	134	68	34
35	17	85	85	43	35	135	68	85
[3] 36	18	36	86	43	86	136	69	36
37	18	87	87	44	37	137	69	87
38	19	38	88	44	88	138	70	38
39	19	89	89	45	39	139	70	89
40	20	40	**90**	45	90	**140**	71	40
41	20	91	91	46	41	141	71	91
42	21	42	92	46	92	142	72	42
43	21	93	93	47	43	143	72	93
44	22	44	94	47	94	[12] 144	73	44
45	22	95	95	48	45	145	73	95
46	23	46	[8] 96	48	96	146	74	46
47	23	97	97	49	47	147	74	97
[4] 48	24	48	98	49	98	148	75	48
49	24	99	99	50	49	149	75	99
50	25	50	**100**	51	0	**150**	76	50

(* Dozens.)

Doz.	£	P
152	77	52
154	78	54
[13] 156	79	56
158	80	58
160	81	60
162	82	62
164	83	64
166	84	66
[14] 168	85	68
170	86	70
172	87	72
174	88	74
175	89	25
176	89	76
178	90	78
[15] 180	91	80
182	92	82
184	93	84
186	94	86
188	95	88
190	96	90
[16] 192	97	92
194	98	94
196	99	96
198	100	98
200	102	0
[17] 204	104	4
205	104	55
210	107	10
215	109	65
[18] 216	110	16
220	112	20
225	114	75
[19] 228	116	28
230	117	30
235	119	85
[20] 240	122	40
245	124	95
250	127	50
255	130	5
260	132	60
265	135	15
270	137	70
275	140	25
280	142	80
285	145	35
[24] 288	146	88
290	147	90
295	150	45
300	153	0

No.	£	P
310	158	10
320	163	20
330	168	30
340	173	40
350	178	50
360	183	60
365	186	15
370	188	70
380	193	80
390	198	90
400	204	0
410	209	10
420	214	20
430	219	30
440	224	40
450	229	50
460	234	60
470	239	70
480	244	80
490	249	90
500	255	0
550	280	50
600	306	0
650	331	50
700	357	0
750	382	50
800	408	0
850	433	50
900	459	0
950	484	50
1000	510	0
1016	518	16
1250	637	50
1500	765	0
1728	881	28
1750	892	50
1760	897	60
2000	1020	0
2240	1142	40
2500	1275	0
3000	1530	0
4000	2040	0
5000	2550	0
6000	3060	0
7000	3570	0
8000	4080	0
9000	4590	0
10,000	5100	0
15,000	7650	0
20,000	10200	0

Grosses.

1.	73	44
2.	146	88
3.	220	32
4.	293	76
5.	367	20
6.	440	64
7.	514	8
8.	587	52
9.	660	96
10.	734	40
11.	807	84

Twelfths

	1.	0	4¼
⅙	2.	0	8½
	3.	0	12¾
⅓	4.	0	17
	5.	0	21¼
½	6.	0	25½
	7.	0	29¾
⅔	8.	0	34
	9.	0	38¼
⅚	10.	0	42½
	11.	0	46¾

Twentieths

10ths				10ths			
	1.	0	2½		11.	0	28
·1	2.	0	5	·6	12.	0	30½
	3.	0	7¾		13.	0	33¼
·2	4.	0	10¼	·7	14.	0	35¾
	5.	0	12¾		15.	0	38¼
·3	6.	0	15¼	·8	16.	0	40¾
	7.	0	17¾		17.	0	43¼
·4	8.	0	20½	·9	18.	0	46
	9.	0	23		19.	0	48½
·5	10.	0	25½		20.	0	51

Sixteenths

	1.	0	3¼		9.	0	28¾
⅛	2.	0	6½	⅝	10.	0	32
	3.	0	9½		11.	0	35
¼	4.	0	12¾	¾	12.	0	38¼
	5.	0	16		13.	0	41½
⅜	6.	0	19¼	⅞	14.	0	44¾
	7.	0	22¼		15.	0	47¾
½	8.	0	25½				

52 Pence 52 Pence

Dozens / No.	£	p	Dozens / No.	£	p	Dozens / No.	£	p	Dozens / No.	£	p	No.	£	p
1	0	52	51	26	52	101	52	52	152	79	4	310	161	20
2	1	4	52	27	4	102	53	4	154	80	8	320	166	40
3	1	56	53	27	56	103	53	56	[13] 156	81	12	330	171	60
4	2	8	54	28	8	104	54	8	158	82	16	340	176	80
5	2	60	55	28	60	105	54	60	160	83	20	350	182	0
*6	3	12	56	29	12	106	55	12	162	84	24	360	187	20
7	3	64	57	29	64	107	55	64	164	85	28	365	189	80
8	4	16	58	30	16	[9] 108	56	16	166	86	32	370	192	40
9	4	68	59	30	68	109	56	68	[14] 168	87	36	380	197	60
10	5	20	[5] **60**	31	20	**110**	57	20	170	88	40	390	202	80
*11	5	72	61	31	72	111	57	72	172	89	44	400	208	0
[1] 12	6	24	62	32	24	112	58	24	174	90	48	410	213	20
13	6	76	63	32	76	113	58	76	175	91	0	420	218	40
14	7	28	64	33	28	114	59	28	176	91	52	430	223	60
15	7	80	65	33	80	115	59	80	178	92	56	440	228	80
16	8	32	66	34	32	116	60	32	[15] 180	93	60	450	234	0
17	8	84	67	34	84	117	60	84	182	94	64	460	239	20
18	9	36	68	35	36	118	61	36	184	95	68	470	244	40
19	9	88	69	35	88	119	61	88	186	96	72	480	249	60
20	10	40	**70**	36	40	**120**	62	40	188	97	76	490	254	80
21	10	92	71	36	92	121	62	92	190	98	80	**500**	260	0
22	11	44	[6] 72	37	44	122	63	44	[16] 192	99	84	550	286	0
23	11	96	73	37	96	123	63	96	194	100	88	600	312	0
[2] 24	12	48	74	38	48	124	64	48	196	101	92	650	338	0
25	13	0	75	39	0	125	65	0	198	102	96	700	364	0
26	13	52	76	39	52	126	65	52	**200**	104	0	750	390	0
27	14	4	77	40	4	127	66	4	[17] 204	106	8	800	416	0
28	14	56	78	40	56	128	66	56	205	106	60	850	442	0
29	15	8	79	41	8	129	67	8	210	109	20	900	468	0
30	15	60	**80**	41	60	**130**	67	60	215	111	80	950	494	0
31	16	12	81	42	12	131	68	12	[18] 216	112	32	**1000**	520	0
32	16	64	82	42	64	[11] 132	68	64	220	114	40	1016	528	32
33	17	16	83	43	16	133	69	16	225	117	0	1250	650	0
34	17	68	[7] 84	43	68	134	69	68	[19] 228	118	56	1500	780	0
35	18	20	85	44	20	135	70	20	230	119	60	1728	898	56
[3] 36	18	72	86	44	72	136	70	72	235	122	20	1750	910	0
37	19	24	87	45	24	137	71	24	[20] 240	124	80	1760	915	20
38	19	76	88	45	76	138	71	76	245	127	40	2000	1040	0
39	20	28	89	46	28	139	72	28	**250**	130	0	2240	1164	80
40	20	80	**90**	46	80	**140**	72	80	255	132	60	2500	1300	0
41	21	32	91	47	32	141	73	32	260	135	20	3000	1560	0
42	21	84	92	47	84	142	73	84	265	137	80	4000	2080	0
43	22	36	93	48	36	143	74	36	270	140	40	**5000**	2600	0
44	22	88	94	48	88	[12] 144	74	88	275	143	0	6000	3120	0
45	23	40	95	49	40	145	75	40	280	145	60	7000	3640	0
46	23	92	[8] 96	49	92	146	75	92	285	148	20	8000	4160	0
47	24	44	97	50	44	147	76	44	[24] 288	149	76	9000	4680	0
[4] 48	24	96	98	50	96	148	76	96	290	150	80	10000	5200	0
49	25	48	99	51	48	149	77	48	295	153	40	15000	7800	0
50	26	0	**100**	52	0	**150**	78	0	**300**	156	0	20000	10400	0

Grosses

1.	74	88
2.	149	76
3.	224	64
4.	299	52
5.	374	40
6.	449	28
7.	524	16
8.	599	4
9.	673	92
10.	748	80
11.	823	68

Twelfths

	1.		4⅓
⅙	2.	0	8⅔
	3.	0	13
⅓	4.	0	17⅓
	5.	0	21⅔
½	6.	0	26
	7.	0	30⅓
⅔	8.	0	34⅔
	9.	0	39
⅚	10.	0	43⅓
	11.	0	47⅔

Twentieths

10ths				10ths			
	1.	0	2⅗		11.	0	28⅗
·1	2.	0	5⅕	·6	12.	0	31⅕
	3.	0	7⅘		13.	0	33⅘
·2	4.	0	10⅖	·7	14.	0	36⅖
	5.	0	13		15.	0	39
·3	6.	0	15⅗	·8	16.	0	41⅗
	7.	0	18⅕		17.	0	44⅕
·4	8.	0	20⅘	·9	18.	0	46⅘
	9.	0	23⅖		19.	0	49⅖
·5	10.	0	26		20.	0	52

Sixteenths

	1.	0	3¼		9.	0	29¼
⅛	2.	0	6½	⅝	10.	0	32½
	3.	0	9¾		11.	0	35¾
¼	4.	0	13	¾	12.	0	39
	5.	0	16¼		13.	0	42¼
⅜	6.	0	19½	⅞	14.	0	45½
	7.	0	22¾		15.	0	48¾
½	8.	0	26				

	£ P		£ P		£ P		£ P		£ P
1	0 53	51	27 3	101	53 53	152	80 56	310	164 30
2	1 6	52	27 56	102	54 6	154	81 62	320	169 60
3	1 59	53	28 9	103	54 59	13 156	82 68	330	174 90
4	2 12	54	28 62	104	55 12	158	83 74	340	180 20
5	2 65	55	29 15	105	55 65	160	84 80	350	185 50
*6	3 18	56	29 68	106	56 18	162	85 86	360	190 80
7	3 71	57	30 21	107	56 71	164	86 92	365	193 45
8	4 24	58	30 74	9 108	57 24	166	87 98	370	196 10
9	4 77	59	31 27	109	57 77	14 168	89 4	380	201 40
10	5 30	5 60	31 80	110	58 30	170	90 10	390	206 70
11	5 83	61	32 33	111	58 83	172	91 16	400	212 0
12	6 36	62	32 86	112	59 36	174	92 22	410	217 30
13	6 89	63	33 39	113	59 89	175	92 75	420	222 60
14	7 42	64	33 92	114	60 42	176	93 28	430	227 90
15	7 95	65	34 45	115	60 95	178	94 34	440	233 20
16	8 48	66	34 98	116	61 48	15 180	95 40	450	238 50
17	9 1	67	35 51	117	62 1	182	96 46	460	243 80
18	9 54	68	36 4	118	62 54	184	97 52	470	249 10
19	10 7	69	36 57	119	63 7	186	98 58	480	254 40
20	10 60	70	37 10	120	63 60	188	99 64	490	259 70
21	11 13	71	37 63	121	64 13	190	100 70	500	265 0
22	11 66	6 72	38 16	122	64 66	16 192	101 76	550	291 50
23	12 19	73	38 69	123	65 19	194	102 82	600	318 0
24	12 72	74	39 22	124	65 72	196	103 88	650	344 50
25	13 25	75	39 75	125	66 25	198	104 94	700	371 0
26	13 78	76	40 28	126	66 78	200	106 0	750	397 50
27	14 31	77	40 81	127	67 31	17 204	108 12	800	424 0
28	14 84	78	41 34	128	67 84	205	108 65	850	450 50
29	15 37	79	41 87	129	68 37	210	111 30	900	477 0
30	15 90	80	42 40	130	68 90	215	113 95	950	503 50
31	16 43	81	42 93	131	69 43	18 216	114 48	1000	530 0
32	16 96	82	43 46	11 132	69 96	220	116 60	1016	538 48
33	17 49	83	43 99	133	70 49	225	119 25	1250	662 50
34	18 2	7 84	44 52	134	71 2	19 228	120 84	1500	795 0
35	18 55	85	45 5	135	71 55	230	121 90	1728	915 84
36	19 8	86	45 58	136	72 8	235	124 55	1750	927 50
37	19 61	87	46 11	137	72 61	20 240	127 20	1760	932 80
38	20 14	88	46 64	138	73 14	245	129 85	2000	1060 0
39	20 67	89	47 17	139	73 67	250	132 50	2240	1187 20
40	21 20	90	47 70	140	74 20	255	135 15	2500	1325 0
41	21 73	91	48 23	141	74 73	260	137 80	3000	1590 0
42	22 26	92	48 76	142	75 26	265	140 45	4000	2120 0
43	22 79	93	49 29	143	75 79	270	143 10	5000	2650 0
44	23 32	94	49 82	12 144	76 32	275	145 75	6000	3180 0
45	23 85	95	50 35	145	76 85	280	148 40	7000	3710 0
46	24 38	8 96	50 88	146	77 38	285	151 5	8000	4240 0
47	24 91	97	51 41	147	77 91	24 288	152 64	9000	4770 0
48	25 44	98	51 94	148	78 44	290	153 70	10000	5300 0
49	25 97	99	52 47	149	78 97	295	156 35	15000	7950 0
50	26 50	100	53 0	150	79 50	300	159 0	20000	10600 0

Grosses.		Twelfths.		Twentieths.				Sixteenths.			
1.	76 32	1.	0 4½	1.	0 2¾	11.	0 29¼	1.	0 3¼	9.	0 29¼
2.	152 64	½2.	0 8½	x 2.	0 5¼	6 12.	0 31½	½2.	0 6¼	½10.	0 33¼
3.	228 96	3.	0 13½	3.	0 8	13.	0 34½	3.	0 10	11.	0 36½
4.	305 28	¼4.	0 17¾	2 4.	0 10½	7 14.	0 37	¼4.	0 13¼	¾12.	0 39¾
5.	381 60	5.	0 22	5.	0 13¼	15.	0 39¾	5.	0 16½	13.	0 43
6.	457 92	½6.	0 26½	3 6.	0 16	8 16.	0 42½	¾6.	0 20	¾14.	0 46¼
7.	534 24	7.	0 31	7.	0 18½	17.	0 45	7.	0 23¼	15.	0 49¾
8.	610 56	¾8.	0 35½	4 8.	0 21¼	9 18.	0 47¾	½8.	0 26½		
9.	686 88	9.	0 39½	9.	0 23¾	19.	0 50¼				
10.	763 20	10.	0 44½	5 10.	0 26½	20.	0 53				
11.	839 52	11.	0 48½								

	£	P		£	P		£	P		£	P		£	P
1	0	54	51	27	54	101	54	54	152	82	8	310	167	40
2	1	8	52	28	8	102	55	8	154	83	16	320	172	80
3	1	62	53	28	62	103	55	62	13 156	84	24	330	178	20
4	2	16	54	29	16	104	56	16	158	85	32	340	183	60
5	2	70	55	29	70	105	56	70	160	86	40	350	189	0
6	3	24	56	30	24	106	57	24	162	87	48	360	194	40
7	3	78	57	30	78	107	57	78	164	88	56	365	197	10
8	4	32	58	31	32	9 108	58	32	166	89	64	370	199	80
9	4	86	59	31	86	109	58	86	14 168	90	72	380	205	20
10	5	40	5 **60**	32	40	**110**	59	40	170	91	80	390	210	60
*11	5	94	61	32	94	111	59	94	172	92	88	400	216	0
1 12	6	48	62	33	48	112	60	48	174	93	96	410	221	40
13	7	2	63	34	2	113	61	2	175	94	50	420	226	80
14	7	56	64	34	56	114	61	56	176	95	4	430	232	20
15	8	10	65	35	10	115	62	10	178	96	12	440	237	60
16	8	64	66	35	64	116	62	64	15 180	97	20	450	243	0
17	9	18	67	36	18	117	63	18	182	98	28	460	248	40
18	9	72	68	36	72	118	63	72	184	99	36	470	253	80
19	10	26	69	37	26	119	64	26	186	100	44	480	259	20
20	10	80	**70**	37	80	**120**	64	80	188	101	52	490	264	60
21	11	34	71	38	34	121	65	34	190	102	60	**500**	270	0
22	11	88	6 72	38	88	122	65	88	16 192	103	68	550	297	0
23	12	42	73	39	42	123	66	42	194	104	76	600	324	0
2 24	12	96	74	39	96	124	66	96	196	105	84	650	351	0
25	13	50	75	40	50	125	67	50	198	106	92	700	378	0
26	14	4	76	41	4	126	68	4	**200**	108	0	750	405	0
27	14	58	77	41	58	127	68	58	17 204	110	16	800	432	0
28	15	12	78	42	12	128	69	12	205	110	70	850	459	0
29	15	66	79	42	66	129	69	66	210	113	40	900	486	0
30	16	20	**80**	43	20	**130**	70	20	215	116	10	950	513	0
31	16	74	81	43	74	131	70	74	18 216	116	64	**1000**	540	0
32	17	28	82	44	28	11 132	71	28	220	118	80	1016	548	64
33	17	82	83	44	82	133	71	82	225	121	50	1250	675	0
34	18	36	7 84	45	36	134	72	36	19 228	123	12	1500	810	0
35	18	90	85	45	90	135	72	90	230	124	20	1728	933	12
3 36	19	44	86	46	44	136	73	44	235	126	90	1750	945	0
37	19	98	87	46	98	137	73	98	20 240	129	60	1760	950	40
38	20	52	88	47	52	138	74	52	245	132	30	2000	1080	0
39	21	6	89	48	6	139	75	6	**250**	135	0	2240	1209	60
40	21	60	**90**	48	60	**140**	75	60	255	137	70	2500	1350	0
41	22	14	91	49	14	141	76	14	260	140	40	3000	1620	0
42	22	68	92	49	68	142	76	68	265	143	10	4000	2160	0
43	23	22	93	50	22	143	77	22	270	145	80	**5000**	2700	0
44	23	76	94	50	76	12 144	77	76	275	148	50	6000	3240	0
45	24	30	95	51	30	145	78	30	280	151	20	7000	3780	0
46	24	84	8 96	51	84	146	78	84	285	153	90	8000	4320	0
47	25	38	97	52	38	147	79	38	24 288	155	52	9000	4860	0
4 48	25	92	98	52	92	148	79	92	290	156	60	10000	5400	0
49	26	46	99	53	46	149	80	46	295	159	30	15000	8100	0
50	27	0	**100**	54	0	**150**	81	0	**300**	162	0	20000	10800	0

*Dozens

Grosses

1.	77	76
2.	155	52
3.	233	28
4.	311	04
5.	388	80
6.	466	56
7.	544	32
8.	622	08
9.	699	84
10.	777	60
11.	855	36

Twelfths

	1.	0	4½
⅙	2.	0	9
	3.	0	13½
⅓	4.	0	18
	5.	0	22½
½	6.	0	27
	7.	0	31½
⅔	8.	0	36
	9.	0	40½
⅚	10.	0	45
	11.	0	49½

Twentieths (10ths)

10ths				10ths			
	1.	0	2¾		11.	0	29¾
·1	2.	0	5½	·6	12.	0	32½
	3.	0	8		13.	0	35
·2	4.	0	10¾	·7	14.	0	37¾
	5.	0	13½		15.	0	40½
·3	6.	0	16¼	·8	16.	0	43¼
	7.	0	19		17.	0	46
·4	8.	0	21½	·9	18.	0	48½
	9.	0	24¼		19.	0	51¼
·5	10.	0	27		20.	0	54

Sixteenths

	1.	0	3½		9.	0	30½
⅛	2.	0	6¾	⅝	10.	0	33¾
	3.	0	10¼		11.	0	37¼
¼	4.	0	13½	¾	12.	0	40½
	5.	0	17		13.	0	44
⅜	6.	0	20¼	⅞	14.	0	47¼
	7.	0	23¾		15.	0	50¾
½	8.	0	27				

	£	P		£	P		£	P		£	P		£	P
1	0	55	51	28	5	101	55	55	152	83	60	310	170	50
2	1	10	52	28	60	102	56	10	154	84	70	320	176	0
3	1	65	53	29	15	103	56	65	[13] 156	85	80	330	181	50
4	2	20	54	29	70	104	57	20	158	86	90	340	187	0
5	2	75	55	30	25	105	57	75	160	88	0	350	192	50
6	3	30	56	30	80	106	58	30	162	89	10	360	198	0
7	3	85	57	31	35	107	58	85	164	90	20	365	200	75
8	4	40	58	31	90	[9] 108	59	40	166	91	30	370	203	50
9	4	95	59	32	45	109	59	95	[14] 168	92	40	380	209	0
10	5	50	[5] **60**	33	0	**110**	60	50	170	93	50	390	214	50
*11	6	5	61	33	55	111	61	5	172	94	60	400	220	0
[1] 12	6	60	62	34	10	112	61	60	174	95	70	410	225	50
13	7	15	63	34	65	113	62	15	175	96	25	420	231	0
14	7	70	64	35	20	114	62	70	176	96	80	430	236	50
15	8	25	65	35	75	115	63	25	178	97	90	440	242	0
16	8	80	66	36	30	116	63	80	[15] 180	99	0	450	247	50
17	9	35	67	36	85	117	64	35	182	100	10	460	253	0
18	9	90	68	37	40	118	64	90	184	101	20	470	258	50
19	10	45	69	37	95	119	65	45	186	102	30	480	264	0
20	11	0	**70**	38	50	**120**	66	0	188	103	40	490	269	50
21	11	55	71	39	5	121	66	55	190	104	50	**500**	275	0
22	12	10	[6] 72	39	60	122	67	10	[16] 192	105	60	550	302	50
23	12	65	73	40	15	123	67	65	194	106	70	600	330	0
[2] 24	13	20	74	40	70	124	68	20	196	107	80	650	357	50
25	13	75	75	41	25	125	68	75	198	108	90	700	385	0
26	14	30	76	41	80	126	69	30	**200**	110	0	750	412	50
27	14	85	77	42	35	127	69	85	[17] 204	112	20	800	440	0
28	15	40	78	42	90	128	70	40	205	112	75	850	467	50
29	15	95	79	43	45	129	70	95	210	115	50	900	495	0
30	16	50	**80**	44	0	**130**	71	50	215	118	25	950	522	50
31	17	5	81	44	55	131	72	5	[18] 216	118	80	**1000**	550	0
32	17	60	82	45	10	[11] 132	72	60	220	121	0	1016	558	80
33	18	15	83	45	65	133	73	15	225	123	75	1250	687	50
34	18	70	[7] 84	46	20	134	73	70	[19] 228	125	40	1500	825	0
35	19	25	85	46	75	135	74	25	230	126	50	1728	950	40
[3] 36	19	80	86	47	30	136	74	80	235	129	25	1750	962	50
37	20	35	87	47	85	137	75	35	[20] 240	132	0	1760	968	0
38	20	90	88	48	40	138	75	90	245	134	75	2000	1100	0
39	21	45	89	48	95	139	76	45	**250**	137	50	2240	1232	0
40	22	0	**90**	49	50	**140**	77	0	255	140	25	2500	1375	0
41	22	55	91	50	5	141	77	55	260	143	0	3000	1650	0
42	23	10	92	50	60	142	78	10	265	145	75	4000	2200	0
43	23	65	93	51	15	143	78	65	270	148	50	5000	2750	0
44	24	20	94	51	70	[12] 144	79	20	275	151	25	6000	3300	0
45	24	75	95	52	25	145	79	75	280	154	0	7000	3850	0
46	25	30	[8] 96	52	80	146	80	30	285	156	75	8000	4400	0
47	25	85	97	53	35	147	80	85	[24] 288	158	40	9000	4950	0
[4] 48	26	40	98	53	90	148	81	40	290	159	50	10000	5500	0
49	26	95	99	54	45	149	81	95	295	162	25	15000	8250	0
50	27	50	**100**	55	0	**150**	82	50	**300**	165	0	20000	11000	0

*Dozens

Grosses

1.	79	20
2.	158	40
3.	237	60
4.	316	80
5.	396	0
6.	475	20
7.	554	40
8.	633	60
9.	712	80
10.	792	0
11.	871	20

Twelfths

	1.	0	4½
1/6	2.	0	9¼
	3.	0	13¾
1/3	4.	0	18¼
	5.	0	23
1/2	6.	0	27½
	7.	0	32
2/3	8.	0	36¾
	9.	0	41¼
5/6	10.	0	45¾
	11.	0	50½

Twentieths

10ths				10ths			
	1.	0	2¾		11.	0	30¼
·1	2.	0	5½	·6	12.	0	33
	3.	0	8¼		13.	0	35¾
·2	4.	0	11	·7	14.	0	38½
	5.	0	13¾		15.	0	41¼
·3	6.	0	16½	·8	16.	0	44
	7.	0	19¼		17.	0	46¾
·4	8.	0	22	·9	18.	0	49½
	9.	0	24¾		19.	0	52¼
·5	10.	0	27½		20.	0	55

Sixteenths

	1.	0	3½		9.	0	31
1/8	2.	0	7	5/8	10.	0	34½
	3.	0	10¼		11.	0	37¾
1/4	4.	0	13¾	3/4	12.	0	41¼
	5.	0	17¼		13.	0	44¾
3/8	6.	0	20¾	7/8	14.	0	48¼
	7.	0	24		15.	0	51½
1/2	8.	0	27½				

	£	P		£	P		£	P		£	P		£	P
1	0	56	51	28	56	101	56	56	152	85	12	310	173	60
2	1	12	52	29	12	102	57	12	154	86	24	320	179	20
3	1	68	53	29	68	103	57	68	156	87	36	330	184	80
4	2	24	54	30	24	104	58	24	158	88	48	340	190	40
5	2	80	55	30	80	105	58	80	160	89	60	350	196	0
*6	3	36	56	31	36	106	59	36	162	90	72	360	201	60
7	3	92	57	31	92	107	59	92	164	91	84	365	204	40
8	4	48	58	32	48	108	60	48	166	92	96	370	207	20
9	5	4	59	33	4	109	61	4	168	94	8	380	212	80
10	5	60	60	33	60	110	61	60	170	95	20	390	218	40
11	6	16	61	34	16	111	62	16	172	96	32	400	224	0
12	6	72	62	34	72	112	62	72	174	97	44	410	229	60
13	7	28	63	35	28	113	63	28	175	98	0	420	235	20
14	7	84	64	35	84	114	63	84	176	98	56	430	240	80
15	8	40	65	36	40	115	64	40	178	99	68	440	246	40
16	8	96	66	36	96	116	64	96	180	100	80	450	252	0
17	9	52	67	37	52	117	65	52	182	101	92	460	257	60
18	10	8	68	38	8	118	66	8	184	103	4	470	263	20
19	10	64	69	38	64	119	66	64	186	104	16	480	268	80
20	11	20	70	39	20	120	67	20	188	105	28	490	274	40
21	11	76	71	39	76	121	67	76	190	106	40	500	280	0
22	12	32	72	40	32	122	68	32	192	107	52	550	308	0
23	12	88	73	40	88	123	68	88	194	108	64	600	336	0
24	13	44	74	41	44	124	69	44	196	109	76	650	364	0
25	14	0	75	42	0	125	70	0	198	110	88	700	392	0
26	14	56	76	42	56	126	70	56	200	112	0	750	420	0
27	15	12	77	43	12	127	71	12	204	114	24	800	448	0
28	15	68	78	43	68	128	71	68	205	114	80	850	476	0
29	16	24	79	44	24	129	72	24	210	117	60	900	504	0
30	16	80	80	44	80	130	72	80	215	120	40	950	532	0
31	17	36	81	45	36	131	73	36	216	120	96	1000	560	0
32	17	92	82	45	92	132	73	92	220	123	20	1016	568	96
33	18	48	83	46	48	133	74	48	225	126	0	1250	700	0
34	19	4	84	47	4	134	75	4	228	127	68	1500	840	0
35	19	60	85	47	60	135	75	60	230	128	80	1728	967	68
36	20	16	86	48	16	136	76	16	235	131	60	1750	980	0
37	20	72	87	48	72	137	76	72	240	134	40	1760	985	60
38	21	28	88	49	28	138	77	28	245	137	20	2000	1120	0
39	21	84	89	49	84	139	77	84	250	140	0	2240	1254	40
40	22	40	90	50	40	140	78	40	255	142	80	2500	1400	0
41	22	96	91	50	96	141	78	96	260	145	60	3000	1680	0
42	23	52	92	51	52	142	79	52	265	148	40	4000	2240	0
43	24	8	93	52	8	143	80	8	270	151	20	5000	2800	0
44	24	64	94	52	64	144	80	64	275	154	0	6000	3360	0
45	25	20	95	53	20	145	81	20	280	156	80	7000	3920	0
46	25	76	96	53	76	146	81	76	285	159	60	8000	4480	0
47	26	32	97	54	32	147	82	32	288	161	28	9000	5040	0
48	26	88	98	54	88	148	82	88	290	162	40	10000	5600	0
49	27	44	99	55	44	149	83	44	295	165	20	15000	8400	0
50	28	0	100	56	0	150	84	0	300	168	0	20000	11200	0

Grosses			Twelfths			Twentieths						Sixteenths					
1.	80	64	1.		4⅔	1.	0	2⅘	11.	0	30⅘	1.	0	3½	9.	0	31½
2.	161	28	⅙ 2.	0	9¼	·1 2.	0	5⅗	·6 12.	0	33⅗	⅛ 2.	0	7	⅝ 10.	0	35
3.	241	92	3.	0	14	3.	0	8⅖	13.	0	36⅖	3.	0	10½	11.	0	38½
4.	322	56	¼ 4.	0	18¾	·2 4.	0	11⅕	7 14.	0	39⅕	¼ 4.	0	14	¾ 12.	0	42
5.	403	20	5.	0	23¼	5.	0	14	15.	0	42	5.	0	17½	13.	0	45½
6.	483	84	⅓ 6.	0	28	·3 6.	0	16⅘	·8 16.	0	44⅘	⅜ 6.	0	21	⅞ 14.	0	49
7.	564	48	7.	0	32½	7.	0	19⅗	17.	0	47⅗	7.	0	24½	15.	0	52½
8.	645	12	⅜ 8.	0	37¼	·4 8.	0	22⅖	·9 18.	0	50⅖	½ 8.	0	28			
9.	725	76	9.	0	42	9.	0	25⅕	19.	0	53⅕						
10.	806	40	⅚ 10.	0	46¾	·5 10.	0	28	20.	0	56						
11.	887	4	11.	0	51¼												

No	£	P	No	£	P	No	£	P	No	£	P	No	£	P
1	0	57	51	29	7	101	57	57	152	86	64	310	176	70
2	1	14	52	29	64	102	58	14	154	87	78	320	182	40
3	1	71	53	30	21	103	58	71	156	88	92	330	188	10
4	2	28	54	30	78	104	59	28	158	90	6	340	193	80
5	2	85	55	31	35	105	59	85	160	91	20	350	199	50
6	3	42	56	31	92	106	60	42	162	92	34	360	205	20
7	3	99	57	32	49	107	60	99	164	93	48	365	208	5
8	4	56	58	33	6	108	61	56	166	94	62	370	210	90
9	5	13	59	33	63	109	62	13	168	95	76	380	216	60
10	5	70	60	34	20	110	62	70	170	96	90	390	222	30
11	6	27	61	34	77	111	63	27	172	98	4	400	228	0
12	6	84	62	35	34	112	63	84	174	99	18	410	233	70
13	7	41	63	35	91	113	64	41	175	99	75	420	239	40
14	7	98	64	36	48	114	64	98	176	100	32	430	245	10
15	8	55	65	37	5	115	65	55	178	101	46	440	250	80
16	9	12	66	37	62	116	66	12	180	102	60	450	256	50
17	9	69	67	38	19	117	66	69	182	103	74	460	262	20
18	10	26	68	38	76	118	67	26	184	104	88	470	267	90
19	10	83	69	39	33	119	67	83	186	106	2	480	273	60
20	11	40	70	39	90	120	68	40	188	107	16	490	279	30
21	11	97	71	40	47	121	68	97	190	108	30	500	285	0
22	12	54	72	41	4	122	69	54	192	109	44	550	313	50
23	13	11	73	41	61	123	70	11	194	110	58	600	342	0
24	13	68	74	42	18	124	70	68	196	111	72	650	370	50
25	14	25	75	42	75	125	71	25	198	112	86	700	399	0
26	14	82	76	43	32	126	71	82	200	114	0	750	427	50
27	15	39	77	43	89	127	72	39	204	116	24	800	456	0
28	15	96	78	44	46	128	72	96	205	116	85	850	484	50
29	16	53	79	45	3	129	73	53	210	119	70	900	513	0
30	17	10	80	45	60	130	74	10	215	122	55	950	541	50
31	17	67	81	46	17	131	74	67	216	123	12	1000	570	0
32	18	24	82	46	74	132	75	24	220	125	40	1016	579	12
33	18	81	83	47	31	133	75	81	225	128	25	1250	712	50
34	19	38	84	47	88	134	76	38	228	129	96	1500	855	0
35	19	95	85	48	45	135	76	95	230	131	10	1728	984	96
36	20	52	86	49	2	136	77	52	235	133	95	1750	997	50
37	21	9	87	49	59	137	78	9	240	136	80	1760	1003	20
38	21	66	88	50	16	138	78	66	245	139	65	2000	1140	0
39	22	23	89	50	73	139	79	23	250	142	50	2240	1276	80
40	22	80	90	51	30	140	79	80	255	145	35	2500	1425	0
41	23	37	91	51	87	141	80	37	260	148	20	3000	1710	0
42	23	94	92	52	44	142	80	94	265	151	5	4000	2280	0
43	24	51	93	53	1	143	81	51	270	153	90	5000	2850	0
44	25	8	94	53	58	144	82	8	275	156	75	6000	3420	0
45	25	65	95	54	15	145	82	65	280	159	60	7000	3990	0
46	26	22	96	54	72	146	83	22	285	162	45	8000	4560	0
47	26	79	97	55	29	147	83	79	288	164	16	9000	5130	0
48	27	36	98	55	86	148	84	36	290	165	30	10000	5700	0
49	27	93	99	56	43	149	84	93	295	168	15	15000	8550	0
50	28	50	100	57	0	150	85	50	300	171	0	20000	11400	0

Dozens markers: 3 = 36, 4 = 48, 5 = 60, 6 = 72, 7 = 84, 8 = 96, 9 = 108, 10 = 120, 11 = 132, 12 = 144, 13 = 156, 14 = 168, 15 = 180, 16 = 192, 17 = 204, 18 = 216, 19 = 228, 20 = 240, 24 = 288.

Grosses			Twelfths			10ths	Twentieths						Sixteenths				
1.	82	8	1.	0	4¾		1.	0	2¾	11.	0	31½	1.	0	3½	9.	0	32
2.	164	16	2.	0	9½	·1	2.	0	5¾	·6 12.	0	34¼	½ 2.	0	7¼	10.	0	35½
3.	246	24	3.	0	14¼		3.	0	8½	13.	0	37	3.	0	10¾	11.	0	39¼
4.	328	32	4.	0	19	·2 4.	0	11½	·7 14.	0	40	¼ 4.	0	14¼	12.	0	42¾
5.	410	40	5.	0	23¾		5.	0	14¼	15.	0	42¾	5.	0	17¾	13.	0	46¼
6.	492	48	6.	0	28½	·3 6.	0	17	·8 16.	0	45½	6.	0	21¼	14.	0	50
7.	574	56	7.	0	33¼		7.	0	20	17.	0	48¼	7.	0	25	15.	0	53½
8.	656	64	8.	0	38	·4 8.	0	22¾	·9 18.	0	51¼	8.	0	28½			
9.	738	72	9.	0	42¾		9.	0	25¾	19.	0	54¼						
10.	820	80	10.	0	47½	·5 10.	0	28½	20.	0	57						
11.	902	88	11.	0	52¼													

58 Pence   58 Pence

*Dozens		£	P	Dozens		£	P	Dozens		£	P	Dozens		£	P		£	P
	1	0	58		51	29	58		101	58	58		152	88	16	310	179	80
	2	1	16		52	30	16		102	59	16		154	89	32	320	185	60
	3	1	74		53	30	74		103	59	74	13	156	90	48	330	191	40
	4	2	32		54	31	32		104	60	32		158	91	64	340	197	20
	5	2	90		55	31	90		105	60	90		160	92	80	350	203	0
	6	3	48		56	32	48		106	61	48		162	93	96	360	208	80
	7	4	6		57	33	6		107	62	6		164	95	12	365	211	70
	8	4	64		58	33	64	9	108	62	64		166	96	28	370	214	60
	9	5	22		59	34	22		109	63	22	14	168	97	44	380	220	40
	10	5	80	5	**60**	34	80		**110**	63	80		170	98	60	390	226	20
*	11	6	38		61	35	38		111	64	38		172	99	76	400	232	0
1	12	6	96		62	35	96		112	64	96		174	100	92	410	237	80
	13	7	54		63	36	54		113	65	54		175	101	50	420	243	60
	14	8	12		64	37	12		114	66	12		176	102	8	430	249	40
	15	8	70		65	37	70		115	66	70		178	103	24	440	255	20
	16	9	28		66	38	28		116	67	28	15	180	104	40	450	261	0
	17	9	86		67	38	86		117	67	86		182	105	56	460	266	80
	18	10	44		68	39	44		118	68	44		184	106	72	470	272	60
	19	11	2		69	40	2		119	69	2		186	107	88	480	278	40
	20	11	60		**70**	40	60	10	**120**	69	60		188	109	4	490	284	20
	21	12	18		71	41	18		121	70	18		190	110	20	**500**	290	0
	22	12	76	6	72	41	76		122	70	76	16	192	111	36	550	319	0
	23	13	34		73	42	34		123	71	34		194	112	52	600	348	0
2	24	13	92		74	42	92		124	71	92		196	113	68	650	377	0
	25	14	50		75	43	50		125	72	50		198	114	84	700	406	0
	26	15	8		76	44	8		126	73	8		**200**	116	0	750	435	0
	27	15	66		77	44	66		127	73	66	17	204	118	32	800	464	0
	28	16	24		78	45	24		128	74	24		205	118	90	850	493	0
	29	16	82		79	45	82		129	74	82		210	121	80	900	522	0
	30	17	40		**80**	46	40		**130**	75	40		215	124	70	950	551	0
	31	17	98		81	46	98		131	75	98	18	216	125	28	**1000**	580	0
	32	18	56		82	47	56	11	132	76	56		220	127	60	1016	589	28
	33	19	14		83	48	14		133	77	14		225	130	50	1250	725	0
	34	19	72	7	84	48	72		134	77	72	19	228	132	24	1500	870	0
	35	20	30		85	49	30		135	78	30		230	133	40	1728	1002	24
3	36	20	88		86	49	88		136	78	88		235	136	30	1750	1015	0
	37	21	46		87	50	46		137	79	46	20	240	139	20	1760	1020	80
	38	22	4		88	51	4		138	80	4		245	142	10	2000	1160	0
	39	22	62		89	51	62		139	80	62		**250**	145	0	2240	1299	20
	40	23	20		**90**	52	20		**140**	81	20		255	147	90	2500	1450	0
	41	23	78		91	52	78		141	81	78		260	150	80	3000	1740	0
	42	24	36		92	53	36		142	82	36		265	153	70	4000	2320	0
	43	24	94		93	53	94		143	82	94		270	156	60	**5000**	2900	0
	44	25	52		94	54	52	12	144	83	52		275	159	50	6000	3480	0
	45	26	10		95	55	10		145	84	10		280	162	40	7000	4060	0
	46	26	68	8	96	55	68		146	84	68		285	165	30	8000	4640	0
	47	27	26		97	56	26		147	85	26	24	288	167	4	9000	5220	0
4	48	27	84		98	56	84		148	85	84		290	168	20	10000	5800	0
	49	28	42		99	57	42		149	86	42		295	171	10	15000	8700	0
	50	29	0		**100**	58	0		**150**	87	0		**300**	174	0	20000	11600	0

Grosses

1.	83	52
2.	167	04
3.	250	56
4.	334	08
5.	417	60
6.	501	12
7.	584	64
8.	668	16
9.	751	68
10.	835	20
11.	918	72

Twelfths

	1.	0	4¾
1/6	2.	0	9¾
	3.	0	14½
1/3	4.	0	19¼
	5.	0	24¼
1/2	6.	0	29
	7.	0	33¾
2/3	8.	0	38¾
	9.	0	43½
5/6	10.	0	48¼
	11.	0	53¼

Twentieths

10ths		U	C	10ths		U	C
	1.	0	3		11.	0	32
·1	2.	0	5¾	·6	12.	0	34¾
	3.	0	8¾		13.	0	37¾
·2	4.	0	11½	·7	14.	0	40½
	5.	0	14½		15.	0	43½
·3	6.	0	17½	·8	16.	0	46½
	7.	0	20¼		17.	0	49¼
·4	8.	0	23¼	·9	18.	0	52¼
	9.	0	26		19.	0	55
·5	10.	0	29		20.	0	58

Sixteenths

	1.	0	3¾		9.	0	32¾
1/8	2.	0	7¼	5/8	10.	0	36¼
	3.	0	11		11.	0	40
1/4	4.	0	14½	3/4	12.	0	43½
	5.	0	18¼		13.	0	47¼
3/8	6.	0	21¾	7/8	14.	0	50¾
	7.	0	25½		15.	0	54½
1/2	8.	0	29				

*Dozens	£	P	Dozens	£	P	Dozens	£	P	Dozens	£	P		£	P
1	0	59	51	30	9	101	59	59	152	89	68	310	182	90
2	1	18	52	30	68	102	60	18	154	90	86	320	188	80
3	1	77	53	31	27	103	60	77	[13] 156	92	4	330	194	70
4	2	36	54	31	86	104	61	36	158	93	22	340	200	60
5	2	95	55	32	45	105	61	95	160	94	40	350	206	50
6	3	54	56	33	4	106	62	54	162	95	58	360	212	40
7	4	13	57	33	63	107	63	13	164	96	76	365	215	35
8	4	72	58	34	22	[9] 108	63	72	166	97	94	370	218	30
9	5	31	59	34	81	109	64	31	[14] 168	99	12	380	224	20
10	5	90	[5] **60**	35	40	**110**	64	90	170	100	30	390	230	10
*11	6	49	61	35	99	111	65	49	172	101	48	400	236	0
[1] 12	7	8	62	36	58	112	66	8	174	102	66	410	241	90
13	7	67	63	37	17	113	66	67	175	103	25	420	247	80
14	8	26	64	37	76	114	67	26	176	103	84	430	253	70
15	8	85	65	38	35	115	67	85	178	105	2	440	259	60
16	9	44	66	38	94	116	68	44	[15] 180	106	20	450	265	50
17	10	3	67	39	53	117	69	3	182	107	38	460	271	40
18	10	62	68	40	12	118	69	62	184	108	56	470	277	30
19	11	21	69	40	71	119	70	21	186	109	74	480	283	20
20	11	80	**70**	41	30	**120**	70	80	188	110	92	490	289	10
21	12	39	71	41	89	121	71	39	190	112	10	**500**	295	0
22	12	98	[6] 72	42	48	122	71	98	[16] 192	113	28	550	324	50
23	13	57	73	43	7	123	72	57	194	114	46	600	354	0
[2] 24	14	16	74	43	66	124	73	16	196	115	64	650	383	50
25	14	75	75	44	25	125	73	75	198	116	82	700	413	0
26	15	34	76	44	84	126	74	34	**200**	118	0	750	442	50
27	15	93	77	45	43	127	74	93	[17] 204	120	36	800	472	0
28	16	52	78	46	2	128	75	52	205	120	95	850	501	50
29	17	11	79	46	61	129	76	11	210	123	90	900	531	0
30	17	70	**80**	47	20	**130**	76	70	215	126	85	950	560	50
31	18	29	81	47	79	131	77	29	[18] 216	127	44	**1000**	590	0
32	18	88	82	48	38	[11] 132	77	88	220	129	80	1016	599	44
33	19	47	83	48	97	133	78	47	225	132	75	1250	737	50
34	20	6	[7] 84	49	56	134	79	6	[19] 228	134	52	1500	885	0
35	20	65	85	50	15	135	79	65	230	135	70	1728	1019	52
[3] 36	21	24	86	50	74	136	80	24	235	138	65	1750	1032	50
37	21	83	87	51	33	137	80	83	[20] 240	141	60	1760	1038	40
38	22	42	88	51	92	138	81	42	245	144	55	2000	1180	0
39	23	1	89	52	51	139	82	1	**250**	147	50	2240	1321	60
40	23	60	**90**	53	10	**140**	82	60	255	150	45	2500	1475	0
41	24	19	91	53	69	141	83	19	260	153	40	3000	1770	0
42	24	78	92	54	28	142	83	78	265	156	35	4000	2360	0
43	25	37	93	54	87	143	84	37	270	159	30	5000	2950	0
44	25	96	94	55	46	[12] 144	84	96	275	162	25	6000	3540	0
45	26	55	95	56	5	145	85	55	280	165	20	7000	4130	0
46	27	14	[8] 96	56	64	146	86	14	285	168	15	8000	4720	0
47	27	73	97	57	23	147	86	73	[24] 288	169	92	9000	5310	0
[4] 48	28	32	98	57	82	148	87	32	290	171	10	10000	5900	0
49	28	91	99	58	41	149	87	91	295	174	5	15000	8850	0
50	29	50	**100**	59	0	**150**	88	50	**300**	177	0	20000	11800	0

Grosses

	£	p
1.	84	96
2.	169	92
3.	254	88
4.	339	84
5.	424	80
6.	509	76
7.	594	72
8.	679	68
9.	764	64
10.	849	60
11.	934	56

Twelfths

		£	p
	1.	0	5
⅙	2.	0	9¾
	3.	0	14¾
⅓	4.	0	19¾
	5.	0	24½
½	6.	0	29½
	7.	0	34½
⅔	8.	0	39¼
	9.	0	44¼
⅚	10.	0	49¼
	11.	0	54

Twentieths

10ths		£	p			£	p
	1.	0	3		11.	0	32½
·1	2.	0	6	·6	12.	0	35½
	3.	0	8¾		13.	0	38¼
·2	4.	0	11¾	·7	14.	0	41¼
	5.	0	14¾		15.	0	44¼
·3	6.	0	17¾	·8	16.	0	47¼
	7.	0	20¾		17.	0	50¼
·4	8.	0	23½	·9	18.	0	53
	9.	0	26½		19.	0	56
·5	10.	0	29½		20.	0	59

Sixteenths

		£	p			£	p
	1.	0	3¾		9.	0	33¼
⅛	2.	0	7½	⅝	10.	0	37
	3.	0	11		11.	0	40½
¼	4.	0	14¾	¾	12.	0	44¼
	5.	0	18½		13.	0	48
⅜	6.	0	22¼	⅞	14.	0	51¾
	7.	0	25¾		15.	0	55¼
½	8.	0	29½				

No.	£	P	No.	£	P	No.	£	P	No.	£	P	No.	£	P
1	0	60	51	30	60	101	60	60	152	91	20	310	186	0
2	1	20	52	31	20	102	61	20	154	92	40	320	192	0
3	1	80	53	31	80	103	61	80	156	93	60	330	198	0
4	2	40	54	32	40	104	62	40	158	94	80	340	204	0
5	3	0	55	33	0	105	63	0	160	96	0	350	210	0
6	3	60	56	33	60	106	63	60	162	97	20	360	216	0
7	4	20	57	34	20	107	64	20	164	98	40	365	219	0
8	4	80	58	34	80	108	64	80	166	99	60	370	222	0
9	5	40	59	35	40	109	65	40	168	100	80	380	228	0
10	6	0	60	36	0	110	66	0	170	102	0	390	234	0
11	6	60	61	36	60	111	66	60	172	103	20	400	240	0
12	7	20	62	37	20	112	67	20	174	104	40	410	246	0
13	7	80	63	37	80	113	67	80	175	105	0	420	252	0
14	8	40	64	38	40	114	68	40	176	105	60	430	258	0
15	9	0	65	39	0	115	69	0	178	106	80	440	264	0
16	9	60	66	39	60	116	69	60	180	108	0	450	270	0
17	10	20	67	40	20	117	70	20	182	109	20	460	276	0
18	10	80	68	40	80	118	70	80	184	110	40	470	282	0
19	11	40	69	41	40	119	71	40	186	111	60	480	288	0
20	12	0	70	42	0	120	72	0	188	112	80	490	294	0
21	12	60	71	42	60	121	72	60	190	114	0	500	300	0
22	13	20	72	43	20	122	73	20	192	115	20	550	330	0
23	13	80	73	43	80	123	73	80	194	116	40	600	360	0
24	14	40	74	44	40	124	74	40	196	117	60	650	390	0
25	15	0	75	45	0	125	75	0	198	118	80	700	420	0
26	15	60	76	45	60	126	75	60	200	120	0	750	450	0
27	16	20	77	46	20	127	76	20	204	122	40	800	480	0
28	16	80	78	46	80	128	76	80	205	123	0	850	510	0
29	17	40	79	47	40	129	77	40	210	126	0	900	540	0
30	18	0	80	48	0	130	78	0	215	129	0	950	570	0
31	18	60	81	48	60	131	78	60	216	129	60	1000	600	0
32	19	20	82	49	20	132	79	20	220	132	0	1016	609	60
33	19	80	83	49	80	133	79	80	225	135	0	1250	750	0
34	20	40	84	50	40	134	80	40	226	135	60	1500	900	0
35	21	0	85	51	0	135	81	0	230	138	0	1728	1036	80
36	21	60	86	51	60	136	81	60	235	141	0	1750	1050	0
37	22	20	87	52	20	137	82	20	240	144	0	1760	1056	0
38	22	80	88	52	80	138	82	80	245	147	0	2000	1200	0
39	23	40	89	53	40	139	83	40	250	150	0	2240	1344	0
40	24	0	90	54	0	140	84	0	255	153	0	2500	1500	0
41	24	60	91	54	60	141	84	60	260	156	0	3000	1800	0
42	25	20	92	55	20	142	85	20	265	159	0	4000	2400	0
43	25	80	93	55	80	143	85	80	270	162	0	5000	3000	0
44	26	40	94	56	40	144	86	40	275	165	0	6000	3600	0
45	27	0	95	57	0	145	87	0	280	168	0	7000	4200	0
46	27	60	96	57	60	146	87	60	285	171	0	8000	4800	0
47	28	20	97	58	20	147	88	20	288	172	80	9000	5400	0
48	28	80	98	58	80	148	88	80	290	174	0	10000	6000	0
49	29	40	99	59	40	149	89	40	295	177	0	15000	9000	0
50	30	0	100	60	0	150	90	0	300	180	0	20000	12000	0

Grosses			Twelfths			10ths	Twentieths			Sixteenths				
1.	86	40	1.	1 0	5		1.	0	3	1.	0	3½	9.	0 33½
2.	172	80	½2.	0	10	x	2.	0	6	2.	0	7½	10.	0 37½
3.	259	20	3.	0	15		3.	0	9	3.	0	11¼	11.	0 41¼
4.	345	60	⅓4.	0	20	2	4.	0	12	4.	0	15	12.	0 45
5.	432	0	5.	0	25		5.	0	15	5.	0	18½	13.	0 48½
6.	518	40	½6.	0	30	3	6.	0	18	6.	0	22½	14.	0 52½
7.	604	80	7.	0	35		7.	0	21	7.	0	26¼	15.	0 56¼
8.	691	20	⅔8.	0	40	4	8.	0	24	8.	0	30		
9.	777	60	9.	0	45		9.	0	27					
10.	864	0	⅚10.	0	50	5	10.	0	30					
11.	950	40	11.	0	55									

Twentieths (continued): 11. 0 33   12. 0 36   13. 0 39   14. 0 42   15. 0 45   16. 0 48   17. 0 51   18. 0 54   19. 0 57   20. 0 60

	£	P		£	P		£	P		£	P		£	P
1	0	61	51	31	11	101	61	61	152	92	72	310	189	10
2	1	22	52	31	72	102	62	22	154	93	94	320	195	20
3	1	83	53	32	33	103	62	83	[13] 156	95	16	330	201	30
4	2	44	54	32	94	104	63	44	158	96	38	340	207	40
5	3	5	55	33	55	105	64	5	160	97	60	350	213	50
*6	3	66	56	34	16	106	64	66	162	98	82	360	219	60
7	4	27	57	34	77	107	65	27	164	100	4	365	222	65
8	4	88	58	35	38	[9] 108	65	88	166	101	26	370	225	70
9	5	49	59	35	99	109	66	49	[14] 168	102	48	380	231	80
10	6	10	[5] 60	36	60	110	67	10	170	103	70	390	237	90
*11	6	71	61	37	21	111	67	71	172	104	92	400	244	0
[1] 12	7	32	62	37	82	112	68	32	174	106	14	410	250	10
13	7	93	63	38	43	113	68	93	175	106	75	420	256	20
14	8	54	64	39	4	114	69	54	176	107	36	430	262	30
15	9	15	65	39	65	115	70	15	178	108	58	440	268	40
16	9	76	66	40	26	116	70	76	[15] 180	109	80	450	274	50
17	10	37	67	40	87	117	71	37	182	111	2	460	280	60
18	10	98	68	41	48	118	71	98	184	112	24	470	286	70
19	11	59	69	42	9	119	72	59	186	113	46	480	292	80
20	12	20	70	42	70	120	73	20	188	114	68	490	298	90
21	12	81	71	43	31	121	73	81	190	115	90	500	305	0
22	13	42	[6] 72	43	92	122	74	42	[16] 192	117	12	550	335	50
23	14	3	73	44	53	123	75	3	194	118	34	600	366	0
[2] 24	14	64	74	45	14	124	75	64	196	119	56	650	396	50
25	15	25	75	45	75	125	76	25	198	120	78	700	427	0
26	15	86	76	46	36	126	76	86	200	122	0	750	457	50
27	16	47	77	46	97	127	77	47	[17] 204	124	44	800	488	0
28	17	8	78	47	58	128	78	8	205	125	5	850	518	50
29	17	69	79	48	19	129	78	69	210	128	10	900	549	0
30	18	30	80	48	80	130	79	30	215	131	15	950	579	50
31	18	91	81	49	41	131	79	91	[18] 216	131	76	1000	610	0
32	19	52	82	50	2	[11] 132	80	52	220	134	20	1016	619	76
33	20	13	83	50	63	133	81	13	225	137	25	1250	762	50
34	20	74	[7] 84	51	24	134	81	74	[19] 228	139	8	1500	915	0
35	21	35	85	51	85	135	82	35	230	140	30	1728	1054	8
[3] 36	21	96	86	52	46	136	82	96	235	143	35	1750	1067	50
37	22	57	87	53	7	137	83	57	[20] 240	146	40	1760	1073	60
38	23	18	88	53	68	138	84	18	245	149	45	2000	1220	0
39	23	79	89	54	29	139	84	79	250	152	50	2240	1366	40
40	24	40	90	54	90	140	85	40	255	155	55	2500	1525	0
41	25	1	91	55	51	141	86	1	260	158	60	3000	1830	0
42	25	62	92	56	12	142	86	62	265	161	65	4000	2440	0
43	26	23	93	56	73	143	87	23	270	164	70	5000	3050	0
44	26	84	94	57	34	[12] 144	87	84	275	167	75	6000	3660	0
45	27	45	95	57	95	145	88	45	280	170	80	7000	4270	0
46	28	6	[8] 96	58	56	146	89	6	285	173	85	8000	4880	0
47	28	67	97	59	17	147	89	67	[24] 288	175	68	9000	5490	0
[4] 48	29	28	98	59	78	148	90	28	290	176	90	10000	6100	0
49	29	89	99	60	39	149	90	89	295	179	95	15000	9150	0
50	30	50	100	61	0	150	91	50	300	183	0	20000	12200	0

Grosses.

1.	87	84
2.	175	68
3.	263	52
4.	351	36
5.	439	20
6.	527	4
7.	614	88
8.	702	72
9.	790	56
10.	878	40
11.	966	24

Twelfths

	1.	0	5
1/6	2.	0	10¼
	3.	0	15¼
1/3	4.	0	20¼
	5.	0	25½
1/2	6.	0	30½
	7.	0	35½
2/3	8.	0	40¾
	9.	0	45¾
5/6	10.	0	50¾
	11.	0	56

Twentieths

10ths				10ths			
	1.	0	3		11.	0	33½
·1	2.	0	6	·6	12.	0	36½
	3.	0	9¼		13.	0	39¾
·2	4.	0	12¼	·7	14.	0	42¾
	5.	0	15¼		15.	0	45¾
·3	6.	0	18¼	8	16.	0	48¾
	7.	0	21¼		17.	0	51¾
·4	8.	0	24½	·9	18.	0	55
	9.	0	27½		19.	0	58
·5	10.	0	30½		20.	0	61

Sixteenths

	1.	0	3¾		9.	0	34¼
1/8	2.	0	7¾	5/8	10.	0	38¼
	3.	0	11½		11.	0	42
1/4	4.	0	15¼	3/4	12.	0	45¾
	5.	0	19		13.	0	49½
3/8	6.	0	23	7/8	14.	0	53½
	7.	0	26¾		15.	0	57¼
1/2	8.	0	30½				

Dozens		£	P
	1	0	62
	2	1	24
	3	1	86
	4	2	48
	5	3	10
*	6	3	72
	7	4	34
	8	4	96
	9	5	58
	10	6	20
*	11	6	82
1	12	7	44
	13	8	6
	14	8	68
	15	9	30
	16	9	92
	17	10	54
	18	11	16
	19	11	78
	20	12	40
	21	13	2
	22	13	64
	23	14	26
2	24	14	88
	25	15	50
	26	16	12
	27	16	74
	28	17	36
	29	17	98
	30	18	60
	31	19	22
	32	19	84
	33	20	46
	34	21	8
	35	21	70
3	36	22	32
	37	22	94
	38	23	56
	39	24	18
	40	24	80
	41	25	42
	42	26	4
	43	26	66
	44	27	28
	45	27	90
	46	28	52
	47	29	14
4	48	29	76
	49	30	38
	50	31	0

Dozens		£	P
	51	31	62
	52	32	24
	53	32	86
	54	33	48
	55	34	10
	56	34	72
	57	35	34
	58	35	96
	59	36	58
5	**60**	37	20
	61	37	82
	62	38	44
	63	39	6
	64	39	68
	65	40	30
	66	40	92
	67	41	54
	68	42	16
	69	42	78
	70	43	40
	71	44	2
6	72	44	64
	73	45	26
	74	45	88
	75	46	50
	76	47	12
	77	47	74
	78	48	36
	79	48	98
	80	49	60
	81	50	22
	82	50	84
	83	51	46
7	84	52	8
	85	52	70
	86	53	32
	87	53	94
	88	54	56
	89	55	18
	90	55	80
	91	56	42
	92	57	4
	93	57	66
	94	58	28
	95	58	90
8	96	59	52
	97	60	14
	98	60	76
	99	61	38
	100	62	0

Dozens		£	P
	101	62	62
	102	63	24
	103	63	86
	104	64	48
	105	65	10
	106	65	72
	107	66	34
9	108	66	96
	109	67	58
	110	68	20
	111	68	82
	112	69	44
	113	70	6
	114	70	68
	115	71	30
	116	71	92
	117	72	54
	118	73	16
	119	73	78
	120	74	40
	121	75	2
	122	75	64
	123	76	26
	124	76	88
	125	77	50
	126	78	12
	127	78	74
	128	79	36
	129	79	98
	130	80	60
	131	81	22
11	132	81	84
	133	82	46
	134	83	8
	135	83	70
	136	84	32
	137	84	94
	138	85	56
	139	86	18
	140	86	80
	141	87	42
	142	88	4
	143	88	66
12	144	89	28
	145	89	90
	146	90	52
	147	91	14
	148	91	76
	149	92	38
	150	93	0

Dozens		£	P
	152	94	24
	154	95	48
13	156	96	72
	158	97	96
	160	99	20
	162	100	44
	164	101	68
	166	102	92
14	168	104	16
	170	105	40
	172	106	64
	174	107	88
	175	108	50
	176	109	12
	178	110	36
15	180	111	60
	182	112	84
	184	114	8
	186	115	32
	188	116	56
	190	117	80
16	192	119	4
	194	120	28
	196	121	52
	198	122	76
	200	124	0
17	204	126	48
	205	127	10
	210	130	20
	215	133	30
18	216	133	92
	220	136	40
	225	139	50
19	228	141	36
	230	142	60
	235	145	70
20	240	148	80
	245	151	90
	250	155	0
	255	158	10
	260	161	20
	265	164	30
	270	167	40
	275	170	50
	280	173	60
	285	176	70
24	288	178	56
	290	179	80
	295	182	90
	300	186	0

	£	P
310	192	20
320	198	40
330	204	60
340	210	80
350	217	0
360	223	20
365	226	30
370	229	40
380	235	60
390	241	80
400	248	0
410	254	20
420	260	40
430	266	60
440	272	80
450	279	0
460	285	20
470	291	40
480	297	60
490	303	80
500	310	0
550	341	0
600	372	0
650	403	0
700	434	0
750	465	0
800	496	0
850	527	0
900	558	0
950	589	0
1000	620	0
1016	629	92
1250	775	0
1500	930	0
1728	1071	36
1750	1085	0
1760	1091	20
2000	1240	0
2240	1388	80
2500	1550	0
3000	1860	0
4000	2480	0
5000	3100	0
6000	3720	0
7000	4340	0
8000	4960	0
9000	5580	0
10000	6200	0
15000	9300	0
20000	12400	0

Grosses

1.	89	28
2.	178	56
3.	267	84
4.	357	12
5.	446	40
6.	535	68
7.	624	96
8.	714	24
9.	803	52
10.	892	80
11.	982	08

Twelfths

	1.		5¼
⅙	2.	0	10¼
	3.	0	15½
⅓	4.	0	20¾
	5.	0	25¾
½	6.	0	31
	7.	0	36¼
⅔	8.	0	41¼
	9.	0	46½
⅚	10.	0	51¾
	11.	0	56¾

Twentieths

10ths			
	1.	0	3
·1	2.	0	6¼
	3.	0	9¼
·2	4.	0	12½
	5.	0	15½
·3	6.	0	18½
	7.	0	21¾
·4	8.	0	24¾
	9.	0	28
·5	10.	0	31
	11.	0	34
·6	12.	0	37¼
	13.	0	40¼
7	14.	0	43½
	15.	0	46½
·8	16.	0	49½
	17.	0	52¾
·9	18.	0	55¾
	19.	0	59
	20.	0	62

Sixteenths

	1.	0	4
⅛	2.	0	7¾
	3.	0	11¾
¼	4.	0	15½
	5.	0	19½
⅜	6.	0	23¼
	7.	0	27¼
½	8.	0	31
	9.	0	35
⅝	10.	0	38¾
	11.	0	42¾
¾	12.	0	46½
	13.	0	50½
⅞	14.	0	54¼
	15.	0	58¼

63 Pence 63 Pence

Dozens.	£	P	Dozens.	£	P	Dozens.	£	P	Doz.	£	P		£	P
1	0	63	51	32	13	101	63	63	152	95	76	310	195	30
2	1	26	52	32	76	102	64	26	154	97	2	320	201	60
3	1	89	53	33	39	103	64	89	[13] 156	98	28	330	207	90
4	2	52	54	34	2	104	65	52	158	99	54	340	214	20
5	3	15	55	34	65	105	66	15	160	100	80	350	220	50
* 6	3	78	56	35	28	106	66	78	162	102	6	360	226	80
7	4	41	57	35	91	107	67	41	164	103	32	365	229	95
8	5	4	58	36	54	[9] 108	68	4	166	104	58	370	233	10
9	5	67	59	37	17	109	68	67	[14] 168	105	84	380	239	40
10	6	30	[5] **60**	37	80	**110**	69	30	170	107	10	390	245	70
11	6	93	61	38	43	111	69	93	172	108	36	400	252	0
*[1] 12	7	56	62	39	6	112	70	56	174	109	62	410	258	30
13	8	19	63	39	69	113	71	19	175	110	25	420	264	60
14	8	82	64	40	32	114	71	82	176	110	88	430	270	90
15	9	45	65	40	95	115	72	45	178	112	14	440	277	20
16	10	8	66	41	58	116	73	8	[15] 180	113	40	450	283	50
17	10	71	67	42	21	117	73	71	182	114	66	460	289	80
18	11	34	68	42	84	118	74	34	184	115	92	470	296	10
19	11	97	69	43	47	119	74	97	186	117	18	480	302	40
20	12	60	**70**	44	10	**120**	75	60	188	118	44	490	308	70
21	13	23	71	44	73	121	76	23	190	119	70	**500**	315	0
22	13	86	[6] 72	45	36	122	76	86	[16] 192	120	96	550	346	50
23	14	49	73	45	99	123	77	49	194	122	22	600	378	0
[2] 24	15	12	74	46	62	124	78	12	196	123	48	650	409	50
25	15	75	75	47	25	125	78	75	198	124	74	700	441	0
26	16	38	76	47	88	126	79	38	**200**	126	0	750	472	50
27	17	1	77	48	51	127	80	1	[17] 204	128	52	800	504	0
28	17	64	78	49	14	128	80	64	205	129	15	850	535	50
29	18	27	79	49	77	129	81	27	210	132	30	900	567	0
30	18	90	**80**	50	40	**130**	81	90	215	135	45	950	598	50
31	19	53	81	51	3	131	82	53	[18] 216	136	8	**1000**	630	0
32	20	16	82	51	66	[11] 132	83	16	220	138	60	1016	640	8
33	20	79	83	52	29	133	83	79	225	141	75	1250	787	50
34	21	42	[7] 84	52	92	134	84	42	[19] 228	143	64	1500	945	0
35	22	5	85	53	55	135	85	5	230	144	90	1728	1088	64
[3] 36	22	68	86	54	18	136	85	68	235	148	5	1750	1102	50
37	23	31	87	54	81	137	86	31	[20] 240	151	20	1760	1108	80
38	23	94	88	55	44	138	86	94	245	154	35	2000	1260	0
39	24	57	89	56	7	139	87	57	**250**	157	50	2240	1411	20
40	25	20	**90**	56	70	**140**	88	20	255	160	65	2500	1575	0
41	25	83	91	57	33	141	88	83	260	163	80	3000	1890	0
42	26	46	92	57	96	142	89	46	265	166	95	4000	2520	0
43	27	9	93	58	59	143	90	9	270	170	10	**5000**	3150	0
44	27	72	94	59	22	[12] 144	90	72	275	173	25	6000	3780	0
45	28	35	95	59	85	145	91	35	280	176	40	7000	4410	0
46	28	98	[8] 96	60	48	146	91	98	285	179	55	8000	5040	0
47	29	61	97	61	11	147	92	61	[24] 288	181	44	9000	5670	0
[4] 48	30	24	98	61	74	148	93	24	290	182	70	10000	6300	0
49	30	87	99	62	37	149	93	87	295	185	85	15000	9450	0
50	31	50	**100**	63	0	**150**	94	50	**300**	189	0	20000	12600	0

Grosses.

1.	90	72
2.	181	44
3.	272	16
4.	362	88
5.	453	60
6.	544	32
7.	635	04
8.	725	76
9.	816	48
10.	907	20
11.	997	92

Twelfths

	1.	0	5¼
$\frac{1}{6}$	2.	0	10½
	3.	0	15¾
$\frac{1}{3}$	4.	0	21
	5.	0	26¼
$\frac{1}{2}$	6.	0	31½
	7.	0	36¾
$\frac{2}{3}$	8.	0	42
	9.	0	47¼
$\frac{5}{6}$	10.	0	52½
	11.	0	57¾

Twentieths (10ths)

10ths				10ths			
	1.	0	3¼		11.	0	34¾
·1	2.	0	6¼	·6	12.	0	37¾
	3.	0	9½		13.	0	41
·2	4.	0	12½	·7	14.	0	44
	5.	0	15¾		15.	0	47¼
·3	6.	0	19	8	16.	0	50½
	7.	0	22		17.	0	53½
·4	8.	0	25¼	·9	18.	0	56¾
	9.	0	28¼		19.	0	59¾
·5	10.	0	31½		20.	0	63

Sixteenths

	1.	0	4		9.	0	35½
$\frac{1}{8}$	2.	0	8	$\frac{5}{8}$	10.	0	39½
	3.	0	11¾		11.	0	43¼
$\frac{1}{4}$	4.	0	15¾	$\frac{3}{4}$	12.	0	47¼
	5.	0	19¾		13.	0	51¼
$\frac{3}{8}$	6.	0	23¾	$\frac{7}{8}$	14.	0	55¼
	7.	0	27½		15.	0	59
$\frac{1}{2}$	8.	0	31½				

No.	£ P	No.	£ P	No.	£ P	No.	£ P	No.	£ P
1	0 64	51	32 64	101	64 64	152	97 28	310	198 40
2	1 28	52	33 28	102	65 28	154	98 56	320	204 80
3	1 92	53	33 92	103	65 92	156	99 84	330	211 20
4	2 56	54	34 56	104	66 56	158	101 12	340	217 60
5	3 20	55	35 20	105	67 20	160	102 40	350	224 0
6	3 84	56	35 84	106	67 84	162	103 68	360	230 40
7	4 48	57	36 48	107	68 48	164	104 96	365	233 60
8	5 12	58	37 12	108	69 12	166	106 24	370	236 80
9	5 76	59	37 76	109	69 76	168	107 52	380	243 20
10	6 40	60	38 40	110	70 40	170	108 80	390	249 60
11	7 4	61	39 4	111	71 4	172	110 8	400	256 0
12	7 68	62	39 68	112	71 68	174	111 36	410	262 40
13	8 32	63	40 32	113	72 32	176	112 64	420	268 80
14	8 96	64	40 96	114	72 96	178	113 92	430	275 20
15	9 60	65	41 60	115	73 60	180	115 20	440	281 60
16	10 24	66	42 24	116	74 24	182	116 48	450	288 0
17	10 88	67	42 88	117	74 88	184	117 76	460	294 40
18	11 52	68	43 52	118	75 52	186	119 4	470	300 80
19	12 16	69	44 16	119	76 16	188	120 32	480	307 20
20	12 80	70	44 80	120	76 80	190	121 60	490	313 60
21	13 44	71	45 44	121	77 44	192	122 88	500	320 0
22	14 8	72	46 8	122	78 8	194	124 16	550	352 0
23	14 72	73	46 72	123	78 72	196	125 44	600	384 0
24	15 36	74	47 36	124	79 36	198	126 72	650	416 0
25	16 0	75	48 0	125	80 0	200	128 0	700	448 0
26	16 64	76	48 64	126	80 64	204	130 56	750	480 0
27	17 28	77	49 28	127	81 28	205	131 20	800	512 0
28	17 92	78	49 92	128	81 92	210	134 40	850	544 0
29	18 56	79	50 56	129	82 56	215	137 60	900	576 0
30	19 20	80	51 20	130	83 20	216	138 24	950	608 0
31	19 84	81	51 84	131	83 84	220	140 80	1000	640 0
32	20 48	82	52 48	132	84 48	225	144 0	1016	650 24
33	21 12	83	53 12	133	85 12	228	145 92	1250	800 0
34	21 76	84	53 76	134	85 76	230	147 20	1500	960 0
35	22 40	85	54 40	135	86 40	235	150 40	1728	1105 92
36	23 4	86	55 4	136	87 4	240	153 60	1750	1120 0
37	23 68	87	55 68	137	87 68	245	156 80	1760	1126 40
38	24 32	88	56 32	138	88 32	250	160 0	2000	1280 0
39	24 96	89	56 96	139	88 96	255	163 20	2240	1433 60
40	25 60	90	57 60	140	89 60	260	166 40	2500	1600 0
41	26 24	91	58 24	141	90 24	265	169 60	3000	1920 0
42	26 88	92	58 88	142	90 88	270	172 80	4000	2560 0
43	27 52	93	59 52	143	91 52	275	176 0	5000	3200 0
44	28 16	94	60 16	144	92 16	280	179 20	6000	3840 0
45	28 80	95	60 80	145	92 80	285	182 40	7000	4480 0
46	29 44	96	61 44	146	93 44	288	184 32	8000	5120 0
47	30 8	97	62 8	147	94 8	290	185 60	9000	5760 0
48	30 72	98	62 72	148	94 72	295	188 80	10000	6400 0
49	31 36	99	63 36	149	95 36	300	192 0	15000	9600 0
50	32 0	100	64 0	150	96 0			20000	12800 0

Grosses		Twelfths		Twentieths		Sixteenths	
1.	92 16	1.	0 5⅓	1. 0 3⅕	11. 0 35⅕	1. 0 4	9. 0 36
2.	184 32	2.	0 10⅔	2. 0 6⅖	12. 0 38⅖	2. 0 8	10. 0 40
3.	276 48	3.	0 16	3. 0 9⅗	13. 0 41⅗	3. 0 12	11. 0 44
4.	368 64	4.	0 21⅓	4. 0 12⅘	14. 0 44⅘	4. 0 16	12. 0 48
5.	460 80	5.	0 26⅔	5. 0 16	15. 0 48	5. 0 20	13. 0 52
6.	552 96	6.	0 32	6. 0 19⅕	16. 0 51⅕	6. 0 24	14. 0 56
7.	645 12	7.	0 37⅓	7. 0 22⅖	17. 0 54⅖	7. 0 28	15. 0 60
8.	737 28	8.	0 42⅔	8. 0 25⅗	18. 0 57⅗	8. 0 32	
9.	829 44	9.	0 48	9. 0 28⅘	19. 0 60⅘		
10.	921 60	10.	0 53⅓	10. 0 32	20. 0 64		
11.	1013 76	11.	0 58⅔				

	£	P		£	P		£	P		£	P		£	P
1	0	65	51	33	15	101	65	65	152	98	80	310	201	50
2	1	30	52	33	80	102	66	30	154	100	10	320	208	0
3	1	95	53	34	45	103	66	95	[13] 156	101	40	330	214	50
4	2	60	54	35	10	104	67	60	158	102	70	340	221	0
5	3	25	55	35	75	105	68	25	160	104	0	350	227	50
6	3	90	56	36	40	106	68	90	162	105	30	360	234	0
7	4	55	57	37	5	107	69	55	164	106	60	365	237	25
8	5	20	58	37	70	[9] 108	70	20	166	107	90	370	240	50
9	5	85	59	38	35	109	70	85	[14] 168	109	20	380	247	0
10	**6**	**50**	[5] **60**	**39**	**0**	**110**	**71**	**50**	170	110	50	390	253	50
*11	7	15	61	39	65	111	72	15	172	111	80	400	260	0
[1] 12	7	80	62	40	30	112	72	80	174	113	10	410	266	50
13	8	45	63	40	95	113	73	45	175	113	75	420	273	0
14	9	10	64	41	60	114	74	10	176	114	40	430	279	50
15	9	75	65	42	25	115	74	75	178	115	70	440	286	0
16	10	40	66	42	90	116	75	40	[15] 180	117	0	450	292	50
17	11	5	67	43	55	117	76	5	182	118	30	460	299	0
18	11	70	68	44	20	118	76	70	184	119	60	470	305	50
19	12	35	69	44	85	119	77	35	186	120	90	480	312	0
20	**13**	**0**	**70**	**45**	**50**	**120**	**78**	**0**	188	122	20	490	318	50
21	13	65	71	46	15	121	78	65	190	123	50	**500**	**325**	**0**
22	14	30	[6] 72	46	80	122	79	30	[16] 192	124	80	550	357	50
23	14	95	73	47	45	123	79	95	194	126	10	600	390	0
[2] 24	15	60	74	48	10	124	80	60	196	127	40	650	422	50
25	16	25	75	48	75	125	81	25	198	128	70	700	455	0
26	16	90	76	49	40	126	81	90	**200**	**130**	**0**	750	487	50
27	17	55	77	50	5	127	82	55	[17] 204	132	60	800	520	0
28	18	20	78	50	70	128	83	20	205	133	25	850	552	50
29	18	85	79	51	35	129	83	85	210	136	50	900	585	0
30	**19**	**50**	**80**	**52**	**0**	**130**	**84**	**50**	215	139	75	950	617	50
31	20	15	81	52	65	131	85	15	[18] 216	140	40	**1000**	**650**	**0**
32	20	80	82	53	30	[11] 132	85	80	220	143	0	1016	660	40
33	21	45	83	53	95	133	86	45	225	146	25	1250	812	50
34	22	10	[7] 84	54	60	134	87	10	[19] 228	148	20	1500	975	0
35	22	75	85	55	25	135	87	75	230	149	50	1728	1123	20
[3] 36	23	40	86	55	90	136	88	40	235	152	75	1750	1137	50
37	24	5	87	56	55	137	89	5	[20] 240	156	0	1760	1144	0
38	24	70	88	57	20	138	89	70	245	159	25	2000	1300	0
39	25	35	89	57	85	139	90	35	**250**	**162**	**50**	2240	1456	0
40	**26**	**0**	**90**	**58**	**50**	**140**	**91**	**0**	255	165	75	2500	1625	0
41	26	65	91	59	15	141	91	65	260	169	0	3000	1950	0
42	27	30	92	59	80	142	92	30	265	172	25	4000	2600	0
43	27	95	93	60	45	143	92	95	270	175	50	5000	3250	0
44	28	60	94	61	10	[12] 144	93	60	275	178	75	6000	3900	0
45	29	25	95	61	75	145	94	25	280	182	0	7000	4550	0
46	29	90	[8] 96	62	40	146	94	90	285	185	25	8000	5200	0
47	30	55	97	63	5	147	95	55	[24] 288	187	20	9000	5850	0
[4] 48	31	20	98	63	70	148	96	20	290	188	50	10000	6500	0
49	31	85	99	64	35	149	96	85	295	191	75	15000	9750	0
50	**32**	**50**	**100**	**65**	**0**	**150**	**97**	**50**	**300**	**195**	**0**	20000	13000	0

*Dozens

Grosses

1.	93	60
2.	187	20
3.	280	80
4.	374	40
5.	468	0
6.	561	60
7.	655	20
8.	748	80
9.	842	40
10.	936	0
11.	1029	60

Twelfths

	1.	0	5½
⅙	2.	0	10¾
	3.	0	16¼
⅓	4.	0	21¾
	5.	0	27
½	6.	0	32½
	7.	0	38
⅔	8.	0	43
	9.	0	48¾
⅚	10.	0	54¼
	11.	0	59½

Twentieths

10ths				10ths			
	1.	0	3¼		11.	0	35¾
·1	2.	0	6½	·6	12.	0	39
	3.	0	9¾		13.	0	42¼
·2	4.	0	13	·7	14.	0	45½
	5.	0	16¼		15.	0	48¾
·3	6.	0	19½	·8	16.	0	52
	7.	0	22¾		17.	0	55¼
·4	8.	0	26	·9	18.	0	58½
	9.	0	29¼		19.	0	61¾
·5	10.	0	32½		20.	0	65

Sixteenths

	1.	0	4		9.	0	36½
⅛	2.	0	8¼	⅝	10.	0	40¾
	3.	0	12¼		11.	0	44¾
¼	4.	0	16¼	¾	12.	0	48¾
	5.	0	20¼		13.	0	52¾
⅜	6.	0	24½	⅞	14.	0	57
	7.	0	28½		15.	0	61
½	8.	0	32½				

No.	£	P		No.	£	P		No.	£	P		Doz	No.	£	P		No.	£	P
1	0	66		51	33	66		101	66	66			152	100	32		310	204	60
2	1	32		52	34	32		102	67	32			154	101	64		320	211	20
3	1	98		53	34	98		103	67	98		13	156	102	96		330	217	80
4	2	64		54	35	64		104	68	64			158	104	28		340	224	40
5	3	30		55	36	30		105	69	30			160	105	60		350	231	0
6	3	96		56	36	96		106	69	96			162	106	92		360	237	60
7	4	62		57	37	62		107	70	62			164	108	24		365	240	90
8	5	28		58	38	28		108	71	28		14	166	109	56		370	244	20
9	5	94		59	38	94		109	71	94			168	110	88		380	250	80
10	6	60		60	39	60		110	72	60			170	112	20		390	257	40
11	7	26		61	40	26		111	73	26			172	113	52		400	264	0
12	7	92		62	40	92		112	73	92			174	114	84		410	270	60
13	8	58		63	41	58		113	74	58			175	115	50		420	277	20
14	9	24		64	42	24		114	75	24			176	116	16		430	283	80
15	9	90		65	42	90		115	75	90			178	117	48		440	290	40
16	10	56		66	43	56		116	76	56		15	180	118	80		450	297	0
17	11	22		67	44	22		117	77	22			182	120	12		460	303	60
18	11	88		68	44	88		118	77	88			184	121	44		470	310	20
19	12	54		69	45	54		119	78	54			186	122	76		480	316	80
20	13	20		70	46	20		120	79	20			188	124	8		490	323	40
21	13	86		71	46	86		121	79	86			190	125	40		500	330	0
22	14	52		72	47	52		122	80	52		16	192	126	72		550	363	0
23	15	18		73	48	18		123	81	18			194	128	4		600	396	0
24	15	84		74	48	84		124	81	84			196	129	36		650	429	0
25	16	50		75	49	50		125	82	50			198	130	68		700	462	0
26	17	16		76	50	16		126	83	16			200	132	0		750	495	0
27	17	82		77	50	82		127	83	82		17	204	134	64		800	528	0
28	18	48		78	51	48		128	84	48			205	135	30		850	561	0
29	19	14		79	52	14		129	85	14			210	138	60		900	594	0
30	19	80		80	52	80		130	85	80			215	141	90		950	627	0
31	20	46		81	53	46		131	86	46		18	216	142	56		1000	660	0
32	21	12		82	54	12		132	87	12			220	145	20		1016	670	56
33	21	78		83	54	78		133	87	78			225	148	50		1250	825	0
34	22	44		84	55	44		134	88	44		19	228	150	48		1500	990	0
35	23	10		85	56	10		135	89	10			230	151	80		1728	1140	48
36	23	76		86	56	76		136	89	76			235	155	10		1750	1155	0
37	24	42		87	57	42		137	90	42		20	240	158	40		1760	1161	60
38	25	8		88	58	8		138	91	8			245	161	70		2000	1320	0
39	25	74		89	58	74		139	91	74			250	165	0		2240	1478	40
40	26	40		90	59	40		140	92	40			255	168	30		2500	1650	0
41	27	6		91	60	6		141	93	6			260	171	60		3000	1980	0
42	27	72		92	60	72		142	93	72			270	178	20		4000	2640	0
43	28	38		93	61	38		143	94	38			275	181	50		5000	3300	0
44	29	4		94	62	4		144	95	4			280	184	80		6000	3960	0
45	29	70		95	62	70		145	95	70			285	188	10		7000	4620	0
46	30	36		96	63	36		146	96	36		24	288	190	8		8000	5280	0
47	31	2		97	64	2		147	97	2			290	191	40		9000	5940	0
48	31	68		98	64	68		148	97	68			295	194	70		10000	6600	0
49	32	34		99	65	34		149	98	34			300	198	0		15000	9900	0
50	33	0		100	66	0		150	99	0							20000	13200	0

Grosses			Twelfths				10ths	Twentieths					Sixteenths		
1.	95	4		1.	0	5½		1.	0	3¼		11.	0	36½
2.	190	8	⅙	2.	0	11	·1	2.	0	6½	·6	12.	0	39½
3.	285	12		3.	0	16½		3.	0	10		13.	0	43
4.	380	16	¼	4.	0	22	·2	4.	0	13¼	·7	14.	0	46¼
5.	475	20		5.	0	27½		5.	0	16½		15.	0	49½
6.	570	24	½	6.	0	33	·3	6.	0	19¾	·8	16.	0	52¾
7.	665	28		7.	0	38½		7.	0	23		17.	0	56
8.	760	32	⅔	8.	0	44	·4	8.	0	26¼	·9	18.	0	59¼
9.	855	36		9.	0	49½		9.	0	29½		19.	0	62¾
10.	950	40	¾	10.	0	55	·5	10.	0	33		20.	0	66
11.	1045	44		11.	0	60½								

Sixteenths:

1.	0	4¼		9.	0	37½
½ 2.	0	8¼	⅝ 10.	0	41¼
3.	0	12½		11.	0	45½
¼ 4.	0	16½	¾ 12.	0	49½
5.	0	20¾		13.	0	53¾
⅜ 6.	0	24¾	⅞ 14.	0	57¾
7.	0	29		15.	0	62
½ 8.	0	33				

	£	P		£	P		£	P		£	P		£	P
1	0	67	51	34	17	101	67	67	152	101	84	310	207	70
2	1	34	52	34	84	102	68	34	154	103	18	320	214	40
3	2	1	53	35	51	103	69	1	13 156	104	52	330	221	10
*4	2	68	54	36	18	104	69	68	158	105	86	340	227	80
5	3	35	55	36	85	105	70	35	160	107	20	350	234	50
6	4	2	56	37	52	106	71	2	162	108	54	360	241	20
7	4	69	57	38	19	107	71	69	164	109	88	365	244	55
8	5	36	58	38	86	108	72	36	166	111	22	370	247	90
9	6	3	59	39	53	9 108	72	36	168	112	56	380	254	60
10	6	70	5 60	40	20	109	73	3	14 168	112	56	390	261	30
11	7	37	61	40	87	110	73	70	170	113	90	400	268	0
1 12	8	4	62	41	54	111	74	37	172	115	24	410	274	70
13	8	71	63	42	21	112	75	4	174	116	58	420	281	40
14	9	38	64	42	88	113	75	71	175	117	25	430	288	10
15	10	5	65	43	55	114	76	38	176	117	92	440	294	80
16	10	72	66	44	22	115	77	5	178	119	26	450	301	50
17	11	39	67	44	89	116	77	72	15 180	120	60	460	308	20
18	12	6	68	45	56	117	78	39	182	121	94	470	314	90
19	12	73	69	46	23	118	79	6	184	123	28	480	321	60
20	13	40	70	46	90	119	79	73	186	124	62	490	328	30
21	14	7	71	47	57	120	80	40	188	125	96	500	335	0
22	14	74	6 72	48	24	121	81	7	190	127	30	550	368	50
23	15	41	73	48	91	122	81	74	16 192	128	64	600	402	0
2 24	16	8	74	49	58	123	82	41	194	129	98	650	435	50
25	16	75	75	50	25	124	83	8	196	131	32	700	469	0
26	17	42	76	50	92	125	83	75	198	132	66	7b0	502	50
27	18	9	77	51	59	126	84	42	200	134	0	800	536	0
28	18	76	78	52	26	127	85	9	17 204	136	68	850	569	50
29	19	43	79	52	93	128	85	76	205	137	35	900	603	0
30	20	10	80	53	60	129	86	43	210	140	70	950	636	50
31	20	77	81	54	27	130	87	10	215	144	5	1000	670	0
32	21	44	82	54	94	131	87	77	18 216	144	72	1016	680	72
33	22	11	83	55	61	11 132	88	44	220	147	40	1250	837	50
34	22	78	7 84	56	28	133	89	11	225	150	75	1500	1005	0
35	23	45	85	56	95	134	89	78	19 228	152	76	1728	1157	76
3 36	24	12	86	57	62	135	90	45	230	154	10	1750	1172	50
37	24	79	87	58	29	136	91	12	235	157	45	1760	1179	20
38	25	46	88	58	96	137	91	79	20 240	160	80	2000	1340	0
39	26	13	89	59	63	138	92	46	245	164	15	2240	1500	80
40	26	80	90	60	30	139	93	13	250	167	50	2500	1675	0
41	27	47	91	60	97	140	93	80	255	170	85	3000	2010	0
42	28	14	92	61	64	141	94	47	260	174	20	4000	2680	0
43	28	81	93	62	31	142	95	14	265	177	55	5000	3350	0
44	29	48	94	62	98	143	95	81	270	180	90	6000	4020	0
45	30	15	95	63	65	12 144	96	48	275	184	25	7000	4690	0
46	30	82	8 96	64	32	145	97	15	280	187	60	8000	5360	0
47	31	49	97	64	99	146	97	82	285	190	95	9000	6030	0
4 48	32	16	98	65	66	147	98	49	24 288	192	96	10000	6700	0
49	32	83	99	66	33	148	99	16	290	194	30	15000	10050	0
50	33	50	100	67	0	149	99	83	295	197	65	20000	13400	0
						150	100	50	300	201	0			

Grosses			Twelfths			10th	Twentieths						Sixteenths				
1.	96	48		1.	0	5½		1.	0	3½	11.	0	36½	1.	0	4¼	9.	0	37½
2.	192	96	½ 2.	0	11½	·1	2.	0	7	·6 12.	0	40½	½ 2.	0	8½	⅝ 10.	0	42
3.	289	44	3.	0	16½		3.	0	10	13.	0	43½	3.	0	12½	11.	0	46
4.	385	92	¼ 4.	0	22½	·2	4.	0	13½	·7 14.	0	47	¼ 4.	0	16½	¾ 12.	0	50½
5.	482	40	5.	0	28		5.	0	16½	15.	0	50½	5.	0	21	13.	0	54½
6.	578	88	⅓ 6.	0	33½	·3	6.	0	20	·8 16.	0	53½	⅜ 6.	0	25½	14.	0	58½
7.	675	36	7.	0	39		7.	0	23½	17.	0	57	7.	0	29½	⅞ 14.	0	58½
8.	771	84	½ 8.	0	44½	·4	8.	0	26½	·9 18.	0	60½	8.	0	33½	15.	0	62½
9.	868	32	9.	0	50½		9.	0	30½	19.	0	63½						
10.	964	80	⅔ 10.	0	55½	·5	10.	0	33½	20.	0	67						
11.	1061	28	11.	0	61½													

*Dozens		£	P	Dozens		£	P	Dozens		£	P	Dozens		£	P		£	P
	1	0	68		51	34	68		101	68	68		152	103	36	310	210	80
	2	1	36		52	35	36		102	69	36		154	104	72	320	217	60
	3	2	4		53	36	4		103	70	4	13	156	106	8	330	224	40
	4	2	72		54	36	72		104	70	72		158	107	44	340	231	20
	5	3	40		55	37	40		105	71	40		160	108	80	350	238	0
	6	4	8		56	38	8		106	72	8		162	110	16	360	244	80
	7	4	76		57	38	76		107	72	76		164	111	52	365	248	20
	8	5	44		58	39	44	9	108	73	44		166	112	88	370	251	60
	9	6	12		59	40	12		109	74	12	14	168	114	24	380	258	40
	10	6	80	5	60	40	80		110	74	80		170	115	60	390	265	20
	11	7	48		61	41	48		111	75	48		172	116	96	400	272	0
*1	12	8	16		62	42	16		112	76	16		174	118	32	410	278	80
	13	8	84		63	42	84		113	76	84		175	119	0	420	285	60
	14	9	52		64	43	52		114	77	52		176	119	68	430	292	40
	15	10	20		65	44	20		115	78	20		178	121	4	440	299	20
	16	10	88		66	44	88		116	78	88	15	180	122	40	450	306	0
	17	11	56		67	45	56		117	79	56		182	123	76	460	312	80
	18	12	24		68	46	24		118	80	24		184	125	12	470	319	60
	19	12	92		69	46	92		119	80	92		186	126	48	480	326	40
	20	13	60		70	47	60	10	120	81	60		188	127	84	490	333	20
	21	14	28		71	48	28		121	82	28		190	129	20	500	340	0
	22	14	96	6	72	48	96		122	82	96	16	192	130	56	550	374	0
	23	15	64		73	49	64		123	83	64		194	131	92	600	408	0
2	24	16	32		74	50	32		124	84	32		196	133	28	650	442	0
	25	17	0		75	51	0		125	85	0		198	134	64	700	476	0
	26	17	68		76	51	68		126	85	68		200	136	0	750	510	0
	27	18	36		77	52	36		127	86	36	17	204	138	72	800	544	0
	28	19	4		78	53	4		128	87	4		205	139	40	850	578	0
	29	19	72		79	53	72		129	87	72		210	142	80	900	612	0
	30	20	40		80	54	40		130	88	40		215	146	20	950	646	0
	31	21	8		81	55	8		131	89	8	18	216	146	88	1000	680	0
	32	21	76		82	55	76	11	132	89	76		220	149	60	1016	690	88
	33	22	44		83	56	44		133	90	44		225	153	0	1250	850	0
	34	23	12	7	84	57	12		134	91	12	19	228	155	4	1500	1020	0
	35	23	80		85	57	80		135	91	80		230	156	40	1728	1175	4
3	36	24	48		86	58	48		136	92	48		235	159	80	1750	1190	0
	37	25	16		87	59	16		137	93	16	20	240	163	20	1760	1196	80
	38	25	84		88	59	84		138	93	84		245	166	60	2000	1360	0
	39	26	52		89	60	52		139	94	52		250	170	0	2240	1523	20
	40	27	20		90	61	20		140	95	20		255	173	40	2500	1700	0
	41	27	88		91	61	88		141	95	88		260	176	80	3000	2040	0
	42	28	56		92	62	56		142	96	56		265	180	20	4000	2720	0
	43	29	24		93	63	24		143	97	24		270	183	60	5000	3400	0
	44	29	92		94	63	92	12	144	97	92		275	187	0	6000	4080	0
	45	30	60		95	64	60		145	98	60		280	190	40	7000	4760	0
	46	31	28	8	96	65	28		146	99	28		285	193	80	8000	5440	0
	47	31	96		97	65	96		147	99	96	24	288	195	84	9000	6120	0
4	48	32	64		98	66	64		148	100	64		290	197	20	10000	6800	0
	49	33	32		99	67	32		149	101	32		295	200	60	15000	10200	0
	50	34	0		100	68	0		150	102	0		300	204	0	20000	13600	0

Grosses

1.	97	92
2.	195	84
3.	293	76
4.	391	68
5.	489	60
6.	587	52
7.	685	44
8.	783	36
9.	881	28
10.	979	20
11.	1077	12

Twelfths

	1.	0	5¾
⅙	2.	0	11¼
	3.	0	17
⅓	4.	0	22¾
	5.	0	28¼
½	6.	0	34
	7.	0	39¾
⅔	8.	0	45¼
	9.	0	51
⅚	10.	0	56¾
	11.	0	62¼

10ths / Twentieths

10ths				10ths			
	1.	0	3½		11.	0	37½
·1	2.	0	6¾	·6	12.	0	40¾
	3.	0	10¼		13.	0	44¼
·2	4.	0	13½	·7	14.	0	47½
	5.	0	17		15.	0	51
·3	6.	0	20½	·8	16.	0	54½
	7.	0	23¾		17.	0	57¾
·4	8.	0	27¼	·9	18.	0	61¼
	9.	0	30½		19.	0	64½
·5	10.	0	34		20.	0	68

Sixteenths

	1.	0	4¼		9.	0	38¼
⅛	2.	0	8½	⅝	10.	0	42½
	3.	0	12¾		11.	0	46¾
¼	4.	0	17	¾	12.	0	51
	5.	0	21¼		13.	0	55¼
⅜	6.	0	25½	⅞	14.	0	59½
	7.	0	29¾		15.	0	63¾
½	8.	0	34				

*Dozens		£	P	Dozens		£	P	Dozens		£	P	Dozens		£	P		£	P
	1	0	69		51	35	19		101	69	69		152	104	88	310	213	90
	2	1	38		52	35	88		102	70	38		154	106	26	320	220	80
	3	2	7		53	36	57		103	71	7	13	156	107	64	330	227	70
	4	2	76		54	37	26		104	71	76		158	109	2	340	234	60
	5	3	45		55	37	95		105	72	45		160	110	40	350	241	50
	6	4	14		56	38	64		106	73	14		162	111	78	360	248	40
	7	4	83		57	39	33		107	73	83		164	113	16	365	251	85
	8	5	52		58	40	2	9	108	74	52		166	114	54	370	255	30
	9	6	21		59	40	71		109	75	21	14	168	115	92	380	262	20
	10	6	90	5	**60**	41	40		**110**	75	90		170	117	30	390	269	10
	11	7	59		61	42	9		111	76	59		172	118	68	400	276	0
1	12	8	28		62	42	78		112	77	28		174	120	6	410	282	90
	13	8	97		63	43	47		113	77	97		175	120	75	420	289	80
	14	9	66		64	44	16		114	78	66		176	121	44	430	296	70
	15	10	35		65	44	85		115	79	35		178	122	82	440	303	60
	16	11	4		66	45	54		116	80	4	15	180	124	20	450	310	50
	17	11	73		67	46	23		117	80	73		182	125	58	460	317	40
	18	12	42		68	46	92		118	81	42		184	126	96	470	324	30
	19	13	11		69	47	61		119	82	11		186	128	34	480	331	20
	20	13	80		**70**	48	30		**120**	82	80		188	129	72	490	338	10
	21	14	49		71	48	99		121	83	49		190	131	10	**500**	**345**	**0**
	22	15	18	6	72	49	68		122	84	18	16	192	132	48	550	379	50
	23	15	87		73	50	37		123	84	87		194	133	86	600	414	0
2	24	16	56		74	51	6		124	85	56		196	135	24	650	448	50
	25	17	25		75	51	75		125	86	25		198	136	62	700	483	0
	26	17	94		76	52	44		126	86	94		**200**	138	0	750	517	50
	27	18	63		77	53	13		127	87	63	17	204	140	76	800	552	0
	28	19	32		78	53	82		128	88	32		205	141	45	850	586	50
	29	20	1		79	54	51		129	89	1		210	144	90	900	621	0
	30	20	70		**80**	55	20		**130**	89	70		215	148	35	950	655	50
	31	21	39		81	55	89		131	90	39	18	216	149	4	**1000**	690	0
	32	22	8		82	56	58	11	132	91	8		220	151	80	1016	701	4
	33	22	77		83	57	27		133	91	77		225	155	25	1250	862	50
	34	23	46	7	84	57	96		134	92	46	19	228	157	32	1500	1035	0
	35	24	15		85	58	65		135	93	15		230	158	70	1728	1192	32
3	36	24	84		86	59	34		136	93	84		235	162	15	1750	1207	50
	37	25	53		87	60	3		137	94	53	20	240	165	60	1760	1214	40
	38	26	22		88	60	72		138	95	22		245	169	5	2000	1380	0
	39	26	91		89	61	41		139	95	91		**250**	172	50	2240	1545	60
	40	27	60		**90**	62	10		**140**	96	60		255	175	95	2500	1725	0
	41	28	29		91	62	79		141	97	29		260	179	40	3000	2070	0
	42	28	98		92	63	48		142	97	98		265	182	85	4000	2760	0
	43	29	67		93	64	17		143	98	67		270	186	30	**5000**	**3450**	**0**
	44	30	36		94	64	86	12	144	99	36		275	189	75	6000	4140	0
	45	31	5		95	65	55		145	100	5		280	193	20	7000	4830	0
	46	31	74	8	96	66	24		146	100	74		285	196	65	8000	5520	0
	47	32	43		97	66	93		147	101	43	24	288	198	72	9000	6210	0
4	48	33	12		98	67	62		148	102	12		290	200	10	10000	6900	0
	49	33	81		99	68	31		149	102	81		295	203	55	15000	10350	0
	50	34	50		**100**	69	0		**150**	103	50		**300**	207	0	20000	13800	0

Grosses

1.	99	36
2.	198	72
3.	298	8
4.	397	44
5.	496	80
6.	596	16
7.	695	52
8.	794	88
9.	894	24
10.	993	60
11.	1092	96

Twelfths

	1.	0	5¾
1/6	2.	0	11½
	3.	0	17¼
1/3	4.	0	23
	5.	0	28¾
1/2	6.	0	34½
	7.	0	40¼
2/3	8.	0	46
	9.	0	51¾
5/6	10.	0	57½
	11.	0	63¼

Twentieths

10ths				10ths			
	1.	0	3½		11.	0	38
·1	2.	0	7	·6	12.	0	41½
	3.	0	10½		13.	0	44¾
·2	4.	0	13¾	·7	14.	0	48¼
	5.	0	17¼		15.	0	51¾
·3	6.	0	20¾	·8	16.	0	55¼
	7.	0	24¼		17.	0	58¾
·4	8.	0	27½	·9	18.	0	62
	9.	0	31		19.	0	65½
·5	10.	0	34½		20.	0	69

Sixteenths

	1.	0	4¼		9.	0	38¾
1/8	2.	0	8¾	5/8	10.	0	43¼
	3.	0	13		11.	0	47½
1/4	4.	0	17¼	3/4	12.	0	51¾
	5.	0	21½		13.	0	56
3/8	6.	0	26	7/8	14.	0	60½
	7.	0	30¼		15.	0	64¾
1/2	8.	0	34½				

No.	£	P	No.	£	P	No.	£	P	No.	£	P	No.	£	P
1	0	70	51	35	70	101	70	70	152	106	40	310	217	0
2	1	40	52	36	40	102	71	40	154	107	80	320	224	0
3	2	10	53	37	10	103	72	10	13 156	109	20	330	231	0
4	2	80	54	37	80	104	72	80	158	110	60	340	238	0
5	3	50	55	38	50	105	73	50	160	112	0	350	245	0
6	4	20	56	39	20	106	74	20	162	113	40	360	252	0
7	4	90	57	39	90	107	74	90	164	114	80	365	255	50
8	5	60	58	40	60	9 108	75	60	166	116	20	370	259	0
9	6	30	59	41	30	109	76	30	14 168	117	60	380	266	0
10	7	0	60	42	0	110	77	0	170	119	0	390	273	0
*11	7	70	61	42	70	111	77	70	172	120	40	400	280	0
12	8	40	62	43	40	112	78	40	174	121	80	410	287	0
13	9	10	63	44	10	113	79	10	176	123	20	420	294	0
14	9	80	64	44	80	114	79	80	178	124	60	430	301	0
15	10	50	65	45	50	115	80	50	15 180	126	0	440	308	0
16	11	20	66	46	20	116	81	20	182	127	40	450	315	0
17	11	90	67	46	90	117	81	90	184	128	80	460	322	0
18	12	60	68	47	60	118	82	60	186	130	20	470	329	0
19	13	30	69	48	30	119	83	30	188	131	60	480	336	0
20	14	0	70	49	0	120	84	0	190	133	0	490	343	0
21	14	70	71	49	70	121	84	70	16 192	134	40	500	350	0
22	15	40	72	50	40	122	85	40	194	135	80	550	385	0
23	16	10	73	51	10	123	86	10	196	137	20	600	420	0
24	16	80	74	51	80	124	86	80	198	138	60	650	455	0
25	17	50	75	52	50	125	87	50	200	140	0	700	490	0
26	18	20	76	53	20	126	88	20	17 204	142	80	750	525	0
27	18	90	77	53	90	127	88	90	205	143	50	800	560	0
28	19	60	78	54	60	128	89	60	210	147	0	850	595	0
29	20	30	79	55	30	129	90	30	18 216	151	20	900	630	0
30	21	0	80	56	0	130	91	0	220	154	0	950	665	0
31	21	70	81	56	70	131	91	70	225	157	50	1000	700	0
32	22	40	82	57	40	11 132	92	40	19 228	159	60	1016	711	20
33	23	10	83	58	10	133	93	10	230	161	0	1250	875	0
34	23	80	7 84	58	80	134	93	80	235	164	50	1500	1050	0
35	24	50	85	59	50	135	94	50	20 240	168	0	1728	1209	60
36	25	20	86	60	20	136	95	20	245	171	50	1750	1225	0
37	25	90	87	60	90	137	95	90	250	175	0	1760	1232	0
38	26	60	88	61	60	138	96	60	255	178	50	2000	1400	0
39	27	30	89	62	30	139	97	30	260	182	0	2240	1568	0
40	28	0	90	63	0	140	98	0	265	185	50	2500	1750	0
41	28	70	91	63	70	141	98	70	270	189	0	3000	2100	0
42	29	40	92	64	40	142	99	40	275	192	50	4000	2800	0
43	30	10	93	65	10	143	100	10	280	196	0	5000	3500	0
44	30	80	94	65	80	12 144	100	80	285	199	50	6000	4200	0
45	31	50	95	66	50	145	101	50	24 288	201	60	7000	4900	0
46	32	20	8 96	67	20	146	102	20	290	203	0	8000	5600	0
47	32	90	97	67	90	147	102	90	295	206	50	9000	6300	0
48	33	60	98	68	60	148	103	60	300	210	0	10000	7000	0
49	34	30	99	69	30	149	104	30				15000	10500	0
50	35	0	100	70	0	150	105	0				20000	14000	0

*Dozens (col 1) · Dozens (col 2) · Dozens (col 3) · Dozens (col 4)

Grosses			Twelfths			10ths	Twentieths						Sixteenths		
1.	100	80	1.	0	5⅚		1.	0	3½	11.	0	38½	1.	0	4⅜
2.	201	60	½2.	0	11⅔	x 2.	0	7		-6 12.	0	42	½2.	0	8¾
3.	302	40	3.	0	17½		3.	0	10½	13.	0	45½	3.	0	13⅛
4.	403	20	¼4.	0	23⅓	-2 4.	0	14		14.	0	49	¼4.	0	17½
5.	504	0	5.	0	29¼		5.	0	17½	-7 15.	0	52½	5.	0	22
6.	604	80	⅙6.	0	35	-3 6.	0	21		16.	0	56	⅜6.	0	26¼
7.	705	60	7.	0	40⅚		7.	0	24½	17.	0	59½	7.	0	30⅝
8.	806	40	⅜8.	0	46⅔	-4 8.	0	28		-8 18.	0	63	½8.	0	35
9.	907	20	9.	0	52½		9.	0	31½	-9 19.	0	66½	9.	0	39⅜
10.	1008	0	⅝10.	0	58⅓	-5 10.	0	35		20.	0	70	⅝10.	0	43¾
11.	1108	80	11.	0	64¼								11.	0	48⅛
													¾12.	0	52½
													13.	0	57
													⅞14.	0	61⅜
													15.	0	65⅝

* Dozens.	£	P	Dozens.	£	P	Dozens.	£	P	Doz.	£	P		£	P
1	0	71	51	36	21	101	71	71	152	107	92	310	220	10
2	1	42	52	36	92	102	72	42	154	109	34	320	227	20
3	2	13	53	37	63	103	73	13	[13] 156	110	76	330	234	30
4	2	84	54	38	34	104	73	84	158	112	18	340	241	40
5	3	55	55	39	5	105	74	55	160	113	60	350	248	50
*6	4	26	56	39	76	106	75	26	162	115	2	360	255	60
7	4	97	57	40	47	107	75	97	164	116	44	365	259	15
8	5	68	58	41	18	[9] 108	76	68	166	117	86	370	262	70
9	6	39	59	41	89	109	77	39	[14] 168	119	28	380	269	80
10	7	10	[5] **60**	42	60	**110**	78	10	170	120	70	390	276	90
*11	7	81	61	43	31	111	78	81	172	122	12	400	284	0
[1] 12	8	52	62	44	2	112	79	52	174	123	54	410	291	10
13	9	23	63	44	73	113	80	23	175	124	25	420	298	20
14	9	94	64	45	44	114	80	94	176	124	96	430	305	30
15	10	65	65	46	15	115	81	65	178	126	38	440	312	40
16	11	36	66	46	86	116	82	36	[15] 180	127	80	450	319	50
17	12	7	67	47	57	117	83	7	182	129	22	460	326	60
18	12	78	68	48	28	118	83	78	184	130	64	470	333	70
19	13	49	69	48	99	119	84	49	186	132	6	480	340	80
20	14	20	**70**	49	70	**120**	85	20	188	133	48	490	347	90
21	14	91	71	50	41	121	85	91	190	134	90	**500**	355	0
22	15	62	[6] 72	51	12	122	86	62	[16] 192	136	32	550	390	50
23	16	33	73	51	83	123	87	33	194	137	74	600	426	0
[2] 24	17	4	74	52	54	124	88	4	196	139	16	650	461	50
25	17	75	75	53	25	125	88	75	198	140	58	700	497	0
26	18	46	76	53	96	126	89	46	**200**	142	0	750	532	50
27	19	17	77	54	67	127	90	17	[17] 204	144	84	800	568	0
28	19	88	78	55	38	128	90	88	205	145	55	850	603	50
29	20	59	79	56	9	129	91	59	210	149	10	900	639	0
30	21	30	**80**	56	80	**130**	92	30	215	152	65	950	674	50
31	22	1	81	57	51	131	93	1	[18] 216	153	36	**1000**	710	0
32	22	72	82	58	22	[11] 132	93	72	220	156	20	1016	721	36
33	23	43	83	58	93	133	94	43	225	159	75	1250	887	50
34	24	14	[7] 84	59	64	134	95	14	[19] 228	161	88	1500	1065	0
35	24	85	85	60	35	135	95	85	230	163	30	1728	1226	88
[3] 36	25	56	86	61	6	136	96	56	235	166	85	1750	1242	50
37	26	27	87	61	77	137	97	27	[20] 240	170	40	1760	1249	60
38	26	98	88	62	48	138	97	98	245	173	95	2000	1420	0
39	27	69	89	63	19	139	98	69	**250**	177	50	2240	1590	40
40	28	40	**90**	63	90	**140**	99	40	255	181	5	2500	1775	0
41	29	11	91	64	61	141	100	11	260	184	60	3000	2130	0
42	29	82	92	65	32	142	100	82	265	188	15	4000	2840	0
43	30	53	93	66	3	143	101	53	270	191	70	**5000**	3550	0
44	31	24	94	66	74	[12] 144	102	24	275	195	25	6000	4260	0
45	31	95	95	67	45	145	102	95	280	198	80	7000	4970	0
46	32	66	[8] 96	68	16	146	103	66	285	202	35	8000	5680	0
47	33	37	97	68	87	147	104	37	[24] 288	204	48	9000	6390	0
[4] 48	34	8	98	69	58	148	105	8	290	205	90	10000	7100	0
49	34	79	99	70	29	149	105	79	295	209	45	15000	10650	0
50	35	50	**100**	71	0	**150**	106	50	**300**	213	0	20000	14200	0

Grosses.

1.	102	24
2.	204	48
3.	306	72
4.	408	96
5.	511	20
6.	613	44
7.	715	68
8.	817	92
9.	920	16
10.	1022	40
11.	1124	64

Twelfths

	1.	0	6
⅙	2.	0	11¾
	3.	0	17¾
⅓	4.	0	23¾
	5.	0	29½
½	6.	0	35½
	7.	0	41½
⅔	8.	0	47¼
	9.	0	53¼
⅚	10.	0	59¼
	11.	0	65

Twentieths (10ths)

	1.	0	3½		11.	0	39
·1	2.	0	7	·6	12.	0	42½
	3.	0	10¾		13.	0	46¼
·2	4.	0	14¼	·7	14.	0	49¾
	5.	0	17¾		15.	0	53¼
·3	6.	0	21¼	·8	16.	0	56¾
	7.	0	24¾		17.	0	60¼
·4	8.	0	28½	·9	18.	0	64
	9.	0	32		19.	0	67½
·5	10.	0	35½		20.	0	71

Sixteenths

	1.	0	4½		9.	0	40
⅛	2.	0	9	⅝	10.	0	44½
	3.	0	13¼		11.	0	48¾
¼	4.	0	17¾	¾	12.	0	53¼
	5.	0	22¼		13.	0	57¾
⅜	6.	0	26¾	⅞	14.	0	62¼
	7.	0	31		15.	0	66½
½	8.	0	35½				

	£ P		£ P		£ P		£ P		£ P
1	0 72	51	36 72	101	72 72	152	109 44	310	223 20
2	1 44	52	37 44	102	73 44	154	110 88	320	230 40
*Dozen 3	2 16	Dozens 53	38 16	Dozens 103	74 16	¹³156	112 32	330	237 60
4	2 88	54	38 88	104	74 88	158	113 76	340	244 80
5	3 60	55	39 60	105	75 60	160	115 20	350	252 0
6	4 32	56	40 32	106	76 32	162	116 64	360	259 20
7	5 4	57	41 4	107	77 4	164	118 8	365	262 80
8	5 76	58	41 76	⁹108	77 76	166	119 52	370	266 40
9	6 48	59	42 48	109	78 48	¹⁴168	120 96	380	273 60
10	7 20	⁵60	43 20	110	79 20	170	122 40	390	280 80
*11	7 92	61	43 92	111	79 92	172	123 84	400	288 0
†12	8 64	62	44 64	112	80 64	174	125 28	410	295 20
13	9 36	63	45 36	113	81 36	175	126 0	420	302 40
14	10 8	64	46 8	114	82 8	176	126 72	430	309 60
15	10 80	65	46 80	115	82 80	178	128 16	440	316 80
16	11 52	66	47 52	116	83 52	¹⁵180	129 60	450	324 0
17	12 24	67	48 24	117	84 24	182	131 4	460	331 20
18	12 96	68	48 96	118	84 96	184	132 48	470	338 40
19	13 68	69	49 68	119	85 68	186	133 92	480	345 60
20	14 40	70	50 40	120	86 40	188	135 36	490	352 80
21	15 12	71	51 12	121	87 12	190	136 80	500	360 0
22	15 84	⁶72	51 84	122	87 84	¹⁶192	138 24	550	396 0
23	16 56	73	52 56	123	88 56	194	139 68	600	432 0
²24	17 28	74	53 28	124	89 28	196	141 12	650	468 0
25	18 0	75	54 0	125	90 0	198	142 56	700	504 0
26	18 72	76	54 72	126	90 72	200	144 0	750	540 0
27	19 44	77	55 44	127	91 44	¹⁷204	146 88	800	576 0
28	20 16	78	56 16	128	92 16	205	147 60	850	612 0
29	20 88	79	56 88	129	92 88	210	151 20	900	648 0
30	21 60	80	57 60	130	93 60	215	154 80	950	684 0
31	22 32	81	58 32	131	94 32	¹⁸216	155 52	1000	720 0
32	23 4	82	59 4	¹¹132	95 4	220	158 40	1016	731 52
33	23 76	83	59 76	133	95 76	225	162 0	1250	900 0
34	24 48	⁷84	60 48	134	96 48	¹⁹228	164 16	1500	1080 0
35	25 20	85	61 20	135	97 20	230	165 60	1728	1244 16
³36	25 92	86	61 92	136	97 92	235	169 20	1750	1260 0
37	26 64	87	62 64	137	98 64	²⁰240	172 80	1760	1267 20
38	27 36	88	63 36	138	99 36	245	176 40	2000	1440 0
39	28 8	89	64 8	139	100 8	250	180 0	2240	1612 80
40	28 80	90	64 80	140	100 80	255	183 60	2500	1800 0
41	29 52	91	65 52	141	101 52	260	187 20	3000	2160 0
42	30 24	92	66 24	142	102 24	265	190 80	4000	2880 0
43	30 96	93	66 96	143	102 96	270	194 40	5000	3600 0
44	31 68	94	67 68	¹²144	103 68	275	198 0	6000	4320 0
45	32 40	95	68 40	145	104 40	280	201 60	7000	5040 0
46	33 12	⁸96	69 12	146	105 12	285	205 20	8000	5760 0
47	33 84	97	69 84	147	105 84	²⁴288	207 36	9000	6480 0
⁴48	34 56	98	70 56	148	106 56	290	208 80	10000	7200 0
49	35 28	99	71 28	149	107 28	295	212 40	15000	10800 0
50	36 0	100	72 0	150	108 0	300	216 0	20000	14400 0

Grosses		Twelfths			10ths Twentieths			Sixteenths	
1.	103 68	1.	1. 0 6		1. 0 3¾	11. 0 39½		1. 0 4½	9. 0 40½
2.	207 36	½	2. 0 12		x 2. 0 7½	·6 12. 0 43¼		½ 2. 0 9	§10. 0 45
3.	311 04	3.	3. 0 18		3. 0 11¼	13. 0 46½		3. 0 13½	11. 0 49½
4.	414 72	¼	4. 0 24		-2 4. 0 14¼	·7 14. 0 50¼		¼ 4. 0 18	¾12. 0 54
5.	518 40	5.	5. 0 30		5. 0 18	15. 0 54		5. 0 22½	13. 0 58½
6.	622 08	⅙	6. 0 36		-3 6. 0 21¼	·8 16. 0 57½		§6. 0 27	13. 0 58½
7.	725 76	7.	7. 0 42		7. 0 25	17. 0 61½		7. 0 31½	¾14. 0 63
8.	829 44	⅞	8. 0 48		-4 8. 0 28¾	·9 18. 0 64½		½8. 0 36	15. 0 67½
9.	933 12	9.	9. 0 54		9. 0 32½	19. 0 68½			
10.	1036 80	⁵⁄₁₀	10. 0 60		-5 10. 0 36	20. 0 72			
11.	1140 48	11.	11. 0 66						

	£	P		£	P		£	P		£	P		£	P
1	0	73	51	37	23	101	73	73	152	110	96	310	226	30
2	1	46	52	37	96	102	74	46	154	112	42	320	233	60
3	2	19	53	38	69	103	75	19	[13] 156	113	88	330	240	90
4	2	92	54	39	42	104	75	92	158	115	34	340	248	20
5	3	65	55	40	15	105	76	65	160	116	80	350	255	50
*6	4	38	56	40	88	106	77	38	162	118	26	360	262	80
7	5	11	57	41	61	107	78	11	164	119	72	365	266	45
8	5	84	58	42	34	[9] 108	78	84	166	121	18	370	270	10
9	6	57	59	43	7	109	79	57	[14] 168	122	64	380	277	40
10	7	30	[5] **60**	43	80	**110**	80	30	170	124	10	390	284	70
*11	8	3	61	44	53	111	81	3	172	125	56	400	292	0
[1] 12	8	76	62	45	26	112	81	76	174	127	2	410	299	30
13	9	49	63	45	99	113	82	49	175	127	75	420	306	60
14	10	22	64	46	72	114	83	22	176	128	48	430	313	90
15	10	95	65	47	45	115	83	95	178	129	94	440	321	20
16	11	68	66	48	18	116	84	68	[15] 180	131	40	450	328	50
17	12	41	67	48	91	117	85	41	182	132	86	460	335	80
18	13	14	68	49	64	118	86	14	184	134	32	470	343	10
19	13	87	69	50	37	119	86	87	186	135	78	480	350	40
20	14	60	**70**	51	10	**120**	87	60	188	137	24	490	357	70
21	15	33	71	51	83	121	88	33	190	138	70	**500**	365	0
22	16	6	[6] 72	52	56	122	89	6	[16] 192	140	16	550	401	50
23	16	79	73	53	29	123	89	79	194	141	62	600	438	0
[2] 24	17	52	74	54	2	124	90	52	196	143	8	650	474	50
25	18	25	75	54	75	125	91	25	198	144	54	700	511	0
26	18	98	76	55	48	126	91	98	**200**	146	0	750	547	50
27	19	71	77	56	21	127	92	71	[17] 204	148	92	800	584	0
28	20	44	78	56	94	128	93	44	205	149	65	850	620	50
29	21	17	79	57	67	129	94	17	210	153	30	900	657	0
30	21	90	**80**	58	40	**130**	94	90	215	156	95	950	693	50
31	22	63	81	59	13	131	95	63	[18] 216	157	68	**1000**	730	0
32	23	36	82	59	86	[11] 132	96	36	220	160	60	1016	741	68
33	24	9	83	60	59	133	97	9	225	164	25	1250	912	50
34	24	82	[7] 84	61	32	134	97	82	[19] 228	166	44	1500	1095	0
35	25	55	85	62	5	135	98	55	230	167	90	1728	1261	44
[3] 36	26	28	86	62	78	136	99	28	235	171	55	1750	1277	50
37	27	1	87	63	51	137	100	1	[20] 240	175	20	1760	1284	80
38	27	74	88	64	24	138	100	74	245	178	85	2000	1460	0
39	28	47	89	64	97	139	101	47	**250**	182	50	2240	1635	20
40	29	20	**90**	65	70	**140**	102	20	255	186	15	2500	1825	0
41	29	93	91	66	43	141	102	93	260	189	80	3000	2190	0
42	30	66	92	67	16	142	103	66	265	193	45	4000	2920	0
43	31	39	93	67	89	143	104	39	270	197	10	**5000**	3650	0
44	32	12	94	68	62	[12] 144	105	12	275	200	75	6000	4380	0
45	32	85	95	69	35	145	105	85	280	204	40	7000	5110	0
46	33	58	[8] 96	70	8	146	106	58	285	208	5	8000	5840	0
47	34	31	97	70	81	147	107	31	[24] 288	210	24	9000	6570	0
[4] 48	35	4	98	71	54	148	108	4	290	211	70	10000	7300	0
49	35	77	99	72	27	149	108	77	295	215	35	15000	10950	0
50	36	50	**100**	73	0	**150**	109	50	**300**	219	0	20000	14600	0

*Dozens.

Grosses.			Twelfths			10ths	Twentieths						Sixteenths					
1.	105	12	1.	0	6		1.	0	3¾	11.	0	40¼	1.	0	4½	9.	0	41
2.	210	24	1/6 2.	0	12¼	·1	2.	0	7¼	·6 12.	0	43¾	1/8 2.	0	9¼	5/8 10.	0	45¾
3.	315	36	3.	0	18¼		3.	0	11	13.	0	47½	3.	0	13¾	11.	0	50¼
4.	420	48	1/3 4.	0	24¼	·2	4.	0	14½	·7 14.	0	51	1/4 4.	0	18¼	3/4 12.	0	54¾
5.	525	60	5.	0	30½		5.	0	18¼	15.	0	54¾	5.	0	22¾	13.	0	59¼
6.	630	72	1/2 6.	0	36½	·3	6.	0	22	8 16.	0	58½	3/8 6.	0	27½	7/8 14.	0	64
7.	735	84	7.	0	42½		7.	0	25½	17.	0	62	7.	0	32	15.	0	68½
8.	840	96	2/3 8.	0	48¾	·4	8.	0	29¼	·9 18.	0	65¾	1/2 8.	0	36½			
9.	946	08	9.	0	54¾		9.	0	32¾	19.	0	69¼						
10.	1051	20	5/6 10.	0	60¾	·5	10.	0	36½	20.	0	73						
11.	1156	32	11.	0	67													

*Dozens

	£	P		£	P		£	P		£	P		£	P
1	0	74	51	37	74	101	74	74	152	112	48	310	229	40
2	1	48	52	38	48	102	75	48	154	113	96	320	236	80
3	2	22	53	39	22	103	76	22	[13] 156	115	44	330	244	20
4	2	96	54	39	96	104	76	96	158	116	92	340	251	60
5	3	70	55	40	70	105	77	70	160	118	40	350	259	0
6	4	44	56	41	44	106	78	44	162	119	88	360	266	40
7	5	18	57	42	18	107	79	18	164	121	36	365	270	10
8	5	92	58	42	92	[9] 108	79	92	166	122	84	370	273	80
9	6	66	59	43	66	109	80	66	[14] 168	124	32	380	281	20
10	7	40	[5] 60	44	40	110	81	40	170	125	80	390	288	60
11	8	14	61	45	14	111	82	14	172	127	28	400	296	0
[*1] 12	8	88	62	45	88	112	82	88	174	128	76	410	303	40
13	9	62	63	46	62	113	83	62	175	129	50	420	310	80
14	10	36	64	47	36	114	84	36	176	130	24	430	318	20
15	11	10	65	48	10	115	85	10	178	131	72	440	325	60
16	11	84	66	48	84	116	85	84	[15] 180	133	20	450	333	0
17	12	58	67	49	58	117	86	58	182	134	68	460	340	40
18	13	32	68	50	32	118	87	32	184	136	16	470	347	80
19	14	6	69	51	6	119	88	6	186	137	64	480	355	20
20	14	80	70	51	80	120	88	80	188	139	12	490	362	60
21	15	54	71	52	54	121	89	54	190	140	60	500	370	0
22	16	28	[6] 72	53	28	122	90	28	[16] 192	142	8	550	407	0
23	17	2	73	54	2	123	91	2	194	143	56	600	444	0
[2] 24	17	76	74	54	76	124	91	76	196	145	4	650	481	0
25	18	50	75	55	50	125	92	50	198	146	52	700	518	0
26	19	24	76	56	24	126	93	24	200	148	0	750	555	0
27	19	98	77	56	98	127	93	98	[17] 204	150	96	800	592	0
28	20	72	78	57	72	128	94	72	205	151	70	850	629	0
29	21	46	79	58	46	129	95	46	210	155	40	900	666	0
30	22	20	80	59	20	130	96	20	215	159	10	950	703	0
31	22	94	81	59	94	131	96	94	[18] 216	159	84	1000	740	0
32	23	68	82	60	68	[11] 132	97	68	220	162	80	1016	751	84
33	24	42	83	61	42	133	98	42	225	166	50	1250	925	0
34	25	16	[7] 84	62	16	134	99	16	[19] 228	168	72	1500	1110	0
35	25	90	85	62	90	135	99	90	230	170	20	1728	1278	72
[3] 36	26	64	86	63	64	136	100	64	235	173	90	1750	1295	0
37	27	38	87	64	38	137	101	38	[20] 240	177	60	1760	1302	40
38	28	12	88	65	12	138	102	12	245	181	30	2000	1480	0
39	28	86	89	65	86	139	102	86	250	185	0	2240	1657	60
40	29	60	90	66	60	140	103	60	255	188	70	2500	1850	0
41	30	34	91	67	34	141	104	34	260	192	40	3000	2220	0
42	31	8	92	68	8	142	105	8	265	196	10	4000	2960	0
43	31	82	93	68	82	143	105	82	270	199	80	5000	3700	0
44	32	56	94	69	56	[12] 144	106	56	275	203	50	6000	4440	0
45	33	30	95	70	30	145	107	30	280	207	20	7000	5180	0
46	34	4	[8] 96	71	4	146	108	4	285	210	90	8000	5920	0
47	34	78	97	71	78	147	108	78	[24] 288	213	12	9000	6660	0
[4] 48	35	52	98	72	52	148	109	52	290	214	60	10000	7400	0
49	36	26	99	73	26	149	110	26	295	218	30	15000	11100	0
50	37	0	100	74	0	150	111	0	300	222	0	20000	14800	0

Grosses

1.	106	56
2.	213	12
3.	319	68
4.	426	24
5.	532	80
6.	639	36
7.	745	92
8.	852	48
9.	959	04
10.	1065	60
11.	1172	16

Twelfths

	1.	0	6¼
⅙	2.	0	12¼
	3.	0	18½
⅓	4.	0	24¾
	5.	0	30¾
½	6.	0	37
	7.	0	43¼
⅔	8.	0	49¼
	9.	0	55½
⅚	10.	0	61¾
	11.	0	67¾

Twentieths

10ths				10ths			
	1.	0	3¾		11.	0	40¾
·1	2.	0	7½	·6	12.	0	44½
	3.	0	11		13.	0	48
·2	4.	0	14¾	·7	14.	0	51¾
	5.	0	18½		15.	0	55½
·3	6.	0	22¼	·8	16.	0	59¼
	7.	0	26		17.	0	63
·4	8.	0	29½	·9	18.	0	66½
	9.	0	33¼		19.	0	70¼
·5	10.	0	37		20.	0	74

Sixteenths

	1.	0	4¾		9.	0	41¾
⅛	2.	0	9¼	⅝	10.	0	46¼
	3.	0	14		11.	0	51
¼	4.	0	18½	¾	12.	0	55½
	5.	0	23¼		13.	0	60¼
⅜	6.	0	27¾	⅞	14.	0	64¾
	7.	0	32½		15.	0	69½
½	8.	0	37				

*Dozens	No.	£	P	Dozens	No.	£	P	Dozens	No.	£	P	Dozens	No.	£	P	No.	£	P
	1	0	75		51	38	25		101	75	75		152	114	0	310	232	50
	2	1	50		52	39	0		102	76	50		154	115	50	320	240	0
	3	2	25		53	39	75		103	77	25	13	156	117	0	330	247	50
	4	3	0		54	40	50		104	78	0		158	118	50	340	255	0
	5	3	75		55	41	25		105	78	75		160	120	0	350	262	50
	6	4	50		56	42	0		106	79	50		162	121	50	360	270	0
	7	5	25		57	42	75		107	80	25		164	123	0	365	273	75
	8	6	0		58	43	50	9	108	81	0		166	124	50	370	277	50
	9	6	75		59	44	25		109	81	75	14	168	126	0	380	285	0
	10	7	50	5	**60**	45	0		**110**	82	50		170	127	50	390	292	50
	11	8	25		61	45	75		111	83	25		172	129	0	400	300	0
*1	12	9	0		62	46	50		112	84	0		174	130	50	410	307	50
	13	9	75		63	47	25		113	84	75		175	131	25	420	315	0
	14	10	50		64	48	0		114	85	50		176	132	0	430	322	50
	15	11	25		65	48	75		115	86	25		178	133	50	440	330	0
	16	12	0		66	49	50		116	87	0	15	180	135	0	450	337	50
	17	12	75		67	50	25		117	87	75		182	136	50	460	345	0
	18	13	50		68	51	0		118	88	50		184	138	0	470	352	50
	19	14	25		69	51	75		119	89	25		186	139	50	480	360	0
	20	15	0		**70**	52	50		**120**	90	0		188	141	0	490	367	50
	21	15	75		71	53	25		121	90	75		190	142	50	**500**	375	0
	22	16	50	6	72	54	0		122	91	50	16	192	144	0	550	412	50
	23	17	25		73	54	75		123	92	25		194	145	50	600	450	0
2	24	18	0		74	55	50		124	93	0		196	147	0	650	487	50
	25	18	75		75	56	25		125	93	75		198	148	50	700	525	0
	26	19	50		76	57	0		126	94	50		**200**	150	0	750	562	50
	27	20	25		77	57	75		127	95	25	17	204	153	0	800	600	0
	28	21	0		78	58	50		128	96	0		205	153	75	850	637	50
	29	21	75		79	59	25		129	96	75		210	157	50	900	675	0
	30	22	50		**80**	60	0		**130**	97	50		215	161	25	950	712	50
	31	23	25		81	60	75		131	98	25	18	216	162	0	**1000**	750	0
	32	24	0		82	61	50	11	132	99	0		220	165	0	1016	762	0
	33	24	75		83	62	25		133	99	75		225	168	75	1250	937	50
	34	25	50	7	84	63	0		134	100	50	19	228	171	0	1500	1125	0
	35	26	25		85	63	75		135	101	25		230	172	50	1728	1296	0
3	36	27	0		86	64	50		136	102	0		235	176	25	1750	1312	50
	37	27	75		87	65	25		137	102	75	20	240	180	0	1760	1320	0
	38	28	50		88	66	0		138	103	50		245	183	75	2000	1500	0
	39	29	25		89	66	75		139	104	25		**250**	187	50	2240	1680	0
	40	30	0		**90**	67	50		**140**	105	0		255	191	25	2500	1875	0
	41	30	75		91	68	25		141	105	75		260	195	0	3000	2250	0
	42	31	50		92	69	0		142	106	50		265	198	75	4000	3000	0
	43	32	25		93	69	75		143	107	25		270	202	50	5000	3750	0
	44	33	0		94	70	50	12	144	108	0		275	206	25	6000	4500	0
	45	33	75		95	71	25		145	108	75		280	210	0	7000	5250	0
	46	34	50	8	96	72	0		146	109	50		285	213	75	8000	6000	0
	47	35	25		97	72	75		147	110	25	24	288	216	0	9000	6750	0
4	48	36	0		98	73	50		148	111	0		290	217	50	10000	7500	0
	49	36	75		99	74	25		149	111	75		295	221	25	15000	11250	0
	50	37	50		**100**	75	0		**150**	112	50		**300**	225	0	20000	15000	0

Grosses	£	P		Twelfths	£	P	10ths	Twentieths	£	P	10ths	Twentieths	£	P		Sixteenths	£	P		Sixteenths	£	P
1.	108	0		1.	0	6¼		1.	0	3¾		11.	0	41¼		1.	0	4¾		9.	0	42¼
2.	216	0	⅙	2.	0	12½	·1	2.	0	7½	·6	12.	0	45	⅛	2.	0	9½	⅝	10.	0	47
3.	324	0		3.	0	18¾		3.	0	11¼		13.	0	48¾		3.	0	14		11.	0	51½
4.	432	0	⅓	4.	0	25	·2	4.	0	15	·7	14.	0	52½	¼	4.	0	18¾	¾	12.	0	56¼
5.	540	0		5.	0	31¼		5.	0	18¾		15.	0	56¼		5.	0	23½		13.	0	61
6.	648	0	½	6.	0	37½	·3	6.	0	22½	·8	16.	0	60	⅜	6.	0	28¼	⅞	14.	0	65¾
7.	756	0		7.	0	43¾		7.	0	26¼		17.	0	63¾		7.	0	32¾		15.	0	70½
8.	864	0	⅔	8.	0	50	·4	8.	0	30	·9	18.	0	67½	½	8.	0	37½				
9.	972	0		9.	0	56¼		9.	0	33¾		19.	0	71¼								
10.	1080	0	⅚	10.	0	62½	·5	10.	0	37½		20.	0	75								
11.	1188	0		11.	0	68¾																

Doz.	No.	£	p	Doz.	No.	£	p	Doz.	No.	£	p	Doz.	No.	£	p	No.	£	p
*Dozens	1	0	76	Dozens	51	38	76	Dozens	101	76	76	Dozens	152	115	52	310	235	60
	2	1	52		52	39	52		102	77	52		154	117	4	320	243	20
	3	2	28		53	40	28		103	78	28	13	156	118	56	330	250	80
	4	3	4		54	41	4		104	79	4		158	120	8	340	258	40
	5	3	80		55	41	80		105	79	80		160	121	60	350	266	0
	6	4	56		56	42	56		106	80	56		162	123	12	360	273	60
	7	5	32		57	43	32		107	81	32		164	124	64	365	277	40
	8	6	8		58	44	8	9	108	82	8		166	126	16	370	281	20
	9	6	84		59	44	84		109	82	84	14	168	127	68	380	288	80
	10	7	60	5	**60**	45	60		**110**	83	60		170	129	20	390	296	40
	11	8	36		61	46	36		111	84	36		172	130	72	400	304	0
*1	12	9	12		62	47	12		112	85	12		174	132	24	410	311	60
	13	9	88		63	47	88		113	85	88		175	133	0	420	319	20
	14	10	64		64	48	64		114	86	64		176	133	76	430	326	80
	15	11	40		65	49	40		115	87	40		178	135	28	440	334	40
	16	12	16		66	50	16		116	88	16	15	180	136	80	450	342	0
	17	12	92		67	50	92		117	88	92		182	138	32	460	349	60
	18	13	68		68	51	68		118	89	68		184	139	84	470	357	20
	19	14	44		69	52	44		119	90	44		186	141	36	480	364	80
	20	15	20		**70**	53	20	10	**120**	91	20		188	142	88	490	372	40
	21	15	96		71	53	96		121	91	96		190	144	40	**500**	380	0
	22	16	72	6	72	54	72		122	92	72	16	192	145	92	550	418	0
	23	17	48		73	55	48		123	93	48		194	147	44	600	456	0
2	24	18	24		74	56	24		124	94	24		196	148	96	650	494	0
	25	19	0		75	57	0		125	95	0		198	150	48	700	532	0
	26	19	76		76	57	76		126	95	76		**200**	152	0	750	570	0
	27	20	52		77	58	52		127	96	52	17	204	155	4	800	608	0
	28	21	28		78	59	28		128	97	28		205	155	80	850	646	0
	29	22	4		79	60	4		129	98	4		210	159	60	900	684	0
	30	22	80		**80**	60	80		**130**	98	80		215	163	40	950	722	0
	31	23	56		81	61	56		131	99	56	18	216	164	16	**1000**	760	0
	32	24	32		82	62	32	11	132	100	32		220	167	20	1016	772	16
	33	25	8		83	63	8		133	101	8		225	171	0	1250	950	0
	34	25	84	7	84	63	84		134	101	84	19	228	173	28	1500	1140	0
	35	26	60		85	64	60		135	102	60		230	174	80	1728	1313	28
3	36	27	36		86	65	36		136	103	36		235	178	60	1750	1330	0
	37	28	12		87	66	12		137	104	12	20	240	182	40	1760	1337	60
	38	28	88		88	66	88		138	104	88		245	186	20	2000	1520	0
	39	29	64		89	67	64		139	105	64		**250**	190	0	2240	1702	40
	40	30	40		**90**	68	40		**140**	106	40		255	193	80	2500	1900	0
	41	31	16		91	69	16		141	107	16		260	197	60	3000	2280	0
	42	31	92		92	69	92		142	107	92		265	201	40	4000	3040	0
	43	32	68		93	70	68		143	108	68		270	205	20	**5000**	3800	0
	44	33	44		94	71	44	12	144	109	44		275	209	0	6000	4560	0
	45	34	20		95	72	20		145	110	20		280	212	80	7000	5320	0
	46	34	96	8	96	72	96		146	110	96		285	216	60	8000	6080	0
	47	35	72		97	73	72		147	111	72	24	288	218	88	9000	6840	0
4	48	36	48		98	74	48		148	112	48		290	220	40	10000	7600	0
	49	37	24		99	75	24		149	113	24		295	224	20	15000	11400	0
	50	38	0		**100**	76	0		**150**	114	0		**300**	228	0	20000	15200	0

Grosses

No.	£	p
1.	109	44
2.	218	88
3.	328	32
4.	437	76
5.	547	20
6.	656	64
7.	766	8
8.	875	52
9.	984	96
10.	1094	40
11.	1203	84

Twelfths

	No.	£	p
	1.	0	6¼
⅙	2.	0	12¾
	3.	0	19
⅓	4.	0	25¼
	5.	0	31¾
½	6.	0	38
	7.	0	44¼
⅔	8.	0	50¾
	9.	0	57
⅚	10.	0	63¼
	11.	0	69¾

Twentieths

10ths	No.	£	p	10ths	No.	£	p
	1.	0	3¾		11.	0	41¾
·1	2.	0	7½	·6	12.	0	45½
	3.	0	11½		13.	0	49½
·2	4.	0	15¼	·7	14.	0	53¼
	5.	0	19		15.	0	57
·3	6.	0	22¾	·8	16.	0	60¾
	7.	0	26½		17.	0	64½
·4	8.	0	30½	·9	18.	0	68½
	9.	0	34¼		19.	0	72¼
·5	10.	0	38		20.	0	76

Sixteenths

	No.	£	p		No.	£	p
	1.	0	4¾		9.	0	42¾
⅛	2.	0	9½	⅝	10.	0	47½
	3.	0	14¼		11.	0	52¼
¼	4.	0	19	¾	12.	0	57
	5.	0	23¾		13.	0	61¾
⅜	6.	0	28½	⅞	14.	0	66½
	7.	0	33¼		15.	0	71¼
½	8.	0	38				

*Dozens

	£	p		£	p		£	p		£	p		£	p
1	0	77	51	39	27	101	77	77	152	117	4	310	238	70
2	1	54	52	40	4	102	78	54	154	118	58	320	246	40
3	2	31	53	40	81	103	79	31	[13] 156	120	12	330	254	10
4	3	8	54	41	58	104	80	8	158	121	66	340	261	80
5	3	85	55	42	35	105	80	85	160	123	20	350	269	50
6	4	62	56	43	12	106	81	62	162	124	74	360	277	20
7	5	39	57	43	89	107	82	39	164	126	28	365	281	5
8	6	16	58	44	66	[9] 108	83	16	166	127	82	370	284	90
9	6	93	59	45	43	109	83	93	[14] 168	129	36	380	292	60
10	7	70	[5] **60**	46	20	**110**	84	70	170	130	90	390	300	30
11	8	47	61	46	97	111	85	47	172	132	44	400	308	0
*[1] 12	9	24	62	47	74	112	86	24	174	133	98	410	315	70
13	10	1	63	48	51	113	87	1	175	134	75	420	323	40
14	10	78	64	49	28	114	87	78	176	135	52	430	331	10
15	11	55	65	50	5	115	88	55	178	137	6	440	338	80
16	12	32	66	50	82	116	89	32	[15] 180	138	60	450	346	50
17	13	9	67	51	59	117	90	9	182	140	14	460	354	20
18	13	86	68	52	36	118	90	86	184	141	68	470	361	90
19	14	63	69	53	13	119	91	63	186	143	22	480	369	60
20	15	40	**70**	53	90	**120**	92	40	188	144	76	490	377	30
21	16	17	71	54	67	121	93	17	190	146	30	**500**	385	0
22	16	94	[6] 72	55	44	122	93	94	[16] 192	147	84	550	423	50
23	17	71	73	56	21	123	94	71	194	149	38	600	462	0
[2] 24	18	48	74	56	98	124	95	48	196	150	92	650	500	50
25	19	25	75	57	75	125	96	25	198	152	46	700	539	0
26	20	2	76	58	52	126	97	2	**200**	154	0	750	577	50
27	20	79	77	59	29	127	97	79	[17] 204	157	8	800	616	0
28	21	56	78	60	6	128	98	56	205	157	85	850	654	50
29	22	33	79	60	83	129	99	33	210	161	70	900	693	0
30	23	10	**80**	61	60	**130**	100	10	215	165	55	950	731	50
31	23	87	81	62	37	131	100	87	[18] 216	166	32	**1000**	770	0
32	24	64	82	63	14	[11] 132	101	64	220	169	40	1016	782	32
33	25	41	83	63	91	133	102	41	225	173	25	1250	962	50
34	26	18	[7] 84	64	68	134	103	18	[19] 228	175	56	1500	1155	0
35	26	95	85	65	45	135	103	95	230	177	10	1728	1330	56
[3] 36	27	72	86	66	22	136	104	72	235	180	95	1750	1347	50
37	28	49	87	66	99	137	105	49	[20] 240	184	80	1760	1355	20
38	29	26	88	67	76	138	106	26	245	188	65	2000	1540	0
39	30	3	89	68	53	139	107	3	**250**	192	50	2240	1724	80
40	30	80	**90**	69	30	**140**	107	80	255	196	35	2500	1925	0
41	31	57	91	70	7	141	108	57	260	200	20	3000	2310	0
42	32	34	92	70	84	142	109	34	265	204	5	4000	3080	0
43	33	11	93	71	61	143	110	11	270	207	90	5000	3850	0
44	33	88	94	72	38	[12] 144	110	88	275	211	75	6000	4620	0
45	34	65	95	73	15	145	111	65	280	215	60	7000	5390	0
46	35	42	[8] 96	73	92	146	112	42	285	219	45	8000	6160	0
47	36	19	97	74	69	147	113	19	[24] 288	221	76	9000	6930	0
[4] 48	36	96	98	75	46	148	113	96	290	223	30	10000	7700	0
49	37	73	99	76	23	149	114	73	295	227	15	15000	11550	0
50	38	50	**100**	77	0	**150**	115	50	**300**	231	0	20000	15400	0

Grosses

1.	110	88
2.	221	76
3.	332	64
4.	443	52
5.	554	40
6.	665	28
7.	776	16
8.	887	4
9.	997	92
10.	1108	80
11.	1219	68

Twelfths

	1.	0	6¼
1/6	2.	0	12¾
	3.	0	19¼
1/3	4.	0	25¾
	5.	0	32
1/2	6.	0	38½
	7.	0	45
2/3	8.	0	51¼
	9.	0	57¾
5/6	10.	0	64¼
	11.	0	70½

Twentieths

10ths				10ths			
	1.	0	3¾		11.	0	42¼
·1	2.	0	7¾	·6	12.	0	46¼
	3.	0	11½		13.	0	50
·2	4.	0	15½	·7	14.	0	54
	5.	0	19¼		15.	0	57¾
·3	6.	0	23	·8	16.	0	61½
	7.	0	27		17.	0	65½
·4	8.	0	30¾	·9	18.	0	69¼
	9.	0	34¾		19.	0	73¼
·5	10.	0	38½		20.	0	77

Sixteenths

	1.	0	4¾		9.	0	43¼
1/8	2.	0	9¾	5/8	10.	0	48¼
	3.	0	14½		11.	0	53
1/4	4.	0	19¼	3/4	12.	0	57¾
	5.	0	24		13.	0	62½
3/8	6.	0	29	7/8	14.	0	67½
	7.	0	33¾		15.	0	72¼
1/2	8.	0	38½				

*Dozens	No.	£	P
	1	0	78
	2	1	56
	3	2	34
	4	3	12
	5	3	90
	6	4	68
	7	5	46
	8	6	24
	9	7	2
	10	7	80
*	11	8	58
1	12	9	36
	13	10	14
	14	10	92
	15	11	70
	16	12	48
	17	13	26
	18	14	4
	19	14	82
	20	15	60
	21	16	38
	22	17	16
	23	17	94
2	24	18	72
	25	19	50
	26	20	28
	27	21	6
	28	21	84
	29	22	62
	30	23	40
	31	24	18
	32	24	96
	33	25	74
	34	26	52
	35	27	30
3	36	28	8
	37	28	86
	38	29	64
	39	30	42
	40	31	20
	41	31	98
	42	32	76
	43	33	54
	44	34	32
	45	35	10
	46	35	88
	47	36	66
4	48	37	44
	49	38	22
	50	39	0

Dozens	No.	£	P
	51	39	78
	52	40	56
	53	41	34
	54	42	12
	55	42	90
	56	43	68
	57	44	46
	58	45	24
	59	46	2
5	**60**	46	80
	61	47	58
	62	48	36
	63	49	14
	64	49	92
	65	50	70
	66	51	48
	67	52	26
	68	53	4
	69	53	82
	70	54	60
	71	55	38
6	72	56	16
	73	56	94
	74	57	72
	75	58	50
	76	59	28
	77	60	6
	78	60	84
	79	61	62
	80	62	40
	81	63	18
	82	63	96
	83	64	74
7	84	65	52
	85	66	30
	86	67	8
	87	67	86
	88	68	64
	89	69	42
	90	70	20
	91	70	98
	92	71	76
	93	72	54
	94	73	32
	95	74	10
8	96	74	88
	97	75	66
	98	76	44
	99	77	22
	100	78	0

Dozens	No.	£	P
	101	78	78
	102	79	56
	103	80	34
	104	81	12
	105	81	90
	106	82	68
	107	83	46
9	108	84	24
	109	85	2
	110	85	80
	111	86	58
	112	87	36
	113	88	14
	114	88	92
	115	89	70
	116	90	48
	117	91	26
	118	92	4
	119	92	82
	120	93	60
	121	94	38
	122	95	16
	123	95	94
	124	96	72
	125	97	50
	126	98	28
	127	99	6
	128	99	84
	129	100	62
	130	101	40
	131	102	18
11	132	102	96
	133	103	74
	134	104	52
	135	105	30
	136	106	8
	137	106	86
	138	107	64
	139	108	42
	140	109	20
	141	109	98
	142	110	76
	143	111	54
12	144	112	32
	145	113	10
	146	113	88
	147	114	66
	148	115	44
	149	116	22
	150	117	0

Dozens	No.	£	P
	152	118	56
	154	120	12
13	156	121	68
	158	123	24
	160	124	80
	162	126	36
	164	127	92
	166	129	48
14	168	131	4
	170	132	60
	172	134	16
	174	135	72
	175	136	50
	176	137	28
	178	138	84
15	180	140	40
	182	141	96
	184	143	52
	186	145	8
	188	146	64
	190	148	20
16	192	149	76
	194	151	32
	196	152	88
	198	154	44
	200	156	0
17	204	159	12
	205	159	90
	210	163	80
	215	167	70
18	216	168	48
	220	171	60
	225	175	50
19	228	177	84
	230	179	40
	235	183	30
20	240	187	20
	245	191	10
	250	195	0
	255	198	90
	260	202	80
	265	206	70
	270	210	60
	275	214	50
	280	218	40
	285	222	30
24	288	224	64
	290	226	20
	295	230	10
	300	234	0

No.	£	P
310	241	80
320	249	60
330	257	40
340	265	20
350	273	0
360	280	80
365	284	70
370	288	60
380	296	40
390	304	20
400	312	0
410	319	80
420	327	60
430	335	40
440	343	20
450	351	0
460	358	80
470	366	60
480	374	40
490	382	20
500	390	0
550	429	0
600	468	0
650	507	0
700	546	0
750	585	0
800	624	0
850	663	0
900	702	0
950	741	0
1000	780	0
1016	792	48
1250	975	0
1500	1170	0
1728	1347	84
1750	1365	0
1760	1372	80
2000	1560	0
2240	1747	20
2500	1950	0
3000	2340	0
4000	3120	0
5000	3900	0
6000	4680	0
7000	5460	0
8000	6240	0
9000	7020	0
10000	7800	0
15000	11700	0
20000	15600	0

Grosses

1.	112	32
2.	224	64
3.	336	96
4.	449	28
5.	561	60
6.	673	92
7.	786	24
8.	898	56
9.	1010	88
10.	1123	20
11.	1235	52

Twelfths

	1.	0	6½
⅙	2.	0	13
	3.	0	19½
⅓	4.	0	26
	5.	0	32½
½	6.	0	39
	7.	0	45½
⅔	8.	0	52
	9.	0	58½
⅚	10.	0	65
	11.	0	71½

Twentieths

10ths			
	1.	0	4
·1	2.	0	7¾
	3.	0	11¾
·2	4.	0	15½
	5.	0	19½
·3	6.	0	23½
	7.	0	27¼
·4	8.	0	31¼
	9.	0	35
·5	10.	0	39
	11.	0	43
·6	12.	0	46¾
	13.	0	50¾
·7	14.	0	54½
	15.	0	58½
·8	16.	0	62½
	17.	0	66¼
·9	18.	0	70¼
	19.	0	74
	20.	0	78

Sixteenths

	1.	0	5
⅛	2.	0	9¾
	3.	0	14¾
¼	4.	0	19½
	5.	0	24½
⅜	6.	0	29¼
	7.	0	34¼
½	8.	0	39
	9.	0	44
⅝	10.	0	48¾
	11.	0	53¾
¾	12.	0	58½
	13.	0	63½
⅞	14.	0	68¼
	15.	0	73¼

Dozens	£	P
1	0	79
2	1	58
3	2	37
4	3	16
*5	3	95
*6	4	74
7	5	53
8	6	32
9	7	11
10	7	90
*11	8	69
12	9	48
13	10	27
14	11	6
15	11	85
16	12	64
17	13	43
18	14	22
19	15	1
20	15	80
21	16	59
22	17	38
23	18	17
24	18	96
25	19	75
26	20	54
27	21	33
28	22	12
29	22	91
30	23	70
31	24	49
32	25	28
33	26	7
34	26	86
35	27	65
*36	28	44
37	29	23
38	30	2
39	30	81
40	31	60
41	32	39
42	33	18
43	33	97
44	34	76
45	35	55
46	36	34
47	37	13
*48	37	92
49	38	71
50	39	50

Dozens	£	P
51	40	29
52	41	8
53	41	87
54	42	66
55	43	45
56	44	24
57	45	3
58	45	82
59	46	61
5 60	47	40
61	48	19
62	48	98
63	49	77
64	50	56
65	51	35
66	52	14
67	52	93
68	53	72
69	54	51
70	55	30
71	56	9
6 72	56	88
73	57	67
74	58	46
75	59	25
76	60	4
77	60	83
78	61	62
79	62	41
80	63	20
81	63	99
82	64	78
83	65	57
7 84	66	36
85	67	15
86	67	94
87	68	73
88	69	52
89	70	31
90	71	10
91	71	89
92	72	68
93	73	47
94	74	26
95	75	5
8 96	75	84
97	76	63
98	77	42
99	78	21
100	79	0

Dozens	£	P
101	79	79
102	80	58
103	81	37
104	82	16
105	82	95
106	83	74
107	84	53
9 108	85	32
109	86	11
110	86	90
111	87	69
112	88	48
113	89	27
114	90	06
115	90	85
116	91	64
117	92	43
118	93	22
119	94	01
120	94	80
121	95	59
122	96	38
123	97	17
124	97	96
125	98	75
126	99	54
127	100	33
128	101	12
129	101	91
130	102	70
131	103	49
11 132	104	28
133	105	07
134	105	86
135	106	65
136	107	44
137	108	23
138	109	02
139	109	81
140	110	60
141	111	39
142	112	18
143	112	97
12 144	113	76
145	114	55
146	115	34
147	116	13
148	116	92
149	117	71
150	118	50

Doz.	£	P
152	120	8
154	121	66
*156	123	24
158	124	82
160	126	40
162	127	98
164	129	56
166	131	14
14 168	132	72
170	134	30
172	135	88
174	137	46
175	138	25
176	139	4
178	140	62
15 180	142	20
182	143	78
184	145	36
186	146	94
188	148	52
190	150	10
16 192	151	68
194	153	26
196	154	84
198	156	42
200	158	0
17 204	161	16
205	161	95
210	165	90
215	169	85
18 216	170	64
220	173	80
225	177	75
19 228	180	12
230	181	70
235	185	65
20 240	189	60
245	193	55
250	197	50
255	201	45
260	205	40
265	209	35
270	213	30
275	217	25
280	221	20
285	225	15
24 288	227	52
290	229	10
295	233	5
300	237	0

	£	P
310	244	90
320	252	80
330	260	70
340	268	60
350	276	50
360	284	40
365	288	35
370	292	30
380	300	20
390	308	10
400	316	0
410	323	90
420	331	80
430	339	70
440	347	60
450	355	50
460	363	40
470	371	30
480	379	20
490	387	10
500	395	0
550	434	50
600	474	0
650	513	50
700	553	0
750	592	50
800	632	0
850	671	50
900	711	0
950	750	50
1000	790	0
1016	802	64
1250	987	50
1500	1185	0
1728	1365	12
1750	1382	50
1760	1390	40
2000	1580	0
2240	1769	60
2500	1975	0
3000	2370	0
4000	3160	0
5000	3950	0
6000	4740	0
7000	5530	0
8000	6320	0
9000	7110	0
10,000	7900	0
15,000	11,850	0
20,000	15,800	0

Grosses.			Twelfths			Twentieths				Sixteenths		
1.	113	76	1.	0	06½		1.	0	4	1.	0	05
2.	227	52	½ 2.	0	13½	x 2.	0	8		½ 2.	0	10
3.	341	28	3.	0	19½		3.	0	11½	3.	0	14½
4.	455	4	¼ 4.	0	26¼	2 4.	0	15½		¼ 4.	0	19½
5.	568	80	5.	0	33		5.	0	19½	5.	0	24½
6.	682	56	½ 6.	0	39½	3 6.	0	23½		½ 6.	0	29½
7.	796	32	7.	0	46		7.	0	27½	7.	0	34½
8.	910	8	¾ 8.	0	52½	4 8.	0	31½		¾ 8.	0	39½
9.	1023	84	9.	0	59½		9.	0	35½	9.	0	44½
10.	1137	60	¾ 10.	0	65½	5 10.	0	39½		¾ 10.	0	49½
11.	1251	36	11.	0	72½		11.	0	43½	11.	0	54½
						6 12.	0	47½		¼ 12.	0	59½
						13.	0	51½		13.	0	64½
						7 14.	0	55½		¾ 14.	0	69½
						15.	0	59½		15.	0	74
						8 16.	0	63½				
						17.	0	67½				
						9 18.	0	71				
						19.	0	75				
						20.	0	79				

	£	p		£	p		£	p		£	p		£	p
1	0	80	51	40	80	101	80	80	152	121	60	310	248	0
2	1	60	52	41	60	102	81	60	154	123	20	320	256	0
3	2	40	53	42	40	103	82	40	[13]156	124	80	330	264	0
4	3	20	54	43	20	104	83	20	158	126	40	340	272	0
5	4	0	55	44	0	105	84	0	160	128	0	350	280	0
*6	4	80	56	44	80	106	84	80	162	129	60	360	288	0
7	5	60	57	45	60	107	85	60	164	131	20	365	292	0
8	6	40	58	46	40	[9]108	86	40	166	132	80	370	296	0
9	7	20	59	47	20	109	87	20	[14]168	134	40	380	304	0
10	8	0	[5]**60**	48	0	**110**	88	0	170	136	0	390	312	0
*11	8	80	61	48	80	111	88	80	172	137	60	400	320	0
[1]12	9	60	62	49	60	112	89	60	174	139	20	410	328	0
13	10	40	63	50	40	113	90	40	175	140	0	420	336	0
14	11	20	64	51	20	114	91	20	176	140	80	430	344	0
15	12	0	65	52	0	115	92	0	178	142	40	440	352	0
16	12	80	66	52	80	116	92	80	[15]180	144	0	450	360	0
17	13	60	67	53	60	117	93	60	182	145	60	460	368	0
18	14	40	68	54	40	118	94	40	184	147	20	470	376	0
19	15	20	69	55	20	119	95	20	186	148	80	480	384	0
20	16	0	**70**	56	0	**120**	96	0	188	150	40	490	392	0
21	16	80	71	56	80	121	96	80	190	152	0	**500**	400	0
22	17	60	[6]72	57	60	122	97	60	[16]192	153	60	550	440	0
23	18	40	73	58	40	123	98	40	194	155	20	600	480	0
[2]24	19	20	74	59	20	124	99	20	196	156	80	650	520	0
25	20	0	75	60	0	125	100	0	198	158	40	700	560	0
26	20	80	76	60	80	126	100	80	**200**	160	0	750	600	0
27	21	60	77	61	60	127	101	60	[17]204	163	20	800	640	0
28	22	40	78	62	40	128	102	40	205	164	0	850	680	0
29	23	20	79	63	20	129	103	20	210	168	0	900	720	0
30	24	0	**80**	64	0	**130**	104	0	215	172	0	950	760	0
31	24	80	81	64	80	131	104	80	[18]216	172	80	**1000**	800	0
32	25	60	82	65	60	[11]132	105	60	220	176	0	1016	812	80
33	26	40	83	66	40	133	106	40	225	180	0	1250	1000	0
34	27	20	[7]84	67	20	134	107	20	[19]228	182	40	1500	1200	0
35	28	0	85	68	0	135	108	0	230	184	0	1728	1382	40
[3]36	28	80	86	68	80	136	108	80	235	188	0	1750	1400	0
37	29	60	87	69	60	137	109	60	[20]240	192	0	1760	1408	0
38	30	40	88	70	40	138	110	40	245	196	0	2000	1600	0
39	31	20	89	71	20	139	111	20	**250**	200	0	2240	1792	0
40	32	0	**90**	72	0	**140**	112	0	255	204	0	2500	2000	0
41	32	80	91	72	80	141	112	80	260	208	0	3000	2400	0
42	33	60	92	73	60	142	113	60	265	212	0	4000	3200	0
43	34	40	93	74	40	143	114	40	270	216	0	**5000**	4000	0
44	35	20	94	75	20	[12]144	115	20	275	220	0	6000	4800	0
45	36	0	95	76	0	145	116	0	280	224	0	7000	5600	0
46	36	80	[8]96	76	80	146	116	80	285	228	0	8000	6400	0
47	37	60	97	77	60	147	117	60	[24]288	230	40	9000	7200	0
[4]48	38	40	98	78	40	148	118	40	290	232	0	10,000	8000	0
49	39	20	99	79	20	149	119	20	295	236	0	15,000	12,000	0
50	40	0	**100**	80	0	**150**	120	0	**300**	240	0	20,000	16,000	0

Grosses.			Twelfths			10ths	Twentieths					Sixteenths					
1.	115	20	1.	0	6¾		1.	0	4	11.	0	44	1.	0	05	9.	0 45
2.	230	40	⅙ 2.	0	13¼	·1	2.	0	8	·6 12.	0	48	⅛ 2.	0	10	⅝ 10.	0 50
3.	345	60	3.	0	20		3.	0	12	13.	0	52	3.	0	15	11.	0 55
4.	460	80	⅓ 4.	0	26¾	·2	4.	0	16	·7 14.	0	56	¼ 4.	0	20	¾ 12.	0 60
5.	576	0	5.	0	33¼		5.	0	20	15.	0	60	5.	0	25	13.	0 65
6.	691	20	½ 6.	0	40	·3	6.	0	24	·8 16.	0	64	⅜ 6.	0	30	⅞ 14.	0 70
7.	806	40	7.	0	46¾		7.	0	28	17.	0	68	7.	0	35	15.	0 75
8.	921	60	⅔ 8.	0	53¼	·4	8.	0	32	·9 18.	0	72	½ 8.	0	40		
9.	1036	80	9.	0	60		9.	0	36	19.	0	76					
10.	1152	0	⅚ 10.	0	66¾	·5	10.	0	40	20.	0	80					
11.	1267	20	11.	0	73¼												

	£ P		£ P		£ P		£ P		£ P
1	0 81	51	41 31	101	81 81	152	123 12	310	251 10
2	1 62	52	42 12	102	82 62	154	124 74	320	259 20
3	2 43	53	42 93	103	83 43	*13* 156	126 36	330	267 30
Dozens 4	3 24	*Dozens* 54	43 74	*Dozens* 104	84 24	158	127 98	340	275 40
5	4 5	55	44 55	105	85 5	160	129 60	350	283 50
6	4 86	56	45 36	106	85 86	162	131 22	360	291 60
7	5 67	57	46 17	107	86 67	*Dozens* 164	132 84	365	295 65
8	6 48	58	46 98	*9* 108	87 48	166	134 46	370	299 70
9	7 29	59	47 79	109	88 29	*14* 168	136 8	380	307 80
10	8 10	*5* 60	48 60	110	89 10	170	137 70	390	315 90
11	8 91	61	49 41	111	89 91	172	139 32	400	324 0
1 12	9 72	62	50 22	112	90 72	174	140 94	410	332 10
13	10 53	63	51 3	113	91 53	176	142 56	420	340 20
14	11 34	64	51 84	114	92 34	178	144 18	430	348 30
15	12 15	65	52 65	115	93 15	*15* 180	145 80	440	356 40
16	12 96	66	53 46	116	93 96	182	147 42	450	364 50
17	13 77	67	54 27	117	94 77	184	149 4	460	372 60
18	14 58	68	55 8	118	95 58	186	150 66	470	380 70
19	15 39	69	55 89	119	96 39	188	152 28	480	388 80
20	16 20	70	56 70	120	97 20	190	153 90	490	396 90
21	17 1	71	57 51	121	98 1	192	155 52	500	405 0
22	17 82	*6* 72	58 32	122	98 82	*16* 192	155 52	550	445 50
23	18 63	73	59 13	123	99 63	194	157 14	600	486 0
2 24	19 44	74	59 94	124	100 44	196	158 76	650	526 50
25	20 25	75	60 75	125	101 25	198	160 38	700	567 0
26	21 6	76	61 56	126	102 6	200	162 0	750	607 50
27	21 87	77	62 37	127	102 87	*17* 204	165 24	800	648 0
28	22 68	78	63 18	128	103 68	205	166 5	850	688 50
29	23 49	79	63 99	129	104 49	210	170 10	900	729 0
30	24 30	80	64 80	130	105 30	215	174 15	950	769 50
31	25 11	81	65 61	131	106 11	*18* 216	174 96	1000	810 0
32	25 92	82	66 42	*11* 132	106 92	220	178 20	1016	822 96
33	26 73	83	67 23	133	107 73	225	182 25	1250	1012 50
34	27 54	*7* 84	68 4	134	108 54	*19* 228	184 68	1500	1215 0
35	28 35	85	68 85	135	109 35	230	186 30	1725	1399 68
3 36	29 16	86	69 66	136	110 16	235	190 35	1750	1417 50
37	29 97	87	70 47	137	110 97	*20* 240	194 40	1760	1425 60
38	30 78	88	71 28	138	111 78	245	198 45	2000	1620 0
39	31 59	89	72 9	139	112 59	250	202 50	2240	1814 40
40	32 40	90	72 90	140	113 40	255	206 55	2500	2025 0
41	33 21	91	73 71	141	114 21	260	210 60	3000	2430 0
42	34 2	92	74 52	142	115 2	265	214 65	4000	3240 0
43	34 83	93	75 33	143	115 83	270	218 70	5000	4050 0
44	35 64	94	76 14	*12* 144	116 64	275	222 75	6000	4860 0
45	36 45	95	76 95	145	117 45	280	226 80	7000	5670 0
46	37 26	*8* 96	77 76	146	118 26	285	230 85	8000	6480 0
47	38 7	97	78 57	147	119 7	*24* 288	233 28	9000	7290 0
4 48	38 88	98	79 38	148	119 88	290	234 90	10000	8100 0
49	39 69	99	80 19	149	120 69	295	238 95	15000	12150 0
50	40 50	100	81 0	150	121 50	300	243 0	20000	16200 0

Grosses		Twelfths		10ths	Twentieths				Sixteenths		
1.	116 64	1.	0 6¾		1.	0 4	11.	0 44½	1.	0 5	9. 0 45½
2.	233 28	⅛ 2.	0 13½	·1	2.	0 8	·6 12.	0 48½	⅛ 2.	0 10¼	⅝10. 0 50¾
3.	349 92	3.	0 20¼		3.	0 12½	13.	0 52½	3.	0 15¼	11. 0 55¾
4.	466 56	¼ 4.	0 27	·2	4.	0 16½	·7 14.	0 56½	¼ 4.	0 20¼	¾12. 0 60¾
5.	583 20	5.	0 33¾		5.	0 20½	15.	0 60½	5.	0 25¼	13. 0 65½
6.	699 84	⅜ 6.	0 40½	·3	6.	0 24½	·8 16.	0 64½	⅜ 6.	0 30½	⅞14. 0 71
7.	816 48	7.	0 47¼		7.	0 28½	17.	0 68½	7.	0 35½	15. 0 76
8.	933 12	½ 8.	0 54	·4	8.	0 32½	·9 18.	0 73	½ 8.	0 40½	
9.	1049 76	9.	0 60¾		9.	0 36½	19.	0 77			
10.	1166 40	⅝10.	0 67½	5	10.	0 40½	20.	0 81			
11.	1283 4	11.	0 74¼								

	£ P		£ P		£ P		£ P		£ P
1	0 82	51	41 82	101	82 82	152	124 64	310	254 20
2	1 64	52	42 64	102	83 64	154	126 28	320	262 40
3	2 46	53	43 46	103	84 46	156	127 92	330	270 60
4	3 28	54	44 28	104	85 28	158	129 56	340	278 80
5	4 10	55	45 10	105	86 10	160	131 20	350	287 0
6	4 92	56	45 92	106	86 92	162	132 84	360	295 20
7	5 74	57	46 74	107	87 74	164	134 48	365	299 30
8	6 56	58	47 56	108	88 56	166	136 12	370	303 40
9	7 38	59	48 38	109	89 38	168	137 76	380	311 60
10	8 20	60	49 20	110	90 20	170	139 40	390	319 80
11	9 2	61	50 2	111	91 2	172	141 4	400	328 0
12	9 84	62	50 84	112	91 84	174	142 68	410	336 20
13	10 66	63	51 66	113	92 66	176	144 32	420	344 40
14	11 48	64	52 48	114	93 48	178	145 96	430	352 60
15	12 30	65	53 30	115	94 30	180	147 60	440	360 80
16	13 12	66	54 12	116	95 12	182	149 24	450	369 0
17	13 94	67	54 94	117	95 94	184	150 88	460	377 20
18	14 76	68	55 76	118	96 76	186	152 52	470	385 40
19	15 58	69	56 58	119	97 58	188	154 16	480	393 60
20	16 40	70	57 40	120	98 40	190	155 80	490	401 80
21	17 22	71	58 22	121	99 22	192	157 44	500	410 0
22	18 4	72	59 4	122	100 4	194	159 8	550	451 0
23	18 86	73	59 86	123	100 86	196	160 72	600	492 0
24	19 68	74	60 68	124	101 68	198	162 36	650	533 0
25	20 50	75	61 50	125	102 50	200	164 0	700	574 0
26	21 32	76	62 32	126	103 32	204	167 28	750	615 0
27	22 14	77	63 14	127	104 14	205	168 10	800	656 0
28	22 96	78	63 96	128	104 96	210	172 20	850	697 0
29	23 78	79	64 78	129	105 78	215	176 30	900	738 0
30	24 60	80	65 60	130	106 60	216	177 12	950	779 0
31	25 42	81	66 42	131	107 42	220	180 40	1000	820 0
32	26 24	82	67 24	132	108 24	225	184 50	1016	833 12
33	27 6	83	68 6	133	109 6	228	186 96	1250	1025 0
34	27 88	84	68 88	134	109 88	230	188 60	1500	1230 0
35	28 70	85	69 70	135	110 70	235	192 70	1728	1416 96
36	29 52	86	70 52	136	111 52	240	196 80	1750	1435 0
37	30 34	87	71 34	137	112 34	245	200 90	1760	1443 20
38	31 16	88	72 16	138	113 16	250	205 0	2000	1640 0
39	31 98	89	72 98	139	113 98	255	209 10	2240	1836 80
40	32 80	90	73 80	140	114 80	260	213 20	2500	2050 0
41	33 62	91	74 62	141	115 62	265	217 30	3000	2460 0
42	34 44	92	75 44	142	116 44	270	221 40	4000	3280 0
43	35 26	93	76 26	143	117 26	275	225 50	5000	4100 0
44	36 8	94	77 8	144	118 8	280	229 60	6000	4920 0
45	36 90	95	77 90	145	118 90	285	233 70	7000	5740 0
46	37 72	96	78 72	146	119 72	288	236 16	8000	6560 0
47	38 54	97	79 54	147	120 54	290	237 80	9000	7380 0
48	39 36	98	80 36	148	121 36	295	241 90	10000	8200 0
49	40 18	99	81 18	149	122 18	300	246 0	15000	12300 0
50	41 0	100	82 0	150	123 0			20000	16400 0

Grosses		Twelfths		10ths	Twentieths		Sixteenths	
1. 118 8		1. 0 6¾			1. 0 4	11. 0 45	1. 0 5¼	9. 0 46¼
2. 236 16		½2. 0 13½		·1	2. 0 8¼	·6 12. 0 49¼	½2. 0 10¼	⅝10. 0 51¼
3. 354 24		3. 0 20¼			3. 0 12¼	13. 0 53¼	3. 0 15½	11. 0 56½
4. 472 32		¼4. 0 27¼		·2	4. 0 16½	·7 14. 0 57½	¼4. 0 20½	¾12. 0 61½
5. 590 40		5. 0 34¼			5. 0 20½	15. 0 61½	5. 0 25¾	13. 0 66¾
6. 708 48		½6. 0 41		·3	6. 0 24¾	·8 16. 0 65¾	⅜6. 0 30¾	⅞14. 0 71¾
7. 826 56		7. 0 47¾			7. 0 28¾	17. 0 69¾	7. 0 36	15. 0 77
8. 944 64		⅜8. 0 54½		·4	8. 0 32¾	·9 18. 0 73¾	⅛8. 0 41	
9. 1062 72		9. 0 61¼			9. 0 37	19. 0 78		
10. 1180 80		⅝10. 0 68¼		·5	10. 0 41	20. 0 82		
11. 1298 88		11. 0 75¼						

	£	P		£	P		£	P		£	P		£	P
1	0	83	51	42	33	101	83	83	152	126	16	310	257	30
2	1	66	52	43	16	102	84	66	154	127	82	320	265	60
3	2	49	53	43	99	103	85	49	¹³156	129	48	330	273	90
4	3	32	54	44	82	104	86	32	158	131	14	340	282	20
5	4	15	55	45	65	105	87	15	160	132	80	350	290	50
*6	4	98	56	46	48	106	87	98	162	134	46	360	298	80
7	5	81	57	47	31	107	88	81	164	136	12	365	302	95
8	6	64	58	48	14	108	89	64	166	137	78	370	307	10
9	7	47	59	48	97	109	90	47	¹⁴168	139	44	380	315	40
10	8	30	⁵60	49	80	110	91	30	170	141	10	390	323	70
11	9	13	61	50	63	111	92	13	172	142	76	400	332	0
12	9	96	62	51	46	112	92	96	174	144	42	410	340	30
13	10	79	63	52	29	113	93	79	176	146	8	420	348	60
14	11	62	64	53	12	114	94	62	178	147	74	430	356	90
15	12	45	65	53	95	115	95	45	¹⁵180	149	40	440	365	20
16	13	28	66	54	78	116	96	28	182	151	6	450	373	50
17	14	11	67	55	61	117	97	11	184	152	72	460	381	80
18	14	94	68	56	44	118	97	94	186	154	38	470	390	10
19	15	77	69	57	27	119	98	77	188	156	4	480	398	40
20	16	60	70	58	10	120	99	60	190	157	70	490	406	70
21	17	43	71	58	93	121	100	43	¹⁶192	159	36	500	415	0
22	18	26	⁶72	59	76	122	101	26	194	161	2	550	456	50
23	19	9	73	60	59	123	102	9	196	162	68	600	498	0
*24	19	92	74	61	42	124	102	92	198	164	34	650	539	50
25	20	75	75	62	25	125	103	75	200	166	0	700	581	0
26	21	58	76	63	8	126	104	58	¹⁷204	169	32	750	622	50
27	22	41	77	63	91	127	105	41	205	170	15	800	664	0
28	23	24	78	64	74	128	106	24	210	174	30	850	705	50
29	24	7	79	65	57	129	107	7	215	178	45	900	747	0
30	24	90	80	66	40	130	107	90	¹⁸216	179	28	950	788	50
31	25	73	81	67	23	131	108	73	220	182	60	1000	830	0
32	26	56	82	68	6	¹¹132	109	56	225	186	75	1016	843	28
33	27	39	83	68	89	133	110	39	¹⁹228	189	24	1250	1037	50
34	28	22	⁷84	69	72	134	111	22	230	190	90	1500	1245	0
35	29	5	85	70	55	135	112	5	235	195	5	1728	1434	24
³36	29	88	86	71	38	136	112	88	²⁰240	199	20	1750	1452	50
37	30	71	87	72	21	137	113	71	245	203	35	1760	1460	80
38	31	54	88	73	4	138	114	54	250	207	50	2000	1660	0
39	32	37	89	73	87	139	115	37	255	211	65	2240	1859	20
40	33	20	90	74	70	140	116	20	260	215	80	2500	2075	0
41	34	3	91	75	53	141	117	3	265	219	95	3000	2490	0
42	34	86	92	76	36	142	117	86	270	224	10	4000	3320	0
43	35	69	93	77	19	143	118	69	275	228	25	5000	4150	0
44	36	52	94	78	2	¹²144	119	52	280	232	40	6000	4980	0
45	37	35	95	78	85	145	120	35	285	236	55	7000	5810	0
46	38	18	⁸96	79	68	146	121	18	²⁴285	239	4	8000	6640	0
47	39	1	97	80	51	147	122	1	290	240	70	9000	7470	0
*48	39	84	98	81	34	148	122	84	295	244	85	10000	8300	0
49	40	67	99	82	17	149	123	67	300	249	0	15000	12450	0
50	41	50	100	83	0	150	124	50				20000	16600	0

Grosses.			Twelfths			1/10th	Twentieths			Sixteenths		
1.	119	52	1.	0	7		1.	0	4¼	1.	0	5¼
2.	239	04	½2.	0	13½	·1	2.	0	8¼	½2.	0	10½
3.	358	56	3.	0	20¼		3.	0	12½	3.	0	15½
4.	478	08	¼4.	0	27½	·2	4.	0	16½	¼4.	0	20¼
5.	597	60	5.	0	34¼		5.	0	20½	5.	0	26
6.	717	12	½6.	0	41½	·3	6.	0	25	½6.	0	31½
7.	836	64	7.	0	48½		7.	0	29	7.	0	36½
8.	956	16	¾8.	0	55½	·4	8.	0	33½	¾8.	0	41½
9.	1075	68	9.	0	62¼		9.	0	37½	9.	0	46¼
10.	1195	20	½10.	0	69½	·5	10.	0	41½	10.	0	52
11.	1314	72	11.	0	76		11.	0	45½	11.	0	57
						·6	12.	0	49½	12.	0	62½
							13.	0	54	13.	0	67½
						·7	14.	0	58	14.	0	72½
							15.	0	62½	15.	0	77½
						·8	16.	0	66½			
							17.	0	70			
						·9	18.	0	74½			
							19.	0	78½			
							20.	0	83			

	£	P		£	P		£	P		£	P		£	P
1	0	84	51	42	84	101	84	84	152	127	68	310	260	40
2	1	68	52	43	68	102	85	68	154	129	36	320	268	80
3	2	52	53	44	52	103	86	52	[13]156	131	4	330	277	20
4	3	36	54	45	36	104	87	36	158	132	72	340	285	60
5	4	20	55	46	20	105	88	20	160	134	40	350	294	0
*6	5	4	56	47	4	106	89	4	162	136	8	360	302	40
7	5	88	57	47	88	107	89	88	164	137	76	365	306	60
8	6	72	58	48	72	[9]108	90	72	166	139	44	370	310	80
9	7	56	59	49	56	109	91	56	[14]168	141	12	380	319	20
10	8	40	[5]**60**	50	40	**110**	92	40	170	142	80	390	327	60
*11	9	24	61	51	24	111	93	24	172	144	48	400	336	0
[1]12	10	8	62	52	8	112	94	8	174	146	16	410	344	40
13	10	92	63	52	92	113	94	92	175	147	0	420	352	80
14	11	76	64	53	76	114	95	76	176	147	84	430	361	20
15	12	60	65	54	60	115	96	60	178	149	52	440	369	60
16	13	44	66	55	44	116	97	44	[15]180	151	20	450	378	0
17	14	28	67	56	28	117	98	28	182	152	88	460	386	40
18	15	12	68	57	12	118	99	12	184	154	56	470	394	80
19	15	96	69	57	96	119	99	96	186	156	24	480	403	20
20	16	80	**70**	58	80	**120**	100	80	188	157	92	490	411	60
21	17	64	71	59	64	121	101	64	190	159	60	**500**	420	0
22	18	48	[6]72	60	48	122	102	48	[16]192	161	28	550	462	0
23	19	32	73	61	32	123	103	32	194	162	96	600	504	0
[2]24	20	16	74	62	16	124	104	16	196	164	64	650	546	0
25	21	0	75	63	0	125	105	0	198	166	32	700	588	0
26	21	84	76	63	84	126	105	84	**200**	168	0	750	630	0
27	22	68	77	64	68	127	106	68	[17]204	171	36	800	672	0
28	23	52	78	65	52	128	107	52	205	172	20	850	714	0
29	24	36	79	66	36	129	108	36	210	176	40	900	756	0
30	25	20	**80**	67	20	**130**	109	20	215	180	60	950	798	0
31	26	4	81	68	4	131	110	4	[18]216	181	44	**1000**	840	0
32	26	88	82	68	88	[11]132	110	88	220	184	80	1016	853	44
33	27	72	83	69	72	133	111	72	225	189	0	1250	1050	0
34	28	56	[7]84	70	56	134	112	56	[19]228	191	52	1500	1260	0
35	29	40	85	71	40	135	113	40	230	193	20	1728	1451	52
[3]36	30	24	86	72	24	136	114	24	235	197	40	1750	1470	0
37	31	8	87	73	8	137	115	8	[20]240	201	60	1760	1478	40
38	31	92	88	73	92	138	115	92	245	205	80	2000	1680	0
39	32	76	89	74	76	139	116	76	**250**	210	0	2240	1881	60
40	33	60	**90**	75	60	**140**	117	60	255	214	20	2500	2100	0
41	34	44	91	76	44	141	118	44	260	218	40	3000	2520	0
42	35	28	92	77	28	142	119	28	265	222	60	4000	3360	0
43	36	12	93	78	12	143	120	12	270	226	80	**5000**	4200	0
44	36	96	94	78	96	[12]144	120	96	275	231	0	6000	5040	0
45	37	80	95	79	80	145	121	80	280	235	20	7000	5880	0
46	38	64	[8]96	80	64	146	122	64	285	239	40	8000	6720	0
47	39	48	97	81	48	147	123	48	[24]288	241	92	9000	7560	0
[4]48	40	32	98	82	32	148	124	32	290	243	60	10000	8400	0
49	41	16	99	83	16	149	125	16	295	247	80	15000	12600	0
50	42	0	**100**	84	0	**150**	126	0	**300**	252	0	20000	16800	0

Grosses

1.	120	96
2.	241	92
3.	362	88
4.	483	84
5.	604	80
6.	725	76
7.	846	72
8.	967	68
9.	1088	64
10.	1209	60
11.	1330	56

Twelfths

	1.	0	7
⅙	2.	0	14
	3.	0	21
⅓	4.	0	28
	5.	0	35
½	6.	0	42
	7.	0	49
⅔	8.	0	56
	9.	0	63
⅚	10.	0	70
	11.	0	77

Twentieths

10ths				10ths			
	1.	0	4¼		11.	0	46¼
·1	2.	0	8½	·6	12.	0	50½
	3.	0	12½		13.	0	54½
·2	4.	0	16¾	·7	14.	0	58¾
	5.	0	21		15.	0	63
·3	6.	0	25¼	·8	16.	0	67¼
	7.	0	29½		17.	0	71½
·4	8.	0	33½	·9	18.	0	75½
	9.	0	37¾		19.	0	79¾
·5	10.	0	42		20.	0	84

Sixteenths

	1.	0	5¼		9.	0	47¼
⅛	2.	0	10½	⅝	10.	0	52½
	3.	0	15¾		11.	0	57¾
¼	4.	0	21	¾	12.	0	63
	5.	0	26¼		13.	0	68¼
⅜	6.	0	31½	⅞	14.	0	73½
	7.	0	36¾		15.	0	78¾
½	8.	0	42				

No.	£ P	No.	£ P	No.	£ P	No.	£ P	No.	£ P
1	0 85	51	43 35	101	85 85	152	129 20	310	263 50
2	1 70	52	44 20	102	86 70	154	130 90	320	272 0
3	2 55	53	45 5	103	87 55	156	132 60	330	280 50
4	3 40	54	45 90	104	88 40	158	134 30	340	289 0
4	4 25	55	46 75	105	89 25	160	136 0	350	297 50
6	5 10	56	47 60	106	90 10	162	137 70	360	306 0
7	5 95	57	48 45	107	90 95	164	139 40	365	310 25
8	6 80	58	49 30	108	91 80	166	141 10	370	314 50
9	7 65	59	50 15	109	92 65	168	142 80	380	323 0
10	8 50	60	51 0	110	93 50	170	144 50	390	331 50
11	9 35	61	51 85	111	94 35	172	146 20	400	340 0
12	10 20	62	52 70	112	95 20	174	147 90	410	348 50
13	11 5	63	53 55	113	96 5	175	148 75	420	357 0
14	11 90	64	54 40	114	96 90	176	149 60	430	365 50
15	12 75	65	55 25	115	97 75	178	151 30	440	374 0
16	13 60	66	56 10	116	98 60	180	153 0	450	382 50
17	14 45	67	56 95	117	99 45	182	154 70	460	391 0
18	15 30	68	57 80	118	100 30	184	156 40	470	399 50
19	16 15	69	58 65	119	101 15	186	158 10	480	408 0
20	17 0	70	59 50	120	102 0	188	159 80	490	416 50
21	17 85	71	60 35	121	102 85	190	161 50	500	425 0
22	18 70	72	61 20	122	103 70	192	163 20	550	467 50
23	19 55	73	62 5	123	104 55	194	164 90	600	510 0
24	20 40	74	62 90	124	105 40	196	166 60	650	552 50
25	21 25	75	63 75	125	106 25	198	168 30	700	595 0
26	22 10	76	64 60	126	107 10	200	170 0	750	637 50
27	22 95	77	65 45	127	107 95	204	173 40	800	680 0
28	23 80	78	66 30	128	108 80	205	174 25	850	722 50
29	24 65	79	67 15	129	109 65	210	178 50	900	765 0
30	25 50	80	68 0	130	110 50	215	182 75	950	807 50
31	26 35	81	68 85	131	111 35	216	183 60	1000	850 0
32	27 20	82	69 70	132	112 20	220	187 0	1016	863 60
33	28 5	83	70 55	133	113 5	225	191 25	1250	1062 50
34	28 90	84	71 40	134	113 90	228	193 80	1500	1275 0
35	29 75	85	72 25	135	114 75	230	195 50	1728	1468 80
36	30 60	86	73 10	136	115 60	235	199 75	1750	1487 50
37	31 45	87	73 95	137	116 45	240	204 0	1760	1496 0
38	32 30	88	74 80	138	117 30	245	208 25	2000	1700 0
39	33 15	89	75 65	139	118 15	250	212 50	2240	1904 0
40	34 0	90	76 50	140	119 0	255	216 75	2500	2125 0
41	34 85	91	77 35	141	119 85	260	221 0	3000	2550 0
42	35 70	92	78 20	142	120 70	265	225 25	4000	3400 0
43	36 55	93	79 5	143	121 55	270	229 50	5000	4250 0
44	37 40	94	79 90	144	122 40	275	233 75	6000	5100 0
45	38 25	95	80 75	145	123 25	280	238 0	7000	5950 0
46	39 10	96	81 60	146	124 10	285	242 25	8000	6800 0
47	39 95	97	82 45	147	124 95	288	244 80	9000	7650 0
48	40 80	98	83 30	148	125 80	290	246 50	10000	8500 0
49	41 65	99	84 15	149	126 65	295	250 75	15000	12750 0
50	42 50	100	85 0	150	127 50	300	255 0	20000	17000 0

Grosses		Twelfths		10ths	Twentieths		Sixteenths	
1.	122 40	1.	0 7	1. 0 4¼	11. 0 46¾		1. 0 5¼	9. 0 47¾
2.	244 80	2.	0 14½	2. 0 8½	12. 0 51		2. 0 10¾	10. 0 53¼
3.	367 20	3.	0 21½	3. 0 12¾	13. 0 55¼		3. 0 16	11. 0 58¼
4.	489 60	4.	0 28½	4. 0 17	14. 0 59½		4. 0 21¼	12. 0 63¾
5.	612 0	5.	0 35½	5. 0 21¼	15. 0 63¾		5. 0 26½	13. 0 69
6.	734 40	6.	0 42½	6. 0 25½	16. 0 68		6. 0 32	14. 0 74¼
7.	856 80	7.	0 49½	7. 0 29¾	17. 0 72¼		7. 0 37½	15. 0 79¾
8.	979 20	8.	0 56½	8. 0 34	18. 0 76½		8. 0 42½	
9.	1101 60	9.	0 63½	9. 0 38¼	19. 0 80¾			
10.	1224 0	10.	0 70½	10. 0 42½	20. 0 85			
11.	1346 40	11.	0 78					

86 Pence

86 Pence

	£	P		£	P		£	P		£	P		£	P
1	0	86	51	43	86	101	86	86	152	130	72	310	266	60
2	1	72	52	44	72	102	87	72	154	132	44	320	275	20
3	2	58	53	45	58	103	88	58	13 156	134	16	330	283	80
4	3	44	54	46	44	104	89	44	158	135	88	340	292	40
5	4	30	55	47	30	105	90	30	160	137	60	350	301	0
6	5	16	56	48	16	106	91	16	162	139	32	360	309	60
7	6	2	57	49	2	107	92	2	164	141	4	365	313	90
8	6	88	58	49	88	9 108	92	88	166	142	76	370	318	20
9	7	74	59	50	74	109	93	74	14 168	144	48	380	326	80
10	**8**	**60**	5 **60**	**51**	**60**	**110**	**94**	**60**	170	146	20	390	335	40
*11	9	46	61	52	46	111	95	46	172	147	92	400	344	0
1 12	10	32	62	53	32	112	96	32	174	149	64	410	352	60
13	11	18	63	54	18	113	97	18	175	150	50	420	361	20
14	12	4	64	55	4	114	98	4	176	151	36	430	369	80
15	12	90	65	55	90	115	98	90	178	153	8	440	378	40
16	13	76	66	56	76	116	99	76	15 180	154	80	450	387	0
17	14	62	67	57	62	117	100	62	182	156	52	460	395	60
18	15	48	68	58	48	118	101	48	184	158	24	470	404	20
19	16	34	69	59	34	119	102	34	186	159	96	480	412	80
20	**17**	**20**	**70**	**60**	**20**	10 **120**	**103**	**20**	188	161	68	490	421	40
21	18	6	71	61	6	121	104	6	190	163	40	**500**	**430**	**0**
22	18	92	6 72	61	92	122	104	92	16 192	165	12	550	473	0
23	19	78	73	62	78	123	105	78	194	166	84	600	516	0
2 24	20	64	74	63	64	124	106	64	196	168	56	650	559	0
25	21	50	75	64	50	125	107	50	198	170	28	700	602	0
26	22	36	76	65	36	126	108	36	**200**	**172**	**0**	750	645	0
27	23	22	77	66	22	127	109	22	17 204	175	44	800	688	0
28	24	8	78	67	8	128	110	8	205	176	30	850	731	0
29	24	94	79	67	94	129	110	94	210	180	60	900	774	0
30	**25**	**80**	**80**	**68**	**80**	**130**	**111**	**80**	215	184	90	950	817	0
31	26	66	81	69	66	131	112	66	18 216	185	76	**1000**	**860**	**0**
32	27	52	82	70	52	11 132	113	52	220	189	20	1016	873	76
33	28	38	83	71	38	133	114	38	225	193	50	1250	1075	0
34	29	24	7 84	72	24	134	115	24	19 228	196	8	1500	1290	0
35	30	10	85	73	10	135	116	10	230	197	80	1728	1486	8
3 36	30	96	86	73	96	136	116	96	235	202	10	1750	1505	0
37	31	82	87	74	82	137	117	82	20 240	206	40	1760	1513	60
38	32	68	88	75	68	138	118	68	245	210	70	2000	1720	0
39	33	54	89	76	54	139	119	54	**250**	**215**	**0**	2240	1926	40
40	**34**	**40**	**90**	**77**	**40**	**140**	**120**	**40**	255	219	30	2500	2150	0
41	35	26	91	78	26	141	121	26	260	223	60	3000	2580	0
42	36	12	92	79	12	142	122	12	265	227	90	4000	3440	0
43	36	98	93	79	98	143	122	98	270	232	20	**5000**	**4300**	**0**
44	37	84	94	80	84	12 144	123	84	275	236	50	6000	5160	0
45	38	70	95	81	70	145	124	70	280	240	80	7000	6020	0
46	39	56	8 96	82	56	146	125	56	285	245	10	8000	6880	0
47	40	42	97	83	42	147	126	42	24 288	247	68	9000	7740	0
4 48	41	28	98	84	28	148	127	28	290	249	40	10000	8600	0
49	42	14	99	85	14	149	128	14	295	253	70	15000	12900	0
50	**43**	**0**	**100**	**86**	**0**	**150**	**129**	**0**	**300**	**258**	**0**	20000	17200	0

*Dozens

Grosses		
1.	123	84
2.	247	68
3.	371	52
4.	495	36
5.	619	20
6.	743	4
7.	866	88
8.	990	72
9.	1114	56
10.	1238	40
11.	1362	24

Twelfths			
	1.	0	7¼
⅙	2.	0	14¼
	3.	0	21½
⅓	4.	0	28¾
	5.	0	35¾
½	6.	0	43
	7.	0	50¼
⅔	8.	0	57¼
	9.	0	64½
⅚	10.	0	71¾
	11.	0	78¾

10ths	Twentieths					
	1.	0	4¼		11.	0 47¼
·1	2.	0	8½	·6	12.	0 51½
	3.	0	13		13.	0 56
·2	4.	0	17¼	·7	14.	0 60¼
	5.	0	21½		15.	0 64½
·3	6.	0	25¾	·8	16.	0 68¾
	7.	0	30		17.	0 73
·4	8.	0	34½	·9	18.	0 77½
	9.	0	38¾		19.	0 81¾
·5	10.	0	43		20.	0 86

Sixteenths							
	1.	0	5½		9.	0	48½
⅛	2.	0	10¾	⅝	10.	0	53¾
	3.	0	16¼		11.	0	59¼
¼	4.	0	21½	¾	12.	0	64½
	5.	0	27		13.	0	70
⅜	6.	0	32¼	⅞	14.	0	75¼
	7.	0	37¾		15.	0	80¾
½	8.	0	43				

* Dozens.	£	P	Dozens.	£	P	Dozens.	£	P	Doz.	£	P		£	P
1	0	87	51	44	37	101	87	87	152	132	24	310	269	70
2	1	74	52	45	24	102	88	74	154	133	98	320	278	40
3	2	61	53	46	11	103	89	61	[13] 156	135	72	330	287	10
4	3	48	54	46	98	104	90	48	158	137	46	340	295	80
5	4	35	55	47	85	105	91	35	160	139	20	350	304	50
6	5	22	56	48	72	106	92	22	162	140	94	360	313	20
7	6	9	57	49	59	107	93	9	164	142	68	365	317	55
8	6	96	58	50	46	[9] 108	93	96	166	144	42	370	321	90
9	7	83	59	51	33	109	94	83	[14] 168	146	16	380	330	60
10	8	70	[5] **60**	52	20	**110**	95	70	170	147	90	390	339	30
*11	9	57	61	53	7	111	96	57	172	149	64	400	348	0
[1] 12	10	44	62	53	94	112	97	44	174	151	38	410	356	70
13	11	31	63	54	81	113	98	31	175	152	25	420	365	40
14	12	18	64	55	68	114	99	18	176	153	12	430	374	10
15	13	5	65	56	55	115	100	5	178	154	86	440	382	80
16	13	92	66	57	42	116	100	92	[15] 180	156	60	450	391	50
17	14	79	67	58	29	117	101	79	182	158	34	460	400	20
18	15	66	68	59	16	118	102	66	184	160	8	470	408	90
19	16	53	69	60	3	119	103	53	186	161	82	480	417	60
20	17	40	**70**	60	90	**120**	104	40	188	163	56	490	426	30
21	18	27	71	61	77	121	105	27	190	165	30	**500**	435	0
22	19	14	[6] 72	62	64	122	106	14	[16] 192	167	4	550	478	50
23	20	1	73	63	51	123	107	1	194	168	78	600	522	0
[2] 24	20	88	74	64	38	124	107	88	196	170	52	650	565	50
25	21	75	75	65	25	125	108	75	198	172	26	700	609	0
26	22	62	76	66	12	126	109	62	**200**	174	0	750	652	50
27	23	49	77	66	99	127	110	49	[17] 204	177	48	800	696	0
28	24	36	78	67	86	128	111	36	205	178	35	850	739	50
29	25	23	79	68	73	129	112	23	210	182	70	900	783	0
30	26	10	**80**	69	60	**130**	113	10	215	187	5	950	826	50
31	26	97	81	70	47	131	113	97	[18] 216	187	92	**1000**	870	0
32	27	84	82	71	34	[11] 132	114	84	220	191	40	1016	883	92
33	28	71	83	72	21	133	115	71	225	195	75	1250	1087	50
34	29	58	[7] 84	73	8	134	116	58	[19] 228	198	36	1500	1305	0
35	30	45	85	73	95	135	117	45	230	200	10	1728	1503	36
[3] 36	31	32	86	74	82	136	118	32	235	204	45	1750	1522	50
37	32	19	87	75	69	137	119	19	[20] 240	208	80	1760	1531	20
38	33	6	88	76	56	138	120	6	245	213	15	2000	1740	0
39	33	93	89	77	43	139	120	93	**250**	217	50	2240	1948	80
40	34	80	**90**	78	30	**140**	121	80	255	221	85	2500	2175	0
41	35	67	91	79	17	141	122	67	260	226	20	3000	2610	0
42	36	54	92	80	4	142	123	54	265	230	55	4000	3480	0
43	37	41	93	80	91	143	124	41	270	234	90	**5000**	4350	0
44	38	28	94	81	78	[12] 144	125	28	275	239	25	6000	5220	0
45	39	15	95	82	65	145	126	15	280	243	60	7000	6090	0
46	40	2	[8] 96	83	52	146	127	2	285	247	95	8000	6960	0
47	40	89	97	84	39	147	127	89	[24] 288	250	56	9000	7830	0
[4] 48	41	76	98	85	26	148	128	76	290	252	30	10000	8700	0
49	42	63	99	86	13	149	129	63	295	256	65	15000	13050	0
50	43	50	**100**	87	0	**150**	130	50	**300**	261	0	20000	17400	0

Grosses.

1.	125	28
2.	250	56
3.	375	84
4.	501	12
5.	626	40
6.	751	68
7.	876	96
8.	1002	24
9.	1127	52
10.	1252	80
11.	1378	08

Twelfths

1.	0	7¼
⅙ 2.	0	14½
3.	0	21¾
⅓ 4.	0	29
5.	0	36¼
½ 6.	0	43½
7.	0	50¾
⅔ 8.	0	58
9.	0	65¼
⅚ 10.	0	72½
11.	0	79¾

Twentieths (10ths)

1.	0	4¼	11.	0	47¾
·1 2.	0	8¾	·6 12.	0	52¼
3.	0	13	13.	0	56½
·2 4.	0	17½	·7 14.	0	61
5.	0	21¾	15.	0	65¼
·3 6.	0	26	8 16.	0	69½
7.	0	30½	17.	0	74
·4 8.	0	34¾	·9 18.	0	78¼
9.	0	39¼	19.	0	82¾
·5 10.	0	43½	20.	0	87

Sixteenths

1.	0	5½	9.	0	49
⅛ 2.	0	11	⅝ 10.	0	54½
3.	0	16¼	11.	0	59¾
¼ 4.	0	21¾	¾ 12.	0	65¼
5.	0	27¼	13.	0	70¾
⅜ 6.	0	32¾	⅞ 14.	0	76¼
7.	0	38	15.	0	81½
½ 8.	0	43½			

	£ P		£ P		£ P		£ P		£ P
1	0 88	51	44 88	101	88 88	152	133 76	310	272 80
2	1 76	52	45 76	102	89 76	154	135 52	320	281 60
3	2 64	53	46 64	103	90 64	13 156	137 28	330	290 40
*Dozens 4	3 52	54	47 52	104	91 52	158	139 4	340	299 20
5	4 40	Dozens 55	48 40	Dozens 105	92 40	Dozens 160	140 80	350	308 0
6	5 28	56	49 28	106	93 28	162	142 56	360	316 80
7	6 16	57	50 16	107	94 16	164	144 32	365	321 20
8	7 4	58	51 4	9 108	95 4	166	146 8	370	325 60
9	7 92	59	51 92	109	95 92	14 168	147 84	380	334 40
10	8 80	5 60	52 80	110	96 80	170	149 60	390	343 20
11	9 68	61	53 68	111	97 68	172	151 36	400	352 0
12	10 56	62	54 56	112	98 56	174	153 12	410	360 80
13	11 44	63	55 44	113	99 44	175	154 0	420	369 60
14	12 32	64	56 32	114	100 32	176	154 88	430	378 40
15	13 20	65	57 20	115	101 20	178	156 64	440	387 20
16	14 8	66	58 8	116	102 8	15 180	158 40	450	396 0
17	14 96	67	58 96	117	102 96	182	160 16	460	404 80
18	15 84	68	59 84	118	103 84	184	161 92	470	413 60
19	16 72	69	60 72	119	104 72	186	163 68	480	422 40
20	17 60	70	61 60	120	105 60	188	165 44	490	431 20
21	18 48	71	62 48	121	106 48	190	167 20	500	440 0
22	19 36	6 72	63 36	122	107 36	16 192	168 96	550	484 0
23	20 24	73	64 24	123	108 24	194	170 72	600	528 0
2 24	21 12	74	65 12	124	109 12	196	172 48	650	572 0
25	22 0	75	66 0	125	110 0	198	174 24	700	616 0
26	22 88	76	66 88	126	110 88	200	176 0	750	660 0
27	23 76	77	67 76	127	111 76	17 204	179 52	800	704 0
28	24 64	78	68 64	128	112 64	205	180 40	850	748 0
29	25 52	79	69 52	129	113 52	210	184 80	900	792 0
30	26 40	80	70 40	130	114 40	215	189 20	950	836 0
31	27 28	81	71 28	131	115 28	18 216	190 8	1000	880 0
32	28 16	82	72 16	11 132	116 16	220	193 60	1016	894 8
33	29 4	83	73 4	133	117 4	225	198 0	1250	1100 0
34	29 92	7 84	73 92	134	117 92	19 228	200 64	1500	1320 0
35	30 80	85	74 80	135	118 80	230	202 40	1728	1520 64
3 36	31 68	86	75 68	136	119 68	235	206 80	1750	1540 0
37	32 56	87	76 56	137	120 56	20 240	211 20	1760	1548 80
38	33 44	88	77 44	138	121 44	245	215 60	2000	1760 0
39	34 32	89	78 32	139	122 32	250	220 0	2240	1971 20
40	35 20	90	79 20	140	123 20	255	224 40	2500	2200 0
41	36 8	91	80 8	141	124 8	260	228 80	3000	2640 0
42	36 96	92	80 96	142	124 96	265	233 20	4000	3520 0
43	37 84	93	81 84	143	125 84	270	237 60	5000	4400 0
44	38 72	94	82 72	12 144	126 72	275	242 0	6000	5280 0
45	39 60	95	83 60	145	127 60	280	246 40	7000	6160 0
46	40 48	8 96	84 48	146	128 48	285	250 80	8000	7040 0
47	41 36	97	85 36	147	129 36	24 288	253 44	9000	7920 0
4 48	42 24	98	86 24	148	130 24	290	255 20	10000	8800 0
49	43 12	99	87 12	149	131 12	295	259 60	15000	13200 0
50	44 0	100	88 0	150	132 0	300	264 0	20000	17600 0

Grosses		Twelfths		10ths / Twentieths		Sixteenths	
1.	126 72	1. 0 07¼		1. 0 4½	11. 0 48½	1. 0 5½	9. 0 49½
2.	253 44	⅙ 2. 0 14¾		⅕ 2. 0 8¾	·6 12. 0 52¾	½ 2. 0 11	½ 10. 0 55
3.	380 16	3. 0 22		3. 0 13¼	13. 0 57¼	3. 0 16½	11. 0 60½
4.	506 88	¾ 4. 0 29¼		·2 4. 0 17⅝	·7 14. 0 61¾	¼ 4. 0 22	12. 0 66
5.	633 60	5. 0 36¼		5. 0 22	15. 0 66	5. 0 27½	½ 12. 0 66
6.	760 32	⅙ 6. 0 44		·3 6. 0 26½	·8 16. 0 70½	6. 0 33	13. 0 71½
7.	887 04	7. 0 51¼		7. 0 30¾	17. 0 74¾	½ 6. 0 33	½ 14. 0 77
8.	1013 76	⅜ 8. 0 58¼		·4 8. 0 35¼	·9 18. 0 79¼	7. 0 38½	14. 0 77
9.	1140 48	9. 0 66		9. 0 39½	19. 0 83½	½ 8. 0 44	15. 0 82½
10.	1267 20	⅚ 10. 0 73¼		·5 10. 0 44	20. 0 88	8. 0 44	
11.	1393 92	11. 0 80¾					

*Dozens	No.	£	P
	1	0	89
	2	1	78
	3	2	67
	4	3	56
	5	4	45
	6	5	34
	7	6	23
	8	7	12
	9	8	1
	10	**8**	**90**
*	11	9	79
1	12	10	68
	13	11	57
	14	12	46
	15	13	35
	16	14	24
	17	15	13
	18	16	2
	19	16	91
	20	**17**	**80**
	21	18	69
	22	19	58
	23	20	47
2	24	21	36
	25	22	25
	26	23	14
	27	24	3
	28	24	92
	29	25	81
	30	**26**	**70**
	31	27	59
	32	28	48
	33	29	37
	34	30	26
	35	31	15
3	36	32	4
	37	32	93
	38	33	82
	39	34	71
	40	**35**	**60**
	41	36	49
	42	37	38
	43	38	27
	44	39	16
	45	40	5
	46	40	94
	47	41	83
4	48	42	72
	49	43	61
	50	**44**	**50**

Dozens	No.	£	P
	51	45	39
	52	46	28
	53	47	17
	54	48	6
	55	48	95
	56	49	84
	57	50	73
	58	51	62
	59	52	51
5	**60**	**53**	**40**
	61	54	29
	62	55	18
	63	56	7
	64	56	96
	65	57	85
	66	58	74
	67	59	63
	68	60	52
	69	61	41
	70	**62**	**30**
	71	63	19
6	72	64	8
	73	64	97
	74	65	86
	75	66	75
	76	67	64
	77	68	53
	78	69	42
	79	70	31
	80	**71**	**20**
	81	72	9
	82	72	98
	83	73	87
7	84	74	76
	85	75	65
	86	76	54
	87	77	43
	88	78	32
	89	79	21
	90	**80**	**10**
	91	80	99
	92	81	88
	93	82	77
	94	83	66
	95	84	55
8	96	85	44
	97	86	33
	98	87	22
	99	88	11
	100	**89**	**0**

Dozens	No.	£	P
	101	89	89
	102	90	78
	103	91	67
	104	92	56
	105	93	45
	106	94	34
	107	95	23
9	108	96	12
	109	97	1
	110	**97**	**90**
	111	98	79
	112	99	68
	113	100	57
	114	101	46
	115	102	35
	116	103	24
	117	104	13
	118	105	2
	119	105	91
	120	**106**	**80**
	121	107	69
	122	108	58
	123	109	47
	124	110	36
	125	111	25
	126	112	14
	127	113	3
	128	113	92
	129	114	81
	130	**115**	**70**
	131	116	59
11	132	117	48
	133	118	37
	134	119	26
	135	120	15
	136	121	4
	137	121	93
	138	122	82
	139	123	71
	140	**124**	**60**
	141	125	49
	142	126	38
	143	127	27
12	144	128	16
	145	129	5
	146	129	94
	147	130	83
	148	131	72
	149	132	61
	150	**133**	**50**

Dozens	No.	£	P
	152	135	28
	154	137	6
13	156	138	84
	158	140	62
	160	142	40
	162	144	18
	164	145	96
	166	147	74
14	168	149	52
	170	151	30
	172	153	8
	174	154	86
	175	155	75
	176	156	64
	178	158	42
15	180	160	20
	182	161	98
	184	163	76
	186	165	54
	188	167	32
	190	169	10
16	192	170	88
	194	172	66
	196	174	44
	198	176	22
	200	**178**	**0**
17	204	181	56
	205	182	45
	210	186	90
	215	191	35
18	216	192	24
	220	195	80
	225	200	25
19	228	202	92
	230	204	70
	235	209	15
20	240	213	60
	245	218	5
	250	**222**	**50**
	255	226	95
	260	231	40
	265	235	85
	270	240	30
	275	244	75
	280	249	20
	285	253	65
24	288	256	32
	290	258	10
	295	262	55
	300	**267**	**0**

No.	£	P
310	275	90
320	284	80
330	293	70
340	302	60
350	311	50
360	320	40
365	324	85
370	329	30
380	338	20
390	347	10
400	356	0
410	364	90
420	373	80
430	382	70
440	391	60
450	400	50
460	409	40
470	418	30
480	427	20
490	436	10
500	**445**	**0**
550	489	50
600	534	0
650	578	50
700	623	0
750	667	50
800	712	0
850	756	50
900	801	0
950	845	50
1000	**890**	**0**
1016	904	24
1250	1112	50
1500	1335	0
1728	1537	92
1750	1557	50
1760	1566	40
2000	1780	0
2240	1993	60
2500	2225	0
3000	2670	0
4000	3560	0
5000	4450	0
6000	5340	0
7000	6230	0
8000	7120	0
9000	8010	0
10000	8900	0
15000	13350	0
20000	17800	0

Grosses

	£	P
1.	128	16
2.	256	32
3.	384	48
4.	512	64
5.	640	80
6.	768	96
7.	897	12
8.	1025	28
9.	1153	44
10.	1281	60
11.	1409	76

Twelfths

		£	P
	1.	0	7½
⅙	2.	0	14¾
	3.	0	22¼
⅓	4.	0	29¾
	5.	0	37
½	6.	0	44½
	7.	0	52
⅔	8.	0	59¼
	9.	0	66¾
⅚	10.	0	74¼
	11.	0	81½

Twentieths

10ths		£	P			£	P
	1.	0	4½		11.	0	49
·1	2.	0	9	·6	12.	0	53½
	3.	0	13¼		13.	0	57¾
·2	4.	0	17¾	·7	14.	0	62¼
	5.	0	22¼		15.	0	66¾
·3	6.	0	26¾	·8	16.	0	71¼
	7.	0	31¼		17.	0	75¾
·4	8.	0	35½	·9	18.	0	80
	9.	0	40		19.	0	84½
·5	10.	0	44½		20.	0	89

Sixteenths

		£	P			£	P
	1.	0	5½		9.	0	50
⅛	2.	0	11¼	⅝	10.	0	55¾
	3.	0	16¾		11.	0	61¼
¼	4.	0	22¼	¾	12	0	66¾
	5.	0	27¾		13.	0	72¼
⅜	6.	0	33½	⅞	14.	0	78
	7.	0	39		15.	0	83½
½	8.	0	44½				

	£	P		£	P		£	P		£	P		£	P
1	0	90	51	45	90	101	90	90	152	136	80	310	279	0
2	1	80	52	46	80	102	91	80	154	138	60	320	288	0
3	2	70	53	47	70	103	92	70	¹³156	140	40	330	297	0
4	3	60	54	48	60	104	93	60	158	142	20	340	306	0
5	4	50	55	49	50	105	94	50	160	144	0	350	315	0
6	5	40	56	50	40	106	95	40	162	145	80	360	324	0
7	6	30	57	51	30	107	96	30	164	147	60	365	328	50
8	7	20	58	52	20	⁹108	97	20	166	149	40	370	333	0
9	8	10	59	53	10	109	98	10	¹⁴168	151	20	380	342	0
10	9	0	⁵60	54	0	110	99	0	170	153	0	390	351	0
*11	9	90	61	54	90	111	99	90	172	154	80	400	360	0
¹12	10	80	62	55	80	112	100	80	174	156	60	410	369	0
13	11	70	63	56	70	113	101	70	175	157	50	420	378	0
14	12	60	64	57	60	114	102	60	176	158	40	430	387	0
15	13	50	65	58	50	115	103	50	178	160	20	440	396	0
16	14	40	66	59	40	116	104	40	¹⁵180	162	0	450	405	0
17	15	30	67	60	30	117	105	30	182	163	80	460	414	0
18	16	20	68	61	20	118	106	20	184	165	60	470	423	0
19	17	10	69	62	10	119	107	10	186	167	40	480	432	0
20	18	0	70	63	0	120	108	0	188	169	20	490	441	0
21	18	90	71	63	90	121	108	90	190	171	0	500	450	0
22	19	80	⁶72	64	80	122	109	80	¹⁶192	172	80	550	495	0
23	20	70	73	65	70	123	110	70	194	174	60	600	540	0
²24	21	60	74	66	60	124	111	60	196	176	40	650	585	0
25	22	50	75	67	50	125	112	50	198	178	20	700	630	0
26	23	40	76	68	40	126	113	40	200	180	0	750	675	0
27	24	30	77	69	30	127	114	30	¹⁷204	183	60	800	720	0
28	25	20	78	70	20	128	115	20	205	184	50	850	765	0
29	26	10	79	71	10	129	116	10	210	189	0	900	810	0
30	27	0	80	72	0	130	117	0	215	193	50	950	855	0
31	27	90	81	72	90	131	117	90	¹⁸216	194	40	1000	900	0
32	28	80	82	73	80	¹¹132	118	80	220	198	0	1016	914	40
33	29	70	83	74	70	133	119	70	225	202	50	1250	1125	0
34	30	60	⁷84	75	60	134	120	60	¹⁹228	205	20	1500	1350	0
35	31	50	85	76	50	135	121	50	230	207	0	1728	1555	20
³36	32	40	86	77	40	136	122	40	235	211	50	1750	1575	0
37	33	30	87	78	30	137	123	30	²⁰240	216	0	1760	1584	0
38	34	20	88	79	20	138	124	20	245	220	50	2000	1800	0
39	35	10	89	80	10	139	125	10	250	225	0	2240	2016	0
40	36	0	90	81	0	140	126	0	255	229	50	2500	2250	0
41	36	90	91	81	90	141	126	90	260	234	0	3000	2700	0
42	37	80	92	82	80	142	127	80	265	238	50	4000	3600	0
43	38	70	93	83	70	143	128	70	270	243	0	5000	4500	0
44	39	60	94	84	60	¹²144	129	60	275	247	50	6000	5400	0
45	40	50	95	85	50	145	130	50	280	252	0	7000	6300	0
46	41	40	⁸96	86	40	146	131	40	285	256	50	8000	7200	0
47	42	30	97	87	30	147	132	30	²⁴288	259	20	9000	8100	0
⁴48	43	20	98	88	20	148	133	20	290	261	0	10000	9000	0
49	44	10	99	89	10	149	134	10	295	265	50	15000	13500	0
50	45	0	100	90	0	150	135	0	300	270	0	20000	18000	0

Grosses		Twelfths			10ths	Twentieths		Sixteenths			
1.	129 60	1/12.	0	7½				1.	0 5¼	9.	0 50¼
2.	259 20	⅙ 2.	0	15	1. 0 4½	11. 0 49½		⅛.	0 11¼	⅝10.	0 56¼
3.	388 80	3.	0	22½	x 2. 0 9	·6 12. 0 54		3.	0 17	11.	0 62
4.	518 40	⅓ 4.	0	30	3. 0 13½	13. 0 58½		¼.	0 22½	¾12.	0 67½
5.	648 00	5.	0	37½	·2 4. 0 18	·7 14. 0 63		5.	0 28¼	13.	0 73¼
6.	777 60	½ 6.	0	45	5. 0 22½	15. 0 67½		⅜.	0 33¾	⅞14.	0 78¾
7.	907 20	7.	0	52½	·3 6. 0 27	·8 16. 0 72		7.	0 39¼	15.	0 84¼
8.	1036 80	⅔ 8.	0	60	7. 0 31½	17. 0 76½		½.	0 45		
9.	1166 40	9.	0	67½	·4 8. 0 36	·9 18. 0 81					
10.	1296 00	⅚10.	0	75	9. 0 40½	19. 0 85½					
11.	1425 60	11.	0	82½	·5 10. 0 45	20. 0 90					

£ — P conversion tables (91 Pence per unit)

Panel 1

doz	n	£	P
	4	3	64
	5	4	55
	6	5	46
	7	6	37
	8	7	28
	9	8	19
	10	9	10
	11	10	1
1	12	10	92
	13	11	83
	14	12	74
	15	13	65
	16	14	56
	17	15	47
	18	16	38
	19	17	29
	20	18	20
	21	19	11
	22	20	2
	23	20	93
2	24	21	84
	25	22	75
	26	23	66
	27	24	57
	28	25	48
	29	26	39
	30	27	30
	31	28	21
	32	29	12
	33	30	3
	34	30	94
	35	31	85
3	36	32	76
	37	33	67
	38	34	58
	39	35	49
	40	36	40
	41	37	31
	42	38	22
	43	39	13
	44	40	4
	45	40	95
	46	41	86
	47	42	77
4	48	43	68
	49	44	59
	50	45	50

Panel 2 (Dozens)

doz	n	£	P
	51	46	41
	52	47	32
	53	48	23
	54	49	14
	55	50	5
	56	50	96
	57	51	87
	58	52	78
	59	53	69
5	60	54	60
	61	55	51
	62	56	42
	63	57	33
	64	58	24
	65	59	15
	66	60	6
	67	60	97
	68	61	88
	69	62	79
	70	63	70
	71	64	61
6	72	65	52
	73	66	43
	74	67	34
	75	68	25
	76	69	16
	77	70	7
	78	70	98
	79	71	89
	80	72	80
	81	73	71
	82	74	62
	83	75	53
7	84	76	44
	85	77	35
	86	78	26
	87	79	17
	88	80	8
	89	80	99
	90	81	90
	91	82	81
	92	83	72
	93	84	63
	94	85	54
	95	86	45
8	96	87	36
	97	88	27
	98	89	18
	99	90	9
	100	91	0

Panel 3 (Dozens)

doz	n	£	P
	101	91	91
	102	92	82
	103	93	73
	104	94	64
	105	95	55
	106	96	46
	107	97	37
9	108	98	28
	109	99	19
	110	100	10
	111	101	1
	112	101	92
	113	102	83
	114	103	74
	115	104	65
	116	105	56
	117	106	47
	118	107	38
	119	108	29
10	120	109	20
	121	110	11
	122	111	2
	123	111	93
	124	112	84
	125	113	75
	126	114	66
	127	115	57
	128	116	48
	129	117	39
	130	118	30
	131	119	21
11	132	120	12
	133	121	3
	134	121	94
	135	122	85
	136	123	76
	137	124	67
	138	125	58
	139	126	49
	140	127	40
	141	128	31
	142	129	22
	143	130	13
12	144	131	4
	145	131	95
	146	132	86
	147	133	77
	148	134	68
	149	135	59
	150	136	50

Panel 4 (Dozens)

doz	n	£	P
	152	138	32
	154	140	14
13	156	141	96
	158	143	78
	160	145	60
	162	147	42
	164	149	24
	166	151	6
14	168	152	88
	170	154	70
	172	156	52
	174	158	34
	175	159	25
	176	160	16
	178	161	98
15	180	163	80
	182	165	62
	184	167	44
	186	169	26
	188	171	8
	190	172	90
16	192	174	72
	194	176	54
	196	178	36
	198	180	18
	200	182	0
17	204	185	64
	205	186	55
	210	191	10
18	216	196	56
	220	200	20
	225	204	75
19	228	207	48
	230	209	30
20	240	218	40
	245	222	95
	250	227	50
	255	232	5
	260	236	60
	265	241	15
	270	245	70
	275	250	25
	280	254	80
	285	259	35
24	288	262	8
	290	263	90
	295	268	45
	300	273	0

Panel 5

n	£	P
310	282	10
320	291	20
330	300	30
340	309	40
350	318	50
360	327	60
365	332	15
370	336	70
380	345	80
390	354	90
400	364	0
410	373	10
420	382	20
430	391	30
440	400	40
450	409	50
460	418	60
470	427	70
480	436	80
490	445	90
500	455	0
550	500	50
600	546	0
650	591	50
700	637	0
750	682	50
800	728	0
850	773	50
900	819	0
950	864	50
1000	910	0
1016	924	56
1250	1137	50
1500	1365	0
1728	1572	48
1750	1592	50
1760	1601	60
2000	1820	0
2240	2038	40
2500	2275	0
3000	2730	0
4000	3640	0
5000	4550	0
6000	5460	0
7000	6370	0
8000	7280	0
9000	8190	0
10000	9100	0
15000	13650	0
20000	18200	0

Grosses

Grosses	£	P
1.	131	4
2.	262	8
3.	393	12
4.	524	16
5.	655	20
6.	786	24
7.	917	28
8.	1048	32
9.	1179	36
10.	1310	40
11.	1441	44

Twelfths

frac	Twelfths	£	P
	1.	0	7½
⅙	2.	0	15¼
	3.	0	22¾
⅓	4.	0	30¼
	5.	0	38
½	6.	0	45½
	7.	0	53
⅔	8.	0	60¾
	9.	0	68¼
⅚	10.	0	75¾
	11.	0	83¼

10ths / Twentieths

10ths	Twentieths	£	P
	1.	0	4½
·1	2.	0	9
	3.	0	13½
·2	4.	0	18¼
	5.	0	22¾
·3	6.	0	27¼
	7.	0	31½
·4	8.	0	36½
	9.	0	41
·5	10.	0	45½
	11.	0	50
·6	12.	0	54½
	13.	0	59½
·7	14.	0	63¾
	15.	0	68¼
·8	16.	0	72¾
	17.	0	77¼
·9	18.	0	82
	19.	0	86½
	20.	0	91

Sixteenths

frac	Sixteenths	£	P
	1.	0	5¾
⅛	2.	0	11½
	3.	0	17
¼	4.	0	22¾
	5.	0	28½
⅜	6.	0	34¼
	7.	0	39¾
½	8.	0	45½
	9.	0	51¼
⅝	10.	0	57
	11.	0	62½
¾	12.	0	68¼
	13.	0	74
⅞	14.	0	79¾
	15.	0	85¼

92 Pence

Doz.	No.	£	P	Doz.	No.	£	P	Doz.	No.	£	P	Doz.	No.	£	P	No.	£	P
*Dozens	1	0	92	Dozens	51	46	92	Dozens	101	92	92	Dozens	152	139	84	310	285	20
	2	1	84		52	47	84		102	93	84		154	141	68	320	294	40
	3	2	76		53	48	76		103	94	76	13	156	143	52	330	303	60
	4	3	68		54	49	68		104	95	68		158	145	36	340	312	80
	5	4	60		55	50	60		105	96	60		160	147	20	350	322	0
	6	5	52		56	51	52		106	97	52		162	149	4	360	331	20
	7	6	44		57	52	44		107	98	44		164	150	88	365	335	80
	8	7	36		58	53	36	9	108	99	36		166	152	72	370	340	40
	9	8	28		59	54	28		109	100	28	14	168	154	56	380	349	60
	10	**9**	**20**	5	**60**	**55**	**20**		**110**	**101**	**20**		170	156	40	390	358	80
*	11	10	12		61	56	12		111	102	12		172	158	24	400	368	0
1	12	11	4		62	57	4		112	103	4		174	160	8	410	377	20
	13	11	96		63	57	96		113	103	96		175	161	0	420	386	40
	14	12	88		64	58	88		114	104	88		176	161	92	430	395	60
	15	13	80		65	59	80		115	105	80		178	163	76	440	404	80
	16	14	72		66	60	72		116	106	72	15	180	165	60	450	414	0
	17	15	64		67	61	64		117	107	64		182	167	44	460	423	20
	18	16	56		68	62	56		118	108	56		184	169	28	470	432	40
	19	17	48		69	63	48		119	109	48		186	171	12	480	441	60
	20	**18**	**40**		**70**	**64**	**40**	10	**120**	**110**	**40**		188	172	96	490	450	80
	21	19	32		71	65	32		121	111	32		190	174	80	**500**	**460**	**0**
	22	20	24	6	72	66	24		122	112	24	16	192	176	64	550	506	0
	23	21	16		73	67	16		123	113	16		194	178	48	600	552	0
2	24	22	8		74	68	8		124	114	8		196	180	32	650	598	0
	25	23	0		75	69	0		125	115	0		198	182	16	700	644	0
	26	23	92		76	69	92		126	115	92		**200**	**184**	**0**	750	690	0
	27	24	84		77	70	84		127	116	84	17	204	187	68	800	736	0
	28	25	76		78	71	76		128	117	76		205	188	60	850	782	0
	29	26	68		79	72	68		129	118	68		210	193	20	900	828	0
	30	**27**	**60**		**80**	**73**	**60**		**130**	**119**	**60**		215	197	80	950	874	0
	31	28	52		81	74	52		131	120	52	18	216	198	72	**1000**	**920**	**0**
	32	29	44		82	75	44	11	132	121	44		220	202	40	1016	934	72
	33	30	36		83	76	36		133	122	36		225	207	0	1250	1150	0
	34	31	28	7	84	77	28		134	123	28	19	228	209	76	1500	1380	0
	35	32	20		85	78	20		135	124	20		230	211	60	1728	1589	76
3	36	33	12		86	79	12		136	125	12		235	216	20	1750	1610	0
	37	34	4		87	80	4		137	126	4	20	240	220	80	1760	1619	20
	38	34	96		88	80	96		138	126	96		245	225	40	2000	1840	0
	39	35	88		89	81	88		139	127	88		**250**	**230**	**0**	2240	2060	80
	40	**36**	**80**		**90**	**82**	**80**		**140**	**128**	**80**		255	234	60	2500	2300	0
	41	37	72		91	83	72		141	129	72		260	239	20	3000	2760	0
	42	38	64		92	84	64		142	130	64		265	243	80	4000	3680	0
	43	39	56		93	85	56		143	131	56		270	248	40	**5000**	**4600**	**0**
	44	40	48		94	86	48	12	144	132	48		275	253	0	6000	5520	0
	45	41	40		95	87	40		145	133	40		280	257	60	7000	6440	0
	46	42	32	8	96	88	32		146	134	32		285	262	20	8000	7360	0
	47	43	24		97	89	24		147	135	24	24	288	264	96	9000	8280	0
4	48	44	16		98	90	16		148	136	16		290	266	80	10000	9200	0
	49	45	8		99	91	8		149	137	8		295	271	40	15000	13800	0
	50	**46**	**0**		**100**	**92**	**0**		**150**	**138**	**0**		**300**	**276**	**0**	20000	18400	0

Grosses

1.	132	48
2.	264	96
3.	397	44
4.	529	92
5.	662	40
6.	794	88
7.	927	36
8.	1059	84
9.	1192	32
10.	1324	80
11.	1457	28

Twelfths

	1.	0	7¾
⅙	2.	0	15¼
	3.	0	23
⅓	4.	0	30¾
	5.	0	38¼
½	6.	0	46
	7.	0	53¾
⅔	8.	0	61¼
	9.	0	69
⅚	10.	0	76¾
	11.	0	84¼

Twentieths

10ths				10ths			
	1.	0	4½		11.	0	50½
·1	2.	0	9¼	·6	12.	0	55¼
	3.	0	13¾		13.	0	59¾
·2	4.	0	18½	·7	14.	0	64½
	5.	0	23		15.	0	69
·3	6.	0	27½	·8	16.	0	73½
	7.	0	32¼		17.	0	78¼
·4	8.	0	36¾	·9	18.	0	82¾
	9.	0	41½		19.	0	87½
·5	10.	0	46		20.	0	92

Sixteenths

	1.	0	5¾		9.	0	51¾
⅛	2.	0	11½	⅝	10.	0	57½
	3.	0	17¼		11.	0	63¼
¼	4.	0	23	¾	12.	0	69
	5.	0	28¾		13.	0	74¾
⅜	6.	0	34½	⅞	14.	0	80½
	7.	0	40¼		15.	0	86¼
½	8.	0	46				

	£	P		£	P		£	P
1	0	93	51	47	43	101	93	93
2	1	86	52	48	36	102	94	86
3	2	79	53	49	29	103	95	79
4	3	72	54	50	22	104	96	72
5	4	65	55	51	15	105	97	65
6	5	58	56	52	8	106	98	58
7	6	51	57	53	1	107	99	51
8	7	44	58	53	94	108	100	44
9	8	37	59	54	87	109	101	37
10	9	30	60	55	80	110	102	30
11	10	23	61	56	73	111	103	23
12	11	16	62	57	66	112	104	16
13	12	9	63	58	59	113	105	9
14	13	2	64	59	52	114	106	2
15	13	95	65	60	45	115	106	95
16	14	88	66	61	38	116	107	88
17	15	81	67	62	31	117	108	81
18	16	74	68	63	24	118	109	74
19	17	67	69	64	17	119	110	67
20	18	60	70	65	10	120	111	60
21	19	53	71	66	3	121	112	53
22	20	46	72	66	96	122	113	46
23	21	39	73	67	89	123	114	39
24	22	32	74	68	82	124	115	32
25	23	25	75	69	75	125	116	25
26	24	18	76	70	68	126	117	18
27	25	11	77	71	61	127	118	11
28	26	4	78	72	54	128	119	4
29	26	97	79	73	47	129	119	97
30	27	90	80	74	40	130	120	90
31	28	83	81	75	33	131	121	83
32	29	76	82	76	26	132	122	76
33	30	69	83	77	19	133	123	69
34	31	62	84	78	12	134	124	62
35	32	55	85	79	5	135	125	55
36	33	48	86	79	98	136	126	48
37	34	41	87	80	91	137	127	41
38	35	34	88	81	84	138	128	34
39	36	27	89	82	77	139	129	27
40	37	20	90	83	70	140	130	20
41	38	13	91	84	63	141	131	13
42	39	6	92	85	56	142	132	6
43	39	99	93	86	49	143	132	99
44	40	92	94	87	42	144	133	92
45	41	85	95	88	35	145	134	85
46	42	78	96	89	28	146	135	78
47	43	71	97	90	21	147	136	71
48	44	64	98	91	14	148	137	64
49	45	57	99	92	7	149	138	57
50	46	50	100	93	0	150	139	50

Left-margin dozen markers: 5 60, 6 72, 7 84, 8 96, 9 108, 10 (110), 11 132, 12 144.

	£	P		£	P
152	141	36	310	288	30
154	143	22	320	297	60
156	145	8	330	306	90
158	146	94	340	316	20
160	148	80	350	325	50
162	150	66	360	334	80
164	152	52	365	339	45
166	154	38	370	344	10
168	156	24	380	353	40
170	158	10	390	362	70
172	159	96	400	372	0
174	161	82	410	381	30
175	162	75	420	390	60
176	163	68	430	399	90
178	165	54	440	409	20
180	167	40	450	418	50
182	169	26	460	427	80
184	171	12	470	437	10
186	172	98	480	446	40
188	174	84	490	455	70
190	176	70	500	465	0
192	178	56	550	511	50
194	180	42	600	558	0
196	182	28	650	604	50
198	184	14	700	651	0
200	186	0	750	697	50
204	189	72	800	744	0
205	190	65	850	790	50
210	195	30	900	837	0
215	199	95	950	883	50
216	200	88	1000	930	0
220	204	60	1016	944	88
225	209	25	1250	1162	50
228	212	4	1500	1395	0
230	213	90	1728	1607	4
235	218	55	1750	1627	50
240	223	20	1760	1636	80
245	227	85	2000	1860	0
250	232	50	2240	2083	20
255	237	15	2500	2325	0
260	241	80	3000	2790	0
265	246	45	4000	3720	0
270	251	10	5000	4650	0
275	255	75	6000	5580	0
280	260	40	7000	6510	0
285	265	5	8000	7440	0
290	269	70	9000	8370	0
295	274	35	10000	9300	0
300	279	0	15000	13950	0
			20000	18600	0

Left-margin dozen markers in 152–300 block: 13 156, Das. 160, 14 168, 15 180, 16 192, 17 204, 18 216, 19 228, 20 240, 24 288.

Grosses.			Twelfths				Twentieths			Sixteenths		
1.	133	92	1.	0	7¾	1.	0	4⅝	11.	0	51¼	1.	0	5⅞
2.	267	84	2.	0	15½	2.	0	9¼	12.	0	55¾	2.	0	11⅝
3.	401	76	3.	0	23¼	3.	0	14	13.	0	60½	3.	0	17½
4.	535	68	4.	0	31	4.	0	18½	14.	0	65	4.	0	23¼
5.	669	60	5.	0	38¾	5.	0	23¼	15.	0	69½	5.	0	29
6.	803	52	6.	0	46½	6.	0	28	16.	0	74¼	6.	0	35
7.	937	44	7.	0	54¼	7.	0	32½	17.	0	79	7.	0	40½
8.	1071	36	8.	0	62	8.	0	37¼	18.	0	83½	8.	0	46¼
9.	1205	28	9.	0	69¾	9.	0	41¾	19.	0	88¼	9.	0	52⅛
10.	1339	20	10.	0	77½	10.	0	46½	20.	0	93	10.	0	58¼
11.	1473	12	11.	0	85¼							11.	0	64
												12.	0	69¾
												13.	0	75½
												14.	0	81¼
												15.	0	87¼

Qty	£	P
1	0	94
2	1	88
3	2	82
4	3	76
5	4	70
6	5	64
7	6	58
8	7	52
9	8	46
10	9	40
11	10	34
12	11	28
13	12	22
14	13	16
15	14	10
16	15	4
17	15	98
18	16	92
19	17	86
20	18	80
21	19	74
22	20	68
23	21	62
24	22	56
25	23	50
26	24	44
27	25	38
28	26	32
29	27	26
30	28	20
31	29	14
32	30	8
33	31	2
34	31	96
35	32	90
36	33	84
37	34	78
38	35	72
39	36	66
40	37	60
41	38	54
42	39	48
43	40	42
44	41	36
45	42	30
46	43	24
47	44	18
48	45	12
49	46	6
50	47	0

Qty	£	P
51	47	94
52	48	88
53	49	82
54	50	76
55	51	70
56	52	64
57	53	58
58	54	52
59	55	46
60	56	40
61	57	34
62	58	28
63	59	22
64	60	16
65	61	10
66	62	4
67	62	98
68	63	92
69	64	86
70	65	80
71	66	74
72	67	68
73	68	62
74	69	56
75	70	50
76	71	44
77	72	38
78	73	32
79	74	26
80	75	20
81	76	14
82	77	8
83	78	2
84	78	96
85	79	90
86	80	84
87	81	78
88	82	72
89	83	66
90	84	60
91	85	54
92	86	48
93	87	42
94	88	36
95	89	30
96	90	24
97	91	18
98	92	12
99	93	6
100	94	0

Qty	£	P
101	94	94
102	95	88
103	96	82
104	97	76
105	98	70
106	99	64
107	100	58
108	101	52
109	102	46
110	103	40
111	104	34
112	105	28
113	106	22
114	107	16
115	108	10
116	109	4
117	109	98
118	110	92
119	111	86
120	112	80
121	113	74
122	114	68
123	115	62
124	116	56
125	117	50
126	118	44
127	119	38
128	120	32
129	121	26
130	122	20
131	123	14
132	124	8
133	125	2
134	125	96
135	126	90
136	127	84
137	128	78
138	129	72
139	130	66
140	131	60
141	132	54
142	133	48
143	134	42
144	135	36
145	136	30
146	137	24
147	138	18
148	139	12
149	140	6
150	141	0

Qty	£	P
152	142	88
154	144	76
156	146	64
158	148	52
160	150	40
162	152	28
164	154	16
166	156	4
168	157	92
170	159	80
172	161	68
174	163	56
176	165	44
178	167	32
180	169	20
182	171	8
184	172	96
186	174	84
188	176	72
190	178	60
192	180	48
194	182	36
196	184	24
198	186	12
200	188	0
204	191	76
205	192	70
210	197	40
215	202	10
216	203	4
220	206	80
225	211	50
228	214	32
230	216	20
235	220	90
240	225	60
245	230	30
250	235	0
255	239	70
260	244	40
265	249	10
270	253	80
275	258	50
280	263	20
285	267	90
288	270	72
290	272	60
295	277	30
300	282	0

Qty	£	P
310	291	40
320	300	80
330	310	20
340	319	60
350	329	0
360	338	40
365	343	10
370	347	80
380	357	20
390	366	60
400	376	0
410	385	40
420	394	80
430	404	20
440	413	60
450	423	0
460	432	40
470	441	80
480	451	20
490	460	60
500	470	0
550	517	0
600	564	0
650	611	0
700	658	0
750	705	0
800	752	0
850	799	0
900	846	0
950	893	0
1000	940	0
1016	955	4
1250	1175	0
1500	1410	0
1728	1624	32
1750	1645	0
1760	1654	40
1800	1692	0
2000	1880	0
2240	2105	60
2500	2350	0
2800	2632	0
3000	2820	0
4000	3760	0
5000	4700	0
6000	5640	0
7000	6580	0
8000	7520	0
9000	8460	0
10000	9400	0
15000	14100	0
20000	18800	0

Grosses		Twelfths		Twentieths		Sixteenths	
1.	135 36	1.	0 7¾	1. 0 4¾	11. 0 51¾	1. 0 6	9. 0 53
2.	270 72	2.	0 15½	2. 0 9½	12. 0 56¼	2. 0 11¾	10. 0 58¾
3.	406 08	3.	0 23¼	3. 0 14	13. 0 61	3. 0 17¾	11. 0 64½
4.	541 44	4.	0 31¼	4. 0 18¾	14. 0 65¾	4. 0 23½	12. 0 70½
5.	676 80	5.	0 39¼	5. 0 23½	15. 0 70½	5. 0 29¼	13. 0 76¼
6.	812 16	6.	0 47	6. 0 28¼	16. 0 75¼	6. 0 35¼	14. 0 82¼
7.	947 52	7.	0 54¾	7. 0 32¾	17. 0 80	7. 0 41¼	15. 0 88¼
8.	1082 88	8.	0 62½	8. 0 37½	18. 0 84½	8. 0 47	
9.	1218 24	9.	0 70¼	9. 0 42¼	19. 0 89¼		
10.	1353 60	10.	0 78¼	10. 0 47	20. 0 94		
11.	1488 96	11.	0 86¼				

	£ P		£ P		£ P		£ P		£ P
1	0 95	51	48 45	101	95 95	152	144 40	310	294 50
2	1 90	52	49 40	102	96 90	154	146 30	320	304 00
3	2 85	53	50 35	103	97 85	13 156	148 20	330	313 50
4	3 80	54	51 30	104	98 80	158	150 10	340	323 00
5	4 75	55	52 25	105	99 75	160	152 0	350	332 50
6	5 70	56	53 20	106	100 70	162	153 90	360	342 00
7	6 65	57	54 15	107	101 65	164	155 80	365	346 75
8	7 60	58	55 10	108	102 60	166	157 70	370	351 50
9	8 55	59	56 5	109	103 55	14 168	159 60	380	361 00
10	9 50	60	57 0	110	104 50	170	161 50	390	370 50
11	10 45	61	57 95	111	105 45	172	163 40	400	380 00
12	11 40	62	58 90	112	106 40	174	165 30	410	389 50
13	12 35	63	59 85	113	107 35	175	166 25	420	399 00
14	13 30	64	60 80	114	108 30	176	167 20	430	408 50
15	14 25	65	61 75	115	109 25	178	169 10	440	418 00
16	15 20	66	62 70	116	110 20	15 180	171 0	450	427 50
17	16 15	67	63 65	117	111 15	182	172 90	460	437 00
18	17 10	68	64 60	118	112 10	184	174 80	470	446 50
19	18 5	69	65 55	119	113 5	186	176 70	480	456 00
20	19 0	70	66 50	120	114 0	188	178 60	490	465 50
21	19 95	71	67 45	121	114 95	190	180 50	500	475 0
22	20 90	72	68 40	122	115 90	16 192	182 40	550	522 50
23	21 85	73	69 35	123	116 85	194	184 30	600	570 0
24	22 80	74	70 30	124	117 80	196	186 20	650	617 50
25	23 75	75	71 25	125	118 75	198	188 10	700	665 0
26	24 70	76	72 20	126	119 70	200	190 0	750	712 50
27	25 65	77	73 15	127	120 65	17 204	193 80	800	760 0
28	26 60	78	74 10	128	121 60	205	194 75	850	807 50
29	27 55	79	75 5	129	122 55	210	199 50	900	855 0
30	28 50	80	76 0	130	123 50	215	204 25	950	902 50
31	29 45	81	76 95	131	124 45	18 216	205 20	1000	950 0
32	30 40	82	77 90	132	125 40	220	209 0	1016	965 20
33	31 35	83	78 85	133	126 35	225	213 75	1250	1187 50
34	32 30	84	79 80	134	127 30	19 228	216 60	1500	1425 0
35	33 25	85	80 75	135	128 25	230	218 50	1728	1641 60
36	34 20	86	81 70	136	129 20	235	223 25	1750	1662 50
37	35 15	87	82 65	137	130 15	20 240	228 0	1760	1672 0
38	36 10	88	83 60	138	131 10	245	232 75	2000	1900 0
39	37 5	89	84 55	139	132 5	250	237 50	2240	2128 0
40	38 0	90	85 50	140	133 0	255	242 25	2500	2375 0
41	38 95	91	86 45	141	133 95	260	247 0	3000	2850 0
42	39 90	92	87 40	142	134 90	265	251 75	4000	3800 0
43	40 85	93	88 35	143	135 85	270	256 50	5000	4750 0
44	41 80	94	89 30	144	136 80	275	261 25	6000	5700 0
45	42 75	95	90 25	145	137 75	280	266 0	7000	6650 0
46	43 70	96	91 20	146	138 70	285	270 75	8000	7600 0
47	44 65	97	92 15	147	139 65	24 288	273 60	9000	8550 0
48	45 60	98	93 10	148	140 60	290	275 50	10000	9500 0
49	46 55	99	94 5	149	141 55	295	280 25	15000	14250 0
50	47 50	100	95 0	150	142 50	300	285 0	20000	19000 0

Grosses		Twelfths		10ths	Twentieths			Sixteenths			
1.	136 80	1.	0 8		1.	0 4¾	11.	0 52¼	1.	0 6	9.	0 53½
2.	273 60	½2.	0 15½	·1	2.	0 9½	·6 12.	0 57	⅛2.	0 12	⅝10.	0 59½
3.	410 40	3.	0 23½		3.	0 14¼	13.	0 61¾	3.	0 17½	11.	0 65½
4.	547 20	¼4.	0 31½	·2	4.	0 19	·7 14.	0 66½	¼4.	0 23½	¾12.	0 71½
5.	684 00	5.	0 39½		5.	0 23¾	15.	0 71¼	5.	0 29½	13.	0 77½
6.	820 80	⅙6.	0 47½	·3	6.	0 28½	·8 16.	0 76	⅜6.	0 35½	⅞14.	0 83½
7.	957 60	7.	0 54½		7.	0 33⅓	·9 18.	0 85½	7.	0 41½	15.	0 89
8.	1094 40	⅓8.	0 63½	·4	8.	0 38	19.	0 90¼	½8.	0 47½		
9.	1231 20	9.	0 71½		9.	0 42¾	20.	0 95				
10.	1368 00	⁵⁄₁₂10.	0 79½	·5	10.	0 47½						
11.	1504 80	11.	0 87									

*Dozens	£	P	Dozens	£	P	Dozens	£	P	Dozens	£	P		£	P
1	0	96	51	48	96	101	96	96	152	145	92	310	297	60
2	1	92	52	49	92	102	97	92	154	147	84	320	307	20
3	2	88	53	50	88	103	98	88	[13] 156	149	76	330	316	80
4	3	84	54	51	84	104	99	84	158	151	68	340	326	40
5	4	80	55	52	80	105	100	80	160	153	60	350	336	0
6	5	76	56	53	76	106	101	76	162	155	52	360	345	60
7	6	72	57	54	72	107	102	72	164	157	44	365	350	40
8	7	68	58	55	68	[9] 108	103	68	166	159	36	370	355	20
9	8	64	59	56	64	109	104	64	[14] 168	161	28	380	364	80
10	9	60	[5] 60	57	60	110	105	60	170	163	20	390	374	40
11	10	56	61	58	56	111	106	56	172	165	12	400	384	0
[1*] 12	11	52	62	59	52	112	107	52	174	167	4	410	393	60
13	12	48	63	60	48	113	108	48	175	168	0	420	403	20
14	13	44	64	61	44	114	109	44	176	168	96	430	412	80
15	14	40	65	62	40	115	110	40	178	170	88	440	422	40
16	15	36	66	63	36	116	111	36	[15] 180	172	80	450	432	0
17	16	32	67	64	32	117	112	32	182	174	72	460	441	60
18	17	28	68	65	28	118	113	28	184	176	64	470	451	20
19	18	24	69	66	24	119	114	24	186	178	56	480	460	80
20	19	20	70	67	20	[10] 120	115	20	188	180	48	490	470	40
21	20	16	71	68	16	121	116	16	190	182	40	500	480	0
22	21	12	[6] 72	69	12	122	117	12	[16] 192	184	32	550	528	0
23	22	8	73	70	8	123	118	8	194	186	24	600	576	0
[2] 24	23	4	74	71	4	124	119	4	196	188	16	650	624	0
25	24	0	75	72	0	125	120	0	198	190	8	700	672	0
26	24	96	76	72	96	126	120	96	200	192	0	750	720	0
27	25	92	77	73	92	127	121	92	[17] 204	195	84	800	768	0
28	26	88	78	74	88	128	122	88	205	196	80	850	816	0
29	27	84	79	75	84	129	123	84	210	201	60	900	864	0
30	28	80	80	76	80	130	124	80	215	206	40	950	912	0
31	29	76	81	77	76	131	125	76	[18] 216	207	36	1000	960	0
32	30	72	82	78	72	[11] 132	126	72	220	211	20	1016	975	36
33	31	68	83	79	68	133	127	68	225	216	0	1250	1200	0
34	32	64	[7] 84	80	64	134	128	64	[19] 228	218	88	1500	1440	0
35	33	60	85	81	60	135	129	60	230	220	80	1728	1658	88
[3] 36	34	56	86	82	56	136	130	56	235	225	60	1750	1680	0
37	35	52	87	83	52	137	131	52	[20] 240	230	40	1760	1689	60
38	36	48	88	84	48	138	132	48	245	235	20	2000	1920	0
39	37	44	89	85	44	139	133	44	250	240	0	2240	2150	40
40	38	40	90	86	40	140	134	40	255	244	80	2500	2400	0
41	39	36	91	87	36	141	135	36	260	249	60	3000	2880	0
42	40	32	92	88	32	142	136	32	265	254	40	4000	3840	0
43	41	28	93	89	28	143	137	28	270	259	20	5000	4800	0
44	42	24	94	90	24	[12] 144	138	24	275	264	0	6000	5760	0
45	43	20	95	91	20	145	139	20	280	268	80	7000	6720	0
46	44	16	[8] 96	92	16	146	140	16	285	273	60	8000	7680	0
47	45	12	97	93	12	147	141	12	[24] 288	276	48	9000	8640	0
[4] 48	46	8	98	94	8	148	142	8	290	278	40	10000	9600	0
49	47	4	99	95	4	149	143	4	295	283	20	15000	14400	0
50	48	0	100	96	0	150	144	0	300	288	0	20000	19200	0

Grosses		
1.	138	24
2.	276	48
3.	414	72
4.	552	96
5.	691	20
6.	829	44
7.	967	68
8.	1105	92
9.	1244	16
10.	1382	40
11.	1520	64

Twelfths		
1.	0	8
[1/6] 2.	0	16
3.	0	24
[1/3] 4.	0	32
5.	0	40
[1/2] 6.	0	48
7.	0	56
[2/3] 8.	0	64
9.	0	72
[5/6] 10.	0	80
11.	0	88

Twentieths (10ths)					
1.	0	4¾	11.	0	52¾
[·1] 2.	0	9½	[·6] 12.	0	57½
3.	0	14½	13.	0	62½
[·2] 4.	0	19¼	[·7] 14.	0	67¼
5.	0	24	15.	0	72
[·3] 6.	0	28¾	[·8] 16.	0	76¾
7.	0	33½	17.	0	81½
[·4] 8.	0	38½	[·9] 18.	0	86½
9.	0	43¼	19.	0	91¼
[·5] 10.	0	48	20.	0	96

Sixteenths					
1.	0	6	9.	0	54
[1/8] 2.	0	12	[5/8] 10.	0	60
3.	0	18	11.	0	66
[1/4] 4.	0	24	[3/4] 12.	0	72
5.	0	30	13.	0	78
[3/8] 6.	0	36	[7/8] 14.	0	84
7.	0	42	15.	0	90
[1/2] 8.	0	48			

*Dozens		£	p	Dozens		£	p	Dozens		£	p	Dozens		£	p		£	p
	1	0	97		51	49	47		101	97	97		152	147	44	310	300	70
	2	1	94		52	50	44		102	98	94		154	149	38	320	310	40
	3	2	91		53	51	41		103	99	91	13	156	151	32	330	320	10
	4	3	88		54	52	38		104	100	88		158	153	26	340	329	80
	5	4	85		55	53	35		105	101	85		160	155	20	350	339	50
	6	5	82		56	54	32		106	102	82		162	157	14	360	349	20
	7	6	79		57	55	29		107	103	79		164	159	8	365	354	5
	8	7	76		58	56	26	9	108	104	76		166	161	2	370	358	90
	9	8	73		59	57	23		109	105	73	14	168	162	96	380	368	60
	10	9	70	5	**60**	58	20		**110**	106	70		170	164	90	390	378	30
	11	10	67		61	59	17		111	107	67		172	166	84	400	388	0
1	12	11	64		62	60	14		112	108	64		174	168	78	410	397	70
	13	12	61		63	61	11		113	109	61		175	169	75	420	407	40
	14	13	58		64	62	8		114	110	58		176	170	72	430	417	10
	15	14	55		65	63	5		115	111	55		178	172	66	440	426	80
	16	15	52		66	64	2		116	112	52	15	180	174	60	450	436	50
	17	16	49		67	64	99		117	113	49		182	176	54	460	446	20
	18	17	46		68	65	96		118	114	46		184	178	48	470	455	90
	19	18	43		69	66	93		119	115	43		186	180	42	480	465	60
	20	19	40		**70**	67	90		**120**	116	40		188	182	36	490	475	30
	21	20	37		71	68	87		121	117	37		190	184	30	500	485	0
	22	21	34	6	72	69	84		122	118	34	16	192	186	24	550	533	50
	23	22	31		73	70	81		123	119	31		194	188	18	600	582	0
2	24	23	28		74	71	78		124	120	28		196	190	12	650	630	50
	25	24	25		75	72	75		125	121	25		198	192	6	700	679	0
	26	25	22		76	73	72		126	122	22		**200**	194	0	750	727	50
	27	26	19		77	74	69		127	123	19	17	204	197	88	800	776	0
	28	27	16		78	75	66		128	124	16		205	198	85	850	824	50
	29	28	13		79	76	63		129	125	13		210	203	70	900	873	0
	30	29	10		**80**	77	60		**130**	126	10		215	208	55	950	921	50
	31	30	7		81	78	57		131	127	7	18	216	209	52	1000	970	0
	32	31	4		82	79	54	11	132	128	4		220	213	40	1016	985	52
	33	32	1		83	80	51		133	129	1		225	218	25	1250	1212	50
	34	32	98	7	84	81	48		134	129	98	19	228	221	16	1500	1455	0
	35	33	95		85	82	45		135	130	95		230	223	10	1728	1676	16
3	36	34	92		86	83	42		136	131	92		235	227	95	1750	1697	50
	37	35	89		87	84	39		137	132	89	20	240	232	80	1760	1707	20
	38	36	86		88	85	36		138	133	86		245	237	65	2000	1940	0
	39	37	83		89	86	33		139	134	83		**250**	242	50	2240	2172	80
	40	38	80		**90**	87	30		**140**	135	80		255	247	35	2500	2425	0
	41	39	77		91	88	27		141	136	77		260	252	20	3000	2910	0
	42	40	74		92	89	24		142	137	74		265	257	5	4000	3880	0
	43	41	71		93	90	21		143	138	71		270	261	90	5000	4850	0
	44	42	68		94	91	18	12	144	139	68		275	266	75	6000	5820	0
	45	43	65		95	92	15		145	140	65		280	271	60	7000	6790	0
	46	44	62	8	96	93	12		146	141	62		285	276	45	8000	7760	0
	47	45	59		97	94	9		147	142	59	24	288	279	36	9000	8730	0
4	48	46	56		98	95	6		148	143	56		290	281	30	10000	9700	0
	49	47	53		99	96	3		149	144	53		295	286	15	15000	14550	0
	50	48	50		**100**	97	0		**150**	145	50		**300**	291	0	20000	19400	0

Grosses

1.	139	68
2.	279	36
3.	419	4
4.	558	72
5.	698	40
6.	838	8
7.	977	76
8.	1117	44
9.	1257	12
10.	1396	80
11.	1536	48

Twelfths

	1.	0	8
⅙	2.	0	16¼
	3.	0	24¼
⅓	4.	0	32¼
	5.	0	40½
½	6.	0	48½
	7.	0	56½
⅔	8.	0	64¾
	9.	0	72¾
⅚	10.	0	80¾
	11.	0	89

Twentieths

10ths				10ths			
	1.	0	4¾		11.	0	53¼
·1	2.	0	9¾	·6	12.	0	58¼
	3.	0	14½		13.	0	63
·2	4.	0	19½	·7	14.	0	68
	5.	0	24¼		15.	0	72¾
·3	6.	0	29	·8	16.	0	77½
	7.	0	34		17.	0	82½
·4	8.	0	38¾	·9	18.	0	87¼
	9.	0	43¾		19.	0	92¼
·5	10.	0	48½		20.	0	97

Sixteenths

	1.	0	6		9.	0	54½
⅛	2.	0	12¼	⅝	10.	0	60¾
	3.	0	18¼		11.	0	66¾
¼	4.	0	24¼	¾	12.	0	72¾
	5.	0	30¼		13.	0	78¾
⅜	6.	0	36½	⅞	14.	0	85
	7.	0	42½		15.	0	91
½	8.	0	48½				

	£	P		£	P		£	P		£	P		£	P
1	0	98	51	49	98	101	98	98	152	148	96	310	303	80
2	1	96	52	50	96	102	99	96	154	150	92	320	313	60
3	2	94	53	51	94	103	100	94	[13] 156	152	88	330	323	40
4	3	92	54	52	92	104	101	92	158	154	84	340	333	20
5	4	90	55	53	90	105	102	90	160	156	80	350	343	0
6	5	88	56	54	88	106	103	88	162	158	76	360	352	80
7	6	86	57	55	86	107	104	86	164	160	72	365	357	70
8	7	84	58	56	84	[9] 108	105	84	166	162	68	370	362	60
9	8	82	59	57	82	109	106	82	[14] 168	164	64	380	372	40
10	9	80	[5] 60	58	80	110	107	80	170	166	60	390	382	20
11	10	78	61	59	78	111	108	78	172	168	56	400	392	0
[*1] 12	11	76	62	60	76	112	109	76	174	170	52	410	401	80
13	12	74	63	61	74	113	110	74	175	171	50	420	411	60
14	13	72	64	62	72	114	111	72	176	172	48	430	421	40
15	14	70	65	63	70	115	112	70	178	174	44	440	431	20
16	15	68	66	64	68	116	113	68	[15] 180	176	40	450	441	0
17	16	66	67	65	66	117	114	66	182	178	36	460	450	80
18	17	64	68	66	64	118	115	64	184	180	32	470	460	60
19	18	62	69	67	62	119	116	62	186	182	28	480	470	40
20	19	60	70	68	60	120	117	60	188	184	24	490	480	20
21	20	58	71	69	58	121	118	58	190	186	20	500	490	0
22	21	56	[6] 72	70	56	122	119	56	[16] 192	188	16	550	539	0
23	22	54	73	71	54	123	120	54	194	190	12	600	588	0
[2] 24	23	52	74	72	52	124	121	52	196	192	8	650	637	0
25	24	50	75	73	50	125	122	50	198	194	4	700	686	0
26	25	48	76	74	48	126	123	48	200	196	0	750	735	0
27	26	46	77	75	46	127	124	46	[17] 204	199	92	800	784	0
28	27	44	78	76	44	128	125	44	205	200	90	850	833	0
29	28	42	79	77	42	129	126	42	210	205	80	900	882	0
30	29	40	80	78	40	130	127	40	215	210	70	950	931	0
31	30	38	81	79	38	131	128	38	[18] 216	211	68	1000	980	0
32	31	36	82	80	36	[11] 132	129	36	220	215	60	1016	995	68
33	32	34	83	81	34	133	130	34	225	220	50	1250	1225	0
34	33	32	[7] 84	82	32	134	131	32	[19] 228	223	44	1500	1470	0
35	34	30	85	83	30	135	132	30	230	225	40	1728	1693	44
[3] 36	35	28	86	84	28	136	133	28	235	230	30	1750	1715	0
37	36	26	87	85	26	137	134	26	[20] 240	235	20	1760	1724	80
38	37	24	88	86	24	138	135	24	245	240	10	2000	1960	0
39	38	22	89	87	22	139	136	22	250	245	0	2240	2195	20
40	39	20	90	88	20	140	137	20	255	249	90	2500	2450	0
41	40	18	91	89	18	141	138	18	260	254	80	3000	2940	0
42	41	16	92	90	16	142	139	16	265	259	70	4000	3920	0
43	42	14	93	91	14	143	140	14	270	264	60	5000	4900	0
44	43	12	94	92	12	[12] 144	141	12	275	269	50	6000	5880	0
45	44	10	95	93	10	145	142	10	280	274	40	7000	6860	0
46	45	8	[8] 96	94	8	146	143	8	285	279	30	8000	7840	0
47	46	6	97	95	6	147	144	6	[24] 288	282	24	9000	8820	0
[4] 48	47	4	98	96	4	148	145	4	290	284	20	10000	9800	0
49	48	2	99	97	2	149	146	2	295	289	10	15000	14700	0
50	49	0	100	98	0	150	147	0	300	294	0	20000	19600	0

*Dozens.

Grosses.

1.	141	12
2.	282	24
3.	423	36
4.	564	48
5.	705	60
6.	846	72
7.	987	84
8.	1128	96
9.	1270	08
10.	1411	20
11.	1552	32

Twelfths

	1.	0	8¼
1/6	2.	0	16¼
	3.	0	24½
1/3	4.	0	32¾
	5.	0	40¾
1/2	6.	0	49
	7.	0	57¼
2/3	8.	0	65¼
	9.	0	73½
5/6	10.	0	81¾
	11.	0	89¾

Twentieths (10ths)

10ths				10ths			
	1.	0	5		11.	0	54
·1	2.	0	9¾	·6	12.	0	58¾
	3.	0	14¾		13.	0	63¾
·2	4.	0	19½	·7	14.	0	68½
	5.	0	24½		15.	0	73½
·3	6.	0	29½	·8	16.	0	78½
	7.	0	34½		17.	0	83¼
·4	8.	0	39¼	·9	18.	0	88¼
	9.	0	44		19.	0	93
·5	10.	0	49		20.	0	98

Sixteenths

	1.	0	6¼		9.	0	55¼
1/8	2.	0	12¼	5/8	10.	0	61¼
	3.	0	18½		11.	0	67½
1/4	4.	0	24½	3/4	12.	0	73½
	5.	0	30¾		13.	0	79¾
3/8	6.	0	36¾	7/8	14.	0	85¾
	7.	0	43		15.	0	92
1/2	8.	0	49				

Dozens*	£	P	Dozens	£	P	Dozens	£	P	Dozens	£	P		£	P
1	0	99	51	50	49	101	99	99	152	150	48	310	306	90
2	1	98	52	51	48	102	100	98	154	152	46	320	316	80
3	2	97	53	52	47	103	101	97	[13] 156	154	44	330	326	70
4	3	96	54	53	46	104	102	96	158	156	42	340	336	60
5	4	95	55	54	45	105	103	95	160	158	40	350	346	50
6	5	94	56	55	44	106	104	94	162	160	38	360	356	40
7	6	93	57	56	43	107	105	93	164	162	36	365	361	35
8	7	92	58	57	42	[9] 108	106	92	166	164	34	370	366	30
9	8	91	59	58	41	109	107	91	[14] 168	166	32	380	376	20
10	9	90	[5] **60**	59	40	**110**	108	90	170	168	30	390	386	10
*11	10	89	61	60	39	111	109	89	172	170	28	400	396	00
[1] 12	11	88	62	61	38	112	110	88	174	172	26	410	405	90
13	12	87	63	62	37	113	111	87	175	173	25	420	415	80
14	13	86	64	63	36	114	112	86	176	174	24	430	425	70
15	14	85	65	64	35	115	113	85	178	176	22	440	435	60
16	15	84	66	65	34	116	114	84	[15] 180	178	20	450	445	50
17	16	83	67	66	33	117	115	83	182	180	18	460	455	40
18	17	82	68	67	32	118	116	82	184	182	16	470	465	30
19	18	81	69	68	31	119	117	81	186	184	14	480	475	20
20	19	80	**70**	69	30	**120**	118	80	188	186	12	490	485	10
21	20	79	71	70	29	121	119	79	190	188	10	**500**	495	0
22	21	78	[6] 72	71	28	122	120	78	[16] 192	190	8	550	544	50
23	22	77	73	72	27	123	121	77	194	192	6	600	594	0
[2] 24	23	76	74	73	26	124	122	76	196	194	4	650	643	50
25	24	75	75	74	25	125	123	75	198	196	2	700	693	0
26	25	74	76	75	24	126	124	74	**200**	198	0	750	742	50
27	26	73	77	76	23	127	125	73	[17] 204	201	96	800	792	0
28	27	72	78	77	22	128	126	72	205	202	95	850	841	50
29	28	71	79	78	21	129	127	71	210	207	90	900	891	0
30	29	70	**80**	79	20	**130**	128	70	215	212	85	950	940	50
31	30	69	81	80	19	131	129	69	[18] 216	213	84	**1000**	990	0
32	31	68	82	81	18	[11] 132	130	68	220	217	80	1016	1005	84
33	32	67	83	82	17	133	131	67	225	222	75	1250	1237	50
34	33	66	[7] 84	83	16	134	132	66	[19] 228	225	72	1500	1485	0
35	34	65	85	84	15	135	133	65	230	227	70	1728	1710	72
[3] 36	35	64	86	85	14	136	134	64	235	232	65	1750	1732	50
37	36	63	87	86	13	137	135	63	[20] 240	237	60	1760	1742	40
38	37	62	88	87	12	138	136	62	245	242	55	2000	1980	0
39	38	61	89	88	11	139	137	61	**250**	247	50	2240	2217	60
40	39	60	**90**	89	10	**140**	138	60	255	252	45	2500	2475	0
41	40	59	91	90	9	141	139	59	260	257	40	3000	2970	0
42	41	58	92	91	8	142	140	58	265	262	35	4000	3960	0
43	42	57	93	92	7	143	141	57	270	267	30	5000	4950	0
44	43	56	94	93	6	[12] 144	142	56	275	272	25	6000	5940	0
45	44	55	95	94	5	145	143	55	280	277	20	7000	6930	0
46	45	54	[8] 96	95	4	146	144	54	285	282	15	8000	7920	0
47	46	53	97	96	3	147	145	53	[24] 288	285	12	9000	8910	0
[4] 48	47	52	98	97	2	148	146	52	290	287	10	10000	9900	0
49	48	51	99	98	1	149	147	51	295	292	5	15000	14850	0
50	49	50	**100**	99	0	**150**	148	50	**300**	297	0	20000	19800	0

Grosses

	£	P
1.	142	56
2.	285	12
3.	427	68
4.	570	24
5.	712	80
6.	855	36
7.	997	92
8.	1140	48
9.	1283	04
10.	1425	60
11.	1568	16

Twelfths

		£	P
	1.	0	8¼
⅙	2.	0	16½
	3.	0	24¾
⅓	4.	0	33
	5.	0	41¼
½	6.	0	49½
	7.	0	57¾
⅔	8.	0	66
	9.	0	74¼
⅚	10.	0	32½
	11.	0	90¾

Twentieths

10ths		£	P	10ths		£	P
	1.	0	5		11.	0	54½
·1	2.	0	10	·6	12.	0	59½
	3.	0	14¾		13.	0	64¼
·2	4.	0	19¾	·7	14.	0	69¼
	5.	0	24¾		15.	0	74¼
·3	6.	0	29¾	·8	16.	0	79¼
	7.	0	34¾		17.	0	84¼
·4	8.	0	39½	·9	18.	0	89
	9.	0	44½		19.	0	94
·5	10.	0	49½		20.	0	99

Sixteenths

		£	P			£	P
	1.	0	6¼		9.	0	55¾
⅛	2.	0	12½	⅝	10.	0	62
	3.	0	18½		11.	0	68
¼	4.	0	24¾	¾	12	0	74¼
	5.	0	31		13.	0	80½
⅜	6.	0	37¼	⅞	14.	0	86¾
	7.	0	43¼		15.	0	92¾
½	8.	0	49½				

£ 1·00

*Dozens		£	P
	1	1	0
	2	2	0
	3	3	0
	4	4	0
	5	5	0
	6	6	0
	7	7	0
	8	8	0
	9	9	0
	10	10	0
*	11	11	0
1	12	12	0
	13	13	0
	14	14	0
	15	15	0
	16	16	0
	17	17	0
	18	18	0
	19	19	0
	20	20	0
	21	21	0
	22	22	0
	23	23	0
2	24	24	0
	25	25	0
	26	26	0
	27	27	0
	28	28	0
	29	29	0
	30	30	0
	31	31	0
	32	32	0
	33	33	0
	34	34	0
	35	35	0
3	36	36	0
	37	37	0
	38	38	0
	39	39	0
	40	40	0
	41	41	0
	42	42	0
	43	43	0
	44	44	0
	45	45	0
	46	46	0
	47	47	0
4	48	48	0
	49	49	0
	50	50	0

Dozens		£	P
	51	51	0
	52	52	0
	53	53	0
	54	54	0
	55	55	0
	56	56	0
	57	57	0
	58	58	0
	59	59	0
5	**60**	60	0
	61	61	0
	62	62	0
	63	63	0
	64	64	0
	65	65	0
	66	66	0
	67	67	0
	68	68	0
	69	69	0
	70	70	0
	71	71	0
6	72	72	0
	75	75	0
	80	80	0
7	84	84	0
	90	90	0
8	96	96	0
	100	100	0
10	120	120	0
	140	140	0
	150	150	0
	160	160	0
	180	180	0
	200	200	0
25	300	300	0
	365	365	0
	400	400	0
	500	500	0
	600	600	0
	700	700	0
	800	800	0
	900	900	0
	1000	1000	0

Twelfths

	1. 0 8¼		7. 0 58¼
⅙	2. 0 16¾	⅔	8. 0 66¾
	3. 0 25		9. 0 75
⅓	4. 0 33¼	⅚	10. 0 83¼
	5. 0 41¾		11. 0 91¾
½	6. 0 50		

Sixteenths

	1. 0 6¼		9. 0 56¼
⅛	2. 0 12½	⅝	10. 0 62½
	3. 0 18¾		11. 0 68¾
¼	4. 0 25	¾	12. 0 75
	5. 0 31¼		13. 0 81¼
⅜	6. 0 37½	⅞	14. 0 87½
	7. 0 43¾		15. 0 93¾
	8. 0 50		

Twentieths

10ths		10ths	
	1. 0 5		11. 0 55
·1	2. 0 10	·6	12. 0 60
	3. 0 15		13. 0 65
·2	4. 0 20	·7	14. 0 70
	5. 0 25		15. 0 75
·3	6. 0 30	·8	16. 0 80
	7. 0 35		17. 0 85
·4	8. 0 40	·9	18. 0 90
	9. 0 45		19. 0 95
·5	10. 0 50		20. 1 0

£ 1·01

*Dozens		£	P
	1	1	1
	2	2	2
	3	3	3
	4	4	4
	5	5	5
	6	6	6
	7	7	7
	8	8	8
	9	9	9
	10	10	10
	11	11	11
1	12	12	12
	13	13	13
	14	14	14
	15	15	15
	16	16	16
	17	17	17
	18	18	18
	19	19	19
	20	20	20
	21	21	21
	22	22	22
	23	23	23
2	24	24	24
	25	25	25
	26	26	26
	27	27	27
	28	28	28
	29	29	29
	30	30	30
	31	31	31
	32	32	32
	33	33	33
	34	34	34
	35	35	35
3	36	36	36
	37	37	37
	38	38	38
	39	39	39
	40	40	40
	41	41	41
	42	42	42
	43	43	43
	44	44	44
	45	45	45
	46	46	46
	47	47	47
4	48	48	48
	49	49	49
	50	50	50

Dozens		£	P
	51	51	51
	52	52	52
	53	53	53
	54	54	54
	55	55	55
	56	56	56
	57	57	57
	58	58	58
	59	59	59
5	**60**	60	60
	61	61	61
	62	62	62
	63	63	63
	64	64	64
	65	65	65
	66	66	66
	67	67	67
	68	68	68
	69	69	69
	70	70	70
	71	71	71
6	72	72	72
	75	75	75
	80	80	80
7	84	84	84
	90	90	90
8	96	96	96
	100	101	0
10	120	121	20
	140	141	40
	150	151	50
	160	161	60
	180	181	80
	200	202	0
25	300	303	0
	365	368	65
	400	404	0
	500	505	0
	600	606	0
	700	707	0
	800	808	0
	900	909	0
	1000	1010	0

Twelfths

	1. 0 8½		7. 0 59
⅙	2. 0 16¾	⅔	8. 0 67¼
	3. 0 25¼		9. 0 75¾
⅓	4. 0 33¾	⅚	10. 0 84¼
	5. 0 42		11. 0 92½
½	6. 0 50½		

Sixteenths

	1. 0 6¼		9. 0 56¾
⅛	2. 0 12¾	⅝	10. 0 63¼
	3. 0 19		11. 0 69½
¼	4. 0 25¼	¾	12. 0 75¾
	5. 0 31½		13. 0 82
⅜	6. 0 38	⅞	14. 0 88½
	7. 0 44¼		15. 0 94¾
½	8. 0 50½		

Twentieths

10ths		10ths	
	1. 0 5		11. 0 55½
·1	2. 0 10	·6	12. 0 60½
	3. 0 15¼		13. 0 65¾
·2	4. 0 20¼	·7	14. 0 70¾
	5. 0 25¼		15. 0 75¾
·3	6. 0 30¼	·8	16. 0 80¾
	7. 0 35½		17. 0 85¾
·4	8. 0 40½	·9	18. 0 91
	9. 0 45½		19. 0 96
·5	10. 0 50½		20. 1 1

£ 1·02

*Dozens		£	P	Dozens		£	P
	1	1	2		51	52	2
	2	2	4		52	53	4
	3	3	6		53	54	6
	4	4	8		54	55	8
	5	5	10		55	56	10
	6	6	12		56	57	12
	7	7	14		57	58	14
	8	8	16		58	59	16
	9	9	18		59	60	18
	10	10	20	5	60	61	20
*	11	11	22		61	62	22
1	12	12	24		62	63	24
	13	13	26		63	64	26
	14	14	28		64	65	28
	15	15	30		65	66	30
	16	16	32		66	67	32
	17	17	34		67	68	34
	18	18	36		68	69	36
	19	19	38		69	70	38
	20	20	40		70	71	40
	21	21	42		71	72	42
	22	22	44	6	72	73	44
	23	23	46		75	76	50
2	24	24	48		80	81	60
	25	25	50	7	84	85	68
	26	26	52		90	91	80
	27	27	54	8	96	97	92
	28	28	56		100	102	0
	29	29	58	10	120	122	40
	30	30	60		140	142	80
	31	31	62		150	153	0
	32	32	64		160	163	20
	33	33	66		180	183	60
	34	34	68		200	204	0
	35	35	70	25	300	306	0
3	36	36	72		365	372	30
	37	37	74		400	408	0
	38	38	76		500	510	0
	39	39	78		600	612	0
	40	40	80		700	714	0
	41	41	82		800	816	0
	42	42	84		900	918	0
	43	43	86		1000	1020	0
	44	44	88				
	45	45	90				
	46	46	92				
	47	47	94				
4	48	48	96				
	49	49	98				
	50	51	0				

Twelfths

	1.	0	8½		7.	0	59½
⅙	2.	0	17	⅔	8.	0	68
	3.	0	25½		9.	0	76½
⅓	4.	0	34	⅚	10.	0	85
	5.	0	42½		11.	0	93½
½	6.	0	51				

Sixteenths

	1.	0	6½		9.	0	57½
⅛	2.	0	12¾	⅝	10.	0	63¾
	3.	0	19¼		11.	0	70¼
¼	4.	0	25½	¾	12.	0	76½
	5.	0	32		13.	0	83
⅜	6.	0	38¼	⅞	14.	0	89¼
	7.	0	44¾		15.	0	95¾
	8.	0	51				

Twentieths

10ths				10ths			
	1.	0	5		11.	0	56
·1	2.	0	10¼	·6	12.	0	61¼
	3.	0	15¼		13.	0	66¼
·2	4.	0	20½	·7	14.	0	71½
	5.	0	25½		15.	0	76½
·3	6.	0	30½	·8	16.	0	81½
	7.	0	35¾		17.	0	86¾
·4	8.	0	40¾	·9	18.	0	91¾
	9.	0	46		19.	0	97
·5	10.	0	51		20.	1	2

£ 1·03

*Dozens		£	P	Dozens		£	P
	1	1	3		51	52	53
	2	2	6		52	53	56
	3	3	9		53	54	59
	4	4	12		54	55	62
	5	5	15		55	56	65
	6	6	18		56	57	68
	7	7	21		57	58	71
	8	8	24		58	59	74
	9	9	27		59	60	77
	10	10	30	5	60	61	80
	11	11	33		61	62	83
1	12	12	36		62	63	86
	13	13	39		63	64	89
	14	14	42		64	65	92
	15	15	45		65	66	95
	16	16	48		66	67	98
	17	17	51		67	69	1
	18	18	54		68	70	4
	19	19	57		69	71	7
	20	20	60		70	72	10
	21	21	63		71	73	13
	22	22	66	6	72	74	16
	23	23	69		75	77	25
2	24	24	72		80	82	40
	25	25	75	7	84	86	52
	26	26	78		90	92	70
	27	27	81	8	96	98	88
	28	28	84		100	103	0
	29	29	87	10	120	123	60
	30	30	90		140	144	20
	31	31	93		150	154	50
	32	32	96		160	164	80
	33	33	99		180	185	40
	34	35	2		200	206	0
	35	36	5	25	300	309	0
3	36	37	8		365	375	95
	37	38	11		400	412	0
	38	39	14		500	515	0
	39	40	17		600	618	0
	40	41	20		700	721	0
	41	42	23		800	824	0
	42	43	26		900	927	0
	43	44	29		1000	1030	0
	44	45	32				
	45	46	35				
	46	47	38				
	47	48	41				
4	48	49	44				
	49	50	47				
	50	51	50				

Twelfths

	1.	0	8½		7.	0	60
⅙	2.	0	17¼	⅔	8.	0	68¾
	3.	0	25¾		9.	0	77¼
⅓	4.	0	34¼	⅚	10.	0	85¾
	5.	0	43		11.	0	94½
½	6.	0	51½				

Sixteenths

	1.	0	6½		9.	0	58
⅛	2.	0	13	⅝	10.	0	64½
	3.	0	19¼		11.	0	70¾
¼	4.	0	25¾	¾	12.	0	77¼
	5.	0	32¼		13.	0	83¾
⅜	6.	0	38¾	⅞	14.	0	90¼
	7.	0	45		15.	0	96½
½	8.	0	51½				

Twentieths

10ths				10ths			
	1.	0	5¼		11.	0	56¾
·1	2.	0	10¼	·6	12.	0	61¾
	3.	0	15½		13.	0	67
·2	4.	0	20½	·7	14.	0	72
	5.	0	25¾		15.	0	77¼
·3	6.	0	31	·8	16.	0	82½
	7.	0	36		17.	0	87½
·4	8.	0	41¼	·9	18.	0	92¾
	9.	0	46¼		19.	0	97¾
·5	10.	0	51½		20.	1	3

£ 1·04

		£	P
*Dozens	1	1	4
	2	2	8
	3	3	12
	4	4	16
	5	5	20
	6	6	24
	7	7	28
	8	8	32
	9	9	36
	10	10	40
	11	11	44
1	12	12	48
	13	13	52
	14	14	56
	15	15	60
	16	16	64
	17	17	68
	18	18	72
	19	19	76
	20	20	80
	21	21	84
	22	22	88
	23	23	92
2	24	24	96
	25	26	0
	26	27	4
	27	28	8
	28	29	12
	29	30	16
	30	31	20
	31	32	24
	32	33	28
	33	34	32
	34	35	36
	35	36	40
3	36	37	44
	37	38	48
	38	39	52
	39	40	56
	40	41	60
	41	42	64
	42	43	68
	43	44	72
	44	45	76
	45	46	80
	46	47	84
	47	48	88
4	48	49	92
	49	50	96
	50	52	0

		£	P
Dozens	51	53	4
	52	54	8
	53	55	12
	54	56	16
	55	57	20
	56	58	24
	57	59	28
	58	60	32
	59	61	36
5	**60**	62	40
	61	63	44
	62	64	48
	63	65	52
	64	66	56
	65	67	60
	66	68	64
	67	69	68
	68	70	72
	69	71	76
	70	72	80
	71	73	84
6	72	74	88
	75	78	0
	80	83	20
7	84	87	36
	90	93	60
8	96	99	84
	100	104	0
10	120	124	80
	140	145	60
	150	156	0
	160	166	40
	180	187	20
	200	208	0
25	300	312	0
	365	379	60
	400	416	0
	500	520	0
	600	624	0
	700	728	0
	800	832	0
	900	936	0
	1000	1040	0

Twelfths

	1.	0 8¾		7.	0 60¾
⅙	2.	0 17¼	⅔	8.	0 69¼
	3.	0 26		9.	0 78
⅓	4.	0 34¾	⅚	10.	0 86¾
	5.	0 43¼		11.	0 95¼
½	6.	0 52			

Sixteenths

	1.	0 6½		9.	0 58½
⅛	2.	0 13	⅝	10.	0 65
	3.	0 19½		11.	0 71½
¼	4.	0 26	¾	12.	0 78
	5.	0 32½		13.	0 84½
⅜	6.	0 39	⅞	14.	0 91
	7.	0 45½		15.	0 97½
	8.	0 52			

Twentieths (10ths)

	1.	0 5¼		11.	0 57¼
·1	2.	0 10½	·6	12.	0 62½
	3.	0 15½		13.	0 67½
·2	4.	0 20¾	·7	14.	0 72¾
	5.	0 26		15.	0 78
·3	6.	0 31¼	·8	16.	0 83¼
	7.	0 36½		17.	0 88½
·4	8.	0 41½	·9	18.	0 93½
	9.	0 46¾		19.	0 98¾
·5	10.	0 52		20.	1 4

£ 1·05

		£	P
*Dozens	1	1	5
	2	2	10
	3	3	15
	4	4	20
	5	5	25
	6	6	30
	7	7	35
	8	8	40
	9	9	45
	10	10	50
	11	11	55
1	12	12	60
	13	13	65
	14	14	70
	15	15	75
	16	16	80
	17	17	85
	18	18	90
	19	19	95
	20	21	0
	21	22	5
	22	23	10
	23	24	15
2	24	25	20
	25	26	25
	26	27	30
	27	28	35
	28	29	40
	29	30	45
	30	31	50
	31	32	55
	32	33	60
	33	34	65
	34	35	70
	35	36	75
3	36	37	80
	37	38	85
	38	39	90
	39	40	95
	40	42	0
	41	43	5
	42	44	10
	43	45	15
	44	46	20
	45	47	25
	46	48	30
	47	49	35
4	48	50	40
	49	51	45
	50	52	50

		£	P
Dozens	51	53	55
	52	54	60
	53	55	65
	54	56	70
	55	57	75
	56	58	80
	57	59	85
	58	60	90
	59	61	95
5	**60**	63	0
	61	64	5
	62	65	10
	63	66	15
	64	67	20
	65	68	25
	66	69	30
	67	70	35
	68	71	40
	69	72	45
	70	73	50
	71	74	55
6	72	75	60
	75	78	75
	80	84	0
7	84	88	20
	90	94	50
8	96	100	80
	100	105	0
10	120	126	0
	140	147	0
	150	157	50
	160	168	0
	180	189	0
	200	210	0
25	300	315	0
	365	383	25
	400	420	0
	500	525	0
	600	630	0
	700	735	0
	800	840	0
	900	945	0
	1000	1050	0

Twelfths

	1.	0 8¾		7.	0 61¼
⅙	2.	0 17½	⅔	8.	0 70
	3.	0 26¼		9.	0 78¾
⅓	4.	0 35	⅚	10.	0 87½
	5.	0 43¾		11.	0 96¼
½	6.	0 52½			

Sixteenths

	1.	0 6½		9.	0 59
⅛	2.	0 13¼	⅝	10.	0 65¾
	3.	0 19¾		11.	0 72¼
¼	4.	0 26¼	¾	12.	0 78¾
	5.	0 32¾		13.	0 85¼
⅜	6.	0 39½	⅞	14.	0 92
	7.	0 46		15.	0 98½
½	8.	0 52½			

Twentieths (10ths)

	1.	0 5¼		11.	0 57¾
·1	2.	0 10½	·6	12.	0 63
	3.	0 15¾		13.	0 68¼
·2	4.	0 21	·7	14.	0 73½
	5.	0 26¼		15.	0 78¾
·3	6.	0 31½	·8	16.	0 84
	7.	0 36¾		17.	0 89¼
·4	8.	0 42	·9	18.	0 94½
	9.	0 47¼		19.	0 99¾
·5	10.	0 52½		20.	1 5

£ 1·06

*Dozens	No.	£	P	Dozens	No.	£	P
	1	1	6		51	54	6
	2	2	12		52	55	12
	3	3	18		53	56	18
	4	4	24		54	57	24
	5	5	30		55	58	30
	6	6	36		56	59	36
	7	7	42		57	60	42
	8	8	48		58	61	48
	9	9	54		59	62	54
	10	10	60	5	**60**	63	60
	11	11	66		61	64	66
1	12	12	72		62	65	72
	13	13	78		63	66	78
	14	14	84		64	67	84
	15	15	90		65	68	90
	16	16	96		66	69	96
	17	18	2		67	71	2
	18	19	8		68	72	8
	19	20	14		69	73	14
	20	21	20		**70**	74	20
	21	22	26		71	75	26
	22	23	32	6	72	76	32
	23	24	38		75	79	50
2	24	25	44		80	84	80
	25	26	50	7	84	89	4
	26	27	56		90	95	40
	27	28	62	8	96	101	76
	28	29	68		100	106	0
	29	30	74	10	120	127	20
	30	31	80		140	148	40
	31	32	86		150	159	0
	32	33	92		160	169	60
	33	34	98		180	190	80
	34	36	4		200	212	0
	35	37	10	25	300	318	0
3	36	38	16		365	386	90
	37	39	22		400	424	0
	38	40	28		500	530	0
	39	41	34		600	636	0
	40	42	40		700	742	0
	41	43	46		800	848	0
	42	44	52		900	954	0
	43	45	58		**1000**	1060	0
	44	46	64				
	45	47	70				
	46	48	76				
	47	49	82				
4	48	50	88				
	49	51	94				
	50	53	0				

Twelfths

	1. 0 8¾		7. 0 61¾
⅙	2. 0 17¾	⅔	8. 0 70¾
	3. 0 26½		9. 0 79½
⅓	4. 0 35¼	⅚	10. 0 88¼
	5. 0 44¼		11. 0 97¼
½	6. 0 53		

Sixteenths

	1. 0 6¾		9. 0 59¾
⅛	2. 0 13¼	⅝	10. 0 66¼
	3. 0 20		11. 0 73
¼	4. 0 26½	¾	12. 0 79½
	5. 0 33¼		13. 0 86¼
⅜	6. 0 39¾	⅞	14. 0 92¾
	7. 0 46½		15. 0 99½
	8. 0 53		

Twentieths

10ths		10ths	
	1. 0 5¼		11. 0 58¼
·1	2. 0 10½	·6	12. 0 63½
	3. 0 16		13. 0 68
·2	4. 0 21¼	·7	14. 0 74¼
	5. 0 26½		15. 0 79½
·3	6. 0 31¾	·8	16. 0 84¾
	7. 0 37		17. 0 90
·4	8. 0 42½	·9	18. 0 95½
	9. 0 47¾		19. 1 0¾
·5	10. 0 53		20. 1 6

£ 1·07

*Dozens	No.	£	P	Dozens	No.	£	P
	1	1	7		51	54	57
	2	2	14		52	55	64
	3	3	21		53	56	71
	4	4	28		54	57	78
	5	5	35		55	58	85
	6	6	42		56	59	92
	7	7	49		57	60	99
	8	8	56		58	62	6
	9	9	63		59	63	13
	10	10	70	5	**60**	64	20
	11	11	77		61	65	27
1	12	12	84		62	66	34
	13	13	91		63	67	41
	14	14	98		64	68	48
	15	16	5		65	69	55
	16	17	12		66	70	62
	17	18	19		67	71	69
	18	19	26		68	72	76
	19	20	33		69	73	83
	20	21	40		**70**	74	90
	21	22	47		71	75	97
	22	23	54	6	72	77	4
	23	24	61		75	80	25
2	24	25	68		80	85	60
	25	26	75	7	84	89	88
	26	27	82		90	96	30
	27	28	89	8	96	102	72
	28	29	96		100	107	0
	29	31	3	10	120	128	40
	30	32	10		140	149	80
	31	33	17		150	160	50
	32	34	24		160	171	20
	33	35	31		180	192	60
	34	36	38		200	214	0
	35	37	45	25	300	321	0
3	36	38	52		365	390	55
	37	39	59		400	428	0
	38	40	66		500	535	0
	39	41	73		600	642	0
	40	42	80		700	749	0
	41	43	87		800	856	0
	42	44	94		900	963	0
	43	46	1		**1000**	1070	0
	44	47	8				
	45	48	15				
	46	49	22				
	47	50	29				
4	48	51	36				
	49	52	43				
	50	53	50				

Twelfths

	1. 0 9		7. 0 62½
⅙	2. 0 17¾	⅔	8. 0 71¼
	3. 0 26¾		9. 0 80¼
⅓	4. 0 35¾	⅚	10. 0 89¼
	5. 0 44½		11. 0 98
½	6. 0 53½		

Sixteenths

	1. 0 6¾		9. 0 60¼
⅛	2. 0 13½	⅝	10. 0 67
	3. 0 20		11. 0 73½
¼	4. 0 26¾	¾	12. 0 80¼
	5. 0 33½		13. 0 87
⅜	6. 0 40¼	⅞	14. 0 93¾
	7. 0 46¾		15. 1 00¼
½	8. 0 53½		

Twentieths

10ths		10ths	
	1. 0 5¼		11. 0 58¾
·1	2. 0 10¾	·6	12. 0 64¼
	3. 0 16		13. 0 69½
·2	4. 0 21½	·7	14. 0 75
	5. 0 26¾		15. 0 80¼
·3	6. 0 32	·8	16. 0 85½
	7. 0 37½		17. 0 91
·4	8. 0 42¾	·9	18. 0 96¼
	9. 0 48¼		19. 1 1¾
·5	10. 0 53½		20. 1 7

£ 1·08

*Dozens		£	P	Dozens		£	P
	1	1	8		51	55	8
	2	2	16		52	56	16
	3	3	24		53	57	24
	4	4	32		54	58	32
	5	5	40		55	59	40
	6	6	48		56	60	48
	7	7	56		57	61	56
	8	8	64		58	62	64
	9	9	72		59	63	72
	10	10	80	5	**60**	64	80
	11	11	88		61	65	88
1	12	12	96		62	66	96
	13	14	4		63	68	4
	14	15	12		64	69	12
	15	16	20		65	70	20
	16	17	28		66	71	28
	17	18	36		67	72	36
	18	19	44		68	73	44
	19	20	52		69	74	52
	20	21	60		**70**	75	60
	21	22	68		71	76	68
	22	23	76	6	72	77	76
	23	24	84		75	81	0
2	24	25	92		80	86	40
	25	27	0	7	84	90	72
	26	28	8		90	97	20
	27	29	16	8	96	103	68
	28	30	24		100	108	0
	29	31	32	10	120	129	60
	30	32	40		140	151	20
	31	33	48		150	162	0
	32	34	56		160	172	80
	33	35	64		180	194	40
	34	36	72		200	216	0
	35	37	80	25	300	324	0
3	36	38	88		365	394	20
	37	39	96		400	432	0
	38	41	4		500	540	0
	39	42	12		600	648	0
	40	43	20		700	756	0
	41	44	28		800	864	0
	42	45	36		900	972	0
	43	46	44		1000	1080	0
	44	47	52				
	45	48	60				
	46	49	68				
	47	50	76				
4	48	51	84				
	49	52	92				
	50	54	0				

Twelfths

	1. 0 9		7. 0 63		
1/6	2. 0 18	2/3	8. 0 72		
	3. 0 27		9. 0 81		
1/3	4. 0 36	5/6	10. 0 90		
	5. 0 45		11. 0 99		
1/2	6. 0 54				

Sixteenths

	1. 0 6¾		9. 0 60¾
1/8	2. 0 13½	5/8	10. 0 67½
	3. 0 20¼		11. 0 74¼
1/4	4. 0 27	3/4	12. 0 81
	5. 0 33¾		13. 0 87¾
3/8	6. 0 40½	7/8	14. 0 94½
	7. 0 47¼		15. 1 1¼
1/2	8. 0 54		

Twentieths (10ths)

	1. 0 5½		11. 0 59½
·1	2. 0 10¾	·6	12. 0 64¾
	3. 0 16¼		13. 0 70¼
·2	4. 0 21½	·7	14. 0 75½
	5. 0 27		15. 0 81
·3	6. 0 32½	·8	16. 0 86½
	7. 0 37¾		17. 0 91¾
·4	8. 0 43½	·9	18. 0 97½
	9. 0 48½		19. 1 2½
·5	10. 0 54		20. 1 8

£ 1·09

*Dozens		£	P	Dozens		£	P
	1	1	9		51	55	59
	2	2	18		52	56	68
	3	3	27		53	57	77
	4	4	36		54	58	86
	5	5	45		55	59	95
	6	6	54		56	61	4
	7	7	63		57	62	13
	8	8	72		58	63	22
	9	9	81		59	64	31
	10	10	90	5	**60**	65	40
	11	11	99		61	66	49
1	12	13	8		62	67	58
	13	14	17		63	68	67
	14	15	26		64	69	76
	15	16	35		65	70	85
	16	17	44		66	71	94
	17	18	53		67	73	3
	18	19	62		68	74	12
	19	20	71		69	75	21
	20	21	80		**70**	76	30
	21	22	89		71	77	39
	22	23	98	6	72	78	48
	23	25	7		75	81	75
2	24	26	16		80	87	20
	25	27	25	7	84	91	56
	26	28	34		90	98	10
	27	29	43	8	96	104	64
	28	30	52		100	109	0
	29	31	61	10	120	130	80
	30	32	70		140	152	60
	31	33	79		150	163	50
	32	34	88		160	174	40
	33	35	97		180	196	20
	34	37	6		200	218	0
	35	38	15	25	300	327	0
3	36	39	24		365	397	85
	37	40	33		400	436	0
	38	41	42		500	545	0
	39	42	51		600	654	0
	40	43	60		700	763	0
	41	44	69		800	872	0
	42	45	78		900	981	0
	43	46	87		1000	1090	0
	44	47	96				
	45	49	5				
	46	50	14				
	47	51	23				
4	48	52	32				
	49	53	41				
	50	54	50				

Twelfths

	1. 0 9		7. 0 63½
1/6	2. 0 18¼	2/3	8. 0 72¾
	3. 0 27¼		9. 0 81¾
1/3	4. 0 36¼	5/6	10. 0 90¾
	5. 0 45½		11. 1 0
1/2	6. 0 54½		

Sixteenths

	1. 0 6¾		9. 0 61¼
1/8	2. 0 13¾	5/8	10. 0 68¼
	3. 0 20½		11. 0 75
1/4	4. 0 27¼	3/4	12. 0 81¾
	5. 0 34		13. 0 88½
3/8	6. 0 41	7/8	14. 0 95½
	7. 0 47¾		15. 1 02¼
1/2	8. 0 54½		

Twentieths (10ths)

	1. 0 5½		11. 0 60
·1	2. 0 11	·6	12. 0 65½
	3. 0 16¼		13. 0 70¾
·2	4. 0 21¾	·7	14. 0 76¼
	5. 0 27½		15. 0 81¾
·3	6. 0 32¾	·8	16. 0 87½
	7. 0 38¼		17. 0 92¾
·4	8. 0 43½	·9	18. 0 98
	9. 0 49		19. 1 3½
·5	10. 0 54½		20. 1 9

£ 1·10

Dozens		£	p	Dozens		£	p
	1	1	10		51	56	10
	2	2	20		52	57	20
	3	3	30		53	58	30
	4	4	40		54	59	40
	5	5	50		55	60	50
	6	6	60		56	61	60
	7	7	70		57	62	70
	8	8	80		58	63	80
	9	9	90		59	64	90
	10	11	0	5	60	66	0
	11	12	10		61	67	10
*1	12	13	20		62	68	20
	13	14	30		63	69	30
	14	15	40		64	70	40
	15	16	50		65	71	50
	16	17	60		66	72	60
	17	18	70		67	73	70
	18	19	80		68	74	80
	19	20	90		69	75	90
	20	22	0		70	77	0
	21	23	10		71	78	10
	22	24	20	6	72	79	20
	23	25	30		75	82	50
2	24	26	40		80	88	0
	25	27	50	7	84	92	40
	26	28	60		90	99	0
	27	29	70	8	96	105	60
	28	30	80		100	110	0
	29	31	90	10	120	132	0
	30	33	0		140	154	0
	31	34	10		150	165	0
	32	35	20		160	176	0
	33	36	30		180	198	0
	34	37	40		200	220	0
	35	38	50	25	300	330	0
3	36	39	60		365	401	50
	37	40	70		400	440	0
	38	41	80		500	550	0
	39	42	90		600	660	0
	40	44	0		700	770	0
	41	45	10		800	880	0
	42	46	20		900	990	0
	43	47	30		1000	1100	0
	44	48	40				
	45	49	50				
	46	50	60				
	47	51	70				
4	48	52	80				
	49	53	90				
	50	55	0				

Twelfths

1.	0 9¼	7.	0 64¼
⅙ 2.	0 18¼	⅔ 8.	0 73¼
3.	0 27½	9.	0 82½
⅓ 4.	0 36¾	⅚ 10.	0 91¾
5.	0 45¾	11.	1 0¾
½ 6.	0 55		

Sixteenths

1.	0 7	9.	0 62
⅛ 2.	0 13¾	⅝ 10.	0 68¾
3.	0 20¾	11.	0 75¾
¼ 4.	0 27½	¾ 12.	0 82½
5.	0 34½	13.	0 89½
⅜ 6.	0 41¼	⅞ 14.	0 96¼
7.	0 48¼	15.	1 3¼
8.	0 55		

Twentieths

10ths			10ths		
	1.	0 5½		11.	0 60½
·1	2.	0 11	·6	12	0 66
	3.	0 16½		13.	0 71½
·2	4.	0 22	·7	14.	0 77
	5.	0 27½		15.	0 82½
·3	6.	0 33	·8	16.	0 88
	7.	0 38½		17.	0 93½
·4	8.	0 44	·9	18.	0 99
	9.	0 49½		19.	1 4½
·5	10.	0 55		20.	1 10

£ 1·11

Dozens		£	p	Dozens		£	p
	1	1	11		51	56	61
	2	2	22		52	57	72
	3	3	33		53	58	83
	4	4	44		54	59	94
	5	5	55		55	61	5
	6	6	66		56	62	16
	7	7	77		57	63	27
	8	8	88		58	64	38
	9	9	99		59	65	49
	10	11	10	5	60	66	60
	11	12	21		61	67	71
1	12	13	32		62	68	82
	13	14	43		63	69	93
	14	15	54		64	71	4
	15	16	65		65	72	15
	16	17	76		66	73	26
	17	18	87		67	74	37
	18	19	98		68	75	48
	19	21	9		69	76	59
	20	22	20		70	77	70
	21	23	31		71	78	81
	22	24	42	6	72	79	92
	23	25	53		75	83	25
2	24	26	64		80	88	80
	25	27	75	7	84	93	24
	26	28	86		90	99	90
	27	29	97	8	96	106	56
	28	31	8		100	111	0
	29	32	19	10	120	133	20
	30	33	30		140	155	40
	31	34	41		150	166	50
	32	35	52		160	177	60
	33	36	63		180	199	80
	34	37	74		200	222	0
	35	38	85	25	300	333	0
3	36	39	96		365	405	15
	37	41	7		400	444	0
	38	42	18		500	555	0
	39	43	29		600	666	0
	40	44	40		700	777	0
	41	45	51		800	888	0
	42	46	62		900	999	0
	43	47	73		1000	1110	0
	44	48	84				
	45	49	95				
	46	51	6				
	47	52	17				
4	48	53	28				
	49	54	39				
	50	55	50				

Twelfths

1.	0 9¼	7.	0 64¾
⅙ 2.	0 18½	⅔ 8.	0 74
3.	0 27¾	9.	0 83¼
⅓ 4.	0 37	⅚ 10.	0 92½
5.	0 46¼	11.	1 1¾
½ 6.	0 55½		

Sixteenths

1.	0 7	9.	0 62½
⅛ 2.	0 14	⅝ 10.	0 69½
3.	0 20¾	11.	0 76¼
¼ 4.	0 27¾	¾ 12.	0 83¼
5.	0 34¾	13.	0 90¼
⅜ 6.	0 41¾	⅞ 14.	0 97¼
7.	0 48½	15.	1 4
½ 8.	0 55½		

Twentieths

10ths			10ths		
	1.	0 5½		11.	0 61
·1	2.	0 11	·6	12.	0 66½
	3.	0 16¾		13.	0 72¼
·2	4.	0 22¼	·7	14.	0 77¾
	5.	0 27¾		15.	0 83¼
·3	6.	0 33¼	·8	16.	0 88¾
	7.	0 38¾		17.	0 94¼
·4	8.	0 44½	·9	18.	1 0
	9.	0 50		19.	1 5½
·5	10.	0 55½		20.	1 11

£ 1·12

Doz.	No.	£	P
	1	1	12
*Dozens	2	2	24
	3	3	36
	4	4	48
	5	5	60
	6	6	72
	7	7	84
	8	8	96
	9	10	8
	10	11	20
	11	12	32
1	12	13	44
	13	14	56
	14	15	68
	15	16	80
	16	17	92
	17	19	4
	18	20	16
	19	21	28
	20	22	40
	21	23	52
	22	24	64
	23	25	76
2	24	26	88
	25	28	0
	26	29	12
	27	30	24
	28	31	36
	29	32	48
	30	33	60
	31	34	72
	32	35	84
	33	36	96
	34	38	8
	35	39	20
3	36	40	32
	37	41	44
	38	42	56
	39	43	68
	40	44	80
	41	45	92
	42	47	4
	43	48	16
	44	49	28
	45	50	40
	46	51	52
	47	52	64
4	48	53	76
	49	54	88
	50	56	0

Doz.	No.	£	P
	51	57	12
Dozens	52	58	24
	53	59	36
	54	60	48
	55	61	60
	56	62	72
	57	63	84
	58	64	96
	59	66	8
5	60	67	20
	61	68	32
	62	69	44
	63	70	56
	64	71	68
	65	72	80
	66	73	92
	67	75	4
	68	76	16
	69	77	28
	70	78	40
	71	79	52
6	72	80	64
	75	84	0
	80	89	60
7	84	94	8
	90	100	80
8	96	107	52
	100	112	0
10	120	134	40
	140	156	80
	150	168	0
	160	179	20
	180	201	60
	200	224	0
25	300	336	0
	365	408	80
	400	448	0
	500	560	0
	600	672	0
	700	784	0
	800	896	0
	900	1008	0
	1000	1120	0

Twelfths

1.	0 9¼	7.	0 65¼
⅙ 2.	0 18¾	⅔ 8.	0 74¾
3.	0 28	9.	0 84
⅓ 4.	0 37¼	⅚ 10.	0 93¼
5.	0 46¾	11.	1 2¾
½ 6.	0 56		

Sixteenths

1.	0 7	9.	0 63
⅛ 2.	0 14	⅝ 10.	0 70
3.	0 21	11.	0 77
¼ 4.	0 28	¾ 12.	0 84
5.	0 35	13.	0 91
⅜ 6.	0 42	⅞ 14.	0 98
7.	0 49	15.	1 5
½ 8.	0 56		

Twentieths (10ths)

1.	0 5½	11.	0 61½
·1 2.	0 11¼	·6 12.	0 67¼
3.	0 16¾	13.	0 72¾
·2 4.	0 22½	·7 14.	0 78½
5.	0 28	15.	0 84
·3 6.	0 33½	·8 16.	0 89½
7.	0 39¼	17.	0 95¼
·4 8.	0 44¾	·9 18.	1 0¾
9.	0 50½	19.	1 6½
·5 10.	0 56	20.	1 12

£ 1·13

Doz.	No.	£	P
	1	1	13
*Dozens	2	2	26
	3	3	39
	4	4	52
	5	5	65
	6	6	78
	7	7	91
	8	9	4
	9	10	17
	10	11	30
	11	12	43
1	12	13	56
	13	14	69
	14	15	82
	15	16	95
	16	18	8
	17	19	21
	18	20	34
	19	21	47
	20	22	60
	21	23	73
	22	24	86
	23	25	99
2	24	27	12
	25	28	25
	26	29	38
	27	30	51
	28	31	64
	29	32	77
	30	33	90
	31	35	3
	32	36	16
	33	37	29
	34	38	42
	35	39	55
3	36	40	68
	37	41	81
	38	42	94
	39	44	7
	40	45	20
	41	46	33
	42	47	46
	43	48	59
	44	49	72
	45	50	85
	46	51	98
	47	53	11
4	48	54	24
	49	55	37
	50	56	50

Doz.	No.	£	P
	51	57	63
Dozens	52	58	76
	53	59	89
	54	61	2
	55	62	15
	56	63	28
	57	64	41
	58	65	54
	59	66	67
5	60	67	80
	61	68	93
	62	70	6
	63	71	19
	64	72	32
	65	73	45
	66	74	58
	67	75	71
	68	76	84
	69	77	97
	70	79	10
	71	80	23
6	72	81	36
	75	84	75
	80	90	40
7	84	94	92
	90	101	70
8	96	108	48
	100	113	0
10	120	135	60
	140	158	20
	150	169	50
	160	180	80
	180	203	40
	200	226	0
25	300	339	0
	365	412	45
	400	452	0
	500	565	0
	600	678	0
	700	791	0
	800	904	0
	900	1017	0
	1000	1130	0

Twelfths

1.	0 9½	7.	0 66
⅙ 2.	0 18¾	⅔ 8.	0 75¼
3.	0 28¼	9.	0 84¾
⅓ 4.	0 37¾	⅚ 10.	94¼
5.	0 47	11.	1 3½
½ 6.	0 56½		

Sixteenths

1.	0 7	9.	0 63½
⅛ 2.	0 14¼	⅝ 10.	0 70¾
3.	0 21¼	11.	0 77¾
¼ 4.	0 28¼	¾ 12.	0 84¾
5.	0 35¼	13.	0 91¾
⅜ 6.	0 42½	⅞ 14.	0 99
7.	0 49½	15.	1 6
½ 8.	0 56½		

Twentieths (10ths)

1.	0 5½	11.	0 62¼
·1 2.	0 11¼	·6 12.	0 67¾
3.	0 17	13.	0 73½
·2 4.	0 22½	·7 14.	0 79
5.	0 28¼	15.	0 84¾
·3 6.	0 34	·8 16.	0 90½
7.	0 39½	17.	0 96
·4 8.	0 45¼	·9 18.	1 1¾
9.	0 50¾	19.	1 7¼
·5 10.	0 56½	20.	1 13

£ 1·14

*Dozens		£	P
	1	1	14
	2	2	28
	3	3	42
	4	4	56
	5	5	70
	6	6	84
	7	7	98
	8	9	12
	9	10	26
	10	11	40
*	11	12	54
1	12	13	68
	13	14	82
	14	15	96
	15	17	10
	16	18	24
	17	19	38
	18	20	52
	19	21	66
	20	22	80
	21	23	94
	22	25	8
	23	26	22
2	24	27	36
	25	28	50
	26	29	64
	27	30	78
	28	31	92
	29	33	6
	30	34	20
	31	35	34
	32	36	48
	33	37	62
	34	38	76
	35	39	90
3	36	41	4
	37	42	18
	38	43	32
	39	44	46
	40	45	60
	41	46	74
	42	47	88
	43	49	2
	44	50	16
	45	51	30
	46	52	44
	47	53	58
4	48	54	72
	49	55	86
	50	57	0

Dozens		£	P
	51	58	14
	52	59	28
	53	60	42
	54	61	56
	55	62	70
	56	63	84
	57	64	98
	58	66	12
	59	67	26
5	**60**	68	40
	61	69	54
	62	70	68
	63	71	82
	64	72	96
	65	74	10
	66	75	24
	67	76	38
	68	77	52
	69	78	66
	70	79	80
	71	80	94
6	72	82	8
	75	85	50
	80	91	20
7	84	95	76
	90	102	60
8	96	109	44
	100	114	0
10	120	136	80
	140	159	60
	150	171	0
	160	182	40
	180	205	20
	200	228	0
25	300	342	0
	365	416	10
	400	456	0
	500	570	0
	600	684	0
	700	798	0
	800	912	0
	900	1026	0
	1000	1140	0

Twelfths

	1. 0 9½		7. 0 66½
1/6	2. 0 19	2/3	8. 0 76
	3. 0 28½		9. 0 85½
1/3	4. 0 38	5/6	10. 0 95
	5. 0 47½		11. 1 4½
1/2	6. 0 57		

Sixteenths

	1. 0 7¼		9. 0 64¼
1/8	2. 0 14¼	5/8	10. 0 71¼
	3. 0 21½		11. 0 78½
1/4	4. 0 28½	3/4	12. 0 85½
	5. 0 35¾		13. 0 92¾
3/8	6. 0 42¾	7/8	14. 0 99¾
	7. 0 50		15. 1 7
	8. 0 57		

Twentieths

10ths			
	1. 0 5¾		11. 0 62¾
·1	2. 0 11½	·6	12 0 68½
	3. 0 17		13. 0 74
·2	4. 0 22¾	·7	14. 0 79¾
	5. 0 28½		15. 0 85½
·3	6. 0 34¼	·8	16. 0 91¼
	7. 0 40		17. 0 97
·4	8. 0 45½	·9	18. 1 2½
	9. 0 51¼		19. 1 8¼
·5	10. 0 57		20. 1 14

£ 1·15

*Dozens		£	P
	1	1	15
	2	2	30
	3	3	45
	4	4	60
	5	5	75
	6	6	90
	7	8	5
	8	9	20
	9	10	35
	10	11	50
	11	12	65
1	12	13	80
	13	14	95
	14	16	10
	15	17	25
	16	18	40
	17	19	55
	18	20	70
	19	21	85
	20	23	0
	21	24	15
	22	25	30
	23	26	45
2	24	27	60
	25	28	75
	26	29	90
	27	31	5
	28	32	20
	29	33	35
	30	34	50
	31	35	65
	32	36	80
	33	37	95
	34	39	10
	35	40	25
3	36	41	40
	37	42	55
	38	43	70
	39	44	85
	40	46	0
	41	47	15
	42	48	30
	43	49	45
	44	50	60
	45	51	75
	46	52	90
	47	54	5
4	48	55	20
	49	56	35
	50	57	50

Dozens		£	P
	51	58	65
	52	59	80
	53	60	95
	54	62	10
	55	63	25
	56	64	40
	57	65	55
	58	66	70
	59	67	85
5	**60**	69	0
	61	70	15
	62	71	30
	63	72	45
	64	73	60
	65	74	75
	66	75	90
	67	77	5
	68	78	20
	69	79	35
	70	80	50
	71	81	65
6	72	82	80
	75	86	25
	80	92	0
7	84	96	60
	90	103	50
8	96	110	40
	100	115	0
10	120	138	0
	140	161	0
	150	172	50
	160	184	0
	180	207	0
	200	230	0
25	300	345	0
	365	419	75
	400	460	0
	500	575	0
	600	690	0
	700	805	0
	800	920	0
	900	1035	0
	1000	1150	0

Twelfths

	1. 0 9½		7. 0 67
1/6	2. 0 19¼	2/3	8. 0 76¾
	3. 0 28¾		9. 0 86¼
1/3	4. 0 38¼	5/6	10. 95¾
	5. 0 48		11. 1 5½
1/2	6. 0 57½		

Sixteenths

	1. 0 7¼		9. 0 64¾
1/8	2. 0 14½	5/8	10. 0 72
	3. 0 21½		11. 0 79
1/4	4. 0 28¾	3/4	12. 0 86¼
	5. 0 36		13. 0 93½
3/8	6. 0 43¼	7/8	14. 1 0¾
	7. 0 50¼		15. 1 7¾
1/2	8. 0 57½		

Twentieths

10ths			
	1. 0 5¾		11. 0 63¼
·1	2. 0 11½	·6	12. 0 69
	3. 0 17¼		13. 0 74¾
·2	4. 0 23	·7	14. 0 80½
	5. 0 28¾		15. 0 86¼
·3	6. 0 34½	·8	16. 0 92
	7. 0 40¼		17. 0 97¾
·4	8. 0 46	·9	18. 1 3½
	9. 0 51¾		19. 1 9¼
·5	10. 0 57½		20. 1 15

£ 1·16

*Dozens

Dozens		£	P
	1	1	16
	2	2	32
	3	3	48
	4	4	64
	5	5	80
	6	6	96
	7	8	12
	8	9	28
	9	10	44
	10	11	60
*	11	12	76
1	12	13	92
	13	15	8
	14	16	24
	15	17	40
	16	18	56
	17	19	72
	18	20	88
	19	22	4
	20	23	20
	21	24	36
	22	25	52
	23	26	68
2	24	27	84
	25	29	0
	26	30	16
	27	31	32
	28	32	48
	29	33	64
	30	34	80
	31	35	96
	32	37	12
	33	38	28
	34	39	44
	35	40	60
3	36	41	76
	37	42	92
	38	44	8
	39	45	24
	40	46	40
	41	47	56
	42	48	72
	43	49	88
	44	51	4
	45	52	20
	46	53	36
	47	54	52
4	48	55	68
	49	56	84
	50	58	0

Dozens		£	P
	51	59	16
	52	60	32
	53	61	48
	54	62	64
	55	63	80
	56	64	96
	57	66	12
	58	67	28
	59	68	44
5	**60**	69	60
	61	70	76
	62	71	92
	63	73	08
	64	74	24
	65	75	40
	66	76	56
	67	77	72
	68	78	88
	69	80	4
	70	81	20
	71	82	36
6	72	83	52
	75	87	0
	80	92	80
7	84	97	44
	90	104	40
8	96	111	36
	100	116	0
10	120	139	20
	140	162	40
	150	174	0
	160	185	60
	180	208	80
	200	232	0
25	300	348	0
	365	423	40
	400	464	0
	500	580	0
	600	696	0
	700	812	0
	800	928	0
	900	1044	0
	1000	1160	0

Twelfths

1.	0	9¾	7.	0	67¾
⅙ 2.	0	19¼	⅔ 8.	0	77¼
3.	0	29	9.	0	87
⅓ 4.	0	38¾	⅚ 10.	0	96¾
5.	0	48¼	11.	1	6¼
½ 6.	0	58			

Sixteenths

1.	0	7¼	9.	0	65¼
⅛ 2.	0	14½	⅝ 10.	0	72½
3.	0	21¾	11.	0	79¾
¼ 4.	0	29	¾ 12.	0	87
5.	0	36¼	13.	0	94¼
⅜ 6.	0	43½	⅞ 14.	1	1½
7.	0	50¾	15.	1	8¾
8.	0	58			

Twentieths

10ths				10ths			
	1.	0	5¾		11.	0	63¾
·1	2.	0	11¾	·6	12	0	69½
	3.	0	17½		13.	0	75½
·2	4.	0	23¼	·7	14.	0	81¼
	5.	0	29		15.	0	87
·3	6.	0	34¾	·8	16.	0	92¾
	7.	0	40½		17.	0	98½
·4	8.	0	46½	·9	18.	1	4½
	9.	0	52¼		19.	1	10¼
·5	10.	0	58		20.	1	16

£ 1·17

*Dozens

Dozens		£	P
	1	1	17
	2	2	34
	3	3	51
	4	4	68
	5	5	85
	6	7	2
	7	8	19
	8	9	36
	9	10	53
	10	11	70
	11	12	87
1	12	14	4
	13	15	21
	14	16	38
	15	17	55
	16	18	72
	17	19	89
	18	21	6
	19	22	23
	20	23	40
	21	24	57
	22	25	74
	23	26	91
2	24	28	8
	25	29	25
	26	30	42
	27	31	59
	28	32	76
	29	33	93
	30	35	10
	31	36	27
	32	37	44
	33	38	61
	34	39	78
	35	40	95
3	36	42	12
	37	43	29
	38	44	46
	39	45	63
	40	46	80
	41	47	97
	42	49	14
	43	50	31
	44	51	48
	45	52	65
	46	53	82
	47	54	99
4	48	56	16
	49	57	33
	50	58	50

Dozens		£	P
	51	59	67
	52	60	84
	53	62	1
	54	63	18
	55	64	35
	56	65	52
	57	66	69
	58	67	86
	59	69	3
5	**60**	70	20
	61	71	37
	62	72	54
	63	73	71
	64	74	88
	65	76	5
	66	77	22
	67	78	39
	68	79	56
	69	80	73
	70	81	90
	71	83	7
6	72	84	24
	75	87	75
	80	93	60
7	84	98	28
	90	105	30
8	96	112	32
	100	117	0
10	120	140	40
	140	163	80
	150	175	50
	160	187	20
	180	210	60
	200	234	0
25	300	351	0
	365	427	5
	400	468	0
	500	585	0
	600	702	0
	700	819	0
	800	936	0
	900	1053	0
	1000	1170	0

Twelfths

1.	0	9¾	7.	0	68¼
⅙ 2.	0	19½	⅔ 8.	0	78
3.	0	29¼	9.	0	87¾
⅓ 4.	0	39	⅚ 10.		97½
5.	0	48¾	11.	1	7¼
½ 6.	0	58½			

Sixteenths

1.	0	7¼	9.	0	65¾
⅛ 2.	0	14¾	⅝ 10.	0	73¼
3.	0	22	11.	0	80½
¼ 4.	0	29¼	¾ 12.	0	87¾
5.	0	36½	13.	0	95
⅜ 6.	0	44	⅞ 14.	1	2½
7.	0	51¼	15.	1	9¾
½ 8.	0	58½			

Twentieths

10ths				10ths			
	1.	0	5¾		11.	0	64¼
·1	2.	0	11¾	·6	12.	0	70¼
	3.	0	17½		13.	0	76
·2	4.	0	23½	·7	14.	0	82
	5.	0	29¼		15.	0	87¾
·3	6.	0	35	·8	16.	0	93½
	7.	0	41		17.	0	99½
·4	8.	0	46¾	·9	18.	1	5¼
	9.	0	52¾		19	1	11¼
·5	10.	0	58½		20.	1	17

£ 1·18

*Dozens		£	P
	1	1	18
	2	2	36
	3	3	54
	4	4	72
	5	5	90
	6	7	8
	7	8	26
	8	9	44
	9	10	62
	10	11	80
	11	12	98
1	12	14	16
	13	15	34
	14	16	52
	15	17	70
	16	18	88
	17	20	6
	18	21	24
	19	22	42
	20	23	60
	21	24	78
	22	25	96
	23	27	14
2	24	28	32
	25	29	50
	26	30	68
	27	31	86
	28	33	4
	29	34	22
	30	35	40
	31	36	58
	32	37	76
	33	38	94
	34	40	12
	35	41	30
3	36	42	48
	37	43	66
	38	44	84
	39	46	2
	40	47	20
	41	48	38
	42	49	56
	43	50	74
	44	51	92
	45	53	10
	46	54	28
	47	55	46
4	48	56	64
	49	57	82
	50	59	0

Dozens		£	P
	51	60	18
	52	61	36
	53	62	54
	54	63	72
	55	64	90
	56	66	8
	57	67	26
	58	68	44
	59	69	62
5	**60**	70	80
	61	71	98
	62	73	16
	63	74	34
	64	75	52
	65	76	70
	66	77	88
	67	79	6
	68	80	24
	69	81	42
	70	82	60
	71	83	78
6	72	84	96
	75	88	50
	80	94	40
7	84	99	12
	90	106	20
8	96	113	28
	100	118	0
10	120	141	60
	140	165	20
	150	177	0
	160	188	80
	180	212	40
	200	236	0
25	300	354	0
	365	430	70
	400	472	0
	500	590	0
	600	708	0
	700	826	0
	800	944	0
	900	1062	0
	1000	1180	0

Twelfths

1. 0 9¾		7. 0 68¾	
⅙	2. 0 19¾	⅔	8. 0 78¾
3. 0 29½		9. 0 88½	
⅓	4. 0 39¼	⅚	10. 0 98¼
5. 0 49¼		11. 1 8¼	
½	6. 0 59		

Sixteenths

	1. 0 7½		9. 0 66½
⅛	2. 0 14¾	⅝	10. 0 73¾
	3. 0 22¼		11. 0 81¼
¼	4. 0 29½	¾	12. 0 88½
	5. 0 37		13. 0 96
⅜	6. 0 44¼	⅞	14. 1 3¼
	7. 0 51¾		15. 1 10¾
	8. 0 59		

Twentieths (10ths)

	1. 0 6		11. 0 65
·1	2. 0 11¾	·6	12 0 70¾
	3. 0 17¾		13. 0 76¾
·2	4. 0 23½	·7	14. 0 83½
	5. 0 29½		15. 0 88½
·3	6. 0 35½	·8	16. 0 94½
	7. 0 41¼		17. 1 0¼
·4	8. 0 47¼	·9	18. 1 6¼
	9. 0 53		19. 1 12
·5	10. 0 59		20. 1 18

£ 1·19

*Dozens		£	P
	1	1	19
	2	2	38
	3	3	57
	4	4	76
	5	5	95
	6	7	14
	7	8	33
	8	9	52
	9	10	71
	10	11	90
	11	13	9
1	12	14	28
	13	15	47
	14	16	66
	15	17	85
	16	19	4
	17	20	23
	18	21	42
	19	22	61
	20	23	80
	21	24	99
	22	26	18
	23	27	37
2	24	28	56
	25	29	75
	26	30	94
	27	32	13
	28	33	32
	29	34	51
	30	35	70
	31	36	89
	32	38	8
	33	39	27
	34	40	46
	35	41	65
3	36	42	84
	37	44	3
	38	45	22
	39	46	41
	40	47	60
	41	48	79
	42	49	98
	43	51	17
	44	52	36
	45	53	55
	46	54	74
	47	55	93
4	48	57	12
	49	58	31
	50	59	50

Dozens		£	P
	51	60	69
	52	61	88
	53	63	7
	54	64	26
	55	65	45
	56	66	64
	57	67	83
	58	69	2
	59	70	21
5	**60**	71	40
	61	72	59
	62	73	78
	63	74	97
	64	76	16
	65	77	35
	66	78	54
	67	79	73
	68	80	92
	69	82	11
	70	83	30
	71	84	49
6	72	85	68
	75	89	25
	80	95	20
7	84	99	96
	90	107	10
8	96	114	24
	100	119	0
10	120	142	80
	140	166	60
	150	178	50
	160	190	40
	180	214	20
	200	238	0
25	300	357	0
	365	434	35
	400	476	0
	500	595	0
	600	714	0
	700	833	0
	800	952	0
	900	1071	0
	1000	1190	0

Twelfths

1. 0 10		7. 0 69½	
⅙	2. 0 19¾	⅔	8. 0 79¼
3. 0 29¾		9. 0 89¼	
⅓	4. 0 39¾	⅚	10. 0 99¼
5. 0 49½		11. 1 9	
½	6. 0 59½		

Sixteenths

	1. 0 7½		9. 0 67
⅛	2. 0 15	⅝	10. 0 74½
	3. 0 22¼		11. 0 81¾
¼	4. 0 29¾	¾	12. 0 89¼
	5. 0 37¼		13. 0 96¾
⅜	6. 0 44¾	⅞	14. 1 4¼
	7. 0 52		15. 1 11½
½	8. 0 59½		

Twentieths (10ths)

	1. 0 6		11. 0 65½
·1	2. 0 12	·6	12. 0 71½
	3. 0 17¾		13. 0 77¼
·2	4. 0 23¾	·7	14. 0 83¼
	5. 0 29¾		15. 0 89¼
·3	6. 0 35¾	·8	16. 0 95¼
	7. 0 41½		17. 1 1¼
·4	8. 0 47½	·9	18. 1 7
	9. 0 53½		19 1 13
·5	10. 0 59½		20. 1 19

£ 1·20

*Dozens		£	P
	1	1	20
	2	2	40
	3	3	60
	4	4	80
	5	6	0
	6	7	20
	7	8	40
	8	9	60
	9	10	80
	10	12	0
	11	13	20
*1	12	14	40
	13	15	60
	14	16	80
	15	18	0
	16	19	20
	17	20	40
	18	21	60
	19	22	80
	20	24	0
	21	25	20
	22	26	40
	23	27	60
2	24	28	80
	25	30	0
	26	31	20
	27	32	40
	28	33	60
	29	34	80
	30	36	0
	31	37	20
	32	38	40
	33	39	60
	34	40	80
	35	42	0
3	36	43	20
	37	44	40
	38	45	60
	39	46	80
	40	48	0
	41	49	20
	42	50	40
	43	51	60
	44	52	80
	45	54	0
	46	55	20
	47	56	40
4	48	57	60
	49	58	80
	50	60	0

Dozens		£	P
	51	61	20
	52	62	40
	53	63	60
	54	64	80
	55	66	0
	56	67	20
	57	68	40
	58	69	60
	59	70	80
5	**60**	72	0
	61	73	20
	62	74	40
	63	75	60
	64	76	80
	65	78	0
	66	79	20
	67	80	40
	68	81	60
	69	82	80
	70	84	0
	71	85	20
6	72	86	40
	75	90	0
	80	96	0
7	84	100	80
	90	108	0
8	96	115	20
	100	120	0
10	120	144	0
	140	168	0
	150	180	0
	160	192	0
	180	216	0
	200	240	0
25	300	360	0
	365	438	0
	400	480	0
	500	600	0
	600	720	0
	700	840	0
	800	960	0
	900	1080	0
	1000	1200	0

Twelfths

	1.	0 10		7.	0 70
1/6	2.	0 20	2/3	8.	0 80
	3.	0 30		9.	0 90
1/3	4.	0 40	5/6	10.	1 0
	5.	0 50		11.	1 10
1/2	6.	0 60			

Sixteenths

	1.	0 7½		9.	0 67½
1/8	2.	0 15	5/8	10.	0 75
	3.	0 22½		11.	0 82½
1/4	4.	0 30	3/4	12.	0 90
	5.	0 37½		13.	0 97½
3/8	6.	0 45	7/8	14.	1 5
	7.	0 52½		15.	1 12½
	8.	0 60			

Twentieths (10ths)

	1.	0 6		11.	0 66
·1	2.	0 12	·6	12	0 72
	3.	0 18		13.	0 78
·2	4.	0 24	·7	14.	0 84
	5.	0 30		15.	0 90
·3	6.	0 36	·8	16.	0 96
	7.	0 42		17.	1 2
·4	8.	0 48	·9	18.	1 8
	9.	0 54		19.	1 14
·5	10.	0 60		20.	1 20

£ 1·21

*Dozens		£	P
	1	1	21
	2	2	42
	3	3	63
	4	4	84
	5	6	5
	6	7	26
	7	8	47
	8	9	68
	9	10	89
	10	12	10
	11	13	31
1	12	14	52
	13	15	73
	14	16	94
	15	18	15
	16	19	36
	17	20	57
	18	21	78
	19	22	99
	20	24	20
	21	25	41
	22	26	62
	23	27	83
2	24	29	4
	25	30	25
	26	31	46
	27	32	67
	28	33	88
	29	35	9
	30	36	30
	31	37	51
	32	38	72
	33	39	93
	34	41	14
	35	42	35
3	36	43	56
	37	44	77
	38	45	98
	39	47	19
	40	48	40
	41	49	61
	42	50	82
	43	52	3
	44	53	24
	45	54	45
	46	55	66
	47	56	87
4	48	58	8
	49	59	29
	50	60	50

Dozens		£	P
	51	61	71
	52	62	92
	53	64	13
	54	65	34
	55	66	55
	56	67	76
	57	68	97
	58	70	18
	59	71	39
5	**60**	72	60
	61	73	81
	62	75	2
	63	76	23
	64	77	44
	65	78	65
	66	79	86
	67	81	7
	68	82	28
	69	83	49
	70	84	70
	71	85	91
6	72	87	12
	75	90	75
	80	96	80
7	84	101	64
	90	108	90
8	96	116	16
	100	121	0
10	120	145	20
	140	169	40
	150	181	50
	160	193	60
	180	217	80
	200	242	0
25	300	363	0
	365	441	65
	400	484	0
	500	605	0
	600	726	0
	700	847	0
	800	968	0
	900	1089	0
	1000	1210	0

Twelfths

	1.	0 10		7.	0 70½
1/6	2.	0 20¼	2/3	8.	0 80¾
	3.	0 30¼		9.	0 90¾
1/3	4.	0 40¼	5/6	10.	1 0¾
	5.	0 50½		11.	1 11
1/2	6.	0 60½			

Sixteenths

	1.	0 7½		9.	0 68
1/8	2.	0 15¼	5/8	10.	0 75¾
	3.	0 22¾		11.	0 83¼
1/4	4.	0 30¼	3/4	12.	0 90¾
	5.	0 37¾		13.	0 98¼
3/8	6.	0 45¼	7/8	14.	1 6
	7.	0 53		15.	1 13½
1/2	8.	0 60½			

Twentieths (10ths)

	1.	0 6		11.	0 66½
·1	2.	0 12	·6	12.	0 72½
	3.	0 18¼		13.	0 78¾
·2	4.	0 24¼	·7	14.	0 84¾
	5.	0 30¼		15.	0 90¾
·3	6.	0 36¼	·8	16.	0 96¾
	7.	0 42¼		17.	1 2¾
·4	8.	0 48½	·9	18.	1 9
	9.	0 54½		19	1 15
·5	10.	0 60½		20.	1 21

£ 1·22

Dozens	Qty	£	P
	1	1	22
	2	2	44
	3	3	66
	4	4	88
	5	6	10
	6	7	32
	7	8	54
	8	9	76
	9	10	98
	10	12	20
*	11	13	42
1	12	14	64
	13	15	86
	14	17	8
	15	18	30
	16	19	52
	17	20	74
	18	21	96
	19	23	18
	20	24	40
	21	25	62
	22	26	84
	23	28	6
2	24	29	28
	25	30	50
	26	31	72
	27	32	94
	28	34	16
	29	35	38
	30	36	60
	31	37	82
	32	39	4
	33	40	26
	34	41	48
	35	42	70
3	36	43	92
	37	45	14
	38	46	36
	39	47	58
	40	48	80
	41	50	2
	42	51	24
	43	52	46
	44	53	68
	45	54	90
	46	56	12
	47	57	34
4	48	58	56
	49	59	78
	50	61	0

Dozens	Qty	£	P
	51	62	22
	52	63	44
	53	64	66
	54	65	88
	55	67	10
	56	68	32
	57	69	54
	58	70	76
	59	71	98
5	**60**	73	20
	61	74	42
	62	75	64
	63	76	86
	64	78	8
	65	79	30
	66	80	52
	67	81	74
	68	82	96
	69	84	18
	70	85	40
	71	86	62
6	72	87	84
	75	91	50
	80	97	60
7	84	102	48
	90	109	80
8	96	117	12
	100	122	0
10	120	146	40
	140	170	80
	150	183	0
	160	195	20
	180	219	60
	200	244	0
25	300	366	0
	365	445	30
	400	488	0
	500	610	0
	600	732	0
	700	854	0
	800	976	0
	900	1098	0
	1000	1220	0

Twelfths

	1.	0 10¼		7.	0 71¼
⅙	2.	0 20¼	⅔	8.	0 81¼
	3.	0 30½		9.	0 91½
⅓	4.	0 40¾	⅚	10.	1 1¾
	5.	0 50¾		11.	1 11¾
½	6.	0 61			

Sixteenths

	1.	0 7¾		9.	0 68¾
⅛	2.	0 15¼	⅝	10.	0 76¼
	3.	0 23		11.	0 84
¼	4.	0 30½	¾	12.	0 91½
	5.	0 38¼		13.	0 99¼
⅜	6.	0 45¾	⅞	14.	1 6¾
	7.	0 53½		15.	1 14½
	8.	0 61			

Twentieths

10ths					
	1.	0 6		11.	0 67
·1	2.	0 12¼	·6	12	0 73¼
	3.	0 18¼		13.	0 79¼
·2	4.	0 24½	·7	14.	0 85½
	5.	0 30½		15.	0 91½
·3	6.	0 36½	·8	16.	0 97½
	7.	0 42¾		17.	1 3¾
·4	8.	0 48¾	·9	18.	1 9¾
	9.	0 55		19.	1 16
·5	10.	0 61		20.	1 22

£ 1·23

Dozens	Qty	£	P
	1	1	23
	2	2	46
	3	3	69
	4	4	92
	5	6	15
	6	7	38
	7	8	61
	8	9	84
	9	11	7
	10	12	30
	11	13	53
1	12	14	76
	13	15	99
	14	17	22
	15	18	45
	16	19	68
	17	20	91
	18	22	14
	19	23	37
	20	24	60
	21	25	83
	22	27	6
	23	28	29
2	24	29	52
	25	30	75
	26	31	98
	27	33	21
	28	34	44
	29	35	67
	30	36	90
	31	38	13
	32	39	36
	33	40	59
	34	41	82
	35	43	5
3	36	44	28
	37	45	51
	38	46	74
	39	47	97
	40	49	20
	41	50	43
	42	51	66
	43	52	89
	44	54	12
	45	55	35
	46	56	58
	47	57	81
4	48	59	4
	49	60	27
	50	61	50

Dozens	Qty	£	P
	51	62	73
	52	63	96
	53	65	19
	54	66	42
	55	67	65
	56	68	88
	57	70	11
	58	71	34
	59	72	57
5	**60**	73	80
	61	75	3
	62	76	26
	63	77	49
	64	78	72
	65	79	95
	66	81	18
	67	82	41
	68	83	64
	69	84	87
	70	86	10
	71	87	33
6	72	88	56
	75	92	25
	80	98	40
7	84	103	32
	90	110	70
8	96	118	8
	100	123	0
10	120	147	60
	140	172	20
	150	184	50
	160	196	80
	180	221	40
	200	246	0
25	300	369	0
	365	448	95
	400	492	0
	500	615	0
	600	738	0
	700	861	0
	800	984	0
	900	1107	0
	1000	1230	0

Twelfths

	1.	0 10¼		7.	0 71¾
⅙	2.	0 20½	⅔	8.	0 82
	3.	0 30¾		9.	0 92¼
⅓	4.	0 41	⅚	10.	1 2½
	5.	0 51¼		11.	1 12¾
½	6.	0 61½			

Sixteenths

	1.	0 7¾		9.	0 69¼
⅛	2.	0 15½	⅝	10.	0 77
	3.	0 23		11.	0 84½
¼	4.	0 30¾	¾	12.	0 92¼
	5.	0 38½		13.	1 0
⅜	6.	0 46¼	⅞	14.	1 7¾
	7.	0 53¾		15.	1 15¼
½	8.	0 61½			

Twentieths

10ths					
	1.	0 6¼		11.	0 67¾
·1	2.	0 12¼	·6	12.	0 73¾
	3.	0 18½		13.	0 80
·2	4.	0 24½	·7	14.	0 86
	5.	0 30¾		15.	0 92¼
·3	6.	0 37	·8	16.	0 98½
	7.	0 43		17.	1 4½
·4	8.	0 49¼	·9	18.	1 10¾
	9.	0 55¼		19	1 16¾
·5	10.	0 61½		20.	1 23

£ 1·24

*Dozens	No.	£	P	Dozens	No.	£	P
	1	1	24		51	63	24
	2	2	48		52	64	48
	3	3	72		53	65	72
	4	4	96		54	66	96
	5	6	20		55	68	20
	6	7	44		56	69	44
	7	8	68		57	70	68
	8	9	92		58	71	92
	9	11	16		59	73	16
	10	12	40	5	**60**	74	40
*	11	13	64		61	75	64
1	12	14	88		62	76	88
	13	16	12		63	78	12
	14	17	36		64	79	36
	15	18	60		65	80	60
	16	19	84		66	81	84
	17	21	8		67	83	8
	18	22	32		68	84	32
	19	23	56		69	85	56
	20	24	80		**70**	86	80
	21	26	4		71	88	4
	22	27	28	6	72	89	28
	23	28	52		75	93	0
2	24	29	76		80	99	20
	25	31	0	7	84	104	16
	26	32	24		90	111	60
	27	33	48	8	96	119	4
	28	34	72		100	124	0
	29	35	96	10	120	148	80
	30	37	20		140	173	60
	31	38	44		150	186	0
	32	39	68		160	198	40
	33	40	92		180	223	20
	34	42	16		200	248	0
	35	43	40	25	300	372	0
3	36	44	64		365	452	60
	37	45	88		400	496	0
	38	47	12		500	620	0
	39	48	36		600	744	0
	40	49	60		700	868	0
	41	50	84		800	992	0
	42	52	8		900	1116	0
	43	53	32		1000	1240	0
	44	54	56				
	45	55	80				
	46	57	4				
	47	58	28				
4	48	59	52				
	49	60	76				
	50	62	0				

Twelfths

	1.	0 10¼		7.	0 72¼
⅙	2.	0 20¾	⅔	8.	0 82¾
	3.	0 31		9.	0 93
⅓	4.	0 41¼	⅚	10.	1 3¼
	5.	0 51¾		11.	1 13¾
½	6.	0 62			

Sixteenths

	1.	0 7¾		9.	0 69¾
⅛	2.	0 15½	⅝	10.	0 77½
	3.	0 23¼		11.	0 85¼
¼	4.	0 31	¾	12.	0 93
	5.	0 38¾		13.	1 0¾
⅜	6.	0 46½	⅞	14.	1 8½
	7.	0 54¼		15.	1 16¼
	8.	0 62			

Twentieths

10ths					
	1.	0 6¼		11.	0 68¼
·1	2.	0 12½	·6	12	0 74½
	3.	0 18½		13.	0 80½
·2	4.	0 24¾	·7	14.	0 86¾
	5.	0 31		15.	0 93
·3	6.	0 37¼	8	16.	0 99¼
	7.	0 43½		17.	1 5½
·4	8.	0 49½	·9	18.	1 11½
	9.	0 55¾		19.	1 17¾
·5	10.	0 62		20.	1 24

£ 1·25

*Dozens	No.	£	P	Dozens	No.	£	P
	1	1	25		51	63	75
	2	2	50		52	65	00
	3	3	75		53	66	25
	4	5	0		54	67	50
	5	6	25		55	68	75
	6	7	50		56	70	00
	7	8	75		57	71	25
	8	10	0		58	72	50
	9	11	25		59	73	75
	10	12	50	5	**60**	75	00
	11	13	75		61	76	25
1	12	15	0		62	77	50
	13	16	25		63	78	75
	14	17	50		64	80	00
	15	18	75		65	81	25
	16	20	0		66	82	50
	17	21	25		67	83	75
	18	22	50		68	85	00
	19	23	75		69	86	25
	20	25	0		**70**	87	50
	21	26	25		71	88	75
	22	27	50	6	72	90	0
	23	28	75		75	93	75
2	24	30	0		80	100	0
	25	31	25	7	84	105	0
	26	32	50		90	112	50
	27	33	75	8	96	120	0
	28	35	0		100	125	0
	29	36	25	10	120	150	0
	30	37	50		140	175	0
	31	38	75		150	187	50
	32	40	0		160	200	0
	33	41	25		180	225	0
	34	42	50		200	250	0
	35	43	75	25	300	375	0
3	36	45	0		365	456	25
	37	46	25		400	500	0
	38	47	50		500	625	0
	39	48	75		600	750	0
	40	50	0		700	875	0
	41	51	25		800	1000	0
	42	52	50		900	1125	0
	43	53	75		1000	1250	0
	44	55	0				
	45	56	25				
	46	57	50				
	47	58	75				
4	48	60	0				
	49	61	25				
	50	62	50				

Twelfths

	1.	0 10½		7.	0 73
⅙	2.	0 20¾	⅔	8.	0 83¼
	3.	0 31¼		9.	0 93¾
⅓	4.	0 41¾	⅚	10.	1 4¼
	5.	0 52		11.	1 14½
½	6.	0 62½			

Sixteenths

	1.	0 7¾		9.	0 70¼
⅛	2.	0 15¾	⅝	10.	0 78¼
	3.	0 23½		11.	0 86
¼	4.	0 31¼	¾	12.	0 93¾
	5.	0 39		13.	1 1½
⅜	6.	0 47	⅞	14.	1 9½
	7.	0 54¾		15.	1 17¼
½	8.	0 62½			

Twentieths

10ths					
	1.	0 6¼		11.	0 68¾
·1	2.	0 12½	·6	12.	0 75
	3.	0 18¾		13.	0 81¼
·2	4.	0 25	·7	14.	0 87½
	5.	0 31¼		15.	0 93¾
·3	6.	0 37½	·8	16.	1 0
	7.	0 43¾		17.	1 6¼
·4	8.	0 50	·9	18.	1 12½
	9.	0 56¼		19	1 18¾
·5	10.	0 62½		20.	1 25

£ 1·26

*Dozens		£	P
	1	1	26
	2	2	52
	3	3	78
	4	5	4
	5	6	30
	6	7	56
	7	8	82
	8	10	8
	9	11	34
	10	12	60
*	11	13	86
1	12	15	12
	13	16	38
	14	17	64
	15	18	90
	16	20	16
	17	21	42
	18	22	68
	19	23	94
	20	25	20
	21	26	46
	22	27	72
	23	28	98
2	24	30	24
	25	31	50
	26	32	76
	27	34	2
	28	35	28
	29	36	54
	30	37	80
	31	39	6
	32	40	32
	33	41	58
	34	42	84
	35	44	10
3	36	45	36
	37	46	62
	38	47	88
	39	49	14
	40	50	40
	41	51	66
	42	52	92
	43	54	18
	44	55	44
	45	56	70
	46	57	96
	47	59	22
4	48	60	48
	49	61	74
	50	63	0

Dozens		£	P
	51	64	26
	52	65	52
	53	66	78
	54	68	4
	55	69	30
	56	70	56
	57	71	82
	58	73	8
	59	74	34
5	60	75	60
	61	76	86
	62	78	12
	63	79	38
	64	80	64
	65	81	90
	66	83	16
	67	84	42
	68	85	68
	69	86	94
	70	88	20
	71	89	46
6	72	90	72
	75	94	50
	80	100	80
7	84	105	84
	90	113	40
8	96	120	96
	100	126	0
10	120	151	20
	140	176	40
	150	189	0
	160	201	60
	180	226	80
	200	252	0
25	300	378	0
	365	459	90
	400	504	0
	500	630	0
	600	756	0
	700	882	0
	800	1008	0
	900	1134	0
	1000	1260	0

Twelfths

	1. 0 10½		7. 0 73½
⅙	2. 0 21	⅔	8. 0 84
	3. 0 31½		9. 0 94½
⅓	4. 0 42	⅚	10. 1 5
	5. 0 52½		11. 1 15½
½	6. 0 63		

Sixteenths

	1. 0 8		9. 0 71
⅛	2. 0 15¾	⅝	10. 0 78¾
	3. 0 23¾		11. 0 86¾
¼	4. 0 31½	¾	12. 0 94½
	5. 0 39½		13. 1 2½
⅜	6. 0 47¼	⅞	14. 1 10¼
	7. 0 55¼		15. 1 18¼
	8. 0 63		

Twentieths (10ths)

	1. 0 6¼		11. 0 69¼
·1	2. 0 12½	·6	12 0 75½
	3. 0 19		13. 0 82
·2	4. 0 25¼	·7	14. 0 88¼
	5. 0 31½		15. 0 94½
·3	6. 0 37¾	·8	16. 1 0¾
	7. 0 44		17. 1 7
·4	8. 0 50½	·9	18. 1 13½
	9. 0 56¾		19. 1 19¾
·5	10. 0 63		20. 1 26

£ 1·27

*Dozens		£	P
	1	1	27
	2	2	54
	3	3	81
	4	5	8
	5	6	35
	6	7	62
	7	8	89
	8	10	16
	9	11	43
	10	12	70
	11	13	97
1	12	15	24
	13	16	51
	14	17	78
	15	19	5
	16	20	32
	17	21	59
	18	22	86
	19	24	13
	20	25	40
	21	26	67
	22	27	94
	23	29	21
2	24	30	48
	25	31	75
	26	33	2
	27	34	29
	28	35	56
	29	36	83
	30	38	10
	31	39	37
	32	40	64
	33	41	91
	34	43	18
	35	44	45
3	36	45	72
	37	46	99
	38	48	26
	39	49	53
	40	50	80
	41	52	7
	42	53	34
	43	54	61
	44	55	88
	45	57	15
	46	58	42
	47	59	69
4	48	60	96
	49	62	23
	50	63	50

Dozens		£	P
	51	64	77
	52	66	04
	53	67	31
	54	68	58
	55	69	85
	56	71	12
	57	72	39
	58	73	66
	59	74	93
5	60	76	20
	61	77	47
	62	78	74
	63	80	01
	64	81	28
	65	82	55
	66	83	82
	67	85	9
	68	86	36
	69	87	63
	70	88	90
	71	90	17
6	72	91	44
	75	95	25
	80	101	60
7	84	106	68
	90	114	30
8	96	121	92
	100	127	0
10	120	152	40
	140	177	80
	150	190	50
	160	203	20
	180	228	60
	200	254	0
25	300	381	0
	365	463	55
	400	508	0
	500	635	0
	600	762	0
	700	889	0
	800	1016	0
	900	1143	0
	1000	1270	0

Twelfths

	1. 0 10½		7. 0 74
⅙	2. 0 21¼	⅔	8. 0 84¾
	3. 0 31¾		9. 0 95¼
⅓	4. 0 42¼	⅚	10. 1 5¾
	5. 0 53		11. 1 16½
½	6. 0 63½		

Sixteenths

	1. 0 8		9. 0 71½
⅛	2. 0 16	⅝	10. 0 79½
	3. 0 23¾		11. 0 87¼
¼	4. 0 31¾	¾	12. 0 95¼
	5. 0 39¾		13. 1 3¼
⅜	6. 0 47¾	⅞	14. 1 11¼
	7. 0 55½		15. 1 19
½	8. 0 63½		

Twentieths (10ths)

	1. 0 6¼		11. 0 69¾
·1	2. 0 12¾	·6	12. 0 76¼
	3. 0 19		13. 0 82½
·2	4. 0 25½	·7	14. 0 89
	5. 0 31¾		15. 0 95¼
·3	6. 0 38	·8	16. 1 1½
	7. 0 44½		17. 1 8
·4	8. 0 50¾	·9	18. 1 14¼
	9. 0 57¼		19 1 20¾
·5	10. 0 63½		20. 1 27

£ 1·28

*Dozens	No.	£	P
	1	1	28
	2	2	56
	3	3	84
	4	5	12
	5	6	40
	6	7	68
	7	8	96
	8	10	24
	9	11	52
	10	12	80
	11	14	8
1	12	15	36
	13	16	64
	14	17	92
	15	19	20
	16	20	48
	17	21	76
	18	23	4
	19	24	32
	20	25	60
	21	26	88
	22	28	16
	23	29	44
2	24	30	72
	25	32	0
	26	33	28
	27	34	56
	28	35	84
	29	37	12
	30	38	40
	31	39	68
	32	40	96
	33	42	24
	34	43	52
	35	44	80
3	36	46	8
	37	47	36
	38	48	64
	39	49	92
	40	51	20
	41	52	48
	42	53	76
	43	55	4
	44	56	32
	45	57	60
	46	58	88
	47	60	16
4	48	61	44
	49	62	72
	50	64	0

Dozens	No.	£	P
	51	65	28
	52	66	56
	53	67	84
	54	69	12
	55	70	40
	56	71	68
	57	72	96
	58	74	24
	59	75	52
5	**60**	76	80
	61	78	8
	62	79	36
	63	80	64
	64	81	92
	65	83	20
	66	84	48
	67	85	76
	68	87	4
	69	88	32
	70	89	60
	71	90	88
6	72	92	16
	75	96	0
	80	102	40
7	84	107	52
	90	115	20
8	96	122	88
	100	128	0
10	120	153	60
	140	179	20
	150	192	0
	160	204	80
	180	230	40
	200	256	0
25	300	384	0
	365	467	20
	400	512	0
	500	640	0
	600	768	0
	700	896	0
	800	1024	0
	900	1152	0
	1000	1280	0

Twelfths

	No.	£	P		No.	£	P
	1.	0	10¾		7.	0	74¾
1/6	2.	0	21¼	2/3	8.	0	85¼
	3.	0	32		9.	0	96
1/3	4.	0	42¾	5/6	10.	1	6¾
	5.	0	53¼		11.	1	17¼
1/2	6.	0	64				

Sixteenths

	No.	£	P		No.	£	P
	1.	0	8		9.	0	72
1/8	2.	0	16	5/8	10.	0	80
	3.	0	24		11.	0	88
1/4	4.	0	32	3/4	12.	0	96
	5.	0	40		13.	1	4
3/8	6.	0	48	7/8	14.	1	12
	7.	0	56		15.	1	20
	8.	0	64				

Twentieths

10ths	No.	£	P	10ths	No.	£	P
	1.	0	6½		11.	0	70½
·1	2.	0	12¾	·6	12	0	76¾
	3.	0	19¼		13.	0	83¼
·2	4.	0	25½	·7	14.	0	89½
	5.	0	32		15.	0	96
·3	6.	0	38½	·8	16.	1	2½
	7.	0	44¾		17.	1	8¾
·4	8.	0	51¼	·9	18.	1	15¼
	9.	0	57½		19.	1	21½
·5	10.	0	64		20.	1	28

£ 1·29

*Dozens	No.	£	P
	1	1	29
	2	2	58
	3	3	87
	4	5	16
	5	6	45
	6	7	74
	7	9	3
	8	10	32
	9	11	61
	10	12	90
	11	14	19
1	12	15	48
	13	16	77
	14	18	6
	15	19	35
	16	20	64
	17	21	93
	18	23	22
	19	24	51
	20	25	80
	21	27	9
	22	28	38
	23	29	67
2	24	30	96
	25	32	25
	26	33	54
	27	34	83
	28	36	12
	29	37	41
	30	38	70
	31	39	99
	32	41	28
	33	42	57
	34	43	86
	35	45	15
3	36	46	44
	37	47	73
	38	49	2
	39	50	31
	40	51	60
	41	52	89
	42	54	18
	43	55	47
	44	56	76
	45	58	5
	46	59	34
	47	60	63
4	48	61	92
	49	63	21
	50	64	50

Dozens	No.	£	P
	51	65	79
	52	67	8
	53	68	37
	54	69	66
	55	70	95
	56	72	24
	57	73	53
	58	74	82
	59	76	11
5	**60**	77	40
	61	78	69
	62	79	98
	63	81	27
	64	82	56
	65	83	85
	66	85	14
	67	86	43
	68	87	72
	69	89	1
	70	90	30
	71	91	59
6	72	92	88
	75	96	75
	80	103	20
7	84	108	36
	90	116	10
8	96	123	84
	100	129	0
10	120	154	80
	140	180	60
	150	193	50
	160	206	40
	180	232	20
	200	258	0
25	300	387	0
	365	470	85
	400	516	0
	500	645	0
	600	774	0
	700	903	0
	800	1032	0
	900	1161	0
	1000	1290	0

Twelfths

	No.	£	P		No.	£	P
	1.	0	10¾		7.	0	75¼
1/6	2.	0	21½	2/3	8.	0	86
	3.	0	32¼		9.	0	96¾
1/3	4.	0	43	5/6	10.	1	7½
	5.	0	53¾		11.	1	18¼
1/2	6.	0	64½				

Sixteenths

	No.	£	P		No.	£	P
	1.	0	8		9.	0	72½
1/8	2.	0	16¼	5/8	10.	0	80¾
	3.	0	24¼		11.	0	88¾
1/4	4.	0	32¼	3/4	12.	0	96¾
	5.	0	40¼		13.	1	4¾
3/8	6.	0	48½	7/8	14.	1	13
	7.	0	56½		15.	1	21
1/2	8.	0	64½				

Twentieths

10ths	No.	£	P	10ths	No.	£	P
	1.	0	6½		11.	0	71
·1	2.	0	13	·6	12.	0	77½
	3.	0	19¼		13.	0	83¾
·2	4.	0	25¾	·7	14.	0	90¼
	5.	0	32¼		15.	0	96¾
·3	6.	0	38¾	·8	16.	1	3¼
	7.	0	45¼		17.	1	9¾
·4	8.	0	51½	·9	18.	1	16
	9.	0	58		19	1	22½
·5	10.	0	64½		20.	1	29

£ 1·30

*Dozens		£	P	Dozens		£	P
	1	1	30		51	66	30
	2	2	60		52	67	60
	3	3	90		53	68	90
	4	5	20		54	70	20
	5	6	50		55	71	50
	6	7	80		56	72	80
	7	9	10		57	74	10
	8	10	40		58	75	40
	9	11	70		59	76	70
	10	**13**	**0**	5	**60**	**78**	**0**
*	11	14	30		61	79	30
1	12	15	60		62	80	60
	13	16	90		63	81	90
	14	18	20		64	83	20
	15	19	50		65	84	50
	16	20	80		66	85	80
	17	22	10		67	87	10
	18	23	40		68	88	40
	19	24	70		69	89	70
	20	**26**	**0**		**70**	**91**	**0**
	21	27	30		71	92	30
	22	28	60	6	72	93	60
	23	29	90		75	97	50
2	24	31	20		80	104	0
	25	32	50	7	84	109	20
	26	33	80		90	117	0
	27	35	10	8	96	124	80
	28	36	40		**100**	**130**	**0**
	29	37	70	10	120	156	0
	30	**39**	**0**		140	182	0
	31	40	30		150	195	0
	32	41	60		160	208	0
	33	42	90		180	234	0
	34	44	20		200	260	0
	35	45	50	25	300	390	0
3	36	46	80		365	474	50
	37	48	10		400	520	0
	38	49	40		500	650	0
	39	50	70		600	780	0
	40	**52**	**0**		700	910	0
	41	53	30		800	1040	0
	42	54	60		900	1170	0
	43	55	90		**1000**	**1300**	**0**
	44	57	20				
	45	58	50				
	46	59	80				
	47	61	10				
4	48	62	40				
	49	63	70				
	50	**65**	**0**				

Twelfths

	1. 0 10¾		7. 0 75¾
⅙	2. 0 21¾	⅔	8. 0 86¾
	3. 0 32½		9. 0 97½
⅓	4. 0 43¼	⅚	10. 1 8¼
	5. 0 54¼		11. 1 19¼
½	6. 0 65		

Sixteenths

	1. 0 8¼		9. 0 73¼
⅛	2. 0 16¼	⅝	10. 0 81¼
	3. 0 24½		11. 0 89½
¼	4. 0 32½	¾	12. 0 97½
	5. 0 40¾		13. 1 5¾
⅜	6. 0 48¾	⅞	14. 1 13¾
	7. 0 57		15. 1 22
	8. 0 65		

Twentieths

10ths		10ths	
	1. 0 6½		11. 0 71½
·1	2. 0 13	·6	12 0 78
	3. 0 19½		13. 0 84½
·2	4. 0 26	·7	14. 0 91
	5. 0 32½		15. 0 97½
·3	6. 0 39	·8	16. 1 4
	7. 0 45½		17. 1 10½
·4	8. 0 52	·9	18. 1 17
	9. 0 58½		19. 1 23½
·5	10. 0 65		20. 1 30

£ 1·31

*Dozens		£	P	Dozens		£	P
	1	1	31		51	66	81
	2	2	62		52	68	12
	3	3	93		53	69	43
	4	5	24		54	70	74
	5	6	55		55	72	5
	6	7	86		56	73	36
	7	9	17		57	74	67
	8	10	48		58	75	98
	9	11	79		59	77	29
	10	**13**	**10**	5	**60**	**78**	**60**
	11	14	41		61	79	91
1	12	15	72		62	81	22
	13	17	3		63	82	53
	14	18	34		64	83	84
	15	19	65		65	85	15
	16	20	96		66	86	46
	17	22	27		67	87	77
	18	23	58		68	89	8
	19	24	89		69	90	39
	20	**26**	**20**		**70**	**91**	**70**
	21	27	51		71	93	1
	22	28	82	6	72	94	32
	23	30	13		75	98	25
2	24	31	44		80	104	80
	25	32	75	7	84	110	4
	26	34	6		90	117	90
	27	35	37	8	96	125	76
	28	36	68		**100**	**131**	**0**
	29	37	99	10	120	157	20
	30	**39**	**30**		140	183	40
	31	40	61		150	196	50
	32	41	92		160	209	60
	33	43	23		180	235	80
	34	44	54		200	262	0
	35	45	85	25	300	393	0
3	36	47	16		365	478	15
	37	48	47		400	524	0
	38	49	78		500	655	0
	39	51	9		600	786	0
	40	**52**	**40**		700	917	0
	41	53	71		800	1048	0
	42	55	2		900	1179	0
	43	56	33		**1000**	**1310**	**0**
	44	57	64				
	45	58	95				
	46	60	26				
	47	61	57				
4	48	62	88				
	49	64	19				
	50	**65**	**50**				

Twelfths

	1. 0 11		7. 0 76½
⅙	2. 0 21¾	⅔	8. 0 87¼
	3. 0 32¾		9. 0 98¼
⅓	4. 0 43¾	⅚	10. 1 9¼
	5. 0 54½		11. 1 20
½	6. 0 65½		

Sixteenths

	1. 0 8¼		9. 0 73¾
⅛	2. 0 16½	⅝	10. 0 82
	3. 0 24½		11. 0 90
¼	4. 0 32¾	¾	12. 0 98¼
	5. 0 41		13. 1 6½
⅜	6. 0 49¼	⅞	14. 1 14¾
	7. 0 57¼		15. 1 22¾
½	8. 0 65½		

Twentieths

10ths		10ths	
	1. 0 6½		11. 0 72
·1	2. 0 13	·6	12. 0 78½
	3. 0 19¾		13. 0 85¼
·2	4. 0 26¼	·7	14. 0 91¾
	5. 0 32¾		15. 0 98¼
·3	6. 0 39¼	·8	16. 1 4¾
	7. 0 45¾		17. 1 11¼
·4	8. 0 52½	·9	18. 1 18
	9. 0 59		19 1 24½
·5	10. 0 65½		20. 1 31

£ 1·32

Dozens		£	P
	1	1	32
	2	2	64
	3	3	96
	4	5	28
	5	6	60
	6	7	92
	7	9	24
	8	10	56
	9	11	88
	10	13	20
	11	14	52
*1	12	15	84
	13	17	16
	14	18	48
	15	19	80
	16	21	12
	17	22	44
	18	23	76
	19	25	8
	20	26	40
	21	27	72
	22	29	4
	23	30	36
2	24	31	68
	25	33	0
	26	34	32
	27	35	64
	28	36	96
	29	38	28
	30	39	60
	31	40	92
	32	42	24
	33	43	56
	34	44	88
	35	46	20
3	36	47	52
	37	48	84
	38	50	16
	39	51	48
	40	52	80
	41	54	12
	42	55	44
	43	56	76
	44	58	8
	45	59	40
	46	60	72
	47	62	4
4	48	63	36
	49	64	68
	50	66	0

Dozens		£	P
	51	67	32
	52	68	64
	53	69	96
	54	71	28
	55	72	60
	56	73	92
	57	75	24
	58	76	56
	59	77	88
5	**60**	79	20
	61	80	52
	62	81	84
	63	83	16
	64	84	48
	65	85	80
	66	87	12
	67	88	44
	68	89	76
	69	91	8
	70	92	40
	71	93	72
6	72	95	4
	75	99	0
	80	105	60
7	84	110	88
	90	118	80
8	96	126	72
	100	132	0
10	120	158	40
	140	184	80
	150	198	0
	160	211	20
	180	237	60
	200	264	0
25	300	396	0
	365	481	80
	400	528	0
	500	660	0
	600	792	0
	700	924	0
	800	1056	0
	900	1188	0
	1000	1320	0

Twelfths

	1.	0 11		7.	0 77
⅙	2.	0 22	⅔	8.	0 88
	3.	0 33		9.	0 99
⅓	4.	0 44	⅚	10.	1 10
	5.	0 55		11.	1 21
½	6.	0 66			

Sixteenths

	1.	0 8¼		9.	0 74¼
⅛	2.	0 16½	⅝	10.	0 82½
	3.	0 24¾		11.	0 90¾
¼	4.	0 33	¾	12.	0 99
	5.	0 41¼		13.	1 7¼
⅜	6.	0 49½	⅞	14.	1 15½
	7.	0 57¾		15.	1 23¾
	8.	0 66			

Twentieths

10ths			10ths		
	1.	0 6½		11.	0 72½
·1	2.	0 13¼	·6	12	0 79¼
	3.	0 19¾		13.	0 85¾
·2	4.	0 26½	·7	14.	0 92½
	5.	0 33		15.	0 99
·3	6.	0 39½	·8	16.	1 5½
	7.	0 46¼		17.	1 12¼
·4	8.	0 52¾	·9	18.	1 18¾
	9.	0 59½		19.	1 25½
·5	10.	0 66		20.	1 32

£ 1·33

Dozens		£	P
	1	1	33
	2	2	66
	3	3	99
	4	5	32
	5	6	65
	6	7	98
	7	9	31
	8	10	64
	9	11	97
	10	13	30
	11	14	63
*1	12	15	96
	13	17	29
	14	18	62
	15	19	95
	16	21	28
	17	22	61
	18	23	94
	19	25	27
	20	26	60
	21	27	93
	22	29	26
	23	30	59
2	24	31	92
	25	33	25
	26	34	58
	27	35	91
	28	37	24
	29	38	57
	30	39	90
	31	41	23
	32	42	56
	33	43	89
	34	45	22
	35	46	55
3	36	47	88
	37	49	21
	38	50	54
	39	51	87
	40	53	20
	41	54	53
	42	55	86
	43	57	19
	44	58	52
	45	59	85
	46	61	18
	47	62	51
4	48	63	84
	49	65	17
	50	66	50

Dozens		£	P
	51	67	83
	52	69	16
	53	70	49
	54	71	82
	55	73	15
	56	74	48
	57	75	81
	58	77	14
	59	78	47
5	**60**	79	80
	61	81	13
	62	82	46
	63	83	79
	64	85	12
	65	86	45
	66	87	78
	67	89	11
	68	90	44
	69	91	77
	70	93	10
	71	94	43
6	72	95	76
	75	99	75
	80	106	40
7	84	111	72
	90	119	70
8	96	127	68
	100	133	0
10	120	159	60
	140	186	20
	150	199	50
	160	212	80
	180	239	40
	200	266	0
25	300	399	0
	365	485	45
	400	532	0
	500	665	0
	600	798	0
	700	931	0
	800	1064	0
	900	1197	0
	1000	1330	0

Twelfths

	1.	0 11		7.	0 77½
⅙	2.	0 22¼	⅔	8.	0 88¾
	3.	0 33¼		9.	0 99¾
⅓	4.	0 44¼	⅚	10.	1 10¾
	5.	0 55½		11.	1 22
½	6.	0 66½			

Sixteenths

	1.	0 8¼		9.	0 74¾
⅛	2.	0 16¾	⅝	10.	0 83¼
	3.	0 25		11.	0 91½
¼	4.	0 33¼	¾	12.	0 99¾
	5.	0 41½		13.	1 8
⅜	6.	0 50	⅞	14.	1 16½
	7.	0 58¼		15.	1 24¾
½	8.	0 66½			

Twentieths

10ths			10ths		
	1.	0 6¾		11.	0 73¼
·1	2.	0 13¼	·6	12.	0 79¾
	3.	0 20		13.	0 86½
·2	4.	0 26½	·7	14.	0 93
	5.	0 33¼		15.	0 99¾
·3	6.	0 40	·8	16.	1 6½
	7.	0 46½		17.	1 13
·4	8.	0 53¼	·9	18.	1 19¾
	9.	0 59¾		19	1 26¼
·5	10.	0 66½		20.	1 33

£ 1·34

Doz.		£	P
	1	1	34
	2	2	68
	3	4	2
	4	5	36
	5	6	70
	6	8	4
	7	9	38
	8	10	72
	9	12	6
	10	13	40
*	11	14	74
1	12	16	8
	13	17	42
	14	18	76
	15	20	10
	16	21	44
	17	22	78
	18	24	12
	19	25	46
	20	26	80
	21	28	14
	22	29	48
	23	30	82
2	24	32	16
	25	33	50
	26	34	84
	27	36	18
	28	37	52
	29	38	86
	30	40	20
	31	41	54
	32	42	88
	33	44	22
	34	45	56
	35	46	90
3	36	48	24
	37	49	58
	38	50	92
	39	52	26
	40	53	60
	41	54	94
	42	56	28
	43	57	62
	44	58	96
	45	60	30
	46	61	64
	47	62	98
4	48	64	32
	49	65	66
	50	67	0

Doz.		£	P
	51	68	34
	52	69	68
	53	71	2
	54	72	36
	55	73	70
	56	75	4
	57	76	38
	58	77	72
	59	79	6
5	**60**	80	40
	61	81	74
	62	83	8
	63	84	42
	64	85	76
	65	87	10
	66	88	44
	67	89	78
	68	91	12
	69	92	46
	70	93	80
	71	95	14
6	72	96	48
	75	100	50
	80	107	20
7	84	112	56
	90	120	60
8	96	128	64
	100	134	0
10	120	160	80
	140	187	60
	150	201	0
	160	214	40
	180	241	20
	200	268	0
25	300	402	0
	365	489	10
	400	536	0
	500	670	0
	600	804	0
	700	938	0
	800	1072	0
	900	1206	0
	1000	1340	0

Twelfths

	1.	0 11¼		7.	0 78¼
⅙	2.	0 22¼	⅔	8.	0 89¼
	3.	0 33½		9.	1 0½
⅓	4.	0 44¾	⅚	10.	1 11¾
	5.	0 55¾		11.	1 22¾
½	6.	0 67			

Sixteenths

	1.	0 8½		9.	0 73½
⅛	2.	0 16¾	⅝	10.	0 83¾
	3.	0 25¼		11.	0 92¼
¼	4.	0 33½	¾	12.	1 0½
	5.	0 42		13.	1 9
⅜	6.	0 50¼	⅞	14.	1 17¼
	7.	0 58¾		15.	1 25¾
	8.	0 67			

Twentieths

10ths			10ths		
	1.	0 6¾		11.	0 73¾
·1	2.	0 13½	·6	12	0 80½
	3.	0 20		13.	0 87
·2	4.	0 27	·7	14.	0 93¾
	5.	0 33½		15.	1 0½
·3	6.	0 40¼	·8	16.	1 7¼
	7.	0 47		17.	1 14
·4	8.	0 53½	·9	18.	1 20½
	9.	0 60¼		19.	1 27¼
·5	10.	0 67		20.	1 34

£ 1·35

Doz.		£	P
	1	1	35
	2	2	70
	3	4	5
	4	5	40
	5	6	75
	6	8	10
	7	9	45
	8	10	80
	9	12	15
	10	13	50
	11	14	85
1	12	16	20
	13	17	55
	14	18	90
	15	20	25
	16	21	60
	17	22	95
	18	24	30
	19	25	65
	20	27	0
	21	28	35
	22	29	70
	23	31	5
2	24	32	40
	25	33	75
	26	35	10
	27	36	45
	28	37	80
	29	39	15
	30	40	50
	31	41	85
	32	43	20
	33	44	55
	34	45	90
	35	47	25
3	36	48	60
	37	49	95
	38	51	30
	39	52	65
	40	54	0
	41	55	35
	42	56	70
	43	58	5
	44	59	40
	45	60	75
	46	62	10
	47	63	45
4	48	64	80
	49	66	15
	50	67	50

Doz.		£	P
	51	68	85
	52	70	20
	53	71	55
	54	72	90
	55	74	25
	56	75	60
	57	76	95
	58	78	30
	59	79	65
5	**60**	81	0
	61	82	35
	62	83	70
	63	85	5
	64	86	40
	65	87	75
	66	89	10
	67	90	45
	68	91	80
	69	93	15
	70	94	50
	71	95	85
6	72	97	20
	75	101	25
	80	108	0
7	84	113	40
	90	121	50
8	96	129	60
	100	135	0
10	120	162	0
	140	189	0
	150	202	50
	160	216	0
	180	243	0
	200	270	0
25	300	405	0
	365	492	75
	400	540	0
	500	675	0
	600	810	0
	700	945	0
	800	1080	0
	900	1215	0
	1000	1350	0

Twelfths

	1.	0 11¼		7.	0 78¾
⅙	2.	0 22½	⅔	8.	0 90
	3.	0 33¾		9.	1 1¼
⅓	4.	0 45	⅚	10.	1 12½
	5.	0 56¼		11.	1 23¾
½	6.	0 67½			

Sixteenths

	1.	0 8½		9.	0 76
⅛	2.	0 17	⅝	10.	0 84½
	3.	0 25¼		11.	0 92¾
¼	4.	0 33¾	¾	12.	1 1¼
	5.	0 42¼		13.	1 9¾
⅜	6.	0 50¾	⅞	14.	1 18¼
	7.	0 59		15.	1 26½
½	8.	0 67½			

Twentieths

10ths			10ths		
	1.	0 6¾		11.	0 74¼
·1	2.	0 13½	·6	12.	0 81
	3.	0 20¼		13.	0 87¾
·2	4.	0 27	·7	14.	0 94½
	5.	0 33¾		15.	1 1¼
·3	6.	0 40½	·8	16.	1 8
	7.	0 47¼		17.	1 14¾
·4	8.	0 54	·9	18.	1 21½
	9.	0 60¾		19	1 28¼
·5	10.	0 67½		20.	1 35

£ 1·36

*Dozens		£	p
	1	1	36
	2	2	72
	3	4	8
	4	5	44
	5	6	80
	6	8	16
	7	9	52
	8	10	88
	9	12	24
	10	13	60
	11	14	96
1	12	16	32
	13	17	68
	14	19	4
	15	20	40
	16	21	76
	17	23	12
	18	24	48
	19	25	84
	20	27	20
	21	28	56
	22	29	92
	23	31	28
2	24	32	64
	25	34	0
	26	35	36
	27	36	72
	28	38	8
	29	39	44
	30	40	80
	31	42	16
	32	43	52
	33	44	88
	34	46	24
	35	47	60
3	36	48	96
	37	50	32
	38	51	68
	39	53	4
	40	54	40
	41	55	76
	42	57	12
	43	58	48
	44	59	84
	45	61	20
	46	62	56
	47	63	92
4	48	65	28
	49	66	64
	50	68	0

Dozens		£	p
	51	69	36
	52	70	72
	53	72	8
	54	73	44
	55	74	80
	56	76	16
	57	77	52
	58	78	88
	59	80	24
5	**60**	81	60
	61	82	96
	62	84	32
	63	85	68
	64	87	4
	65	88	40
	66	89	76
	67	91	12
	68	92	48
	69	93	84
	70	95	20
	71	96	56
6	72	97	92
	75	102	0
	80	108	80
7	84	114	24
	90	122	40
8	96	130	56
	100	136	0
10	120	163	20
	140	190	40
	150	204	0
	160	217	60
	180	244	80
	200	272	0
25	300	408	0
	365	496	40
	400	544	0
	500	680	0
	600	816	0
	700	952	0
	800	1088	0
	900	1224	0
	1000	1360	0

Twelfths

		£	p			£	p
	1.	0	11¼		7.	0	79¼
⅙	2.	0	22¾	⅔	8.	0	90¾
	3.	0	34		9.	1	2
⅓	4.	0	45¼	⅚	10.	1	13¼
	5.	0	56¾		11.	1	24¾
½	6.	0	68				

Sixteenths

		£	p			£	p
	1.	0	8½		9.	0	76½
⅛	2.	0	17	⅝	10.	0	85
	3.	0	25½		11.	0	93½
¼	4.	0	34	¾	12.	1	2
	5.	0	42½		13.	1	10½
⅜	6.	0	51	⅞	14.	1	19
	7.	0	59½		15.	1	27½
	8.	0	68				

Twentieths

10ths		£	p			£	p
	1.	0	6¾		11.	0	74¾
·1	2.	0	13½	·6	12	0	81½
	3.	0	20½		13.	0	88½
·2	4.	0	27¼	·7	14.	0	95¼
	5.	0	34		15.	1	2
·3	6.	0	40¾	·8	16.	1	8¾
	7.	0	47½		17.	1	15½
·4	8.	0	54½	·9	18.	1	22½
	9.	0	61¼		19.	1	29¼
·5	10.	0	68		20.	1	36

£ 1·37

*Dozens		£	p
	1	1	37
	2	2	74
	3	4	11
	4	5	48
	5	6	85
	6	8	22
	7	9	59
	8	10	96
	9	12	33
	10	13	70
	11	15	7
1	12	16	44
	13	17	81
	14	19	18
	15	20	55
	16	21	92
	17	23	29
	18	24	66
	19	26	3
	20	27	40
	21	28	77
	22	30	14
	23	31	51
2	24	32	88
	25	34	25
	26	35	62
	27	36	99
	28	38	36
	29	39	73
	30	41	10
	31	42	47
	32	43	84
	33	45	21
	34	46	58
	35	47	95
3	36	49	32
	37	50	69
	38	52	6
	39	53	43
	40	54	80
	41	56	17
	42	57	54
	43	58	91
	44	60	28
	45	61	65
	46	63	2
	47	64	39
4	48	65	76
	49	67	13
	50	68	50

Dozens		£	p
	51	69	87
	52	71	24
	53	72	61
	54	73	98
	55	75	35
	56	76	72
	57	78	9
	58	79	46
	59	80	83
5	**60**	82	20
	61	83	57
	62	84	94
	63	86	31
	64	87	68
	65	89	5
	66	90	42
	67	91	79
	68	93	16
	69	94	53
	70	95	90
	71	97	27
6	72	98	64
	75	102	75
	80	109	60
7	84	115	8
	90	123	30
8	96	131	52
	100	137	0
10	120	164	40
	140	191	80
	150	205	50
	160	219	20
	180	246	60
	200	274	0
25	300	411	0
	365	500	5
	400	548	0
	500	685	0
	600	822	0
	700	959	0
	800	1096	0
	900	1233	0
	1000	1370	0

Twelfths

		£	p			£	p
	1.	0	11½		7.	0	80
⅙	2.	0	22¾	⅔	8.	0	91¼
	3.	0	34¼		9.	1	2¾
⅓	4.	0	45¾	⅚	10.	1	14¼
	5.	0	57		11.	1	25½
½	6.	0	68½				

Sixteenths

		£	p			£	p
	1.	0	8½		9.	0	77
⅛	2.	0	17¼	⅝	10.	0	85¾
	3.	0	25¾		11.	0	94¼
¼	4.	0	34¼	¾	12.	1	2¾
	5.	0	42¾		13.	1	11¼
⅜	6.	0	51½	⅞	14.	1	20
	7.	0	60		15.	1	28½
½	8.	0	68½				

Twentieths

10ths		£	p			£	p
	1.	0	6¾		11.	0	75¼
·1	2.	0	13¾	·6	12.	0	82¼
	3.	0	20½		13.	0	89
·2	4.	0	27½	·7	14.	0	96
	5.	0	34¼		15.	1	2¾
·3	6.	0	41	·8	16.	1	9½
	7.	0	48		17.	1	16½
·4	8.	0	54¾	·9	18.	1	23¼
	9.	0	61¾		19	1	30¼
·5	10.	0	68½		20.	1	37

£ 1·38

*Dozens		£	P	Dozens		£	P
	1	1	38		51	70	38
	2	2	76		52	71	76
	3	4	14		53	73	14
	4	5	52		54	74	52
	5	6	90		55	75	90
	6	8	28		56	77	28
	7	9	66		57	78	66
	8	11	4		58	80	4
	9	12	42		59	81	42
	10	13	80	5	**60**	82	80
*	11	15	18		61	84	18
1	12	16	56		62	85	56
	13	17	94		63	86	94
	14	19	32		64	88	32
	15	20	70		65	89	70
	16	22	8		66	91	8
	17	23	46		67	92	46
	18	24	84		68	93	84
	19	26	22		69	95	22
	20	27	60		**70**	96	60
	21	28	98		71	97	98
	22	30	36	6	72	99	36
	23	31	74		75	103	50
2	24	33	12		80	110	40
	25	34	50	7	84	115	92
	26	35	88		90	124	20
	27	37	26	8	96	132	48
	28	38	64		100	138	0
	29	40	2	10	120	165	60
	30	41	40		140	193	20
	31	42	78		150	207	0
	32	44	16		160	220	80
	33	45	54		180	248	40
	34	46	92		200	276	0
	35	48	30	25	300	414	0
3	36	49	68		365	503	70
	37	51	6		400	552	0
	38	52	44		500	690	0
	39	53	82		600	828	0
	40	55	20		700	966	0
	41	56	58		800	1104	0
	42	57	96		900	1242	0
	43	59	34		1000	1380	0
	44	60	72				
	45	62	10				
	46	63	48				
	47	64	86				
4	48	66	24				
	49	67	62				
	50	69	0				

Twelfths

1.	0	11½	7.	0	80½
⅙2.	0	23	⅔ 8.	0	92
3.	0	34½	9.	1	3½
⅓4.	0	46	⅚10.	1	15
5.	0	57½	11.	1	26½
½6.	0	69			

Sixteenths

1.	0	8¾	9.	0	77¾
⅛2.	0	17¼	⅝10.	0	86¼
3.	0	26	11.	0	95
¼4.	0	34½	¾12.	1	3½
5.	0	43¼	13.	1	12¼
⅜6.	0	51¾	⅞14.	1	20¾
7.	0	60½	15.	1	29½
8.	0	69			

Twentieths

10ths				10ths			
	1.	0	7		11.	0	76
·1	2.	0	13¾	·6	12	0	82¾
	3.	0	20¾		13.	0	89¾
·2	4.	0	27½	·7	14.	0	96½
	5.	0	34½		15.	1	3½
·3	6.	0	41½	·8	16.	1	10½
	7.	0	48¼		17.	1	17¼
·4	8.	0	55¼	·9	18.	1	24¼
	9.	0	62		19.	1	31
·5	10.	0	69		20.	1	38

£ 1·39

*Dozens		£	P	Dozens		£	P
	1	1	39		51	70	89
	2	2	78		52	72	28
	3	4	17		53	73	67
	4	5	56		54	75	6
	5	6	95		55	76	45
	6	8	34		56	77	84
	7	9	73		57	79	23
	8	11	12		58	80	62
	9	12	51		59	82	1
	10	13	90	5	**60**	83	40
	11	15	29		61	84	79
1	12	16	68		62	86	18
	13	18	7		63	87	57
	14	19	46		64	88	96
	15	20	85		65	90	35
	16	22	24		66	91	74
	17	23	63		67	93	13
	18	25	2		68	94	52
	19	26	41		69	95	91
	20	27	80		**70**	97	30
	21	29	19		71	98	69
	22	30	58	6	72	100	8
	23	31	97		75	104	25
2	24	33	36		80	111	20
	25	34	75	7	84	116	76
	26	36	14		90	125	10
	27	37	53	8	96	133	44
	28	38	92		100	139	0
	29	40	31	10	120	166	80
	30	41	70		140	194	60
	31	43	9		150	208	50
	32	44	48		160	222	40
	33	45	87		180	250	20
	34	47	26		200	278	0
	35	48	65	25	300	417	0
3	36	50	4		365	507	35
	37	51	43		400	556	0
	38	52	82		500	695	0
	39	54	21		600	834	0
	40	55	60		700	973	0
	41	56	99		800	1112	0
	42	58	38		900	1251	0
	43	59	77		1000	1390	0
	44	61	16				
	45	62	55				
	46	63	94				
	47	65	33				
4	48	66	72				
	49	68	11				
	50	69	50				

Twelfths

1.	0	11½	7.	0	81
⅙2.	0	23¼	⅔ 8.	0	92¾
3.	0	34¾	9.	1	4¼
⅓4.	0	46¼	⅚10.	1	15¾
5.	0	58	11.	1	27½
½6.	0	69½			

Sixteenths

1.	0	8¾	9.	0	78¼
⅛2.	0	17¼	⅝10.	0	87
3.	0	26	11.	0	95½
¼4.	0	34¾	¾12.	1	4¼
5.	0	43½	13.	1	13
⅜6.	0	52¼	⅞14.	1	21¾
7.	0	60¾	15.	1	30½
½8.	0	69½			

Twentieths

10ths				10ths			
	1.	0	7		11.	0	76½
·1	2.	0	14	·6	12.	0	83½
	3.	0	20¾		13.	0	90¼
·2	4.	0	27¾	·7	14.	0	97¼
	5.	0	34¾		15.	1	4¼
·3	6.	0	41¾	·8	16.	1	1¼
	7.	0	48¾		17.	1	18¼
·4	8.	0	55½	·9	18.	1	25
	9.	0	62½		19	1	32
·5	10.	0	69½		20.	1	39

£ 1·40

*Dozens

	£	P
1	1	40
2	2	80
3	4	20
4	5	60
5	7	0
6	8	40
7	9	80
8	11	20
9	12	60
10	14	0
11	15	40
[1] 12	16	80
13	18	20
14	19	60
15	21	0
16	22	40
17	23	80
18	25	20
19	26	60
20	28	0
21	29	40
22	30	80
23	32	20
[2] 24	33	60
25	35	0
26	36	40
27	37	80
28	39	20
29	40	60
30	42	0
31	43	40
32	44	80
33	46	20
34	47	60
35	49	0
[3] 36	50	40
37	51	80
38	53	20
39	54	60
40	56	0
41	57	40
42	58	80
43	60	20
44	61	60
45	63	0
46	64	40
47	65	80
[4] 48	67	20
49	68	60
50	70	0

Dozens

	£	P
51	71	40
52	72	80
53	74	20
54	75	60
55	77	0
56	78	40
57	79	80
58	81	20
59	82	60
[5] **60**	84	0
61	85	40
62	86	80
63	88	20
64	89	60
65	91	0
66	92	40
67	93	80
68	95	20
69	96	60
70	98	0
71	99	40
[6] 72	100	80
75	105	0
80	112	0
[7] 84	117	60
90	126	0
[8] 96	134	40
100	140	0
[10] 120	168	0
140	196	0
150	210	0
160	224	0
180	252	0
200	280	0
[25] 300	420	0
365	511	0
400	560	0
500	700	0
600	840	0
700	980	0
800	1120	0
900	1260	0
1000	1400	0

Twelfths

1.	0	11¾	7.	0	81¾
⅙ 2.	0	23¼	⅔ 8.	0	93¼
3.	0	35	9.	1	5
⅓ 4.	0	46¾	⅚ 10.	1	16¾
5.	0	58¼	11.	1	28¼
½ 6.	0	70			

Sixteenths

1.	0	8¾	9.	0	78¾
⅛ 2.	0	17½	⅝ 10.	0	87½
3.	0	26¼	11.	0	96¼
¼ 4.	0	35	¾ 12.	1	5
5.	0	43¾	13.	1	13¾
⅜ 6.	0	52½	⅞ 14.	1	22½
7.	0	61¼	15.	1	31¼
½ 8.	0	70			

Twentieths (10ths)

10ths				10ths			
	1.	0	7		11.	0	77
·1	2.	0	14	·6	12	0	84
	3.	0	21		13.	0	91
·2	4.	0	28	·7	14.	0	98
	5.	0	35		15.	1	5
·3	6.	0	42	·8	16.	1	12
	7.	0	49		17.	1	19
·4	8.	0	56	·9	18.	1	26
	9.	0	63		19.	1	33
·5	10.	0	70		20.	1	40

£ 1·41

*Dozens

	£	P
1	1	41
2	2	82
3	4	23
4	5	64
5	7	5
6	8	46
7	9	87
8	11	28
9	12	69
10	14	10
11	15	51
[1] 12	16	92
13	18	33
14	19	74
15	21	15
16	22	56
17	23	97
18	25	38
19	26	79
20	28	20
21	29	61
22	31	2
23	32	43
[2] 24	33	84
25	35	25
26	36	66
27	38	7
28	39	48
29	40	89
30	42	30
31	43	71
32	45	12
33	46	53
34	47	94
35	49	35
[3] 36	50	76
37	52	17
38	53	58
39	54	99
40	56	40
41	57	81
42	59	22
43	60	63
44	62	4
45	63	45
46	64	86
47	66	27
[4] 48	67	68
49	69	9
50	70	50

Dozens

	£	P
51	71	91
52	73	32
53	74	73
54	76	14
55	77	55
56	78	96
57	80	37
58	81	78
59	83	19
[5] **60**	84	60
61	86	1
62	87	42
63	88	83
64	90	24
65	91	65
66	93	6
67	94	47
68	95	88
69	97	29
70	98	70
71	100	11
[6] 72	101	52
75	105	75
80	112	80
[7] 84	118	44
90	126	90
[8] 96	135	36
100	141	0
[10] 120	169	20
140	197	40
150	211	50
160	225	60
180	253	80
200	282	0
[25] 300	423	0
365	514	65
400	564	0
500	705	0
600	846	0
700	987	0
800	1128	0
900	1269	0
1000	1410	0

Twelfths

1.	0	11¾	7.	0	82¼
⅙ 2.	0	23½	⅔ 8.	0	94
3.	0	35¼	9.	1	5¾
⅓ 4.	0	47	⅚ 10.	1	17½
5.	0	58¾	11.	1	29¼
½ 6.	0	70½			

Sixteenths

1.	0	8¾	9.	0	79¼
⅛ 2.	0	17¾	⅝ 10.	0	88¼
3.	0	26½	11.	0	97
¼ 4.	0	35¼	¾ 12.	1	5¾
5.	0	44	13.	1	14½
⅜ 6.	0	53	⅞ 14.	1	23½
7.	0	61¾	15.	1	32¼
½ 8.	0	70½			

Twentieths (10ths)

10ths				10ths			
	1.	0	7		11.	0	77½
·1	2.	0	14	·6	12.	0	84½
	3.	0	21¼		13.	0	91¾
·2	4.	0	28¼	·7	14.	0	98¾
	5.	0	35¼		15.	1	5¾
·3	6.	0	42¼	·8	16.	1	12¾
	7.	0	49¼		17.	1	19¾
·4	8.	0	56½	·9	18.	1	27
	9.	0	63½		19	1	34
·5	10.	0	70½		20.	1	41

£ 1·42

*Dozens		£	P
	1	1	42
	2	2	84
	3	4	26
	4	5	68
	5	7	10
	6	8	52
	7	9	94
	8	11	36
	9	12	78
	10	14	20
	11	15	62
1	12	17	4
	13	18	46
	14	19	88
	15	21	30
	16	22	72
	17	24	14
	18	25	56
	19	26	98
	20	28	40
	21	29	82
	22	31	24
	23	32	66
2	24	34	8
	25	35	50
	26	36	92
	27	38	34
	28	39	76
	29	41	18
	30	42	60
	31	44	2
	32	45	44
	33	46	86
	34	48	28
	35	49	70
3	36	51	12
	37	52	54
	38	53	96
	39	55	38
	40	56	80
	41	58	22
	42	59	64
	43	61	6
	44	62	48
	45	63	90
	46	65	32
	47	66	74
4	48	68	16
	49	69	58
	50	71	0

Dozens		£	P
	51	72	42
	52	73	84
	53	75	26
	54	76	68
	55	78	10
	56	79	52
	57	80	94
	58	82	36
	59	83	78
5	**60**	85	20
	61	86	62
	62	88	4
	63	89	46
	64	90	88
	65	92	30
	66	93	72
	67	95	14
	68	96	56
	69	97	98
	70	99	40
	71	100	82
6	72	102	24
	75	106	50
	80	113	60
7	84	119	28
	90	127	80
8	96	136	32
	100	142	0
10	120	170	40
	140	198	80
	150	213	0
	160	227	20
	180	255	60
	200	284	0
25	300	426	0
	365	518	30
	400	568	0
	500	710	0
	600	852	0
	700	994	0
	800	1136	0
	900	1278	0
	1000	1420	0

Twelfths

	1.	0 11¾		7.	0 82¾
1/6	2.	0 23¾	2/3	8.	0 94¾
	3.	0 35½		9.	1 6½
1/3	4.	0 47¼	5/6	10.	1 18¼
	5.	0 59¼		11.	1 30¼
1/2	6.	0 71			

Sixteenths

	1.	0 9		9.	0 80
1/8	2.	0 17¾	5/8	10.	0 88¾
	3.	0 26¾		11.	0 97¾
1/4	4.	0 35½	3/4	12.	1 6½
	5.	0 44½		13.	1 15½
3/8	6.	0 53¼	7/8	14.	1 24¼
	7.	0 62¼		15.	1 33¼
	8.	0 71			

Twentieths

10ths			10ths		
	1.	0 7		11.	0 78
·1	2.	0 14¼	·6	12	0 85¼
	3.	0 21¼		13.	0 92¼
·2	4.	0 28½	·7	14.	0 99½
	5.	0 35½		15.	1 6½
·3	6.	0 42½	·8	16.	1 13½
	7.	0 49¾		17.	1 20¾
·4	8.	0 56¾	·9	18.	1 27¾
	9.	0 64		19.	1 35
·5	10.	0 71		20.	1 42

£ 1·43

*Dozens		£	P
	1	1	43
	2	2	86
	3	4	29
	4	5	72
	5	7	15
	6	8	58
	7	10	1
	8	11	44
	9	12	87
	10	14	30
	11	15	73
1	12	17	16
	13	18	59
	14	20	2
	15	21	45
	16	22	88
	17	24	31
	18	25	74
	19	27	17
	20	28	60
	21	30	3
	22	31	46
	23	32	89
2	24	34	32
	25	35	75
	26	37	18
	27	38	61
	28	40	4
	29	41	47
	30	42	90
	31	44	33
	32	45	76
	33	47	19
	34	48	62
	35	50	5
3	36	51	48
	37	52	91
	38	54	34
	39	55	77
	40	57	20
	41	58	63
	42	60	6
	43	61	49
	44	62	92
	45	64	35
	46	65	78
	47	67	21
4	48	68	64
	49	70	7
	50	71	50

Dozens		£	P
	51	72	93
	52	74	36
	53	75	79
	54	77	22
	55	78	65
	56	80	8
	57	81	51
	58	82	94
	59	84	37
5	**60**	85	80
	61	87	23
	62	88	66
	63	90	9
	64	91	52
	65	92	95
	66	94	38
	67	95	81
	68	97	24
	69	98	67
	70	100	10
	71	101	53
6	72	102	96
	75	107	25
	80	114	40
7	84	120	12
	90	128	70
8	96	137	28
	100	143	0
10	120	171	60
	140	200	20
	150	214	50
	160	228	80
	180	257	40
	200	286	0
25	300	429	0
	365	521	95
	400	572	0
	500	715	0
	600	858	0
	700	1001	0
	800	1144	0
	900	1287	0
	1000	1430	0

Twelfths

	1.	0 12		7.	0 83½
1/6	2.	0 23¾	2/3	8.	0 95¼
	3.	0 35¾		9.	1 7¼
1/3	4.	0 47¾	5/6	10.	1 19¼
	5.	0 59½		11.	1 31
1/2	6.	0 71½			

Sixteenths

	1.	0 9		9.	0 80½
1/8	2.	0 18	5/8	10.	0 89½
	3.	0 26¾		11.	0 98¼
1/4	4.	0 35¾	3/4	12.	1 7¼
	5.	0 44¾		13.	1 16¼
3/8	6.	0 53¾	7/8	14.	1 25¼
	7.	0 62½		15.	1 34
1/2	8.	0 71½			

Twentieths

10ths			10ths		
	1.	0 7¼		11.	0 78¾
·1	2.	0 14¼	·6	12.	0 85¾
	3.	0 21½		13.	0 93
·2	4.	0 28½	·7	14.	1 0
	5.	0 35¾		15.	1 7¼
·3	6.	0 43	·8	16.	1 14½
	7.	0 50		17.	1 21½
·4	8.	0 57¼	·9	18.	1 28¾
	9.	0 64¼		19	1 35¾
·5	10.	0 71½		20.	1 43

£ 1·44

*Dozens		£	P
	1	1	44
	2	2	88
	3	4	32
	4	5	76
	5	7	20
	6	8	64
	7	10	8
	8	11	52
	9	12	96
	10	14	40
	11	15	84
*1	12	17	28
	13	18	72
	14	20	16
	15	21	60
	16	23	4
	17	24	48
	18	25	92
	19	27	36
	20	28	80
	21	30	24
	22	31	68
	23	33	12
2	24	34	56
	25	36	0
	26	37	44
	27	38	88
	28	40	32
	29	41	76
	30	43	20
	31	44	64
	32	46	8
	33	47	52
	34	48	96
	35	50	40
3	36	51	84
	37	53	28
	38	54	72
	39	56	16
	40	57	60
	41	59	4
	42	60	48
	43	61	92
	44	63	36
	45	64	80
	46	66	24
	47	67	68
4	48	69	12
	49	70	56
	50	72	0

Dozens		£	P
	51	73	44
	52	74	88
	53	76	32
	54	77	76
	55	79	20
	56	80	64
	57	82	8
	58	83	52
	59	84	96
5	**60**	86	40
	61	87	84
	62	89	28
	63	90	72
	64	92	16
	65	93	60
	66	95	4
	67	96	48
	68	97	92
	69	99	36
	70	100	80
	71	102	24
6	72	103	68
	75	108	0
	80	115	20
7	84	120	96
	90	129	60
8	96	138	24
	100	144	0
10	120	172	80
	140	201	60
	150	216	0
	160	230	40
	180	259	20
	200	288	0
25	300	432	0
	365	525	60
	400	576	0
	500	720	0
	600	864	0
	700	1008	0
	800	1152	0
	900	1296	0
	1000	1440	0

Twelfths

	1.	0	12		7.	0	84
⅙	2.	0	24	⅔	8.	0	96
	3.	0	36		9.	1	8
⅓	4.	0	48	⅚	10.	1	20
	5.	0	60		11.	1	32
½	6.	0	72				

Sixteenths

	1.	0	9		9.	0	81
⅛	2.	0	18	⅝	10.	0	90
	3.	0	27		11.	0	99
¼	4.	0	36	¾	12.	1	8
	5.	0	45		13.	1	17
⅜	6.	0	54	⅞	14.	1	26
	7.	0	63		15.	1	35
	8.	0	72				

Twentieths

10ths							
	1.	0	7¼		11.	0	79¼
·1	2.	0	14½	·6	12	0	86½
	3.	0	21½		13.	0	93½
·2	4.	0	28¾	·7	14.	1	0¾
	5.	0	36		15.	1	8
·3	6.	0	43¼	·8	16.	1	15¼
	7.	0	50½		17.	1	22½
·4	8.	0	57½	·9	18.	1	29½
	9.	0	64¾		19.	1	36¾
·5	10.	0	72		20.	1	44

£ 1·45

*Dozens		£	P
	1	1	45
	2	2	90
	3	4	35
	4	5	80
	5	7	25
	6	8	70
	7	10	15
	8	11	60
	9	13	5
	10	14	50
	11	15	95
1	12	17	40
	13	18	85
	14	20	30
	15	21	75
	16	23	20
	17	24	65
	18	26	10
	19	27	55
	20	29	0
	21	30	45
	22	31	90
	23	33	35
2	24	34	80
	25	36	25
	26	37	70
	27	39	15
	28	40	60
	29	42	5
	30	43	50
	31	44	95
	32	46	40
	33	47	85
	34	49	30
	35	50	75
3	36	52	20
	37	53	65
	38	55	10
	39	56	55
	40	58	0
	41	59	45
	42	60	90
	43	62	35
	44	63	80
	45	65	25
	46	66	70
	47	68	15
4	48	69	60
	49	71	5
	50	72	50

Dozens		£	P
	51	73	95
	52	75	40
	53	76	85
	54	78	30
	55	79	75
	56	81	20
	57	82	65
	58	84	10
	59	85	55
5	**60**	87	0
	61	88	45
	62	89	90
	63	91	35
	64	92	80
	65	94	25
	66	95	70
	67	97	15
	68	98	60
	69	100	5
	70	101	50
	71	102	95
6	72	104	40
	75	108	75
	80	116	0
7	84	121	80
	90	130	50
8	96	139	20
	100	145	0
10	120	174	0
	140	203	0
	150	217	50
	160	232	0
	180	261	0
	200	290	0
25	300	435	0
	365	529	25
	400	580	0
	500	725	0
	600	870	0
	700	1015	0
	800	1160	0
	900	1305	0
	1000	1450	0

Twelfths

	1.	0	12		7.	0	84½
⅙	2.	0	24¼	⅔	8.	0	96¾
	3.	0	36¼		9.	1	8¾
⅓	4.	0	48¼	⅚	10.	1	20¾
	5.	0	60½		11.	1	33
½	6.	0	72½				

Sixteenths

	1.	0	9		9.	0	81½
⅛	2.	0	18¼	⅝	10.	0	90¾
	3.	0	27¼		11.	0	99¾
¼	4.	0	36¼	¾	12.	1	8¾
	5.	0	45¼		13.	1	17¾
⅜	6.	0	54½	⅞	14.	1	27
	7.	0	63½		15.	1	36
½	8.	0	72½				

Twentieths

10ths							
	1.	0	7¼		11.	0	79¾
·1	2.	0	14½	·6	12.	0	87
	3.	0	21¾		13.	0	94¼
·2	4.	0	29	·7	14.	1	1½
	5.	0	36¼		15.	1	8¾
·3	6.	0	43½	·8	16.	1	16
	7.	0	50¾		17.	1	23¼
·4	8.	0	58	·9	18.	1	30½
	9.	0	65¼		19	1	37¾
·5	10.	0	72½		20.	1	45

£ 1·46

*Dozens	No.	£	P	Dozens	No.	£	P
	1	1	46		51	74	46
	2	2	92		52	75	92
	3	4	38		53	77	38
	4	5	84		54	78	84
	5	7	30		55	80	30
	6	8	76		56	81	76
	7	10	22		57	83	22
	8	11	68		58	84	68
	9	13	14		59	86	14
	10	14	60	5	**60**	87	60
	11	16	6		61	89	6
1	12	17	52		62	90	52
	13	18	98		63	91	98
	14	20	44		64	93	44
	15	21	90		65	94	90
	16	23	36		66	96	36
	17	24	82		67	97	82
	18	26	28		68	99	28
	19	27	74		69	100	74
	20	29	20		**70**	102	20
	21	30	66		71	103	66
	22	32	12	6	72	105	12
	23	33	58		75	109	50
2	24	35	4		80	116	80
	25	36	50	7	84	122	64
	26	37	96		90	131	40
	27	39	42	8	96	140	16
	28	40	88		**100**	146	0
	29	42	34	10	120	175	20
	30	43	80		140	204	40
	31	45	26		150	219	0
	32	46	72		160	233	60
	33	48	18		180	262	80
	34	49	64		200	292	0
	35	51	10	25	300	438	0
3	36	52	56		365	532	90
	37	54	2		400	584	0
	38	55	48		500	730	0
	39	56	94		600	876	0
	40	58	40		700	1022	0
	41	59	86		800	1168	0
	42	61	32		900	1314	0
	43	62	78		**1000**	1460	0
	44	64	24				
	45	65	70				
	46	67	16				
	47	68	62				
4	48	70	8				
	49	71	54				
	50	73	0				

Twelfths

	1.	0	12¼		7.	0	85¼
⅙	2.	0	24¼	⅔	8.	0	97¼
	3.	0	36½		9.	1	9½
⅓	4.	0	48¾	⅚	10.	1	21¾
	5.	0	60¾		11.	1	33¾
½	6.	0	73				

Sixteenths

	1.	0	9¼		9.	0	82¼
⅛	2.	0	18¼	⅝	10.	0	91¼
	3.	0	27½		11.	1	0½
¼	4.	0	36½	¾	12.	1	9½
	5.	0	45¾		13.	1	18¾
⅜	6.	0	54¾	⅞	14.	1	27¾
	7.	0	64		15.	1	37
	8.	0	73				

Twentieths

10ths				10ths			
	1.	0	7¼		11.	0	80¼
·1	2.	0	14½	·6	12	0	87½
	3.	0	22		13.	0	95
·2	4.	0	29¼	·7	14.	1	2¼
	5.	0	36½		15.	1	9½
·3	6.	0	43¾	·8	16.	1	16¾
	7.	0	51		17.	1	24
·4	8.	0	58½	·9	18.	1	31½
	9.	0	65¾		19.	1	38¾
·5	10.	0	73		20.	1	46

£ 1·47

*Dozens	No.	£	P	Dozens	No.	£	P
	1	1	47		51	74	97
	2	2	94		52	76	44
	3	4	41		53	77	91
	4	5	88		54	79	38
	5	7	35		55	80	85
	6	8	82		56	82	32
	7	10	29		57	83	79
	8	11	76		58	85	26
	9	13	23		59	86	73
	10	14	70	5	**60**	88	20
	11	16	17		61	89	67
1	12	17	64		62	91	14
	13	19	11		63	92	61
	14	20	58		64	94	8
	15	22	5		65	95	55
	16	23	52		66	97	2
	17	24	99		67	98	49
	18	26	46		68	99	96
	19	27	93		69	101	43
	20	29	40		**70**	102	90
	21	30	87		71	104	37
	22	32	34	6	72	105	84
	23	33	81		75	110	25
2	24	35	28		80	117	60
	25	36	75	7	84	123	48
	26	38	22		90	132	30
	27	39	69	8	96	141	12
	28	41	16		**100**	147	0
	29	42	63	10	120	176	40
	30	44	10		140	205	80
	31	45	57		150	220	50
	32	47	4		160	235	20
	33	48	51		180	264	60
	34	49	98		200	294	0
	35	51	45	25	300	441	0
3	36	52	92		365	536	55
	37	54	39		400	588	0
	38	55	86		500	735	0
	39	57	33		600	882	0
	40	58	80		700	1029	0
	41	60	27		800	1176	0
	42	61	74		900	1323	0
	43	63	21		**1000**	1470	0
	44	64	68				
	45	66	15				
	46	67	62				
	47	69	9				
4	48	70	56				
	49	72	3				
	50	73	50				

Twelfths

	1.	0	12¼		7.	0	85¾
⅙	2.	0	24½	⅔	8.	0	98
	3.	0	36¾		9.	1	10¼
⅓	4.	0	49	⅚	10.	1	22½
	5.	0	61¼		11.	1	34¾
½	6.	0	73½				

Sixteenths

	1.	0	9¼		9.	0	82¾
⅛	2.	0	18½	⅝	10.	0	92
	3.	0	27½		11.	1	1
¼	4.	0	36¾	¾	12.	1	10¼
	5.	0	46		13.	1	19½
⅜	6.	0	55¼	⅞	14.	1	28¾
	7.	0	64¼		15.	1	37¾
½	8.	0	73½				

Twentieths

10ths				10ths			
	1.	0	7¼		11.	0	80¾
·1	2.	0	14¾	·6	12.	0	88¼
	3.	0	22		13.	0	95½
·2	4.	0	29½	·7	14.	1	3
	5.	0	36¾		15.	1	10¼
·3	6.	0	44	·8	16.	1	17½
	7.	0	51½		17.	1	25
·4	8.	0	58¾	·9	18.	1	32¼
	9.	0	66¼		19	1	39¾
·5	10.	0	73½		20.	1	47

£ 1·48

*Dozens

	£	P		£	P
1	1	48	51	75	48
2	2	96	52	76	96
3	4	44	53	78	44
4	5	92	54	79	92
5	7	40	55	81	40
6	8	88	56	82	88
7	10	36	57	84	36
8	11	84	58	85	84
9	13	32	59	87	32
10	14	80	[5] **60**	88	80
11	16	28	61	90	28
[*1] 12	17	76	62	91	76
13	19	24	63	93	24
14	20	72	64	94	72
15	22	20	65	96	20
16	23	68	66	97	68
17	25	16	67	99	16
18	26	64	68	100	64
19	28	12	69	102	12
20	29	60	**70**	103	60
21	31	8	71	105	8
22	32	56	[6] 72	106	56
23	34	4	75	111	0
[2] 24	35	52	80	118	40
25	37	0	[7] 84	124	32
26	38	48	90	133	20
27	39	96	[8] 96	142	8
28	41	44	100	148	0
29	42	92	[10] 120	177	60
30	44	40	140	207	20
31	45	88	150	222	0
32	47	36	160	236	80
33	48	84	180	266	40
34	50	32	200	296	0
35	51	80	[25] 300	444	0
[3] 36	53	28	365	540	20
37	54	76	400	592	0
38	56	24	500	740	0
39	57	72	600	888	0
40	59	20	700	1036	0
41	60	68	800	1184	0
42	62	16	900	1332	0
43	63	64	1000	1480	0
44	65	12			
45	66	60			
46	68	8			
47	69	56			
[4] 48	71	4			
49	72	52			
50	74	0			

Twelfths

1. 0 12¼	7. 0 86¼
⅙ 2. 0 24¾	⅔ 8. 0 98¾
3. 0 37	9. 1 11
⅓ 4. 0 49¼	⅚ 10. 1 23¼
5. 0 61¾	11. 1 35¾
½ 6. 0 74	

Sixteenths

1. 0 9¼	9. 0 83¼
⅛ 2. 0 18½	⅝ 10. 0 92½
3. 0 27¾	11. 1 1¾
¼ 4. 0 37	¾ 12. 1 11
5. 0 46¼	13. 1 20¼
⅜ 6. 0 55½	⅞ 14. 1 29½
7. 0 64¾	15. 1 38¾
8. 0 74	

10ths / Twentieths

	1. 0 7½		11. 0 81½
·1	2. 0 14¾	·6	12. 0 88¾
	3. 0 22¼		13. 0 96¼
·2	4. 0 29½	·7	14. 1 3½
	5. 0 37		15. 1 11
·3	6. 0 44½	·8	16. 1 18½
	7. 0 51¾		17. 1 25¾
·4	8. 0 59¼	·9	18. 1 33¼
	9. 0 66¾		19. 1 40½
·5	10. 0 74		20. 1 48

£ 1·49

*Dozens

	£	P		£	P
1	1	49	51	75	99
2	2	98	52	77	48
3	4	47	53	78	97
4	5	96	54	80	46
5	7	45	55	81	95
6	8	94	56	83	44
7	10	43	57	84	93
8	11	92	58	86	42
9	13	41	59	87	91
10	14	90	[5] **60**	89	40
11	16	39	61	90	89
[1] 12	17	88	62	92	38
13	19	37	63	93	87
14	20	86	64	95	36
15	22	35	65	96	85
16	23	84	66	98	34
17	25	33	67	99	83
18	26	82	68	101	32
19	28	31	69	102	81
20	29	80	**70**	104	30
21	31	29	71	105	79
22	32	78	[6] 72	107	28
23	34	27	75	111	75
[2] 24	35	76	80	119	20
25	37	25	[7] 84	125	16
26	38	74	90	134	10
27	40	23	[8] 96	143	4
28	41	72	100	149	0
29	43	21	[10] 120	178	80
30	44	70	140	208	60
31	46	19	150	223	50
32	47	68	160	238	40
33	49	17	180	268	20
34	50	66	200	298	0
35	52	15	[25] 300	447	0
[3] 36	53	64	365	543	85
37	55	13	400	596	0
38	56	62	500	745	0
39	58	11	600	894	0
40	59	60	700	1043	0
41	61	9	800	1192	0
42	62	58	900	1341	0
43	64	7	1000	1490	0
44	65	56			
45	67	5			
46	68	54			
47	70	3			
[4] 48	71	52			
49	73	1			
50	74	50			

Twelfths

1. 0 12½	7. 0 87
⅙ 2. 0 24¾	⅔ 8. 0 99¼
3. 0 37¼	9. 1 11¾
⅓ 4. 0 49¾	⅚ 10. 1 24¼
5. 0 62	11. 1 36½
½ 6. 0 74½	

Sixteenths

1. 0 9¼	9. 0 83¾
⅛ 2. 0 18¾	⅝ 10. 0 93½
3. 0 28	11. 1 2½
¼ 4. 0 37¼	¾ 12. 1 11¾
5. 0 46½	13. 1 21
⅜ 6. 0 56	⅞ 14. 1 30½
7. 0 65¼	15. 1 39¾
½ 8. 0 74½	

10ths / Twentieths

	1. 0 7½		11. 0 82
·1	2. 0 15	·6	12. 0 89½
	3. 0 22¼		13. 0 96¾
·2	4. 0 29¾	·7	14. 1 4¼
	5. 0 37¼		15. 1 11¾
·3	6. 0 44¾	·8	16. 1 19¼
	7. 0 52¼		17. 1 26¾
·4	8. 0 59½	·9	18. 1 34
	9. 0 67		19 1 41½
·5	10. 0 74½		20. 1 49

£ 1·50

*Dozens		£	P
	1	1	50
	2	3	0
	3	4	50
	4	6	0
	5	7	50
	6	9	0
	7	10	50
	8	12	0
	9	13	50
	10	15	0
	11	16	50
1	12	18	0
	13	19	50
	14	21	0
	15	22	50
	16	24	0
	17	25	50
	18	27	0
	19	28	50
	20	30	0
	21	31	50
	22	33	0
	23	34	50
2	24	36	0
	25	37	50
	26	39	0
	27	40	50
	28	42	0
	29	43	50
	30	45	0
	31	46	50
	32	48	0
	33	49	50
	34	51	0
	35	52	50
3	36	54	0
	37	55	50
	38	57	0
	39	58	50
	40	60	0
	41	61	50
	42	63	0
	43	64	50
	44	66	0
	45	67	50
	46	69	0
	47	70	50
4	48	72	0
	49	73	50
	50	75	0

Dozens		£	P
	51	76	50
	52	78	0
	53	79	50
	54	81	0
	55	82	50
	56	84	0
	57	85	50
	58	87	0
	59	88	50
5	**60**	90	0
	61	91	50
	62	93	0
	63	94	50
	64	96	0
	65	97	50
	66	99	0
	67	100	50
	68	102	0
	69	103	50
	70	105	0
	71	106	50
6	72	108	0
	75	112	50
	80	120	0
7	84	126	0
	90	135	0
8	96	144	0
	100	150	0
10	120	180	0
	140	210	0
	150	225	0
	160	240	0
	180	270	0
	200	300	0
25	300	450	0
	365	547	50
	400	600	0
	500	750	0
	600	900	0
	700	1050	0
	800	1200	0
	900	1350	0
	1000	1500	0

Twelfths

	1. 0 12½		7. 0 87½
1/6	2. 0 25	2/3	8. 1 0
	3. 0 37½		9. 1 12½
1/3	4. 0 50	5/6	10. 1 25
	5. 0 62½		11. 1 37½
1/2	6. 0 75		

Sixteenths

	1. 0 9½		9. 0 84½
1/8	2. 0 18¾	5/8	10. 0 93¾
	3. 0 28¼		11. 1 3¼
1/4	4. 0 37½	3/4	12. 1 12½
	5. 0 47		13. 1 22
3/8	6. 0 56¼	7/8	14. 1 31¼
	7. 0 65¾		15. 1 40¾
	8. 0 75		

Twentieths

10ths			
	1. 0 7½		11. 0 82½
·1	2. 0 15	·6	12 0 90
	3. 0 22½		13. 0 97½
·2	4. 0 30	·7	14. 1 5
	5. 0 37½		15. 1 12½
·3	6. 0 45	·8	16. 1 20
	7. 0 52½		17. 1 27½
·4	8. 0 60	·9	18. 1 35
	9. 0 67½		19. 1 42½
·5	10. 0 75		20. 1 50

£ 1·51

*Dozens		£	P
	1	1	51
	2	3	2
	3	4	53
	4	6	4
	5	7	55
	6	9	6
	7	10	57
	8	12	8
	9	13	59
	10	15	10
	11	16	61
1	12	18	12
	13	19	63
	14	21	14
	15	22	65
	16	24	16
	17	25	67
	18	27	18
	19	28	69
	20	30	20
	21	31	71
	22	33	22
	23	34	73
2	24	36	24
	25	37	75
	26	39	26
	27	40	77
	28	42	28
	29	43	79
	30	45	30
	31	46	81
	32	48	32
	33	49	83
	34	51	34
	35	52	85
3	36	54	36
	37	55	87
	38	57	38
	39	58	89
	40	60	40
	41	61	91
	42	63	42
	43	64	93
	44	66	44
	45	67	95
	46	69	46
	47	70	97
4	48	72	48
	49	73	99
	50	75	50

Dozens		£	P
	51	77	1
	52	78	52
	53	80	3
	54	81	54
	55	83	5
	56	84	56
	57	86	7
	58	87	58
	59	89	9
5	**60**	90	60
	61	92	11
	62	93	62
	63	95	13
	64	96	64
	65	98	15
	66	99	66
	67	101	17
	68	102	68
	69	104	19
	70	105	70
	71	107	21
6	72	108	72
	75	113	25
	80	120	80
7	84	126	84
	90	135	90
8	96	144	96
	100	151	0
10	120	181	20
	140	211	40
	150	226	50
	160	241	60
	180	271	80
	200	302	0
25	300	453	0
	365	551	15
	400	604	0
	500	755	0
	600	906	0
	700	1057	0
	800	1208	0
	900	1359	0
	1000	1510	0

Twelfths

	1. 0 12½		7. 0 88
1/6	2. 0 25¼	2/3	8. 1 0¾
	3. 0 37¾		9. 1 13¼
1/3	4. 0 50¼	5/6	10. 1 25¾
	5. 0 63		11. 1 38½
1/2	6. 0 75½		

Sixteenths

	1. 0 9½		9. 0 85
1/8	2. 0 19	5/8	10. 0 94½
	3. 0 28¼		11. 1 3¾
1/4	4. 0 37¾	3/4	12. 1 13¼
	5. 0 47¼		13. 1 22¾
3/8	6. 0 56¾	7/8	14. 1 32¼
	7. 0 66		15. 1 41½
1/2	8. 0 75½		

Twentieths

10ths			
	1. 0 7½		11. 0 83
·1	2. 0 15	·6	12. 0 90½
	3. 0 22¾		13. 0 98¼
·2	4. 0 30¼	·7	14. 1 5¾
	5. 0 37¾		15. 1 13¼
·3	6. 0 45¼	·8	16. 1 20¾
	7. 0 52¾		17. 1 28¼
·4	8. 0 60½	·9	18. 1 36
	9. 0 68		19 1 43½
·5	10. 0 75½		20. 1 51

£ 1·52

*Dozens		£	P	Dozens		£	P
	1	1	52		51	77	52
	2	3	4		52	79	4
	3	4	56		53	80	56
	4	6	8		54	82	8
	5	7	60		55	83	60
	6	9	12		56	85	12
	7	10	64		57	86	64
	8	12	16		58	88	16
	9	13	68		59	89	68
	10	15	20	5	**60**	91	20
	11	16	72		61	92	72
1*	12	18	24		62	94	24
	13	19	76		63	95	76
	14	21	28		64	97	28
	15	22	80		65	98	80
	16	24	32		66	100	32
	17	25	84		67	101	84
	18	27	36		68	103	36
	19	28	88		69	104	88
	20	30	40		**70**	106	40
	21	31	92		71	107	92
	22	33	44	6	72	109	44
	23	34	96		75	114	0
2	24	36	48		80	121	60
	25	38	0	7	84	127	68
	26	39	52		90	136	80
	27	41	4	8	96	145	92
	28	42	56		100	152	0
	29	44	8	10	120	182	40
	30	45	60		140	212	80
	31	47	12		150	228	0
	32	48	64		160	243	20
	33	50	16		180	273	60
	34	51	68		200	304	0
	35	53	20	25	300	456	0
3	36	54	72		365	554	80
	37	56	24		400	608	0
	38	57	76		500	760	0
	39	59	28		600	912	0
	40	60	80		700	1064	0
	41	62	32		800	1216	0
	42	63	84		900	1368	0
	43	65	36		1000	1520	0
	44	66	88				
	45	68	40				
	46	69	92				
	47	71	44				
4	48	72	96				
	49	74	48				
	50	76	0				

Twelfths

	1.	0 12¾		7.	0 88¾
⅙	2.	0 25¼	⅔	8.	1 1¼
	3.	0 38		9.	1 14
⅓	4.	0 50¾	⅚	10.	1 26¾
	5.	0 63¼		11.	1 39¼
½	6.	0 76			

Sixteenths

	1.	0 9½		9.	0 85½
⅛	2.	0 19	⅝	10.	0 95
	3.	0 28½		11.	1 4½
¼	4.	0 38	¾	12.	1 14
	5.	0 47½		13.	1 23½
⅜	6.	0 57	⅞	14.	1 33
	7.	0 66½		15.	1 42½
	8.	0 76			

Twentieths (10ths)

	1.	0 7½		11.	0 83½
·1	2.	0 15¼	·6	12	0 91¼
	3.	0 22¾		13.	0 98¾
·2	4.	0 30½	·7	14.	1 6½
	5.	0 38		15.	1 14
·3	6.	0 45½	·8	16.	1 21½
	7.	0 53¼		17.	1 29¼
·4	8.	0 60¾	·9	18.	1 36¾
	9.	0 68½		19.	1 44½
·5	10.	0 76		20.	1 52

£ 1·53

*Dozens		£	P	Dozens		£	P
	1	1	53		51	78	3
	2	3	6		52	79	56
	3	4	59		53	81	9
	4	6	12		54	82	62
	5	7	65		55	84	15
	6	9	18		56	85	68
	7	10	71		57	87	21
	8	12	24		58	88	74
	9	13	77		59	90	27
	10	15	30	5	**60**	91	80
	11	16	83		61	93	33
1	12	18	36		62	94	86
	13	19	89		63	96	39
	14	21	42		64	97	92
	15	22	95		65	99	45
	16	24	48		66	100	98
	17	26	1		67	102	51
	18	27	54		68	104	4
	19	29	7		69	105	57
	20	30	60		**70**	107	10
	21	32	13		71	108	63
	22	33	66	6	72	110	16
	23	35	19		75	114	75
2	24	36	72		80	122	40
	25	38	25	7	84	128	52
	26	39	78		90	137	70
	27	41	31	8	96	146	88
	28	42	84		100	153	0
	29	44	37	10	120	183	60
	30	45	90		140	214	20
	31	47	43		150	229	50
	32	48	96		160	244	80
	33	50	49		180	275	40
	34	52	2		200	306	0
	35	53	55	25	300	459	0
3	36	55	8		365	558	45
	37	56	61		400	612	0
	38	58	14		500	765	0
	39	59	67		600	918	0
	40	61	20		700	1071	0
	41	62	73		800	1224	0
	42	64	26		900	1377	0
	43	65	79		1000	1530	0
	44	67	32				
	45	68	85				
	46	70	38				
	47	71	91				
4	48	73	44				
	49	74	97				
	50	76	50				

Twelfths

	1.	0 12¾		7.	0 89¼
⅙	2.	0 25½	⅔	8.	1 2
	3.	0 38¼		9.	1 14¾
⅓	4.	0 51	⅚	10.	1 27½
	5.	0 63¾		11.	1 40¼
½	6.	0 76½			

Sixteenths

	1.	0 9½		9.	0 86
⅛	2.	0 19¼	⅝	10.	0 95¾
	3.	0 28¾		11.	1 5¼
¼	4.	0 38¼	¾	12.	1 14¾
	5.	0 47¾		13.	1 24¼
⅜	6.	0 57½	⅞	14.	1 34
	7.	0 67		15.	1 43½
½	8.	0 76½			

Twentieths (10ths)

	1.	0 7¾		11.	0 84¼
·1	2.	0 15¼	·6	12.	0 91¾
	3.	0 23		13.	0 99½
·2	4.	0 30½	·7	14.	1 7
	5.	0 38¼		15.	1 14¾
·3	6.	0 46	·8	16.	1 22½
	7.	0 53½		17	1 30
·4	8.	0 61¼	·9	18.	1 37¾
	9.	0 68¾		19	1 45¼
·5	10.	0 76½		20.	1 53

£ 1·54

*Dozens		£	P
	1	1	54
	2	3	8
	3	4	62
	4	6	16
	5	7	70
	6	9	24
	7	10	78
	8	12	32
	9	13	86
	10	15	40
	11	16	94
1	12	18	48
	13	20	2
	14	21	56
	15	23	10
	16	24	64
	17	26	18
	18	27	72
	19	29	26
	20	30	80
	21	32	34
	22	33	88
	23	35	42
2	24	36	96
	25	38	50
	26	40	4
	27	41	58
	28	43	12
	29	44	66
	30	46	20
	31	47	74
	32	49	28
	33	50	82
	34	52	36
	35	53	90
3	36	55	44
	37	56	98
	38	58	52
	39	60	6
	40	61	60
	41	63	14
	42	64	68
	43	66	22
	44	67	76
	45	69	30
	46	70	84
	47	72	38
4	48	73	92
	49	75	46
	50	77	0

Dozens		£	P
	51	78	54
	52	80	8
	53	81	62
	54	83	16
	55	84	70
	56	86	24
	57	87	78
	58	89	32
	59	90	86
5	60	92	40
	61	93	94
	62	95	48
	63	97	2
	64	98	56
	65	100	10
	66	101	64
	67	103	18
	68	104	72
	69	106	26
	70	107	80
	71	109	34
6	72	110	88
	75	115	50
	80	123	20
7	84	129	36
	90	138	60
8	96	147	84
	100	154	0
10	120	184	80
	140	215	60
	150	231	0
	160	246	40
	180	277	20
	200	308	0
25	300	462	0
	365	562	10
	400	616	0
	500	770	0
	600	924	0
	700	1078	0
	800	1232	0
	900	1386	0
	1000	1540	0

Twelfths

1. 0 12¾		7. 0 89¾	
⅙	2. 0 25¾	⅔	8. 1 2¾
	3. 0 38½		9. 1 15½
⅓	4. 0 51¼	⅚	10. 1 28¼
	5. 0 64¼		11. 1 41¼
½	6. 0 77		

Sixteenths

	1. 0 9¾		9. 0 86¾
⅛	2. 0 19¼	⅝	10. 0 96¼
	3. 0 29		11. 1 6
¼	4. 0 38½	¾	12. 1 15½
	5. 0 48¼		13. 1 25¼
⅜	6. 0 57¾	⅞	14. 1 34¾
	7. 0 67½		15. 1 44½
	8. 0 77		

Twentieths (10ths)

	1. 0 7¾		11. 0 84¾
·1	2. 0 15½	·6	12. 0 92½
	3. 0 23		13. 1 0
·2	4. 0 30¾	·7	14. 1 7¾
	5. 0 38½		15. 1 15½
·3	6. 0 46¼	·8	16. 1 23¼
	7. 0 54		17. 1 31
·4	8. 0 61½	·9	18. 1 38½
	9. 0 69¼		19. 1 46¼
·5	10. 0 77		20. 1 54

£ 1·55

*Dozens		£	P
	1	1	55
	2	3	10
	3	4	65
	4	6	20
	5	7	75
	6	9	30
	7	10	85
	8	12	40
	9	13	95
	10	15	50
	11	17	5
1	12	18	60
	13	20	15
	14	21	70
	15	23	25
	16	24	80
	17	26	35
	18	27	90
	19	29	45
	20	31	0
	21	32	55
	22	34	10
	23	35	65
2	24	37	20
	25	38	75
	26	40	30
	27	41	85
	28	43	40
	29	44	95
	30	46	50
	31	48	5
	32	49	60
	33	51	15
	34	52	70
	35	54	25
3	36	55	80
	37	57	35
	38	58	90
	39	60	45
	40	62	0
	41	63	55
	42	65	10
	43	66	65
	44	68	20
	45	69	75
	46	71	30
	47	72	85
4	48	74	40
	49	75	95
	50	77	50

Dozens		£	P
	51	79	5
	52	80	60
	53	82	15
	54	83	70
	55	85	25
	56	86	80
	57	88	35
	58	89	90
	59	91	45
5	60	93	0
	61	94	55
	62	96	10
	63	97	65
	64	99	20
	65	100	75
	66	102	30
	67	103	85
	68	105	40
	69	106	95
	70	108	50
	71	110	5
6	72	111	60
	75	116	25
	80	124	0
7	84	130	20
	90	139	50
8	96	148	80
	100	155	0
10	120	186	0
	140	217	0
	150	232	50
	160	248	0
	180	279	0
	200	310	0
25	300	465	0
	365	565	75
	400	620	0
	500	775	0
	600	930	0
	700	1085	0
	800	1240	0
	900	1395	0
	1000	1550	0

Twelfths

	1. 0 13		7. 0 90½
⅙	2. 0 25¾	⅔	8. 1 3¼
	3. 0 38¾		9. 1 16¼
⅓	4. 0 51¾	⅚	10. 1 29¼
	5. 0 64½		11. 1 42
½	6. 0 77½		

Sixteenths

	1. 0 9¾		9. 0 87¼
⅛	2. 0 19½	⅝	10. 0 97
	3. 0 29		11. 1 6½
¼	4. 0 38¾	¾	12. 1 16¼
	5. 0 48½		13. 1 26
⅜	6. 0 58¼	⅞	14. 1 35¾
	7. 0 67¾		15. 1 45½
½	8. 0 77½		

Twentieths (10ths)

	1. 0 7¾		11. 0 85¼
·1	2. 0 15½	·6	12. 0 93
	3. 0 23¼		13. 1 0¾
·2	4. 0 31	·7	14. 1 8½
	5. 0 38¾		15. 1 16¼
·3	6. 0 46½	·8	16. 1 24
	7. 0 54¼		17. 1 31¾
·4	8. 0 62	·9	18. 1 39½
	9. 0 69¾		19 1 47¼
·5	10. 0 77½		20. 1 55

£ 1·56

*Dozens		£	P
	1	1	56
	2	3	12
	3	4	68
	4	6	24
	5	7	80
	6	9	36
	7	10	92
	8	12	48
	9	14	4
	10	15	60
	11	17	16
1	12	18	72
	13	20	28
	14	21	84
	15	23	40
	16	24	96
	17	26	52
	18	28	8
	19	29	64
	20	31	20
	21	32	76
	22	34	32
	23	35	88
2	24	37	44
	25	39	0
	26	40	56
	27	42	12
	28	43	68
	29	45	24
	30	46	80
	31	48	36
	32	49	92
	33	51	48
	34	53	4
	35	54	60
3	36	56	16
	37	57	72
	38	59	28
	39	60	84
	40	62	40
	41	63	96
	42	65	52
	43	67	8
	44	68	64
	45	70	20
	46	71	76
	47	73	32
4	48	74	88
	49	76	44
	50	78	0

Dozens		£	P
	51	79	56
	52	81	12
	53	82	68
	54	84	24
	55	85	80
	56	87	36
	57	88	92
	58	90	48
	59	92	4
5	60	93	60
	61	95	16
	62	96	72
	63	98	28
	64	99	84
	65	101	40
	66	102	96
	67	104	52
	68	106	8
	69	107	64
	70	109	20
	71	110	76
6	72	112	32
	75	117	0
	80	124	80
7	84	131	4
	90	140	40
8	96	149	76
	100	156	0
10	120	187	20
	140	218	40
	150	234	0
	160	249	60
	180	280	80
	200	312	0
25	300	468	0
	365	569	40
	400	624	0
	500	780	0
	600	936	0
	700	1092	0
	800	1248	0
	900	1404	0
	1000	1560	0

Twelfths

	1.	0	13		7.	0	91
⅙	2.	0	26	⅔	8.	1	4
	3.	0	39		9.	1	17
⅓	4.	0	52	⅚	10.	1	30
	5.	0	65		11.	1	43
½	6.	0	78				

Sixteenths

	1.	0	9¾		9.	0	87¾
⅛	2.	0	19½	⅝	10.	0	97½
	3.	0	29¼		11.	1	7¼
¼	4.	0	39	¾	12.	1	17
	5.	0	48¾		13.	1	26¾
⅜	6.	0	58½	⅞	14.	1	36½
	7.	0	68¼		15.	1	46¼
	8.	0	78				

Twentieths

10ths							
	1.	0	7¾		11.	0	85¾
·1	2.	0	15½	·6	12	0	93½
	3.	0	23½		13.	1	1½
·2	4.	0	31¼	·7	14.	1	9¼
	5.	0	39		15.	1	17
·3	6.	0	46¾	·8	16.	1	24¾
	7.	0	54½		17.	1	32½
·4	8.	0	62½	·9	18.	1	40½
	9.	0	70¼		19.	1	48¼
·5	10.	0	78		20.	1	56

£ 1·57

*Dozens		£	P
	1	1	57
	2	3	14
	3	4	71
	4	6	28
	5	7	85
	6	9	42
	7	10	99
	8	12	56
	9	14	13
	10	15	70
	11	17	27
1	12	18	84
	13	20	41
	14	21	98
	15	23	55
	16	25	12
	17	26	69
	18	28	26
	19	29	83
	20	31	40
	21	32	97
	22	34	54
	23	36	11
2	24	37	68
	25	39	25
	26	40	82
	27	42	39
	28	43	96
	29	45	53
	30	47	10
	31	48	67
	32	50	24
	33	51	81
	34	53	38
	35	54	95
3	36	56	52
	37	58	9
	38	59	66
	39	61	23
	40	62	80
	41	64	37
	42	65	94
	43	67	51
	44	69	8
	45	70	65
	46	72	22
	47	73	79
4	48	75	36
	49	76	93
	50	78	50

Dozens		£	P
	51	80	7
	52	81	64
	53	83	21
	54	84	78
	55	86	35
	56	87	92
	57	89	49
	58	91	6
	59	92	63
5	60	94	20
	61	95	77
	62	97	34
	63	98	91
	64	100	48
	65	102	5
	66	103	62
	67	105	19
	68	106	76
	69	108	33
	70	109	90
	71	111	47
6	72	113	4
	75	117	75
	80	125	60
7	84	131	88
	90	141	30
8	96	150	72
	100	157	0
10	120	188	40
	140	219	80
	150	235	50
	160	251	20
	180	282	60
	200	314	0
25	300	471	0
	365	573	5
	400	628	0
	500	785	0
	600	942	0
	700	1099	0
	800	1256	0
	900	1413	0
	1000	1570	0

Twelfths

	1.	0	13		7.	0	91½
⅙	2.	0	26¼	⅔	8.	1	4¾
	3.	0	39¼		9.	1	17¾
⅓	4.	0	52¼	⅚	10.	1	30¾
	5.	0	65½		11.	1	44
½	6.	0	78½				

Sixteenths

	1.	0	9¾		9.	0	88¼
⅛	2.	0	19¾	⅝	10.	0	98¼
	3.	0	29½		11.	1	8
¼	4.	0	39¼	¾	12.	1	17¾
	5.	0	49		13.	1	27½
⅜	6.	0	59	⅞	14.	1	37½
	7.	0	68¾		15.	1	47¼
½	8.	0	78½				

Twentieths

10ths							
	1.	0	7¾		11.	0	86¼
·1	2.	0	15¾	·6	12.	0	94¼
	3.	0	23½		13.	1	2
·2	4.	0	31½	·7	14.	1	10
	5.	0	39¼		15.	1	17¾
·3	6.	0	47	·8	16.	1	25½
	7.	0	55		17.	1	33½
·4	8.	0	62¾	·9	18.	1	41
	9.	0	70¾		19	1	49¼
·5	10.	0	78½		20.	1	57

£ 1·58

*Dozens	No.	£	P	Dozens	No.	£	P
	1	1	58		51	80	58
	2	3	16		52	82	16
	3	4	74		53	83	74
	4	6	32		54	85	32
	5	7	90		55	86	90
	6	9	48		56	88	48
	7	11	6		57	90	6
	8	12	64		58	91	64
	9	14	22		59	93	22
	10	15	80	5	**60**	94	80
	11	17	38		61	96	38
*1	12	18	96		62	97	96
	13	20	54		63	99	54
	14	22	12		64	101	12
	15	23	70		65	102	70
	16	25	28		66	104	28
	17	26	86		67	105	86
	18	28	44		68	107	44
	19	30	2		69	109	2
	20	31	60		**70**	110	60
	21	33	18		71	112	18
	22	34	76	6	72	113	76
	23	36	34		75	118	50
2	24	37	92		80	126	40
	25	39	50	7	84	132	72
	26	41	8		90	142	20
	27	42	66	8	96	151	68
	28	44	24		100	158	0
	29	45	82	10	120	189	60
	30	47	40		140	221	20
	31	48	98		150	237	0
	32	50	56		160	252	80
	33	52	14		180	284	40
	34	53	72		200	316	0
	35	55	30	25	300	474	0
3	36	56	88		365	576	70
	37	58	46		400	632	0
	38	60	4		500	790	0
	39	61	62		600	948	0
	40	63	20		700	1106	0
	41	64	78		800	1264	0
	42	66	36		900	1422	0
	43	67	94		1000	1580	0
	44	69	52				
	45	71	10				
	46	72	68				
	47	74	26				
4	48	75	84				
	49	77	42				
	50	79	0				

Twelfths

	1. 0 13¼		7. 0 92¼
⅙	2. 0 26¼	⅔	8. 1 5¼
	3. 0 39½		9. 1 18½
⅓	4. 0 52¾	⅚	10. 1 31¾
	5. 0 65¾		11. 1 44¾
½	6. 0 79		

Sixteenths

	1. 0 10		9. 0 89
⅛	2. 0 19¾	⅝	10. 0 98¾
	3. 0 29¾		11. 1 8¾
¼	4. 0 39½	¾	12. 1 18½
	5. 0 49½		13. 1 28½
⅜	6. 0 59¼	⅞	14. 1 38¼
	7. 0 69¼		15. 1 48¼
	8. 0 79		

Twentieths

10ths		10ths	
	1. 0 8		11. 0 87
·1	2. 0 15¾	·6	12 0 94¾
	3. 0 23¾		13. 1 2¾
·2	4. 0 31½	·7	14. 1 10½
	5. 0 39½		15. 1 18½
·3	6. 0 47½	·8	16. 1 26½
	7. 0 55¼		17. 1 34¼
·4	8. 0 63¼	·9	18. 1 42¼
	9. 0 71		19. 1 50
·5	10. 0 79		20. 1 58

£ 1·59

*Dozens	No.	£	P	Dozens	No.	£	P
	1	1	59		51	81	9
	2	3	18		52	82	68
	3	4	77		53	84	27
	4	6	36		54	85	86
	5	7	95		55	87	45
	6	9	54		56	89	4
	7	11	13		57	90	63
	8	12	72		58	92	22
	9	14	31		59	93	81
	10	15	90	5	**60**	95	40
	11	17	49		61	96	99
1	12	19	8		62	98	58
	13	20	67		63	100	17
	14	22	26		64	101	76
	15	23	85		65	103	35
	16	25	44		66	104	94
	17	27	3		67	106	53
	18	28	62		68	108	12
	19	30	21		69	109	71
	20	31	80		**70**	111	30
	21	33	39		71	112	89
	22	34	98	6	72	114	48
	23	36	57		75	119	25
2	24	38	16		80	127	20
	25	39	75	7	84	133	56
	26	41	34		90	143	10
	27	42	93	8	96	152	64
	28	44	52		100	159	0
	29	46	11	10	120	190	80
	30	47	70		140	222	60
	31	49	29		150	238	50
	32	50	88		160	254	40
	33	52	47		180	286	20
	34	54	6		200	318	0
	35	55	65	25	300	477	0
3	36	57	24		365	580	35
	37	58	83		400	636	0
	38	60	42		500	795	0
	39	62	1		600	954	0
	40	63	60		700	1113	0
	41	65	19		800	1272	0
	42	66	78		900	1431	0
	43	68	37		1000	1590	0
	44	69	96				
	45	71	55				
	46	73	14				
	47	74	73				
4	48	76	32				
	49	77	91				
	50	79	50				

Twelfths

	1. 0 13¼		7. 0 92¾
⅙	2. 0 26½	⅔	8. 1 6
	3. 0 39¾		9. 1 19¼
⅓	4. 0 53	⅚	10. 1 32½
	5. 0 66¼		11. 1 45¾
½	6. 0 79½		

Sixteenths

	1. 0 10		9. 0 89½
⅛	2. 0 20	⅝	10. 0 99½
	3. 0 29¾		11. 1 9¼
¼	4. 0 39¾	¾	12. 1 19¼
	5. 0 49¾		13. 1 29¼
⅜	6. 0 59¾	⅞	14. 1 39¼
	7. 0 69½		15. 1 49
½	8. 0 79½		

Twentieths

10ths		10ths	
	1. 0 8		11. 0 87½
·1	2. 0 16	·6	12. 0 95½
	3. 0 23¾		13. 1 3¼
·2	4. 0 31¾	·7	14. 1 11½
	5. 0 39¾		15. 1 19¼
·3	6. 0 47¾	·8	16. 1 27¼
	7. 0 55¾		17. 1 35¼
·4	8. 0 63½	·9	18. 1 43
	9. 0 71½		19 1 51
·5	10. 0 79½		20. 1 59

£ 1·60

		£	p
	1	1	60
*Dozens	2	3	20
	3	4	80
	4	6	40
	5	8	0
	6	9	60
	7	11	20
	8	12	80
	9	14	40
	10	16	0
	11	17	60
1	12	19	20
	13	20	80
	14	22	40
	15	24	0
	16	25	60
	17	27	20
	18	28	80
	19	30	40
	20	32	0
	21	33	60
	22	35	20
	23	36	80
2	24	38	40
	25	40	0
	26	41	60
	27	43	20
	28	44	80
	29	46	40
	30	48	0
	31	49	60
	32	51	20
	33	52	80
	34	54	40
	35	56	0
3	36	57	60
	37	59	20
	38	60	80
	39	62	40
	40	64	0
	41	65	60
	42	67	20
	43	68	80
	44	70	40
	45	72	0
	46	73	60
	47	75	20
4	48	76	80
	49	78	40
	50	80	0

		£	p
	51	81	60
Dozens	52	83	20
	53	84	80
	54	86	40
	55	88	0
	56	89	60
	57	91	20
	58	92	80
	59	94	40
5	**60**	96	0
	61	97	60
	62	99	20
	63	100	80
	64	102	40
	65	104	0
	66	105	60
	67	107	20
	68	108	80
	69	110	40
	70	112	0
	71	113	60
6	72	115	20
	75	120	0
	80	128	0
7	84	134	40
	90	144	0
8	96	153	60
	100	160	0
10	120	192	0
	140	224	0
	150	240	0
	160	256	0
	180	288	0
	200	320	0
25	300	480	0
	365	584	0
	400	640	0
	500	800	0
	600	960	0
	700	1120	0
	800	1280	0
	900	1440	0
	1000	1600	0

Twelfths

1. 0 13¼	7. 0 93¼
⅙2. 0 26¾	⅔ 8. 1 6¾
3. 0 40	9. 1 20
⅓4. 0 53¼	⅚10. 1 33¼
5. 0 66¾	11. 1 46¾
½6. 0 80	

Sixteenths

1. 0 10	9. 0 90
⅛2. 0 20	⅝10. 1 0
3. 0 30	11. 1 10
¼4. 0 40	¾12. 1 20
5. 0 50	13. 1 30
⅜6. 0 60	⅞14. 1 40
7. 0 70	15. 1 50
8. 0 80	

Twentieths

10ths		10ths	
	1. 0 8		11. 0 88
·1	2. 0 16	·6	12 0 96
	3. 0 24		13. 1 4
·2	4. 0 32	·7	14. 1 12
	5. 0 40		15. 1 20
·3	6. 0 48	·8	16. 1 28
	7. 0 56		17. 1 36
·4	8. 0 64	·9	18. 1 44
	9. 0 72		19. 1 52
·5	10. 0 80		20. 1 60

£ 1·61

		£	p
	1	1	61
*Dozens	2	3	22
	3	4	83
	4	6	44
	5	8	5
	6	9	66
	7	11	27
	8	12	88
	9	14	49
	10	16	10
	11	17	71
1	12	19	32
	13	20	93
	14	22	54
	15	24	15
	16	25	76
	17	27	37
	18	28	98
	19	30	59
	20	32	20
	21	33	81
	22	35	42
	23	37	3
2	24	38	64
	25	40	25
	26	41	86
	27	43	47
	28	45	8
	29	46	69
	30	48	30
	31	49	91
	32	51	52
	33	53	13
	34	54	74
	35	56	35
3	36	57	96
	37	59	57
	38	61	18
	39	62	79
	40	64	40
	41	66	1
	42	67	62
	43	69	23
	44	70	84
	45	72	45
	46	74	6
	47	75	67
4	48	77	28
	49	78	89
	50	80	50

		£	p
	51	82	11
Dozens	52	83	72
	53	85	33
	54	86	94
	55	88	55
	56	90	16
	57	91	77
	58	93	38
	59	94	99
5	**60**	96	60
	61	98	21
	62	99	82
	63	101	43
	64	103	4
	65	104	65
	66	106	26
	67	107	87
	68	109	48
	69	111	9
	70	112	70
	71	114	31
6	72	115	92
	75	120	75
	80	128	80
7	84	135	24
	90	144	90
8	96	154	56
	100	161	0
10	120	193	20
	140	225	40
	150	241	50
	160	257	60
	180	289	80
	200	322	0
25	300	483	0
	365	587	65
	400	644	0
	500	805	0
	600	966	0
	700	1127	0
	800	1288	0
	900	1449	0
	1000	1610	0

Twelfths

1. 0 13½	7. 0 94
⅙2. 0 26¾	⅔ 8. 1 7¼
3. 0 40¼	9. 1 20¾
⅓4. 0 53¾	⅚10. 1 34¼
5. 0 67	11. 1 47½
½6. 0 80½	

Sixteenths

1. 0 10	9. 0 90½
⅛2. 0 20¼	⅝10. 0 0¾
3. 0 30¼	11. 1 10¾
¼4. 0 40¼	¾12. 1 20¾
5. 0 50¼	13. 1 30¾
⅜6. 0 60½	⅞14. 1 41
7. 0 70½	15. 1 51
½8. 0 80½	

Twentieths

10ths		10ths	
	1. 0 8		11. 0 88½
·1	2. 0 16	·6	12. 0 96½
	3. 0 24¼		13. 1 4¾
·2	4. 0 32¼	·7	14. 1 12¾
	5 0 40¼		15. 1 20¾
·3	6. 0 48¼	·8	16. 1 28
	7. 0 56¼		17. 1 36¾
·4	8. 0 64½	·9	18. 1 45¾
	9. 0 72½		19 1 53
·5	10. 0 80½		20. 1 61

£ 1·62

*Dozens		£	P
	1	1	62
	2	3	24
	3	4	86
	4	6	48
	5	8	10
	6	9	72
	7	11	34
	8	12	96
	9	14	58
	10	16	20
	11	17	82
1	12	19	44
	13	21	6
	14	22	68
	15	24	30
	16	25	92
	17	27	54
	18	29	16
	19	30	78
	20	32	40
	21	34	2
	22	35	64
	23	37	26
2	24	38	88
	25	40	50
	26	42	12
	27	43	74
	28	45	36
	29	46	98
	30	48	60
	31	50	22
	32	51	84
	33	53	46
	34	55	8
	35	56	70
3	36	58	32
	37	59	94
	38	61	56
	39	63	18
	40	64	80
	41	66	42
	42	68	4
	43	69	66
	44	71	28
	45	72	90
	46	74	52
	47	76	14
4	48	77	76
	49	79	38
	50	81	0

Dozens		£	P
	51	82	62
	52	84	24
	53	85	86
	54	87	48
	55	89	10
	56	90	72
	57	92	34
	58	93	96
	59	95	58
5	**60**	97	20
	61	98	82
	62	100	44
	63	102	6
	64	103	68
	65	105	30
	66	106	92
	67	108	54
	68	110	16
	69	111	78
	70	113	40
	71	115	2
6	72	116	64
	75	121	50
	80	129	60
7	84	136	8
	90	145	80
8	96	155	52
	100	162	0
10	120	194	40
	140	226	80
	150	243	0
	160	259	20
	180	291	60
	200	324	0
25	300	486	0
	365	591	30
	400	648	0
	500	810	0
	600	972	0
	700	1134	0
	800	1296	0
	900	1458	0
	1000	1620	0

Twelfths

	1. 0 13½		7. 0 94½
⅙	2. 0 27	⅔	8. 1 8
	3. 0 40½		9. 1 21½
⅓	4. 0 54	⅚	10. 1 35
	5. 0 67½		11. 1 48½
½	6. 0 81		

Sixteenths

	1. 0 10¼		9. 0 91¼
⅛	2. 0 20¼	⅝	10. 1 1¼
	3. 0 30½		11. 1 11½
¼	4. 0 40½	¾	12. 1 21½
	5. 0 50¾		13. 1 31¾
⅜	6. 0 60¾	⅞	14. 1 41¾
	7. 0 71		15. 1 52
	8. 0 81		

Twentieths

10ths		10ths	
	1. 0 8		11. 0 89
·1	2. 0 16¼	·6	12 0 97¼
	3. 0 24¼		13. 1 5¼
·2	4. 0 32½	·7	14. 1 13½
	5. 0 40½		15. 1 21½
·3	6. 0 48½	·8	16. 1 29½
	7. 0 56¾		17. 1 37¾
·4	8. 0 64¾	·9	18. 1 45¾
	9. 0 73		19. 1 54
·5	10. 0 81		20. 1 62

£ 1·63

*Dozens		£	P
	1	1	63
	2	3	26
	3	4	89
	4	6	52
	5	8	15
	6	9	78
	7	11	41
	8	13	4
	9	14	67
	10	16	30
	11	17	93
1	12	19	56
	13	21	19
	14	22	82
	15	24	45
	16	26	8
	17	27	71
	18	29	34
	19	30	97
	20	32	60
	21	34	23
	22	35	86
	23	37	49
2	24	39	12
	25	40	75
	26	42	38
	27	44	1
	28	45	64
	29	47	27
	30	48	90
	31	50	53
	32	52	16
	33	53	79
	34	55	42
	35	57	5
3	36	58	68
	37	60	31
	38	61	94
	39	63	57
	40	65	20
	41	66	83
	42	68	46
	43	70	9
	44	71	72
	45	73	35
	46	74	98
	47	76	61
4	48	78	24
	49	79	87
	50	81	50

Dozens		£	P
	51	83	13
	52	84	76
	53	86	39
	54	88	2
	55	89	65
	56	91	28
	57	92	91
	58	94	54
	59	96	17
5	**60**	97	80
	61	99	43
	62	101	6
	63	102	69
	64	104	32
	65	105	95
	66	107	58
	67	109	21
	68	110	84
	69	112	47
	70	114	10
	71	115	73
6	72	117	36
	75	122	25
	80	130	40
7	84	136	92
	90	146	70
8	96	156	48
	100	163	0
10	120	195	60
	140	228	20
	150	244	50
	160	260	80
	180	293	40
	200	326	0
25	300	489	0
	365	594	95
	400	652	0
	500	815	0
	600	978	0
	700	1141	0
	800	1304	0
	900	1467	0
	1000	1630	0

Twelfths

	1. 0 13½		7. 0 95
⅙	2. 0 27¼	⅔	8. 1 8¾
	3. 0 40¾		9. 1 22¼
⅓	4. 0 54¼	⅚	10. 1 35¾
	5. 0 68		11. 1 49½
½	6. 0 81½		

Sixteenths

	1. 0 10¼		9. 0 91¾
⅛	2. 0 20½	⅝	10. 1 2
	3. 0 30½		11. 1 12
¼	4. 0 40¾	¾	12. 1 22¼
	5. 0 51		13. 1 32½
⅜	6. 0 61¼	⅞	14. 1 42¾
	7. 0 71¼		15. 1 52¾
½	8. 0 81½		

Twentieths

10ths		10ths	
	1. 0 8¼		11. 0 89¾
·1	2. 0 16¼	·6	12. 0 97¾
	3. 0 24½		13. 1 6
·2	4. 0 32½	·7	14. 1 14
	5 0 40¾		15. 1 22¼
·3	6. 0 49	·8	16. 1 30½
	7. 0 57		17. 1 38½
·4	8. 0 65¼	·9	18. 1 46¾
	9. 0 73¼		19 1 54¾
·5	10. 0 81½		20. 1 63

£ 1·64

*Dozens		£	P
	1	1	64
	2	3	28
	3	4	92
	4	6	56
	5	8	20
	6	9	84
	7	11	48
	8	13	12
	9	14	76
	10	16	40
	11	18	4
*1	12	19	68
	13	21	32
	14	22	96
	15	24	60
	16	26	24
	17	27	88
	18	29	52
	19	31	16
	20	32	80
	21	34	44
	22	36	8
	23	37	72
2	24	39	36
	25	41	0
	26	42	64
	27	44	28
	28	45	92
	29	47	56
	30	49	20
	31	50	84
	32	52	48
	33	54	12
	34	55	76
	35	57	40
3	36	59	4
	37	60	68
	38	62	32
	39	63	96
	40	65	60
	41	67	24
	42	68	88
	43	70	52
	44	72	16
	45	73	80
	46	75	44
	47	77	8
4	48	78	72
	49	80	36
	50	82	0

Dozens		£	P
	51	83	64
	52	85	28
	53	86	92
	54	88	56
	55	90	20
	56	91	84
	57	93	48
	58	95	12
	59	96	76
5	**60**	98	40
	61	100	4
	62	101	68
	63	103	32
	64	104	96
	65	106	60
	66	108	24
	67	109	88
	68	111	52
	69	113	16
	70	114	80
	71	116	44
6	72	118	8
	75	123	0
	80	131	20
7	84	137	76
	90	147	60
8	96	157	44
	100	164	0
10	120	196	80
	140	229	60
	150	246	0
	160	262	40
	180	295	20
	200	328	0
25	300	492	0
	365	598	60
	400	656	0
	500	820	0
	600	984	0
	700	1148	0
	800	1312	0
	900	1476	0
	1000	1640	0

Twelfths

	1. 0 13¾		7. 0 95¾
⅙	2. 0 27¼	⅔	8. 1 9¼
	3. 0 41		9. 1 23
⅓	4. 0 54¾	⅚	10. 1 36¾
	5. 0 68¼		11. 1 50¼
½	6. 0 82		

Sixteenths

	1. 0 10¼		9. 0 92¼
⅛	2. 0 20½	⅝	10. 1 2½
	3. 0 30¾		11. 1 12¾
¼	4. 0 41	¾	12. 1 23
	5. 0 51¼		13. 1 33¼
⅜	6. 0 61½	⅞	14. 1 43½
	7. 0 71¾		15. 1 53¾
	8. 0 82		

Twentieths

10ths			
	1. 0 8¼		11. 0 90¼
·1	2. 0 16½	·6	12 0 98½
	3. 0 24½		13. 1 6½
·2	4. 0 32¾	·7	14. 1 14¾
	5. 0 41		15. 1 23
·3	6. 0 49¼	·8	16. 1 31¼
	7. 0 57½		17. 1 39½
·4	8. 0 65½	·9	18. 1 47½
	9. 0 73¾		19. 1 55¾
·5	10. 0 82		20. 1 64

£ 1·65

*Dozens		£	P
	1	1	65
	2	3	30
	3	4	95
	4	6	60
	5	8	25
	6	9	90
	7	11	55
	8	13	20
	9	14	85
	10	16	50
	11	18	15
1	12	19	80
	13	21	45
	14	23	10
	15	24	75
	16	26	40
	17	28	5
	18	29	70
	19	31	35
	20	33	0
	21	34	65
	22	36	30
	23	37	95
2	24	39	60
	25	41	25
	26	42	90
	27	44	55
	28	46	20
	29	47	85
	30	49	50
	31	51	15
	32	52	80
	33	54	45
	34	56	10
	35	57	75
3	36	59	40
	37	61	5
	38	62	70
	39	64	35
	40	66	0
	41	67	65
	42	69	30
	43	70	95
	44	72	60
	45	74	25
	46	75	90
	47	77	55
4	48	79	20
	49	80	85
	50	82	50

Dozens		£	P
	51	84	15
	52	85	80
	53	87	45
	54	89	10
	55	90	75
	56	92	40
	57	94	5
	58	95	70
	59	97	35
5	**60**	99	0
	61	100	65
	62	102	30
	63	103	95
	64	105	60
	65	107	25
	66	108	90
	67	110	55
	68	112	20
	69	113	85
	70	115	50
	71	117	15
6	72	118	80
	75	123	75
	80	132	0
7	84	138	60
	90	148	50
8	96	158	40
	100	165	0
10	120	198	0
	140	231	0
	150	247	50
	160	264	0
	180	297	0
	200	330	0
25	300	495	0
	365	602	25
	400	660	0
	500	825	0
	600	990	0
	700	1155	0
	800	1320	0
	900	1485	0
	1000	1650	0

Twelfths

	1. 0 13¾		7. 0 96¼
⅙	2. 0 27½	⅔	8. 1 10
	3. 0 41¼		9. 1 23¾
⅓	4. 0 55	⅚	10. 1 37½
	5. 0 68¾		11. 1 51¼
½	6. 0 82½		

Sixteenths

	1. 0 10¼		9. 0 92¾
⅛	2. 0 20¾	⅝	10. 1 3¼
	3. 0 31		11. 1 13½
¼	4. 0 41¼	¾	12. 1 23¾
	5. 0 51½		13. 1 34
⅜	6. 0 62	⅞	14. 1 44¼
	7. 0 72¼		15. 1 54¾
½	8. 0 82½		

Twentieths

10ths			
	1. 0 8¼		11. 0 90¾
·1	2. 0 16½	·6	12. 0 99
	3. 0 24¾		13. 1 7¼
·2	4. 0 33	·7	14. 1 15½
	5 0 41¼		15. 1 23¾
·3	6. 0 49½	·8	16. 1 32
	7. 0 57¾		17. 1 40¼
·4	8. 0 66	·9	18. 1 48½
	9. 0 74¼		19 1 56¾
·5	10. 0 82½		20. 1 65

£ 1·66

*Dozens		£	p
	1	1	66
	2	3	32
	3	4	98
	4	6	64
	5	8	30
	6	9	96
	7	11	62
	8	13	28
	9	14	94
	10	16	60
	11	18	26
1	12	19	92
	13	21	58
	14	23	24
	15	24	90
	16	26	56
	17	28	22
	18	29	88
	19	31	54
	20	33	20
	21	34	86
	22	36	52
	23	38	18
2	24	39	84
	25	41	50
	26	43	16
	27	44	82
	28	46	48
	29	48	14
	30	49	80
	31	51	46
	32	53	12
	33	54	78
	34	56	44
	35	58	10
3	36	59	76
	37	61	42
	38	63	8
	39	64	74
	40	66	40
	41	68	6
	42	69	72
	43	71	38
	44	73	4
	45	74	70
	46	76	36
	47	78	2
4	48	79	68
	49	81	34
	50	83	0

Dozens		£	p
	51	84	66
	52	86	32
	53	87	98
	54	89	64
	55	91	30
	56	92	96
	57	94	62
	58	96	28
	59	97	94
5	**60**	99	60
	61	101	26
	62	102	92
	63	104	58
	64	106	24
	65	107	90
	66	109	56
	67	111	22
	68	112	88
	69	114	54
	70	116	20
	71	117	86
6	72	119	52
	75	124	50
	80	132	80
7	84	139	44
	90	149	40
8	96	159	36
	100	166	0
10	120	199	20
	140	232	40
	150	249	0
	160	265	60
	180	298	80
	200	332	0
25	300	498	0
	365	605	90
	400	664	0
	500	830	0
	600	996	0
	700	1162	0
	800	1328	0
	900	1494	0
	1000	1660	0

Twelfths

	1.	0 13¾		7.	0 96¾
1/6	2.	0 27¾	2/3	8.	1 10¾
	3.	0 41½		9.	1 24½
1/3	4.	0 55¼	5/6	10.	1 38¼
	5.	0 69¼		11.	1 52¼
1/2	6.	0 83			

Sixteenths

	1.	0 10½		9.	0 93½
1/8	2.	0 20¾	5/8	10.	1 3¾
	3.	0 31¼		11.	1 14¼
1/4	4.	0 41½	3/4	12.	1 24½
	5.	0 52		13.	1 35
3/8	6.	0 62¼	7/8	14.	1 45¼
	7.	0 72¾		15.	1 55¾
	8.	0 83			

Twentieths

10ths			10ths		
	1.	0 8¼		11.	0 91¼
·1	2.	0 16½	·6	12	0 99¾
	3.	0 25		13.	1 8
·2	4.	0 33¼	·7	14.	1 16¼
	5.	0 41½		15.	1 24½
·3	6.	0 49¾	·8	16.	1 32¾
	7.	0 58		17.	1 41
·4	8.	0 66¼	·9	18.	1 49¼
	9.	0 74¾		19.	1 57¾
·5	10.	0 83		20.	1 66

£ 1·67

*Dozens		£	p
	1	1	67
	2	3	34
	3	5	1
	4	6	68
	5	8	35
	6	10	2
	7	11	69
	8	13	36
	9	15	3
	10	16	70
	11	18	37
1	12	20	4
	13	21	71
	14	23	38
	15	25	5
	16	26	72
	17	28	39
	18	30	6
	19	31	73
	20	33	40
	21	35	7
	22	36	74
	23	38	41
2	24	40	8
	25	41	75
	26	43	42
	27	45	9
	28	46	76
	29	48	43
	30	50	10
	31	51	77
	32	53	44
	33	55	11
	34	56	78
	35	58	45
3	36	60	12
	37	61	79
	38	63	46
	39	65	13
	40	66	80
	41	68	47
	42	70	14
	43	71	81
	44	73	48
	45	75	15
	46	76	82
	47	78	49
4	48	80	16
	49	81	83
	50	83	50

Dozens		£	p
	51	85	17
	52	86	84
	53	88	51
	54	90	18
	55	91	85
	56	93	52
	57	95	19
	58	96	86
	59	98	53
5	**60**	100	20
	61	101	87
	62	103	54
	63	105	21
	64	106	88
	65	108	55
	66	110	22
	67	111	89
	68	113	56
	69	115	23
	70	116	90
	71	118	57
6	72	120	24
	75	125	25
	80	133	60
7	84	140	28
	90	150	30
8	96	160	32
	100	167	0
10	120	200	40
	140	233	80
	150	250	50
	160	267	20
	180	300	60
	200	334	0
25	300	501	0
	365	609	55
	400	668	0
	500	835	0
	600	1002	0
	700	1169	0
	800	1336	0
	900	1503	0
	1000	1670	0

Twelfths

	1.	0 14		7.	0 97½
1/6	2.	0 27¾	2/3	8.	1 11¼
	3.	0 41¾		9.	1 25¼
1/3	4.	0 55¾	5/6	10.	1 39¼
	5.	0 69½		11.	1 53
1/2	6.	0 83½			

Sixteenths

	1.	0 10½		9.	0 94
1/8	2.	0 21	5/8	10.	1 4½
	3.	0 31¼		11.	1 14¾
1/4	4.	0 41¾	3/4	12.	1 25¼
	5.	0 52¼		13.	1 35¾
3/8	6.	0 62¾	7/8	14.	1 46¼
	7.	0 73		15.	1 56½
1/2	8.	0 83½			

Twentieths

10ths			10ths		
	1.	0 8¼		11.	0 91¾
·1	2.	0 16¾	·6	12.	1 0¼
	3.	0 25		13.	1 8½
·2	4.	0 33½	·7	14.	1 17
	5	0 41¾		15.	1 25¼
·3	6.	0 50	·8	16.	1 33½
	7.	0 58½		17.	1 42
·4	8.	0 66¾	·9	18.	1 50¼
	9.	0 75¼		19	1 58¾
·5	10.	0 83½		20.	1 67

£ 1·68

*Dozens		£	P
	1	1	68
	2	3	36
	3	5	4
	4	6	72
	5	8	40
	6	10	8
	7	11	76
	8	13	44
	9	15	12
	10	16	80
	11	18	48
1	12	20	16
	13	21	84
	14	23	52
	15	25	20
	16	26	88
	17	28	56
	18	30	24
	19	31	92
	20	33	60
	21	35	28
	22	36	96
	23	38	64
2	24	40	32
	25	42	0
	26	43	68
	27	45	36
	28	47	4
	29	48	72
	30	50	40
	31	52	8
	32	53	76
	33	55	44
	34	57	12
	35	58	80
3	36	60	48
	37	62	16
	38	63	84
	39	65	52
	40	67	20
	41	68	88
	42	70	56
	43	72	24
	44	73	92
	45	75	60
	46	77	28
	47	78	96
4	48	80	64
	49	82	32
	50	84	0

Dozens		£	P
	51	85	68
	52	87	36
	53	89	4
	54	90	72
	55	92	40
	56	94	8
	57	95	76
	58	97	44
	59	99	12
5	**60**	100	80
	61	102	48
	62	104	16
	63	105	84
	64	107	52
	65	109	20
	66	110	88
	67	112	56
	68	114	24
	69	115	92
	70	117	60
	71	119	28
6	72	120	96
	75	126	0
	80	134	40
7	84	141	12
	90	151	20
8	96	161	28
	100	168	0
10	120	201	60
	140	235	20
	150	252	0
	160	268	80
	180	302	40
	200	336	0
25	300	504	0
	365	613	20
	400	672	0
	500	840	0
	600	1008	0
	700	1176	0
	800	1344	0
	900	1512	0
	1000	1680	0

Twelfths

	1.	0	14		7.	0	98
1/6	2.	0	28	2/3	8.	1	12
	3.	0	42		9.	1	26
1/3	4.	0	56	5/6	10.	1	40
	5.	0	70		11.	1	54
½	6.	0	84				

Sixteenths

	1.	0	10½		9.	0	94½
⅛	2.	0	21	⅝	10.	1	5
	3.	0	31½		11.	1	15½
¼	4.	0	42	¾	12.	1	26
	5.	0	52½		13.	1	36½
⅜	6.	0	63	⅞	14.	1	47
	7.	0	73½		15.	1	57½
	8.	0	84				

Twentieths

10ths				10ths			
	1.	0	8½		11.	0	92½
·1	2.	0	16¾	·6	12	1	0¾
	3.	0	25¼		13.	1	9¼
·2	4.	0	33½	·7	14.	1	17½
	5.	0	42		15.	1	26
·3	6.	0	50½	·8	16.	1	34½
	7.	0	58¾		17.	1	42¾
·4	8.	0	67¼	·9	18.	1	51¼
	9.	0	75½		19.	1	59½
·5	10.	0	84		20.	1	68

£ 1·69

*Dozens		£	P
	1	1	69
	2	3	38
	3	5	7
	4	6	76
	5	8	45
	6	10	14
	7	11	83
	8	13	52
	9	15	21
	10	16	90
	11	18	59
1	12	20	28
	13	21	97
	14	23	66
	15	25	35
	16	27	4
	17	28	73
	18	30	42
	19	32	11
	20	33	80
	21	35	49
	22	37	18
	23	38	87
2	24	40	56
	25	42	25
	26	43	94
	27	45	63
	28	47	32
	29	49	1
	30	50	70
	31	52	39
	32	54	8
	33	55	77
	34	57	46
	35	59	15
3	36	60	84
	37	62	53
	38	64	22
	39	65	91
	40	67	60
	41	69	29
	42	70	98
	43	72	67
	44	74	36
	45	76	5
	46	77	74
	47	79	43
4	48	81	12
	49	82	81
	50	84	50

Dozens		£	P
	51	86	19
	52	87	88
	53	89	57
	54	91	26
	55	92	95
	56	94	64
	57	96	33
	58	98	2
	59	99	71
5	**60**	101	40
	61	103	9
	62	104	78
	63	106	47
	64	108	16
	65	109	85
	66	111	54
	67	113	23
	68	114	92
	69	116	61
	70	118	30
	71	119	99
6	72	121	68
	75	126	75
	80	135	20
7	84	141	96
	90	152	10
8	96	162	24
	100	169	0
10	120	202	80
	140	236	60
	150	253	50
	160	270	40
	180	304	20
	200	338	0
25	300	507	0
	365	616	85
	400	676	0
	500	845	0
	600	1014	0
	700	1183	0
	800	1352	0
	900	1521	0
	1000	1690	0

Twelfths

	1.	0	14		7.	0	98½
1/6	2.	0	28¼	2/3	8.	1	12¾
	3.	0	42¼		9.	1	26¾
1/3	4.	0	56¼	5/6	10.	1	40¾
	5.	0	70½		11.	1	55
½	6.	0	84½				

Sixteenths

	1.	0	10½		9.	0	95
⅛	2.	0	21¼	⅝	10.	1	5¾
	3.	0	31¾		11.	1	16¼
¼	4.	0	42¼	¾	12.	1	26¾
	5.	0	52¾		13.	1	37¼
⅜	6.	0	63½	⅞	14.	1	48
	7.	0	74		15.	1	58½
½	8.	0	84½				

Twentieths

10ths				10ths			
	1.	0	8½		11.	0	93
·1	2.	0	17	·6	12.	1	1½
	3.	0	25¼		13.	1	9¾
·2	4.	0	33¾	·7	14.	1	18¼
	5	0	42¼		15.	1	26¾
·3	6.	0	50¾	·8	16.	1	35¼
	7.	0	59¼		17.	1	43¾
·4	8.	0	67½	·9	18.	1	52
	9.	0	76		19	1	60½
·5	10.	0	84½		20.	1	69

£ 1·70

*Dozens

		£	P			£	P
	1	1	70		51	86	70
	2	3	40		52	88	40
	3	5	10		53	90	10
	4	6	80		54	91	80
	5	8	50		55	93	50
	6	10	20		56	95	20
	7	11	90		57	96	90
	8	13	60		58	98	60
	9	15	30		59	100	30
	10	17	0	5	**60**	102	0
	11	18	70		61	103	70
†1	12	20	40		62	105	40
	13	22	10		63	107	10
	14	23	80		64	108	80
	15	25	50		65	110	50
	16	27	20		66	112	20
	17	28	90		67	113	90
	18	30	60		68	115	60
	19	32	30		69	117	30
	20	34	0		**70**	119	0
	21	35	70		71	120	70
	22	37	40	6	72	122	40
	23	39	10		75	127	50
2	24	40	80		80	136	0
	25	42	50	7	84	142	80
	26	44	20		90	153	0
	27	45	90	8	96	163	20
	28	47	60		100	170	0
	29	49	30	10	120	204	0
	30	51	0		140	238	0
	31	52	70		150	255	0
	32	54	40		160	272	0
	33	56	10		180	306	0
	34	57	80		200	340	0
	35	59	50	25	300	510	0
3	36	61	20		365	620	50
	37	62	90		400	680	0
	38	64	60		500	850	0
	39	66	30		600	1020	0
	40	68	0		700	1190	0
	41	69	70		800	1360	0
	42	71	40		900	1530	0
	43	73	10		1000	1700	0
	44	74	80				
	45	76	50				
	46	78	20				
	47	79	90				
4	48	81	60				
	49	83	30				
	50	85	0				

Twelfths

1. 0 14¼		7. 0 99¼
⅙2. 0 28¼	⅔	8. 1 13¼
3. 0 42½		9. 1 27½
⅓4. 0 56¾	⅚	10. 1 41¾
5. 0 70¾		11. 1 55¾
½6. 0 85		

Sixteenths

1. 0 10¾	9. 0 95¾
⅛2. 0 21¼	⅝10. 1 6¼
3. 0 32	11. 1 17
¼4. 0 42½	¾12. 1 27½
5. 0 53¼	13. 1 38¼
⅜6. 0 63¾	⅞14. 1 48¾
7. 0 74½	15. 1 59½
8. 0 85	

Twentieths (10ths)

	1. 0 8½		11. 0 93½
·1	2. 0 17	·6	12. 1 2
	3. 0 25½		13. 1 10½
·2	4. 0 34	·7	14. 1 19
	5. 0 42½		15. 1 27½
·3	6. 0 51	·8	16. 1 36
	7. 0 59½		17. 1 44½
·4	8. 0 68	·9	18. 1 53
	9. 0 76½		19. 1 61½
·5	10. 0 85		20. 1 70

£ 1·71

*Dozens

		£	P			£	P
	1	1	71		51	87	21
	2	3	42		52	88	92
	3	5	13		53	90	63
	4	6	84		54	92	34
	5	8	55		55	94	5
	6	10	26		56	95	76
	7	11	97		57	97	47
	8	13	68		58	99	18
	9	15	39		59	100	89
	10	17	10	5	**60**	102	60
	11	18	81		61	104	31
1	12	20	52		62	106	2
	13	22	23		63	107	73
	14	23	94		64	109	44
	15	25	65		65	111	15
	16	27	36		66	112	86
	17	29	7		67	114	57
	18	30	78		68	116	28
	19	32	49		69	117	99
	20	34	20		**70**	119	70
	21	35	91		71	121	41
	22	37	62	6	72	123	12
	23	39	33		75	128	25
2	24	41	4		80	136	80
	25	42	75	7	84	143	64
	26	44	46		90	153	90
	27	46	17	8	96	164	16
	28	47	88		100	171	0
	29	49	59	10	120	205	20
	30	51	30		140	239	40
	31	53	1		150	256	50
	32	54	72		160	273	60
	33	56	43		180	307	80
	34	58	14		200	342	0
	35	59	85	25	300	513	0
3	36	61	56		365	624	15
	37	63	27		400	684	0
	38	64	98		500	855	0
	39	66	69		600	1026	0
	40	68	40		700	1197	0
	41	70	11		800	1368	0
	42	71	82		900	1539	0
	43	73	53		1000	1710	0
	44	75	24				
	45	76	95				
	46	78	66				
	47	80	37				
4	48	82	8				
	49	83	79				
	50	85	50				

Twelfths

1. 0 14¼		7. 0 99¾
⅙2. 0 28½	⅔	8. 1 14
3. 0 42¾		9. 1 28¼
⅓4. 0 57	⅚	10. 1 42½
5. 0 71¼		11. 1 56¾
½6. 0 85½		

Sixteenths

1. 0 10¾	9. 0 96¼
⅛2. 0 21¼	⅝10. 1 7
3. 0 32	11. 1 17½
¼4. 0 42¾	¾12. 1 28¼
5. 0 53½	13. 1 39
⅜6. 0 64¼	⅞14. 1 49½
7. 0 74¾	15. 1 60¼
½8. 0 85½	

Twentieths (10ths)

	1. 0 8½		11. 0 94
·1	2. 0 17	·6	12. 1 2½
	3. 0 25¾		13. 1 11
·2	4. 0 34¼	·7	14. 1 19¾
	5 0 42¾		15. 1 28¼
·3	6. 0 51¼	·8	16. 1 36¾
	7. 0 59¾		17. 1 45¼
·4	8. 0 68½	·9	18. 1 54
	9. 0 77		19 1 62½
·5	10. 0 85½		20. 1 71

£ 1·72

*Dozens

	£	P	Dozens	£	P
1	1	72	51	87	72
2	3	44	52	89	44
3	5	16	53	91	16
4	6	88	54	92	88
5	8	60	55	94	60
6	10	32	56	96	32
7	12	4	57	98	4
8	13	76	58	99	76
9	15	48	59	101	48
10	17	20	[5] **60**	103	20
11	18	92	61	104	92
*1 12	20	64	62	106	64
13	22	36	63	108	36
14	24	8	64	110	8
15	25	80	65	111	80
16	27	52	66	113	52
17	29	24	67	115	24
18	30	96	68	116	96
19	32	68	69	118	68
20	34	40	**70**	120	40
21	36	12	71	122	12
22	37	84	[6] 72	123	84
23	39	56	75	129	0
[2] 24	41	28	80	137	60
25	43	0	[7] 84	144	48
26	44	72	90	154	80
27	46	44	[8] 96	165	12
28	48	16	100	172	0
29	49	88	[10] 120	206	40
30	51	60	140	240	80
31	53	32	150	258	0
32	55	4	160	275	20
33	56	76	180	309	60
34	58	48	200	344	0
35	60	20	[25] 300	516	0
[3] 36	61	92	365	627	80
37	63	64	400	688	0
38	65	36	500	860	0
39	67	8	600	1032	0
40	68	80	700	1204	0
41	70	52	800	1376	0
42	72	24	900	1548	0
43	73	96	1000	1720	0
44	75	68			
45	77	40			
46	79	12			
47	80	84			
[4] 48	82	56			
49	84	28			
50	86	0			

Twelfths

1.	0 14¼	7.	1 0¼
⅙ 2.	0 28¾	⅔ 8.	1 14¾
3.	0 43	9.	1 29
⅓ 4.	0 57¼	⅚ 10.	1 43¼
5.	0 71¾	11.	1 57¾
½ 6.	0 86		

Sixteenths

1.	0 10¾	9.	0 96¾
⅛ 2.	0 21½	⅝ 10.	1 7½
3.	0 32¼	11.	1 18¼
¼ 4.	0 43	¾ 12.	1 29
5.	0 53¾	13.	1 39¾
⅜ 6.	0 64½	⅞ 14.	1 50½
7.	0 75¼	15.	1 61¼
8.	0 86		

Twentieths (10ths)

10ths			10ths		
	1.	0 8½		11.	0 94½
·1	2.	0 17¼	·6	12.	1 3¼
	3.	0 25¾		13.	1 11¾
·2	4.	0 34½	·7	14.	1 20½
	5.	0 43		15.	1 29
·3	6.	0 51½	·8	16.	1 37½
	7.	0 60¼		17.	1 46¼
·4	8.	0 68¾	·9	18.	1 54¾
	9.	0 77½		19.	1 63½
·5	10.	0 86		20.	1 72

£ 1·73

*Dozens

	£	P	Dozens	£	P
1	1	73	51	88	23
2	3	46	52	89	96
3	5	19	53	91	69
4	6	92	54	93	42
5	8	65	55	95	15
6	10	38	56	96	88
7	12	11	57	98	61
8	13	84	58	100	34
9	15	57	59	102	7
10	17	30	[5] **60**	103	80
11	19	3	61	105	53
[1] 12	20	76	62	107	26
13	22	49	63	108	99
14	24	22	64	110	72
15	25	95	65	112	45
16	27	68	66	114	18
17	29	41	67	115	91
18	31	14	68	117	64
19	32	87	69	119	37
20	34	60	**70**	121	10
21	36	33	71	122	83
22	38	6	[6] 72	124	56
23	39	79	75	129	75
[2] 24	41	52	80	138	40
25	43	25	[7] 84	145	32
26	44	98	90	155	70
27	46	71	[8] 96	166	8
28	48	44	100	173	0
29	50	17	[10] 120	207	60
30	51	90	140	242	20
31	53	63	150	259	50
32	55	36	160	276	80
33	57	9	180	311	40
34	58	82	200	346	0
35	60	55	[25] 300	519	0
[3] 36	62	28	365	631	45
37	64	1	400	692	0
38	65	74	500	865	0
39	67	47	600	1038	0
40	69	20	700	1211	0
41	70	93	800	1384	0
42	72	66	900	1557	0
43	74	39	1000	1730	0
44	76	12			
45	77	85			
46	79	58			
47	81	31			
[4] 48	83	4			
49	84	77			
50	86	50			

Twelfths

1.	0 14½	7.	1 1
⅙ 2.	0 28¾	⅔ 8.	1 15¼
3.	0 43¼	9.	1 29¾
⅓ 4.	0 57¾	⅚ 10.	1 44¼
5.	0 72'	11.	1 58½
½ 6.	0 86½		

Sixteenths

1.	0 10¾	9.	0 97¼
⅛ 2.	0 21¾	⅝ 10.	1 8¼
3.	0 32½	11.	1 19
¼ 4.	0 43¼	¾ 12.	1 29¾
5.	0 54	13.	1 40½
⅜ 6.	0 65	⅞ 14.	1 51½
7.	0 75¾	15.	1 62¼
½ 8.	0 86½		

Twentieths (10ths)

10ths			10ths		
	1.	0 8¾		11.	0 95¼
·1	2.	0 17¼	·6	12.	1 3¾
	3.	0 26		13.	1 12
·2	4.	0 34½	·7	14.	1 21½
	5	0 43¼		15.	1 29
·3	6.	0 52	·8	16.	1 38½
	7.	0 60½		17.	1 47½
·4	8.	0 69¼	·9	18.	1 55
	9.	0 77¾		19	1 64¼
·5	10.	0 86½		20.	1 73½

£ 1·74

*Dozens		£	P	Dozens		£	P
	1	1	74		51	88	74
	2	3	48		52	90	48
	3	5	22		53	92	22
	4	6	96		54	93	96
	5	8	70		55	95	70
	6	10	44		56	97	44
	7	12	18		57	99	18
	8	13	92		58	100	92
	9	15	66		59	102	66
	10	17	40	5	**60**	104	40
*	11	19	14		61	106	14
1	12	20	88		62	107	88
	13	22	62		63	109	62
	14	24	36		64	111	36
	15	26	10		65	113	10
	16	27	84		66	114	84
	17	29	58		67	116	58
	18	31	32		68	118	32
	19	33	6		69	120	6
	20	34	80		**70**	121	80
	21	36	54		71	123	54
	22	38	28	6	72	125	28
	23	40	2		75	130	50
2	24	41	76		80	139	20
	25	43	50	7	84	146	16
	26	45	24		90	156	60
	27	46	98	8	96	167	4
	28	48	72		**100**	174	0
	29	50	46	10	120	208	80
	30	52	20		140	243	60
	31	53	94		150	261	0
	32	55	68		160	278	40
	33	57	42		180	313	20
	34	59	16		200	348	0
	35	60	90	25	300	522	0
3	36	62	64		365	635	10
	37	64	38		400	696	0
	38	66	12		500	870	0
	39	67	86		600	1044	0
	40	69	60		700	1218	0
	41	71	34		800	1392	0
	42	73	8		900	1566	0
	43	74	82		**1000**	**1740**	**0**
	44	76	56				
	45	78	30				
	46	80	4				
	47	81	78				
4	48	83	52				
	49	85	26				
	50	87	0				

Twelfths

	1. 0 14½		7. 1 1½
⅙	2. 0 29	⅔	8. 1 16
	3. 0 43½		9. 1 30½
⅓	4. 0 58	⅚	10. 1 45
	5. 0 72½		11. 1 59½
½	6. 0 87		

Sixteenths

	1. 0 11		9. 0 98
⅛	2. 0 21¾	⅝	10. 1 8¾
	3. 0 32¾		11. 1 19¾
¼	4. 0 43½	¾	12. 1 30½
	5. 0 54½		13. 1 41½
⅜	6. 0 65¼	⅞	14. 1 52¼
	7. 0 76¼		15. 1 63¼
	8. 0 87		

Twentieths

10ths			
	1. 0 8¾		11. 0 95¾
·1	2. 0 17½	·6	12. 1 4½
	3. 0 26		13. 1 13
·2	4. 0 34¾	·7	14. 1 21¾
	5. 0 43½		15. 1 30½
·3	6. 0 52¼	·8	16. 1 39¼
	7. 0 61		17. 1 48
·4	8. 0 69½	·9	18. 1 56½
	9. 0 78¼		19. 1 65¼
·5	10. 0 87		20. 1 74

£ 1·75

*Dozens		£	P	Dozens		£	P
	1	1	75		51	89	25
	2	3	50		52	91	0
	3	5	25		53	92	75
	4	7	0		54	94	50
	5	8	75		55	96	25
	6	10	50		56	98	0
	7	12	25		57	99	75
	8	14	0		58	101	50
	9	15	75		59	103	25
	10	17	50	5	**60**	105	0
	11	19	25		61	106	75
1	12	21	0		62	108	50
	13	22	75		63	110	25
	14	24	50		64	112	0
	15	26	25		65	113	75
	16	28	0		66	115	50
	17	29	75		67	117	25
	18	31	50		68	119	0
	19	33	25		69	120	75
	20	35	0		**70**	122	50
	21	36	75		71	124	25
	22	38	50	6	72	126	0
	23	40	25		75	131	25
2	24	42	0		80	140	0
	25	43	75	7	84	147	0
	26	45	50		90	157	50
	27	47	25	8	96	168	0
	28	49	0		**100**	175	0
	29	50	75	10	120	210	0
	30	52	50		140	245	0
	31	54	25		150	262	50
	32	56	0		160	280	0
	33	57	75		180	315	0
	34	59	50		200	350	0
	35	61	25	25	300	525	0
3	36	63	0		365	638	75
	37	64	75		400	700	0
	38	66	50		500	875	0
	39	68	25		600	1050	0
	40	70	0		700	1225	0
	41	71	75		800	1400	0
	42	73	50		900	1575	0
	43	75	25		**1000**	**1750**	**0**
	44	77	0				
	45	78	75				
	46	80	50				
	47	82	25				
4	48	84	0				
	49	85	75				
	50	87	50				

Twelfths

	1. 0 14½		7. 1 2
⅙	2. 0 29¼	⅔	8. 1 16¾
	3. 0 43¾		9. 1 31¼
⅓	4. 0 58¼	⅚	10. 1 45¾
	5. 0 73		11. 1 60½
½	6. 0 87½		

Sixteenths

	1. 0 11		9. 0 98½
⅛	2. 0 22	⅝	10. 1 9½
	3. 0 32¾		11. 1 20¼
¼	4. 0 43¾	¾	12. 1 31¼
	5. 0 54¾		13. 1 42¼
⅜	6. 0 65¾	⅞	14. 1 53¼
	7. 0 76½		15. 1 64
½	8. 0 87½		

Twentieths

10ths			
	1. 0 8¾		11. 0 96¼
·1	2. 0 17½	·6	12. 1 5
	3. 0 26¼		13. 1 13¾
·2	4. 0 35	·7	14. 1 22½
	5 0 43¾		15. 1 31¼
·3	6. 0 52½	·8	16. 1 40
	7. 0 61¼		17. 1 48¾
·4	8. 0 70	·9	18. 1 57½
	9. 0 78¾		19 1 66¼
·5	10. 0 87½		20. 1 75

£ 1·76

*Dozens		£	P	Dozens		£	P
	1	1	76		51	89	76
	2	3	52		52	91	52
	3	5	28		53	93	28
	4	7	4		54	95	4
	5	8	80		55	96	80
	6	10	56		56	98	56
	7	12	32		57	100	32
	8	14	8		58	102	8
	9	15	84		59	103	84
	10	17	60	5	**60**	105	60
	11	19	36		61	107	36
*1	12	21	12		62	109	12
	13	22	88		63	110	88
	14	24	64		64	112	64
	15	26	40		65	114	40
	16	28	16		66	116	16
	17	29	92		67	117	92
	18	31	68		68	119	68
	19	33	44		69	121	44
	20	35	20		**70**	123	20
	21	36	96		71	124	96
	22	38	72	6	72	126	72
	23	40	48		75	132	0
2	24	42	24		80	140	80
	25	44	0	7	84	147	84
	26	45	76		90	158	40
	27	47	52	8	96	168	96
	28	49	28		100	176	0
	29	51	4	10	120	211	20
	30	52	80		140	246	40
	31	54	56		150	264	0
	32	56	32		160	281	60
	33	58	8		180	316	80
	34	59	84		200	352	0
	35	61	60	25	300	528	0
3	36	63	36		365	642	40
	37	65	12		400	704	0
	38	66	88		500	880	0
	39	68	64		600	1056	0
	40	70	40		700	1232	0
	41	72	16		800	1408	0
	42	73	92		900	1584	0
	43	75	68		1000	1760	0
	44	77	44				
	45	79	20				
	46	80	96				
	47	82	72				
4	48	84	48				
	49	86	24				
	50	88	0				

Twelfths

1.	0 14⅔	7.	1 2⅔
⅙ 2.	0 29⅓	⅔ 8.	1 17⅓
3.	0 44	9.	1 32
⅓ 4.	0 58⅔	⅚ 10.	1 46⅔
5.	0 73⅓	11.	1 61⅓
½ 6.	0 88		

Sixteenths

1.	0 11	9.	0 99
⅛ 2.	0 22	⅝ 10.	1 10
3.	0 33	11.	1 21
¼ 4.	0 44	¾ 12.	1 32
5.	0 55	13.	1 43
⅜ 6.	0 66	⅞ 14.	1 54
7.	0 77	15.	1 65
8.	0 88		

Twentieths

10ths					
	1.	0 8¾		11.	0 96¾
·1	2.	0 17½	·6	12.	1 5½
	3.	0 26½		13.	1 14½
·2	4.	0 35¼	·7	14.	1 23¼
	5.	0 44		15.	1 32
·3	6.	0 52¾	·8	16.	1 40¾
	7.	0 61½		17.	1 49½
·4	8.	0 70½	·9	18.	1 58½
	9.	0 79¼		19.	1 67¼
·5	10.	0 88		20.	1 76

£ 1·77

*Dozens		£	P	Dozens		£	P
	1	1	77		51	90	27
	2	3	54		52	92	4
	3	5	31		53	93	81
	4	7	8		54	95	58
	5	8	85		55	97	35
	6	10	62		56	99	12
	7	12	39		57	100	89
	8	14	16		58	102	66
	9	15	93		59	104	43
	10	17	70	5	**60**	106	20
	11	19	47		61	107	97
1	12	21	24		62	109	74
	13	23	1		63	111	51
	14	24	78		64	113	28
	15	26	55		65	115	5
	16	28	32		66	116	82
	17	30	9		67	118	59
	18	31	86		68	120	36
	19	33	63		69	122	13
	20	35	40		**70**	123	90
	21	37	17		71	125	67
	22	38	94	6	72	127	44
	23	40	71		75	132	75
2	24	42	48		80	141	60
	25	44	25	7	84	148	68
	26	46	2		90	159	30
	27	47	79	8	96	169	92
	28	49	56		100	177	0
	29	51	33	10	120	212	40
	30	53	10		140	247	80
	31	54	87		150	265	50
	32	56	64		160	283	20
	33	58	41		180	318	60
	34	60	18		200	354	0
	35	61	95	25	300	531	0
3	36	63	72		365	646	5
	37	65	49		400	708	0
	38	67	26		500	885	0
	39	69	3		600	1062	0
	40	70	80		700	1239	0
	41	72	57		800	1416	0
	42	74	34		900	1593	0
	43	76	11		1000	1770	0
	44	77	88				
	45	79	65				
	46	81	42				
	47	83	19				
4	48	84	96				
	49	86	73				
	50	88	50				

Twelfths

1.	0 14¾	7.	1 3¼
⅙ 2.	0 29½	⅔ 8.	1 18
3.	0 44¼	9.	1 32¾
⅓ 4.	0 59	⅚ 10.	1 47½
5.	0 73¾	11.	1 62¼
½ 6.	0 88½		

Sixteenths

1.	0 11	9.	0 99½
⅛ 2.	0 22¼	⅝ 10.	1 10¾
3.	0 33¼	11.	1 21¾
¼ 4.	0 44¼	¾ 12.	1 32¾
5.	0 55¼	13.	1 43¾
⅜ 6.	0 66½	⅞ 14.	1 55
7.	0 77½	15.	1 66
½ 8.	0 88½		

Twentieths

10ths					
	1.	0 8¾		11.	0 97¼
·1	2.	0 17¾	·6	12.	1 6¼
	3.	0 26½		13.	1 15
·2	4.	0 35½	·7	14.	1 24
	5	0 44¼		15.	1 32¾
·3	6.	0 53	·8	16.	1 41½
	7.	0 62		17.	1 50½
·4	8.	0 70¾	·9	18.	1 59¼
	9.	0 79¾		19	1 68¼
·5	10.	0 88½		20.	1 77

£ 1·78

		£	P
	1	1	78
*Dozens	2	3	56
	3	5	34
	4	7	12
	5	8	90
	6	10	68
	7	12	46
	8	14	24
	9	16	2
	10	17	80
	11	19	58
*1	12	21	36
	13	23	14
	14	24	92
	15	26	70
	16	28	48
	17	30	26
	18	32	4
	19	33	82
	20	35	60
	21	37	38
	22	39	16
	23	40	94
2	24	42	72
	25	44	50
	26	46	28
	27	48	6
	28	49	84
	29	51	62
	30	53	40
	31	55	18
	32	56	96
	33	58	74
	34	60	52
	35	62	30
3	36	64	8
	37	65	86
	38	67	64
	39	69	42
	40	71	20
	41	72	98
	42	74	76
	43	76	54
	44	78	32
	45	80	10
	46	81	88
	47	83	66
4	48	85	44
	49	87	22
	50	89	0

Dozens		£	P
	51	90	78
	52	92	56
	53	94	34
	54	96	12
	55	97	90
	56	99	68
	57	101	46
	58	103	24
	59	105	2
5	**60**	106	80
	61	108	58
	62	110	36
	63	112	14
	64	113	92
	65	115	70
	66	117	48
	67	119	26
	68	121	4
	69	122	82
	70	124	60
	71	126	38
6	72	128	16
	75	133	50
	80	142	40
7	84	149	52
	90	160	20
8	96	170	88
	100	178	0
10	120	213	60
	140	249	20
	150	267	0
	160	284	80
	180	320	40
	200	356	0
25	300	534	0
	365	649	70
	400	712	0
	500	890	0
	600	1068	0
	700	1246	0
	800	1424	0
	900	1602	0
	1000	1780	0

Twelfths

	1.	0 14¾		7.	1 3¾
⅙	2.	0 29¾	⅔	8.	1 18¾
	3.	0 44½		9.	1 33½
⅓	4.	0 59¼	⅚	10.	1 48¼
	5.	0 74¼		11.	1 63¼
½	6.	0 89			

Sixteenths

	1.	0 11¼		9.	1 0¼
⅛	2.	0 22¼	⅝	10.	1 11¼
	3.	0 33½		11.	1 22½
¼	4.	0 44½	¾	12.	1 33½
	5.	0 55¾		13.	1 44¾
⅜	6.	0 66¾	⅞	14.	1 55¾
	7.	0 78		15.	1 67
	8.	0 89			

Twentieths

10ths					
	1.	0 9		11.	0 79
·1	2.	0 17¾	·6	12.	1 6¾
	3.	0 26¾		13.	1 15¾
·2	4.	0 35½	·7	14.	1 24½
	5.	0 44½		15.	1 33½
·3	6.	0 53½	·8	16.	1 42½
	7.	0 62¼		17.	1 51¼
·4	8.	0 71¼	·9	18.	1 60¼
	9.	0 80		19.	1 69
·5	10.	0 89		20.	1 78

£ 1·79

		£	P
	1	1	79
*Dozens	2	3	58
	3	5	37
	4	7	16
	5	8	95
	6	10	74
	7	12	53
	8	14	32
	9	16	11
	10	17	90
	11	19	69
1	12	21	48
	13	23	27
	14	25	6
	15	26	85
	16	28	64
	17	30	43
	18	32	22
	19	34	1
	20	35	80
	21	37	59
	22	39	38
	23	41	17
2	24	42	96
	25	44	75
	26	46	54
	27	48	33
	28	50	12
	29	51	91
	30	53	70
	31	55	49
	32	57	28
	33	59	7
	34	60	86
	35	62	65
3	36	64	44
	37	66	23
	38	68	2
	39	69	81
	40	71	60
	41	73	39
	42	75	18
	43	76	97
	44	78	76
	45	80	55
	46	82	34
	47	84	13
4	48	85	92
	49	87	71
	50	89	50

Dozens		£	P
	51	91	29
	52	93	8
	53	94	87
	54	96	66
	55	98	45
	56	100	24
	57	102	3
	58	103	82
	59	105	61
5	**60**	107	40
	61	109	19
	62	110	98
	63	112	77
	64	114	56
	65	116	35
	66	118	14
	67	119	93
	68	121	72
	69	123	51
	70	125	30
	71	127	9
6	72	128	88
	75	134	25
	80	143	20
7	84	150	36
	90	161	10
8	96	171	84
	100	179	0
10	120	214	80
	140	250	60
	150	268	50
	160	286	40
	180	322	20
	200	358	0
25	300	537	0
	365	653	35
	400	716	0
	500	895	0
	600	1074	0
	700	1253	0
	800	1432	0
	900	1611	0
	1000	1790	0

Twelfths

	1.	0 15		7.	1 4½
⅙	2.	0 29¾	⅔	8.	1 19¼
	3.	0 44¾		9.	1 34¼
⅓	4.	0 59¾	⅚	10.	1 49¼
	5.	0 74½		11.	1 64
½	6.	0 89½			

Sixteenths

	1.	0 11¼		9.	1 0¾
⅛	2.	0 22½	⅝	10.	1 12
	3.	0 33½		11.	1 23
¼	4.	0 44¾	¾	12.	1 34¼
	5.	0 56		13.	1 45½
⅜	6.	0 67¼	⅞	14.	1 56½
	7.	0 78¼		15.	1 67¾
½	8.	0 89½			

Twentieths

10ths					
	1.	0 9		11.	0 98½
·1	2.	0 18	·6	12.	1 7½
	3.	0 26¾		13.	1 16¼
·2	4.	0 35¾	·7	14.	1 25¼
	5	0 44¾		15.	1 34¼
·3	6.	0 53¾	·8	16.	1 43¼
	7.	0 62½		17.	1 52¼
·4	8.	0 71½	·9	18.	1 61
	9.	0 80½		19	1 70
·5	10.	0 89½		20.	1 79

£ 1·80

*Dozens		£	P
	1	1	80
	2	3	60
	3	5	40
	4	7	20
	5	9	0
	6	10	80
	7	12	60
	8	14	40
	9	16	20
	10	18	0
	11	19	80
*1	12	21	60
	13	23	40
	14	25	20
	15	27	0
	16	28	80
	17	30	60
	18	32	40
	19	34	20
	20	36	0
	21	37	80
	22	39	60
	23	41	40
2	24	43	20
	25	45	0
	26	46	80
	27	48	60
	28	50	40
	29	52	20
	30	54	0
	31	55	80
	32	57	60
	33	59	40
	34	61	20
	35	63	0
3	36	64	80
	37	66	60
	38	68	40
	39	70	20
	40	72	0
	41	73	80
	42	75	60
	43	77	40
	44	79	20
	45	81	0
	46	82	80
	47	84	60
4	48	86	40
	49	88	20
	50	90	0

Dozens		£	P
	51	91	80
	52	93	60
	53	95	40
	54	97	20
	55	99	0
	56	100	80
	57	102	60
	58	104	40
	59	106	20
5	**60**	108	0
	61	109	80
	62	111	60
	63	113	40
	64	115	20
	65	117	0
	66	118	80
	67	120	60
	68	122	40
	69	124	20
	70	126	0
	71	127	80
6	72	129	60
	75	135	0
	80	144	0
7	84	151	20
	90	162	0
8	96	172	80
	100	180	0
10	120	216	0
	140	252	0
	150	270	0
	160	288	0
	180	324	0
	200	360	0
25	300	540	0
	365	657	0
	400	720	0
	500	900	0
	600	1080	0
	700	1260	0
	800	1440	0
	900	1620	0
	1000	1800	0

Twelfths

	1.	0 15		7.	1 5
1/6	2.	0 30	2/3	8.	1 20
	3.	0 45		9.	1 35
1/3	4.	0 60	5/6	10.	1 50
	5.	0 75		11.	1 65
½	6.	0 90			

Sixteenths

	1.	0 11¼		9.	1 1¼
⅛	2.	0 22½	⅝	10.	1 12½
	3.	0 33¾		11.	1 23¾
¼	4.	0 45	¾	12.	1 35
	5.	0 56¼		13.	1 46¼
⅜	6.	0 67½	⅞	14.	1 57
	7.	0 78¾		15.	1 68¾
	8.	0 90			

Twentieths

10ths			10ths		
	1.	0 9		11.	0 99
·1	2.	0 18	·6	12	1 8
	3.	0 27		13.	1 17
·2	4.	0 36	·7	14.	1 26
	5.	0 45		15.	1 35
·3	6.	0 54	·8	16.	1 44
	7.	0 63		17.	1 53
·4	8.	0 72	·9	18.	1 62
	9.	0 81		19.	1 71
·5	10.	0 90		20.	1 80

£ 1·81

*Dozens		£	P
	1	1	81
	2	3	62
	3	5	43
	4	7	24
	5	9	5
	6	10	86
	7	12	67
	8	14	48
	9	16	29
	10	18	10
	11	19	91
1	12	21	72
	13	23	53
	14	25	34
	15	27	15
	16	28	96
	17	30	77
	18	32	58
	19	34	39
	20	36	20
	21	38	1
	22	39	82
	23	41	63
2	24	43	44
	25	45	25
	26	47	6
	27	48	87
	28	50	68
	29	52	49
	30	54	30
	31	56	11
	32	57	92
	33	59	73
	34	61	54
	35	63	35
3	36	65	16
	37	66	97
	38	68	78
	39	70	59
	40	72	40
	41	74	21
	42	76	2
	43	77	83
	44	79	64
	45	81	45
	46	83	26
	47	85	7
4	48	86	88
	49	88	69
	50	90	50

Dozens		£	P
	51	92	31
	52	94	12
	53	95	93
	54	97	74
	55	99	55
	56	101	36
	57	103	17
	58	104	98
	59	106	79
5	**60**	108	60
	61	110	41
	62	112	22
	63	114	3
	64	115	84
	65	117	65
	66	119	46
	67	121	27
	68	123	8
	69	124	89
	70	126	70
	71	128	51
6	72	130	32
	75	135	75
	80	144	80
7	84	152	4
	90	162	90
8	96	173	76
	100	181	0
10	120	217	20
	140	253	40
	150	271	50
	160	289	60
	180	325	80
	200	362	0
25	300	543	0
	365	660	65
	400	724	0
	500	905	0
	600	1086	0
	700	1267	0
	800	1448	0
	900	1629	0
	1000	1810	0

Twelfths

	1.	0 15		7.	1 5½
1/6	2.	0 30¼	2/3	8.	1 20¾
	3.	0 45¼		9.	1 35¾
1/3	4.	0 60¼	5/6	10.	1 50¾
	5.	0 75½		11.	1 66
½	6.	0 90½			

Sixteenths

	1.	0 11½		9.	1 1¾
⅛	2.	0 22¾	⅝	10.	1 13¼
	3.	0 34		11.	1 24½
¼	4.	0 45¼	¾	12.	1 35¾
	5.	0 56¼		13.	1 47
⅜	6.	0 68	⅞	14.	1 58½
	7.	0 79¼		15.	1 69¾
½	8.	0 90½			

Twentieths

10ths			10ths		
	1.	0 9		11.	0 99½
·1	2.	0 18	·6	12.	1 8½
	3.	0 27¼		13.	1 17¾
·2	4.	0 36¼	·7	14.	1 26¾
	5	0 45¼		15.	1 35¾
·3	6.	0 54¼	·8	16.	1 44¾
	7.	0 63¼		17.	1 53¾
·4	8.	0 72½	·9	18.	1 63
	9.	0 81½		19	1 72
·5	10.	0 90½		20.	1 81

£ 1·82

*Dozens	No.	£	P
	1	1	82
	2	3	64
	3	5	46
	4	7	28
	5	9	10
	6	10	92
	7	12	74
	8	14	56
	9	16	38
	10	18	20
*	11	20	2
1	12	21	84
	13	23	66
	14	25	48
	15	27	30
	16	29	12
	17	30	94
	18	32	76
	19	34	58
	20	36	40
	21	38	22
	22	40	4
	23	41	86
2	24	43	68
	25	45	50
	26	47	32
	27	49	14
	28	50	96
	29	52	78
	30	54	60
	31	56	42
	32	58	24
	33	60	6
	34	61	88
	35	63	70
3	36	65	52
	37	67	34
	38	69	16
	39	70	98
	40	72	80
	41	74	62
	42	76	44
	43	78	26
	44	80	8
	45	81	90
	46	83	72
	47	85	54
4	48	87	36
	49	89	18
	50	91	0

Dozens	No.	£	P
	51	92	82
	52	94	64
	53	96	46
	54	98	28
	55	100	10
	56	101	92
	57	103	74
	58	105	56
	59	107	38
5	**60**	109	20
	61	111	2
	62	112	84
	63	114	66
	64	116	48
	65	118	30
	66	120	12
	67	121	94
	68	123	76
	69	125	58
	70	127	40
	71	129	22
6	72	131	4
	75	136	50
	80	145	60
7	84	152	88
	90	163	80
8	96	174	72
	100	182	0
10	120	218	40
	140	254	80
	150	273	0
	160	291	20
	180	327	60
	200	364	0
25	300	546	0
	365	664	30
	400	728	0
	500	910	0
	600	1092	0
	700	1274	0
	800	1456	0
	900	1638	0
	1000	1820	0

Twelfths

	1.	0	15¼		7.	1	6¼
⅙	2.	0	30¼	⅔	8.	1	21¼
	3.	0	45½		9.	1	36½
⅓	4.	0	60¾	⅚	10.	1	51¾
	5.	0	75¾		11.	1	66¾
½	6.	0	91				

Twentieths

10ths							
	1.	0	9		11.	1	0
·1	2.	0	18¼	·6	12	1	9¼
	3.	0	27¼		13.	1	18¼
·2	4.	0	36½	·7	14.	1	27½
	5.	0	45½		15.	1	36½
·3	6.	0	54½	·8	16.	1	45½
	7.	0	63¾		17.	1	54¾
·4	8.	0	72¾	·9	18.	1	63¾
	9.	0	82		19.	1	73
·5	10.	0	91		20.	1	82

Sixteenths

	1.	0	11½		9.	1	2½
⅛	2.	0	22¾	⅝	10.	1	13¾
	3.	0	34¼		11.	1	25¼
¼	4.	0	45½	¾	12.	1	36½
	5.	0	57		13.	1	48
⅜	6.	0	68¼	⅞	14.	1	59½
	7.	0	79¾		15.	1	70¾
	8.	0	91				

£ 1·83

*Dozens	No.	£	P
	1	1	83
	2	3	66
	3	5	49
	4	7	32
	5	9	15
	6	10	98
	7	12	81
	8	14	64
	9	16	47
	10	18	30
	11	20	13
1	12	21	96
	13	23	79
	14	25	62
	15	27	45
	16	29	28
	17	31	11
	18	32	94
	19	34	77
	20	36	60
	21	38	43
	22	40	26
	23	42	9
2	24	43	92
	25	45	75
	26	47	58
	27	49	41
	28	51	24
	29	53	7
	30	54	90
	31	56	73
	32	58	56
	33	60	39
	34	62	22
	35	64	5
3	36	65	88
	37	67	71
	38	69	54
	39	71	37
	40	73	20
	41	75	3
	42	76	86
	43	78	69
	44	80	52
	45	82	35
	46	84	18
	47	86	1
4	48	87	84
	49	89	67
	50	91	50

Dozens	No.	£	P
	51	93	33
	52	95	16
	53	96	99
	54	98	82
	55	100	65
	56	102	48
	57	104	31
	58	106	14
	59	107	97
5	**60**	109	80
	61	111	63
	62	113	46
	63	115	29
	64	117	12
	65	118	95
	66	120	78
	67	122	61
	68	124	44
	69	126	27
	70	128	10
	71	129	93
6	72	131	76
	75	137	25
	80	146	40
7	84	153	72
	90	164	70
8	96	175	68
	100	183	0
10	120	219	60
	140	256	20
	150	274	50
	160	292	80
	180	329	40
	200	366	0
25	300	549	0
	365	667	95
	400	732	0
	500	915	0
	600	1098	0
	700	1281	0
	800	1464	0
	900	1647	0
	1000	1830	0

Twelfths

	1.	0	15¼		7.	1	6¾
⅙	2.	0	30½	⅔	8.	1	22
	3.	0	45¾		9.	1	37¼
⅓	4.	0	61	⅚	10.	1	52½
	5.	0	76¼		11.	1	67¾
½	6.	0	91½				

Twentieths

10ths							
	1.	0	9¼		11.	1	0¾
·1	2.	0	18¼	·6	12.	1	9¾
	3.	0	27½		13.	1	19
·2	4.	0	36½	·7	14.	1	28
	5	0	45¾		15.	1	37¼
·3	6.	0	55	·8	16.	1	46½
	7.	0	64		17.	1	55½
·4	8.	0	73¼	·9	18.	1	64¾
	9.	0	82¼		19	1	73¾
·5	10.	0	91½		20.	1	83

Sixteenths

	1.	0	11½		9.	1	3
⅛	2.	0	23	⅝	10.	1	14½
	3.	0	34¼		11.	1	25¾
¼	4.	0	45¾	¾	12.	1	37¼
	5.	0	57½		13.	1	48¾
⅜	6.	0	68¾	⅞	14.	1	60¼
	7.	0	80		15.	1	71½
½	8.	0	91½				

£ 1·84

*Dozens		£	p
	1	1	84
	2	3	68
	3	5	52
	4	7	36
	5	9	20
	6	11	4
	7	12	88
	8	14	72
	9	16	56
	10	18	40
	11	20	24
*1	12	22	8
	13	23	92
	14	25	76
	15	27	60
	16	29	44
	17	31	28
	18	33	12
	19	34	96
	20	36	80
	21	38	64
	22	40	48
	23	42	32
2	24	44	16
	25	46	0
	26	47	84
	27	49	68
	28	51	52
	29	53	36
	30	55	20
	31	57	4
	32	58	88
	33	60	72
	34	62	56
	35	64	40
3	36	66	24
	37	68	8
	38	69	92
	39	71	76
	40	73	60
	41	75	44
	42	77	28
	43	79	12
	44	80	96
	45	82	80
	46	84	64
	47	86	48
4	48	88	32
	49	90	16
	50	92	0

Dozens		£	p
	51	93	84
	52	95	68
	53	97	52
	54	99	36
	55	101	20
	56	103	4
	57	104	88
	58	106	72
	59	108	56
5	**60**	110	40
	61	112	24
	62	114	8
	63	115	92
	64	117	76
	65	119	60
	66	121	44
	67	123	28
	68	125	12
	69	126	96
	70	128	80
	71	130	64
6	72	132	48
	75	138	0
	80	147	20
7	84	154	56
	90	165	60
8	96	176	64
	100	184	0
10	120	220	80
	140	257	60
	150	276	0
	160	294	40
	180	331	20
	200	368	0
25	300	552	0
	365	671	60
	400	736	0
	500	920	0
	600	1104	0
	700	1288	0
	800	1472	0
	900	1656	0
	1000	1840	0

Sixteenths

1.	0	11½	9.	1	3½
⅛ 2.	0	23	⅝ 10.	1	15
3.	0	34½	11.	1	26½
¼ 4.	0	46	¾ 12.	1	38
5.	0	57½	13.	1	49½
⅜ 6.	0	69	⅞ 14.	1	61
7.	0	80½	15	1	72½
½ 8.	0	92			

Twelfths

1.	0	15¼	7.	1	7¼
⅙ 2.	0	30¾	⅔ 8.	1	22¾
3.	0	46	9.	1	38
⅓ 4.	0	61¼	⅚ 10.	1	53¼
5.	0	76¾	11.	1	68¾
½ 6.	0	92			

Twentieths

10ths				10ths			
	1.	0	9¼		11.	1	1¼
·1	2.	0	18½	·6	12	1	10½
	3.	0	27½		13.	1	19½
·2	4.	0	36¾	·7	14.	1	28¾
	5.	0	46		15.	1	38
·3	6.	0	55¼	·8	16.	1	47¼
	7.	0	64½		17.	1	56½
·4	8.	0	73½	·9	18.	1	65½
	9.	0	82¾		19.	1	74¾
·5	10.	0	92		20.	1	84

£ 1·85

*Dozens		£	p
	1	1	85
	2	3	70
	3	5	55
	4	7	40
	5	9	25
	6	11	10
	7	12	95
	8	14	80
	9	16	65
	10	18	50
	11	20	35
1	12	22	20
	13	24	5
	14	25	90
	15	27	75
	16	29	60
	17	31	45
	18	33	30
	19	35	15
	20	37	0
	21	38	85
	22	40	70
	23	42	55
2	24	44	40
	25	46	25
	26	48	10
	27	49	95
	28	51	80
	29	53	65
	30	55	50
	31	57	35
	32	59	20
	33	61	5
	34	62	90
	35	64	75
3	36	66	60
	37	68	45
	38	70	30
	39	72	15
	40	74	0
	41	75	85
	42	77	70
	43	79	55
	44	81	40
	45	83	25
	46	85	10
	47	86	95
4	48	88	80
	49	90	65
	50	92	50

Dozens		£	p
	51	94	35
	52	96	20
	53	98	5
	54	99	90
	55	101	75
	56	103	60
	57	105	45
	58	107	30
	59	109	15
5	**60**	111	0
	61	112	85
	62	114	70
	63	116	55
	64	118	40
	65	120	25
	66	122	10
	67	123	95
	68	125	80
	69	127	65
	70	129	50
	71	131	35
6	72	133	20
	75	138	75
	80	148	0
7	84	155	40
	90	166	50
8	96	177	60
	100	185	0
10	120	222	0
	140	259	0
	150	277	50
	160	296	0
	180	333	0
	200	370	0
25	300	555	0
	365	675	25
	400	740	0
	500	925	0
	600	1110	0
	700	1295	0
	800	1480	0
	900	1665	0
	1000	1850	0

Sixteenths

1.	0	11½	9.	1	4
⅛ 2.	0	23¼	⅝ 10.	1	15¾
3.	0	34¾	11.	1	27¼
¼ 4.	0	46¼	¾ 12.	1	38¾
5.	0	57¾	13.	1	50¼
⅜ 6.	0	69½	⅞ 14.	1	62
7.	0	81	15.	1	73½
½ 8.	0	92½			

Twelfths

1.	0	15½	7.	1	8
⅙ 2.	0	30¾	⅔ 8.	1	23¼
3.	0	46¼	9.	1	38¾
⅓ 4.	0	61¾	⅚ 10.	1	54¼
5.	0	77	11.	1	69½
½ 6.	0	92½			

Twentieths

10ths				10ths			
	1.	0	9¼		11.	1	1¾
·1	2.	0	18½	·6	12.	1	11
	3.	0	27¾		13.	1	20¼
·2	4.	0	37	·7	14.	1	29½
	5	0	46¼		15.	1	38¾
·3	6.	0	55½	·8	16.	1	48
	7.	0	64¾		17.	1	57¼
·4	8.	0	74	·9	18.	1	66½
	9	0	83¼		19	1	75¾
·5	10.	0	92½		20.	1	85

£ 1·86

*Dozens

Dozens	Qty	£	P
	1	1	86
	2	3	72
	3	5	58
	4	7	44
	5	9	30
	6	11	16
	7	13	2
	8	14	88
	9	16	74
	10	18	60
	11	20	46
1	12	22	32
	13	24	18
	14	26	4
	15	27	90
	16	29	76
	17	31	62
	18	33	48
	19	35	34
	20	37	20
	21	39	6
	22	40	92
	23	42	78
2	24	44	64
	25	46	50
	26	48	36
	27	50	22
	28	52	8
	29	53	94
	30	55	80
	31	57	66
	32	59	52
	33	61	38
	34	63	24
	35	65	10
3	36	66	96
	37	68	82
	38	70	68
	39	72	54
	40	74	40
	41	76	26
	42	78	12
	43	79	98
	44	81	84
	45	83	70
	46	85	56
	47	87	42
4	48	89	28
	49	91	14
	50	93	0

Dozens	Qty	£	P
	51	94	86
	52	96	72
	53	98	58
	54	100	44
	55	102	30
	56	104	16
	57	106	2
	58	107	88
	59	109	74
5	60	111	60
	61	113	46
	62	115	32
	63	117	18
	64	119	4
	65	120	90
	66	122	76
	67	124	62
	68	126	48
	69	128	34
	70	130	20
	71	132	6
6	72	133	92
	75	139	50
	80	148	80
7	84	156	24
	90	167	40
8	96	178	56
	100	186	0
10	120	223	20
	140	260	40
	150	279	0
	160	297	60
	180	334	80
	200	372	0
25	300	558	0
	365	678	90
	400	744	0
	500	930	0
	600	1116	0
	700	1302	0
	800	1488	0
	900	1674	0
	1000	1860	0

Twelfths

	1. 0 15½		7. 1 8½
⅙	2. 0 31	⅔	8. 1 24
	3. 0 46½		9. 1 39½
⅓	4. 0 62	⅚	10. 1 55
	5. 0 77½		11. 1 70½
½	6. 0 93		

Sixteenths

	1. 0 11¾		9. 1 4¾
⅛	2. 0 23¼	⅝	10. 1 16¼
	3. 0 35		11. 1 28
¼	4. 0 46½	¾	12. 1 39½
	5. 0 58¼		13. 1 51¼
⅜	6. 0 69¾	⅞	14. 1 62¾
	7. 0 81½		15. 1 74½
	8. 0 93		

Twentieths (10ths)

10ths		10ths	
	1. 0 9¼		11. 1 2¼
·1	2. 0 18½	·6	12 1 11½
	3. 0 28		13. 1 21
·2	4. 0 37¼	·7	14. 1 30¼
	5. 0 46½		15. 1 39½
·3	6. 0 55¾	8	16. 1 48¾
	7. 0 65		17. 1 58
·4	8. 0 74½	·9	18. 1 67½
	9. 0 83¾		19. 1 76¾
·5	10. 0 93		20. 1 86

£ 1·87

*Dozens

Dozens	Qty	£	P
	1	1	87
	2	3	74
	3	5	61
	4	7	48
	5	9	35
	6	11	22
	7	13	9
	8	14	96
	9	16	83
	10	18	70
	11	20	57
1	12	22	44
	13	24	31
	14	26	18
	15	28	5
	16	29	92
	17	31	79
	18	33	66
	19	35	53
	20	37	40
	21	39	27
	22	41	14
	23	43	1
2	24	44	88
	25	46	75
	26	48	62
	27	50	49
	28	52	36
	29	54	23
	30	56	10
	31	57	97
	32	59	84
	33	61	71
	34	63	58
	35	65	45
3	36	67	32
	37	69	19
	38	71	6
	39	72	93
	40	74	80
	41	76	67
	42	78	54
	43	80	41
	44	82	28
	45	84	15
	46	86	2
	47	87	89
4	48	89	76
	49	91	63
	50	93	50

Dozens	Qty	£	P
	51	95	37
	52	97	24
	53	99	11
	54	100	98
	55	102	85
	56	104	72
	57	106	59
	58	108	46
	59	110	33
5	60	112	20
	61	114	7
	62	115	94
	63	117	81
	64	119	68
	65	121	55
	66	123	42
	67	125	29
	68	127	16
	69	129	3
	70	130	90
	71	132	77
6	72	134	64
	75	140	25
	80	149	60
7	84	157	8
	90	168	30
8	96	179	52
	100	187	0
10	120	224	40
	140	261	80
	150	280	50
	160	299	20
	180	336	60
	200	374	0
25	300	561	0
	365	682	55
	400	748	0
	500	935	0
	600	1122	0
	700	1309	0
	800	1496	0
	900	1683	0
	1000	1870	0

Twelfths

	1. 0 15½		7. 1 9
⅙	2. 0 31¼	⅔	8. 1 24¾
	3. 0 46¾		9. 1 40¼
⅓	4. 0 62¼	⅚	10. 1 55¾
	5. 0 78		11. 1 71½
½	6. 0 93½		

Sixteenths

	1. 0 11¾		9. 1 5¼
⅛	2. 0 23½	⅝	10. 1 17
	3. 0 35		11. 1 28½
¼	4. 0 46¾	¾	12. 1 40¼
	5. 0 58½		13. 1 52
⅜	6. 0 70¼	⅞	14. 1 63¾
	7. 0 81¾		15. 1 75¼
½	8. 0 93½		

Twentieths (10ths)

10ths		10ths	
	1. 0 9¼		11. 1 2¾
·1	2. 0 18¾	·6	12. 1 12¼
	3. 0 28		13. 1 21½
·2	4. 0 37½	·7	14. 1 31
	5 0 46¾		15. 1 40¼
·3	6. 0 56	·8	16. 1 49½
	7. 0 65½		17. 1 59
·4	8. 0 74¾	·9	18. 1 68¼
	9. 0 84¼		19 1 77¾
·5	10. 0 93½		20. 1 87

£ 1·88

*Dozens

Dozens	Qty	£	P
	1	1	88
	2	3	76
	3	5	64
	4	7	52
	5	9	40
	6	11	28
	7	13	16
	8	15	4
	9	16	92
	10	18	80
	11	20	68
*1	12	22	56
	13	24	44
	14	26	32
	15	28	20
	16	30	8
	17	31	96
	18	33	84
	19	35	72
	20	37	60
	21	39	48
	22	41	36
	23	43	24
2	24	45	12
	25	47	0
	26	48	88
	27	50	76
	28	52	64
	29	54	52
	30	56	40
	31	58	28
	32	60	16
	33	62	4
	34	63	92
	35	65	80
3	36	67	68
	37	69	56
	38	71	44
	39	73	32
	40	75	20
	41	77	8
	42	78	96
	43	80	84
	44	82	72
	45	84	60
	46	86	48
	47	88	36
4	48	90	24
	49	92	12
	50	94	0

Dozens	Qty	£	P
	51	95	88
	52	97	76
	53	99	64
	54	101	52
	55	103	40
	56	105	28
	57	107	16
	58	109	4
	59	110	92
5	**60**	112	80
	61	114	68
	62	116	56
	63	118	44
	64	120	32
	65	122	20
	66	124	8
	67	125	96
	68	127	84
	69	129	72
	70	131	60
	71	133	48
6	72	135	36
	75	141	0
	80	150	40
7	84	157	92
	90	169	20
8	96	180	48
	100	188	0
10	120	225	60
	140	263	20
	150	282	0
	160	300	80
	180	338	40
	200	376	0
25	300	564	0
	365	686	20
	400	752	0
	500	940	0
	600	1128	0
	700	1316	0
	800	1504	0
	900	1692	0
	1000	1880	0

Twelfths

	1. 0 15¾		7. 1 9¾
⅙	2. 0 31¼	⅔	8. 1 25¼
	3. 0 47		9. 1 41
⅓	4. 0 62¾	⅚	10. 1 56¾
	5. 0 78¼		11. 1 72¼
½	6. 0 94		

Sixteenths

	1. 0 11¾		9. 1 5¾
⅛	2. 0 23½	⅝	10. 1 17½
	3. 0 35¼		11. 1 29¼
¼	4. 0 47	¾	12. 1 41
	5. 0 58¾		13. 1 52¾
⅜	6. 0 70½	⅞	14. 1 64½
	7. 0 82¼		15. 1 76¼
	8. 0 94		

Twentieths

10ths			
	1. 0 9½		11. 1 3½
·1	2. 0 18¾	·6	12 1 12¾
	3. 0 28¼		13. 1 22¼
·2	4. 0 37½	·7	14. 1 31½
	5. 0 47		15. 1 41
·3	6. 0 56½	8	16. 1 50½
	7. 0 65¾		17. 1 59¾
·4	8. 0 75¼	·9	18. 1 69¼
	9. 0 84½		19. 1 78½
·5	10. 0 94		20. 1 88

£ 1·89

*Dozens

Dozens	Qty	£	P
	1	1	89
	2	3	78
	3	5	67
	4	7	56
	5	9	45
	6	11	34
	7	13	23
	8	15	12
	9	17	1
	10	18	90
	11	20	79
1	12	22	68
	13	24	57
	14	26	46
	15	28	35
	16	30	24
	17	32	13
	18	34	2
	19	35	91
	20	37	80
	21	39	69
	22	41	58
	23	43	47
2	24	45	36
	25	47	25
	26	49	14
	27	51	3
	28	52	92
	29	54	81
	30	56	70
	31	58	59
	32	60	48
	33	62	37
	34	64	26
	35	66	15
3	36	68	4
	37	69	93
	38	71	82
	39	73	71
	40	75	60
	41	77	49
	42	79	38
	43	81	27
	44	83	16
	45	85	5
	46	86	94
	47	88	83
4	48	90	72
	49	92	61
	50	94	50

Dozens	Qty	£	P
	51	96	39
	52	98	28
	53	100	17
	54	102	6
	55	103	95
	56	105	84
	57	107	73
	58	109	62
	59	111	51
5	**60**	113	40
	61	115	29
	62	117	18
	63	119	7
	64	120	96
	65	122	85
	66	124	74
	67	126	63
	68	128	52
	69	130	41
	70	132	30
	71	134	19
6	72	136	8
	75	141	75
	80	151	20
7	84	158	76
	90	170	10
8	96	181	44
	100	189	0
10	120	226	80
	140	264	60
	150	283	50
	160	302	40
	180	340	20
	200	378	0
25	300	567	0
	365	689	85
	400	756	0
	500	945	0
	600	1134	0
	700	1323	0
	800	1512	0
	900	1701	0
	1000	1890	0

Twelfths

	1. 0 15¾		7. 1 10¼
⅙	2. 0 31½	⅔	8. 1 26
	3. 0 47¼		9. 1 41¾
⅓	4. 0 63	⅚	10. 1 57½
	5. 0 78¾		11. 1 73¼
½	6. 0 94½		

Sixteenths

	1. 0 11¾		9. 1 6¼
⅛	2. 0 23¾	⅝	10. 1 18¼
	3. 0 35½		11. 1 30
¼	4. 0 47¼	¾	12. 1 41¾
	5. 0 59		13. 1 53½
⅜	6. 0 71	⅞	14. 1 65½
	7. 0 82¾		15. 1 77¼
½	8. 0 94½		

Twentieths

10ths			
	1. 0 9½		11. 1 4
·1	2. 0 19	·6	12. 1 13½
	3. 0 28¼		13. 1 22¾
·2	4. 0 37¾	·7	14. 1 32¼
	5 0 47¼		15. 1 41¾
·3	6. 0 56¾	·8	16. 1 51¼
	7. 0 66¼		17. 1 60¾
·4	8. 0 75½	·9	18. 1 70
	9. 0 85		19 1 79½
·5	10. 0 94½		20. 1 89

£ 1·90

*Dozens		£	P
	1	1	90
	2	3	80
	3	5	70
	4	7	60
	5	9	50
	6	11	40
	7	13	30
	8	15	20
	9	17	10
	10	19	0
*	11	20	90
1	12	22	80
	13	24	70
	14	26	60
	15	28	50
	16	30	40
	17	32	30
	18	34	20
	19	36	10
	20	38	0
	21	39	90
	22	41	80
	23	43	70
2	24	45	60
	25	47	50
	26	49	40
	27	51	30
	28	53	20
	29	55	10
	30	57	0
	31	58	90
	32	60	80
	33	62	70
	34	64	60
	35	66	50
3	36	68	40
	37	70	30
	38	72	20
	39	74	10
	40	76	0
	41	77	90
	42	79	80
	43	81	70
	44	83	60
	45	85	50
	46	87	40
	47	89	30
4	48	91	20
	49	93	10
	50	95	0

Dozens		£	P
	51	96	90
	52	98	80
	53	100	70
	54	102	60
	55	104	50
	56	106	40
	57	108	30
	58	110	20
	59	112	10
5	**60**	114	0
	61	115	90
	62	117	80
	63	119	70
	64	121	60
	65	123	50
	66	125	40
	67	127	30
	68	129	20
	69	131	10
	70	133	0
	71	134	90
6	72	136	80
	75	142	50
	80	152	0
7	84	159	60
	90	171	0
8	96	182	40
	100	190	0
10	120	228	0
	140	266	0
	150	285	0
	160	304	0
	180	342	0
	200	380	0
25	300	570	0
	365	693	50
	400	760	0
	500	950	0
	600	1140	0
	700	1330	0
	800	1520	0
	900	1710	0
	1000	1900	0

Twelfths

	1. 0 15¾		7. 1 10¾
⅙	2. 0 31¾	⅔	8. 1 26¾
	3. 0 47½		9. 1 42½
⅓	4. 0 63¼	⅚	10. 1 58¼
	5. 0 79¼		11. 1 74¼
½	6. 0 95		

Sixteenths

	1. 0 12		9. 1 7
⅛	2. 0 23¾	⅝	10. 1 18¾
	3. 0 35¾		11. 1 30¾
¼	4. 0 47½	¾	12. 1 42½
	5. 0 59½		13. 1 54½
⅜	6. 0 71¼	⅞	14. 1 66¼
	7. 0 83¼		15. 1 78¼
½	8. 0 95		

Twentieths

10ths			
	1. 0 9½		11. 1 4½
·1	2. 0 19	·6	12. 1 14
	3. 0 28½		13. 1 23½
·2	4. 0 38	·7	14. 1 33
	5. 0 47½		15. 1 42½
·3	6. 0 57	·8	16. 1 52
	7. 0 66½		17. 1 61½
·4	8. 0 76	·9	18. 1 71
	9. 0 85½		19. 1 80½
·5	10. 0 95		20. 1 90

£ 1·91

*Dozens		£	P
	1	1	91
	2	3	82
	3	5	73
	4	7	64
	5	9	55
	6	11	46
	7	13	37
	8	15	28
	9	17	19
	10	19	10
	11	21	1
1	12	22	92
	13	24	83
	14	26	74
	15	28	65
	16	30	56
	17	32	47
	18	34	38
	19	36	29
	20	38	20
	21	40	11
	22	42	2
	23	43	93
2	24	45	84
	25	47	75
	26	49	66
	27	51	57
	28	53	48
	29	55	39
	30	57	30
	31	59	21
	32	61	12
	33	63	3
	34	64	94
	35	66	85
3	36	68	76
	37	70	67
	38	72	58
	39	74	49
	40	76	40
	41	78	31
	42	80	22
	43	82	13
	44	84	4
	45	85	95
	46	87	86
	47	89	77
4	48	91	68
	49	93	59
	50	95	50

Dozens		£	P
	51	97	41
	52	99	32
	53	101	23
	54	103	14
	55	105	5
	56	106	96
	57	108	87
	58	110	78
	59	112	69
5	**60**	114	60
	61	116	51
	62	118	42
	63	120	33
	64	122	24
	65	124	15
	66	126	6
	67	127	97
	68	129	88
	69	131	79
	70	133	70
	71	135	61
6	72	137	52
	75	143	25
	80	152	80
7	84	160	44
	90	171	90
8	96	183	36
	100	191	0
10	120	229	20
	140	267	40
	150	286	50
	160	305	60
	180	343	80
	200	382	0
25	300	573	0
	365	697	15
	400	764	0
	500	955	0
	600	1146	0
	700	1337	0
	800	1528	0
	900	1719	0
	1000	1910	0

Twelfths

	1. 0 16		7. 1 11½
⅙	2. 0 31¾	⅔	8. 1 27¼
	3. 0 47¾		9. 1 43¼
⅓	4. 0 63¾	⅚	10. 1 59¼
	5. 0 79½		11. 1 75
½	6. 0 95½		

Sixteenths

	1. 0 12		9. 1 7½
⅛	2. 0 24	⅝	10. 1 19½
	3. 0 35¾		11. 1 31¼
¼	4. 0 47¾	¾	12. 1 43¼
	5. 0 59¾		13. 1 55¼
⅜	6. 0 71¾	⅞	14. 1 67¼
	7. 0 83½		15. 1 79
½	8. 0 95½		

Twentieths

10ths			
	1. 0 9½		11. 1 5
·1	2. 0 19	·6	12. 1 14½
	3. 0 28¾		13. 1 24¼
·2	4. 0 38¼	·7	14. 1 33¾
	5. 0 47¾		15. 1 43¼
·3	6. 0 57¼	·8	16. 1 52¾
	7. 0 66¾		17. 1 62¼
·4	8. 0 76½	·9	18. 1 72
	9. 0 86		19. 1 81½
·5	10. 0 95½		20. 1 91

£ 1·92

Dozens	No.	£	P
	1	1	92
	2	3	84
	3	5	76
	4	7	68
	5	9	60
	6	11	52
	7	13	44
	8	15	36
	9	17	28
	10	19	20
	11	21	12
*1	12	23	4
	13	24	96
	14	26	88
	15	28	80
	16	30	72
	17	32	64
	18	34	56
	19	36	48
	20	38	40
	21	40	32
	22	42	24
	23	44	16
2	24	46	8
	25	48	0
	26	49	92
	27	51	84
	28	53	76
	29	55	68
	30	57	60
	31	59	52
	32	61	44
	33	63	36
	34	65	28
	35	67	20
3	36	69	12
	37	71	4
	38	72	96
	39	74	88
	40	76	80
	41	78	72
	42	80	64
	43	82	56
	44	84	48
	45	86	40
	46	88	32
	47	90	24
4	48	92	16
	49	94	8
	50	96	0

Dozens	No.	£	P
	51	97	92
	52	99	84
	53	101	76
	54	103	68
	55	105	60
	56	107	52
	57	109	44
	58	111	36
	59	113	28
5	**60**	115	20
	61	117	12
	62	119	4
	63	120	96
	64	122	88
	65	124	80
	66	126	72
	67	128	64
	68	130	56
	69	132	48
	70	134	40
	71	136	32
6	72	138	24
	75	144	0
	80	153	60
7	84	161	28
	90	172	80
8	96	184	32
	100	192	0
10	120	230	40
	140	268	80
	150	288	0
	160	307	20
	180	345	60
	200	384	0
25	300	576	0
	365	700	80
	400	768	0
	500	960	0
	600	1152	0
	700	1344	0
	800	1536	0
	900	1728	0
	1000	1920	0

*Dozens

Twelfths

	1. 0 16		7. 1 12
⅙	2. 0 32	⅔	8. 1 28
	3. 0 48		9. 1 44
⅓	4. 0 64	⅚	10. 1 60
	5. 0 80		11. 1 76
½	6. 0 96		

Sixteenths

	1. 0 12		9. 1 8
⅛	2. 0 24	⅝	10. 1 20
	3. 0 36		11. 1 32
¼	4. 0 48	¾	12. 1 44
	5. 0 60		13. 1 56
⅜	6. 0 72	⅞	14. 1 68
	7. 0 84		15. 1 80
	8. 0 96		

Twentieths

10ths		10ths	
	1. 0 9½		11. 1 5½
·1	2. 0 19¼	·6	12. 1 15¼
	3. 0 28¾		13. 1 24¾
·2	4. 0 38½	·7	14. 1 34½
	5. 0 48		15. 1 44
·3	6. 0 57½	·8	16. 1 53½
	7. 0 67¼		17. 1 63¼
·4	8. 0 76¾	·9	18. 1 72¾
	9. 0 86½		19. 1 82½
·5	10. 0 96		20. 1 92

£ 1·93

Dozens	No.	£	P
	1	1	93
	2	3	86
	3	5	79
	4	7	72
	5	9	65
	6	11	58
	7	13	51
	8	15	44
	9	17	37
	10	19	30
	11	21	23
1	12	23	16
	13	25	9
	14	27	2
	15	28	95
	16	30	88
	17	32	81
	18	34	74
	19	36	67
	20	38	60
	21	40	53
	22	42	46
	23	44	39
2	24	46	32
	25	48	25
	26	50	18
	27	52	11
	28	54	4
	29	55	97
	30	57	90
	31	59	83
	32	61	76
	33	63	69
	34	65	62
	35	67	55
3	36	69	48
	37	71	41
	38	73	34
	39	75	27
	40	77	20
	41	79	13
	42	81	6
	43	82	99
	44	84	92
	45	86	85
	46	88	78
	47	90	71
4	48	92	64
	49	94	57
	50	96	50

Dozens	No.	£	P
	51	98	43
	52	100	36
	53	102	29
	54	104	22
	55	106	15
	56	108	8
	57	110	1
	58	111	94
	59	113	87
5	**60**	115	80
	61	117	73
	62	119	66
	63	121	59
	64	123	52
	65	125	45
	66	127	38
	67	129	31
	68	131	24
	69	133	17
	70	135	10
	71	137	3
6	72	138	96
	75	144	75
	80	154	40
7	84	162	12
	90	173	70
8	96	185	28
	100	193	0
10	120	231	60
	140	270	20
	150	289	50
	160	308	80
	180	347	40
	200	386	0
25	300	579	0
	365	704	45
	400	772	0
	500	965	0
	600	1158	0
	700	1351	0
	800	1544	0
	900	1737	0
	1000	1930	0

Twelfths

	1. 0 16		7. 1 12½
⅙	2. 0 32¼	⅔	8. 1 28¾
	3. 0 48¼		9. 1 44¾
⅓	4. 0 64¼	⅚	10. 1 60¾
	5. 0 80½		11. 1 77
½	6. 0 96½		

Sixteenths

	1. 0 12		9. 1 8½
⅛	2. 0 24¼	⅝	10. 1 20¾
	3. 0 36¼		11. 1 32¾
¼	4. 0 48¼	¾	12. 1 44¾
	5. 0 60¼		13. 1 56¾
⅜	6. 0 72½	⅞	14. 1 69
	7. 0 84½		15. 1 81
½	8. 0 96½		

Twentieths

10ths		10ths	
	1. 0 9¾		11. 1 6¼
·1	2. 0 19¼	·6	12. 1 15¾
	3. 0 29		13. 1 25½
·2	4. 0 38½	·7	14. 1 35
	5 0 48¼		15. 1 44¾
·3	6. 0 58	·8	16. 1 54½
	7. 0 67½		17. 1 64
·4	8. 0 77¼	·9	18. 1 73¾
	9. 0 86¾		19 1 83¼
·5	10. 0 96½		20. 1 93

£ 1·94

*Dozens		£	P
	1	1	94
	2	3	88
	3	5	82
	4	7	76
	5	9	70
	6	11	64
	7	13	58
	8	15	52
	9	17	46
	10	19	40
	11	21	34
1	12	23	28
	13	25	22
	14	27	16
	15	29	10
	16	31	4
	17	32	98
	18	34	92
	19	36	86
	20	38	80
	21	40	74
	22	42	68
	23	44	62
2	24	46	56
	25	48	50
	26	50	44
	27	52	38
	28	54	32
	29	56	26
	30	58	20
	31	60	14
	32	62	8
	33	64	2
	34	65	96
	35	67	90
3	36	69	84
	37	71	78
	38	73	72
	39	75	66
	40	77	60
	41	79	54
	42	81	48
	43	83	42
	44	85	36
	45	87	30
	46	89	24
	47	91	18
4	48	93	12
	49	95	6
	50	97	0

Dozens		£	P
	51	98	94
	52	100	88
	53	102	82
	54	104	76
	55	106	70
	56	108	64
	57	110	58
	58	112	52
	59	114	46
5	**60**	116	40
	61	118	34
	62	120	28
	63	122	22
	64	124	16
	65	126	10
	66	128	4
	67	129	98
	68	131	92
	69	133	86
	70	135	80
	71	137	74
6	72	139	68
	75	145	50
	80	155	20
7	84	162	96
	90	174	60
8	96	186	24
	100	194	0
10	120	232	80
	140	271	60
	150	291	0
	160	310	40
	180	349	20
	200	388	0
25	300	582	0
	365	708	10
	400	776	0
	500	970	0
	600	1164	0
	700	1358	0
	800	1552	0
	900	1746	0
	1000	1940	0

Twelfths

	1. 0 16¼		7. 1 13¼
⅙	2. 0 32¼	⅔	8. 1 29¼
	3. 0 48½		9. 1 45½
⅓	4. 0 64¾	⅚	10. 1 61¾
	5. 0 80¾		11. 1 77¾
½	6. 0 97		

Sixteenths

	1. 0 12¼		9. 1 9¼
⅛	2. 0 24¼	⅝	10. 1 21¼
	3. 0 36½		11. 1 33½
¼	4. 0 48½	¾	12. 1 45½
	5. 0 60¾		13. 1 57¾
⅜	6. 0 72¾	⅞	14. 1 69¾
	7. 0 85		15. 1 82
	8. 0 97		

Twentieths

10ths			
	1. 0 9¾		11. 1 6¾
·1	2. 0 19½	·6	12 1 16½
	3. 0 29		13. 1 26
·2	4. 0 38¾	·7	14. 1 35¾
	5. 0 48½		15. 1 45½
·3	6. 0 58¼	·8	16. 1 55¼
	7. 0 68		17. 1 65
·4	8. 0 77½	·9	18. 1 74½
	9. 0 87¼		19. 1 84¼
·5	10. 0 97		20. 1 94

£ 1·95

*Dozens		£	P
	1	1	95
	2	3	90
	3	5	85
	4	7	80
	5	9	75
	6	11	70
	7	13	65
	8	15	60
	9	17	55
	10	19	50
	11	21	45
1	12	23	40
	13	25	35
	14	27	30
	15	29	25
	16	31	20
	17	33	15
	18	35	10
	19	37	5
	20	39	0
	21	40	95
	22	42	90
	23	44	85
2	24	46	80
	25	48	75
	26	50	70
	27	52	65
	28	54	60
	29	56	55
	30	58	50
	31	60	45
	32	62	40
	33	64	35
	34	66	30
	35	68	25
3	36	70	20
	37	72	15
	38	74	10
	39	76	5
	40	78	0
	41	79	95
	42	81	90
	43	83	85
	44	85	80
	45	87	75
	46	89	70
	47	91	65
4	48	93	60
	49	95	55
	50	97	50

Dozens		£	P
	51	99	45
	52	101	40
	53	103	35
	54	105	30
	55	107	25
	56	109	20
	57	111	15
	58	113	10
	59	115	5
5	**60**	117	0
	61	118	95
	62	120	90
	63	122	85
	64	124	80
	65	126	75
	66	128	70
	67	130	65
	68	132	60
	69	134	55
	70	136	50
	71	138	45
6	72	140	40
	75	146	25
	80	156	0
7	84	163	80
	90	175	50
8	96	187	20
	100	195	0
10	120	234	0
	140	273	0
	150	292	50
	160	312	0
	180	351	0
	200	390	0
25	300	585	0
	365	711	75
	400	780	0
	500	975	0
	600	1170	0
	700	1365	0
	800	1560	0
	900	1755	0
	1000	1950	0

Twelfths

	1. 0 16¼		7. 1 13¾
⅙	2. 0 32½	⅔	8. 1 30
	3. 0 48¾		9. 1 46¼
⅓	4. 0 65	⅚	10. 1 62½
	5. 0 81¼		11. 1 78¾
½	6. 0 97½		

Sixteenths

	1. 0 12¼		9. 1 9¾
⅛	2. 0 24½	⅝	10. 1 22
	3. 0 36½		11. 1 34
¼	4. 0 48¾	¾	12. 1 46¼
	5. 0 61		13. 1 58½
⅜	6. 0 73¼	⅞	14. 1 70¾
	7. 0 85¼		15. 1 82¾
½	8. 0 97½		

Twentieths

10ths			
	1. 0 9¾		11. 1 7¼
·1	2. 0 19½	·6	12. 1 17
	3. 0 29¼		13. 1 26¾
·2	4. 0 39	·7	14. 1 36½
	5 0 48¾		15. 1 46¼
·3	6. 0 58½	·8	16. 1 56
	7. 0 68¼		17. 1 65¾
·4	8. 0 78	·9	18. 1 75½
	9. 0 87¾		19 1 85¼
·5	10. 0 97½		20. 1 95

£ 1·96

*Dozens		£	P
	1	1	96
	2	3	92
	3	5	88
	4	7	84
	5	9	80
	6	11	76
	7	13	72
	8	15	68
	9	17	64
	10	19	60
*	11	21	56
1	12	23	52
	13	25	48
	14	27	44
	15	29	40
	16	31	36
	17	33	32
	18	35	28
	19	37	24
	20	39	20
	21	41	16
	22	43	12
	23	45	8
2	24	47	4
	25	49	0
	26	50	96
	27	52	92
	28	54	88
	29	56	84
	30	58	80
	31	60	76
	32	62	72
	33	64	68
	34	66	64
	35	68	60
3	36	70	56
	37	72	52
	38	74	48
	39	76	44
	40	78	40
	41	80	36
	42	82	32
	43	84	28
	44	86	24
	45	88	20
	46	90	16
	47	92	12
4	48	94	8
	49	96	4
	50	98	0

Dozens		£	P
	51	99	96
	52	101	92
	53	103	88
	54	105	84
	55	107	80
	56	109	76
	57	111	72
	58	113	68
	59	115	64
5	**60**	117	60
	61	119	56
	62	121	52
	63	123	48
	64	125	44
	65	127	40
	66	129	36
	67	131	32
	68	133	28
	69	135	24
	70	137	20
	71	139	16
6	72	141	12
	75	147	0
	80	156	80
7	84	164	64
	90	176	40
8	96	188	16
	100	196	0
10	120	235	20
	140	274	40
	150	294	0
	160	313	60
	180	352	80
	200	392	0
25	300	588	0
	365	715	40
	400	784	0
	500	980	0
	600	1176	0
	700	1372	0
	800	1568	0
	900	1764	0
	1000	1960	0

Twelfths

	1. 0 16¼	7. 1 14¼
⅙	2. 0 32¾	⅔ 8. 1 30¾
	3. 0 49	9. 1 47
⅓	4. 0 65¼	⅚ 10. 1 63¼
	5. 0 81¾	11. 1 79¾
½	6. 0 98	

Sixteenths

	1. 0 12¼	9. 1 10¼
⅛	2. 0 24½	⅝ 10. 1 22½
	3. 0 36¾	11. 1 34¾
¼	4. 0 49	¾ 12. 1 47
	5. 0 61¼	13. 1 59¼
⅜	6. 0 73½	⅞ 14. 1 71½
	7. 0 85¾	15. 1 83¾
	8. 0 98	

Twentieths (10ths)

	1. 0 9¾		11. 1 7¾
·1	2. 0 19½	·6	12. 1 17½
	3. 0 29¼		13. 1 27¼
·2	4. 0 39¼	·7	14. 1 37¼
	5. 0 49		15. 1 47
·3	6. 0 58¾	·8	16. 1 56¾
	7. 0 68½		17. 1 66½
·4	8. 0 78½	·9	18. 1 76½
	9. 0 88¼		19. 1 86¼
·5	10. 0 98		20. 1 96

£ 1·97

*Dozens		£	P
	1	1	97
	2	3	94
	3	5	91
	4	7	88
	5	9	85
	6	11	82
	7	13	79
	8	15	76
	9	17	73
	10	19	70
	11	21	67
1	12	23	64
	13	25	61
	14	27	58
	15	29	55
	16	31	52
	17	33	49
	18	35	46
	19	37	43
	20	39	40
	21	41	37
	22	43	34
	23	45	31
2	24	47	28
	25	49	25
	26	51	22
	27	53	19
	28	55	16
	29	57	13
	30	59	10
	31	61	7
	32	63	4
	33	65	1
	34	66	98
	35	68	95
3	36	70	92
	37	72	89
	38	74	86
	39	76	83
	40	78	80
	41	80	77
	42	82	74
	43	84	71
	44	86	68
	45	88	65
	46	90	62
	47	92	59
4	48	94	56
	49	96	53
	50	98	50

Dozens		£	P
	51	100	47
	52	102	44
	53	104	41
	54	106	38
	55	108	35
	56	110	32
	57	112	29
	58	114	26
	59	116	23
5	**60**	118	20
	61	120	17
	62	122	14
	63	124	11
	64	126	8
	65	128	5
	66	130	2
	67	131	99
	68	133	96
	69	135	93
	70	137	90
	71	139	87
6	72	141	84
	75	147	75
	80	157	60
7	84	165	48
	90	177	30
8	96	189	12
	100	197	0
10	120	236	40
	140	275	80
	150	295	50
	160	315	20
	180	354	60
	200	394	0
25	300	591	0
	365	719	5
	400	788	0
	500	985	0
	600	1182	0
	700	1379	0
	800	1576	0
	900	1773	0
	1000	1970	0

Twelfths

	1. 0 16½	7. 1 15
⅙	2. 0 32¾	⅔ 8. 1 31¼
	3. 0 49¼	9. 1 47¾
⅓	4. 0 65¾	⅚ 10. 1 64¼
	5. 0 82	11. 1 80½
½	6. 0 98½	

Sixteenths

	1. 0 12¼	9. 1 10¾
⅛	2. 0 24¾	⅝ 10. 1 23¼
	3. 0 37	11. 1 35½
¼	4. 0 49¼	¾ 12. 1 47¾
	5. 0 61½	13. 1 60
⅜	6. 0 74	⅞ 14. 1 72½
	7. 0 86¼	15. 1 84¾
½	8. 0 98½	

Twentieths (10ths)

	1. 0 9¾		11. 1 8½
·1	2. 0 19¾	·6	12. 1 18¼
	3. 0 29½		13. 1 28
·2	4. 0 39½	·7	14. 1 38
	5 0 49¼		15. 1 47¾
·3	6. 0 59	·8	16. 1 57½
	7. 0 69		17. 1 67½
·4	8. 0 78¾	·9	18. 1 77¼
	9. 0 88¾		19 1 87¼
·5	10. 0 98½		20. 1 97

£ 1·98

Dozens	No.	£	P	Dozens	No.	£	P
	1	1	98		51	100	98
	2	3	96		52	102	96
	3	5	94		53	104	94
	4	7	92		54	106	92
	5	9	90		55	108	90
	6	11	88		56	110	88
	7	13	86		57	112	86
	8	15	84		58	114	84
	9	17	82		59	116	82
	10	19	80	5	**60**	118	80
*	11	21	78		61	120	78
1	12	23	76		62	122	76
	13	25	74		63	124	74
	14	27	72		64	126	72
	15	29	70		65	128	70
	16	31	68		66	130	68
	17	33	66		67	132	66
	18	35	64		68	134	64
	19	37	62		69	136	62
	20	39	60		**70**	138	60
	21	41	58		71	140	58
	22	43	56	6	72	142	56
	23	45	54		75	148	50
2	24	47	52		80	158	40
	25	49	50	7	84	166	32
	26	51	48		90	178	20
	27	53	46	8	96	190	8
	28	55	44		100	198	0
	29	57	42	9	108	213	84
	30	59	40		112	221	76
	31	61	38	10	120	237	60
	32	63	36	11	132	261	36
	33	65	34	12	144	285	12
	34	67	32		200	396	0
	35	69	30	25	300	594	0
3	36	71	28		365	722	70
	37	73	26		400	792	0
	38	75	24		500	990	0
	39	77	22		600	1188	0
	40	79	20		700	1386	0
	41	81	18		800	1584	0
	42	83	16		900	1782	0
	43	85	14		1000	1980	0
	44	87	12				
	45	89	10				
	46	91	8				
	47	93	6				
4	48	95	4				
	49	97	2				
	50	99	0				

*Dozens

Twelfths

1.	0	16½	7.	1	15½
⅙ 2.	0	33	⅔ 8.	1	32
3.	0	49½	9.	1	48½
⅓ 4.	0	66	⅚ 10.	1	65
5.	0	82½	11.	1	81½
½ 6.	0	99			

Sixteenths

1.	0	12½	9.	1	11½
⅛ 2.	0	24¾	⅝ 10.	1	23¾
3.	0	37¼	11.	1	36¼
¼ 4.	0	49½	¾ 12.	1	48½
5.	0	62	13.	1	61
⅜ 6.	0	74¼	⅞ 14.	1	73¼
7.	0	86¾	15.	1	85¾
½ 8.	0	99			

Twentieths (10ths)

1.	0	10	11.	1	9
·1 2.	0	19¾	·6 12.	1	18¾
3.	0	29¾	13.	1	28¾
·2 4.	0	39½	·7 14.	1	38½
5.	0	49½	15.	1	48½
·3 6.	0	59½	·8 16.	1	58½
7.	0	69¼	17.	1	68¼
·4 8.	0	79¼	·9 18.	1	78¼
9.	0	89	19.	1	88
·5 10.	0	99	20.	1	98

£ 1·99

Dozens	No.	£	P	Dozens	No.	£	P
	1	1	99		51	101	49
	2	3	98		52	103	48
	3	5	97		53	105	47
	4	7	96		54	107	46
	5	9	95		55	109	45
	6	11	94		56	111	44
	7	13	93		57	113	43
	8	15	92		58	115	42
	9	17	91		59	117	41
	10	19	90	5	**60**	119	40
	11	21	89		61	121	39
1	12	23	88		62	123	38
	13	25	87		63	125	37
	14	27	86		64	127	36
	15	29	85		65	129	35
	16	31	84		66	131	34
	17	33	83		67	133	33
	18	35	82		68	135	32
	19	37	81		69	137	31
	20	39	80		**70**	139	30
	21	41	79		71	141	29
	22	43	78	6	72	143	28
	23	45	77		75	149	25
2	24	47	76		80	159	20
	25	49	75	7	84	167	16
	26	51	74		90	179	10
	27	53	73	8	96	191	4
	28	55	72		100	199	0
	29	57	71	9	108	214	92
	30	59	70		112	222	88
	31	61	69	10	120	238	80
	32	63	68	11	132	262	68
	33	65	67	12	144	286	56
	34	67	66		200	398	0
	35	69	65	25	300	597	0
3	36	71	64		365	726	35
	37	73	63		400	796	0
	38	75	62		500	995	0
	39	77	61		600	1194	0
	40	79	60		700	1393	0
	41	81	59		800	1592	0
	42	83	58		900	1791	0
	43	85	57		1000	1990	0
	44	87	56				
	45	89	55				
	46	91	54				
	47	93	53				
4	48	95	52				
	49	97	51				
	50	99	50				

*Dozens

Twelfths

1.	0	16½	7.	1	16
⅙ 2.	0	33¼	⅔ 8.	1	32¾
3.	0	49¾	9.	1	49¼
⅓ 4.	0	66¼	⅚ 10.	1	65¾
5.	0	83	11.	1	82½
½ 6.	0	99½			

Sixteenths

1.	0	12½	9.	1	12
⅛ 2.	0	25	⅝ 10.	1	24½
3.	0	37¼	11.	1	36¾
¼ 4.	0	49¾	¾ 12.	1	49¼
5.	0	62¼	13.	1	61¾
⅜ 6.	0	74¾	⅞ 14.	1	74¼
7.	0	87	15.	1	86½
½ 8.	0	99½			

Twentieths (10ths)

1.	0	10	11.	1	9½
·1 2.	0	20	·6 12.	1	19½
3.	0	29¾	13.	1	29¼
·2 4.	0	39¾	·7 14.	1	39¼
5.	0	49¾	15.	1	49¼
·3 6.	0	59¾	·8 16.	1	59¼
7.	0	69¾	17.	1	69¼
·4 8.	0	79½	·9 18.	1	79
9.	0	89½	19.	1	89
·5 10.	0	99½	20.	1	99

EXTENSION

from

£2·05 to £9·05

rising by

5 PENNY INTERVALS

No.	£2·05 £	£2·05 p	£2·10 £	£2·10 p	£2·15 £	£2·15 p	No.	£2·05 £	£2·05 p	£2·10 £	£2·10 p	£2·15 £	£2·15 p
1	2	05	2	10	2	15	51	104	55	107	10	109	65
2	4	10	4	20	4	30	52	106	60	109	20	111	80
3	6	15	6	30	6	45	53	108	65	111	30	113	95
4	8	20	8	40	8	60	54	110	70	113	40	116	10
5	10	25	10	50	10	75	55	112	75	115	50	118	25
6	12	30	12	60	12	90	56	114	80	117	60	120	40
7	14	35	14	70	15	05	57	116	85	119	70	122	55
8	16	40	16	80	17	20	58	118	90	121	80	124	70
9	18	45	18	90	19	35	59	120	95	123	90	126	85
10	20	50	21	00	21	50	60	123	00	126	00	129	00
11	22	55	23	10	23	65	61	125	05	128	10	131	15
12	24	60	25	20	25	80	62	127	10	130	20	133	30
13	26	65	27	30	27	95	63	129	15	132	30	135	45
14	28	70	29	40	30	10	64	131	20	134	40	137	60
15	30	75	31	50	32	25	65	133	25	136	50	139	75
16	32	80	33	60	34	40	66	135	30	138	60	141	90
17	34	85	35	70	36	55	67	137	35	140	70	144	05
18	36	90	37	80	38	70	68	139	40	142	80	146	20
19	38	95	39	90	40	85	69	141	45	144	90	148	35
20	41	00	42	00	43	00	70	143	50	147	00	150	50
21	43	05	44	10	45	15	71	145	55	149	10	152	65
22	45	10	46	20	47	30	72	147	60	151	20	154	80
23	47	15	48	30	49	45	73	149	65	153	30	156	95
24	49	20	50	40	51	60	74	151	70	155	40	159	10
25	51	25	52	50	53	75	75	153	75	157	50	161	25
26	53	30	54	60	55	90	76	155	80	159	60	163	40
27	55	35	56	70	58	05	77	157	85	161	70	165	55
28	57	40	58	80	60	20	78	159	90	163	80	167	70
29	59	45	60	90	62	35	79	161	95	165	90	169	85
30	61	50	63	00	64	50	80	164	00	168	00	172	00
31	63	55	65	10	66	65	81	166	05	170	10	174	15
32	65	60	67	20	68	80	82	168	10	172	20	176	30
33	67	65	69	30	70	95	83	170	15	174	30	178	45
34	69	70	71	40	73	10	84	172	20	176	40	180	60
35	71	75	73	50	75	25	85	174	25	178	50	182	75
36	73	80	75	60	77	40	86	176	30	180	60	184	90
37	75	85	77	70	79	55	87	178	35	182	70	187	05
38	77	90	79	80	81	70	88	180	40	184	80	189	20
39	79	95	81	90	83	85	89	182	45	186	90	191	35
40	82	00	84	00	86	00	90	184	50	189	00	193	50
41	84	05	86	10	88	15	91	186	55	191	10	195	65
42	86	10	88	20	90	30	92	188	60	193	20	197	80
43	88	15	90	30	92	45	93	190	65	195	30	199	95
44	90	20	92	40	94	60	94	192	70	197	40	202	10
45	92	25	94	50	96	75	95	194	75	199	50	204	25
46	94	30	96	60	98	90	96	196	80	201	60	206	40
47	96	35	98	70	101	05	97	198	85	203	70	208	55
48	98	40	100	80	103	20	98	200	90	205	80	210	70
49	100	45	102	90	105	35	99	202	95	207	90	212	85
50	102	50	105	00	107	50	100	205	00	210	00	215	00
¼	0·5125		0·525		0·5375		¾	1·5375		1·575		1·6125	
½	1·0250		1·050		1·0750		1¼	2·5625		2·625		2·6875	

No.	£2·05 £	p	£2·10 £	p	£2·15 £	p	No.	£2·05 £	p	£2·10 £	p	£2·15 £	p
101	207	05	212	10	217	15	Doz155	317	75	325	50	333	25
102	209	10	214	20	219	30	13156	319	80	327	60	335	40
103	211	15	216	30	221	45	165	338	25	346	50	354	75
104	213	20	218	40	223	60	14168	344	40	352	80	361	20
105	215	25	220	50	225	75	175	358	75	367	50	376	25
106	217	30	222	60	227	90	15180	369	00	378	00	387	00
107	219	35	224	70	230	05	185	379	25	388	50	397	75
9108	221	40	226	80	232	20	16192	393	60	403	20	412	80
109	223	45	228	90	234	35	195	399	75	409	50	419	25
110	225	50	231	00	236	50	200	410	00	420	00	430	00
111	227	55	233	10	238	65	17204	418	20	428	40	438	60
112	229	60	235	20	240	80	205	420	25	430	50	440	75
113	231	65	237	30	242	95	215	440	75	451	50	462	25
114	233	70	239	40	245	10	18216	442	80	453	60	464	40
115	235	75	241	50	247	25	224	459	20	470	40	481	60
116	237	80	243	60	249	40	225	461	25	472	50	483	75
117	239	85	245	70	251	55	19228	467	40	478	80	490	20
118	241	90	247	80	253	70	235	481	75	493	50	505	25
119	243	95	249	90	255	85	245	502	25	514	50	526	75
10120	246	00	252	00	258	00	250	512	50	525	00	537	50
121	248	05	254	10	260	15	21252	516	60	529	20	541	80
122	250	10	256	20	262	30	255	522	75	535	50	548	25
123	252	15	258	30	264	45	265	543	25	556	50	569	75
124	254	20	260	40	266	60	272	557	60	571	20	584	80
125	256	25	262	50	268	75	275	563	75	577	50	591	25
126	258	30	264	60	270	90	280	574	00	588	00	602	00
127	260	35	266	70	273	05	285	584	25	598	50	612	75
128	262	40	268	80	275	20	288	590	40	604	80	619	20
129	264	45	270	90	277	35	295	604	75	619	50	634	25
130	266	50	273	00	279	50	300	615	00	630	00	645	00
131	268	55	275	10	281	65	325	666	25	682	50	698	75
11132	270	60	277	20	283	80	336	688	80	705	60	722	40
133	272	65	279	30	285	95	365	748	25	766	50	784	75
134	274	70	281	40	288	10	375	768	75	787	50	806	25
135	276	75	283	50	290	25	400	820	00	840	00	860	00
136	278	80	285	60	292	40	425	871	25	892	50	913	75
137	280	85	287	70	294	55	432	885	60	907	20	928	80
138	282	90	289	80	296	70	475	973	75	997	50	1021	25
139	284	95	291	90	298	85	480	984	00	1008	00	1032	00
140	287	00	294	00	301	00	500	1025	00	1050	00	1075	00
141	289	05	296	10	303	15	504	1033	20	1058	40	1083	60
142	291	10	298	20	305	30	576	1180	80	1209	60	1238	40
143	293	15	300	30	307	45	600	1230	00	1260	00	1290	00
12144	295	20	302	40	309	60	700	1435	00	1470	00	1505	00
145	297	25	304	50	311	75	750	1537	50	1575	00	1612	50
146	299	30	306	60	313	90	800	1640	00	1680	00	1720	00
147	301	35	308	70	316	05	900	1845	00	1890	00	1935	00
148	303	40	310	80	318	20	1000	2050	00	2100	00	2150	00
149	305	45	312	90	320	35	2500	5125	00	5250	00	5375	00
150	307	50	315	00	322	50	5000	10250	·0	10500	·0	10750	·0
1016	2082·80		2133·60		2184·40		1728	3542·40		3628·80		3715·20	
1296	2656·80		2721·60		2786·40		1760	3608·00		3696·00		3784·00	

No.	£2·20 £	£2·20 p	£2·25 £	£2·25 p	£2·30 £	£2·30 p	No.	£2·20 £	£2·20 p	£2·25 £	£2·25 p	£2·30 £	£2·30 p
1	2	20	2	25	2	30	51	112	20	114	75	117	30
2	4	40	4	50	4	60	52	114	40	117	00	119	60
3	6	60	6	75	6	90	53	116	60	119	25	121	90
4	8	80	9	00	9	20	54	118	80	121	50	124	20
5	11	00	11	25	11	50	55	121	00	123	75	126	50
6	13	20	13	50	13	80	56	123	20	126	00	128	80
7	15	40	15	75	16	10	57	125	40	128	25	131	10
8	17	60	18	00	18	40	58	127	60	130	50	133	40
9	19	80	20	25	20	70	59	129	80	132	75	135	70
10	22	00	22	50	23	00	60	132	00	135	00	138	00
11	24	20	24	75	25	30	61	134	20	137	25	140	30
12	26	40	27	00	27	60	62	136	40	139	50	142	60
13	28	60	29	25	29	90	63	138	60	141	75	144	90
14	30	80	31	50	32	20	64	140	80	144	00	147	20
15	33	00	33	75	34	50	65	143	00	146	25	149	50
16	35	20	36	00	36	80	66	145	20	148	50	151	80
17	37	40	38	25	39	10	67	147	40	150	75	154	10
18	39	60	40	50	41	40	68	149	60	153	00	156	40
19	41	80	42	75	43	70	69	151	80	155	25	158	70
20	44	00	45	00	46	00	70	154	00	157	50	161	00
21	46	20	47	25	48	30	71	156	20	159	75	163	30
22	48	40	49	50	50	60	72	158	40	162	00	165	60
23	50	60	51	75	52	90	73	160	60	164	25	167	90
24	52	80	54	00	55	20	74	162	80	166	50	170	20
25	55	00	56	25	57	50	75	165	00	168	75	172	50
26	57	20	58	50	59	80	76	167	20	171	00	174	80
27	59	40	60	75	62	10	77	169	40	173	25	177	10
28	61	60	63	00	64	40	78	171	60	175	50	179	40
29	63	80	65	25	66	70	79	173	80	177	75	181	70
30	66	00	67	50	69	00	80	176	00	180	00	184	00
31	68	20	69	75	71	30	81	178	20	182	25	186	30
32	70	40	72	00	73	60	82	180	40	184	50	188	60
33	72	60	74	25	75	90	83	182	60	186	75	190	90
34	74	80	76	50	78	20	84	184	80	189	00	193	20
35	77	00	78	75	80	50	85	187	00	191	25	195	50
36	79	20	81	00	82	80	86	189	20	193	50	197	80
37	81	40	83	25	85	10	87	191	40	195	75	200	10
38	83	60	85	50	87	40	88	193	60	198	00	202	40
39	85	80	87	75	89	70	89	195	80	200	25	204	70
40	88	00	90	00	92	00	90	198	00	202	50	207	00
41	90	20	92	25	94	30	91	200	20	204	75	209	30
42	92	40	94	50	96	60	92	202	40	207	00	211	60
43	94	60	96	75	98	90	93	204	60	209	25	213	90
44	96	80	99	00	101	20	94	206	80	211	50	216	20
45	99	00	101	25	103	50	95	209	00	213	75	218	50
46	101	20	103	50	105	80	96	211	20	216	00	220	80
47	103	40	105	75	108	10	97	213	40	218	25	223	10
48	105	60	108	00	110	40	98	215	60	220	50	225	40
49	107	80	110	25	112	70	99	217	80	222	75	227	70
50	110	00	112	50	115	00	100	220	00	225	00	230	00
¼	0·550		0·5625		0·5750		¾	1·650		1·6875		1·7250	
½..	1·10		1·1250		1·150		1¼..	2·750		2·8125		2·8750	

No.	£2·20		£2·25		£2·30	
	£	p	£	p	£	p
101	222	20	227	25	232	30
102	224	40	229	50	234	60
103	226	60	231	75	236	90
104	228	80	234	00	239	20
105	231	00	236	25	241	50
106	233	20	238	50	243	80
107	235	40	240	75	246	10
[9]108	237	60	243	00	248	40
109	239	80	245	25	250	70
110	242	00	247	50	253	00
111	244	20	249	75	255	30
112	246	40	252	00	257	60
113	248	60	254	25	259	90
114	250	80	256	50	262	20
115	253	00	258	75	264	50
116	255	20	261	00	266	80
117	257	40	263	25	269	10
118	259	60	265	50	271	40
119	261	80	267	75	273	70
[10]120	264	00	270	00	276	00
121	266	20	272	25	278	30
122	268	40	274	50	280	60
123	270	60	276	75	282	90
124	272	80	279	00	285	20
125	275	00	281	25	287	50
126	277	20	283	50	289	80
127	279	40	285	75	292	10
128	281	60	288	00	294	40
129	283	80	290	25	296	70
130	286	00	292	50	299	00
131	288	20	294	75	301	30
[11]132	290	40	297	00	303	60
133	292	60	299	25	305	90
134	294	80	301	50	308	20
135	297	00	303	75	310	50
136	299	20	306	00	312	80
137	301	40	308	25	315	10
138	303	60	310	50	317	40
139	305	80	312	75	319	70
140	308	00	315	00	322	00
141	310	20	317	25	324	30
142	312	40	319	50	326	60
143	314	60	321	75	328	90
[12]144	316	80	324	00	331	20
145	319	00	326	25	333	50
146	321	20	328	50	335	80
147	323	40	330	75	338	10
148	325	60	333	00	340	40
149	327	80	335	25	342	70
150	330	00	337	50	345	00
1016	2235·20		2286·00		2336·80	
1296	2851·20		2916·00		2980·80	

No.	£2·20		£2·25		£2·30	
155	341	00	348	75	356	50
[13]156	343	20	351	00	358	80
165	363	00	371	25	379	50
[14]168	369	60	378	00	386	40
175	385	00	393	75	402	50
[15]180	396	00	405	00	414	00
185	407	00	416	25	425	50
[16]192	422	40	432	00	441	60
195	429	00	438	75	448	50
200	440	00	450	00	460	00
[17]204	448	80	459	00	469	20
205	451	00	461	25	471	50
215	473	00	483	75	494	50
[18]216	475	20	486	00	496	80
224	492	80	504	00	515	20
225	495	00	506	25	517	50
[19]228	501	60	513	00	524	40
235	517	00	528	75	540	50
245	539	00	551	25	563	50
250	550	00	562	50	575	00
[21]252	554	40	567	00	579	60
255	561	00	573	75	586	50
265	583	00	596	25	609	50
272	598	40	612	00	625	60
275	605	00	618	75	632	50
280	616	00	630	00	644	00
285 (2 gross)	627	00	641	25	655	50
288 (2 gross)	633	60	648	00	662	40
295	649	00	663	75	678	50
300	660	00	675	00	690	00
325	715	00	731	25	747	50
336	739	20	756	00	772	80
365	803	00	821	25	839	50
375	825	00	843	75	862	50
400	880	00	900	00	920	00
425 (3 gr.)	935	00	956	25	977	50
432 (3 gr.)	950	40	972	00	993	60
475	1045	00	1068	75	1092	50
480	1056	00	1080	00	1104	00
500	1100	00	1125	00	1150	00
504 (4 gr.)	1108	80	1134	00	1159	20
576 (4 gr.)	1267	20	1296	00	1324	80
600	1320	00	1350	00	1380	00
700	1540	00	1575	00	1610	00
750	1650	00	1687	50	1725	00
800	1760	00	1800	00	1840	00
900	1980	00	2025	00	2070	00
1000	2200	00	2250	00	2300	00
2500	5500	00	5625	00	5750	00
5000	11000	·0	11250	·0	11500	·0
1728	3801·60		3888·00		3974·40	
1760	3872·00		3960·00		4048·00	

No.	£2·35		£2·40		£2·45		No.	£2·35		£2·40		£2·45	
	£	P	£	P	£	P		£	P	£	P	£	P
1	2	35	2	40	2	45	51	119	85	122	40	124	95
2	4	70	4	80	4	90	52	122	20	124	80	127	40
3	7	05	7	20	7	35	53	124	55	127	20	129	85
4	9	40	9	60	9	80	54	126	90	129	60	132	30
5	11	75	12	00	12	25	55	129	25	132	00	134	75
6	14	10	14	40	14	70	56	131	60	134	40	137	20
7	16	45	16	80	17	15	57	133	95	136	80	139	65
8	18	80	19	20	19	60	58	136	30	139	20	142	10
9	21	15	21	60	22	05	59	138	65	141	60	144	55
10	23	50	24	00	24	50	60	141	00	144	00	147	00
11	25	85	26	40	26	95	61	143	35	146	40	149	45
12	28	20	28	80	29	40	62	145	70	148	80	151	90
13	30	55	31	20	31	85	63	148	05	151	20	154	35
14	32	90	33	60	34	30	64	150	40	153	60	156	80
15	35	25	36	00	36	75	65	152	75	156	00	159	25
16	37	60	38	40	39	20	66	155	10	158	40	161	70
17	39	95	40	80	41	65	67	157	45	160	80	164	15
18	42	30	43	20	44	10	68	159	80	163	20	166	60
19	44	65	45	60	46	55	69	162	15	165	60	169	05
20	47	00	48	00	49	00	70	164	50	168	00	171	50
21	49	35	50	40	51	45	71	166	85	170	40	173	95
22	51	70	52	80	53	90	72	169	20	172	80	176	40
23	54	05	55	20	56	35	73	171	55	175	20	178	85
24	56	40	57	60	58	80	74	173	90	177	60	181	30
25	58	75	60	00	61	25	75	176	25	180	00	183	75
26	61	10	62	40	63	70	76	178	60	182	40	186	20
27	63	45	64	80	66	15	77	180	95	184	80	188	65
28	65	80	67	20	68	60	78	183	30	187	20	191	10
29	68	15	69	60	71	05	79	185	65	189	60	193	55
30	70	50	72	00	73	50	80	188	00	192	00	196	00
31	72	85	74	40	75	95	81	190	35	194	40	198	45
32	75	20	76	80	78	40	82	192	70	196	80	200	90
33	77	55	79	20	80	85	83	195	05	199	20	203	35
34	79	90	81	60	83	30	84	197	40	201	60	205	80
35	82	25	84	00	85	75	85	199	75	204	00	208	25
36	84	60	86	40	88	20	86	202	10	206	40	210	70
37	86	95	88	80	90	65	87	204	45	208	80	213	15
38	89	30	91	20	93	10	88	206	80	211	20	215	60
39	91	65	93	60	95	55	89	209	15	213	60	218	05
40	94	00	96	00	98	00	90	211	50	216	00	220	50
41	96	35	98	40	100	45	91	213	85	218	40	222	95
42	98	70	100	80	102	90	92	216	20	220	80	225	40
43	101	05	103	20	105	35	93	218	55	223	20	227	85
44	103	40	105	60	107	80	94	220	90	225	60	230	30
45	105	75	108	00	110	25	95	223	25	228	00	232	75
46	108	10	110	40	112	70	96	225	60	230	40	235	20
47	110	45	112	80	115	15	97	227	95	232	80	237	65
48	112	80	115	20	117	60	98	230	30	235	20	240	10
49	115	15	117	60	120	05	99	232	65	237	60	242	55
50	117	50	120	00	122	50	100	235	00	240	00	245	00

	£2·35	£2·40	£2·45		£2·35	£2·40	£2·45
⅛	0·5875	0·60	0·6125	¾	1·7625	1·80	1·8875
¼	1·1750	1·20	1·2250	1¼	2·9375	3·00	3·0625

No.	£2·35		£2·40		£2·45	
	£	p	£	p	£	p
101	237	35	242	40	247	45
102	239	70	244	80	249	90
103	242	05	247	20	252	35
104	244	40	249	60	254	80
105	246	75	252	00	257	25
106	249	10	254	40	259	70
107	251	45	256	80	262	15
9 108	253	80	259	20	264	60
109	256	15	261	60	267	05
110	258	50	264	00	269	50
111	260	85	266	40	271	95
112	263	20	268	80	274	40
113	265	55	271	20	276	85
114	267	90	273	60	279	30
115	270	25	276	00	281	75
116	272	60	278	40	284	20
117	274	95	280	80	286	65
118	277	30	283	20	289	10
119	279	65	285	60	291	55
10 120	282	00	288	00	294	00
121	284	35	290	40	296	45
122	286	70	292	80	298	90
123	289	05	295	20	301	35
124	291	40	297	60	303	80
125	293	75	300	00	306	25
126	296	10	302	40	308	70
127	298	45	304	80	311	15
128	300	80	307	20	313	60
129	303	15	309	60	316	05
130	305	50	312	00	318	50
131	307	85	314	40	320	95
11 132	310	20	316	80	323	40
133	312	55	319	20	325	85
134	314	90	321	60	328	30
135	317	25	324	00	330	75
136	319	60	326	40	333	20
137	321	95	328	80	335	65
138	324	30	331	20	338	10
139	326	65	333	60	340	55
140	329	00	336	00	343	00
141	331	35	338	40	345	45
142	333	70	340	80	347	90
143	336	05	343	20	350	35
12 144	338	40	345	60	352	80
145	340	75	348	00	355	25
146	343	10	350	40	357	70
147	345	45	352	80	360	15
148	347	80	355	20	362	60
149	350	15	357	60	365	05
150	352	50	360	00	367	50
1016	2387·60		2438·40		2489·20	
1296	3045·60		3110·40		3175·20	

No.	£2·35		£2·40		£2·45	
	£	p	£	p	£	p
Doz 155	364	25	372	00	379	75
13 156	366	60	374	40	382	20
165	387	75	396	00	404	25
14 168	394	80	403	20	411	60
175	411	25	420	00	428	75
15 180	423	00	432	00	441	00
185	434	75	444	00	453	25
16 192	451	20	460	80	470	40
195	458	25	468	00	477	75
200	470	00	480	00	490	00
17 204	479	40	489	60	499	80
205	481	75	492	00	502	25
215	505	25	516	00	526	75
18 216	507	60	518	40	529	20
224	526	40	537	60	548	80
225	528	75	540	00	551	25
19 228	535	80	547	20	558	60
235	552	25	564	00	575	75
245	575	75	588	00	600	25
250	587	50	600	00	612	50
21 252	592	20	604	80	617	40
255	599	25	612	00	624	75
265	622	75	636	00	649	25
272	639	20	652	80	666	40
275	646	25	660	00	673	75
280	658	00	672	00	686	00
285	669	75	684	00	698	25
2 gross 288	676	80	691	20	705	60
295	693	25	708	00	722	75
300	705	00	720	00	735	00
325	763	75	780	00	796	25
336	789	60	806	40	823	20
365	857	75	876	00	894	25
375	881	25	900	00	918	75
400	940	00	960	00	980	00
425	998	75	1020	00	1041	25
3 gr. 432	1015	20	1036	80	1058	40
475	1116	25	1140	00	1163	75
480	1128	00	1152	00	1176	00
500	1175	00	1200	00	1225	00
504	1184	40	1209	60	1234	80
4 gr. 576	1353	60	1382	40	1411	20
600	1410	00	1440	00	1470	00
700	1645	00	1680	00	1715	00
750	1762	50	1800	00	1837	50
800	1880	00	1920	00	1960	00
900	2115	00	2160	00	2205	00
1000	2350	00	2400	00	2450	00
2500	5875	00	6000	00	6125	00
5000	11750	·0	12000	·0	12250	·0
1728	4060·80		4147·20		4283·60	
1760	4136·00		4224·00		4312·00	

No.	£2·50 £	P	£2·55 £	P	£2·60 £	P	No.	£2·50 £	P	£2·55 £	P	£2·60 £	P
1	2	50	2	55	2	60	51	127	50	130	05	132	60
2	5	00	5	10	5	20	52	130	00	132	60	135	20
3	7	50	7	65	7	80	53	132	50	135	15	137	80
4	10	00	10	20	10	40	54	135	00	137	70	140	40
5	12	50	12	75	13	00	55	137	50	140	25	143	00
6	15	00	15	30	15	60	56	140	00	142	80	145	60
7	17	50	17	85	18	20	57	142	50	145	35	148	20
8	20	00	20	40	20	80	58	145	00	147	90	150	80
9	22	50	22	95	23	40	59	147	50	150	45	153	40
10	25	00	25	50	26	00	60	150	00	153	00	156	00
11	27	50	28	05	28	60	61	152	50	155	55	158	60
12	30	00	30	60	31	20	62	155	00	158	10	161	20
13	32	50	33	15	33	80	63	157	50	160	65	163	80
14	35	00	35	70	36	40	64	160	00	163	20	166	40
15	37	50	38	25	39	00	65	162	50	165	75	169	00
16	40	00	40	80	41	60	66	165	00	168	30	171	60
17	42	50	43	35	44	20	67	167	50	170	85	174	20
18	45	00	45	90	46	80	68	170	00	173	40	176	80
19	47	50	48	45	49	40	69	172	50	175	95	179	40
20	50	00	51	00	52	00	70	175	00	178	50	182	00
21	52	50	53	55	54	60	71	177	50	181	05	184	60
22	55	00	56	10	57	20	72	180	00	183	60	187	20
23	57	50	58	65	59	80	73	182	50	186	15	189	80
24	60	00	61	20	62	40	74	185	00	188	70	192	40
25	62	50	63	75	65	00	75	187	50	191	25	195	00
26	65	00	66	30	67	60	76	190	00	193	80	197	60
27	67	50	68	85	70	20	77	192	50	196	35	200	20
28	70	00	71	40	72	80	78	195	00	198	90	202	80
29	72	50	73	95	75	40	79	197	50	201	45	205	40
30	75	00	76	50	78	00	80	200	00	204	00	208	00
31	77	50	79	05	80	60	81	202	50	206	55	210	60
32	80	00	81	60	83	20	82	205	00	209	10	213	20
33	82	50	84	15	85	80	83	207	50	211	65	215	80
34	85	00	86	70	88	40	84	210	00	214	20	218	40
35	87	50	89	25	91	00	85	212	50	216	75	221	00
36	90	00	91	80	93	00	86	215	00	219	30	223	60
37	92	50	94	35	96	20	87	217	50	221	85	226	20
38	95	00	96	90	98	80	88	220	00	224	40	228	80
39	97	50	99	45	101	40	89	222	50	226	95	231	40
40	100	00	102	00	104	00	90	225	00	229	50	234	00
41	102	50	104	55	106	60	91	227	50	232	05	236	60
42	105	00	107	10	109	20	92	230	00	234	60	239	20
43	107	50	109	65	111	80	93	232	50	237	15	241	80
44	110	00	112	20	114	40	94	235	00	239	70	244	40
45	112	50	114	75	117	00	95	237	50	242	25	247	00
46	115	00	117	30	119	60	96	240	00	244	80	249	60
47	117	50	119	85	122	20	97	242	50	247	35	252	20
48	120	00	122	40	124	80	98	245	00	249	90	254	80
49	122	50	124	95	127	40	99	247	50	252	45	257	40
50	125	00	127	50	130	00	100	250	00	255	00	260	00
¼	0·625		0·6375		0·650		¾	1·875		1·9125		1·95	
½	1·250		1·2750		1·80		1¼	3·125		3·1875		3·25	

Dozens.

No.	£2·50 £	p	£2·55 £	p	£2·60 £	p
101	252	50	257	55	262	60
102	255	00	260	10	265	20
103	257	50	262	65	267	80
104	260	00	265	20	270	40
105	262	50	267	75	273	00
106	265	00	270	30	275	60
107	267	50	272	85	278	20
⁹108	270	00	275	40	280	80
109	272	50	277	95	283	40
110	275	00	280	50	286	00
111	277	50	283	05	288	60
112	280	00	285	60	291	20
113	282	50	288	15	293	80
114	285	00	290	70	296	40
115	287	50	293	25	299	00
116	290	00	295	80	301	60
117	292	50	298	35	304	20
118	295	00	300	90	306	80
119	297	50	303	45	309	40
¹⁰120	300	00	306	00	312	00
121	302	50	308	55	314	60
122	305	00	311	10	317	20
123	307	50	313	65	319	80
124	310	00	316	20	322	40
125	312	50	318	75	325	00
126	315	00	321	30	327	60
127	317	50	323	85	330	20
128	320	00	326	40	332	80
129	322	50	328	95	335	40
130	325	00	331	50	338	00
131	327	50	334	05	340	60
¹¹132	330	00	336	60	343	20
133	332	50	339	15	345	80
134	335	00	341	70	348	40
135	337	50	344	25	351	00
136	340	00	346	80	353	60
137	342	50	349	35	356	20
138	345	00	351	90	358	80
139	347	50	354	45	361	40
140	350	00	357	00	364	00
141	352	50	359	55	366	60
142	355	00	362	10	369	20
143	357	50	364	65	371	80
¹²144	360	00	367	20	374	40
145	362	50	369	75	377	00
146	365	00	372	30	379	60
147	367	50	374	85	382	20
148	370	00	377	40	384	80
149	372	50	379	95	387	40
150	375	00	382	50	390	00
1016	2540·00		2590·80		2641·60	
1296	3240·00		3304·80		3369·60	

No.	£2·50 £	p	£2·55 £	p	£2·60 £	p
155	387	50	395	25	403	00
¹³156	390	00	397	80	405	60
165	412	50	420	75	429	00
¹⁴168	420	00	428	40	436	80
175	437	50	446	25	455	00
¹⁵180	450	00	459	00	468	00
185	462	50	471	75	481	00
¹⁶192	480	00	489	60	499	20
195	487	50	497	25	507	00
200	500	00	510	00	520	00
¹⁷204	510	00	520	20	530	40
205	512	50	522	75	533	00
215	537	50	548	25	559	00
¹⁸216	540	00	550	80	561	60
224	560	00	571	20	582	40
225	562	50	573	75	585	00
¹⁹228	570	00	581	40	592	80
235	587	50	599	25	611	00
245	612	50	624	75	637	00
250	625	00	637	50	650	00
²¹252	630	00	642	60	655	20
255	637	50	650	25	663	00
265	662	50	675	75	689	00
272	680	00	693	60	707	20
275	687	50	701	25	715	00
280	700	00	714	00	728	00
285	712	50	726	75	741	00
2 gross 288	720	00	734	40	748	80
295	737	50	752	25	767	00
300	750	00	765	00	780	00
325	812	50	828	75	845	00
336	840	00	856	80	873	60
365	912	50	930	75	949	00
375	937	50	956	25	975	00
400	1000	00	1020	00	1040	00
3 gr. 425	1062	50	1083	75	1105	00
432	1080	00	1101	60	1123	20
475	1187	50	1211	25	1235	00
480	1200	00	1224	00	1248	00
500	1250	00	1275	00	1300	00
4 gr. 504	1260	00	1285	20	1310	40
576	1440	00	1468	80	1497	60
600	1500	00	1530	00	1560	00
700	1750	00	1785	00	1820	00
750	1875	00	1912	50	1950	00
800	2000	00	2040	00	2080	00
900	2250	00	2295	00	2340	00
1000	2500	00	2550	00	2600	00
2500	6250	00	6375	00	6500	00
5000	12500	·0	12750	·0	13000	·0
1728	4320·00		4406·40		4492·80	
1760	4400·00		4488·00		4576·00	

No.	£2·65 £	p	£2·70 £	p	£2·75 £	p
1	2	65	2	70	2	75
2	5	30	5	40	5	50
3	7	95	8	10	8	25
4	10	60	10	80	11	00
5	13	25	13	50	13	75
6	15	90	16	20	16	50
7	18	55	18	90	19	25
8	21	20	21	60	22	00
9	23	85	24	30	24	75
10	26	50	27	00	27	50
11	29	15	29	70	30	25
12	31	80	32	40	33	00
13	34	45	35	10	35	75
14	37	10	37	80	38	50
15	39	75	40	50	41	25
16	42	40	43	20	44	00
17	45	05	45	90	46	75
18	47	70	48	60	49	50
19	50	35	51	30	52	25
20	53	00	54	00	55	00
21	55	65	56	70	57	75
22	58	30	59	40	60	50
23	60	95	62	10	63	25
24	63	60	64	80	66	00
25	66	25	67	50	68	75
26	68	90	70	20	71	50
27	71	55	72	90	74	25
28	74	20	75	60	77	00
29	76	85	78	30	79	75
30	79	50	81	00	82	50
31	82	15	83	70	85	25
32	84	80	86	40	88	00
33	87	45	89	10	90	75
34	90	10	91	80	93	50
35	92	75	94	50	96	25
36	95	40	97	20	99	00
37	98	05	99	90	101	75
38	100	70	102	60	104	50
39	103	35	105	30	107	25
40	106	00	108	00	110	00
41	108	65	110	70	112	75
42	111	30	113	40	115	50
43	113	95	116	10	118	25
44	116	60	118	80	121	00
45	119	25	121	50	123	75
46	121	90	124	20	126	50
47	124	55	126	90	129	25
48	127	20	129	60	132	00
49	129	85	132	30	134	75
50	132	50	135	00	137	50

Dozens.

No.	£2·65 £	p	£2·70 £	p	£2·75 £	p
51	135	15	137	70	140	25
52	137	80	140	40	143	00
53	140	45	143	10	145	75
54	143	10	145	80	148	50
55	145	75	148	50	151	25
56	148	40	151	20	154	00
57	151	05	153	90	156	75
58	153	70	156	60	159	50
59	156	35	159	30	162	25
60	159	00	162	00	165	00
61	161	65	164	70	167	75
62	164	30	167	40	170	50
63	166	95	170	10	173	25
64	169	60	172	80	176	00
65	172	25	175	50	178	75
66	174	90	178	20	181	50
67	177	55	180	90	184	25
68	180	20	183	60	187	00
69	182	85	186	30	189	75
70	185	50	189	00	192	50
71	188	15	191	70	195	25
72	190	80	194	40	198	00
73	193	45	197	10	200	75
74	196	10	199	80	203	50
75	198	75	202	50	206	25
76	201	40	205	20	209	00
77	204	05	207	90	211	75
78	206	70	210	60	214	50
79	209	35	213	30	217	25
80	212	00	216	00	220	00
81	214	65	218	70	222	75
82	217	30	221	40	225	50
83	219	95	224	10	228	25
84	222	60	226	80	231	00
85	225	25	229	50	233	75
86	227	90	232	20	236	50
87	230	55	234	90	239	25
88	233	20	237	60	242	00
89	235	85	240	30	244	75
90	238	50	243	00	247	50
91	241	15	245	70	250	25
92	243	80	248	40	253	00
93	246	45	251	10	255	75
94	249	10	253	80	258	50
95	251	75	256	50	261	25
96	254	40	259	20	264	00
97	257	05	261	90	266	75
98	259	70	264	60	269	50
99	262	35	267	30	272	25
100	265	00	270	00	275	00

Dozens.

	£2·65	£2·70	£2·75		£2·65	£2·70	£2·75
¼	0·6625	0·675	0·6875	¾	1·9875	2·025	2·0625
½..	1·3250	1·350	1·3750	1¼..	3·3125	3·375	3·4375

No.	£2·65		£2·70		£2·75		No.	£2·65		£2·70		£2·75	
	£	p	£	p	£	p		£	p	£	p	£	p
101	267	65	272	70	277	75	5 155	410	75	418	50	426	25
102	270	30	275	40	280	50	13 156	413	40	421	20	429	00
103	272	95	278	10	283	25	165	437	25	445	50	453	75
104	275	60	280	80	286	00	14 168	445	20	453	60	462	00
105	278	25	283	50	288	75	175	463	75	472	50	481	25
106	280	90	286	20	291	50	15 180	477	00	486	00	495	00
107	283	55	288	90	294	25	185	490	25	499	50	508	75
9 108	286	20	291	60	297	00	16 192	508	80	518	40	528	00
109	288	85	294	30	299	75	195	516	75	526	50	536	25
110	291	50	297	00	302	50	200	530	00	540	00	550	00
111	294	15	299	70	305	25	17 204	540	60	550	80	561	00
112	296	80	302	40	308	00	205	543	25	553	50	563	75
113	299	45	305	10	310	75	215	569	75	580	50	591	25
114	302	10	307	80	313	50	18 216	572	40	583	20	594	00
115	304	75	310	50	316	25	224	593	60	604	80	616	00
116	307	40	313	20	319	00	225	596	25	607	50	618	75
117	310	05	315	90	321	75	19 228	604	20	615	60	627	00
118	312	70	318	60	324	50	235	622	75	634	50	646	25
119	315	35	321	30	327	25	245	649	25	661	50	673	75
10 120	318	00	324	00	330	00	250	662	50	675	00	687	50
121	320	65	326	70	332	75	21 252	667	80	680	40	693	00
122	323	30	329	40	335	50	255	675	75	688	50	701	25
123	325	95	332	10	338	25	265	702	25	715	50	728	75
124	328	60	334	80	341	00	272	720	80	734	40	748	00
125	331	25	337	50	343	75	275	728	75	742	50	756	25
126	333	90	340	20	346	50	280	742	00	756	00	770	00
127	336	55	342	90	349	25	285	755	25	769	50	783	75
128	339	20	345	60	352	00	288	763	20	777	60	792	00
129	341	85	348	30	354	75	295	781	75	796	50	811	25
130	344	50	351	00	357	50	300	795	00	810	00	825	00
131	347	15	353	70	360	25	325	861	25	877	50	893	75
11 132	349	80	356	40	363	00	336	890	40	907	20	924	00
133	352	45	359	10	365	75	365	967	25	985	50	1003	75
134	355	10	361	80	368	50	375	993	75	1012	50	1031	25
135	357	75	364	50	371	25	400	1060	00	1080	00	1100	00
136	360	40	367	20	374	00	425	1126	25	1147	50	1168	75
137	363	05	369	90	376	75	432	1144	80	1166	40	1188	00
138	365	70	372	60	379	50	475	1258	75	1282	50	1306	25
139	368	35	375	30	382	25	480	1272	00	1296	00	1320	00
140	371	00	378	00	385	00	500	1325	00	1350	00	1375	00
141	373	65	380	70	387	75	504	1335	60	1360	80	1386	00
142	376	30	383	40	390	50	576	1526	40	1555	20	1584	00
143	378	95	386	10	393	25	600	1590	00	1620	00	1650	00
12 144	381	60	388	80	396	00	700	1855	00	1890	00	1925	00
145	384	25	391	50	398	75	750	1987	50	2025	00	2062	50
146	386	90	394	20	401	50	800	2120	00	2160	00	2200	00
147	389	55	396	90	404	25	900	2385	00	2430	00	2475	00
148	392	20	399	60	407	00	1000	2650	00	2700	00	2750	00
149	394	85	402	30	409	75	2500	6625	00	6750	00	6875	00
150	397	50	405	00	412	50	5000	13250	0	13500	0	13750	0
1016	2692·40		2743·20		2794·00		1728	4579·20		4665·60		4752·00	
1296	3434·40		3499·20		3564·00		1760	4664·00		4752·00		4840·00	

No.	£2·80		£2·85		£2·90		No.	£2·80		£2·85		£2·90	
	£	P	£	P	£	P		£	P	£	P	£	P
1	2	80	2	85	2	90	51	142	80	145	35	147	90
2	5	60	5	70	5	80	52	145	60	148	20	150	80
3	8	40	8	55	8	70	53	148	40	151	05	153	70
4	11	20	11	40	11	60	54	151	20	153	90	156	60
5	14	00	14	25	14	50	55	154	00	156	75	159	50
6	16	80	17	10	17	40	56	156	80	159	60	162	40
7	19	60	19	95	20	30	57	159	60	162	45	165	30
8	22	40	22	80	23	20	58	162	40	165	30	168	20
9	25	20	25	65	26	10	59	165	20	168	15	171	10
10	28	00	28	50	29	00	60	168	00	171	00	174	00
11	30	80	31	35	31	90	61	170	80	173	85	176	90
12	33	60	34	20	34	80	62	173	60	176	70	179	80
13	36	40	37	05	37	70	63	176	40	179	55	182	70
14	39	20	39	90	40	60	64	179	20	182	40	185	60
15	42	00	42	75	43	50	65	182	00	185	25	188	50
16	44	80	45	60	46	40	66	184	80	188	10	191	40
17	47	60	48	45	49	30	67	187	60	190	95	194	30
18	50	40	51	30	52	20	68	190	40	193	80	197	20
19	53	20	54	15	55	10	69	193	20	196	65	200	10
20	56	00	57	00	58	00	70	196	00	199	50	203	00
21	58	80	59	85	60	90	71	198	80	202	35	205	90
22	61	60	62	70	63	80	72	201	60	205	20	208	80
23	64	40	65	55	66	70	73	204	40	208	05	211	70
24	67	20	68	40	69	60	74	207	20	210	90	214	60
25	70	00	71	25	72	50	75	210	00	213	75	217	50
26	72	80	74	10	75	40	76	212	80	216	60	220	40
27	75	60	76	95	78	30	77	215	60	219	45	223	30
28	78	40	79	80	81	20	78	218	40	222	30	226	20
29	81	20	82	65	84	10	79	221	20	225	15	229	10
30	84	00	85	50	87	00	80	224	00	228	00	232	00
31	86	80	88	35	89	90	81	226	80	230	85	234	90
32	89	60	91	20	92	80	82	229	60	233	70	237	80
33	92	40	94	05	95	70	83	232	40	236	55	240	70
34	95	20	96	90	98	60	84	235	20	239	40	243	60
35	98	00	99	75	101	50	85	238	00	242	25	246	50
36	100	80	102	60	104	40	86	240	80	245	10	249	40
37	103	60	105	45	107	30	87	243	60	247	95	252	30
38	106	40	108	30	110	20	88	246	40	250	80	255	20
39	109	20	111	15	113	10	89	249	20	253	65	258	10
40	112	00	114	00	116	00	90	252	00	256	50	261	00
41	114	80	116	85	118	90	91	254	80	259	35	263	90
42	117	60	119	70	121	80	92	257	60	262	20	266	80
43	120	40	122	55	124	70	93	260	40	265	05	269	70
44	123	20	125	40	127	60	94	263	20	267	90	272	60
45	126	00	128	25	130	50	95	266	00	270	75	275	50
46	128	80	131	10	133	40	96	268	80	273	60	278	40
47	131	60	133	95	136	30	97	271	60	276	45	281	30
48	134	40	136	80	139	20	98	274	40	279	30	284	20
49	137	20	139	65	142	10	99	277	20	282	15	287	10
50	140	00	142	50	145	00	100	280	00	285	00	290	00

Note on left margin: *Dozens.*

	£2·80	£2·85	£2·90		£2·80	£2·85	£2·90
¼	0·70	0·7125	0·725	¾	2·10	2·1375	2·175
½ ..	1·40	1·4250	1·450	1¼ ..	3·50	3·5625	3·625

No. | £2·80 | £2·85 | £2·90

No.	£2·80	£2·85	£2·90
101	282 80	287 85	292 90
102	285 60	290 70	295 80
103	288 40	293 55	298 70
104	291 20	296 40	301 60
105	294 00	299 25	304 50
106	296 80	302 10	307 40
107	299 60	304 95	310 30
108	302 40	307 80	313 20
109	305 20	310 65	316 10
110	308 00	313 50	319 00
111	310 80	316 35	321 90
112	313 60	319 20	324 80
113	316 40	322 05	327 70
114	319 20	324 90	330 60
115	322 00	327 75	333 50
116	324 80	330 60	336 40
117	327 60	333 45	339 30
118	330 40	336 30	342 20
119	333 20	339 15	345 10
120	336 00	342 00	348 00
121	338 80	344 85	350 90
122	341 60	347 70	353 80
123	344 40	350 55	356 70
124	347 20	353 40	359 60
125	350 00	356 25	362 50
126	352 80	359 10	365 40
127	355 60	361 95	368 30
128	358 40	364 80	371 20
129	361 20	367 65	374 10
130	364 00	370 50	377 00
131	366 80	373 35	379 90
132	369 60	376 20	382 80
133	372 40	379 05	385 70
134	375 20	381 90	388 60
135	378 00	384 75	391 50
136	380 80	387 60	394 40
137	383 60	390 45	397 30
138	386 40	393 30	400 20
139	389 00	396 15	403 10
140	392 00	399 00	406 00
141	394 80	401 85	408 90
142	397 60	404 70	411 80
143	400 40	407 55	414 70
144	403 20	410 40	417 60
145	406 00	413 25	420 50
146	408 80	416 10	423 40
147	411 60	418 95	426 30
148	414 40	421 80	429 20
149	417 20	424 65	432 10
150	420 00	427 50	435 00

No.	£2·80	£2·85	£2·90
155	434 00	441 75	449 50
156	436 80	444 60	452 40
165	462 00	470 25	478 50
168	470 40	478 80	487 20
175	490 00	498 75	507 50
180	504 00	513 00	522 00
185	518 00	527 25	536 50
192	537 60	547 20	556 80
195	546 00	555 75	565 50
200	560 00	570 00	580 00
204	571 20	581 40	591 60
205	574 00	584 25	594 50
215	602 00	612 75	623 50
216	604 80	615 60	626 40
224	627 20	638 40	649 60
225	630 00	641 25	652 50
228	638 40	649 80	661 20
235	658 00	669 75	681 50
245	686 00	698 25	710 50
250	700 00	712 50	725 00
252	705 60	718 20	730 80
255	714 00	726 75	739 50
265	742 00	755 25	768 50
272	761 60	775 20	788 80
275	770 00	783 75	797 50
280	784 00	798 00	812 00
285	798 00	812 25	826 50
288	806 40	820 80	835 20
295	826 00	840 75	855 50
300	840 00	855 00	870 00
325	910 00	926 25	942 50
336	940 80	957 60	974 40
365	1022 00	1040 25	1058 50
375	1050 00	1068 75	1087 50
400	1120 00	1140 00	1160 00
425	1190 00	1211 25	1232 50
432	1209 60	1231 20	1252 80
475	1330 00	1353 75	1377 50
480	1344 00	1368 00	1392 00
500	1400 00	1425 00	1450 00
504	1411 20	1436 40	1461 60
576	1612 80	1641 60	1670 40
600	1680 00	1710 00	1740 00
700	1960 00	1995 00	2030 00
750	2100 00	2137 50	2175 00
800	2240 00	2280 00	2320 00
900	2520 00	2565 00	2610 00
1000	2800 00	2850 00	2900 00
2500	7000 00	7125 00	7250 00
5000	14000 ·0	14250 ·0	14500 ·0

No.	£2·80	£2·85	£2·90	No.	£2·80	£2·85	£2·90
1016	2844·80	2895·60	2946·40	1728	4838·40	4924·80	5011·20
1296	3628·80	3693·60	3758·40	1760	4928·00	5016·00	5104·00

No.	£2.95 £	£2.95 p	£3.00 £	£3.00 p	£3.05 £	£3.05 p
1	2	95	3	00	3	05
2	5	90	6	00	6	10
3	8	85	9	00	9	15
4	11	80	12	00	12	20
5	14	75	15	00	15	25
6	17	70	18	00	18	30
7	20	65	21	00	21	35
8	23	60	24	00	24	40
9	26	55	27	00	27	45
10	29	50	30	00	30	50
11	32	45	33	00	33	55
12	35	40	36	00	36	60
13	38	35	39	00	39	65
14	41	30	42	00	42	70
15	44	25	45	00	45	75
16	47	20	48	00	48	80
17	50	15	51	00	51	85
18	53	10	54	00	54	90
19	56	05	57	00	57	95
20	59	00	60	00	61	00
21	61	95	63	00	64	05
22	64	90	66	00	67	10
23	67	85	69	00	70	15
24	70	80	72	00	73	20
25	73	75	75	00	76	25
26	76	70	78	00	79	30
27	79	65	81	00	82	35
28	82	60	84	00	85	40
29	85	55	87	00	88	45
30	88	50	90	00	91	50
31	91	45	93	00	94	55
32	94	40	96	00	97	60
33	97	35	99	00	100	65
34	100	30	102	00	103	70
35	103	25	105	00	106	75
36	106	20	108	00	109	80
37	109	15	111	00	112	85
38	112	10	114	00	115	90
39	115	05	117	00	118	95
40	118	00	120	00	122	00
41	120	95	123	00	125	05
42	123	90	126	00	128	10
43	126	85	129	00	131	15
44	129	80	132	00	134	20
45	132	75	135	00	137	25
46	135	70	138	00	140	30
47	138	65	141	00	143	35
48	141	60	144	00	146	40
49	144	55	147	00	149	45
50	147	50	150	00	152	50

No.	£2.95 £	£2.95 p	£3.00 £	£3.00 p	£3.05 £	£3.05 p
51	150	45	153	00	155	55
52	153	40	156	00	158	60
53	156	35	159	00	161	65
54	159	30	162	00	164	70
55	162	25	165	00	167	75
56	165	20	168	00	170	80
57	168	15	171	00	173	85
58	171	10	174	00	176	90
59	174	05	177	00	179	95
60	177	00	180	00	183	00
61	179	95	183	00	186	05
62	182	90	186	00	189	10
63	185	85	189	00	192	15
64	188	80	192	00	195	20
65	191	75	195	00	198	25
66	194	70	198	00	201	30
67	197	65	201	00	204	35
68	200	60	204	00	207	40
69	203	55	207	00	210	45
70	206	50	210	00	213	50
71	209	45	213	00	216	55
72	212	40	216	00	219	60
73	215	35	219	00	222	65
74	218	30	222	00	225	70
75	221	25	225	00	228	75
76	224	20	228	00	231	80
77	227	15	231	00	234	85
78	230	10	234	00	237	90
79	233	05	237	00	240	95
80	236	00	240	00	244	00
81	238	95	243	00	247	05
82	241	90	246	00	250	10
83	244	85	249	00	253	15
84	247	80	252	00	256	20
85	250	75	255	00	259	25
86	253	70	258	00	262	30
87	256	65	261	00	265	35
88	259	60	264	00	268	40
89	262	55	267	00	271	45
90	265	50	270	00	274	50
91	268	45	273	00	277	55
92	271	40	276	00	280	60
93	274	35	279	00	283	65
94	277	30	282	00	286	70
95	280	25	285	00	289	75
96	283	20	288	00	292	80
97	286	15	291	00	295	85
98	289	10	294	00	298	90
99	292	05	297	00	301	95
100	295	00	300	00	305	00

	£2.95	£3.00	£3.05
¼	0·7375	0·75	0·7625
½..	1·4750	1·50	1·5250
¾	2·2125	2·25	2·2875
1¼..	3·6875	3·75	3·8125

(Left column marked "Dozens.")

No.	£2·95	£3·00	£3·05
101	297 95	303 00	308 05
102	300 90	306 00	311 10
103	303 85	309 00	314 15
104	306 80	312 00	317 20
105	309 75	315 00	320 25
106	312 70	318 00	323 30
107	315 65	321 00	326 35
9 108	318 60	324 00	329 40
109	321 55	327 00	332 45
110	324 50	330 00	335 50
111	327 45	333 00	338 55
112	330 40	336 00	341 60
113	333 35	339 00	344 65
114	336 30	342 00	347 70
115	339 25	345 00	350 75
116	342 20	348 00	353 80
117	345 15	351 00	356 85
118	348 10	354 00	359 90
119	351 05	357 00	362 95
10 120	354 00	360 00	366 00
121	356 95	363 00	369 05
122	359 90	366 00	372 10
123	362 85	369 00	375 15
124	365 80	372 00	378 20
125	368 75	375 00	381 25
126	371 70	378 00	384 30
127	374 65	381 00	387 35
128	377 60	384 00	390 40
129	380 55	387 00	393 45
130	383 50	390 00	396 50
131	386 45	393 00	399 55
11 132	389 40	396 00	402 60
133	392 35	399 00	405 65
134	395 30	402 00	408 70
135	398 25	405 00	411 75
136	401 20	408 00	414 80
137	404 15	411 00	417 85
138	407 10	414 00	420 90
139	410 05	417 00	423 95
140	413 00	420 00	427 00
141	415 95	423 00	430 05
142	418 90	426 00	433 10
143	421 85	429 00	436 15
12 144	424 80	432 00	439 20
145	427 75	435 00	442 25
146	430 70	438 00	445 30
147	433 65	441 00	448 35
148	436 60	444 00	451 40
149	439 55	447 00	454 45
150	442 50	450 00	457 50
1016	2997·20	3048·00	3098·80
1296	3823·20	3888·00	3952·80

No.	£2·95	£3·00	£3·05
155	457 25	465 00	472 75
13 156	460 20	468 00	475 80
165	486 75	495 00	503 25
14 168	495 60	504 00	512 40
175	516 25	525 00	533 75
15 180	531 00	540 00	549 00
185	545 75	555 00	564 25
16 192	566 40	576 00	585 60
195	575 25	585 00	594 75
200	590 00	600 00	610 00
17 204	601 80	612 00	622 20
205	604 75	615 00	625 25
215	634 25	645 00	655 75
18 216	637 20	648 00	658 80
224	660 80	672 00	683 20
225	663 75	675 00	686 25
19 228	672 60	684 00	695 40
235	693 25	705 00	716 75
245	722 75	735 00	747 25
250	737 50	750 00	762 50
21 252	743 40	756 00	768 60
255	752 25	765 00	777 75
265	781 75	795 00	808 25
272	802 40	816 00	829 60
275	811 25	825 00	838 75
280	826 00	840 00	854 00
285	840 75	855 00	869 25
288	849 60	864 00	878 40
295	870 25	885 00	899 75
300	885 00	900 00	915 00
325	958 75	975 00	991 25
336	991 20	1008 00	1024 80
365	1076 75	1095 00	1113 25
375	1106 25	1125 00	1143 75
400	1180 00	1200 00	1220 00
425	1253 75	1275 00	1296 25
432	1274 40	1296 00	1317 60
475	1401 25	1425 00	1448 75
480	1416 00	1440 00	1464 00
500	1475 00	1500 00	1525 00
504	1486 80	1512 00	1537 20
576	1699 20	1728 00	1756 80
600	1770 00	1800 00	1830 00
700	2065 00	2100 00	2135 00
750	2212 50	2250 00	2287 50
800	2360 00	2400 00	2440 00
900	2655 00	2700 00	2745 00
1000	2950 00	3000 00	3050 00
2500	7375 00	7500 00	7625 00
5000	14750 ·0	15000 ·0	15250 ·0
1728	5097·60	5184·00	5270·40
1760	5192·00	5280·00	5368·00

Doz · 2 gross · 3 gr. · 4 gr.

No.	£3·10		£3·15		£3·20	
	£	P	£	P	£	P
1	3	10	3	15	3	20
2	6	20	6	30	6	40
3	9	30	9	45	9	60
4	12	40	12	60	12	80
5	15	50	15	75	16	00
6	18	60	18	90	19	20
7	21	70	22	05	22	40
8	24	80	25	20	25	60
9	27	90	28	35	28	80
10	31	00	31	50	32	00
11	34	10	34	65	35	20
12	37	20	37	80	38	40
13	40	30	40	95	41	60
14	43	40	44	10	44	80
15	46	50	47	25	48	00
16	49	60	50	40	51	20
17	52	70	53	55	54	40
18	55	80	56	70	57	60
19	58	90	59	85	60	80
20	62	00	63	00	64	00
21	65	10	66	15	67	20
22	68	20	69	30	70	40
23	71	30	72	45	73	60
24	74	40	75	60	76	80
25	77	50	78	75	80	00
26	80	60	81	90	83	20
27	83	70	85	05	86	40
28	86	80	88	20	89	60
29	89	90	91	35	92	80
30	93	00	94	50	96	00
31	96	10	97	65	99	20
32	99	20	100	80	102	40
33	102	30	103	95	105	60
34	105	40	107	10	108	80
35	108	50	110	25	112	00
36	111	60	113	40	115	20
37	114	70	116	55	118	40
38	117	80	119	70	121	60
39	120	90	122	85	124	80
40	124	00	126	00	128	00
41	127	10	129	15	131	20
42	130	20	132	30	134	40
43	133	30	135	45	137	60
44	136	40	138	60	140	80
45	139	50	141	75	144	00
46	142	60	144	90	147	20
47	145	70	148	05	150	40
48	148	80	151	20	153	60
49	151	90	154	35	156	80
50	155	00	157	50	160	00

No.	£3·10		£3·15		£3·20	
	£	P	£	P	£	P
51	158	10	160	65	163	20
52	161	20	163	80	166	40
53	164	30	166	95	169	60
54	167	40	170	10	172	86
55	170	50	173	25	176	00
56	173	60	176	40	179	20
57	176	70	179	55	182	40
58	179	80	182	70	185	60
59	182	90	185	85	188	80
60	186	00	189	00	192	00
61	189	10	192	15	195	20
62	192	20	195	30	198	40
63	195	30	198	45	201	60
64	198	40	201	60	204	80
65	201	50	204	75	208	00
66	204	60	207	90	211	20
67	207	70	211	05	214	40
68	210	80	214	20	217	60
69	213	90	217	35	220	80
70	217	00	220	50	224	00
71	220	10	223	65	227	20
72	223	20	226	80	230	40
73	226	30	229	95	233	60
74	229	40	233	10	236	80
75	232	50	236	25	240	00
76	235	60	239	40	243	20
77	238	70	242	55	246	40
78	241	80	245	70	249	60
79	244	90	248	85	252	80
80	248	00	252	00	256	00
81	251	10	255	15	259	20
82	254	20	258	30	262	40
83	257	30	261	45	265	60
84	260	40	264	60	268	80
85	263	50	267	75	272	00
86	266	60	270	90	275	20
87	269	70	274	05	278	40
88	272	80	277	20	281	60
89	275	90	280	35	284	80
90	279	00	283	50	288	00
91	282	10	286	65	291	20
92	285	20	289	80	294	40
93	288	30	292	95	297	60
94	291	40	296	10	300	80
95	294	50	299	25	304	00
96	297	60	302	40	307	20
97	300	70	305	55	310	40
98	303	80	308	70	313	60
99	306	90	311	85	316	80
100	310	00	315	00	320	00

	£3·10	£3·15	£3·20		£3·10	£3·15	£3·20
¼	0·775	0·7875	0·80	¾	2·325	2·3625	2·40
½..	1·550	1·5750	1·60	1¼..	3·875	3·9375	4·00

No.	£3·10 £	P	£3·15 £	P	£3·20 £	P
101	313	10	318	15	323	20
102	316	20	321	30	326	40
103	319	30	324	45	329	60
104	322	40	327	60	332	80
105	325	50	330	75	336	00
106	328	60	333	90	339	20
107	331	70	337	05	342	40
[9]108	334	80	340	20	345	60
109	337	90	343	35	348	80
110	341	00	346	50	352	00
111	344	10	349	65	355	20
112	347	20	352	80	358	40
113	350	30	355	95	361	60
114	353	40	359	10	364	80
115	356	50	362	25	368	00
116	359	60	365	40	371	20
117	362	70	368	55	374	40
118	365	80	371	70	377	60
119	368	90	374	85	380	80
[10]120	372	00	378	00	384	00
121	375	10	381	15	387	20
122	378	20	384	30	390	40
123	381	30	387	45	393	60
124	384	40	390	60	396	80
125	387	50	393	75	400	00
126	390	60	396	90	403	20
127	393	70	400	05	406	40
128	396	80	403	20	409	60
129	399	90	406	35	412	80
130	403	00	409	50	416	00
131	406	10	412	65	419	20
[11]132	409	20	415	80	422	40
133	412	30	418	95	425	60
134	415	40	422	10	428	80
135	418	50	425	25	432	00
136	421	60	428	40	435	20
137	424	70	431	55	438	40
138	427	80	434	70	441	60
139	430	90	437	85	444	80
140	434	00	441	00	448	00
141	437	10	444	15	451	20
142	440	20	447	30	454	40
143	443	30	450	45	457	60
[12]144	446	40	453	60	460	80
145	449	50	456	75	464	00
146	452	60	459	90	467	20
147	455	70	463	05	470	40
148	458	80	466	20	473	60
149	461	90	469	35	476	80
150	465	00	472	50	480	00
1016	3149·60		3200·40		3251·20	
1296	4017·60		4082·40		4147·20	

No.	£3·10 £	P	£3·15 £	P	£3·20 £	P
[12oz] 155	480	50	488	25	496	00
[13]156	483	60	491	40	499	20
165	511	50	519	75	528	00
[14]168	520	80	529	20	537	60
175	542	50	551	25	560	00
[15]180	558	00	567	00	576	00
185	573	50	582	75	592	00
[16]192	595	20	604	80	614	40
195	604	50	614	25	624	00
200	620	00	630	00	640	00
[17]204	632	40	642	60	652	80
205	635	50	645	75	656	00
215	666	50	677	25	688	00
[18]216	669	60	680	40	691	20
224	694	40	705	60	716	80
225	697	50	708	75	720	00
[19]228	706	80	718	20	729	60
235	728	50	740	25	752	00
245	759	50	771	75	784	00
250	775	00	787	50	800	00
[21]252	781	20	793	80	806	40
255	790	50	803	25	816	00
265	821	50	834	75	848	00
272	843	20	856	80	870	40
275	852	50	866	25	880	00
280	868	00	882	00	896	00
285	883	50	897	75	912	00
2 stars 288	892	80	907	20	921	60
295	914	50	929	25	944	00
300	930	00	945	00	960	00
325	1007	50	1023	75	1040	00
336	1041	60	1058	40	1075	20
365	1131	50	1149	75	1168	00
375	1162	50	1181	25	1200	00
400	1240	00	1260	00	1280	00
3 gr. 425	1317	50	1338	75	1360	00
432	1339	20	1360	80	1382	40
475	1472	50	1496	25	1520	00
480	1488	00	1512	00	1536	00
500	1550	00	1575	00	1600	00
4 gr. 504	1562	40	1587	60	1612	80
576	1785	60	1814	40	1843	20
600	1860	00	1890	00	1920	00
700	2170	00	2205	00	2240	00
750	2325	00	2362	50	2400	00
800	2480	00	2520	00	2560	00
900	2790	00	2835	00	2880	00
1000	3100	00	3150	00	3200	00
2500	7750	00	7875	00	8000	00
5000	15,500·0		15,750·0		16,000·0	
1728	5356·80		5443·20		5529·60	
1760	5456·00		5544·00		5632·00	

No.	£3·25		£3·30		£3·35		No.	£3·25		£3·30		£3·35	
	£	P	£	P	£	P		£	P	£	P	£	P
1	3	25	3	30	3	35	51	165	75	168	30	170	85
2	6	50	6	60	6	70	52	169	00	171	60	174	20
3	9	75	9	90	10	05	53	172	25	174	90	177	55
4	13	00	13	20	13	40	54	175	50	178	20	180	90
5	16	25	16	50	16	75	55	178	75	181	50	184	25
6	19	50	19	80	20	10	56	182	00	184	80	187	60
7	22	75	23	10	23	45	57	185	25	188	10	190	95
8	26	00	26	40	26	80	58	188	50	191	40	194	30
9	29	25	29	70	30	15	59	191	75	194	70	197	65
10	32	50	33	00	33	50	60	195	00	198	00	201	00
11	35	75	36	30	36	85	61	198	25	201	30	204	35
12	39	00	39	60	40	20	62	201	50	204	60	207	70
13	42	25	42	90	43	55	63	204	75	207	90	211	05
14	45	50	46	20	46	90	64	208	00	211	20	214	40
15	48	75	49	50	50	25	65	211	25	214	50	217	75
16	52	00	52	80	53	60	66	214	50	217	80	221	10
17	55	25	56	10	56	95	67	217	75	221	10	224	45
18	58	50	59	40	60	30	68	221	00	224	40	227	80
19	61	75	62	70	63	65	69	224	25	227	70	231	15
20	65	00	66	00	67	00	70	227	50	231	00	234	50
21	68	25	69	30	70	35	71	230	75	234	30	237	85
22	71	50	72	60	73	70	72	234	00	237	60	241	20
23	74	75	75	90	77	05	73	237	25	240	90	244	55
24	78	00	79	20	80	40	74	240	50	244	20	247	90
25	81	25	82	50	83	75	75	243	75	247	50	251	25
26	84	50	85	80	87	10	76	247	00	250	80	254	60
27	87	75	89	10	90	45	77	250	25	254	10	257	95
28	91	00	92	40	93	80	78	253	50	257	40	261	30
29	94	25	95	70	97	15	79	256	75	260	70	264	65
30	97	50	99	00	100	50	80	260	00	264	00	268	00
31	100	75	102	30	103	85	81	263	25	267	30	271	35
32	104	00	105	60	107	20	82	266	50	270	60	274	70
33	107	25	108	90	110	55	83	269	75	273	90	278	05
34	110	50	112	20	113	90	84	273	00	277	20	281	40
35	113	75	115	50	117	25	85	276	25	280	50	284	75
36	117	00	118	80	120	60	86	279	50	283	80	288	10
37	120	25	122	10	123	95	87	282	75	287	10	291	45
38	123	50	125	40	127	30	88	286	00	290	40	294	80
39	126	75	128	70	130	65	89	289	25	293	70	298	15
40	130	00	132	00	134	00	90	292	50	297	00	301	50
41	133	25	135	30	137	35	91	295	75	300	30	304	85
42	136	50	138	60	140	70	92	299	00	303	60	308	20
43	139	75	141	90	144	05	93	302	25	306	90	311	55
44	143	00	145	20	147	40	94	305	50	310	20	314	90
45	146	25	148	50	150	75	95	308	75	313	50	318	25
46	149	50	151	80	154	10	96	312	00	316	80	321	60
47	152	75	155	10	157	45	97	315	25	320	10	324	95
48	156	00	158	40	160	80	98	318	50	323	40	328	30
49	159	25	161	70	164	15	99	321	75	326	70	331	65
50	162	50	165	00	167	50	100	325	00	330	00	335	00
¼	0·8125		0·825		0·8375		¾	2·4375		2·475		2·5125	
½	1·6250		1·650		1·6750		1¼	4·0625		4·125		4·1875	

No.	£3·25 £	P	£3·30 £	P	£3·35 £	P
101	328	25	333	30	338	35
102	331	50	336	60	341	70
103	334	75	339	90	345	05
104	338	00	343	20	348	40
105	341	25	346	50	351	75
106	344	50	349	80	355	10
107	347	75	353	10	358	45
9 108	351	00	356	40	361	80
109	354	25	359	70	365	15
110	357	50	363	00	368	50
111	360	75	366	30	371	85
112	364	00	369	60	375	20
113	367	25	372	90	378	55
114	370	50	376	20	381	90
115	373	75	379	50	385	25
116	377	00	382	80	388	60
117	380	25	386	10	391	95
118	383	50	389	40	395	30
119	386	75	392	70	398	65
10 120	390	00	396	00	402	00
121	393	25	399	30	405	35
122	396	50	402	60	408	70
123	399	75	405	90	412	05
124	403	00	409	20	415	40
125	406	25	412	50	418	75
126	409	50	415	80	422	10
127	412	75	419	10	425	45
128	416	00	422	40	428	80
129	419	25	425	70	432	15
130	422	50	429	00	435	50
131	425	75	432	30	438	85
11 132	429	00	435	60	442	20
133	432	25	438	90	445	55
134	435	50	442	20	448	90
135	438	75	445	50	452	25
136	442	00	448	80	455	60
137	445	25	452	10	458	95
138	448	50	455	40	462	30
139	451	75	458	70	465	65
140	455	00	462	00	469	00
141	458	25	465	30	472	35
142	461	50	468	60	475	70
143	464	75	471	90	479	05
12 144	468	00	475	20	482	40
145	471	25	478	50	485	75
146	474	50	481	80	489	10
147	477	75	485	10	492	45
148	481	00	488	40	495	80
149	484	25	491	70	499	15
150	487	50	495	00	502	50
1016	3302	00	3352	80	3403	60
1296	4212	00	4276	80	4341	60

No.	£3·25 £	P	£3·30 £	P	£3·35 £	P
155	503	75	511	50	519	25
13 156	507	00	514	80	522	60
165	536	25	544	50	552	75
14 168	546	00	554	40	562	80
175	568	75	577	50	586	25
15 180	585	00	594	00	603	00
185	601	25	610	50	619	75
16 192	624	00	633	60	643	20
195	633	75	643	50	653	25
200	650	00	660	00	670	00
17 204	663	00	673	20	683	40
205	666	25	676	50	686	75
215	698	75	709	50	720	25
18 216	702	00	712	80	723	60
224	728	00	739	20	750	40
225	731	25	742	50	753	75
19 228	741	00	752	40	763	80
235	763	75	775	50	787	25
245	796	25	808	50	820	75
250	812	50	825	00	837	50
21 252	819	00	831	60	844	20
255	828	75	841	50	854	25
265	861	25	874	50	887	75
272	884	00	897	60	911	20
275	893	75	907	50	921	25
s gross 280	910	00	924	00	938	00
285	926	25	940	50	954	75
2 gross 288	936	00	950	40	964	80
295	958	75	973	50	988	25
300	975	00	990	00	1005	00
325	1056	25	1072	50	1088	75
336	1092	00	1108	80	1125	60
365	1186	25	1204	50	1222	75
375	1218	75	1237	50	1256	25
400	1300	00	1320	00	1340	00
3 gr. 425	1381	25	1402	50	1423	75
3 gr. 432	1404	00	1425	60	1447	20
475	1543	75	1567	50	1591	25
480	1560	00	1584	00	1608	00
500	1625	00	1650	00	1675	00
4 gr. 504	1638	00	1663	20	1688	40
4 gr. 576	1872	00	1900	80	1929	60
600	1950	00	1980	00	2010	00
700	2275	00	2310	00	2345	00
750	2437	50	2475	00	2512	50
800	2600	00	2640	00	2680	00
900	2925	00	2970	00	3015	00
1000	3250	00	3300	00	3350	00
2500	8125	00	8250	00	8375	00
5000	16250	0	16500	0	16750	0
1728	5616	00	5702	40	5788	80
1760	5720	00	5808	00	5896	00

No.	£3·40		£3·45		£3·50		No.	£3·40		£3·45		£3·50	
	£	p	£	p	£	p		£	p	£	p	£	p
1	3	40	3	45	3	50	51	173	40	175	95	178	50
2	6	80	6	90	7	00	52	176	80	179	40	182	00
3	10	20	10	35	10	50	53	180	20	182	85	185	50
4	13	60	13	80	14	00	54	183	60	186	30	189	00
5	17	00	17	25	17	50	55	187	00	189	75	192	50
6	20	40	20	70	21	00	56	190	40	193	20	196	00
7	23	80	24	15	24	50	57	193	80	196	65	199	50
8	27	20	27	60	28	00	58	197	20	200	10	203	00
9	30	60	31	05	31	50	59	200	60	203	55	206	50
10	34	00	34	50	35	00	60	204	00	207	00	210	00
11	37	40	37	95	38	50	61	207	40	210	45	213	50
12	40	80	41	40	42	00	62	210	80	213	90	217	00
13	44	20	44	85	45	50	63	214	20	217	35	220	50
14	47	60	48	30	49	00	64	217	60	220	80	224	00
15	51	00	51	75	52	50	65	221	00	224	25	227	50
16	54	40	55	20	56	00	66	224	40	227	70	231	00
17	57	80	58	65	59	50	67	227	80	231	15	234	50
18	61	20	62	10	63	00	68	231	20	234	60	238	00
19	64	60	65	55	66	50	69	234	60	238	05	241	50
20	68	00	69	00	70	00	70	238	00	241	50	245	00
21	71	40	72	45	73	50	71	241	40	244	95	248	50
22	74	80	75	90	77	00	72	244	80	248	40	252	00
23	78	20	79	35	80	50	73	248	20	251	85	255	50
24	81	60	82	80	84	00	74	251	60	255	30	259	00
25	85	00	86	25	87	50	75	255	00	258	75	262	50
26	88	40	89	70	91	00	76	258	40	262	20	266	00
27	91	80	93	15	94	50	77	261	80	265	65	269	50
28	95	20	96	60	98	00	78	265	20	269	10	273	00
29	98	60	100	05	101	50	79	268	60	272	55	276	50
30	102	00	103	50	105	00	80	272	00	276	00	280	00
31	105	40	106	95	108	50	81	275	40	279	45	283	50
32	108	80	110	40	112	00	82	278	80	282	90	287	00
33	112	20	113	85	115	50	83	282	20	286	35	290	50
34	115	60	117	30	119	00	84	285	60	289	80	294	00
35	119	00	120	75	122	50	85	289	00	293	25	297	50
36	122	40	124	20	126	00	86	292	40	296	70	301	00
37	125	80	127	65	129	50	87	295	80	300	15	304	50
38	129	20	131	10	133	00	88	299	20	303	60	308	00
39	132	60	134	55	136	50	89	302	60	307	05	311	50
40	136	00	138	00	140	00	90	306	00	310	50	315	00
41	139	40	141	45	143	50	91	309	40	313	95	318	50
42	142	80	144	90	147	00	92	312	80	317	40	322	00
43	146	20	148	35	150	50	93	316	20	320	85	325	50
44	149	60	151	80	154	00	94	319	60	324	30	329	00
45	153	00	155	25	157	50	95	323	00	327	75	332	50
46	156	40	158	70	161	00	96	326	40	331	20	336	00
47	159	80	162	15	164	50	97	329	80	334	65	339	50
48	163	20	165	60	168	00	98	333	20	338	10	343	00
49	166	60	169	05	171	50	99	336	60	341	55	346	50
50	170	00	172	50	175	00	100	340	00	345	00	350	00
¼	0·85		0·8625		0·875		¾	2·55		2·5875		2·625	
½	1·70		1·7250		1·750		1½	4·25		4·3125		4·375	

Dozens.

No.	£3·40 £	p	£3·45 £	p	£3·50 £	p	No.	£3·40 £	p	£3·45 £	p	£3·50 £	p
101	343	40	348	45	353	50	Doz 155	527	00	534	75	542	50
102	346	80	351	90	357	00	13 156	530	40	538	20	546	00
103	350	20	355	35	360	50	165	561	00	569	25	577	50
104	353	60	358	80	364	00	14 168	571	20	579	60	588	00
105	357	00	362	25	367	50	175	595	00	603	75	612	50
106	360	40	365	70	371	00	15 180	612	00	621	00	630	00
107	363	80	369	15	374	50	185	629	00	638	25	647	50
9 108	367	20	372	60	378	00	16 192	652	80	662	40	672	00
109	370	60	376	05	381	50	195	663	00	672	75	682	50
110	374	00	379	50	385	00	200	680	00	690	00	700	00
111	377	40	382	95	388	50	17 204	693	60	703	80	714	00
112	380	80	386	40	392	00	205	697	00	707	25	717	50
113	384	20	389	85	395	50	215	731	00	741	75	752	50
114	387	60	393	30	399	00	18 216	734	40	745	20	756	00
115	391	00	396	75	402	50	224	761	60	772	80	784	00
116	394	40	400	20	406	00	225	765	00	776	25	787	50
117	397	80	403	65	409	50	19 228	775	20	786	60	798	00
118	401	20	407	10	413	00	235	799	00	810	75	822	50
119	404	60	410	55	416	50	245	833	00	845	25	857	50
10 120	408	00	414	00	420	00	250	850	00	862	50	875	00
121	411	40	417	45	423	50	21 252	856	80	869	40	882	00
122	414	80	420	90	427	00	255	867	00	879	75	892	50
123	418	20	424	35	430	50	265	901	00	914	25	927	50
124	421	60	427	80	434	00	272	924	80	938	40	952	00
125	425	00	431	25	437	50	275	935	00	948	75	962	50
126	428	40	434	70	441	00	280	952	00	966	00	980	00
127	431	80	438	15	444	50	285	969	00	983	25	997	50
128	435	20	441	60	448	00	2 gross 288	979	20	993	60	1008	00
129	438	60	445	05	451	50	295	1003	00	1017	75	1032	50
130	442	00	448	50	455	00	300	1020	00	1035	00	1050	00
131	445	40	451	95	458	50	325	1105	00	1121	25	1137	50
11 132	448	80	455	40	462	00	336	1142	40	1159	20	1176	00
133	452	20	458	85	465	50	365	1241	00	1259	25	1277	50
134	455	60	462	30	469	00	375	1275	00	1293	75	1312	50
135	459	00	465	75	472	50	400	1360	00	1380	00	1400	00
136	462	40	469	20	476	00	3 gr. 425	1445	00	1466	25	1487	50
137	465	80	472	65	479	50	432	1468	80	1490	40	1512	00
138	469	20	476	10	483	00	475	1615	00	1638	75	1662	50
139	472	60	479	55	486	50	480	1632	00	1656	00	1680	00
140	476	00	483	00	490	00	500	1700	00	1725	00	1750	00
141	479	40	486	45	493	50	4 gr. 504	1713	60	1738	80	1764	00
142	482	80	489	90	497	00	576	1958	40	1987	20	2016	00
143	486	20	493	35	500	50	600	2040	00	2070	00	2100	00
12 144	489	60	496	80	504	00	700	2380	00	2415	00	2450	00
145	493	00	500	25	507	50	750	2550	00	2587	50	2625	00
146	496	40	503	70	511	00	800	2720	00	2760	00	2800	00
147	499	80	507	15	514	50	900	3060	00	3105	00	3150	00
148	503	20	510	60	518	00	1000	3400	00	3450	00	3500	00
149	506	60	514	05	521	50	2500	8500	00	8625	00	8750	00
150	510	00	517	50	525	00	5000	17000	·0	17250	·0	17500	·0
1016	3454·40		3505·20		3556·00		1728	5875·20		5961·60		6048·00	
1296	4406·40		4471·20		4536·00		1760	5984·00		6072·00		6160·00	

No.	£3·55 £	p	£3·60 £	p	£3·65 £	p	No.	£3·55 £	p	£3·60 £	p	£3·65 £	p
1	3	55	3	60	3	65	51	181	05	183	60	186	15
2	7	10	7	20	7	30	52	184	60	187	20	189	80
3	10	65	10	80	10	95	53	188	15	190	80	193	45
4	14	20	14	40	14	60	54	191	70	194	40	197	10
5	17	75	18	00	18	25	55	195	25	198	00	200	75
6	21	30	21	60	21	90	56	198	80	201	60	204	40
7	24	85	25	20	25	55	57	202	35	205	20	208	05
8	28	40	28	80	29	20	58	205	90	208	80	211	70
9	31	95	32	40	32	85	59	209	45	212	40	215	35
10	35	50	36	00	36	50	60	213	00	216	00	219	00
*11	39	05	39	60	40	15	61	216	55	219	60	222	65
i12	42	60	43	20	43	80	62	220	10	223	20	226	30
13	46	15	46	80	47	45	63	223	65	226	80	229	95
14	49	70	50	40	51	10	64	227	20	230	40	233	60
15	53	25	54	00	54	75	65	230	75	234	00	237	25
16	56	80	57	60	58	40	66	234	30	237	60	240	90
17	60	35	61	20	62	05	67	237	85	241	20	244	55
18	63	90	64	80	65	70	68	241	40	244	80	248	20
19	67	45	68	40	69	35	69	244	95	248	40	251	85
20	71	00	72	00	73	00	70	248	50	252	00	255	50
21	74	55	75	60	76	65	71	252	05	255	60	259	15
22	78	10	79	20	80	30	⁶72	255	60	259	20	262	80
23	81	65	82	80	83	95	73	259	15	262	80	266	45
²24	85	20	86	40	87	60	74	262	70	266	40	270	10
25	88	75	90	00	91	25	75	266	25	270	00	273	75
26	92	30	93	60	94	90	76	269	80	273	60	277	40
27	95	85	97	20	98	55	77	273	35	277	20	281	05
28	99	40	100	80	102	20	78	276	90	280	80	284	70
29	102	95	104	40	105	85	79	280	45	284	40	288	35
30	106	50	108	00	109	50	80	284	00	288	00	292	00
31	110	05	111	60	113	15	81	287	55	291	60	295	65
32	113	60	115	20	116	80	82	291	10	295	20	299	30
33	117	15	118	80	120	45	83	294	65	298	80	302	95
34	120	70	122	40	124	10	⁷84	298	20	302	40	306	60
35	124	25	126	00	127	75	85	301	75	306	00	310	25
³36	127	80	129	60	131	40	86	305	30	309	60	313	90
37	131	35	133	20	135	05	87	308	85	313	20	317	55
38	134	90	136	80	138	70	88	312	40	316	80	321	20
39	138	45	140	40	142	35	89	315	95	320	40	324	85
40	142	00	144	00	146	00	90	319	50	324	00	328	50
41	145	55	147	60	149	65	91	323	05	327	60	332	15
42	149	10	151	20	153	30	92	326	60	331	20	335	80
43	152	65	154	80	156	95	93	330	15	334	80	339	45
44	156	20	158	40	160	60	94	333	70	338	40	343	10
45	159	75	162	00	164	25	95	337	25	342	00	346	75
46	163	30	165	60	167	90	⁸96	340	80	345	60	350	40
47	166	85	169	20	171	55	97	344	35	349	20	354	05
48	170	40	172	80	175	20	98	347	90	352	80	357	70
49	173	95	176	40	178	85	99	351	45	356	40	361	35
50	177	50	180	00	182	50	100	355	00	360	00	365	00
¼	0·8875		0·90		0·9125		¾	2·6625		2·70		2·7375	
½	1·7750		1·80		1·8250		1¼	4·4375		4·50		4·5625	

Dozens. (left column, marks at 11, 12, 24, 36, 48) · *Dozens.* (right column, marks at 60, 72, 84, 96)

No. £3·55 £3·60 £3·65   No. £3·55 £3·60 £3·65

No.	£3·55 £	p	£3·60 £	p	£3·65 £	p	No.	£3·55 £	p	£3·60 £	p	£3·65 £	p
101	358	55	363	60	368	65	Doz 155	550	25	558	00	565	75
102	362	10	367	20	372	30	13 156	553	80	561	60	569	40
103	365	65	370	80	375	95	165	585	75	594	00	602	25
104	369	20	374	40	379	60	14 168	596	40	604	80	613	20
105	372	75	378	00	383	25	175	621	25	630	00	638	75
106	376	30	381	60	386	90	15 180	639	00	648	00	657	00
107	379	85	385	20	390	55	185	656	75	666	00	675	25
108	383	40	388	80	394	20	16 192	681	60	691	20	700	80
109	386	95	392	40	397	85	195	692	25	702	00	711	75
110	390	50	396	00	401	50	200	710	00	720	00	730	00
111	394	05	399	60	405	15	17 204	724	20	734	40	744	60
112	397	60	403	20	408	80	205	727	75	738	00	748	25
113	401	15	406	80	412	45	215	763	25	774	00	784	75
114	404	70	410	40	416	10	18 216	766	80	777	60	788	40
115	408	25	414	00	419	75	224	795	20	806	40	817	60
116	411	80	417	60	423	40	225	798	75	810	00	821	25
117	415	35	421	20	427	05	19 228	809	40	820	80	832	20
118	418	90	424	80	430	70	235	834	25	846	00	857	75
119	422	45	428	40	434	35	245	869	75	882	00	894	25
10 120	426	00	432	00	438	00	250	887	50	900	00	912	50
121	429	55	435	60	441	65	21 252	894	60	907	20	919	80
122	433	10	439	20	445	30	255	905	25	918	00	930	75
123	436	65	442	80	448	95	265	940	75	954	00	967	25
124	440	20	446	40	452	60	272	965	60	979	20	992	80
125	443	75	450	00	456	25	275	976	25	990	00	1003	75
126	447	30	453	60	459	90	280	994	00	1008	00	1022	00
127	450	85	457	20	463	55	285	1011	75	1026	00	1040	25
128	454	40	460	80	467	20	288	1022	40	1036	80	1051	20
129	457	95	464	40	470	85	295	1047	25	1062	00	1076	75
130	461	50	468	00	474	50	300	1065	00	1080	00	1095	00
131	465	05	471	60	478	15	325	1153	75	1170	00	1186	25
11 132	468	60	475	20	481	80	336	1192	80	1209	60	1226	40
133	472	15	478	80	485	45	365	1295	75	1314	00	1332	25
134	475	70	482	40	489	10	375	1331	25	1350	00	1368	75
135	479	25	486	00	492	75	400	1420	00	1440	00	1460	00
136	482	80	489	60	496	40	425	1508	75	1530	00	1551	25
137	486	35	493	20	500	05	3 gr. 432	1533	60	1555	20	1576	80
138	489	90	496	80	503	70	475	1686	25	1710	00	1733	75
139	493	45	500	40	507	35	480	1704	00	1728	00	1752	00
140	497	00	504	00	511	00	500	1775	00	1800	00	1825	00
141	500	55	507	60	514	65	504	1789	20	1814	40	1839	60
142	504	10	511	20	518	30	4 gr. 576	2044	80	2073	60	2102	40
143	507	65	514	80	521	95	600	2130	00	2160	00	2190	00
12 144	511	20	518	40	525	60	700	2485	00	2520	00	2555	00
145	514	75	522	00	529	25	750	2662	50	2700	00	2737	50
146	518	30	525	60	532	90	800	2840	00	2880	00	2920	00
147	521	85	529	20	536	55	900	3195	00	3240	00	3285	00
148	525	40	532	80	540	20	1000	3550	00	3600	00	3650	00
149	528	95	536	40	543	85	2500	8875	00	9000	00	9125	00
150	532	50	540	00	547	50	5000	17750	·0	18000	·0	18250	·0
1016	3606	80	3657	60	3708	40	1728	6134	40	6220	80	6307	20
1296	4600	80	4665	60	4730	40	1760	6248	00	6336	00	6424	00

No.	£3·70		£3·75		£3·80		No.	£3·70		£3·75		£3·80	
	£	p	£	p	£	p		£	p	£	p	£	p
1	3	70	3	75	3	80	51	188	70	191	25	193	80
2	7	40	7	50	7	60	52	192	40	195	00	197	60
3	11	10	11	25	11	40	53	196	10	198	75	201	40
4	14	80	15	00	15	20	54	199	80	202	50	205	20
5	18	50	18	75	19	00	55	203	50	206	25	209	00
6	22	20	22	50	22	80	56	207	20	210	00	212	80
7	25	90	26	25	26	60	57	210	90	213	75	216	60
8	29	60	30	00	30	40	58	214	60	217	50	220	40
9	33	30	33	75	34	20	59	218	30	221	25	224	20
10	37	00	37	50	38	00	60	222	00	225	00	228	00
11	40	70	41	25	41	80	61	225	70	228	75	231	80
12	44	40	45	00	45	60	62	229	40	232	50	235	60
13	48	10	48	75	49	40	63	233	10	236	25	239	40
14	51	80	52	50	53	20	64	236	80	240	00	243	20
15	55	50	56	25	57	00	65	240	50	243	75	247	00
16	59	20	60	00	60	80	66	244	20	247	50	250	80
17	62	90	63	75	64	60	67	247	90	251	25	254	60
18	66	60	67	50	68	40	68	251	60	255	00	258	40
19	70	30	71	25	72	20	69	255	30	258	75	262	20
20	74	00	75	00	76	00	70	259	00	262	50	266	00
21	77	70	78	75	79	80	71	262	70	266	25	269	80
22	81	40	82	50	83	60	72	266	40	270	00	273	60
23	85	10	86	25	87	40	73	270	10	273	75	277	40
24	88	80	90	00	91	20	74	273	80	277	50	281	20
25	92	50	93	75	95	00	75	277	50	281	25	285	00
26	96	20	97	50	98	80	76	281	20	285	00	288	80
27	99	90	101	25	102	60	77	284	90	288	75	292	60
28	103	60	105	00	106	40	78	288	60	292	50	296	40
29	107	30	108	75	110	20	79	292	30	296	25	300	20
30	111	00	112	50	114	00	80	296	00	300	00	304	00
31	114	70	116	25	117	80	81	299	70	303	75	307	80
32	118	40	120	00	121	60	82	303	40	307	50	311	60
33	122	10	123	75	125	40	83	307	10	311	25	315	40
34	125	80	127	50	129	20	84	310	80	315	00	319	20
35	129	50	131	25	133	00	85	314	50	318	75	323	00
36	133	20	135	00	136	80	86	318	20	322	50	326	80
37	136	90	138	75	140	60	87	321	90	326	25	330	60
38	140	60	142	50	144	40	88	325	60	330	00	334	40
39	144	30	146	25	148	20	89	329	30	333	75	338	20
40	148	00	150	00	152	00	90	333	00	337	50	342	00
41	151	70	153	75	155	80	91	336	70	341	25	345	80
42	155	40	157	50	159	60	92	340	40	345	00	349	60
43	159	10	161	25	163	40	93	344	10	348	75	353	40
44	162	80	165	00	167	20	94	347	80	352	50	357	20
45	166	50	168	75	171	00	95	351	50	356	25	361	00
46	170	20	172	50	174	80	96	355	20	360	00	364	80
47	173	90	176	25	178	60	97	358	90	363	75	368	60
48	177	60	180	00	182	40	98	362	60	367	50	372	40
49	181	30	183	75	186	20	99	366	30	371	25	376	20
50	185	00	187	50	190	00	100	370	00	375	00	380	00

	£3·70	£3·75	£3·80		£3·70	£3·75	£3·80
¼	0·925	0·9375	0·95	¾	2·775	2·8125	2·85
½	1·850	1·8750	1·90	1¼	4·625	4·6875	4·75

No.	£3·70		£3·75		£3·80		No.	£3·70		£3·75		£3·80	
	£	p	£	p	£	p		£	p	£	p	£	p
101	373	70	378	75	383	80	155	573	50	581	25	589	00
102	377	40	382	50	387	60	13156	577	20	585	00	592	80
103	381	10	386	25	391	40	165	610	50	618	75	627	00
104	384	80	390	00	395	20	14168	621	60	630	00	638	40
105	388	50	393	75	399	00	175	647	50	656	25	665	00
106	392	20	397	50	402	80	15180	666	00	675	00	684	00
107	395	90	401	25	406	60	185	684	50	693	75	703	00
108	399	60	405	00	410	40	16192	710	40	720	00	729	60
109	403	30	408	75	414	20	195	721	50	731	25	741	00
110	407	00	412	50	418	00	200	740	00	750	00	760	00
111	410	70	416	25	421	80	17204	754	80	765	00	775	20
112	414	40	420	00	425	60	205	758	50	768	75	779	00
113	418	10	423	75	429	40	215	795	50	806	25	817	00
114	421	80	427	50	433	20	18216	799	20	810	00	820	80
115	425	50	431	25	437	00	224	828	80	840	00	851	20
116	429	20	435	00	440	80	225	832	50	843	75	855	00
117	432	90	438	75	444	60	19228	843	60	855	00	866	40
118	436	60	442	50	448	40	235	869	50	881	25	893	00
119	440	30	446	25	452	20	245	906	50	918	75	931	00
120	444	00	450	00	456	00	250	925	00	937	50	950	00
121	447	70	453	75	459	80	21252	932	40	945	00	957	60
122	451	40	457	50	463	60	255	943	50	956	25	969	00
123	455	10	461	25	467	40	265	980	50	993	75	1007	00
124	458	80	465	00	471	20	272	1006	40	1020	00	1033	60
125	462	50	468	75	475	00	275	1017	50	1031	25	1045	00
126	466	20	472	50	478	80	280	1036	00	1050	00	1064	00
127	469	90	476	25	482	60	285	1054	50	1068	75	1083	00
128	473	60	480	00	486	40	288	1065	60	1080	00	1094	40
129	477	30	483	75	490	20	295	1091	50	1106	25	1121	00
130	481	00	487	50	494	00	300	1110	00	1125	00	1140	00
131	484	70	491	25	497	80	325	1202	50	1218	75	1235	00
11132	488	40	495	00	501	60	336	1243	20	1260	00	1276	80
133	492	10	498	75	505	40	365	1350	50	1368	75	1387	00
134	495	80	502	50	509	20	375	1387	50	1406	25	1425	00
135	499	50	506	25	513	00	400	1480	00	1500	00	1520	00
136	503	20	510	00	516	80	425	1572	50	1593	75	1615	00
137	506	90	513	75	520	60	432	1598	40	1620	00	1641	60
138	510	60	517	50	524	40	475	1757	50	1781	25	1805	00
139	514	30	521	25	528	20	480	1776	00	1800	00	1824	00
140	518	00	525	00	532	00	500	1850	00	1875	00	1900	00
141	521	70	528	75	535	80	504	1864	80	1890	00	1915	20
142	525	40	532	50	539	60	576	2131	20	2160	00	2188	80
143	529	10	536	25	543	40	600	2220	00	2250	00	2280	00
12144	532	80	540	00	547	20	700	2590	00	2625	00	2660	00
145	536	50	543	75	551	00	750	2775	00	2812	50	2850	00
146	540	20	547	50	554	80	800	2960	00	3000	00	3040	00
147	543	90	551	25	558	60	900	3330	00	3375	00	3420	00
148	547	60	555	00	562	40	1000	3700	00	3750	00	3800	00
149	551	30	558	75	566	20	2500	9250	00	9375	00	9500	00
150	555	00	562	50	570	00	5000	18500	·0	18750	·0	19000	·0
1016	3759	20	3810	00	3860	80	1728	6393	60	6480	00	6566	40
1296	4795	20	4860	00	4924	80	1760	6512	00	6600	00	6688	00

No.	£3·85		£3·90		£3·95		No.	£3·85		£3·90		£3·95	
	£	P	£	P	£	P		£	P	£	P	£	P
1	3	85	3	90	3	95	51	196	35	198	90	201	45
2	7	70	7	80	7	90	52	200	20	202	80	205	40
3	11	55	11	70	11	85	53	204	05	206	70	209	35
4	15	40	15	60	15	80	54	207	90	210	60	213	30
5	19	25	19	50	19	75	55	211	75	214	50	217	25
6	23	10	23	40	23	70	56	215	60	218	40	221	20
7	26	95	27	30	27	65	57	219	45	222	30	225	15
8	30	80	31	20	31	60	58	223	30	226	20	229	10
9	34	65	35	10	35	55	59	227	15	230	10	233	05
10	38	50	39	00	39	50	60	231	00	234	00	237	00
11	42	35	42	90	43	45	61	234	85	237	90	240	95
12	46	20	46	80	47	40	62	238	70	241	80	244	90
13	50	05	50	70	51	35	63	242	55	245	70	248	85
14	53	90	54	60	55	30	64	246	40	249	60	252	80
15	57	75	58	50	59	25	65	250	25	253	50	256	75
16	61	60	62	40	63	20	66	254	10	257	40	260	70
17	65	45	66	30	67	15	67	257	95	261	30	264	65
18	69	30	70	20	71	10	68	261	80	265	20	268	60
19	73	15	74	10	75	05	69	265	65	269	10	272	55
20	77	00	78	00	79	00	70	269	50	273	00	276	50
21	80	85	81	90	82	95	71	273	35	276	90	280	45
22	84	70	85	80	86	90	72	277	20	280	80	284	40
23	88	55	89	70	90	85	73	281	05	284	70	288	35
24	92	40	93	60	94	80	74	284	90	288	60	292	30
25	96	25	97	50	98	75	75	288	75	292	50	296	25
26	100	10	101	40	102	70	76	292	60	296	40	300	20
27	103	95	105	30	106	65	77	296	45	300	30	304	15
28	107	80	109	20	110	60	78	300	30	304	20	308	10
29	111	65	113	10	114	55	79	304	15	308	10	312	05
30	115	50	117	00	118	50	80	308	00	312	00	316	00
31	119	35	120	90	122	45	81	311	85	315	90	319	95
32	123	20	124	80	126	40	82	315	70	319	80	323	90
33	127	05	128	70	130	35	83	319	55	323	70	327	85
34	130	90	132	60	134	30	84	323	40	327	60	331	80
35	134	75	136	50	138	25	85	327	25	331	50	335	75
36	138	60	140	40	142	20	86	331	10	335	40	339	70
37	142	45	144	30	146	15	87	334	95	339	30	343	65
38	146	30	148	20	150	10	88	338	80	343	20	347	60
39	150	15	152	10	154	05	89	342	65	347	10	351	55
40	154	00	156	00	158	00	90	346	50	351	00	355	50
41	157	85	159	90	161	95	91	350	35	354	90	359	45
42	161	70	163	80	165	90	92	354	20	358	80	363	40
43	165	55	167	70	169	85	93	358	05	362	70	367	35
44	169	40	171	60	173	80	94	361	90	366	60	371	30
45	173	25	175	50	177	75	95	365	75	370	50	375	25
46	177	10	179	40	181	70	96	369	60	374	40	379	20
47	180	95	183	30	185	65	97	373	45	378	30	383	15
48	184	80	187	20	189	60	98	377	30	382	20	387	10
49	188	65	191	10	193	55	99	381	15	386	10	391	05
50	192	50	195	00	197	50	100	385	00	390	00	395	00
¼	0·9625		0·975		0·9875		¾	2·8875		2·925		2·9625	
½	1·9250		1·950		1·9750		1¼	4·8125		4·875		4·9375	

No.	£3·85 £	P	£3·90 £	P	£3·95 £	P
101	388	85	393	90	398	95
102	392	70	397	80	402	90
103	396	55	401	70	406	85
104	400	40	405	60	410	80
105	404	25	409	50	414	75
106	408	10	413	40	418	70
107	411	95	417	30	422	65
108	415	80	421	20	426	60
109	419	65	425	10	430	55
110	423	50	429	00	434	50
111	427	35	432	90	438	45
112	431	20	436	80	442	40
113	435	05	440	70	446	35
114	438	90	444	60	450	30
115	442	75	448	50	454	25
116	446	60	452	40	458	20
117	450	45	456	30	462	15
118	454	30	460	20	466	10
119	458	15	464	10	470	05
120	462	00	468	00	474	00
121	465	85	471	90	477	95
122	469	70	475	80	481	90
123	473	55	479	70	485	85
124	477	40	483	60	489	80
125	481	25	487	50	493	75
126	485	10	491	40	497	70
127	488	95	495	30	501	65
128	492	80	499	20	505	60
129	496	65	503	10	509	55
130	500	50	507	00	513	50
131	504	35	510	90	517	45
11 132	508	20	514	80	521	40
133	512	05	518	70	525	35
134	515	90	522	60	529	30
135	519	75	526	50	533	25
136	523	60	530	40	537	20
137	527	45	534	30	541	15
138	531	30	538	20	545	10
139	535	15	542	10	549	05
140	539	00	546	00	553	00
141	542	85	549	90	556	95
142	546	70	553	80	560	90
143	550	55	557	70	564	85
12 144	554	40	561	60	568	80
145	558	25	565	50	572	75
146	562	10	569	40	576	70
147	565	95	573	30	580	65
148	569	80	577	20	584	60
149	573	65	581	10	588	55
150	577	50	585	00	592	50
1016	3911	60	3962	40	4013	20
1296	4989	60	5054	40	5119	20

No.	£3·85 £	P	£3·90 £	P	£3·95 £	P
155	596	75	604	50	612	25
13 156	600	60	608	40	616	20
165	635	25	643	50	651	75
14 168	646	80	655	20	663	60
175	673	75	682	50	691	25
15 180	693	00	702	00	711	00
185	712	25	721	50	730	75
16 192	739	20	748	80	758	40
195	750	75	760	50	770	25
200	770	00	780	00	790	00
17 204	785	40	795	60	805	80
205	789	25	799	50	809	75
215	827	75	838	50	849	25
18 216	831	60	842	40	853	20
224	862	40	873	00	884	80
225	866	25	877	50	888	75
19 228	877	80	889	20	900	60
235	904	75	916	50	928	25
245	943	25	955	50	967	75
250	962	50	975	00	987	50
21 252	970	20	982	80	995	40
255	981	75	994	50	1007	25
265	1020	25	1033	50	1046	75
272	1047	20	1060	80	1074	40
275	1058	75	1072	50	1086	25
280	1078	00	1092	00	1106	00
285	1097	25	1111	50	1125	75
2 gross 288	1108	80	1123	20	1137	60
295	1135	75	1150	50	1165	25
300	1155	00	1170	00	1185	00
325	1251	25	1267	50	1283	75
336	1293	60	1310	40	1327	20
365	1405	25	1423	50	1441	75
375	1443	75	1462	50	1481	25
400	1540	00	1560	00	1580	00
3 gr. 425	1636	25	1657	50	1678	75
432	1663	20	1684	80	1706	40
475	1828	75	1852	50	1876	25
480	1848	00	1872	00	1896	00
500	1925	00	1950	00	1975	00
4 gr. 504	1940	40	1965	60	1990	80
576	2217	60	2246	40	2275	20
600	2310	00	2340	00	2370	00
700	2695	00	2730	00	2765	00
750	2887	50	2925	00	2962	50
800	3080	00	3120	00	3160	00
900	3465	00	3510	00	3555	00
1000	3850	00	3900	00	3950	00
2500	9625	00	9750	00	9875	00
5000	19250	0	19500	0	19750	0
1728	6652	80	6739	20	6825	60
1760	6776	00	6864	00	6952	00

No.	£4·00 £	P	£4·05 £	P	£4·10 £	P	No.	£4·00 £	P	£4·05 £	P	£4·10 £	P
1	4	00	4	05	4	10	51	204	00	206	55	209	10
2	8	00	8	10	8	20	52	208	00	210	60	213	20
3	12	00	12	15	12	30	53	212	00	214	65	217	30
4	16	00	16	20	16	40	54	216	00	218	70	221	40
5	20	00	20	25	20	50	55	220	00	222	75	225	50
6	24	00	24	30	24	60	56	224	00	226	80	229	60
7	28	00	28	35	28	70	57	228	00	230	85	233	70
8	32	00	32	40	32	80	58	232	00	234	90	237	80
9	36	00	36	45	36	90	59	236	00	238	95	241	90
10	40	00	40	50	41	00	60	240	00	243	00	246	00
11	44	00	44	55	45	10	61	244	00	247	05	250	10
12	48	00	48	60	49	20	62	248	00	251	10	254	20
13	52	00	52	65	53	30	63	252	00	255	15	258	30
14	56	00	56	70	57	40	64	256	00	259	20	262	40
15	60	00	60	75	61	50	65	260	00	263	25	266	50
16	64	00	64	80	65	60	66	264	00	267	30	270	60
17	68	00	68	85	69	70	67	268	00	271	35	274	70
18	72	00	72	90	73	80	68	272	00	275	40	278	80
19	76	00	76	95	77	90	69	276	00	279	45	282	90
20	80	00	81	00	82	00	70	280	00	283	50	287	00
21	84	00	85	05	86	10	71	284	00	287	55	291	10
22	88	00	89	10	90	20	72	288	00	291	60	295	20
23	92	00	93	15	94	30	73	292	00	295	65	299	30
24	96	00	97	20	98	40	74	296	00	299	70	303	40
25	100	00	101	25	102	50	75	300	00	303	75	307	50
26	104	00	105	30	106	60	76	304	00	307	80	311	60
27	108	00	109	35	110	70	77	308	00	311	85	315	70
28	112	00	113	40	114	80	78	312	00	315	90	319	80
29	116	00	117	45	118	90	79	316	00	319	95	323	90
30	120	00	121	50	123	00	80	320	00	324	00	328	00
31	124	00	125	55	127	10	81	324	00	328	05	332	10
32	128	00	129	60	131	20	82	328	00	332	10	336	20
33	132	00	133	65	135	30	83	332	00	336	15	340	30
34	136	00	137	70	139	40	84	336	00	340	20	344	40
35	140	00	141	75	143	50	85	340	00	344	25	348	50
36	144	00	145	80	147	60	86	344	00	348	30	352	60
37	148	00	149	85	151	70	87	348	00	352	35	356	70
38	152	00	153	90	155	80	88	352	00	356	40	360	80
39	156	00	157	95	159	90	89	356	00	360	45	364	90
40	160	00	162	00	164	00	90	360	00	364	50	369	00
41	164	00	166	05	168	10	91	364	00	368	55	373	10
42	168	00	170	10	172	20	92	368	00	372	60	377	20
43	172	00	174	15	176	30	93	372	00	376	65	381	30
44	176	00	178	20	180	40	94	376	00	380	70	385	40
45	180	00	182	25	184	50	95	380	00	384	75	389	50
46	184	00	186	30	188	60	96	384	00	388	80	393	60
47	188	00	190	35	192	70	97	388	00	392	85	397	70
48	192	00	194	40	196	80	98	392	00	396	90	401	80
49	196	00	198	45	200	90	99	396	00	400	95	405	90
50	200	00	202	50	205	00	100	400	00	405	00	410	00
¼	1·00		1·0125		1·025		½	3·00		3·0375		3·0750	
½	2·00		2·0250		2·050		1¼	5·00		5·0625		5·1250	

No.	£4·00 £	p	£4·05 £	p	£4·10 £	p	No.	£4·00 £	p	£4·05 £	p	£4·10 £	p
101	404	00	409	05	414	10	155	620	00	627	75	635	50
102	408	00	413	10	418	20	13156	624	00	631	80	639	60
103	412	00	417	15	422	30	165	660	00	668	25	676	50
104	416	00	421	20	426	40	14168	672	00	680	40	688	80
105	420	00	425	25	430	50	175	700	00	708	75	717	50
106	424	00	429	30	434	60	15180	720	00	729	00	738	00
107	428	00	433	35	438	70	185	740	00	749	25	758	50
9108	432	00	437	40	442	80	16192	768	00	777	60	787	20
109	436	00	441	45	446	90	195	780	00	789	75	799	50
110	440	00	445	50	451	10	200	800	00	810	00	820	00
111	444	00	449	55	455	10	17204	816	00	826	20	836	40
112	448	00	453	60	459	20	205	820	00	830	25	840	50
113	452	00	457	65	463	30	215	860	00	870	75	881	50
114	456	00	461	70	467	40	18216	864	00	874	80	885	60
115	460	00	465	75	471	50	224	896	00	907	20	918	40
116	464	00	469	80	475	60	225	900	00	911	25	922	50
117	468	00	473	85	479	70	19228	912	00	923	40	934	80
118	472	00	477	90	483	80	235	940	00	951	75	963	50
119	476	00	481	95	487	90	245	980	00	992	25	1004	50
10120	480	00	486	00	492	00	250	1000	00	1012	50	1025	00
121	484	00	490	05	496	10	21252	1008	00	1020	60	1033	20
122	488	00	494	10	500	20	255	1020	00	1032	75	1045	50
123	492	00	498	15	504	30	265	1060	00	1073	25	1086	50
124	496	00	502	20	508	40	272	1088	00	1101	60	1115	20
125	500	00	506	25	512	50	275	1100	00	1113	75	1127	50
126	504	00	510	30	516	60	280	1120	00	1134	00	1148	00
127	508	00	514	35	520	70	285	1140	00	1154	25	1168	00
128	512	00	518	40	524	80	288	1152	00	1166	40	1180	80
129	516	00	522	45	528	90	295	1180	00	1194	75	1209	50
130	520	00	526	50	533	00	300	1200	00	1215	00	1230	00
131	524	00	530	55	537	10	325	1300	00	1316	25	1332	50
11132	528	00	534	60	541	20	336	1344	00	1360	80	1377	60
133	532	00	538	65	545	30	365	1460	00	1478	25	1496	50
134	536	00	542	70	549	40	375	1500	00	1518	75	1537	50
135	540	00	546	75	553	50	400	1600	00	1620	00	1640	00
136	544	00	550	80	557	60	425	1700	00	1721	25	1742	50
137	548	00	554	85	561	70	432	1728	00	1749	60	1771	20
138	552	00	558	90	565	80	475	1900	00	1923	75	1947	50
139	556	00	562	95	569	90	480	1920	00	1944	00	1968	00
140	560	00	567	00	574	00	500	2000	00	2025	00	2050	00
141	564	00	571	05	578	10	504	2016	00	2041	20	2066	40
142	568	00	575	10	582	20	576	2304	00	2332	80	2361	60
143	572	00	579	15	586	30	600	2400	00	2430	00	2460	00
12144	576	00	583	20	590	40	700	2800	00	2835	00	2870	00
145	580	00	587	25	594	50	750	3000	00	3037	50	3075	00
146	584	00	591	30	598	60	800	3200	00	3240	00	3280	00
147	588	00	595	35	602	70	900	3600	00	3645	00	3690	00
148	592	00	599	40	606	80	1000	4000	00	4050	00	4100	00
149	596	00	603	45	610	90	2500	10000	·0	10125	·0	10250	·0
150	600	00	607	50	615	00	5000	20000	·0	20250	·0	20500	·0

1016	4064·00	4114·80	4165·60	1728	6912·00	6998·40	7084·80
1296	5184·00	5248·80	5313·60	1760	7040·00	7128·00	7216·00

No.	£4·15		£4·20		£4·25		No.	£4·15		£4·20		£4·25	
	£	P	£	P	£	P		£	P	£	P	£	P
1	4	15	4	20	4	25	51	211	65	214	20	216	75
2	8	30	8	40	8	50	52	215	80	218	40	221	00
3	12	45	12	60	12	75	53	219	95	222	60	225	25
4	16	60	16	80	17	00	54	224	10	226	80	229	50
5	20	75	21	00	21	25	55	228	25	231	00	233	75
6	24	90	25	20	25	50	56	232	40	235	20	238	00
7	29	05	29	40	29	75	57	236	55	239	40	242	25
8	33	20	33	60	34	00	58	240	70	243	60	246	50
9	37	35	37	80	38	25	59	244	85	247	80	250	75
10	41	50	42	00	42	50	60	249	00	252	00	255	00
11	45	65	46	20	46	75	61	253	15	256	20	259	25
12	49	80	50	40	51	00	62	257	30	260	40	263	50
13	53	95	54	60	55	25	63	261	45	264	60	267	75
14	58	10	58	80	59	50	64	265	60	268	80	272	00
15	62	25	63	00	63	75	65	269	75	273	00	276 · 25
16	66	40	67	20	68	00	66	273	90	277	20	280	50
17	70	55	71	40	72	25	67	278	05	281	40	284	75
18	74	70	75	60	76	50	68	282	20	285	60	289	00
19	78	85	79	80	80	75	69	286	35	289	80	293	25
20	83	00	84	00	85	00	70	290	50	294	00	297	50
21	87	15	88	20	89	25	71	294	65	298	20	301	75
22	91	30	92	40	93	50	72	298	80	302	40	306	00
23	95	45	96	60	97	75	73	302	95	306	60	310	25
24	99	60	100	80	102	00	74	307	10	310	80	314	50
25	103	75	105	00	106	25	75	311	25	315	00	318	75
26	107	90	109	20	110	50	76	315	40	319	20	323	00
27	112	05	113	40	114	75	77	319	55	323	40	327	25
28	116	20	117	60	119	00	78	323	70	327	60	331	50
29	120	35	121	80	123	25	79	327	85	331	80	335	75
30	124	50	126	00	127	50	80	332	00	336	00	340	00
31	128	65	130	20	131	75	81	336	15	340	20	344	25
32	132	80	134	40	136	00	82	340	30	344	40	348	50
33	136	95	138	60	140	25	83	344	45	348	60	352	75
34	141	10	142	80	144	50	84	348	60	352	80	357	00
35	145	25	147	00	148	75	85	352	75	357	00	361	25
36	149	40	151	20	153	00	86	356	90	361	20	365	50
37	153	55	155	40	157	25	87	361	05	365	40	369	75
38	157	70	159	60	161	50	88	365	20	369	60	374	00
39	161	85	163	80	165	75	89	369	35	373	80	378	25
40	166	00	168	00	170	00	90	373	50	378	00	382	50
41	170	15	172	20	174	25	91	377	65	382	20	386	75
42	174	30	176	40	178	50	92	381	80	386	40	391	00
43	178	45	180	60	182	75	93	385	95	390	60	395	25
44	182	60	184	80	187	00	94	390	10	394	80	399	50
45	186	75	189	00	191	25	95	394	25	399	00	403	75
46	190	90	193	20	195	50	96	398	40	403	20	408	00
47	195	05	197	40	199	75	97	402	55	407	40	412	25
48	199	20	201	60	204	00	98	406	70	411	60	416	50
49	203	35	205	80	208	25	99	410	85	415	80	420	75
50	207	50	210	00	212	50	100	415	00	420	00	425	00
¼	1·0875		1·05		1·0625		¾	3·1125		3·15		3·1875	
½..	2·0750		2·10		2·1250		1¼..	5·1875		5·25		5·3125	

No.	£4·15 £	p	£4·20 £	p	£4·25 £	p	No.	£4·15 £	p	£4·20 £	p	£4·25 £	p
101	419	15	424	20	429	25	155	643	25	651	00	658	75
102	423	30	428	40	433	50	13156	647	40	655	20	663	00
103	427	45	432	60	437	75	165	684	75	693	00	701	25
104	431	60	436	80	442	00	14168	697	20	705	60	714	00
105	435	75	441	00	446	25	175	726	25	735	00	743	75
106	439	90	445	20	450	50	15180	747	00	756	00	765	00
107	444	05	449	40	454	75	185	767	75	777	00	786	25
9108	448	20	453	60	459	00	16192	796	80	806	40	816	00
109	452	35	457	80	463	25	195	809	25	819	00	828	75
110	456	50	462	00	467	50	200	830	00	840	00	850	00
111	460	65	466	20	471	75	17204	846	60	856	80	867	00
112	464	80	470	40	476	00	205	850	75	861	00	871	25
113	468	95	474	60	480	25	215	892	25	903	00	913	75
114	473	10	478	80	484	50	18216	896	40	907	20	918	00
115	477	25	483	00	488	75	224	929	60	940	80	952	00
116	481	40	487	20	493	00	225	933	75	945	00	956	25
117	485	55	491	40	497	25	19228	946	20	957	60	969	00
118	489	70	495	60	501	50	235	975	25	987	00	998	75
119	493	85	499	80	505	75	245	1016	75	1029	00	1041	25
120	498	00	504	00	510	00	250	1037	50	1050	00	1062	50
121	502	15	508	20	514	25	21252	1045	80	1058	40	1071	00
122	506	30	512	40	518	50	255	1058	25	1071	00	1083	75
123	510	45	516	60	522	75	265	1099	75	1113	00	1126	25
124	514	60	520	80	527	00	272	1128	80	1142	40	1156	00
125	518	75	525	00	531	25	275	1141	25	1155	00	1168	75
126	522	90	529	20	535	50	280	1162	00	1176	00	1190	00
127	527	05	533	40	539	75	285	1182	75	1197	00	1211	25
128	531	20	537	60	544	00	2 gross 288	1195	20	1209	60	1224	00
129	535	35	541	80	548	25	295	1224	25	1239	00	1253	75
130	539	50	546	00	552	50	300	1245	00	1260	00	1275	00
131	543	65	550	20	556	75	325	1348	75	1365	00	1381	25
132	547	80	554	40	561	00	336	1394	40	1411	20	1428	00
133	551	95	558	60	565	25	365	1514	75	1533	00	1551	25
134	556	10	562	80	569	50	375	1556	25	1575	00	1593	75
135	560	25	567	00	573	75	400	1660	00	1680	00	1700	00
136	564	40	571	20	578	00	3 gr. 425	1763	75	1785	00	1806	25
137	568	55	575	40	582	25	432	1792	80	1814	40	1836	00
138	572	70	579	60	586	50	475	1971	25	1995	00	2018	75
139	576	85	583	80	590	75	480	1992	00	2016	00	2040	00
140	581	00	588	00	595	00	500	2075	00	2100	00	2125	00
141	585	15	592	20	599	25	4 gr. 504	2091	60	2116	80	2142	00
142	589	30	596	40	603	50	576	2390	40	2419	20	2448	00
143	593	45	600	60	607	75	600	2490	00	2520	00	2550	00
12144	597	60	604	80	612	00	700	2905	00	2940	00	2975	00
145	601	75	609	00	616	25	750	3112	50	3150	00	3187	50
146	605	90	613	20	620	50	800	3320	00	3360	00	3400	00
147	610	05	617	40	624	75	900	3735	00	3780	00	3825	00
148	614	20	621	60	629	00	1000	4150	00	4200	00	4250	00
149	618	35	625	80	633	25	2500	10375	·0	10500	·0	10625	·0
150	622	50	630	00	637	50	5000	20750	·0	21000	·0	21250	·0
1016	4216·40		4267·20		4318·00		1728	7171·20		7257·60		7344·00	
1296	5378·40		5443·20		5508·00		1760	7304·00		7392·00		7480·00	

No.	£4·30 £	P	£4·35 £	P	£4·40 £	P
1	4	30	4	35	4	40
2	8	60	8	70	8	80
3	12	90	13	05	13	20
4	17	20	17	40	17	60
5	21	50	21	75	22	00
6	25	80	26	10	26	40
7	30	10	30	45	30	80
8	34	40	34	80	35	20
9	38	70	39	15	39	60
10	43	00	43	50	44	00
11	47	30	47	85	48	40
12	51	60	52	20	52	80
13	55	90	56	55	57	20
14	60	20	60	90	61	60
15	64	50	65	25	66	00
16	68	80	69	60	70	40
17	73	10	73	95	74	80
18	77	40	78	30	79	20
19	81	70	82	65	83	60
20	86	00	87	00	88	00
21	90	30	91	35	92	40
22	94	60	95	70	96	80
23	98	90	100	05	101	20
24	103	20	104	40	105	60
25	107	50	108	75	110	00
26	111	80	113	10	114	40
27	116	10	117	45	118	80
28	120	40	121	80	123	20
29	124	70	126	15	127	60
30	129	00	130	50	132	00
31	133	30	134	85	136	40
32	137	60	139	20	140	80
33	141	90	143	55	145	20
34	146	20	147	90	149	60
35	150	50	152	25	154	00
36	154	80	156	60	158	40
37	159	10	160	95	162	80
38	163	40	165	30	167	20
39	167	70	169	65	171	60
40	172	00	174	00	176	00
41	176	30	178	35	180	40
42	180	60	182	70	184	80
43	184	90	187	05	189	20
44	189	20	191	40	193	60
45	193	50	195	75	198	00
46	197	80	200	10	202	40
47	202	10	204	45	206	80
48	206	40	208	80	211	20
49	210	70	213	15	215	60
50	215	00	217	50	220	00

No.	£4·30 £	P	£4·35 £	P	£4·40 £	P
51	219	30	221	85	224	40
52	223	60	226	20	228	80
53	227	90	230	55	233	20
54	232	20	234	90	237	60
55	236	50	239	25	242	00
56	240	80	243	60	246	40
57	245	10	247	95	250	80
58	249	40	252	30	255	20
59	253	70	256	65	259	60
60	258	00	261	00	264	00
61	262	30	265	35	268	40
62	266	60	269	70	272	80
63	270	90	274	05	277	20
64	275	20	278	40	281	60
65	279	50	282	75	286	00
66	283	80	287	10	290	40
67	288	10	291	45	294	80
68	292	40	295	80	299	20
69	296	70	300	15	303	60
70	301	00	304	50	308	00
71	305	30	308	85	312	40
72	309	60	313	20	316	80
73	313	90	317	55	321	20
74	318	20	321	90	325	60
75	322	50	326	25	330	00
76	326	80	330	60	334	40
77	331	10	334	95	338	80
78	335	40	339	30	343	20
79	339	70	343	65	347	60
80	344	00	348	00	352	00
81	348	30	352	35	356	40
82	352	60	356	70	360	80
83	356	90	361	05	365	20
84	361	20	365	40	369	60
85	365	50	369	75	374	00
86	369	80	374	10	378	40
87	374	10	378	45	382	80
88	378	40	382	80	387	20
89	382	70	387	15	391	60
90	387	00	391	50	396	00
91	391	30	395	85	400	40
92	395	60	400	20	404	80
93	399	90	404	55	409	20
94	404	20	408	90	413	60
95	408	50	413	25	418	00
96	412	80	417	60	422	40
97	417	10	421	95	426	80
98	421	40	426	30	431	20
99	425	70	430	65	435	60
100	430	00	435	00	440	00

	£4·30	£4·35	£4·40		£4·30	£4·35	£4·40
¼	1·075	1·0875	1·10	¾	3·225	3·2625	3·30
½	2·150	2·1750	2·20	1¼	5·375	5·4875	5·50

No. | £4·30 £ / p | £4·35 £ / p | £4·40 £ / p

No.	£4·30 £	p	£4·35 £	p	£4·40 £	p
101	434	30	439	35	444	40
102	438	60	443	70	448	80
103	442	90	448	05	453	20
104	447	20	452	40	457	60
105	451	50	456	75	462	00
106	455	80	461	10	466	40
107	460	10	465	45	470	80
108	464	40	469	80	475	20
109	468	70	474	15	479	60
110	473	00	478	50	484	00
111	477	30	482	85	488	40
112	481	60	487	20	492	80
113	485	90	491	55	497	20
114	490	20	495	90	501	60
115	494	50	500	25	506	00
116	498	80	504	60	510	40
117	503	10	508	95	514	80
118	507	40	513	30	519	20
119	511	70	517	65	523	60
120	516	00	522	00	528	00
121	520	30	526	35	532	40
122	524	60	530	70	536	80
123	528	90	535	05	541	20
124	533	20	539	40	545	60
125	537	50	543	75	550	00
126	541	80	548	10	554	40
127	546	10	552	45	558	80
128	550	40	556	80	563	20
129	554	70	561	15	567	60
30	559	00	565	50	572	00
131	563	30	569	85	576	40
132	567	60	574	20	580	80
133	571	90	578	55	585	20
134	576	20	582	90	589	60
135	580	50	587	25	594	00
136	584	80	591	60	598	40
137	589	10	595	95	602	80
138	593	40	600	30	607	20
139	597	70	604	65	611	60
40	602	00	609	00	616	00
141	606	30	613	35	620	40
142	610	60	617	70	624	80
143	614	90	622	05	629	20
144	619	20	626	40	633	60
145	623	50	630	75	638	00
146	627	80	635	10	642	40
147	632	10	639	45	646	80
148	636	40	643	80	651	20
149	640	70	648	15	655	60
50	645	00	652	50	660	00
016	4368	80	4419	60	4470	40
296	5572	80	5687	60	5702	40

No.	£4·30 £	p	£4·35 £	p	£4·40 £	p
155	666	50	674	25	682	55
[13]156	670	80	678	60	686	40
165	709	50	717	75	726	00
[14]168	722	40	730	80	739	20
175	752	50	761	25	770	00
[15]180	774	00	783	00	792	00
185	795	50	804	75	814	00
[16]192	825	60	835	20	844	80
195	838	50	848	25	858	00
200	860	00	870	00	880	00
[17]204	877	20	887	40	897	60
205	881	50	891	75	902	00
215	924	50	935	25	946	00
[18]216	928	80	939	60	950	40
224	963	20	974	40	985	60
225	967	50	978	75	990	00
[19]228	980	40	991	80	1003	20
235	1010	50	1022	25	1034	00
245	1053	50	1065	75	1078	00
250	1075	00	1087	50	1100	00
[21]252	1083	60	1096	20	1108	80
255	1096	50	1109	25	1122	00
265	1139	50	1152	75	1166	00
272	1169	60	1183	20	1196	80
275	1182	50	1196	25	1210	00
280	1204	00	1218	00	1232	00
285	1225	50	1239	75	1254	00
2 gross 288	1238	40	1252	80	1267	20
295	1268	50	1283	25	1298	00
300	1290	00	1305	00	1320	00
325	1397	50	1413	75	1430	00
336	1444	80	1461	60	1478	40
365	1569	50	1587	75	1606	00
375	1612	50	1631	25	1650	00
400	1720	00	1740	00	1760	00
425	1827	50	1848	75	1870	00
3 gr. 432	1857	60	1879	20	1900	80
475	2042	50	2066	25	2090	00
480	2064	00	2088	00	2112	00
500	2150	00	2175	00	2200	00
4 gr. 504	2167	20	2192	40	2217	60
576	2476	80	2505	60	2534	40
600	2580	00	2610	00	2640	00
700	3010	00	3045	00	3080	00
750	3225	00	3262	50	3300	00
800	3440	00	3480	00	3520	00
900	3870	00	3915	00	3960	00
1000	4300	00	4350	00	4400	00
2500	10750	·0	10875	·0	11000	·0
5000	21500	·0	21750	·0	22000	·0
1728	7430	40	7516	80	7603	20
1760	7568	00	7656	00	7744	00

No.	£4·45 £	P	£4·50 £	P	£4·55 £	P	No.	£4·45 £	P	£4·50 £	P	£4·55 £	P
1	4	45	4	50	4	55	51	226	95	229	50	232	05
2	8	90	9	00	9	10	52	231	40	234	00	236	60
3	13	35	13	50	13	65	53	235	85	238	50	241	15
4	17	80	18	00	18	20	54	240	30	243	00	245	70
5	22	25	22	50	22	75	55	244	75	247	50	250	25
6	26	70	27	00	27	30	56	249	20	252	00	254	80
7	31	15	31	50	31	85	57	253	65	256	50	259	35
8	35	60	36	00	36	40	58	258	10	261	00	263	90
9	40	05	40	50	40	95	59	262	55	265	50	268	45
10	44	50	45	00	45	50	60	267	00	270	00	273	00
11	48	95	49	50	50	05	61	271	45	274	50	277	55
12	53	40	54	00	54	60	62	275	90	279	00	282	10
13	57	85	58	50	59	15	63	280	35	283	50	286	65
14	62	30	63	00	63	70	64	284	80	288	00	291	20
15	66	75	67	50	68	25	65	289	25	292	50	295	75
16	71	20	72	00	72	80	66	293	70	297	00	300	30
17	75	65	76	50	77	35	67	298	15	301	50	304	85
18	80	10	81	00	81	90	68	302	60	306	00	309	40
19	84	55	85	50	86	45	69	307	05	310	50	313	95
20	89	00	90	00	91	00	70	311	50	315	00	318	50
21	93	45	94	50	95	55	71	315	95	319	50	323	05
22	97	90	99	00	100	10	72	320	40	324	00	327	60
23	102	35	103	50	104	65	73	324	85	328	50	332	15
24	106	80	108	00	109	20	74	329	30	333	00	336	70
25	111	25	112	50	113	75	75	333	75	337	50	341	25
26	115	70	117	00	118	30	76	338	20	342	00	345	80
27	120	15	121	50	122	85	77	342	65	346	50	350	35
28	124	60	126	00	127	40	78	347	10	351	00	354	90
29	129	05	130	50	131	95	79	351	55	355	50	359	45
30	133	50	135	00	136	50	80	356	00	360	00	364	00
31	137	95	139	50	141	05	81	360	45	364	50	368	55
32	142	40	144	00	145	60	82	364	90	369	00	373	10
33	146	85	148	50	150	15	83	369	35	373	50	377	65
34	151	30	153	00	154	70	84	373	80	378	00	382	20
35	155	75	157	50	159	25	85	378	25	382	50	386	75
36	160	20	162	00	163	80	86	382	70	387	00	391	30
37	164	65	166	50	168	35	87	387	15	391	50	395	85
38	169	10	171	00	172	90	88	391	60	396	00	400	40
39	173	55	175	50	177	45	89	396	05	400	50	404	95
40	178	00	180	00	182	00	90	400	50	405	00	409	50
41	182	45	184	50	186	55	91	404	95	409	50	414	05
42	186	90	189	00	191	10	92	409	40	414	00	418	60
43	191	35	193	50	195	65	93	413	85	418	50	423	15
44	195	80	198	00	200	20	94	418	30	423	00	427	70
45	200	25	202	50	204	75	95	422	75	427	50	432	25
46	204	70	207	00	209	30	96	427	20	432	00	436	80
47	209	15	211	50	213	85	97	431	65	436	50	441	35
48	213	60	216	00	218	40	98	436	10	441	00	445	90
49	218	05	220	50	222	95	99	440	55	445	50	450	45
50	222	50	225	00	227	50	100	445	00	450	00	455	00

	£4·45	£4·50	£4·55		£4·45	£4·50	£4·55
¼	1·1125	1·125	1·1375	¾	3·3375	3·375	3·4125
½	2·2250	2·250	2·2750	1¼	5·5625	5·625	5·6875

No.	£4.45 £	P	£4.50 £	P	£4.55 £	P
101	449	45	454	50	459	55
102	453	90	459	00	464	10
103	458	35	463	50	468	65
104	462	80	468	00	473	20
105	467	25	472	50	477	75
106	471	70	477	00	482	30
107	476	15	481	50	486	85
108	480	60	486	00	491	40
109	485	05	490	50	495	95
110	489	50	495	00	500	50
111	493	95	499	50	505	05
112	498	40	504	00	509	60
113	502	85	508	50	514	15
114	507	30	513	00	518	70
115	511	75	517	50	523	25
116	516	20	522	00	527	80
117	520	65	526	50	532	35
118	525	10	531	00	536	90
119	529	55	535	50	541	45
120	534	00	540	00	546	00
121	538	45	544	50	550	55
122	542	90	549	00	555	10
123	547	35	553	50	559	65
124	551	80	558	00	564	20
125	556	25	562	50	568	75
126	560	70	567	00	573	30
127	565	15	571	50	577	85
128	569	60	576	00	582	40
129	574	05	580	50	586	95
130	578	50	585	00	591	50
131	582	95	589	50	596	05
132	587	40	594	00	600	60
133	591	85	598	50	605	15
134	596	30	603	00	609	70
135	600	75	607	50	614	25
136	605	20	612	00	618	80
137	609	65	616	50	623	35
138	614	10	621	00	627	90
139	618	55	625	50	632	45
140	623	00	630	00	637	00
141	627	45	634	50	641	55
142	631	90	639	00	646	10
143	636	35	643	50	650	65
144	640	80	648	00	655	20
145	645	25	652	50	659	75
146	649	70	657	00	664	30
147	654	15	661	50	668	85
148	658	60	666	00	673	40
149	663	05	670	50	677	95
150	667	50	675	00	682	50
1016	4521	20	4572	00	4622	80
1296	5767	20	5832	00	5896	80

No.	£4.45 £	P	£4.50 £	P	£4.55 £	P
Doz 155	689	75	697	50	705	25
13 156	694	20	702	00	709	80
165	734	25	742	50	750	75
14 168	747	60	756	00	764	40
175	778	75	787	50	796	25
15 180	801	00	810	00	819	00
185	823	25	832	50	841	75
16 192	854	40	864	00	873	60
195	867	75	877	50	887	25
200	890	00	900	00	910	00
17 204	907	80	918	00	928	20
205	912	25	922	50	932	75
215	956	75	967	50	978	25
18 216	961	20	972	00	982	80
224	996	80	1008	00	1019	20
225	1001	25	1012	50	1023	75
19 228	1014	60	1026	00	1037	40
235	1045	75	1057	50	1069	25
245	1090	25	1102	50	1114	75
250	1112	50	1125	00	1137	50
21 252	1121	40	1134	00	1146	60
255	1134	75	1147	50	1160	25
265	1179	25	1192	50	1205	75
272	1210	40	1224	00	1237	60
275	1223	75	1237	50	1251	25
280	1246	00	1260	00	1274	00
285	1268	25	1282	50	1296	75
288	1281	60	1296	00	1310	40
295	1312	50	1327	50	1342	25
300	1335	00	1350	00	1365	00
325	1446	25	1462	50	1478	75
336	1495	20	1512	00	1528	80
365	1624	25	1642	50	1660	75
375	1668	75	1687	50	1706	25
400	1780	00	1800	00	1820	00
425	1891	25	1912	50	1933	75
432	1922	40	1944	00	1965	60
475	2113	75	2137	50	2161	25
480	2136	00	2160	00	2184	00
500	2225	00	2250	00	2275	00
504	2242	80	2268	00	2293	20
576	2563	20	2592	00	2620	80
600	2670	00	2700	00	2730	00
700	3115	00	3150	00	3185	00
750	3337	50	3375	00	3412	50
800	3560	00	3600	00	3640	00
900	4005	00	4050	00	4095	00
1000	4450	00	4500	00	4550	00
2500	11125	0	11250	0	11375	0
5000	22250	0	22500	0	22750	0
1728	7689	60	7776	00	7862	40
1760	7832	00	7920	00	8008	00

No.	£4·60		£4·65		£4·70		No.	£4·60		£4·65		£4·70	
	£	P	£	P	£	P		£	P	£	P	£	P
1	4	60	4	65	4	70	51	234	60	237	15	239	70
2	9	20	9	30	9	40	52	239	20	241	80	244	40
3	13	80	13	95	14	10	53	243	80	246	45	249	10
4	18	40	18	60	18	80	54	248	40	251	10	253	80
5	23	00	23	25	23	50	55	253	00	255	75	258	50
6	27	60	27	90	28	20	56	257	60	260	40	263	20
7	32	20	32	55	32	90	57	262	20	265	05	267	90
8	36	80	37	20	37	60	58	266	80	269	70	272	60
9	41	40	41	85	42	30	59	271	40	274	35	277	30
10	46	00	46	50	47	00	60	276	00	279	00	282	00
11	50	60	51	15	51	70	61	280	60	283	65	286	70
12	55	20	55	80	56	40	62	285	20	288	30	291	40
13	59	80	60	45	61	10	63	289	80	292	95	296	10
14	64	40	65	10	65	80	64	294	40	297	60	300	80
15	69	00	69	75	70	50	65	299	00	302	25	305	50
16	73	60	74	40	75	20	66	303	60	306	90	310	20
17	78	20	79	05	79	90	67	308	20	311	55	314	90
18	82	80	83	70	84	60	68	312	80	316	20	319	60
19	87	40	88	35	89	30	69	317	40	320	85	324	30
20	92	00	93	00	94	00	70	322	00	325	50	329	00
21	96	60	97	65	98	70	71	326	60	330	15	333	70
22	101	20	102	30	103	40	72	331	20	334	80	338	40
23	105	80	106	95	108	10	73	335	80	339	45	343	10
24	110	40	111	60	112	80	74	340	40	344	10	347	80
25	115	00	116	25	117	50	75	345	00	348	75	352	50
26	119	60	120	90	122	20	76	349	60	353	40	357	20
27	124	20	125	55	126	90	77	354	20	358	05	361	90
28	128	80	130	20	131	60	78	358	80	362	70	366	60
29	133	40	134	85	136	30	79	363	40	367	35	371	30
30	138	00	139	50	141	00	80	368	00	372	00	376	00
31	142	60	144	15	145	70	81	372	60	376	65	380	70
32	147	20	148	80	150	40	82	377	20	381	30	385	40
33	151	80	153	45	155	10	83	381	80	385	95	390	10
34	156	40	158	10	159	80	84	386	40	390	60	394	80
35	161	00	162	75	164	50	85	391	00	395	25	399	50
36	165	60	167	40	169	20	86	395	60	399	90	404	20
37	170	20	172	05	173	90	87	400	20	404	55	408	90
38	174	80	176	70	178	60	88	404	80	409	20	413	60
39	179	40	181	35	183	30	89	409	40	413	85	418	30
40	184	00	186	00	188	00	90	414	00	418	50	423	00
41	188	60	190	65	192	70	91	418	60	423	15	427	70
42	193	20	195	30	197	40	92	423	20	427	80	432	40
43	197	80	199	95	202	10	93	427	80	432	45	437	10
44	202	40	204	60	206	80	94	432	40	437	10	441	80
45	207	00	209	25	211	50	95	437	00	441	75	446	50
46	211	60	213	90	216	20	96	441	60	446	40	451	20
47	216	20	218	55	220	90	97	446	20	451	05	455	90
48	220	80	223	20	225	60	98	450	80	455	70	460	60
49	225	40	227	85	230	30	99	455	40	460	35	465	30
50	230	00	232	50	235	00	100	460	00	465	00	470	00

	£4·60	£4·65	£4·70		£4·60	£4·65	£4·70
¼	1·15	1·1625	1·175	¾	3·45	3·4875	3·525
½ ..	2·30	2·3250	2·350	1¼ ..	5·75	5·8125	5·875

No.	£4·60	£4·65	£4·70	No.	£4·60	£4·65	£4·70
	£ p	£ p	£ p		£ p	£ p	£ p
101	464 60	469 65	474 70	155	713 00	720 75	728 50
102	469 20	474 30	479 40	156	717 60	725 40	733 20
103	473 80	478 95	484 10	165	759 00	767 25	775 50
104	478 40	483 60	488 80	168	772 80	781 20	789 60
105	483 00	488 25	493 50	175	805 00	813 75	822 50
106	487 60	492 90	498 20	180	828 00	837 00	846 00
107	492 20	497 55	502 90	185	851 00	860 25	869 50
108	496 80	502 20	507 60	192	883 20	892 80	902 40
109	501 40	506 85	512 30	195	897 00	906 75	916 50
110	506 00	511 50	517 00	200	920 00	930 00	940 00
111	510 60	516 15	521 70	204	938 40	948 60	958 80
112	515 20	520 80	526 40	205	943 00	953 25	963 50
113	519 80	525 45	531 10	215	989 00	999 75	1010 50
114	524 40	530 10	535 80	216	993 60	1004 40	1015 20
115	529 00	534 75	540 50	224	1030 40	1041 60	1052 80
116	533 60	539 40	545 20	225	1035 00	1046 25	1057 50
117	538 20	544 05	549 90	228	1048 80	1060 20	1071 60
118	542 80	548 70	554 60	235	1081 00	1092 75	1104 50
119	547 40	553 35	559 30	245	1127 00	1139 25	1151 50
120	552 00	558 00	564 00	250	1150 00	1162 50	1175 00
121	556 60	562 65	568 70	252	1159 20	1171 80	1184 40
122	561 20	567 30	573 40	255	1173 00	1185 75	1198 50
123	565 80	571 95	578 10	265	1219 00	1232 25	1245 50
124	570 40	576 60	582 80	272	1251 20	1264 80	1278 40
125	575 00	581 25	587 50	275	1265 00	1278 75	1292 50
126	579 60	585 90	592 20	280	1288 00	1302 00	1316 00
127	584 20	590 55	596 90	285	1311 00	1325 25	1339 50
128	588 80	595 20	601 60	288	1324 80	1339 20	1353 60
129	593 40	599 85	606 30	295	1357 00	1371 75	1386 50
130	598 00	604 50	611 00	300	1380 00	1395 00	1410 00
131	602 60	609 15	615 70	325	1495 00	1511 25	1527 50
132	607 20	613 80	620 40	336	1545 60	1562 40	1579 20
133	611 80	618 45	625 10	365	1679 00	1697 25	1715 50
134	616 40	623 10	629 80	375	1725 00	1743 75	1762 50
135	621 00	627 75	634 50	400	1840 00	1860 00	1880 00
136	625 60	632 40	639 20	425	1955 00	1976 25	1997 50
137	630 20	637 05	643 90	432	1987 20	2008 80	2030 40
138	634 80	641 70	648 60	475	2185 00	2208 75	2232 50
139	639 40	646 35	653 30	480	2208 00	2232 00	2256 00
140	644 00	651 00	658 00	500	2300 00	2325 00	2350 00
141	648 60	655 65	662 70	504	2318 40	2343 60	2368 80
142	653 20	660 30	667 40	576	2649 60	2678 40	2707 20
143	657 80	664 95	672 10	600	2760 00	2790 00	2820 00
144	662 40	669 60	676 80	700	3220 00	3255 00	3290 00
145	667 00	674 25	681 50	750	3450 00	3487 50	3525 00
146	671 60	678 90	686 20	800	3680 00	3720 00	3760 00
147	676 20	683 55	690 90	900	4140 00	4185 00	4230 00
148	680 80	688 20	695 60	1000	4600 00	4650 00	4700 00
149	685 40	692 85	700 30	2500	11500 ·0	11625 ·0	11750 ·0
150	690 00	697 50	705 00	5000	23000 ·0	23250 ·0	23500 ·0
1016	4673·60	4724·40	4775·20	1728	7948·80	8035·20	8121·60
1296	5961·00	6026·40	6091·20	1760	8096·00	8184·00	8272·00

*Dozens.

No.	£4·75 £	p	£4·80 £	p	£4·85 £	p
1	4	75	4	80	4	85
2	9	50	9	60	9	70
3	14	25	14	40	14	55
4	19	00	19	20	19	40
5	23	75	24	00	24	25
6	28	50	28	80	29	10
7	33	25	33	60	33	95
8	38	00	38	40	38	80
9	42	75	43	20	43	65
10	47	50	48	00	48	50
11	52	25	52	80	53	35
[1]* 12	57	00	57	60	58	20
13	61	75	62	40	63	05
14	66	50	67	20	67	90
15	71	25	72	00	72	75
16	76	00	76	80	77	60
17	80	75	81	60	82	45
18	85	50	86	40	87	30
19	90	25	91	20	92	15
20	95	00	96	00	97	00
21	99	75	100	80	101	85
22	104	50	105	60	106	70
23	109	25	110	40	111	55
[2] 24	114	00	115	20	116	40
25	118	75	120	00	121	25
26	123	50	124	80	126	10
27	128	25	129	60	130	95
28	133	00	134	40	135	80
29	137	75	139	20	140	65
30	142	50	144	00	145	50
31	147	25	148	80	150	35
32	152	00	153	60	155	20
33	156	75	158	40	160	05
34	161	50	163	20	164	90
35	166	25	168	00	169	75
[3] 36	171	00	172	80	174	60
37	175	75	177	60	179	45
38	180	50	182	40	184	30
39	185	25	187	20	189	15
40	190	00	192	00	194	00
41	194	75	196	80	198	85
42	199	50	201	60	203	70
43	204	25	206	40	208	55
44	209	00	211	20	213	40
45	213	75	216	00	218	25
46	218	50	220	80	223	10
47	223	25	225	60	227	95
[4] 48	228	00	230	40	232	80
49	232	75	235	20	237	65
50	237	50	240	00	242	50
¼	1·1875		1·20		1·2125	
½..	2·3750		2·40		2·4250	
51	242	25	244	80	247	35
52	247	00	249	60	252	20
53	251	75	254	40	257	05
54	256	50	259	20	261	90
55	261	25	264	00	266	75
56	266	00	268	80	271	60
57	270	75	273	60	276	45
58	275	50	278	40	281	30
59	280	25	283	20	286	15
[5]* **60**	285	00	288	00	291	00
61	289	75	292	80	295	85
62	294	50	297	60	300	70
63	299	25	302	40	305	55
64	304	00	307	20	310	40
65	308	75	312	00	315	25
66	313	50	316	80	320	10
67	318	25	321	60	324	95
68	323	00	326	40	329	80
69	327	75	331	20	334	65
70	332	50	336	00	339	50
71	337	25	340	80	344	35
[6] 72	342	00	345	60	349	20
73	346	75	350	40	354	05
74	351	50	355	20	358	90
75	356	25	360	00	363	75
76	361	00	364	80	368	60
77	365	75	369	60	373	45
78	370	50	374	40	378	30
79	375	25	379	20	383	15
80	380	00	384	00	388	00
81	384	75	388	80	392	85
82	389	50	393	60	397	70
83	394	25	398	40	402	55
[7] 84	399	00	403	20	407	40
85	403	75	408	00	412	25
86	408	50	412	80	417	10
87	413	25	417	60	421	95
88	418	00	422	40	426	80
89	422	75	427	20	431	65
90	427	50	432	00	436	50
91	432	25	436	80	441	35
92	437	00	441	60	446	20
93	441	75	446	40	451	05
94	446	50	451	20	455	90
95	451	25	456	00	460	75
[8] 96	456	00	460	80	465	60
97	460	75	465	60	470	45
98	465	50	470	40	475	30
99	470	25	475	20	480	15
100	475	00	480	00	485	00
¾	3·5625		3·60		3·6375	
1¼..	5·9375		6·00		6·0625	

No.	£4·75		£4·80		£4·85		No.	£4·75		£4·80		£4·85	
	£	P	£	P	£	P		£	P	£	P	£	P
101	479	75	484	80	489	85	155	736	25	744	00	751	75
102	484	50	489	60	494	70	13156	741	00	748	80	756	60
103	489	25	494	40	499	55	165	783	75	792	00	800	25
104	494	00	499	20	504	40	14168	798	00	806	40	814	80
105	498	75	504	00	509	25	175	831	25	840	00	848	75
106	503	50	508	80	514	10	15180	855	00	864	00	873	00
107	508	25	513	60	518	95	185	878	75	888	00	897	25
9108	513	00	518	40	523	80	16192	912	00	921	60	931	20
109	517	75	523	20	528	65	195	926	25	936	00	945	75
110	522	50	528	00	533	50	200	950	00	960	00	970	00
111	527	25	532	80	538	35	17204	969	00	979	20	989	40
112	532	00	537	60	543	20	205	973	75	984	00	994	25
113	536	75	542	40	548	05	215	1021	25	1032	00	1042	75
114	541	50	547	20	552	90	18216	1026	00	1036	80	1047	60
115	546	25	552	00	557	75	224	1064	00	1075	20	1086	40
116	551	00	556	80	562	60	225	1068	75	1080	00	1091	25
117	555	75	561	60	567	45	19228	1083	00	1094	40	1105	80
118	560	50	566	40	572	30	235	1116	25	1128	00	1139	75
119	565	25	571	20	577	15	245	1163	75	1176	00	1188	25
10120	570	00	576	00	582	00	250	1187	50	1200	00	1212	50
121	574	75	580	80	586	85	21252	1197	00	1209	60	1222	20
122	579	50	585	60	591	70	255	1211	25	1224	00	1236	75
123	584	25	590	40	596	55	265	1258	75	1272	00	1285	25
124	589	00	595	20	601	40	272	1292	00	1305	60	1319	20
125	593	75	600	00	606	25	275	1306	25	1320	00	1333	75
126	598	50	604	80	611	10	280	1330	00	1344	00	1358	00
127	603	25	609	60	615	95	285	1353	75	1368	00	1382	25
128	608	00	614	40	620	80	2 288	1368	00	1382	40	1396	80
129	612	75	619	20	625	65	295	1401	25	1416	00	1430	75
130	617	50	624	00	630	50	300	1425	00	1440	00	1455	00
131	622	25	628	80	635	35	325	1543	75	1560	00	1576	25
11132	627	00	633	60	640	20	336	1596	00	1612	80	1629	60
133	631	75	638	40	645	05	365	1733	75	1752	00	1770	25
134	636	50	643	20	649	90	375	1781	25	1800	00	1818	75
135	641	25	648	00	654	75	400	1900	00	1920	00	1940	00
136	646	00	652	80	659	60	425	2018	75	2040	00	2061	25
137	650	75	657	60	664	45	3 432	2052	00	2073	60	2095	20
138	655	50	662	40	669	30	475	2256	25	2280	00	2303	75
139	660	25	667	20	674	15	480	2280	00	2304	00	2328	00
140	665	00	672	00	679	00	500	2375	00	2400	00	2425	00
141	669	75	676	80	683	85	504	2394	00	2419	20	2444	40
142	674	50	681	60	688	70	4 576	2736	00	2764	80	2793	60
143	679	25	686	40	693	55	600	2850	00	2880	00	2910	00
12144	684	00	691	20	698	40	700	3325	00	3360	00	3395	00
145	688	75	696	00	703	25	750	3562	50	3600	00	3637	50
146	693	50	700	80	708	10	800	3800	00	3840	00	3880	00
147	698	25	705	60	712	95	900	4275	00	4320	00	4365	00
148	703	00	710	40	717	80	1000	4750	00	4800	00	4850	00
149	707	75	715	20	722	65	2500	11875	·0	12000	·0	12125	·0
150	712	50	720	00	727	50	5000	23750	·0	24000	·0	24250	·0
1016	4826·00		4876·80		4927·60		1728	8208·00		8294·40		8380·80	
1296	6156·00		6220·80		6285·60		1760	8360·00		8448·00		8536·00	

• Dozens.

No.	£4·90 £	p	£4·95 £	p	£5·00 £	p
1	4	90	4	95	5	00
2	9	80	9	90	10	00
3	14	70	14	85	15	00
4	19	60	19	80	20	00
5	24	50	24	75	25	00
6	29	40	29	70	30	00
7	34	30	34	65	35	00
8	39	20	39	60	40	00
9	44	10	44	55	45	00
10	49	00	49	50	50	00
* 11	53	90	54	45	55	00
[1] 12	58	80	59	40	60	00
13	63	70	64	35	65	00
14	68	60	69	30	70	00
15	73	50	74	25	75	00
16	78	40	79	20	80	00
17	83	30	84	15	85	00
18	88	20	89	10	90	00
19	93	10	94	05	95	00
20	98	00	99	00	100	00
21	102	90	103	95	105	00
22	107	80	108	90	110	00
23	112	70	113	85	115	00
[2] 24	117	60	118	80	120	00
25	122	50	123	75	125	00
26	127	40	128	70	130	00
27	132	30	133	65	135	00
28	137	20	138	60	140	00
29	142	10	143	55	145	00
30	147	00	148	50	150	00
31	151	90	153	45	155	00
32	156	80	158	40	160	00
33	161	70	163	35	165	00
34	166	60	168	30	170	00
35	171	50	173	25	175	00
[3] 36	176	40	178	20	180	00
37	181	30	183	15	185	00
38	186	20	188	10	190	00
39	191	10	193	05	195	00
40	196	00	198	00	200	00
41	200	90	202	95	205	00
42	205	80	207	90	210	00
43	210	70	212	85	215	00
44	215	60	217	80	220	00
45	220	50	222	75	225	00
46	225	40	227	70	230	00
47	230	30	232	65	235	00
[4] 48	235	20	237	60	240	00
49	240	10	242	55	245	00
50	245	00	247	50	250	00
¼	1·225		1·2375		1·25	
½..	2·450		2·4750		2·50	

• Dozens.

No	£4·90 £	p	£4·95 £	p	£5·00 £	p
51	249	90	252	45	255	00
52	254	80	257	40	260	00
53	259	70	262	35	265	00
54	264	60	267	30	270	00
55	269	50	272	25	275	00
56	274	40	277	20	280	00
57	279	30	282	15	285	00
58	284	20	287	10	290	00
59	289	10	292	05	295	00
* [5] **60**	294	00	297	00	300	00
61	298	90	301	95	305	00
62	303	80	306	90	310	00
63	308	70	311	85	315	00
64	313	60	316	80	320	00
65	318	50	321	75	325	00
66	323	40	326	70	330	00
67	328	30	331	65	335	00
68	333	20	336	60	340	00
69	338	10	341	55	345	00
70	343	00	346	50	350	00
71	347	90	351	45	355	00
[6] 72	352	80	356	40	360	00
73	357	70	361	35	365	00
74	362	60	366	30	370	00
75	367	50	371	25	375	00
76	372	40	376	20	380	00
77	377	30	381	15	385	00
78	382	20	386	10	390	00
79	387	10	391	05	395	00
80	392	00	396	00	400	00
81	396	90	400	95	405	00
82	401	80	405	90	410	00
83	406	70	410	85	415	00
[7] 84	411	60	415	80	420	00
85	416	50	420	75	425	00
86	421	40	425	70	430	00
87	426	30	430	65	435	00
88	431	20	435	60	440	00
89	436	10	440	55	445	00
90	441	00	445	50	450	00
91	445	90	450	45	455	00
92	450	80	455	40	460	00
93	455	70	460	35	465	00
94	460	60	465	30	470	00
95	465	50	470	25	475	00
[8] 96	470	40	475	20	480	00
97	475	30	480	15	485	00
98	480	20	485	10	490	00
99	485	10	490	05	495	00
100	490	00	495	00	500	00
¾	3·675		3·7125		3·75	
1¼..	6·125		6·1875		6·25	

No.	£4.90 £	p	£4.95 £	p	£5.00 £	p
101	494	90	499	95	505	00
102	499	80	504	90	510	00
103	504	70	509	85	515	00
104	509	60	514	80	520	00
105	514	50	519	75	525	00
106	519	40	524	70	530	00
107	524	30	529	65	535	00
108	529	20	534	60	540	00
109	534	10	539	55	545	00
110	539	00	544	50	550	00
111	543	90	549	45	555	00
112	548	80	554	40	560	00
113	553	70	559	35	565	00
114	558	60	564	30	570	00
115	563	50	569	25	575	00
116	568	40	574	20	580	00
117	573	30	579	15	585	00
118	578	20	584	10	590	00
119	583	10	589	05	595	00
120	588	00	594	00	600	00
121	592	90	598	95	605	00
122	597	80	603	90	610	00
123	602	70	608	85	615	00
124	607	60	613	80	620	00
125	612	50	618	75	625	00
126	617	40	623	70	630	00
127	622	30	628	65	635	00
128	627	20	633	60	640	00
129	632	10	638	55	645	00
130	637	00	643	50	650	00
131	641	90	648	45	655	00
132	646	80	653	40	660	00
133	651	70	658	35	665	00
134	656	60	663	30	670	00
135	661	50	668	25	675	00
136	666	40	673	20	680	00
137	671	30	678	15	685	00
138	676	20	683	10	690	00
139	681	10	688	05	695	00
140	686	00	693	00	700	00
141	690	90	697	95	705	00
142	695	80	702	90	710	00
143	700	70	707	85	715	00
144	705	60	712	80	720	00
145	710	50	717	75	725	00
146	715	40	722	70	730	00
147	720	30	727	65	735	00
148	725	20	732	60	740	00
149	730	10	737	55	745	00
150	735	00	742	50	750	00
1016	4978	40	5029	20	5080	00
1296	6350	40	6415	20	6480	00

No.	£4.90 £	p	£4.95 £	p	£5.00 £	p
155	759	50	767	25	775	00
156	764	40	772	20	780	00
165	808	50	816	75	825	00
168	823	20	831	60	840	00
175	857	50	866	25	875	00
180	882	00	891	00	900	00
185	906	50	915	75	925	00
192	940	80	950	40	960	00
195	955	50	965	25	975	00
200	980	00	990	00	1000	00
204	999	60	1009	80	1020	00
205	1004	50	1014	75	1025	00
215	1053	50	1064	25	1075	00
216	1058	40	1069	20	1080	00
224	1097	60	1108	80	1120	00
225	1102	50	1113	75	1125	00
228	1117	20	1128	60	1140	00
235	1151	50	1163	25	1175	00
245	1200	50	1212	75	1225	00
250	1225	00	1237	50	1250	00
252	1234	80	1247	40	1260	00
255	1249	50	1262	25	1275	00
265	1298	50	1311	75	1325	00
272	1332	80	1346	40	1360	00
275	1347	50	1361	25	1375	00
280	1372	00	1386	00	1400	00
285	1396	50	1410	75	1425	00
288	1411	20	1425	60	1440	00
295	1445	50	1460	25	1475	00
300	1470	00	1485	00	1500	00
325	1592	50	1608	75	1625	00
336	1646	40	1663	20	1680	00
365	1788	50	1806	75	1825	00
375	1837	50	1856	25	1875	00
400	1960	00	1980	00	2000	00
425	2082	50	2103	75	2125	00
432	2116	80	2138	40	2160	00
475	2327	50	2351	25	2375	00
480	2352	00	2376	00	2400	00
500	2450	00	2475	00	2500	00
504	2469	60	2494	80	2520	00
576	2822	40	2851	20	2880	00
600	2940	00	2970	00	3000	00
700	3430	00	3465	00	3500	00
750	3675	00	3712	50	3750	00
800	3920	00	3960	00	4000	00
900	4410	00	4455	00	4500	00
1000	4900	00	4950	00	5000	00
2500	12250	·0	12375	·0	12500	·0
5000	24500	·0	24750	·0	25000	·0
1728	8467	20	8553	60	8640	00
1760	8624	00	8712	00	8800	00

No.	£5·05 £	p	£5·10 £	p	£5·15 £	p	No.	£5·05 £	p	£5·10 £	p	£5·15 £	p
1	5	05	5	10	5	15	51	257	55	260	10	262	65
2	10	10	10	20	10	30	52	262	60	265	20	267	80
3	15	15	15	30	15	45	53	267	65	270	30	272	95
4	20	20	20	40	20	60	54	272	70	275	40	278	10
5	25	25	25	50	25	75	55	277	75	280	50	283	25
6	30	30	30	60	30	90	56	282	80	285	60	288	40
7	35	35	35	70	36	05	57	287	85	290	70	293	55
8	40	40	40	80	41	20	58	292	90	295	80	298	70
9	45	45	45	90	46	35	59	297	95	300	90	303	85
10	50	50	51	00	51	50	60	303	00	306	00	309	00
11	55	55	56	10	56	65	61	308	05	311	10	314	15
12	60	60	61	20	61	80	62	313	10	316	20	319	30
13	65	65	66	30	66	95	63	318	15	321	30	324	45
14	70	70	71	40	72	10	64	323	20	326	40	329	60
15	75	75	76	50	77	25	65	328	25	331	50	334	75
16	80	80	81	60	82	40	66	333	30	336	60	339	90
17	85	85	86	70	87	55	67	338	35	341	70	345	05
18	90	90	91	80	92	70	68	343	40	346	80	350	20
19	95	95	96	90	97	85	69	348	45	351	90	355	35
20	101	00	102	00	103	00	70	353	50	357	00	360	50
21	106	05	107	10	108	15	71	358	55	362	10	365	65
22	111	10	112	20	113	30	72	363	60	367	20	370	80
23	116	15	117	30	118	45	73	368	65	372	30	375	95
24	121	20	122	40	123	60	74	373	70	377	40	381	10
25	126	25	127	50	128	75	75	378	75	382	50	386	25
26	131	30	132	60	133	90	76	383	80	387	60	391	40
27	136	35	137	70	139	05	77	388	85	392	70	396	55
28	141	40	142	80	144	20	78	393	90	397	80	401	70
29	146	45	147	90	149	35	79	398	95	402	90	406	85
30	151	50	153	00	154	50	80	404	00	408	00	412	00
31	156	55	158	10	159	65	81	409	05	413	10	417	15
32	161	60	163	20	164	80	82	414	10	418	20	422	30
33	166	65	168	30	169	95	83	419	15	423	30	427	45
34	171	70	173	40	175	10	84	424	20	428	40	432	60
35	176	75	178	50	180	25	85	429	25	433	50	437	75
36	181	80	183	60	185	40	86	434	30	438	60	442	90
37	186	85	188	70	190	55	87	439	35	443	70	448	05
38	191	90	193	80	195	70	88	444	40	448	80	453	20
39	196	95	198	90	200	85	89	449	45	453	90	458	35
40	202	00	204	00	206	00	90	454	50	459	00	463	50
41	207	05	209	10	211	15	91	459	55	464	10	468	65
42	212	10	214	20	216	30	92	464	60	469	20	473	80
43	217	15	219	30	221	45	93	469	65	474	30	478	95
44	222	20	224	40	226	60	94	474	70	479	40	484	10
45	227	25	229	50	231	75	95	479	75	484	50	489	25
46	232	30	234	60	236	90	96	484	80	489	60	494	40
47	237	35	239	70	242	05	97	489	85	494	70	499	55
48	242	40	244	80	247	20	98	494	90	499	80	504	70
49	247	45	249	90	252	35	99	499	95	504	90	509	85
50	252	50	255	00	257	50	100	505	00	510	00	515	00

¼	1·2625	1·275	1·2875	¾	3·7875	3·825	3·8625
½..	2·5250	2·550	2·5750	1¼..	6·3125	6·375	6·4375

Dozens. (marginal note alongside rows 1–12 and 51–62)

No.	£5·05 £	P	£5·10 £	P	£5·15 £	P
101	510	05	515	10	520	15
102	515	10	520	20	525	30
103	520	15	525	30	530	45
104	525	20	530	40	535	60
105	530	25	535	50	540	75
106	535	30	540	60	545	90
107	540	35	545	70	551	05
9 108	545	40	550	80	556	20
109	550	45	555	90	561	35
10 110	555	50	561	00	566	50
111	560	55	566	10	571	65
112	565	60	571	20	576	80
113	570	65	576	30	581	95
114	575	70	581	40	587	10
115	580	75	586	50	592	25
116	585	80	591	60	597	40
117	590	85	596	70	602	55
118	595	90	601	80	607	70
119	600	95	606	90	612	85
10 120	606	00	612	00	618	00
121	611	05	617	10	623	15
122	616	10	622	20	628	30
123	621	15	627	30	633	45
124	626	20	632	40	638	60
125	631	25	637	50	643	75
126	636	30	642	60	648	90
127	641	35	647	70	654	05
128	646	40	652	80	659	20
129	651	45	657	90	664	35
130	656	50	663	00	669	50
131	661	55	668	10	674	65
11 132	666	60	673	20	679	80
133	671	65	678	30	684	95
134	676	70	683	40	690	10
135	681	75	688	50	695	25
136	686	80	693	60	700	40
137	691	85	698	70	705	55
138	696	90	703	80	710	70
139	701	95	708	90	715	85
140	707	00	714	00	721	00
141	712	05	719	10	726	15
142	717	10	724	20	731	30
143	722	15	729	30	736	45
12 144	727	20	734	40	741	60
145	732	25	739	50	746	75
146	737	30	744	60	751	90
147	742	35	749	70	757	05
148	747	40	754	80	762	20
149	752	45	759	90	767	35
150	757	50	765	00	772	50
1016	5180·80		5181·60		5232·40	
1296	6544·80		6609·60		6674·40	

No.	£5·05 £	P	£5·10 £	P	£5·15 £	P
13 155	782	75	790	50	798	25
156	787	80	795	60	803	40
165	833	25	841	50	849	75
14 168	848	40	856	80	865	20
175	883	75	892	50	901	25
15 180	909	00	918	00	927	00
185	934	25	943	50	952	75
16 192	969	60	979	20	988	80
195	984	75	994	50	1004	25
200	1010	00	1020	00	1030	00
17 204	1030	20	1040	40	1050	60
205	1035	25	1045	50	1055	75
215	1085	75	1096	50	1107	25
18 216	1090	80	1101	60	1112	40
224	1131	20	1142	40	1153	60
225	1136	25	1147	50	1158	75
19 228	1151	40	1162	80	1174	20
235	1186	75	1198	50	1210	25
245	1237	25	1249	50	1261	75
250	1262	50	1275	00	1287	50
21 252	1272	60	1285	20	1297	80
255	1287	75	1300	50	1313	25
265	1338	25	1351	50	1364	75
272	1373	60	1387	20	1400	80
275	1388	75	1402	50	1416	25
280	1414	00	1428	00	1442	00
2 gross 285	1439	25	1453	50	1467	75
288	1454	40	1468	80	1483	20
295	1489	75	1504	50	1519	25
300	1515	00	1530	00	1545	00
325	1641	25	1657	50	1673	75
336	1696	80	1713	60	1730	40
365	1843	25	1861	50	1879	75
375	1893	75	1912	50	1931	25
400	2020	00	2040	00	2060	00
425	2146	25	2167	50	2188	75
3 gr. 432	2181	60	2203	20	2224	80
475	2398	75	2422	50	2446	25
480	2424	00	2448	00	2472	00
500	2525	00	2550	00	2575	00
4 gr. 504	2545	20	2570	40	2595	60
576	2908	80	2937	60	2966	40
600	3030	00	3060	00	3090	00
700	3535	00	3570	00	3605	00
750	3787	50	3825	00	3862	50
800	4040	00	4080	00	4120	00
900	4545	00	4590	00	4635	00
1000	5050	00	5100	00	5150	00
2500	12625	·0	12750	·0	12875	·0
5000	25250	·0	25500	·0	25750	·0
1728	8726·40		8812·80		8899·20	
1760	8888·00		8976·00		9064·00	

No.	£5·20		£5·25		£5·30		No.	£5·20		£5·25		£5·30	
	£	P	£	P	£	P		£	P	£	P	£	P
1	5	20	5	25	5	30	51	265	20	267	75	270	30
2	10	40	10	50	10	60	52	270	40	273	00	275	60
3	15	60	15	75	15	90	53	275	60	278	25	280	90
4	20	80	21	00	21	20	54	280	80	283	50	286	20
5	26	00	26	25	26	50	55	286	00	288	75	291	50
6	31	20	31	50	31	80	56	291	20	294	00	296	80
7	36	40	36	75	37	10	57	296	40	299	25	302	10
8	41	60	42	00	42	40	58	301	60	304	50	307	40
9	46	80	47	25	47	70	59	306	80	309	75	312	70
10	52	00	52	50	53	00	60	312	00	315	00	318	00
11	57	20	57	75	58	30	61	317	20	320	25	323	30
12	62	40	63	00	63	60	62	322	40	325	50	328	60
13	67	60	68	25	68	90	63	327	60	330	75	333	90
14	72	80	73	50	74	20	64	332	80	336	00	339	20
15	78	00	78	75	79	50	65	338	00	341	25	344	50
16	83	20	84	00	84	80	66	343	20	346	50	349	80
17	88	40	89	25	90	10	67	348	40	351	75	355	10
18	93	60	94	50	95	40	68	353	60	357	00	360	40
19	98	80	99	75	100	70	69	358	80	362	25	365	70
20	104	00	105	00	106	00	70	364	00	367	50	371	00
21	109	20	110	25	111	30	71	369	20	372	75	376	30
22	114	40	115	50	116	60	72	374	40	378	00	381	60
23	119	60	120	75	121	90	73	379	60	383	25	386	90
24	124	80	126	00	127	20	74	384	80	388	50	392	20
25	130	00	131	25	132	50	75	390	00	393	75	397	50
26	135	20	136	50	137	80	76	395	20	399	00	402	80
27	140	40	141	75	143	10	77	400	40	404	25	408	10
28	145	60	147	00	148	40	78	405	60	409	50	413	40
29	150	80	152	25	153	70	79	410	80	414	75	418	70
30	156	00	157	50	159	00	80	416	00	420	00	424	00
31	161	20	162	75	164	30	81	421	20	425	25	429	30
32	166	40	168	00	169	60	82	426	40	430	50	434	60
33	171	60	173	25	174	90	83	431	60	435	75	439	90
34	176	80	178	50	180	20	84	436	80	441	00	445	20
35	182	00	183	75	185	50	85	442	00	446	25	450	50
36	187	20	189	00	190	80	86	447	20	451	50	455	80
37	192	40	194	25	196	10	87	452	40	456	75	461	10
38	197	60	199	50	201	40	88	457	60	462	00	466	40
39	202	80	204	75	206	70	89	462	80	467	25	471	70
40	208	00	210	00	212	00	90	468	00	472	50	477	00
41	213	20	215	25	217	30	91	473	20	477	75	482	30
42	218	40	220	50	222	60	92	478	40	483	00	487	60
43	223	60	225	75	227	90	93	483	60	488	25	492	90
44	228	80	231	00	233	20	94	488	80	493	50	498	20
45	234	00	236	25	238	50	95	494	00	498	75	503	50
46	239	20	241	50	243	80	96	499	20	504	00	508	80
47	244	40	246	75	249	10	97	504	40	509	25	514	10
48	249	60	252	00	254	40	98	509	60	514	50	519	40
49	254	80	257	25	259	70	99	514	80	519	75	524	70
50	260	00	262	50	265	00	100	520	00	525	00	530	00

	£5·20	£5·25	£5·30		£5·20	£5·25	£5·30
¼	1·30	1·3125	1·325	¾	3·90	3·9375	3·975
½	2·60	2·6250	2·650	1¼	6·50	6·5625	6·625

Left

No.	£5·20 £	P	£5·25 £	P	£5·30 £	P
101	525	20	530	25	535	30
102	530	40	535	50	540	60
103	535	60	540	75	545	90
104	540	80	546	00	551	20
105	546	00	551	25	556	50
106	551	20	556	50	561	80
107	556	40	561	75	567	10
9108	561	60	567	00	572	40
109	566	80	572	25	577	70
110	572	00	577	50	583	00
111	577	20	582	75	588	30
112	582	40	588	00	593	60
113	587	60	593	25	598	90
114	592	80	598	50	604	20
115	598	00	603	75	609	50
116	603	20	609	00	614	80
117	608	40	614	25	620	10
118	613	60	619	50	625	40
119	618	80	624	75	630	70
10120	624	00	630	00	636	00
121	629	20	635	25	641	30
122	634	40	640	50	646	60
123	639	60	645	75	651	90
124	644	80	651	00	657	20
125	650	00	656	25	662	50
126	655	20	661	50	667	80
127	660	40	666	75	673	10
128	665	60	672	00	678	40
129	670	80	677	25	683	70
30	676	00	682	50	689	00
131	681	20	687	75	694	30
132	686	40	693	00	699	60
133	691	60	698	25	704	90
134	696	80	703	50	710	20
135	702	00	708	75	715	50
136	707	20	714	00	720	80
137	712	40	719	25	726	10
138	717	60	724	50	731	40
139	722	80	729	75	736	70
40	728	00	735	00	742	00
141	733	20	740	25	747	30
142	738	40	745	50	752	60
143	743	60	750	75	757	90
12144	748	80	756	00	763	20
145	754	00	761	25	768	50
146	759	20	766	50	773	80
147	764	40	771	75	779	10
148	769	60	777	00	784	40
149	774	80	782	25	789	70
150	780	00	787	50	795	00
1016	5283	20	5334	00	5384	80
1296	6739	20	6804	00	6868	80

Right

No.	£5·20 £	P	£5·25 £	P	£5·30 £	P
155	806	00	813	75	821	50
18156	811	20	819	00	826	80
165	858	00	866	25	874	50
14168	873	60	882	00	890	40
175	910	00	918	75	927	50
15180	936	00	945	00	954	00
185	962	00	971	25	980	50
16192	998	40	1008	00	1017	60
195	1014	00	1023	75	1033	50
200	1040	00	1050	00	1060	00
17204	1060	80	1071	00	1081	20
205	1066	00	1076	25	1086	50
215	1118	00	1128	75	1139	50
18216	1123	20	1134	00	1144	80
224	1164	80	1176	00	1187	20
225	1170	00	1181	25	1192	50
19228	1185	60	1197	00	1208	40
235	1222	00	1233	75	1245	50
245	1274	00	1286	25	1298	50
250	1300	00	1312	50	1325	00
21252	1310	40	1323	00	1335	60
255	1326	00	1338	75	1351	50
265	1378	00	1391	25	1404	50
272	1414	40	1428	00	1441	60
275	1430	00	1443	75	1457	50
280	1456	00	1470	00	1484	00
285	1482	00	1496	25	1510	50
2 gross 288	1497	60	1512	00	1526	40
295	1534	00	1548	75	1563	50
300	1560	00	1575	00	1590	00
325	1690	00	1706	25	1722	50
336	1747	20	1764	00	1780	80
365	1898	00	1916	25	1934	50
375	1950	00	1968	75	1987	50
400	2080	00	2100	00	2120	00
425	2210	00	2231	25	2252	50
3 gr. 432	2246	40	2268	00	2289	60
475	2470	00	2493	75	2517	50
480	2496	00	2520	00	2544	00
500	2600	00	2625	00	2650	00
504	2620	80	2646	00	2671	20
4 gr. 576	2995	20	3024	00	3052	80
600	3120	00	3150	00	3180	00
700	3640	00	3675	00	3710	00
750	3900	00	3937	50	3975	00
800	4160	00	4200	00	4240	00
900	4680	00	4725	00	4770	00
1000	5200	00	5250	00	5300	00
2500	13000	0	13125	0	13250	0
5000	26000	00	26250	0	26500	0
1728	8985	60	9072	00	9158	40
1760	9152	00	9240	00	9328	00

No.	£5·35		£5·40		£5·45		No.	£5·35		£5·40		£5·45	
	£	P	£	P	£	P		£	P	£	P	£	P
1	5	35	5	40	5	45	51	272	85	275	40	277	95
2	10	70	10	80	10	90	52	278	20	280	80	283	40
3	16	05	16	20	16	35	53	283	55	286	20	288	85
4	21	40	21	60	21	80	54	288	90	291	60	294	30
5	26	75	27	00	27	25	55	294	25	297	00	299	75
6	32	10	32	40	32	70	56	299	60	302	40	305	20
7	37	45	37	80	38	15	57	304	95	307	80	310	65
8	42	80	43	20	43	60	58	310	30	313	20	316	10
9	48	15	48	60	49	05	59	315	65	318	60	321	55
10	53	50	54	00	54	50	60	321	00	324	00	327	00
11	58	85	59	40	59	95	61	326	35	329	40	332	45
12	64	20	64	80	65	40	62	331	70	334	80	337	90
13	69	55	70	20	70	85	63	337	05	340	20	343	35
14	74	90	75	60	76	30	64	342	40	345	60	348	80
15	80	25	81	00	81	75	65	347	75	351	00	354	25
16	85	60	86	40	87	20	66	353	10	356	40	359	70
17	90	95	91	80	92	65	67	358	45	361	80	365	15
18	96	30	97	20	98	10	68	363	80	367	20	370	60
19	101	65	102	60	103	55	69	369	15	372	60	376	05
20	107	00	108	00	109	00	70	374	50	378	00	381	50
21	112	35	113	40	114	45	71	379	85	383	40	386	95
22	117	70	118	80	119	90	72	385	20	388	80	392	40
23	123	05	124	20	125	35	73	390	55	394	20	397	85
24	128	40	129	60	130	80	74	395	90	399	60	403	30
25	133	75	135	00	136	25	75	401	25	405	00	408	75
26	139	10	140	40	141	70	76	406	60	410	40	414	20
27	144	45	145	80	147	15	77	411	95	415	80	419	65
28	149	80	151	20	152	60	78	417	30	421	20	425	10
29	155	15	156	60	158	05	79	422	65	426	60	430	55
30	160	50	162	00	163	50	80	428	00	432	00	436	00
31	165	85	167	40	168	95	81	433	35	437	40	441	45
32	171	20	172	80	174	40	82	438	70	442	80	446	90
33	176	55	178	20	179	85	83	444	05	448	20	452	35
34	181	90	183	60	185	30	84	449	40	453	60	457	80
35	187	25	189	00	190	75	85	454	75	459	00	463	25
36	192	60	194	40	196	20	86	460	10	464	40	468	70
37	197	95	199	80	201	65	87	465	45	469	80	474	15
38	203	30	205	20	207	10	88	470	80	475	20	479	60
39	208	65	210	60	212	55	89	476	15	480	60	485	05
40	214	00	216	00	218	00	90	481	50	486	00	490	50
41	219	35	221	40	223	45	91	486	85	491	40	495	95
42	224	70	226	80	228	90	92	492	20	496	80	501	40
43	230	05	232	20	234	35	93	497	55	502	20	506	85
44	235	40	237	60	239	80	94	502	90	507	60	512	30
45	240	75	243	00	245	25	95	508	25	513	00	517	75
46	246	10	248	40	250	70	96	513	60	518	40	523	20
47	251	45	253	80	256	15	97	518	95	523	80	528	65
48	256	80	259	20	261	60	98	524	30	529	20	534	10
49	262	15	264	60	267	05	99	529	65	534	60	539	55
50	267	50	270	00	272	50	100	535	00	540	00	545	00

	£5·35	£5·40	£5·45		£5·35	£5·40	£5·45
¼	1·3375	1·35	1·3625	¾	4·0125	4·05	4·0875
½	2·6750	2·70	2·7250	1¼	6·6875	6·75	6·8125

No. £5·35 £5·40 £5·45 | No. £5·35 £5·40 £5·45

No.	£5·35 £	p	£5·40 £	p	£5·45 £	p
101	540	35	545	40	550	45
102	545	70	550	80	555	90
103	551	05	556	20	561	35
104	556	40	561	60	566	80
105	561	75	567	00	572	25
106	567	10	572	40	577	70
107	572	45	577	80	583	15
9108	577	80	583	20	588	60
109	583	15	588	60	594	05
110	588	50	594	00	599	50
111	593	85	599	40	604	95
112	599	20	604	80	610	40
113	604	55	610	20	615	85
114	609	90	615	60	621	30
115	615	25	621	00	626	75
116	620	60	626	40	632	20
117	625	95	631	80	637	65
118	631	30	637	20	643	10
119	636	65	642	60	648	55
10120	642	00	648	00	654	00
121	647	35	653	40	659	45
122	652	70	658	80	664	90
123	658	05	664	20	670	35
124	663	40	669	60	675	80
125	668	75	675	00	681	25
126	674	10	680	40	686	70
127	679	45	685	80	692	15
128	684	80	691	20	697	60
129	690	15	696	60	703	05
130	695	50	702	00	708	50
131	700	85	707	40	713	95
11132	706	20	712	80	719	40
133	711	55	718	20	724	85
134	716	90	723	60	730	30
135	722	25	729	00	735	75
136	727	60	734	40	741	20
137	732	95	739	80	746	65
138	738	30	745	20	752	10
139	743	65	750	60	757	55
140	749	00	756	00	763	00
141	754	35	761	40	768	45
142	759	70	766	80	773	90
143	765	05	772	20	779	35
12144	770	40	777	80	784	80
145	775	75	783	00	790	25
146	781	10	788	40	795	70
147	786	45	793	80	801	15
148	791	80	799	20	806	60
149	797	15	804	60	812	05
150	802	50	810	00	817	50
1016	5435·60		5486·40		5537·20	
1296	6983·60		6998·40		7063·20	

No.	£5·35 £	p	£5·40 £	p	£5·45 £	p
155	829	25	837	00	844	75
13156	834	60	842	40	850	20
165	882	75	891	00	899	25
14168	898	80	907	20	915	60
175	936	25	945	00	953	75
15180	963	00	972	00	981	00
185	989	75	999	00	1008	25
16192	1027	20	1036	80	1046	40
195	1043	25	1053	00	1062	75
200	1070	00	1080	00	1090	00
17204	1091	40	1101	60	1111	80
205	1096	75	1107	00	1117	25
215	1150	25	1161	00	1171	75
18216	1155	60	1166	40	1177	20
224	1198	40	1209	60	1220	80
225	1203	75	1215	00	1226	25
19228	1219	80	1231	20	1242	60
235	1257	25	1269	00	1280	75
245	1310	75	1323	00	1335	25
250	1337	50	1350	00	1362	50
21252	1348	20	1360	80	1373	40
255	1364	25	1377	00	1389	75
265	1417	75	1431	00	1444	25
272	1455	20	1468	80	1482	40
275	1471	50	1485	00	1498	75
280	1498	00	1512	00	1526	00
285	1524	75	1539	00	1553	25
288	1540	80	1555	20	1569	60
295	1578	25	1593	00	1607	75
300	1605	00	1620	00	1635	00
325	1738	75	1755	00	1771	25
336	1797	60	1814	40	1831	20
365	1952	75	1971	00	1989	25
375	2006	25	2025	00	2043	75
400	2140	00	2160	00	2180	00
425	2273	75	2295	00	2316	25
432	2311	20	2332	80	2354	40
475	2541	25	2565	00	2588	75
480	2568	00	2592	00	2616	00
500	2675	00	2700	00	2725	00
504	2696	40	2721	60	2746	80
576	3081	60	3110	40	3139	20
600	3210	00	3240	00	3270	00
700	3745	00	3780	00	3815	00
750	4012	50	4050	00	4087	50
800	4280	00	4320	00	4360	00
900	4815	00	4860	00	4905	00
1000	5350	00	5400	00	5450	00
2500	13375	·0	13500	:0	13625	·0
5000	26750	·0	27000	·0	27250	·0
1728	9244·80		9331·20		9417·60	
1760	9416·00		9504·00		9592·00	

No.	£5·50		£5·55		£5·60		No.	£5·50		£5·55		£5·60	
	£	P	£	P	£	P		£	P	£	P	£	P
1	5	50	5	55	5	60	51	280	50	283	05	285	60
2	11	00	11	10	11	20	52	286	00	288	60	291	20
3	16	50	16	65	16	80	53	291	50	294	15	296	80
4	22	00	22	20	22	40	54	297	00	299	70	302	40
5	27	50	27	75	28	00	55	302	50	305	25	308	00
6	33	00	33	30	33	60	56	308	00	310	80	313	60
7	38	50	38	85	39	20	57	313	50	316	35	319	20
8	44	00	44	40	44	80	58	319	00	321	90	324	80
9	49	50	49	95	50	40	59	324	50	327	45	330	40
10	55	00	55	50	56	00	60	330	00	333	00	336	00
11	60	50	61	05	61	60	61	335	50	338	55	341	60
12	66	00	66	60	67	20	62	341	00	344	10	347	20
13	71	50	72	15	72	80	63	346	50	349	65	352	80
14	77	00	77	70	78	40	64	352	00	355	20	358	40
15	82	50	83	25	84	00	65	357	50	360	75	364	00
16	88	00	88	80	89	60	66	363	00	366	30	369	60
17	93	50	94	35	95	20	67	368	50	371	85	375	20
18	99	00	99	90	100	80	68	374	00	377	40	380	80
19	104	50	105	45	106	40	69	379	50	382	95	386	40
20	110	00	111	00	112	00	70	385	00	388	50	392	00
21	115	50	116	55	117	60	71	390	50	394	05	397	60
22	121	00	122	10	123	20	72	396	00	399	60	403	20
23	126	50	127	65	128	80	73	401	50	405	15	408	80
24	132	00	133	20	134	40	74	407	00	410	70	414	40
25	137	50	138	75	140	00	75	412	50	416	25	420	00
26	143	00	144	30	145	60	76	418	00	421	80	425	60
27	148	50	149	85	151	20	77	423	50	427	35	431	20
28	154	00	155	40	156	80	78	429	00	432	90	436	80
29	159	50	160	95	162	40	79	434	50	438	45	442	40
30	165	00	166	50	168	00	80	440	00	444	00	448	00
31	170	50	172	05	173	60	81	445	50	449	55	453	60
32	176	00	177	60	179	20	82	451	00	455	10	459	20
33	181	50	183	15	184	80	83	456	50	460	65	464	80
34	187	00	188	70	190	40	84	462	00	466	20	470	40
35	192	50	194	25	196	00	85	467	50	471	75	476	00
36	198	00	199	80	201	60	86	473	00	477	30	481	60
37	203	50	205	35	207	20	87	478	50	482	85	487	20
38	209	00	210	90	212	80	88	484	00	488	40	492	80
39	214	50	216	45	218	40	89	489	50	493	95	498	40
40	220	00	222	00	224	00	90	495	00	499	50	504	00
41	225	50	227	55	229	60	91	500	50	505	05	509	60
42	231	00	233	10	235	20	92	506	00	510	60	515	20
43	236	50	238	65	240	80	93	511	50	516	15	520	80
44	242	00	244	20	246	40	94	517	00	521	70	526	40
45	247	50	249	75	252	00	95	522	50	527	25	532	00
46	253	00	255	30	257	60	96	528	00	532	80	537	60
47	258	50	260	85	263	20	97	533	50	538	35	543	20
48	264	00	266	40	268	80	98	539	00	543	90	548	80
49	269	50	271	95	274	40	99	544	50	549	45	554	40
50	275	00	277	50	280	00	100	550	00	555	00	560	00
¼	1·375		1·3875		1·40		¾	4·125		4·1625		4·20	
½	2·750		2·7750		2·80		1¼	6·875		6·9375		7·00	

No.	£5·50 £ p	£5·55 £ p	£5·60 £ p
101	555 50	560 55	565 60
102	561 00	566 10	571 20
103	566 50	571 65	576 80
104	572 00	577 20	582 40
105	577 50	582 75	588 00
106	583 00	588 30	593 60
107	588 50	593 85	599 20
9108	594 00	599 40	604 80
109	599 50	604 95	610 40
110	605 00	610 50	616 00
111	610 50	616 05	621 60
112	616 00	621 60	627 20
113	621 50	627 15	632 80
114	627 00	632 70	638 40
115	632 50	638 25	644 00
116	638 00	643 80	649 60
117	643 50	649 35	655 20
118	649 00	654 90	660 80
119	654 50	660 45	666 40
10120	660 00	666 00	672 00
121	665 50	671 55	677 60
122	671 00	677 10	683 20
123	676 50	682 65	688 80
124	682 00	688 20	694 40
125	687 50	693 75	700 00
126	693 00	699 30	705 60
127	698 50	704 85	711 20
128	704 00	710 40	716 80
129	709 50	715 95	722 40
130	715 00	721 05	728 00
131	720 50	727 05	733 60
11132	726 00	732 60	739 20
133	731 50	738 15	744 80
134	737 00	743 70	750 40
135	742 50	749 25	756 00
136	748 00	754 80	761 60
137	753 50	760 35	767 20
138	759 00	765 90	772 80
139	764 50	771 45	778 40
140	770 00	777 00	784 00
141	775 50	782 55	789 60
142	781 00	788 10	795 20
143	786 50	793 65	800 80
12144	792 00	799 20	806 40
145	797 50	804 75	812 00
146	803 00	810 30	817 60
147	808 50	815 85	823 20
148	814 00	821 40	828 80
149	819 50	826 95	834 40
150	825 00	832 50	840 00
1016	5588·00	5638·80	5689·60
1296	7128·00	7192·80	7257·60

No.	£5·50 £ p	£5·55 £ p	£5·60 £ p
155	852 50	860 25	868 00
¹³156	858 00	865 80	873 60
165	907 50	915 75	924 00
¹⁴168	924 00	932 40	940 80
175	962 50	971 25	980 00
¹⁵180	990 00	999 00	1008 00
185	1017 50	1026 75	1036 00
¹⁶192	1056 00	1065 60	1075 20
195	1072 50	1082 25	1092 00
200	1100 00	1110 00	1120 00
¹⁷204	1122 00	1132 20	1142 40
205	1127 50	1137 75	1148 00
215	1182 50	1193 25	1204 00
¹⁸216	1188 00	1198 80	1209 60
224	1232 00	1243 20	1254 40
225	1237 50	1248 75	1260 00
¹⁹228	1254 00	1265 40	1276 80
235	1292 50	1304 25	1316 00
245	1347 50	1359 75	1372 00
250	1375 00	1387 50	1400 00
²¹252	1386 00	1398 60	1411 20
255	1402 50	1415 25	1428 00
265	1457 50	1470 75	1484 00
272	1496 00	1509 60	1523 20
275	1512 50	1526 25	1540 00
280	1540 00	1554 00	1568 00
285	1567 50	1581 75	1596 00
288	1584 00	1598 40	1612 80
295	1622 50	1637 25	1652 00
300	1650 00	1665 00	1680 00
325	1787 50	1803 75	1820 00
336	1848 00	1864 80	1881 60
365	2007 50	2025 75	2044 00
375	2062 50	2081 25	2100 00
400	2200 00	2220 00	2240 00
425	2337 50	2358 75	2380 00
432	2376 00	2397 60	2419 20
475	2612 50	2636 25	2660 00
480	2640 00	2664 00	2688 00
500	2750 00	2775 00	2800 00
504	2772 00	2797 20	2822 40
576	3168 00	3196 80	3225 60
600	3300 00	3330 00	3360 00
700	3850 00	3885 00	3920 00
750	4125 00	4162 50	4200 00
800	4400 00	4440 00	4480 00
900	4950 00	4995 00	5040 00
1000	5500 00	5550 00	5600 00
2500	13750 ·0	13875 ·0	14000 ·0
5000	27500 ·0	27750 ·0	28000 ·0
1728	9504·00	9590·40	9676·80
1760	9680·00	9768·00	9856·00

(Side labels in right-hand No. column: Dez, 2 gross, 3 gr., 4 gr.)

No.	£5·65 £	P	£5·70 £	P	£5·75 £	P	No.	£5·65 £	P	£5·70 £	P	£5·75 £	P
1	5	65	5	70	5	75	51	288	15	290	70	293	25
2	11	30	11	40	11	50	52	293	80	296	40	299	00
3	16	95	17	10	17	25	53	299	45	302	10	304	75
4	22	60	22	80	23	00	54	305	10	307	80	310	50
5	28	25	28	50	28	75	55	310	75	313	50	316	25
6	33	90	34	20	34	50	56	316	40	319	20	322	00
7	39	55	39	90	40	25	57	322	05	324	90	327	75
8	45	20	45	60	46	00	58	327	70	330	60	333	50
9	50	85	51	30	51	75	59	333	35	336	30	339	25
10	56	50	57	00	57	50	60	339	00	342	00	345	00
11	62	15	62	70	63	25	61	344	65	347	70	350	75
12	67	80	68	40	69	00	62	350	30	353	40	356	50
13	73	45	74	10	74	75	63	355	95	359	10	362	25
14	79	10	79	80	80	50	64	361	60	364	80	368	00
15	84	75	85	50	86	25	65	367	25	370	50	373	75
16	90	40	91	20	92	00	66	372	90	376	20	379	50
17	96	05	96	90	97	75	67	378	55	381	90	385	25
18	101	70	102	60	103	50	68	384	20	387	60	391	00
19	107	35	108	30	109	25	69	389	85	393	30	396	75
20	113	00	114	00	115	00	70	395	50	399	00	402	50
21	118	65	119	70	120	75	71	401	15	404	70	408	25
22	124	30	125	40	126	50	72	406	80	410	40	414	00
23	129	95	131	10	132	25	73	412	45	416	10	419	75
24	135	60	136	80	138	00	74	418	10	421	80	425	50
25	141	25	142	50	143	75	75	423	75	427	50	431	25
26	146	90	148	20	149	50	76	429	40	433	20	437	00
27	152	55	153	90	155	25	77	435	05	438	90	442	75
28	158	20	159	60	161	00	78	440	70	444	60	448	50
29	163	85	165	30	166	75	79	446	35	450	30	454	25
30	169	50	171	00	172	50	80	452	00	456	00	460	00
31	175	15	176	70	178	25	81	457	65	461	70	465	75
32	180	80	182	40	184	00	82	463	30	467	40	471	50
33	186	45	188	10	189	75	83	468	95	473	10	477	25
34	192	10	193	80	195	50	84	474	60	478	80	483	00
35	197	75	199	50	201	25	85	480	25	484	50	488	75
36	203	40	205	20	207	00	86	485	90	490	20	494	50
37	209	05	210	90	212	75	87	491	55	495	90	500	25
38	214	70	216	60	218	50	88	497	20	501	60	506	00
39	220	35	222	30	224	25	89	502	85	507	30	511	75
40	226	00	228	00	230	00	90	508	50	513	00	517	50
41	231	65	233	70	235	75	91	514	15	518	70	523	25
42	237	30	239	40	241	50	92	519	80	524	40	529	00
43	242	95	245	10	247	25	93	525	45	530	10	534	75
44	248	60	250	80	253	00	94	531	10	535	80	540	50
45	254	25	256	50	258	75	95	536	75	541	50	546	25
46	259	90	262	20	264	50	96	542	40	547	20	552	00
47	265	55	267	90	270	25	97	548	05	552	90	557	75
48	271	20	273	60	276	00	98	553	70	558	60	563	50
49	276	85	279	30	281	75	99	559	35	564	30	569	25
50	282	50	285	00	287	50	100	565	00	570	00	575	00
¼	1·4125		1·425		1·4375		¾	4·2375		4·275		4·3125	
½..	2·8250		2·850		2·8750		1¼..	7·0625		7·125		7·1875	

No.	£5·65		£5·70		£5·75	
	£	p	£	p	£	p
101	570	65	575	70	580	75
102	576	30	581	40	586	50
103	581	95	587	10	592	25
104	587	60	592	80	598	00
105	593	25	598	50	603	75
106	598	90	604	20	609	50
107	604	55	609	90	615	25
9108	610	20	615	60	621	00
109	615	85	621	30	626	75
110	621	50	627	00	632	50
111	627	15	632	70	638	25
112	632	80	638	40	644	00
113	638	45	644	10	649	75
114	644	10	649	80	655	50
115	649	75	655	50	661	25
116	655	40	661	20	667	00
117	661	05	666	90	672	75
118	666	70	672	60	678	50
119	672	35	678	30	684	25
10120	678	00	684	00	690	00
121	683	65	689	70	695	75
122	689	30	695	40	701	50
123	694	95	701	10	707	25
124	700	60	706	80	713	00
125	706	25	712	50	718	75
126	711	90	718	20	724	50
127	717	55	723	90	730	25
128	723	20	729	60	736	00
129	728	85	735	30	741	75
130	734	50	741	00	747	50
131	740	15	746	70	753	25
11132	745	80	752	40	759	00
133	751	45	758	10	764	75
134	757	10	763	80	770	50
135	762	75	769	50	776	25
136	768	40	775	20	782	00
137	774	05	780	90	787	75
138	779	70	786	60	793	50
139	785	35	792	30	799	25
140	791	00	798	00	805	00
141	796	65	803	70	810	75
142	802	30	809	40	816	50
143	807	95	815	10	822	25
12144	813	60	820	80	828	00
145	819	25	826	50	833	75
146	824	90	832	20	839	50
147	830	55	837	90	845	25
148	836	20	843	60	851	00
149	841	85	849	30	856	75
150	847	50	855	00	862	50
1016	5740·40		5791·20		5842·00	
1296	7822·40		7887·20		7452·00	

No.	£5·65		£5·70		£5·75	
	£	p	£	p	£	p
Doz 155	875	75	883	50	891	25
13156	881	40	889	20	897	00
165	932	25	940	50	948	75
14168	949	20	957	60	966	00
175	988	75	997	50	1006	25
15180	1017	00	1026	00	1035	00
185	1045	25	1054	50	1063	75
16192	1084	80	1094	40	1104	00
195	1101	75	1111	50	1121	25
200	1130	00	1140	00	1150	00
17204	1152	60	1162	80	1173	00
205	1158	25	1168	50	1178	75
215	1214	75	1225	50	1236	25
18216	1220	40	1231	20	1242	00
224	1265	60	1276	80	1288	00
225	1271	25	1282	50	1293	75
19228	1288	20	1299	60	1311	00
235	1327	75	1339	50	1351	25
245	1384	25	1396	50	1408	75
250	1412	50	1425	00	1437	50
21252	1423	80	1436	40	1449	00
255	1440	75	1453	50	1466	25
265	1497	25	1510	50	1523	75
272	1536	80	1550	40	1564	00
275	1553	75	1567	50	1581	25
2 gross 280	1582	00	1596	00	1610	00
285	1610	25	1624	50	1638	75
288	1627	20	1641	60	1656	00
295	1666	75	1681	50	1696	25
300	1695	00	1710	00	1725	00
325	1836	25	1852	50	1868	75
336	1898	40	1915	20	1932	00
365	2062	25	2080	50	2098	75
375	2118	75	2137	50	2156	25
400	2260	00	2280	00	2300	00
3 gr. 425	2401	25	2422	50	2443	75
432	2440	80	2462	40	2484	00
475	2683	75	2707	50	2731	25
480	2712	00	2736	00	2760	00
500	2825	00	2850	00	2875	00
4 gr. 504	2847	60	2872	80	2898	00
576	3254	40	3283	20	3312	00
600	3390	00	3420	00	3450	00
700	3955	00	3990	00	4025	00
750	4237	50	4275	00	4312	50
800	4520	00	4560	00	4600	00
900	5085	00	5130	00	5175	00
1000	5650	00	5700	00	5750	00
2500	14125	·0	14250	·0	14375	·0
5000	28250	·0	28500	·0	28750	·0
1728	9763·20		9849·60		9936·00	
1760	9944·00		10032·00		10120·00	

No.	£5·80		£5·85		£5·90		No.	£5·80		£5·85		£5·90	
	£	P	£	P	£	P		£	P	£	P	£	P
1	5	80	5	85	5	90	51	295	80	298	35	300	90
2	11	60	11	70	11	80	52	301	60	304	20	306	80
3	17	40	17	55	17	70	53	307	40	310	05	312	70
4	23	20	23	40	23	60	54	313	20	315	90	318	60
5	29	00	29	25	29	50	55	319	00	321	75	324	50
6	34	80	35	10	35	40	56	324	80	327	60	330	40
7	40	60	40	95	41	30	57	330	60	333	45	336	30
8	46	40	46	80	47	20	58	336	40	339	30	342	20
9	52	20	52	65	53	10	59	342	20	345	15	348	10
10	58	00	58	50	59	00	60	348	00	351	00	354	00
11	63	80	64	35	64	90	61	353	80	356	85	359	90
12	69	60	70	20	70	80	62	359	60	362	70	365	80
13	75	40	76	05	76	70	63	365	40	368	55	371	70
14	81	20	81	90	82	60	64	371	20	374	40	377	60
15	87	00	87	75	88	50	65	377	00	380	25	383	50
16	92	80	93	60	94	40	66	382	80	386	10	389	40
17	98	60	99	45	100	30	67	388	60	391	95	395	30
18	104	40	105	30	106	20	68	394	40	397	80	401	20
19	110	20	111	15	112	10	69	400	20	403	65	407	10
20	116	00	117	00	118	00	70	406	00	409	50	413	00
21	121	80	122	85	123	90	71	411	80	415	35	418	90
22	127	60	128	70	129	80	72	417	60	421	20	424	80
23	133	40	134	55	135	70	73	423	40	427	05	430	70
24	139	20	140	40	141	60	74	429	20	432	90	436	60
25	145	00	146	25	147	50	75	435	00	438	75	442	50
26	150	80	152	10	153	40	76	440	80	444	60	448	40
27	156	60	157	95	159	30	77	446	60	450	45	454	30
28	162	40	163	80	165	20	78	452	40	456	30	460	20
29	168	20	169	65	171	10	79	458	20	462	15	466	10
30	174	00	175	50	177	00	80	464	00	468	00	472	00
31	179	80	181	35	182	90	81	469	80	473	85	477	90
32	185	60	187	20	188	80	82	475	60	479	70	483	80
33	191	40	193	05	194	70	83	481	40	485	55	489	70
34	197	20	198	90	200	60	84	487	20	491	40	495	60
35	203	00	204	75	206	50	85	493	00	497	25	501	50
36	208	80	210	60	212	40	86	498	80	503	10	507	40
37	214	60	216	45	218	30	87	504	60	508	95	513	30
38	220	40	222	30	224	20	88	510	40	514	80	519	20
39	226	20	228	15	230	10	89	516	20	520	65	525	10
40	232	00	234	00	236	00	90	522	00	526	50	531	00
41	237	80	239	85	241	90	91	527	80	532	35	536	90
42	243	60	245	70	247	80	92	533	60	538	20	542	80
43	249	40	251	55	253	70	93	539	40	544	05	548	70
44	255	20	257	40	259	60	94	545	20	549	90	554	60
45	261	00	263	25	265	50	95	551	00	555	75	560	50
46	266	80	269	10	271	40	96	556	80	561	60	566	40
47	272	60	274	95	277	30	97	562	60	567	45	572	30
48	278	40	280	80	283	20	98	568	40	573	30	578	20
49	284	20	286	65	289	10	99	574	20	579	15	584	10
50	290	00	292	50	295	00	100	580	00	585	00	590	00
¼	1·45		1·4625		1·475		¾	4·35		4·3875		4·4250	
½	2·90		2·9250		2·950		1¼	7·25		7·3125		7·3750	

Dozens. (left), *Dozens.* (right)

No.	£5·80		£5·85		£5·90	
	£	p	£	p	£	p
101	585	80	590	85	595	90
102	591	60	596	70	601	80
103	597	40	602	55	607	70
104	603	20	608	40	613	60
105	609	00	614	25	619	50
106	614	80	620	10	625	40
107	620	60	625	95	631	30
[9]108	626	40	631	80	637	20
109	632	20	637	65	643	10
110	638	00	643	50	649	00
111	643	80	649	35	654	90
112	649	60	655	20	660	80
113	655	40	661	05	666	70
114	661	20	666	90	672	60
115	667	00	672	75	678	50
116	672	80	678	60	684	40
117	678	60	684	45	690	30
118	684	40	690	30	696	20
119	690	20	696	15	702	10
[10]120	696	00	702	00	708	00
121	701	80	707	85	713	90
122	707	60	713	70	719	80
123	713	40	719	55	725	70
124	719	20	725	40	731	60
125	725	00	731	25	737	50
126	730	80	737	10	743	40
127	736	60	742	95	749	30
128	742	40	748	80	755	20
129	748	20	754	65	761	10
130	754	00	760	50	767	00
131	759	80	766	35	772	90
[11]132	765	60	772	20	778	80
133	771	40	778	05	784	70
134	777	20	783	90	790	60
135	783	00	789	75	796	50
136	788	80	795	60	802	40
137	794	60	801	45	808	30
138	800	40	807	30	814	20
139	806	20	813	15	820	10
140	812	00	819	00	826	00
141	817	80	824	85	831	90
142	823	60	830	70	837	80
143	829	40	836	55	843	70
[12]144	835	20	842	40	849	60
145	841	00	848	25	855	50
146	846	80	854	10	861	40
147	852	60	859	95	867	30
148	858	40	865	80	873	20
149	864	20	871	65	879	10
150	870	00	877	50	885	00
1016	5892·80		5943·60		5994·40	
1296	7516·80		7581·60		7646·40	

No.	£5·80		£5·85		£5·90	
	£	p	£	p	£	p
155	899	00	906	75	914	50
[13]156	904	80	912	60	920	40
165	957	00	965	25	973	50
[14]168	974	40	982	80	991	20
175	1015	00	1023	75	1032	50
[15]180	1044	00	1053	00	1062	00
185	1073	00	1082	25	1091	50
[16]192	1113	60	1123	20	1132	80
195	1131	00	1140	75	1150	50
200	1160	00	1170	00	1180	00
[17]204	1183	20	1193	40	1203	60
205	1189	00	1199	25	1209	50
215	1247	00	1257	75	1268	50
[18]216	1252	80	1263	60	1274	40
224	1299	20	1310	40	1321	60
225	1305	00	1316	25	1327	50
[19]228	1322	40	1333	80	1345	20
235	1363	00	1374	75	1386	50
245	1421	00	1433	25	1445	50
250	1450	00	1462	50	1475	00
[21]252	1461	60	1474	20	1486	80
255	1479	00	1491	75	1504	50
265	1537	00	1550	25	1563	50
272	1577	60	1591	20	1604	80
275	1595	00	1608	75	1622	50
280	1624	00	1638	00	1652	00
285	1653	00	1667	25	1681	50
2 gross 288	1670	40	1684	80	1699	20
295	1711	00	1725	75	1740	50
300	1740	00	1755	00	1770	00
325	1885	00	1901	25	1917	50
336	1948	80	1965	60	1982	40
365	2117	00	2135	25	2153	50
375	2175	00	2193	75	2212	50
400	2320	00	2340	00	2360	00
425	2465	00	2486	25	2507	50
3 gr. 432	2505	60	2527	20	2548	80
475	2755	00	2778	75	2802	50
480	2784	00	2808	00	2832	00
500	2900	00	2925	00	2950	00
504	2923	20	2948	40	2973	60
4 gr. 576	3340	80	3369	60	3398	40
600	3480	00	3510	00	3540	00
700	4060	00	4095	00	4130	00
750	4350	00	4387	50	4425	00
800	4640	00	4680	00	4720	00
900	5220	00	5265	00	5310	00
1000	5800	00	5850	00	5900	00
2500	14500	·0	14625	·0	14750	·0
5000	29000	·0	29250	·0	29500	·0
1728	10022·40		10108·80		10195·20	
1760	10208·00		10296·00		10384·00	

No.	£5·95 £	P	£6·00 £	P	£6·05 £	P	No.	£5·95 £	P	£6·00 £	P	£6·05 £	P
1	5	95	6	00	6	05	51	303	45	306	00	308	55
2	11	90	12	00	12	10	52	309	40	312	00	314	60
3	17	85	18	00	18	15	53	315	35	318	00	320	65
4	23	80	24	00	24	20	54	321	30	324	00	326	70
5	29	75	30	00	30	25	55	327	25	330	00	332	75
6	35	70	36	00	36	30	56	333	20	336	00	338	80
7	41	65	42	00	42	35	57	339	15	342	00	344	85
8	47	60	48	00	48	40	58	345	10	348	00	350	90
9	53	55	54	00	54	45	59	351	05	354	00	356	95
10	59	50	60	00	60	50	60	357	00	360	00	363	00
11	65	45	66	00	66	55	61	362	95	366	00	369	05
12	71	40	72	00	72	60	62	368	90	372	00	375	10
13	77	35	78	00	78	65	63	374	85	378	00	381	15
14	83	30	84	00	84	70	64	380	80	384	00	387	20
15	89	25	90	00	90	75	65	386	75	390	00	393	25
16	95	20	96	00	96	80	66	392	70	396	00	399	30
17	101	15	102	00	102	85	67	398	65	402	00	405	35
18	107	10	108	00	108	90	68	404	60	408	00	411	40
19	113	05	114	00	114	95	69	410	55	414	00	417	45
20	119	00	120	00	121	00	70	416	50	420	00	423	50
21	124	95	126	00	127	05	71	422	45	426	00	429	55
22	130	90	132	00	133	10	72	428	40	432	00	435	60
23	136	85	138	00	139	15	73	434	35	438	00	441	65
24	142	80	144	00	145	20	74	440	30	444	00	447	70
25	148	75	150	00	151	25	75	446	25	450	00	453	75
26	154	70	156	00	157	30	76	452	20	456	00	459	80
27	160	65	162	00	163	35	77	458	15	462	00	465	85
28	166	60	168	00	169	40	78	464	10	468	00	471	90
29	172	55	174	00	175	45	79	470	05	474	00	477	95
30	178	50	180	00	181	50	80	476	00	480	00	484	00
31	184	45	186	00	187	55	81	481	95	486	00	490	05
32	190	40	192	00	193	60	82	487	90	492	00	496	10
33	196	35	198	00	199	65	83	493	85	498	00	502	15
34	202	30	204	00	205	70	84	499	80	504	00	508	20
35	208	25	210	00	211	75	85	505	75	510	00	514	25
36	214	20	216	00	217	80	86	511	70	516	00	520	30
37	220	15	222	00	223	85	87	517	65	522	00	526	35
38	226	10	228	00	229	90	88	523	60	528	00	532	40
39	232	05	234	00	235	95	89	529	55	534	00	538	45
40	238	00	240	00	242	00	90	535	50	540	00	544	50
41	243	95	246	00	248	05	91	541	45	546	00	550	55
42	249	90	252	00	254	10	92	547	40	552	00	556	60
43	255	85	258	00	260	15	93	553	35	558	00	562	65
44	261	80	264	00	266	20	94	559	30	564	00	568	70
45	267	75	270	00	272	25	95	565	25	570	00	574	75
46	273	70	276	00	278	30	96	571	20	576	00	580	80
47	279	65	282	00	284	35	97	577	15	582	00	586	85
48	285	60	288	00	290	40	98	583	10	588	00	592	90
49	291	55	294	00	296	45	99	589	05	594	00	598	95
50	297	50	300	00	302	50	100	595	00	600	00	605	00
¼	1·4875		1·50		1·5125		¾	4·4625		4·50		4·5375	
½..	2·9750		3·00		3·0250		1¼..	7·4375		7·50		7·5625	

(Left margin marked "Dozens." alongside rows 3–6 and 53–56)

No.	£5·95 £	p	£6·00 £	p	£6·05 £	p
101	600	95	606	00	611	05
102	606	90	612	00	617	10
103	612	85	618	00	623	15
104	618	80	624	00	629	20
105	624	75	630	00	635	25
106	630	70	636	00	641	30
107	636	65	642	00	647	35
9 108	642	60	648	00	653	40
109	648	55	654	00	659	45
110	654	50	660	00	665	50
111	660	45	666	00	671	55
112	666	40	672	00	677	60
113	672	35	678	00	683	65
114	678	30	684	00	689	70
115	684	25	690	00	695	75
116	690	20	696	00	701	80
117	696	15	702	00	707	85
118	702	10	708	00	713	90
119	708	05	714	00	719	95
10 120	714	00	720	00	726	00
121	719	95	726	00	732	05
122	725	90	732	00	738	10
123	731	85	738	00	744	15
124	737	80	744	00	750	20
125	743	75	750	00	756	25
126	749	70	756	00	762	30
127	755	65	762	00	768	35
128	761	60	768	00	774	40
129	767	55	774	00	780	45
130	773	50	780	00	786	50
131	779	45	786	00	792	55
11 132	785	40	792	00	798	60
133	791	35	798	00	804	65
134	797	30	804	00	810	70
135	803	25	810	00	816	75
136	809	20	816	00	822	80
137	815	15	822	00	828	85
138	821	10	828	00	834	90
139	827	05	834	00	840	95
140	833	00	840	00	847	00
141	838	95	846	00	853	05
142	844	90	852	00	859	10
143	850	85	858	00	865	15
12 144	856	80	864	00	871	20
145	862	75	870	00	877	25
146	868	70	876	00	883	30
147	874	65	882	00	889	35
148	880	60	888	00	895	40
149	886	55	894	00	901	45
150	892	50	900	00	907	50
1016	6045	20	6096	00	6146	80
1296	7711	20	7776	00	7840	80

No.	£5·95 £	p	£6·00 £	p	£6·05 £	p
Doz 155	922	25	930	00	937	75
13 156	928	20	936	00	943	80
165	981	75	990	00	998	25
14 168	999	60	1008	00	1016	40
175	1041	25	1050	00	1058	75
15 180	1071	00	1080	00	1089	00
185	1100	75	1110	00	1119	25
16 192	1142	40	1152	00	1161	60
195	1160	25	1170	00	1179	75
200	1190	00	1200	00	1210	00
17 204	1213	80	1224	00	1234	20
205	1219	75	1230	00	1240	25
215	1279	25	1290	00	1300	75
18 216	1285	20	1296	00	1306	80
224	1332	80	1344	00	1355	20
225	1338	75	1350	00	1361	25
19 228	1356	60	1368	00	1379	40
235	1398	25	1410	00	1421	75
245	1457	75	1470	00	1482	25
250	1487	50	1500	00	1512	50
21 252	1499	40	1512	00	1524	60
255	1517	25	1530	00	1542	75
265	1576	75	1590	00	1603	25
272	1618	40	1632	00	1645	60
275	1636	25	1650	00	1663	75
280	1666	00	1680	00	1694	00
285	1695	75	1710	00	1724	25
2 gross 288	1713	60	1728	00	1742	40
295	1755	25	1770	00	1784	75
300	1785	00	1800	00	1815	00
325	1933	75	1950	00	1966	25
336	1999	20	2016	00	2032	80
365	2171	75	2190	00	2208	25
375	2231	25	2250	00	2268	75
400	2380	00	2400	00	2420	00
3 gr. 425	2528	75	2550	00	2571	25
432	2570	40	2592	00	2613	60
475	2826	25	2850	00	2873	75
480	2856	00	2880	00	2904	00
500	2975	00	3000	00	3025	00
4 gr. 504	2998	80	3024	00	3049	20
576	3427	20	3456	00	3484	80
600	3570	00	3600	00	3630	00
700	4165	00	4200	00	4235	00
750	4462	50	4500	00	4537	50
800	4760	00	4800	00	4840	00
900	5355	00	5400	00	5445	00
1000	5950	00	6000	00	6050	00
2500	14875	·0	15000	·0	15125	·0
5000	29750	·0	30000	·0	30250	·0
1728	10281	60	10368	00	10454	40
1760	10472	00	10560	00	10648	00

No.	£6·10		£6·15		£6·20		No.	£6·10		£6·15		£6·20	
	£	P	£	P	£	P		£	P	£	P	£	P
1	6	10	6	15	6	20	51	311	10	313	65	316	20
2	12	20	12	30	12	40	52	317	20	319	80	322	40
3	18	30	18	45	18	60	53	323	30	325	95	328	60
4	24	40	24	60	24	80	54	329	40	332	10	334	80
5	30	50	30	75	31	00	55	335	50	338	25	341	00
6	36	60	36	90	37	20	56	341	60	344	40	347	20
7	42	70	43	05	43	40	57	347	70	350	55	353	40
8	48	80	49	20	49	60	58	353	80	356	70	359	60
9	54	90	55	35	55	80	59	359	90	362	85	365	80
10	61	00	61	50	62	00	60	366	00	369	00	372	00
11	67	10	67	65	68	20	61	372	10	375	15	378	20
12	73	20	73	80	74	40	62	378	20	381	30	384	40
13	79	30	79	95	80	60	63	384	30	387	45	390	60
14	85	40	86	10	86	80	64	390	40	393	60	396	80
15	91	50	92	25	93	00	65	396	50	399	75	403	00
16	97	60	98	40	99	20	66	402	60	405	90	409	20
17	103	70	104	55	105	40	67	408	70	412	05	415	40
18	109	80	110	70	111	60	68	414	80	418	20	421	60
19	115	90	116	85	117	80	69	420	90	424	35	427	80
20	122	00	123	00	124	00	70	427	00	430	50	434	00
21	128	10	129	15	130	20	71	433	10	436	65	440	20
22	134	20	135	30	136	40	72	439	20	442	80	446	40
23	140	30	141	45	142	60	73	445	30	448	95	452	60
24	146	40	147	60	148	80	74	451	40	455	10	458	80
25	152	50	153	75	155	00	75	457	50	461	25	465	00
26	158	60	159	90	161	20	76	463	60	467	40	471	20
27	164	70	166	05	167	40	77	469	70	473	55	477	40
28	170	80	172	20	173	60	78	475	80	479	70	483	60
29	176	90	178	35	179	80	79	481	90	485	85	489	80
30	183	00	184	50	186	00	80	488	00	492	00	496	00
31	189	10	190	65	192	20	81	494	10	498	15	502	20
32	195	20	196	80	198	40	82	500	20	504	30	508	40
33	201	30	202	95	204	60	83	506	30	510	45	514	60
34	207	40	209	10	210	80	84	512	40	516	60	520	80
35	213	50	215	25	217	00	85	518	50	522	75	527	00
36	219	60	221	40	223	20	86	524	60	528	90	533	20
37	225	70	227	55	229	40	87	530	70	535	05	539	40
38	231	80	233	70	235	60	88	536	80	541	20	545	60
39	237	90	239	85	241	80	89	542	90	547	35	551	80
40	244	00	246	00	248	00	90	549	00	553	50	558	00
41	250	10	252	15	254	20	91	555	10	559	65	564	20
42	256	20	258	30	260	40	92	561	20	565	80	570	40
43	262	30	264	45	266	60	93	567	30	571	95	576	60
44	268	40	270	60	272	80	94	573	40	578	10	582	80
45	274	50	276	75	279	00	95	579	50	584	25	589	00
46	280	60	282	90	285	20	96	585	60	590	40	595	20
47	286	70	289	05	291	40	97	591	70	596	55	601	40
48	292	80	295	20	297	60	98	597	80	602	70	607	60
49	298	90	301	35	303	80	99	603	90	608	85	613	80
50	305	00	307	50	310	00	100	610	00	615	00	620	00
⅛	1·525		1·5375		1·55		¾	4·575		4·6125		4·65	
¼	3·050		3·0750		3·10		1¼	7·625		7·6875		7·75	

No.	£6·10 £	P	£6·15 £	P	£6·20 £	P
101	616	10	621	15	626	20
102	622	20	627	30	632	40
103	628	30	633	45	638	60
104	634	40	639	60	644	80
105	640	50	645	75	651	00
106	646	60	651	90	657	20
107	652	70	658	05	663	40
°108	658	80	664	20	669	60
109	664	90	670	35	675	80
110	671	00	676	50	682	00
111	677	10	682	65	688	20
112	683	20	688	80	694	40
113	689	30	694	95	700	60
114	695	40	701	10	706	80
115	701	50	707	25	713	00
116	707	60	713	40	719	20
117	713	70	719	55	725	40
118	719	80	725	70	731	60
119	725	90	731	85	737	80
°120	732	00	738	00	744	00
121	738	10	744	15	750	20
122	744	20	750	30	756	40
123	750	30	756	45	762	60
124	756	40	762	60	768	80
125	762	50	768	75	775	00
126	768	60	774	90	781	20
127	774	70	781	05	787	40
128	780	80	787	20	793	60
129	786	90	793	35	799	80
130	793	00	799	50	806	00
131	799	10	805	65	812	20
x1132	805	20	811	80	818	40
133	811	30	817	95	824	60
134	817	40	824	10	830	80
135	823	50	830	25	837	00
136	829	60	836	40	843	20
137	835	70	842	55	849	40
138	841	80	848	70	855	60
139	847	90	854	85	861	80
140	854	00	861	00	868	00
141	860	10	867	15	874	20
142	866	20	873	30	880	40
143	872	30	879	45	886	60
12144	878	40	885	60	892	80
145	884	50	891	75	899	00
146	890	60	897	90	905	20
147	896	70	904	05	911	40
148	902	80	910	20	917	60
149	908	90	916	35	923	80
150	915	00	922	50	930	00
1016	6197·60		6248·40		6299·20	
1296	7905·60		7970·40		8035·20	

No.	£6·10 £	P	£6·15 £	P	£6·20 £	P
Doz 155	945	50	953	25	961	00
13 156	951	60	959	40	967	20
165	1006	50	1014	75	1023	00
14 168	1024	80	1033	20	1041	60
175	1067	50	1076	25	1085	00
15 180	1098	00	1107	00	1116	00
185	1128	50	1137	75	1147	00
16 192	1171	20	1180	80	1190	40
195	1189	50	1199	25	1209	00
200	1220	00	1230	00	1240	00
17 204	1244	40	1254	60	1264	80
205	1250	50	1260	75	1271	00
215	1311	50	1322	25	1333	00
18 216	1317	60	1328	40	1339	20
224	1366	40	1377	60	1388	80
225	1372	50	1383	75	1395	00
19 228	1390	80	1402	20	1413	60
235	1433	50	1445	25	1457	00
245	1494	50	1506	75	1519	00
250	1525	00	1537	50	1550	00
21 252	1537	20	1549	80	1562	40
255	1555	50	1568	25	1581	00
265	1616	50	1629	75	1643	00
272	1659	20	1672	80	1686	40
275	1677	50	1691	25	1705	00
280	1708	00	1722	00	1736	00
285	1738	50	1752	75	1767	00
2 gross 288	1756	80	1771	20	1785	60
295	1799	50	1814	25	1829	00
300	1830	00	1845	00	1860	00
325	1982	50	1998	75	2015	00
336	2049	60	2066	40	2083	20
365	2226	50	2244	75	2263	00
375	2287	50	2306	25	2325	00
400	2440	00	2460	00	2480	00
3 gr. 425	2592	50	2613	75	2635	00
432	2635	20	2656	80	2678	40
475	2897	50	2921	25	2945	00
480	2928	00	2952	00	2976	00
500	3050	00	3075	00	3100	00
4 gr. 504	3074	40	3099	60	3124	80
576	3513	60	3542	40	3571	20
600	3660	00	3690	00	3720	00
700	4270	00	4305	00	4340	00
750	4575	00	4612	50	4650	00
800	4880	00	4920	00	4960	00
900	5490	00	5535	00	5580	00
1000	6100	00	6150	00	6200	00
2500	15250	·0	15375	·0	15500	·0
5000	30500	·0	30750	·0	31000	·0
1728	10540·80		10627·20		10713·60	
1760	10736·00		10824·00		10912·00	

No.	£6·25		£6·30		£6·35		No.	£6·25		£6·30		£6·35	
	£	P	£	P	£	P		£	P	£	P	£	P
1	6	25	6	30	6	35	51	318	75	321	30	323	85
2	12	50	12	60	12	70	52	325	00	327	60	330	20
3	18	75	18	90	19	05	53	331	25	333	90	336	55
4	25	00	25	20	25	40	54	337	50	340	20	342	90
5	31	25	31	50	31	75	55	343	75	346	50	349	25
6	37	50	37	80	38	10	56	350	00	352	80	355	60
7	43	75	44	10	44	45	57	356	25	359	10	361	95
8	50	00	50	40	50	80	58	362	50	365	40	368	30
9	56	25	56	70	57	15	59	368	75	371	70	374	65
10	62	50	63	00	63	50	60	375	00	378	00	381	00
11	68	75	69	30	69	85	61	381	25	384	30	387	35
12	75	00	75	60	76	20	62	387	50	390	60	393	70
13	81	25	81	90	82	55	63	393	75	396	90	400	05
14	87	50	88	20	88	90	64	400	00	403	20	406	40
15	93	75	94	50	95	25	65	406	25	409	50	412	75
16	100	00	100	80	101	60	66	412	50	415	80	419	10
17	106	25	107	10	107	95	67	418	75	422	10	425	45
18	112	50	113	40	114	30	68	425	00	428	40	431	80
19	118	75	119	70	120	65	69	431	25	434	70	438	15
20	125	00	126	00	127	00	70	437	50	441	00	444	50
21	131	25	132	30	133	35	71	443	75	447	30	450	85
22	137	50	138	60	139	70	72	450	00	453	60	457	20
23	143	75	144	90	146	05	73	456	25	459	90	463	55
24	150	00	151	20	152	40	74	462	50	466	20	469	90
25	156	25	157	50	158	75	75	468	75	472	50	476	25
26	162	50	163	80	165	10	76	475	00	478	80	482	60
27	168	75	170	10	171	45	77	481	25	485	10	488	95
28	175	00	176	40	177	80	78	487	50	491	40	495	30
29	181	25	182	70	184	15	79	493	75	497	70	501	65
30	187	50	189	00	190	50	80	500	00	504	00	508	00
31	193	75	195	30	196	85	81	506	25	510	30	514	35
32	200	00	201	60	203	20	82	512	50	516	60	520	70
33	206	25	207	90	209	55	83	518	75	522	90	527	05
34	212	50	214	20	215	90	84	525	00	529	20	533	40
35	218	75	220	50	222	25	85	531	25	535	50	539	75
36	225	00	226	80	228	60	86	537	50	541	80	546	10
37	231	25	233	10	234	95	87	543	75	548	10	552	45
38	237	50	239	40	241	30	88	550	00	554	40	558	80
39	243	75	245	70	247	65	89	556	25	560	70	565	15
40	250	00	252	00	254	00	90	562	50	567	00	571	50
41	256	25	258	30	260	35	91	568	75	573	30	577	85
42	262	50	264	60	266	70	92	575	00	579	60	584	20
43	268	75	270	90	273	05	93	581	25	585	90	590	55
44	275	00	277	20	279	40	94	587	50	592	20	596	9C
45	281	25	283	50	285	75	95	593	75	598	50	603	25
46	287	50	289	80	292	10	96	600	00	604	80	609	60
47	293	75	296	10	298	45	97	606	25	611	10	615	95
48	300	00	302	40	304	80	98	612	50	617	40	622	30
49	306	25	308	70	311	15	99	618	75	623	70	628	65
50	312	50	315	00	317	50	100	625	00	630	00	635	00
¼	1·5625		1·575		1·5875		¾	4·6875		4·725		4·7625	
½	3·1250		3·150		3·1750		1¼	7·8125		7·875		7·9375	

No.	£6.25 £	P	£6.30 £	P	£6.35 £	P
101	631	25	636	30	641	35
102	637	50	642	60	647	70
103	643	75	648	90	654	05
104	650	00	655	20	660	40
105	656	25	661	50	666	75
106	662	50	667	80	673	10
107	668	75	674	10	679	45
108	675	00	680	40	685	80
109	681	25	686	70	692	15
10	687	50	693	00	698	50
111	693	75	699	30	704	85
112	700	00	705	60	711	20
113	706	25	711	90	717	55
114	712	50	718	20	723	90
115	718	75	724	50	730	25
116	725	00	730	80	736	60
117	731	25	737	10	742	95
118	737	50	743	40	749	30
119	743	75	749	70	755	65
120	750	00	756	00	762	00
121	756	25	762	30	768	35
122	762	50	768	60	774	70
123	768	75	774	90	781	05
124	775	00	781	20	787	40
125	781	25	787	50	793	75
126	787	50	793	80	800	10
127	793	75	800	10	806	45
128	800	00	806	40	812	80
129	806	25	812	70	819	15
130	812	50	819	00	825	50
131	818	75	825	30	831	85
132	825	00	831	60	838	20
133	831	25	837	90	844	55
134	837	50	844	20	850	90
135	843	75	850	50	857	25
136	850	00	856	80	863	60
137	856	25	863	10	869	95
138	862	50	869	40	876	30
139	868	75	875	70	882	65
140	875	00	882	00	889	00
141	881	25	888	30	895	35
142	887	50	894	60	901	70
143	893	75	900	90	908	05
144	900	00	907	20	914	40
145	906	25	913	50	920	75
146	912	50	919	80	927	10
147	918	75	926	10	933	45
148	925	00	932	40	939	80
149	931	25	938	70	946	15
150	937	50	945	00	952	50
1016	6350	00	6400	80	6451	60
1296	8100	00	8164	80	8229	60

No.	£6.25 £	P	£6.30 £	P	£6.35 £	P
155	968	75	976	50	984	25
13 156	975	00	982	80	990	60
165	1031	25	1039	50	1047	75
14 168	1050	00	1058	40	1066	80
175	1093	75	1102	50	1111	25
15 180	1125	00	1134	00	1143	00
185	1156	25	1165	50	1174	75
16 192	1200	00	1209	60	1219	20
195	1218	75	1228	50	1238	25
200	1250	00	1260	00	1270	00
17 204	1275	00	1285	20	1295	40
205	1281	25	1291	50	1301	75
215	1343	75	1354	50	1365	25
18 216	1350	00	1360	80	1371	60
224	1400	00	1411	20	1422	40
225	1406	25	1417	50	1428	75
19 228	1425	00	1436	40	1447	80
235	1468	75	1480	50	1492	25
245	1531	25	1543	50	1555	75
250	1562	50	1575	00	1587	50
21 252	1575	00	1587	60	1600	20
255	1593	75	1606	50	1619	25
265	1656	25	1669	50	1682	75
272	1700	00	1713	60	1727	20
275	1718	75	1732	50	1746	25
280	1750	00	1764	00	1778	00
285	1781	25	1795	50	1809	75
2 gross 288	1800	00	1814	40	1828	80
295	1843	75	1858	50	1873	25
300	1875	00	1890	00	1905	00
325	2031	25	2047	50	2063	75
336	2100	00	2116	80	2133	60
365	2281	25	2299	50	2317	75
375	2343	75	2362	50	2381	25
400	2500	00	2520	00	2540	00
425	2656	25	2677	50	2698	75
3 yr. 432	2700	00	2721	60	2743	20
475	2968	75	2992	50	3016	25
480	3000	00	3024	00	3048	00
500	3125	00	3150	00	3175	00
4 yr. 504	3150	00	3175	20	3200	40
576	3600	00	3628	80	3657	60
600	3750	00	3780	00	3810	00
700	4375	00	4410	00	4445	00
750	4687	50	4725	00	4762	50
800	5000	00	5040	00	5080	00
900	5625	00	5670	00	5715	00
1000	6250	00	6300	00	6350	00
2500	15625	0	15750	0	15875	0
5000	31250	0	31500	0	31750	0
1728	10800	00	10886	40	10972	80
1760	11000	00	11088	00	11176	00

No.	£6·40 £	p	£6·45 £	p	£6·50 £	p	No.	£6·40 £	p	£6·45 £	p	£6·50 £	p
1	6	40	6	45	6	50	51	326	40	328	95	331	50
2	12	80	12	90	13	00	52	332	80	335	40	338	00
3	19	20	19	35	19	50	53	339	20	341	85	344	50
4	25	60	25	80	26	00	54	345	60	348	30	351	00
5	32	00	32	25	32	50	55	352	00	354	75	357	50
6	38	40	38	70	39	00	56	358	40	361	20	364	00
7	44	80	45	15	45	50	57	364	80	367	65	370	50
8	51	20	51	60	52	00	58	371	20	374	10	377	00
9	57	60	58	05	58	50	59	377	60	380	55	383	50
10	64	00	64	50	65	00	60	384	00	387	00	390	00
11	70	40	70	95	71	50	61	390	40	393	45	396	50
12	76	80	77	40	78	00	62	396	80	399	90	403	00
13	83	20	83	85	84	50	63	403	20	406	35	409	50
14	89	60	90	30	91	00	64	409	60	412	80	416	00
15	96	00	96	75	97	50	65	416	00	419	25	422	50
16	102	40	103	20	104	00	66	422	40	425	70	429	00
17	108	80	109	65	110	50	67	428	80	432	15	435	50
18	115	20	116	10	117	00	68	435	20	438	60	442	00
19	121	60	122	55	123	50	69	441	60	445	05	448	50
20	128	00	129	00	130	00	70	448	00	451	50	455	00
21	134	40	135	45	136	50	71	454	40	457	95	461	50
22	140	80	141	90	143	00	72	460	80	464	40	468	00
23	147	20	148	35	149	50	73	467	20	470	85	474	50
24	153	60	154	80	156	00	74	473	60	477	30	481	00
25	160	00	161	25	162	50	75	480	00	483	75	487	50
26	166	40	167	70	169	00	76	486	40	490	20	494	00
27	172	80	174	15	175	50	77	492	80	496	15	500	50
28	179	20	180	60	182	00	78	499	20	503	10	507	00
29	185	60	187	05	188	50	79	505	60	509	55	513	50
30	192	00	193	50	195	00	80	512	00	516	00	520	00
31	198	40	199	95	201	50	81	518	40	522	45	526	50
32	204	80	206	40	208	00	82	524	80	528	90	533	00
33	211	20	212	85	214	50	83	531	20	535	35	539	50
34	217	60	219	30	221	00	84	537	60	541	80	546	00
35	224	00	225	75	227	50	85	544	00	548	25	552	50
36	230	40	232	20	234	00	86	550	40	554	70	559	00
37	236	80	238	65	240	50	87	556	80	561	15	565	50
38	243	20	245	10	247	00	88	563	20	567	60	572	00
39	249	60	251	55	253	50	89	569	60	574	05	578	50
40	256	00	258	00	260	00	90	576	00	580	50	585	00
41	262	40	264	45	266	50	91	582	40	586	95	591	50
42	268	80	270	90	273	00	92	588	80	593	40	598	00
43	275	20	277	35	279	50	93	595	20	599	85	604	50
44	281	60	283	80	286	00	94	601	60	606	30	611	00
45	288	00	290	25	292	50	95	608	00	612	75	617	50
46	294	40	296	70	299	00	96	614	40	619	20	624	00
47	300	80	303	15	305	50	97	620	80	625	65	630	50
48	307	20	309	60	312	00	98	627	20	632	10	637	00
49	313	60	316	05	318	50	99	633	60	638	55	643	50
50	320	00	322	50	325	00	100	640	00	645	00	650	00
¼	1·600		1·6125		1·625		¾	4·80		4·8375		4·875	
½	3·200		3·2250		3·250		1¼	8·00		8·0625		8·125	

No.	£6·40 £ p	£6·45 £ p	£6·50 £ p	No.	£6·40 £ p	£6·45 £ p	£6·50 £ p
101	646 40	651 45	656 50	155	992 00	999 75	1007 50
102	652 80	657 90	663 00	156	998 40	1006 20	1014 00
103	659 20	664 35	669 50	165	1056 00	1064 25	1072 50
104	665 60	670 80	676 00	168	1075 20	1083 60	1092 00
105	672 00	677 25	682 50	175	1120 00	1128 75	1137 50
106	678 40	683 70	689 00	180	1152 00	1161 00	1170 00
107	684 80	690 15	695 50	185	1184 00	1193 25	1202 50
108	691 20	696 60	702 00	192	1228 80	1238 40	1248 00
109	697 60	703 05	708 50	195	1248 00	1257 75	1267 50
110	704 00	709 50	715 00	200	1280 00	1290 00	1300 00
111	710 40	715 95	721 50	204	1305 60	1315 80	1326 00
112	716 80	722 40	728 00	205	1312 00	1322 25	1332 50
113	723 20	728 85	734 50	215	1376 00	1386 75	1397 50
114	729 60	735 30	741 00	216	1382 40	1393 20	1404 00
115	736 00	741 75	747 50	224	1433 60	1444 80	1456 00
116	742 40	748 20	754 00	225	1440 00	1451 25	1462 50
117	748 80	754 65	760 50	228	1459 20	1470 60	1482 00
118	755 20	761 10	767 00	235	1504 00	1515 75	1527 50
119	761 60	767 55	773 50	245	1568 00	1580 25	1592 50
120	768 00	774 00	780 00	250	1600 00	1612 50	1625 00
121	774 40	780 45	786 50	252	1612 80	1625 40	1638 00
122	780 80	786 90	793 00	255	1632 00	1644 75	1657 50
123	787 20	793 35	799 50	265	1696 00	1709 25	1722 50
124	793 60	799 80	806 00	272	1740 80	1754 40	1768 00
125	800 00	806 25	812 50	275	1760 00	1773 75	1787 50
126	806 40	812 70	819 00	280	1792 00	1806 00	1820 00
127	812 80	819 15	825 50	285	1824 00	1838 25	1852 50
128	819 20	825 60	832 00	288	1843 20	1857 60	1872 00
129	825 60	832 05	838 50	295	1888 00	1902 75	1917 50
130	832 00	838 50	845 00	300	1920 00	1935 00	1950 00
131	838 40	844 95	851 50	325	2080 00	2096 25	2112 50
132	844 80	851 40	858 00	336	2150 40	2167 20	2184 00
133	851 20	857 85	864 50	365	2336 00	2354 25	2372 50
134	857 60	864 30	871 00	375	2400 00	2418 75	2437 50
135	864 00	870 75	877 50	400	2560 00	2580 00	2600 00
136	870 40	877 20	884 00	425	2720 00	2741 25	2762 50
137	876 80	883 65	890 50	432	2764 80	2786 40	2808 00
138	883 20	890 10	897 00	475	3040 00	3063 75	3087 50
139	889 60	896 55	903 50	480	3072 00	3096 00	3120 00
140	896 00	903 00	910 00	500	3200 00	3225 00	3250 00
141	902 40	909 45	916 50	504	3225 60	3250 80	3276 00
142	908 80	915 90	923 00	576	3686 40	3715 20	3744 00
143	915 20	922 35	929 50	600	3840 00	3870 00	3900 00
144	921 60	928 80	936 00	700	4480 00	4515 00	4550 00
145	928 00	935 25	942 50	750	4800 00	4837 50	4875 00
146	934 40	941 70	949 00	800	5120 00	5160 00	5200 00
147	940 80	948 15	955 50	900	5760 00	5805 00	5850 00
148	947 20	954 60	962 00	1000	6400 00	6450 00	6500 00
149	953 60	961 05	968 50	2500	16000 ·0	16125 ·0	16250 ·0
150	960 00	967 50	975 00	5000	32000 ·0	32250 ·0	32500 ·0
1016	6502·40	6553·20	6604·00	1728	11059·20	11145·60	11232·00
1296	8294·40	8359·20	8424·00	1760	11264·00	11352·00	11440·00

No.	£6·55		£6·60		£6·65		No.	£6·55		£6·60		£6·65	
	£	p	£	p	£	p		£	p	£	p	£	p
1	6	55	6	60	6	65	51	334	05	336	60	339	15
2	13	10	13	20	13	30	52	340	60	343	20	345	80
3	19	65	19	80	19	95	53	347	15	349	80	352	45
4	26	20	26	40	26	60	54	353	70	356	40	359	10
5	32	75	33	00	33	25	55	360	25	363	00	365	75
6	39	30	39	60	39	90	56	366	80	369	60	372	40
7	45	85	46	20	46	55	57	373	35	376	20	379	05
8	52	40	52	80	53	20	58	379	90	382	80	385	70
9	58	95	59	40	59	85	59	386	45	389	40	392	35
10	65	50	66	00	66	50	60	393	00	396	00	399	00
11	72	05	72	60	73	15	61	399	55	402	60	405	65
12	78	60	79	20	79	80	62	406	10	409	20	412	30
13	85	15	85	80	86	45	63	412	65	415	80	418	95
14	91	70	92	40	93	10	64	419	20	422	40	425	60
15	98	25	99	00	99	75	65	425	75	429	00	432	25
16	104	80	105	60	106	40	66	432	30	435	60	438	90
17	111	35	112	20	113	05	67	438	85	442	20	445	55
18	117	90	118	80	119	70	68	445	40	448	80	452	20
19	124	45	125	40	126	35	69	451	95	455	40	458	85
20	131	00	132	00	133	00	70	458	50	462	00	465	50
21	137	55	138	60	139	65	71	465	05	468	60	472	15
22	144	10	145	20	146	30	72	471	60	475	20	478	80
23	150	65	151	80	152	95	73	478	15	481	80	485	45
24	157	20	158	40	159	60	74	484	70	488	40	492	10
25	163	75	165	00	166	25	75	491	25	495	00	498	75
26	170	30	171	60	172	90	76	497	80	501	60	505	40
27	176	85	178	20	179	55	77	504	35	508	20	512	05
28	183	40	184	80	186	20	78	510	90	514	80	518	70
29	189	95	191	40	192	85	79	517	45	521	40	525	35
30	196	50	198	00	199	50	80	524	00	528	00	532	00
31	203	05	204	60	206	15	81	530	55	534	60	538	65
32	209	60	211	20	212	80	82	537	10	541	20	545	30
33	216	15	217	80	219	45	83	543	65	547	80	551	95
34	222	70	224	40	226	10	84	550	20	554	40	558	60
35	229	25	231	00	232	75	85	556	75	561	00	565	25
36	235	80	237	60	239	40	86	563	30	567	60	571	90
37	242	35	244	20	246	05	87	569	85	574	20	578	55
38	248	90	250	80	252	70	88	576	40	580	80	585	20
39	255	45	257	40	259	35	89	582	95	587	40	591	85
40	262	00	264	00	266	00	90	589	50	594	00	598	50
41	268	55	270	60	272	65	91	596	05	600	60	605	15
42	275	10	277	20	279	30	92	602	60	607	20	611	80
43	281	65	283	80	285	95	93	609	15	613	80	618	45
44	288	20	290	40	292	60	94	615	70	620	40	625	10
45	294	75	297	00	299	25	95	622	25	627	00	631	75
46	301	30	303	60	305	90	96	628	80	633	60	638	40
47	307	85	310	20	312	55	97	635	35	640	20	645	05
48	314	40	316	80	319	20	98	641	90	646	80	651	70
49	320	95	323	40	325	85	99	648	45	653	40	658	35
50	327	50	330	00	332	50	100	655	00	660	00	665	00
¼	1·6375		1·65		1·6625		¾	4·9125		4·95		4·9875	
½..	3·2750		3·30		3·3250		1¼..	8·1875		8·25		8·3125	

No.	£6·55		£6·60		£6·65	
	£	P	£	P	£	P
101	661	55	666	60	671	65
102	668	10	673	20	678	30
103	674	65	679	80	684	95
104	681	20	686	40	691	60
105	687	75	693	00	698	25
106	694	30	699	60	704	90
107	700	85	706	20	711	55
108	707	40	712	80	718	20
109	713	95	719	40	724	85
110	720	50	726	00	731	50
111	727	05	732	60	738	15
112	733	60	739	20	744	80
113	740	15	745	80	751	45
114	746	70	752	40	758	10
115	753	25	759	00	764	75
116	759	80	765	60	771	40
117	766	35	772	20	778	05
118	772	90	778	80	784	70
119	779	45	785	40	791	35
120	786	00	792	00	798	00
121	792	55	798	60	804	65
122	799	10	805	20	811	30
123	805	65	811	80	817	95
124	812	20	818	40	824	60
125	818	75	825	00	831	25
126	825	30	831	60	837	90
127	831	85	838	20	844	55
128	838	40	844	80	851	20
129	844	95	851	40	857	85
130	851	50	858	00	864	50
131	858	05	864	60	871	15
132	864	60	871	20	877	80
133	871	15	877	80	884	45
134	877	70	884	40	891	10
135	884	25	891	00	897	75
136	890	80	897	60	904	40
137	897	35	904	20	911	05
138	903	90	910	80	917	70
139	910	45	917	40	924	35
140	917	00	924	00	931	00
141	923	55	930	60	937	65
142	930	10	937	20	944	30
143	936	65	943	80	950	95
144	943	20	950	40	957	60
145	949	75	957	00	964	25
146	956	30	963	60	970	90
147	962	85	970	20	977	55
148	969	40	976	80	984	20
149	975	95	983	40	990	85
150	982	50	990	00	997	50
1016	6654	80	6705	60	6756	40
1296	8488	80	8553	60	8618	40

No.	£6·55		£6·60		£6·65	
	£	P	£	P	£	P
Dz 155	1015	25	1023	00	1030	75
13 156	1021	80	1029	60	1037	40
165	1080	75	1089	00	1097	25
14 168	1100	40	1108	80	1117	20
175	1146	25	1155	00	1163	75
15 180	1179	00	1188	00	1197	00
185	1211	75	1221	00	1230	25
16 192	1257	60	1267	20	1276	80
195	1277	25	1287	00	1296	75
200	1310	00	1320	00	1330	00
17 204	1336	20	1346	40	1356	60
205	1342	75	1353	00	1363	25
215	1408	25	1419	00	1429	75
18 216	1414	20	1425	60	1436	40
224	1467	20	1478	40	1489	60
225	1473	75	1485	00	1496	25
19 228	1493	40	1504	80	1516	20
235	1539	25	1551	00	1562	75
245	1604	75	1617	00	1629	25
250	1637	50	1650	00	1662	50
21 252	1650	60	1663	20	1675	80
255	1670	25	1683	00	1695	75
265	1735	75	1749	00	1762	25
272	1781	60	1795	20	1808	80
275	1801	25	1815	00	1828	75
280	1834	00	1848	00	1862	00
285	1866	75	1881	00	1895	25
288	1886	40	1900	80	1915	20
295	1932	25	1947	00	1961	75
300	1965	00	1980	00	1995	00
325	2128	75	2145	00	2161	25
336	2200	80	2217	60	2234	40
365	2390	75	2409	00	2427	25
375	2456	25	2475	00	2493	75
400	2620	00	2640	00	2660	00
425	2783	75	2805	00	2826	25
432	2829	60	2851	20	2872	80
475	3111	25	3135	00	3158	75
480	3144	00	3168	00	3192	00
500	3275	00	3300	00	3325	00
504	3301	20	3326	40	3351	60
576	3772	80	3801	60	3830	40
600	3930	00	3960	00	3990	00
700	4585	00	4620	00	4655	00
750	4912	50	4950	00	4987	50
800	5240	00	5280	00	5320	00
900	5895	00	5940	00	5985	00
1000	6550	00	6600	00	6650	00
2500	16375	0	16500	0	16625	0
5000	32750	0	33000	0	33250	0
1728	11318	40	11404	80	11491	20
1760	11528	00	11616	00	11704	00

No.	£6·70 £ P	£6·75 £ P	£6·80 £ P	No.	£6·70 £ P	£6·75 £ P	£6·80 £ P
1	6 70	6 75	6 80	51	341 70	344 25	346 80
2	13 40	13 50	13 60	52	348 40	351 00	353 60
3	20 10	20 25	20 40	53	355 10	357 75	360 40
4	26 80	27 00	27 20	54	361 80	364 50	367 20
5	33 50	33 75	34 00	55	368 50	371 25	374 00
6	40 20	40 50	40 80	56	375 20	378 00	380 80
7	46 90	47 25	47 60	57	381 90	384 75	387 60
8	53 60	54 00	54 40	58	388 60	391 50	394 40
9	60 30	60 75	61 20	59	395 30	398 25	401 20
10	67 00	67 50	68 00	60	402 00	405 00	408 00
11	73 70	74 25	74 80	61	408 70	411 75	414 80
12	80 40	81 00	81 60	62	415 40	418 50	421 60
13	87 10	87 75	88 40	63	422 10	425 25	428 40
14	93 80	94 50	95 20	64	428 80	432 00	435 20
15	100 50	101 25	102 00	65	435 50	438 75	442 00
16	107 20	108 00	108 80	66	442 20	445 50	448 80
17	113 90	114 75	115 60	67	448 90	452 25	455 60
18	120 60	121 50	122 40	68	455 60	459 00	462 40
19	127 30	128 25	129 20	69	462 30	465 75	469 20
20	134 00	135 00	136 00	70	469 00	472 50	476 00
21	140 70	141 75	142 80	71	475 70	479 25	482 80
22	147 40	148 50	149 60	72	482 40	486 00	489 60
23	154 10	155 25	156 40	73	489 10	492 75	496 40
24	160 80	162 00	163 20	74	495 80	499 50	503 20
25	167 50	168 75	170 00	75	502 50	506 25	510 00
26	174 20	175 50	176 80	76	509 20	513 00	516 80
27	180 90	182 25	183 60	77	515 90	519 75	523 60
28	187 60	189 00	190 40	78	522 60	526 50	530 40
29	194 30	195 75	197 20	79	529 30	533 25	537 20
30	201 00	202 50	204 00	80	536 00	540 00	544 00
31	207 70	209 25	210 80	81	542 70	546 75	550 80
32	214 40	216 00	217 60	82	549 40	553 50	557 60
33	221 10	222 75	224 40	83	556 10	560 25	564 40
34	227 80	229 50	231 20	84	562 80	567 00	571 20
35	234 50	236 25	238 00	85	569 50	573 75	578 00
36	241 20	243 00	244 80	86	576 20	580 50	584 80
37	247 90	249 75	251 60	87	582 90	587 25	591 60
38	254 60	256 50	258 40	88	589 60	594 00	598 40
39	261 30	263 25	265 20	89	596 30	600 75	605 20
40	268 00	270 00	272 00	90	603 00	607 50	612 00
41	274 70	276 75	278 80	91	609 70	614 25	618 80
42	281 40	283 50	285 60	92	616 40	621 00	625 60
43	288 10	290 25	292 40	93	623 10	627 75	632 40
44	294 80	297 00	299 20	94	629 80	634 50	639 20
45	301 50	303 75	306 00	95	636 50	641 25	646 00
46	308 20	310 50	312 80	96	643 20	648 00	652 80
47	314 90	317 25	319 60	97	649 90	654 75	659 60
48	321 60	324 00	326 40	98	656 60	661 50	666 40
49	328 30	330 75	333 20	99	663 30	668 25	673 20
50	335 00	337 50	340 00	100	670 00	675 00	680 00
$\frac{1}{4}$	1·675	1·6875	1·70	$\frac{3}{4}$	5·025	5·0625	5·10
$\frac{1}{2}$..	3·350	3·3750	3·40	$1\frac{1}{4}$..	8·375	8·4375	8·50

• Dozens.

No.	£6·70 £ p	£6·75 £ p	£6·80 £ p
101	676 70	681 75	686 80
102	683 40	688 50	693 60
103	690 10	695 25	700 40
104	696 80	702 00	707 20
105	703 50	708 75	714 00
106	710 20	715 50	720 80
107	716 90	722 25	727 60
108	723 60	729 00	734 40
109	730 30	735 75	741 20
110	737 00	742 50	748 00
111	743 70	749 25	754 80
112	750 40	756 00	761 60
113	757 10	762 75	768 40
114	763 80	769 50	775 20
115	770 50	776 25	782 00
116	777 20	783 00	788 80
117	783 90	789 75	795 60
118	790 60	796 50	802 40
119	797 30	803 25	809 20
120	804 00	810 00	816 00
121	810 70	816 75	822 80
122	817 40	823 50	829 60
123	824 10	830 25	836 40
124	830 80	837 00	843 20
125	837 50	843 75	850 00
126	844 20	850 50	856 80
127	850 90	857 25	863 60
128	857 60	864 00	870 40
129	864 30	870 75	877 20
130	871 00	877 50	884 00
131	877 70	884 25	890 80
132	884 40	891 00	897 60
133	891 10	897 75	904 40
134	897 80	904 50	911 20
135	904 50	911 25	918 00
136	911 20	918 00	924 80
137	917 90	924 75	931 60
138	924 60	931 50	938 40
139	931 30	938 25	945 20
140	938 00	945 00	952 00
141	944 70	951 75	958 80
142	951 40	958 50	965 60
143	958 10	965 25	972 40
144	964 80	972 00	979 20
145	971 50	978 75	986 00
146	978 20	985 50	992 80
147	984 90	992 25	999 60
148	991 60	999 00	1006 40
149	998 30	1005 75	1013 20
150	1005 00	1012 50	1020 00
1016	6807·20	6858·00	6908·80
1296	8683·20	8748·00	8812·80

No.	£6·70 £ p	£6·75 £ p	£6·80 £ p
Doz 155	1038 50	1046 25	1054 00
13 156	1045 20	1053 00	1060 80
165	1105 50	1113 75	1122 00
14 168	1125 60	1134 00	1142 40
175	1172 50	1181 25	1190 00
15 180	1206 00	1215 00	1224 00
185	1239 50	1248 75	1258 00
16 192	1286 40	1296 00	1305 60
195	1306 50	1316 25	1326 00
200	1340 00	1350 00	1360 00
17 204	1366 80	1377 00	1387 20
205	1373 50	1383 75	1394 00
215	1440 50	1451 25	1462 00
18 216	1447 20	1458 00	1468 80
224	1500 80	1512 00	1523 20
225	1507 50	1518 75	1530 00
19 228	1527 60	1539 00	1550 40
235	1574 50	1586 25	1598 00
245	1641 50	1653 75	1666 00
250	1675 00	1687 50	1700 00
21 252	1688 40	1701 00	1713 60
255	1708 50	1721 25	1734 00
265	1775 50	1788 75	1802 00
272	1822 40	1836 00	1849 60
275	1842 50	1856 25	1870 00
280	1876 00	1890 00	1904 00
285	1909 50	1923 75	1938 00
2 gross 288	1929 60	1944 00	1958 40
295	1976 50	1991 25	2006 00
300	2010 00	2025 00	2040 00
325	2177 50	2193 75	2210 00
336	2251 20	2268 00	2284 80
365	2445 50	2463 75	2482 00
375	2512 50	2531 25	2550 00
400	2680 00	2700 00	2720 00
8 gr. 425	2847 50	2868 75	2890 00
432	2894 40	2916 00	2937 60
475	3182 50	3206 25	3230 00
480	3216 00	3240 00	3264 00
500	3350 00	3375 00	3400 00
4 gr. 504	3376 80	3402 00	3427 20
576	3859 20	3888 00	3916 80
600	4020 00	4050 00	4080 00
700	4690 00	4725 00	4760 00
750	5025 00	5062 50	5100 00
800	5360 00	5400 00	5440 00
900	6030 00	6075 00	6120 00
1000	6700 00	6750 00	6800 00
2500	16750 0	16875 0	17000 0
5000	33500 0	33750 0	34000 0
1728	11577·60	11664·00	11750·40
1760	11792·00	11880·00	11968·00

No.	£6·85		£6·90		£6·95		No.	£6·85		£6·90		£6·95	
	£	p	£	p	£	p		£	p	£	p	£	p
1	6	85	6	90	6	95	51	349	35	351	90	354	45
2	13	70	13	80	13	90	52	356	20	358	80	361	40
3	20	55	20	70	20	85	53	363	05	365	70	368	35
4	27	40	27	60	27	80	54	369	90	372	60	375	30
5	34	25	34	50	34	75	55	376	75	379	50	382	25
6	41	10	41	40	41	70	56	383	60	386	40	389	20
7	47	95	48	30	48	65	57	390	45	393	30	396	15
8	54	80	55	20	55	60	58	397	30	400	20	403	10
9	61	65	62	10	62	55	59	404	15	407	10	410	05
10	68	50	69	00	69	50	60	411	00	414	00	417	00
11	75	35	75	90	76	45	61	417	85	420	90	423	95
12	82	20	82	80	83	40	62	424	70	427	80	430	90
13	89	05	89	70	90	35	63	431	55	434	70	437	85
14	95	90	96	60	97	30	64	438	40	441	60	444	80
15	102	75	103	50	104	25	65	445	25	448	50	451	75
16	109	60	110	40	111	20	66	452	10	455	40	458	70
17	116	45	117	30	118	15	67	458	95	462	30	465	65
18	123	30	124	20	125	10	68	465	80	469	20	472	60
19	130	15	131	10	132	05	69	472	65	476	10	479	55
20	137	00	138	00	139	00	70	479	50	483	00	486	50
21	143	85	144	90	145	95	71	486	35	489	90	493	45
22	150	70	151	80	152	90	72	493	20	496	80	500	40
23	157	55	158	70	159	85	73	500	05	503	70	507	35
24	164	40	165	60	166	80	74	506	90	510	60	514	30
25	171	25	172	50	173	75	75	513	75	517	50	521	25
26	178	10	179	40	180	70	76	520	60	524	40	528	20
27	184	95	186	30	187	65	77	527	45	531	30	535	15
28	191	80	193	20	194	60	78	534	30	538	20	542	10
29	198	65	200	10	201	55	79	541	15	545	10	549	05
30	205	50	207	00	208	50	80	548	00	552	00	556	00
31	212	35	213	90	215	45	81	554	85	558	90	562	95
32	219	20	220	80	222	40	82	561	70	565	80	569	90
33	226	05	227	70	229	35	83	568	55	572	70	576	85
34	232	90	234	60	236	30	84	575	40	579	60	583	80
35	239	75	241	50	243	25	85	582	25	586	50	590	75
36	246	60	248	40	250	20	86	589	10	593	40	597	70
37	253	45	255	30	257	15	87	595	95	600	30	604	65
38	260	30	262	20	264	10	88	602	80	607	20	611	60
39	267	15	269	10	271	05	89	609	65	614	10	618	55
40	274	00	276	00	278	00	90	616	50	621	00	625	50
41	280	85	282	90	284	95	91	623	35	627	90	632	45
42	287	70	289	80	291	90	92	630	20	634	80	639	40
43	294	55	296	70	298	85	93	637	05	641	70	646	35
44	301	40	303	60	305	80	94	643	90	648	60	653	30
45	308	25	310	50	312	75	95	650	75	655	50	660	25
46	315	10	317	40	319	70	96	657	60	662	40	667	20
47	321	95	324	30	326	65	97	664	45	669	30	674	15
48	328	80	331	20	333	60	98	671	30	676	20	681	10
49	335	65	338	10	340	55	99	678	15	683	10	688	05
50	342	50	345	00	347	50	100	685	00	690	00	695	00
¼	1·7125		1·725		1·7375		¾	5·1375		5·175		5·2125	
½..	3·4250		3·450		3·4750		1¼..	8·5625		8·625		8·6875	

Dozens. (left column) · *Dozens.* (right column)

No.	£6·85		£6·90		£6·95	
	£	p	£	p	£	p
101	691	85	696	90	701	95
102	698	70	703	80	708	90
103	705	55	710	70	715	85
104	712	40	717	60	722	80
105	719	25	724	50	729	75
106	726	10	731	40	736	70
107	732	95	738	30	743	65
108	739	80	745	20	750	60
109	746	65	752	10	757	55
110	753	50	759	00	764	50
111	760	35	765	90	771	45
112	767	20	772	80	778	40
113	774	05	779	70	785	35
114	780	90	786	60	792	30
115	787	75	793	50	799	25
116	794	60	800	40	806	20
117	801	45	807	30	813	15
118	808	30	814	20	820	10
119	815	15	821	10	827	05
120	822	00	828	00	834	00
121	828	85	834	90	840	95
122	835	70	841	80	847	90
123	842	55	848	70	854	85
124	849	40	855	60	861	80
125	856	25	862	50	868	75
126	863	10	869	40	875	70
127	869	95	876	30	882	65
128	876	80	883	20	889	60
129	883	65	890	10	896	55
130	890	50	897	00	903	50
131	897	35	903	90	910	45
132	904	20	910	80	917	40
133	911	05	917	70	924	35
134	917	90	924	60	931	30
135	924	75	931	50	938	25
136	931	60	938	40	945	20
137	938	45	945	30	952	15
138	945	30	952	20	959	10
139	952	15	959	10	966	05
140	959	00	966	00	973	00
141	965	85	972	90	979	95
142	972	70	979	80	986	90
143	979	55	986	70	993	85
144	986	40	993	60	1000	80
145	993	25	1000	50	1007	75
146	1000	10	1007	40	1014	70
147	1006	95	1014	30	1021	65
148	1013	80	1021	20	1028	60
149	1020	65	1028	10	1035	55
150	1027	50	1035	00	1042	50
1016	6959·60		7010·40		7061·20	
1296	8877·60		8942·40		9007·20	

No.	£6·85		£6·90		£6·95	
	£	p	£	p	£	p
155	1061	75	1069	50	1077	25
156	1068	60	1076	40	1084	20
165	1130	25	1138	50	1146	75
168	1150	80	1159	20	1167	60
175	1198	75	1207	50	1216	25
180	1233	00	1242	00	1251	00
185	1267	25	1276	50	1285	75
192	1315	20	1324	80	1334	40
195	1335	75	1345	50	1355	25
200	1370	00	1380	00	1390	00
204	1397	40	1407	60	1417	80
205	1404	25	1414	50	1424	75
215	1472	75	1483	50	1494	25
216	1479	60	1490	40	1501	20
224	1534	40	1545	60	1556	80
225	1541	25	1552	50	1563	75
228	1561	80	1573	20	1584	60
235	1609	75	1621	50	1633	25
245	1678	25	1690	50	1702	75
250	1712	50	1725	00	1737	50
252	1726	20	1738	80	1751	40
255	1746	75	1759	50	1772	25
265	1815	25	1828	50	1841	75
272	1863	20	1876	80	1890	40
275	1883	75	1897	50	1911	25
280	1918	00	1932	00	1946	00
285	1952	25	1966	50	1980	75
288	1972	80	1987	20	2001	60
295	2020	75	2035	50	2050	25
300	2055	00	2070	00	2085	00
325	2226	25	2242	50	2258	75
336	2301	60	2318	40	2335	20
365	2500	25	2518	50	2536	75
375	2568	75	2587	50	2606	25
400	2740	00	2760	00	2780	00
425	2911	25	2932	50	2953	75
432	2959	20	2980	80	3002	40
475	3253	75	3277	50	3301	25
480	3288	00	3312	00	3336	00
500	3425	00	3450	00	3475	00
504	3452	40	3477	60	3502	80
576	3945	60	3974	40	4003	20
600	4110	00	4140	00	4170	00
700	4795	00	4830	00	4865	00
750	5137	50	5175	00	5212	50
800	5480	00	5520	00	5560	00
900	6165	00	6210	00	6255	00
1000	6850	00	6900	00	6950	00
2500	17125	·0	17250	·0	17375	·0
5000	34250	·0	34500	·0	34750	·0
1728	11836·80		11923·20		12009·60	
1760	12056·00		12144·00		12232·00	

No.	£7·00		£7·05		£7·10		No.	£7·00		£7·05		£7·10	
	£	P	£	P	£	P		£	P	£	P	£	P
1	7	00	7	05	7	10	51	357	00	359	55	362	10
2	14	00	14	10	14	20	52	364	00	366	60	369	20
3	21	00	21	15	21	30	53	371	00	373	65	376	30
4	28	00	28	20	28	40	54	378	00	380	70	383	40
5	35	00	35	25	35	50	55	385	00	387	75	390	50
6	42	00	42	30	42	60	56	392	00	394	80	397	60
7	49	00	49	35	49	70	57	399	00	401	85	404	70
8	56	00	56	40	56	80	58	406	00	408	90	411	80
9	63	00	63	45	63	90	59	413	00	415	95	418	90
10	70	00	70	50	71	00	60	420	00	423	00	426	00
11	77	00	77	55	78	10	61	427	00	430	05	433	10
12	84	00	84	60	85	20	62	434	00	437	10	440	20
13	91	00	91	65	92	30	63	441	00	444	15	447	30
14	98	00	98	70	99	40	64	448	00	451	20	454	40
15	105	00	105	75	106	50	65	455	00	458	25	461	50
16	112	00	112	80	113	60	66	462	00	465	30	468	60
17	119	00	119	85	120	70	67	469	00	472	35	475	70
18	126	00	126	90	127	80	68	476	00	479	40	482	80
19	133	00	133	95	134	90	69	483	00	486	45	489	90
20	140	00	141	00	142	00	70	490	00	493	50	497	00
21	147	00	148	05	149	10	71	497	00	500	55	504	10
22	154	00	155	10	156	20	72	504	00	507	60	511	20
23	161	00	162	15	163	30	73	511	00	514	65	518	30
24	168	00	169	20	170	40	74	518	00	521	70	525	40
25	175	00	176	25	177	50	75	525	00	528	75	532	50
26	182	00	183	30	184	60	76	532	00	535	80	539	60
27	189	00	190	35	191	70	77	539	00	542	85	546	70
28	196	00	197	40	198	80	78	546	00	549	90	553	80
29	203	00	204	45	205	90	79	553	00	556	95	560	90
30	210	00	211	50	213	00	80	560	00	564	00	568	00
31	217	00	218	55	220	10	81	567	00	571	05	575	10
32	224	00	225	60	227	20	82	574	00	578	10	582	20
33	231	00	232	65	234	30	83	581	00	585	15	589	30
34	238	00	239	70	241	40	84	588	00	592	20	596	40
35	245	00	246	75	248	50	85	595	00	599	25	603	50
36	252	00	253	80	255	60	86	602	00	606	30	610	60
37	259	00	260	85	262	70	87	609	00	613	35	617	70
38	266	00	267	90	269	80	88	616	00	620	40	624	80
39	273	00	274	95	276	90	89	623	00	627	45	631	90
40	280	00	282	00	284	00	90	630	00	634	50	639	00
41	287	00	289	05	291	10	91	637	00	641	55	646	10
42	294	00	296	10	298	20	92	644	00	648	60	653	20
43	301	00	303	15	305	30	93	651	00	655	65	660	30
44	308	00	310	20	312	40	94	658	00	662	70	667	40
45	315	00	317	25	319	50	95	665	00	669	75	674	50
46	322	00	324	30	326	60	96	672	00	676	80	681	60
47	329	00	331	35	333	70	97	679	00	683	85	688	70
48	336	00	338	40	340	80	98	686	00	690	90	695	80
49	343	00	345	45	347	90	99	693	00	697	95	702	90
50	350	00	352	50	355	00	100	700	00	705	00	710	00
¼	1·75		1·7625		1·775		¾	5·25		5·2875		5·325	
½	3·50		3·5250		3·550		1¼	8·75		8·8125		8·875	

No.	£7·00 £	p	£7·05 £	p	£7·10 £	p
101	707	00	712	05	717	10
102	714	00	719	10	724	20
103	721	00	726	15	731	30
104	728	00	733	20	738	40
105	735	00	740	25	745	50
106	742	00	747	30	752	60
107	749	00	754	35	759	70
9 108	756	00	761	40	766	80
109	763	00	768	45	773	90
110	770	00	775	50	781	00
111	777	00	782	55	788	10
112	784	00	789	60	795	20
113	791	00	796	65	802	30
114	798	00	803	70	809	40
115	805	00	810	75	816	50
116	812	00	817	80	823	60
117	819	00	824	85	830	70
118	826	00	831	90	837	80
119	833	00	838	95	844	90
10 120	840	00	846	00	852	00
121	847	00	853	05	859	10
122	854	00	860	10	866	20
123	861	00	867	15	873	30
124	868	00	874	20	880	40
125	875	00	881	25	887	50
126	882	00	888	30	894	60
127	889	00	895	35	901	70
128	896	00	902	40	908	80
129	903	00	909	45	915	90
130	910	00	916	50	923	00
131	917	00	923	55	930	10
11 132	924	00	930	60	937	20
133	931	00	937	65	944	30
134	938	00	944	70	951	40
135	945	00	951	75	958	50
136	952	00	958	80	965	60
137	959	00	965	85	972	70
138	966	00	972	90	979	80
139	973	00	979	95	986	90
140	980	00	987	00	994	00
141	987	00	994	05	1001	10
142	994	00	1001	10	1008	20
143	1001	00	1008	15	1015	30
12 144	1008	00	1015	20	1022	40
145	1015	00	1022	25	1029	50
146	1022	00	1029	30	1036	60
147	1029	00	1036	35	1043	70
148	1036	00	1043	40	1050	80
149	1043	00	1050	45	1057	90
150	1050	00	1057	50	1065	00

No.	£7·00 £	p	£7·05 £	p	£7·10 £	p
155 *Doz*	1085	00	1092	75	1100	50
13 156	1092	00	1099	80	1107	60
165	1155	00	1163	25	1171	50
14 168	1176	00	1184	40	1192	80
175	1225	00	1233	75	1242	50
15 180	1260	00	1269	00	1278	00
185	1295	00	1304	25	1313	50
16 192	1344	00	1353	60	1363	20
195	1365	00	1374	75	1384	50
200	1400	00	1410	00	1420	00
17 204	1428	00	1438	20	1448	40
205	1435	00	1445	25	1455	50
215	1505	00	1515	75	1526	50
18 216	1512	00	1522	80	1533	60
224	1568	00	1579	20	1590	40
225	1575	00	1586	25	1597	50
19 228	1596	00	1607	40	1618	80
235	1645	00	1656	75	1668	50
245	1715	00	1727	25	1739	50
250	1750	00	1762	50	1775	00
21 252	1764	00	1776	60	1789	20
255	1785	00	1797	75	1810	50
265	1855	00	1868	25	1881	50
272	1904	00	1917	60	1931	20
275	1925	00	1938	75	1952	50
280	1960	00	1974	00	1988	00
285 *2 gross*	1995	00	2009	25	2023	50
288	2016	00	2030	40	2044	80
295	2065	00	2079	75	2094	50
300	2100	00	2115	00	2130	00
325	2275	00	2291	25	2307	50
336	2352	00	2368	80	2385	60
365	2555	00	2573	25	2591	50
375	2625	00	2643	75	2662	50
400	2800	00	2820	00	2840	00
425 *3 gr.*	2975	00	2996	25	3017	50
432	3024	00	3045	60	3067	20
475	3325	00	3348	75	3372	50
480	3360	00	3384	00	3408	00
500	3500	00	3525	00	3550	00
504 *4 gr.*	3528	00	3553	20	3578	40
576	4032	00	4060	80	4089	60
600	4200	00	4230	00	4260	00
700	4900	00	4935	00	4970	00
750	5250	00	5287	50	5325	00
800	5600	00	5640	00	5680	00
900	6300	00	6345	00	6390	00
1000	7000	00	7050	00	7100	00
2500	17500	0	17625	0	17750	0
5000	35000	0	35250	0	35500	0

No.	£7·00	£7·05	£7·10	No.	£7·00	£7·05	£7·10
1016	7112·00	7162·80	7213·60	1728	12096·00	12182·40	12268·80
1296	9072·00	9136·80	9201·60	1760	12320·00	12408·00	12496·00

No.	£7·15	£7·20	£7·25	No.	£7·15	£7·20	£7·25
1	7 15	7 20	7 25	51	364 65	367 20	369 75
2	14 30	14 40	14 50	52	371 80	374 40	377 00
3	21 45	21 60	21 75	53	378 95	381 60	384 25
4	28 60	28 80	29 00	54	386 10	388 80	391 50
5	35 75	36 00	36 25	55	393 25	396 00	398 75
6	42 90	43 20	43 50	56	400 40	403 20	406 00
7	50 05	50 40	50 75	57	407 55	410 40	413 25
8	57 20	57 60	58 00	58	414 70	417 60	420 50
9	64 35	64 80	65 25	59	421 85	424 80	427 75
10	71 50	72 00	72 50	60	429 00	432 00	435 00
11	78 65	79 20	79 75	61	436 15	439 20	442 25
12	85 80	86 40	87 00	62	443 30	446 40	449 50
13	92 95	93 60	94 25	63	450 45	453 60	456 75
14	100 10	100 80	101 50	64	457 60	460 80	464 00
15	107 25	108 00	108 75	65	464 75	468 00	471 25
16	114 40	115 20	116 00	66	471 90	475 20	478 50
17	121 55	122 40	123 25	67	479 05	482 40	485 75
18	128 70	129 60	130 50	68	486 20	489 60	493 00
19	135 85	136 80	137 75	69	493 35	496 80	500 25
20	143 00	144 00	145 00	70	500 50	504 00	507 50
21	150 15	151 20	152 25	71	507 65	511 20	514 75
22	157 30	158 40	159 50	72	514 80	518 40	522 00
23	164 45	165 60	166 75	73	521 95	525 60	529 25
24	171 60	172 80	174 00	74	529 10	532 80	536 50
25	178 75	180 00	181 25	75	536 25	540 00	543 75
26	185 90	187 20	188 50	76	543 40	547 20	551 00
27	193 05	194 40	195 75	77	550 55	554 40	558 25
28	200 20	201 60	203 00	78	557 70	561 60	565 50
29	207 35	208 80	210 25	79	564 85	568 80	572 75
30	214 50	216 00	217 50	80	572 00	576 00	580 00
31	221 65	223 20	224 75	81	579 15	583 20	587 25
32	228 80	230 40	232 00	82	586 30	590 40	594 50
33	235 95	237 60	239 25	83	593 45	597 60	601 75
34	243 10	244 80	246 50	84	600 60	604 80	609 00
35	250 25	252 00	253 75	85	607 75	612 00	616 25
36	257 40	259 20	261 00	86	614 90	619 20	623 50
37	264 55	266 40	268 25	87	622 05	626 40	630 75
38	271 70	273 60	275 50	88	629 20	633 60	638 00
39	278 85	280 80	282 75	89	636 35	640 80	645 25
40	286 00	288 00	290 00	90	643 50	648 00	652 50
41	293 15	295 20	297 25	91	650 65	655 20	659 75
42	300 30	302 40	304 50	92	657 80	662 40	667 00
43	307 45	309 60	311 75	93	664 95	669 60	674 25
44	314 60	316 80	319 00	94	672 10	676 80	681 50
45	321 75	324 00	326 25	95	679 25	684 00	688 75
46	328 90	331 20	333 50	96	686 40	691 20	696 00
47	336 05	338 40	340 75	97	693 55	698 40	703 25
48	343 20	345 60	348 00	98	700 70	705 60	710 50
49	350 35	352 80	355 25	99	707 85	712 80	717 75
50	357 50	360 00	362 50	100	715 00	720 00	725 00
¼	1·7875	1·80	1·8125	¾	5·3625	5·40	5·4375
½..	3·5750	3·60	3·6250	1¼..	8·9875	9·00	9·0625

Dozens.

No.	£7·15 £ P	£7·20 £ P	£7·25 £ P
101	722 15	727 20	732 25
102	729 30	734 40	739 50
103	736 45	741 60	746 75
104	743 60	748 80	754 00
105	750 75	756 00	761 25
106	757 90	763 20	768 50
107	765 05	770 40	775 75
108	772 20	777 60	783 00
109	779 35	784 80	790 25
110	786 50	792 00	797 50
111	793 65	799 20	804 75
112	800 80	806 40	812 00
113	807 95	813 60	819 25
114	815 10	820 80	826 50
115	822 25	828 00	833 75
116	829 40	835 20	841 00
117	836 55	842 40	848 25
118	843 70	849 60	855 50
119	850 85	856 80	862 75
120	858 00	864 00	870 00
121	865 15	871 20	877 25
122	872 30	878 40	884 50
123	879 45	885 60	891 75
124	886 60	892 80	899 00
125	893 75	900 00	906 25
126	900 90	907 20	913 50
127	908 05	914 40	920 75
128	915 20	921 60	928 00
129	922 35	928 80	935 25
130	929 50	936 00	942 50
131	936 65	943 20	949 75
132	943 80	950 40	957 00
133	950 95	957 60	964 25
134	958 10	964 80	971 50
135	965 25	972 00	978 75
136	972 40	979 20	986 00
137	979 55	986 40	993 25
138	986 70	993 60	1000 50
139	993 85	1000 80	1007 75
140	1001 00	1008 00	1015 00
141	1008 15	1015 20	1022 25
142	1015 30	1022 40	1029 50
143	1022 45	1029 60	1036 75
144	1029 60	1036 80	1044 00
145	1036 75	1044 00	1051 25
146	1043 90	1051 20	1058 50
147	1051 05	1058 40	1065 75
148	1058 20	1065 60	1073 00
149	1065 35	1072 80	1080 25
150	1072 50	1080 00	1087 50
1016	7264 40	7315 20	7366 00
1296	9266 40	9331 20	9396 00

No.	£7·15 £ P	£7·20 £ P	£7·25 £ P
155	1108 25	1116 00	1123 75
156	1115 40	1123 20	1131 00
165	1179 75	1188 00	1196 25
168	1201 20	1209 60	1218 00
175	1251 25	1260 00	1268 75
180	1287 00	1296 00	1305 00
185	1322 75	1332 00	1341 25
192	1372 80	1382 40	1392 00
195	1394 25	1404 00	1413 75
200	1430 00	1440 00	1450 00
204	1458 60	1468 80	1479 00
205	1465 75	1476 00	1486 25
215	1537 25	1548 00	1558 75
216	1544 40	1555 20	1566 00
224	1601 60	1612 80	1624 00
225	1608 75	1620 00	1631 25
228	1630 20	1641 60	1653 00
235	1680 25	1692 00	1703 75
245	1751 75	1764 00	1776 25
250	1787 50	1800 00	1812 50
252	1801 80	1814 40	1827 00
255	1823 25	1836 00	1848 75
265	1894 75	1908 00	1921 25
272	1944 80	1958 40	1972 00
275	1966 25	1980 00	1993 75
280	2002 00	2016 00	2030 00
285	2037 75	2052 00	2066 25
288	2059 20	2073 60	2088 00
295	2109 25	2124 00	2138 75
300	2145 00	2160 00	2175 00
325	2323 75	2340 00	2356 25
336	2402 40	2419 20	2436 00
365	2609 75	2628 00	2646 25
375	2681 25	2700 00	2718 75
400	2860 00	2880 00	2900 00
425	3038 75	3060 00	3081 25
432	3088 80	3110 40	3132 00
475	3396 25	3420 00	3443 75
480	3432 00	3456 00	3480 00
500	3575 00	3600 00	3625 00
504	3603 60	3628 80	3654 00
576	4118 40	4147 20	4176 00
600	4290 00	4320 00	4350 00
700	5005 00	5040 00	5075 00
750	5362 50	5400 00	5437 50
800	5720 00	5760 00	5800 00
900	6435 00	6480 00	6525 00
1000	7150 00	7200 00	7250 00
2500	17875 ·0	18000 ·0	18125 ·0
5000	35750 ·0	36000 ·0	36250 ·0
1728	12355 20	12441 60	12528 00
1760	12584 00	12672 00	12760 00

Marginal markers on right table: ¹³ (156), ¹⁴ (168), ¹⁵ (180), ¹⁶ (192), ¹⁷ (204), ¹⁸ (216), ¹⁹ (228), ²¹ (252), "2 gross" (288), "8 yr." (425), "4 yr." (576).

No.	£7·30 £	P	£7·35 £	P	£7·40 £	P
1	7	30	7	35	7	40
2	14	60	14	70	14	80
3	21	90	22	05	22	20
4	29	20	29	40	29	60
5	36	50	36	75	37	00
6	43	80	44	10	44	40
7	51	10	51	45	51	80
8	58	40	58	80	59	20
9	65	70	66	15	66	60
10	73	00	73	50	74	00
11	80	30	80	85	81	40
12	87	60	88	20	88	80
13	94	90	95	55	96	20
14	102	20	102	90	103	60
15	109	50	110	25	111	00
16	116	80	117	60	118	40
17	124	10	124	95	125	80
18	131	40	132	30	133	20
19	138	70	139	65	140	60
20	146	00	147	00	148	00
21	153	30	154	35	155	40
22	160	60	161	70	162	80
23	167	90	169	05	170	20
24	175	20	176	40	177	60
25	182	50	183	75	185	00
26	189	80	191	10	192	40
27	197	10	198	45	199	80
28	204	40	205	80	207	20
29	211	70	213	15	214	60
30	219	00	220	50	222	00
31	226	30	227	85	229	40
32	233	60	235	20	236	80
33	240	90	242	55	244	20
34	248	20	249	90	251	60
35	255	50	257	25	259	00
36	262	80	264	60	266	40
37	270	10	271	95	273	80
38	277	40	279	30	281	20
39	284	70	286	65	288	60
40	292	00	294	00	296	00
41	299	30	301	35	303	40
42	306	60	308	70	310	80
43	313	90	316	05	318	20
44	321	20	323	40	325	60
45	328	50	330	75	333	00
46	335	80	338	10	340	40
47	343	10	345	45	347	80
48	350	40	352	80	355	20
49	357	70	360	15	362	60
50	365	00	367	50	370	00

(Left column marked *Dozens.* at rows 3–9; reference marks at rows 11, 12, 24, 36, 48.)

No.	£7·30 £	P	£7·35 £	P	£7·40 £	P
51	372	30	374	85	377	40
52	379	60	382	20	384	80
53	386	90	389	55	392	20
54	394	20	396	90	399	60
55	401	50	404	25	407	00
56	408	80	411	60	414	40
57	416	10	418	95	421	80
58	423	40	426	30	429	20
59	430	70	433	65	436	60
60	438	00	441	00	444	00
61	445	30	448	35	451	40
62	452	60	455	70	458	80
63	459	90	463	05	466	20
64	467	20	470	40	473	60
65	474	50	477	75	481	00
66	481	80	485	10	488	40
67	489	10	492	45	495	80
68	496	40	499	80	503	20
69	503	70	507	15	510	60
70	511	00	514	50	518	00
71	518	30	521	85	525	40
72	525	60	529	20	532	80
73	532	90	536	55	540	20
74	540	20	543	90	547	60
75	547	50	551	25	555	00
76	554	80	558	60	562	40
77	562	10	565	95	569	80
78	569	40	573	30	577	20
79	576	70	580	65	584	60
80	584	00	588	00	592	00
81	591	30	595	35	599	40
82	598	60	602	70	606	80
83	605	90	610	05	614	20
84	613	20	617	40	621	60
85	620	50	624	75	629	00
86	627	80	632	10	636	40
87	635	10	639	45	643	80
88	642	40	646	80	651	20
89	649	70	654	15	658	60
90	657	00	661	50	666	00
91	664	30	668	85	673	40
92	671	60	676	20	680	80
93	678	90	683	55	688	20
94	686	20	690	90	695	60
95	693	50	698	25	703	00
96	700	80	705	60	710	40
97	708	10	712	95	717	80
98	715	40	720	30	725	20
99	722	70	727	65	732	60
100	730	00	735	00	740	00

(Left column marked *Dozens.* at rows 53–59; reference marks at rows 59, 60, 72, 84, 96.)

	£7·30	£7·35	£7·40		£7·30	£7·35	£7·40
¼	1·825	1·8375	1·85	¾	5·475	5·5125	5·55
½..	3·650	3·6750	3·70	1¼..	9·125	9·1875	9·25

No.	£7·30	£7·35	£7·40
	£ p	£ p	£ p
101	737 30	742 35	747 40
102	744 60	749 70	754 80
103	751 90	757 05	762 20
104	759 20	764 40	769 60
105	766 50	771 75	777 00
106	773 80	779 10	784 40
107	781 10	786 45	791 80
108	788 40	793 80	799 20
109	795 70	801 15	806 60
110	803 00	808 50	814 00
111	810 30	815 85	821 40
112	817 60	823 20	828 80
113	824 90	830 55	836 20
114	832 20	837 90	843 60
115	839 50	845 25	851 00
116	846 80	852 60	858 40
117	854 10	859 95	865 80
118	861 40	867 30	873 20
119	868 70	874 65	880 60
120	876 00	882 00	888 00
121	883 30	889 35	895 40
122	890 60	896 70	902 80
123	897 90	904 05	910 20
124	905 20	911 40	917 60
125	912 50	918 75	925 00
126	919 80	926 10	932 40
127	927 10	933 45	939 80
128	934 40	940 80	947 20
129	941 70	948 15	954 60
130	949 00	955 50	962 00
131	956 30	962 85	969 40
132	963 60	970 20	976 80
133	970 90	977 55	984 20
134	978 20	984 90	991 60
135	985 50	992 25	999 00
136	992 80	999 60	1006 40
137	1000 10	1006 95	1013 80
138	1007 40	1014 30	1021 20
139	1014 70	1021 65	1028 60
140	1022 00	1029 00	1036 00
141	1029 30	1036 35	1043 40
142	1036 60	1043 70	1050 80
143	1043 90	1051 05	1058 20
144	1051 20	1058 40	1065 60
145	1058 50	1065 75	1073 00
146	1065 80	1073 10	1080 40
147	1073 10	1080 45	1087 80
148	1080 40	1087 80	1095 20
149	1087 70	1095 15	1102 60
150	1095 00	1102 50	1110 00
1016	7416·80	7467·60	7518·40
1296	9460·80	9525·60	9590·40

No.	£7·30	£7·35	£7·40
	£ p	£ p	£ p
Doz. 155	1131 50	1139 25	1147 00
13 156	1138 80	1146 60	1154 40
165	1204 50	1212 75	1221 00
14 168	1226 40	1234 80	1243 20
175	1277 50	1286 25	1295 00
15 180	1314 00	1323 00	1332 00
185	1350 50	1359 75	1369 00
16 192	1401 60	1411 20	1420 80
195	1423 50	1433 25	1443 00
200	1460 00	1470 00	1480 00
17 204	1489 20	1499 40	1509 60
205	1496 50	1506 75	1517 00
215	1569 50	1580 25	1591 00
18 216	1576 80	1587 60	1598 40
224	1635 20	1646 40	1657 60
225	1642 50	1653 75	1665 00
19 228	1664 40	1675 80	1687 20
235	1715 50	1727 25	1739 00
245	1788 50	1800 75	1813 00
250	1825 00	1837 50	1850 00
21 252	1839 60	1852 20	1864 80
255	1861 50	1874 25	1887 00
265	1934 50	1947 75	1961 00
272	1985 60	1999 20	2012 80
275	2007 50	2021 25	2035 00
280	2044 00	2058 00	2072 00
285	2080 50	2094 75	2109 00
2 gross 288	2102 40	2116 80	2131 20
295	2153 50	2168 25	2183 00
300	2190 00	2205 00	2220 00
325	2372 50	2388 75	2405 00
336	2452 80	2469 60	2486 40
365	2664 50	2682 75	2701 00
375	2737 50	2756 25	2775 00
400	2920 00	2940 00	2960 00
425	3102 50	3123 75	3145 00
432	3153 60	3175 20	3196 80
475	3467 50	3491 25	3515 00
480	3504 00	3528 00	3552 00
500	3650 00	3675 00	3700 00
504	3679 20	3704 40	3729 60
576	4204 80	4233 60	4262 40
600	4380 00	4410 00	4440 00
700	5110 00	5145 00	5180 00
750	5475 00	5512 50	5550 00
800	5840 00	5880 00	5920 00
900	6570 00	6615 00	6660 00
1000	7300 00	7350 00	7400 00
2500	18250 ·0	18375 ·0	18500 ·0
5000	36500 ·0	36750 ·0	37000 ·0
1728	12614·40	12700·80	12787·20
1760	12848·00	12936·00	13024·00

No.	£7·45 £	p	£7·50 £	p	£7·55 £	p	No.	£7·45 £	p	£7·50 £	p	£7·55 £	p
1	7	45	7	50	7	55	51	379	95	382	50	385	05
2	14	90	15	00	15	10	52	387	40	390	00	392	60
3	22	35	22	50	22	65	53	394	85	397	50	400	15
4	29	80	30	00	30	20	54	402	30	405	00	407	70
5	37	25	37	50	37	75	55	409	75	412	50	415	25
6	44	70	45	00	45	30	56	417	20	420	00	422	80
7	52	15	52	50	52	85	57	424	65	427	50	430	35
8	59	60	60	00	60	40	58	432	10	435	00	437	90
9	67	05	67	50	67	95	59	439	55	442	50	445	45
10	74	50	75	00	75	50	60	447	00	450	00	453	00
11	81	95	82	50	83	05	61	454	45	457	50	460	55
12	89	40	90	00	90	60	62	461	90	465	00	468	10
13	96	85	97	50	98	15	63	469	35	472	50	475	65
14	104	30	105	00	105	70	64	476	80	480	00	483	20
15	111	75	112	50	113	25	65	484	25	487	50	490	75
16	119	20	120	00	120	80	66	491	70	495	00	498	30
17	126	65	127	50	128	35	67	499	15	502	50	505	85
18	134	10	135	00	135	90	68	506	60	510	00	513	40
19	141	55	142	50	143	45	69	514	05	517	50	520	95
20	149	00	150	00	151	00	70	521	50	525	00	528	50
21	156	45	157	50	158	55	71	528	95	532	50	536	05
22	163	90	165	00	166	10	72	536	40	540	00	543	60
23	171	35	172	50	173	65	73	543	85	547	50	551	15
24	178	80	180	00	181	20	74	551	30	555	00	558	70
25	186	25	187	50	188	75	75	558	75	562	50	566	25
26	193	70	195	00	196	30	76	566	20	570	00	573	80
27	201	15	202	50	203	85	77	573	65	577	50	581	35
28	208	60	210	00	211	40	78	581	10	585	00	588	90
29	216	05	217	50	218	95	79	588	55	592	50	596	45
30	223	50	225	00	226	50	80	596	00	600	00	604	00
31	230	95	232	50	234	05	81	603	45	607	50	611	55
32	238	40	240	00	241	60	82	610	90	615	00	619	10
33	245	85	247	50	249	15	83	618	35	622	50	626	65
34	253	30	255	00	256	70	84	625	80	630	00	634	20
35	260	75	262	50	264	25	85	633	25	637	50	641	75
36	268	20	270	00	271	80	86	640	70	645	00	649	30
37	275	65	277	50	279	35	87	648	15	652	50	656	85
38	283	10	285	00	286	90	88	655	60	660	00	664	40
39	290	55	292	50	294	45	89	663	05	667	50	671	95
40	298	00	300	00	302	00	90	670	50	675	00	679	50
41	305	45	307	50	309	55	91	677	95	682	50	687	05
42	312	90	315	00	317	10	92	685	40	690	00	694	60
43	320	35	322	50	324	65	93	692	85	697	50	702	15
44	327	80	330	00	332	20	94	700	30	705	00	709	70
45	335	25	337	50	339	75	95	707	75	712	50	717	25
46	342	70	345	00	347	30	96	715	20	720	00	724	80
47	350	15	352	50	354	85	97	722	65	727	50	732	35
48	357	60	360	00	362	40	98	730	10	735	00	739	90
49	365	05	367	50	369	95	99	737	55	742	50	747	45
50	372	50	375	00	377	50	100	745	00	750	00	755	00
¼	1·8625		1·875		1·8875		¾	5·5875		5·625		5·6625	
½..	3·7250		3·750		3·7750		1¼..	9·3125		9·375		9·4875	

Dozens.

No.	£7·45	£7·50	£7·55	No.	£7·45	£7·50	£7·55
101	752 45	757 50	762 55	155	1154 75	1162 50	1170 25
102	759 90	765 00	770 10	[13] 156	1162 20	1170 00	1177 80
103	767 35	772 50	777 65	165	1229 25	1237 50	1245 75
104	774 80	780 00	785 20	[14] 168	1251 60	1260 00	1268 40
105	782 25	787 50	792 75	175	1303 75	1312 50	1321 25
106	789 70	795 00	800 30	[15] 180	1341 00	1350 00	1359 00
107	797 15	802 50	807 85	185	1378 25	1387 50	1396 75
[9] 108	804 60	810 00	815 40	[16] 192	1430 40	1440 00	1449 60
109	812 05	817 50	822 95	195	1452 75	1462 50	1472 25
110	819 50	825 00	830 50	200	1490 00	1500 00	1510 00
111	826 95	832 50	838 05	[17] 204	1519 80	1530 00	1540 20
112	834 40	840 00	845 60	205	1527 25	1537 50	1547 75
113	841 85	847 50	853 15	215	1601 75	1612 50	1623 25
114	849 30	855 00	860 70	[18] 216	1609 20	1620 00	1630 80
115	856 75	862 50	868 25	224	1668 80	1680 00	1691 20
116	864 20	870 00	875 80	225	1676 25	1687 50	1698 75
117	871 65	877 50	883 35	[19] 228	1698 60	1710 00	1721 40
118	879 10	885 00	890 90	235	1750 75	1762 50	1774 25
119	886 55	892 50	898 45	245	1825 25	1837 50	1849 75
[10] 120	894 00	900 00	906 00	250	1862 50	1875 00	1887 50
121	901 45	907 50	913 55	[21] 252	1877 40	1890 00	1902 60
122	908 90	915 00	921 10	255	1899 75	1912 50	1925 25
123	916 35	922 50	928 65	265	1974 25	1987 50	2000 75
124	923 80	930 00	936 20	272	2026 40	2040 00	2053 60
125	931 25	937 50	943 75	275	2048 75	2062 50	2076 25
126	938 70	945 00	951 30	280	2086 00	2100 00	2114 00
127	946 15	952 50	958 85	285	2123 25	2137 50	2151 75
128	953 60	960 00	966 40	288 (2 gross)	2145 60	2160 00	2174 40
129	961 05	967 50	973 95	295	2197 75	2212 50	2227 25
130	968 50	975 00	981 50	300	2235 00	2250 00	2265 00
131	975 95	982 50	989 05	325	2421 25	2437 50	2453 75
[11] 132	983 40	990 00	996 60	336	2503 20	2520 00	2536 80
133	990 85	997 50	1004 15	365	2719 25	2737 50	2755 75
134	998 30	1005 00	1011 70	375	2793 75	2812 50	2831 25
135	1005 75	1012 50	1019 25	400	2980 00	3000 00	3020 00
136	1013 20	1020 00	1026 80	425	3166 25	3187 50	3208 75
137	1020 65	1027 50	1034 35	432 (3 gr.)	3218 40	3240 00	3261 60
138	1028 10	1035 00	1041 90	475	3538 75	3562 50	3586 25
139	1035 55	1042 50	1049 45	480	3576 00	3600 00	3624 00
140	1043 00	1050 00	1057 00	500	3725 00	3750 00	3775 00
141	1050 45	1057 50	1064 55	504	3754 80	3780 00	3805 20
142	1057 90	1065 00	1072 10	576 (4 gr.)	4291 20	4320 00	4348 80
143	1065 35	1072 50	1079 65	600	4470 00	4500 00	4530 00
[12] 144	1072 80	1080 00	1087 20	700	5215 00	5250 00	5285 00
145	1080 25	1087 50	1094 75	750	5587 50	5625 00	5662 50
146	1087 70	1095 00	1102 30	800	5960 00	6000 00	6040 00
147	1095 15	1102 50	1109 85	900	6705 00	6750 00	6795 00
148	1102 60	1110 00	1117 40	1000	7450 00	7500 00	7550 00
149	1110 05	1117 50	1124 95	2500	18625 ·0	18750 ·0	18875 ·0
150	1117 50	1125 00	1132 50	5000	37250 ·0	37500 ·0	37750 ·0
1016	7569 20	7620 00	7670 80	1728	12873 60	12960 00	13046 40
1296	9655 20	9720 00	9784 80	1760	13112 00	13200 00	13288 00

No.	£7·60 £	P	£7·65 £	P	£7·70 £	P	No.	£7·60 £	P	£7·65 £	P	£7·70 £	P
1	7	60	7	65	7	70	51	387	60	390	15	392	70
2	15	20	15	30	15	40	52	395	20	397	80	400	40
3	22	80	22	95	23	10	53	402	80	405	45	408	10
4	30	40	30	60	30	80	54	410	40	413	10	415	80
5	38	00	38	25	38	50	55	418	00	420	75	423	50
6	45	60	45	90	46	20	56	425	60	428	40	431	20
7	53	20	53	55	53	90	57	433	20	436	05	438	90
8	60	80	61	20	61	60	58	440	80	443	70	446	60
9	68	40	68	85	69	30	59	448	40	451	35	454	30
10	76	00	76	50	77	00	60	456	00	459	00	462	00
11	83	60	84	15	84	70	61	463	60	466	65	469	70
12	91	20	91	80	92	40	62	471	20	474	30	477	40
13	98	80	99	45	100	10	63	478	80	481	95	485	10
14	106	40	107	10	107	80	64	486	40	489	60	492	80
15	114	00	114	75	115	50	65	494	00	497	25	500	50
16	121	60	122	40	123	20	66	501	60	504	90	508	20
17	129	20	130	05	130	90	67	509	20	512	55	515	90
18	136	80	137	70	138	60	68	516	80	520	20	523	60
19	144	40	145	35	146	30	69	524	40	527	85	531	30
20	152	00	153	00	154	00	70	532	00	535	50	539	00
21	159	60	160	65	161	70	71	539	60	543	15	546	70
22	167	20	168	30	169	40	72	547	20	550	80	554	40
23	174	80	175	95	177	10	73	554	80	558	45	562	10
24	182	40	183	60	184	80	74	562	40	566	10	569	80
25	190	00	191	25	192	50	75	570	00	573	75	577	50
26	197	60	198	90	200	20	76	577	60	581	40	585	20
27	205	20	206	55	207	90	77	585	20	589	05	592	90
28	212	80	214	20	215	60	78	592	80	596	70	600	60
29	220	40	221	85	223	30	79	600	40	604	35	608	30
30	228	00	229	50	231	00	80	608	00	612	00	616	00
31	235	60	237	15	238	70	81	615	60	619	65	623	70
32	243	20	244	80	246	40	82	623	20	627	30	631	40
33	250	80	252	45	254	10	83	630	80	634	95	639	10
34	258	40	260	10	261	80	84	638	40	642	60	646	80
35	266	00	267	75	269	50	85	646	00	650	25	654	50
36	273	60	275	40	277	20	86	653	60	657	90	662	20
37	281	20	283	05	284	90	87	661	20	665	55	669	90
38	288	80	290	70	292	60	88	668	80	673	20	677	60
39	296	40	298	35	300	30	89	676	40	680	85	685	30
40	304	00	306	00	308	00	90	684	00	688	50	693	00
41	311	60	313	65	315	70	91	691	60	696	15	700	70
42	319	20	321	30	323	40	92	699	20	703	80	708	40
43	326	80	328	95	331	10	93	706	80	711	45	716	10
44	334	40	336	60	338	80	94	714	40	719	10	723	80
45	342	00	344	25	346	50	95	722	00	726	75	731	50
46	349	60	351	90	354	20	96	729	60	734	40	739	20
47	357	20	359	55	361	90	97	737	20	742	05	746	90
48	364	80	367	20	369	60	98	744	80	749	70	754	60
49	372	40	374	85	377	30	99	752	40	757	35	762	30
50	380	00	382	50	385	00	100	760	00	765	00	770	00
¼	1·90		1·9125		1·925		¾	5·70		5·7375		5·775	
½..	3·80		3·8250		3·850		1¼..	9·50		9·5625		9·625	

No.	£7·60 £	P	£7·65 £	P	£7·70 £	P
101	767	60	772	65	777	70
102	775	20	780	30	785	40
103	782	80	787	95	793	10
104	790	40	795	60	800	80
105	798	00	803	25	808	50
106	805	60	810	90	816	20
107	813	20	818	55	823	90
9 108	820	80	826	20	831	60
109	828	40	833	85	839	30
110	836	00	841	50	847	00
111	843	60	849	15	854	70
112	851	20	856	80	862	40
113	858	80	864	45	870	10
114	866	40	872	10	877	80
115	874	00	879	75	885	50
116	881	60	887	40	893	20
117	889	20	895	05	900	90
118	896	80	902	70	908	60
119	904	40	910	35	916	30
10 120	912	00	918	00	924	00
121	919	60	925	65	931	70
122	927	20	933	30	939	40
123	934	80	940	95	947	10
124	942	40	948	60	954	80
125	950	00	956	25	962	50
126	957	60	963	90	970	20
127	965	20	971	55	977	90
128	972	80	979	20	985	60
129	980	40	986	85	993	30
130	988	00	994	50	1001	00
131	995	60	1002	15	1008	70
11 132	1003	20	1009	80	1016	40
133	1010	80	1017	45	1024	10
134	1018	40	1025	10	1031	80
135	1026	00	1032	75	1039	50
136	1033	60	1040	40	1047	20
137	1041	20	1048	05	1054	90
138	1048	80	1055	70	1062	60
139	1056	40	1063	35	1070	30
140	1064	00	1071	00	1078	00
141	1071	60	1078	65	1085	70
142	1079	20	1086	30	1093	40
143	1086	80	1093	95	1101	10
12 144	1094	40	1101	60	1108	80
145	1102	00	1109	25	1116	50
146	1109	60	1116	90	1124	20
147	1117	20	1124	55	1131	90
148	1124	80	1132	20	1139	60
149	1132	40	1139	85	1147	30
150	1140	00	1147	50	1155	00

No.	£7·60 £	P	£7·65 £	P	£7·70 £	P
Doz 155	1178	00	1185	75	1193	50
13 156	1185	60	1193	40	1201	20
165	1254	00	1262	25	1270	50
14 168	1276	80	1285	20	1293	60
175	1330	00	1338	75	1347	50
15 180	1368	00	1377	00	1386	00
185	1406	00	1415	25	1424	50
16 192	1459	20	1468	80	1478	40
195	1482	00	1491	75	1501	50
200	1520	00	1530	00	1540	00
17 204	1550	40	1560	60	1570	80
205	1558	00	1568	25	1578	50
215	1634	00	1644	75	1655	50
18 216	1641	60	1652	40	1663	20
224	1702	40	1713	60	1724	80
225	1710	00	1721	25	1732	50
19 228	1732	80	1744	20	1755	60
235	1786	00	1797	75	1809	50
245	1862	00	1874	25	1886	50
250	1900	00	1912	50	1925	00
21 252	1915	20	1927	80	1940	40
. 255	1938	00	1950	75	1963	50
265	2014	00	2027	25	2040	50
272	2067	20	2080	80	2094	40
275	2090	00	2103	75	2117	50
280	2128	00	2142	00	2156	00
285	2166	00	2180	25	2194	50
2 gross 288	2188	80	2203	20	2217	60
295	2242	00	2256	75	2271	50
300	2280	00	2295	00	2310	00
325	2470	00	2486	25	2502	50
336	2553	60	2570	40	2587	20
365	2774	00	2792	25	2810	50
375	2850	00	2868	75	2887	50
400	3040	00	3060	00	3080	00
425	3230	00	3251	25	3272	50
3 gr. 432	3283	20	3304	80	3326	40
475	3610	00	3633	75	3657	50
480	3648	00	3672	00	3696	00
500	3800	00	3825	00	3850	00
4 gr. 504	3830	40	3855	60	3880	80
576	4377	60	4406	40	4435	20
600	4560	00	4590	00	4620	00
700	5320	00	5355	00	5390	00
750	5700	00	5737	50	5775	00
800	6080	00	6120	00	6160	00
900	6840	00	6885	00	6930	00
1000	7600	00	7650	00	7700	00
2500	19000	·0	19125	·0	19250	·0
5000	38000	·0	38250	0	38500	0

1016	7721·60	7772·40	7828·20
1296	9849·60	9914·40	9979·20

1728	13182·80	13219·20	13305·60
1760	13876·00	13464·00	13552·00

No.	£7·75		£7·80		£7·85		No.	£7·75		£7·80		£7·85	
	£	P	£	P	£	P		£	P	£	P	£	P
1	7	75	7	80	7	85	51	395	25	397	80	400	35
2	15	50	15	60	15	70	52	403	00	405	60	408	20
3	23	25	23	40	23	55	53	410	75	413	40	416	05
4	31	00	31	20	31	40	54	418	50	421	20	423	90
5	38	75	39	00	39	25	55	426	25	429	00	431	75
6	46	50	46	80	47	10	56	434	00	436	80	439	60
7	54	25	54	60	54	95	57	441	75	444	60	447	45
8	62	00	62	40	62	80	58	449	50	452	40	455	30
9	69	75	70	20	70	65	59	457	25	460	20	463	15
10	77	50	78	00	78	50	60	465	00	468	00	471	00
11	85	25	85	80	86	35	61	472	75	475	80	478	85
12	93	00	93	60	94	20	62	480	50	483	60	486	70
13	100	75	101	40	102	05	63	488	25	491	40	494	55
14	108	50	109	20	109	90	64	496	00	499	20	502	40
15	116	25	117	00	117	75	65	503	75	507	00	510	25
16	124	00	124	80	125	60	66	511	50	514	80	518	10
17	131	75	132	60	133	45	67	519	25	522	60	525	95
18	139	50	140	40	141	30	68	527	00	530	40	533	80
19	147	25	148	20	149	15	69	534	75	538	20	541	65
20	155	00	156	00	157	00	70	542	50	546	00	549	50
21	162	75	163	80	164	85	71	550	25	553	80	557	35
22	170	50	171	60	172	70	72	558	00	561	60	565	20
23	178	25	179	40	180	55	73	565	75	569	40	573	05
24	186	00	187	20	188	40	74	573	50	577	20	580	90
25	193	75	195	00	196	25	75	581	25	585	00	588	75
26	201	50	202	80	204	10	76	589	00	592	80	596	60
27	209	25	210	60	211	95	77	596	75	600	60	604	45
28	217	00	218	40	219	80	78	604	50	608	40	612	30
29	224	75	226	20	227	65	79	612	25	616	20	620	15
30	232	50	234	00	235	50	80	620	00	624	00	628	00
31	240	25	241	80	243	35	81	627	75	631	80	635	85
32	248	00	249	60	251	20	82	635	50	639	60	643	70
33	255	75	257	40	259	05	83	643	25	647	40	651	55
34	263	50	265	20	266	90	84	651	00	655	20	659	40
35	271	25	273	00	274	75	85	658	75	663	00	667	25
36	279	00	280	80	282	60	86	666	50	670	80	675	10
37	286	75	288	60	290	45	87	674	25	678	60	682	95
38	294	50	296	40	298	30	88	682	00	686	40	690	80
39	302	25	304	20	306	15	89	689	75	694	20	698	65
40	310	00	312	00	314	00	90	697	50	702	00	706	50
41	317	75	319	80	321	85	91	705	25	709	80	714	35
42	325	50	327	60	329	70	92	713	00	717	60	722	20
43	333	25	335	40	337	55	93	720	75	725	40	730	05
44	341	00	343	20	345	40	94	728	50	733	20	737	90
45	348	75	351	00	353	25	95	736	25	741	00	745	75
46	356	50	358	80	361	10	96	744	00	748	80	753	60
47	364	25	366	60	368	95	97	751	75	756	60	761	45
48	372	00	374	40	376	80	98	759	50	764	40	769	30
49	379	75	382	20	384	65	99	767	25	772	20	777	15
50	387	50	390	00	392	50	100	775	00	780	00	785	00
¼	1·9375		1·95		1·9625		½	5·8125		5·85		5·8875	
½..	3·8750		3·90		3·925		1¼..	9·6875		9·75		9·8125	

No.	£7·75 £ P	£7·80 £ P	£7·85 £ P
101	782 75	787 80	792 85
102	790 50	795 60	800 70
103	798 25	803 40	808 55
104	806 00	811 20	816 40
105	813 75	819 00	824 25
106	821 50	826 80	832 10
107	829 25	834 60	839 95
•108	837 00	842 40	847 80
109	844 75	850 20	855 65
110	852 50	858 00	863 50
111	860 25	865 80	871 35
112	868 00	873 60	879 20
113	875 75	881 40	887 05
114	883 50	889 20	894 90
115	891 25	897 00	902 75
116	899 00	904 80	910 60
117	906 75	912 60	918 45
118	914 50	920 40	926 30
119	922 25	928 20	934 15
¹⁰120	930 00	936 00	942 00
121	937 75	943 80	949 85
122	945 50	951 60	957 70
123	953 25	959 40	965 55
124	961 00	967 20	973 40
125	968 75	975 00	981 25
126	976 50	982 80	989 10
127	984 25	990 60	996 95
128	992 00	998 40	1004 80
129	999 75	1006 20	1012 65
130	1007 50	1014 00	1020 50
131	1015 25	1021 80	1028 35
¹¹132	1023 00	1029 60	1036 20
133	1030 75	1037 40	1044 05
134	1038 50	1045 20	1051 90
135	1046 25	1053 00	1059 75
136	1054 00	1060 80	1067 60
137	1061 75	1068 60	1075 45
138	1069 50	1076 40	1083 30
139	1077 25	1084 20	1091 15
140	1085 00	1092 00	1099 00
141	1092 75	1099 80	1106 85
142	1100 50	1107 60	1114 70
143	1108 25	1115 40	1122 55
¹²144	1116 00	1123 20	1130 40
145	1123 75	1131 00	1138 25
146	1131 50	1138 80	1146 10
147	1139 25	1146 60	1153 95
148	1147 00	1154 40	1161 80
149	1154 75	1162 20	1169 65
150	1162 50	1170 00	1177 50
1016	7874 00	7924 80	7975 60
1296	10044 00	10108 80	10173 60

No.	£7·75 £ P	£7·80 £ P	£7·85 £ P
Dz 155	1201 25	1209 00	1216 75
¹³156	1209 00	1216 00	1224 60
165	1278 75	1287 00	1295 25
¹⁴168	1302 00	1310 40	1318 80
175	1356 25	1365 00	1373 75
¹⁵180	1395 00	1404 00	1413 00
185	1433 75	1443 00	1452 25
¹⁶192	1488 00	1497 60	1507 20
195	1511 25	1521 00	1530 75
200	1550 00	1560 00	1570 00
¹⁷204	1581 00	1591 20	1601 40
205	1588 75	1599 00	1609 25
215	1666 25	1677 00	1687 75
¹⁸216	1674 00	1684 80	1695 60
224	1736 00	1747 20	1758 40
225	1743 75	1755 00	1766 25
¹⁹228	1767 00	1778 40	1789 80
235	1821 25	1833 00	1844 75
245	1898 75	1911 00	1923 25
250	1937 50	1950 00	1962 50
²¹252	1953 00	1965 60	1978 20
255	1976 25	1989 00	2001 75
265	2053 75	2067 00	2080 25
272	2108 00	2121 60	2135 20
275	2131 25	2145 00	2158 75
280	2170 00	2184 00	2198 00
285	2208 75	2223 00	2237 25
2 gross 288	2232 00	2246 40	2260 80
295	2286 25	2301 00	2315 75
300	2325 00	2340 00	2355 00
325	2518 75	2535 00	2551 25
336	2604 00	2620 80	2637 60
365	2828 75	2847 00	2865 25
375	2906 25	2925 00	2943 75
400	3100 00	3120 00	3140 00
425	3293 75	3315 00	3336 25
432	3348 00	3369 60	3391 20
475	3681 25	3705 00	3728 75
480	3720 00	3744 00	3768 00
500	3875 00	3900 00	3925 00
504	3906 00	3931 20	3956 40
576	4464 00	4492 80	4521 60
600	4650 00	4680 00	4710 00
700	5425 00	5460 00	5495 00
750	5812 50	5850 00	5887 50
800	6200 00	6240 00	6280 00
900	6975 00	7020 00	7065 00
1000	7750 00	7800 00	7850 00
2500	19375 0	19500 00	19625 0
5000	38750 00	39000 00	39250 0
1728	13392 00	13478 40	13564 80
1760	13640 00	13728 00	13816 00

No.	£7·90		£7·95		£8·00		No.	£7·90		£7·95		£8·00	
	£	P	£	P	£	P		£	P	£	P	£	P
1	7	90	7	95	8	00	51	402	90	405	45	408	00
2	15	80	15	90	16	00	52	410	80	413	40	416	00
3	23	70	23	85	24	00	53	418	70	421	35	424	00
4	31	60	31	80	32	00	54	426	60	429	30	432	00
5	39	50	39	75	40	00	55	434	50	437	25	440	00
6	47	40	47	70	48	00	56	442	40	445	20	448	00
7	55	30	55	65	56	00	57	450	30	453	15	456	00
8	63	20	63	60	64	00	58	458	20	461	10	464	00
9	71	10	71	55	72	00	59	466	10	469	05	472	00
10	79	00	79	50	80	00	60	474	00	477	00	480	00
11	86	90	87	45	88	00	61	481	90	484	95	488	00
12	94	80	95	40	96	00	62	489	80	492	90	496	00
13	102	70	103	35	104	00	63	497	70	500	85	504	00
14	110	60	111	30	112	00	64	505	60	508	80	512	00
15	118	50	119	25	120	00	65	513	50	516	75	520	00
16	126	40	127	20	128	00	66	521	40	524	70	528	00
17	134	30	135	15	136	00	67	529	30	532	65	536	00
18	142	20	143	10	144	00	68	537	20	540	60	544	00
19	150	10	151	05	152	00	69	545	10	548	55	552	00
20	158	00	159	00	160	00	70	553	00	556	50	560	00
21	165	90	166	95	168	00	71	560	90	564	45	568	00
22	173	80	174	90	176	00	72	568	80	572	40	576	00
23	181	70	182	85	184	00	73	576	70	580	35	584	00
24	189	60	190	80	192	00	74	584	60	588	30	592	00
25	197	50	198	75	200	00	75	592	50	596	25	600	00
26	205	40	206	70	208	00	76	600	40	604	20	608	00
27	213	30	214	65	216	00	77	608	30	612	15	616	00
28	221	20	222	60	224	00	78	616	20	620	10	624	00
29	229	10	230	55	232	00	79	624	10	628	05	632	00
30	237	00	238	50	240	00	80	632	00	636	00	640	00
31	244	90	246	45	248	00	81	639	90	643	95	648	00
32	252	80	254	40	256	00	82	647	80	651	90	656	00
33	260	70	262	35	264	00	83	655	70	659	85	664	00
34	268	60	270	30	272	00	84	663	60	667	80	672	00
35	276	50	278	25	280	00	85	671	50	675	75	680	00
36	284	40	286	20	288	00	86	679	40	683	70	688	00
37	292	30	294	15	296	00	87	687	30	691	65	696	00
38	300	20	302	10	304	00	88	695	20	699	60	704	00
39	308	10	310	05	312	00	89	703	10	707	55	712	00
40	316	00	318	00	320	00	90	711	00	715	50	720	00
41	323	90	325	95	328	00	91	718	90	723	45	728	00
42	331	80	333	90	336	00	92	726	80	731	40	736	00
43	339	70	341	85	344	00	93	734	70	739	35	744	00
44	347	60	349	80	352	00	94	742	60	747	30	752	00
45	355	50	357	75	360	00	95	750	50	755	25	760	00
46	363	40	365	70	368	00	96	758	40	763	20	768	00
47	371	30	373	65	376	00	97	766	30	771	15	776	00
48	379	20	381	60	384	00	98	774	20	779	10	784	00
49	387	10	389	55	392	00	99	782	10	787	05	792	00
50	395	00	397	50	400	00	100	790	00	795	00	800	00
¼	1·975		1·9875		2·00		¾	5·925		5·9625		6·00	
½	3·950		3·9750		4·00		1¼	9·875		9·9375		10·00	

No.	£7·90	£7·95	£8·00	No.	£7·90	£7·95	£8·00
	£ p	£ p	£ p		£ p	£ p	£ p
101	797 90	802 95	808 00	155	1224 50	1232 25	1240 00
102	805 80	810 90	816 00	156	1232 40	1240 20	1248 00
103	813 70	818 85	824 00	165	1303 50	1311 75	1320 00
104	821 60	826 80	832 00	168	1327 20	1335 60	1344 00
105	829 50	834 75	840 00	175	1382 50	1391 25	1400 00
106	837 40	842 70	848 00	180	1422 00	1431 00	1440 00
107	845 30	850 65	856 00	185	1461 50	1470 75	1480 00
108	853 20	858 60	864 00	192	1516 80	1526 40	1536 00
109	861 10	866 55	872 00	195	1540 50	1550 25	1560 00
110	869 00	874 50	880 00	200	1580 00	1590 00	1600 00
111	876 90	882 45	888 00	204	1611 60	1621 80	1632 00
112	884 80	890 40	896 00	205	1619 50	1629 75	1640 00
113	892 70	898 35	904 00	215	1698 50	1709 25	1720 00
114	900 60	906 30	912 00	216	1706 40	1717 20	1728 00
115	908 50	914 25	920 00	224	1769 60	1780 80	1792 00
116	916 40	922 20	928 00	225	1777 50	1788 75	1800 00
117	924 30	930 15	936 00	228	1801 20	1812 60	1824 00
118	932 20	938 10	944 00	235	1856 50	1868 25	1880 00
119	940 10	946 05	952 00	245	1935 50	1947 75	1960 00
120	948 00	954 00	960 00	250	1975 00	1987 50	2000 00
121	955 90	961 95	968 00	252	1990 80	2003 40	2016 00
122	963 80	969 90	976 00	255	2014 50	2027 25	2040 00
123	971 70	977 85	984 00	265	2093 50	2106 75	2120 00
124	979 60	985 80	992 00	272	2148 80	2162 40	2176 00
125	987 50	993 75	1000 00	275	2172 50	2186 25	2200 00
126	995 40	1001 70	1008 00	280	2212 00	2226 00	2240 00
127	1003 30	1009 60	1016 00	285	2251 50	2265 75	2280 00
128	1011 20	1017 60	1024 00	288	2275 20	2289 60	2304 00
129	1019 10	1025 55	1032 00	295	2330 50	2345 25	2360 00
130	1027 00	1033 50	1040 00	300	2370 00	2385 00	2400 00
131	1034 90	1041 45	1048 00	325	2567 50	2583 75	2600 00
132	1042 80	1049 40	1056 00	336	2654 40	2671 20	2688 00
133	1050 70	1057 35	1064 00	365	2883 50	2901 75	2920 00
134	1058 60	1065 30	1072 00	375	2962 50	2981 25	3000 00
135	1066 50	1073 25	1080 00	400	3160 00	3180 00	3200 00
136	1074 40	1081 20	1088 00	425	3357 50	3378 75	3400 00
137	1082 30	1089 15	1096 00	432	3412 80	3434 40	3456 00
138	1090 20	1097 10	1104 00	475	3752 50	3776 25	3800 00
139	1098 10	1105 05	1112 00	480	3792 00	3816 00	3840 00
140	1106 00	1113 00	1120 00	500	3950 00	3975 00	4000 00
141	1113 90	1120 95	1128 00	504	3981 60	4006 80	4032 00
142	1121 80	1128 90	1136 00	576	4550 40	4579 20	4608 00
143	1129 70	1136 85	1144 00	600	4740 00	4770 00	4800 00
144	1137 60	1144 80	1152 00	700	5530 00	5565 00	5600 00
145	1145 50	1152 75	1160 00	750	5925 00	5962 50	6000 00
146	1153 40	1160 70	1168 00	800	6320 00	6360 00	6400 00
147	1161 30	1168 65	1176 00	900	7110 00	7155 00	7200 00
148	1169 20	1176 60	1184 00	1000	7900 00	7950 00	8000 00
149	1177 10	1184 55	1192 00	2500	19750 0	19875 0	20000 0
150	1185 00	1192 50	1200 00	5000	39500 0	39750 0	40000 0
1016	8026·40	8077·20	8128·00	1728	13651·20	13787·60	13824·00
1296	10238·40	10303·20	10368·00	1760	13904·00	13992·00	14080·00

No.	£8·05 £	P	£8·10 £	P	£8·15 £	P	No.	£8·05 £	P	£8·10 £	P	£8·15 £	P
1	8	05	8	10	8	15	51	410	55	413	10	415	65
2	16	10	16	20	16	30	52	418	60	421	20	423	80
3	24	15	24	30	24	45	53	426	65	429	30	431	95
4	32	20	32	40	32	60	54	434	70	437	40	440	10
5	40	25	40	50	40	75	55	442	75	445	50	448	25
6	48	30	48	60	48	90	56	450	80	453	60	456	40
7	56	35	56	70	57	05	57	458	85	461	70	464	55
8	64	40	64	80	65	20	58	466	90	469	80	472	70
9	72	45	72	90	73	35	59	474	95	477	90	480	85
10	80	50	81	00	81	50	60	483	00	486	00	489	00
11	88	55	89	10	89	65	61	491	05	494	10	497	15
12	96	60	97	20	97	80	62	499	10	502	20	505	30
13	104	65	105	30	105	95	63	507	15	510	30	513	45
14	112	70	113	40	114	10	64	515	20	518	40	521	60
15	120	75	121	50	122	25	65	523	25	526	50	529	75
16	128	80	129	60	130	40	66	531	30	534	60	537	90
17	136	85	137	70	138	55	67	539	35	542	70	546	05
18	144	90	145	80	146	70	68	547	40	550	80	554	20
19	152	95	153	90	154	85	69	555	45	558	90	562	35
20	161	00	162	00	163	00	70	563	50	567	00	570	50
21	169	05	170	10	171	15	71	571	55	575	10	578	65
22	177	10	178	20	179	30	72	579	60	583	20	586	80
23	185	15	186	30	187	45	73	587	65	591	30	594	95
24	193	20	194	40	195	60	74	595	70	599	40	603	10
25	201	25	202	50	203	75	75	603	75	607	50	611	25
26	209	30	210	60	211	90	76	611	80	615	60	619	40
27	217	35	218	70	220	05	77	619	85	623	70	627	55
28	225	40	226	80	228	20	78	627	90	631	80	635	70
29	233	45	234	90	236	35	79	635	95	639	90	643	85
30	241	50	243	00	244	50	80	644	00	648	00	652	00
31	249	55	251	10	252	65	81	652	05	656	10	660	15
32	257	60	259	20	260	80	82	660	10	664	20	668	30
33	265	65	267	30	268	95	83	668	15	672	30	676	45
34	273	70	275	40	277	10	84	676	20	680	40	684	60
35	281	75	283	50	285	25	85	684	25	688	50	692	75
36	289	80	291	60	293	40	86	692	30	696	60	700	90
37	297	85	299	70	301	55	87	700	35	704	70	709	05
38	305	90	307	80	309	70	88	708	40	712	80	717	20
39	313	95	315	90	317	85	89	716	45	720	90	725	35
40	322	00	324	00	326	00	90	724	50	729	00	733	50
41	330	05	332	10	334	15	91	732	55	737	10	741	65
42	338	10	340	20	342	30	92	740	60	745	20	749	80
43	346	15	348	30	350	45	93	748	65	753	30	757	95
44	354	20	356	40	358	60	94	756	70	761	40	766	10
45	362	25	364	50	366	75	95	764	75	769	50	774	25
46	370	30	372	60	374	90	96	772	80	777	60	782	40
47	378	35	380	70	383	05	97	780	85	785	70	790	55
48	386	40	388	80	391	20	98	788	90	793	80	798	70
49	394	45	396	90	399	35	99	796	95	801	90	806	85
50	402	50	405	00	407	50	100	805	00	810	00	815	00

Left column labelled *Dozens.* ; right column labelled *Dozens.*

	£8·05	£8·10	£8·15		£8·05	£8·10	£8·15
¼	2·0125	2·025	2·0375	¾	6·0375	6·075	6·1125
½	4·025	4·05	4·075	1¼	10·0625	10·125	10·1875

No.	£8·05 £ p	£8·10 £ p	£8·15 £ p
101	813 05	818 10	823 15
102	821 10	826 20	831 30
103	829 15	834 30	839 45
104	837 20	842 40	847 60
105	845 25	850 50	855 75
106	853 30	858 60	863 90
107	861 35	866 70	872 05
108	869 40	874 80	880 20
109	877 45	882 90	888 35
110	885 50	891 00	896 50
111	893 55	899 10	904 65
112	901 60	907 20	912 80
113	909 65	915 30	920 95
114	917 70	923 40	929 10
115	925 75	931 50	937 25
116	933 80	939 60	945 40
117	941 85	947 70	953 55
118	949 90	955 80	961 70
119	957 95	963 90	969 85
120	966 00	972 00	978 00
121	974 05	980 10	986 15
122	982 10	988 20	994 30
123	990 15	996 30	1002 45
124	998 20	1004 40	1010 60
125	1006 25	1012 50	1018 75
126	1014 30	1020 60	1026 90
127	1022 35	1028 70	1035 05
128	1030 40	1036 80	1043 20
129	1038 45	1044 90	1051 35
130	1046 50	1053 00	1059 50
131	1054 55	1061 10	1067 65
132	1062 60	1069 20	1075 80
133	1070 65	1077 30	1083 95
134	1078 70	1085 40	1092 10
135	1086 75	1093 50	1100 25
136	1094 80	1101 60	1108 40
137	1102 85	1109 70	1116 55
138	1110 90	1117 80	1124 70
139	1118 95	1125 90	1132 85
140	1127 00	1134 00	1141 00
141	1135 05	1142 10	1149 15
142	1143 10	1150 20	1157 30
143	1151 15	1158 30	1165 45
144	1159 20	1166 40	1173 60
145	1167 25	1174 50	1181 75
146	1175 30	1182 60	1189 90
147	1183 35	1190 70	1198 05
148	1191 40	1198 80	1206 20
149	1199 45	1206 90	1214 35
150	1207 50	1215 00	1222 50
1016	8178 80	8229 60	8280 40
1296	10482 80	10497 60	10562 40

No.	£8·05 £ p	£8·10 £ p	£8·15 £ p
Doz 155	1247 75	1255 50	1263 25
13 156	1255 80	1263 60	1271 40
165	1328 25	1336 50	1344 75
14 168	1352 40	1360 80	1369 20
175	1408 75	1417 50	1426 25
15 180	1449 00	1458 00	1467 00
185	1489 25	1498 50	1507 75
16 192	1545 60	1555 20	1564 80
195	1569 75	1579 50	1589 25
200	1610 00	1620 00	1630 00
17 204	1642 20	1652 40	1662 60
205	1650 25	1660 50	1670 75
215	1730 75	1741 50	1752 25
18 216	1738 80	1749 60	1760 40
224	1803 20	1814 40	1825 60
225	1811 25	1822 50	1833 75
19 228	1835 40	1846 80	1858 20
235	1891 75	1903 50	1915 25
245	1972 25	1984 50	1996 75
250	2012 50	2025 00	2037 50
21 252	2028 60	2041 20	2053 80
255	2052 75	2065 50	2078 25
265	2133 25	2146 50	2159 75
272	2189 60	2203 20	2216 80
275	2213 75	2227 50	2241 25
280	2254 00	2268 00	2282 00
285	2294 25	2308 50	2322 75
2 gross 288	2318 40	2332 80	2347 20
295	2374 75	2389 50	2404 25
300	2415 00	2430 00	2445 00
325	2616 25	2632 50	2648 75
336	2704 80	2721 60	2738 40
365	2938 25	2956 50	2974 75
375	3018 75	3037 50	3056 25
400	3220 00	3240 00	3260 00
3 gr. 425	3421 25	3442 50	3463 75
3 432	3477 60	3499 20	3520 80
475	3823 75	3847 50	3871 25
480	3864 00	3888 00	3912 00
500	4025 00	4050 00	4075 00
4 gr. 504	4057 20	4082 40	4107 60
4 576	4636 80	4665 60	4694 40
600	4830 00	4860 00	4890 00
700	5635 00	5670 00	5705 00
750	6037 50	6075 00	6112 50
800	6440 00	6480 00	6520 00
900	7245 00	7290 00	7335 00
1000	8050 00	8100 00	8150 00
2500	20125 0	20250 0	20375 0
5000	40250 0	40500 0	40750 0
1728	13910 40	13996 80	14083 20
1760	14168 00	14256 00	14344 00

No.	£8·20 £ P	£8·25 £ P	£8·30 £ P	No.	£8·20 £ P	£8·25 £ P	£8·30 £ P
1	8 20	8 25	8 30	51	418 20	420 75	423 30
2	16 40	16 50	16 60	52	426 40	429 00	431 60
3	24 60	24 75	24 90	53	434 60	437 25	439 90
4	32 80	33 00	33 20	54	442 80	445 50	448 20
5	41 00	41 25	41 50	55	451 00	453 75	456 50
6	49 20	49 50	49 80	56	459 20	462 00	464 80
7	57 40	57 75	58 10	57	467 40	470 25	473 10
8	65 60	66 00	66 40	58	475 60	478 50	481 40
9	73 80	74 25	74 70	59	483 80	486 75	489 70
10	82 00	82 50	83 00	60	492 00	495 00	498 00
11	90 20	90 75	91 30	61	500 20	503 25	506 30
12	98 40	99 00	99 60	62	508 40	511 50	514 60
13	106 60	107 25	107 90	63	516 60	519 75	522 90
14	114 80	115 50	116 20	64	524 80	528 00	531 20
15	123 00	123 75	124 50	65	533 00	536 25	539 50
16	131 20	132 00	132 80	66	541 20	544 50	547 80
17	139 40	140 25	141 10	67	549 40	552 75	556 10
18	147 60	148 50	149 40	68	557 60	561 00	564 40
19	155 80	156 75	157 70	69	565 80	569 25	572 70
20	164 00	165 00	166 00	70	574 00	577 50	581 00
21	172 20	173 25	174 30	71	582 20	585 75	589 30
22	180 40	181 50	182 60	72	590 40	594 00	597 60
23	188 60	189 75	190 90	73	598 60	602 25	605 90
24	196 80	198 00	199 20	74	606 80	610 50	614 20
25	205 00	206 25	207 50	75	615 00	618 75	622 50
26	213 20	214 50	215 80	76	623 20	627 00	630 80
27	221 40	222 75	224 10	77	631 40	635 25	639 10
28	229 60	231 00	232 40	78	639 60	643 50	647 40
29	237 80	239 25	240 70	79	647 80	651 75	655 70
30	246 00	247 50	249 00	80	656 00	660 00	664 00
31	254 20	255 75	257 30	81	664 20	668 25	672 30
32	262 40	264 00	265 60	82	672 40	676 50	680 60
33	270 60	272 25	273 90	83	680 60	684 75	688 90
34	278 80	280 50	282 20	84	688 80	693 00	697 20
35	287 00	288 75	290 50	85	697 00	701 25	705 50
36	295 20	297 00	298 80	86	705 20	709 50	713 80
37	303 40	305 25	307 10	87	713 40	717 75	722 10
38	311 60	313 50	315 40	88	721 60	726 00	730 40
39	319 80	321 75	323 70	89	729 80	734 25	738 70
40	328 00	330 00	332 00	90	738 00	742 50	747 00
41	336 20	338 25	340 30	91	746 20	750 75	755 30
42	344 40	346 50	348 60	92	754 40	759 00	763 60
43	352 60	354 75	356 90	93	762 60	767 25	771 90
44	360 80	363 00	365 20	94	770 80	775 50	780 20
45	369 00	371 25	373 50	95	779 00	783 75	788 50
46	377 20	379 50	381 80	96	787 20	792 00	796 80
47	385 40	387 75	390 10	97	795 40	800 25	805 10
48	393 60	396 00	398 40	98	803 60	808 50	813 40
49	401 80	404 25	406 70	99	811 80	816 75	821 70
50	410 00	412 50	415 00	100	820 00	825 00	830 00
¼	2·05	2·0625	2·075	¾	6·15	6·1875	6·225
½..	4·10	4·1250	4·150	1¼..	10·25	10·3125	10·375

No.	£8·20	£8·25	£8·30	No.	£8·20	£8·25	£8·30
	£ p	£ p	£ p		£ p	£ p	£ p
101	828 20	833 25	838 30	155	1271 00	1278 75	1286 50
102	836 40	841 50	846 60	13 156	1279 20	1287 00	1294 80
103	844 60	849 75	854 90	165	1353 00	1361 25	1369 50
104	852 80	858 00	863 20	14 168	1377 60	1386 00	1394 40
105	861 00	866 25	871 50	175	1435 00	1443 75	1452 50
106	869 20	874 50	879 80	15 180	1476 00	1485 00	1494 00
107	877 40	882 75	888 10	185	1517 00	1526 25	1535 50
108	885 60	891 00	896 40	16 192	1574 40	1584 00	1593 60
109	893 80	899 25	904 70	195	1599 00	1608 75	1618 50
10	902 00	907 50	913 00	200	1640 00	1650 00	1660 00
111	910 20	915 75	921 30	17 204	1672 80	1683 00	1693 20
112	918 40	924 00	929 60	205	1681 00	1691 25	1701 50
113	926 60	932 25	937 90	215	1763 00	1773 75	1784 50
114	934 80	940 50	946 20	18 216	1771 20	1782 00	1792 80
115	943 00	948 75	954 50	224	1836 80	1848 00	1859 20
116	951 20	957 00	962 80	225	1845 00	1856 25	1867 50
117	959 40	965 25	971 10	19 228	1869 60	1881 00	1892 40
118	967 60	973 50	979 40	235	1927 00	1938 75	1950 50
119	975 80	981 75	987 70	245	2009 00	2021 25	2033 50
120	984 00	990 00	996 00	250	2050 00	2062 50	2075 00
121	992 20	998 25	1004 30	21 252	2066 40	2079 00	2091 60
122	1000 40	1006 50	1012 60	255	2091 00	2103 75	2116 50
123	1008 60	1014 75	1020 90	265	2173 00	2186 25	2199 50
124	1016 80	1023 00	1029 20	272	2230 40	2244 00	2257 60
125	1025 00	1031 25	1037 50	275	2255 00	2268 75	2282 50
126	1033 20	1039 50	1045 80	280	2296 00	2310 00	2324 00
127	1041 40	1047 75	1054 10	285	2337 00	2351 25	2365 50
128	1049 60	1056 00	1062 40	2 gross 288	2361 60	2376 00	2390 40
129	1057 80	1064 25	1070 70	295	2419 00	2433 75	2448 50
30	1066 00	1072 50	1079 00	300	2460 00	2475 00	2490 00
131	1074 20	1080 75	1087 30	325	2665 00	2681 25	2697 50
132	1082 40	1089 00	1095 60	336	2755 20	2772 00	2788 80
133	1090 60	1097 25	1103 90	365	2993 00	3011 25	3029 50
134	1098 80	1105 50	1112 20	375	3075 00	3093 75	3112 50
135	1107 00	1113 75	1120 50	400	3280 00	3300 00	3320 00
136	1115 20	1122 00	1128 80	425	3485 00	3506 25	3527 50
137	1123 40	1130 25	1137 10	3 gr. 432	3542 40	3564 00	3585 60
138	1131 60	1138 50	1145 40	475	3895 00	3918 75	3942 50
139	1139 80	1146 75	1153 70	480	3936 00	3960 00	3984 00
140	1148 00	1155 00	1162 00	500	4100 00	4125 00	4150 00
141	1156 20	1163 25	1170 30	504	4132 80	4158 00	4183 20
142	1164 40	1171 50	1178 60	4 gr. 576	4723 20	4752 00	4780 80
143	1172 60	1179 75	1186 90	600	4920 00	4950 00	4980 00
144	1180 80	1188 00	1195 20	700	5740 00	5775 00	5810 00
145	1189 00	1196 25	1203 50	750	6150 00	6187 50	6225 00
146	1197 20	1204 50	1211 80	800	6560 00	6600 00	6640 00
147	1205 40	1212 75	1220 10	900	7380 00	7425 00	7470 00
148	1213 60	1221 00	1228 40	1000	8200 00	8250 00	8300 00
149	1221 80	1229 25	1236 70	2500	20500 ·0	20625 ·0	20750 ·0
150	1230 00	1237 50	1245 00	5000	41000 ·0	41250 ·0	41500 ·0
1016	8831·20	8382·00	8432·80	1728	14169·60	14256·00	14842·40
1296	10627·20	10692·00	10756·80	1760	14432·00	14520·00	14608·00

No.	£8·35		£8·40		£8·45		No.	£8·35		£8·40		£8·45	
	£	P	£	P	£	P		£	P	£	P	£	P
1	8	35	8	40	8	45	51	425	85	428	40	430	95
2	16	70	16	80	16	90	52	434	20	436	80	439	40
3	25	05	25	20	25	35	53	442	55	445	20	447	85
4	33	40	33	60	33	80	54	450	90	453	60	456	30
5	41	75	42	00	42	25	55	459	25	462	00	464	75
6	50	10	50	40	50	70	56	467	60	470	40	473	20
7	58	45	58	80	59	15	57	475	95	478	80	481	65
8	66	80	67	20	67	60	58	484	30	487	20	490	10
9	75	15	75	60	76	05	59	492	65	495	60	498	55
10	83	50	84	00	84	50	60	501	00	504	00	507	00
11	91	85	92	40	92	95	61	509	35	512	40	515	45
12	100	20	100	80	101	40	62	517	70	520	80	523	90
13	108	55	109	20	109	85	63	526	05	529	20	532	35
14	116	90	117	60	118	30	64	534	40	537	60	540	80
15	125	25	126	00	126	75	65	542	75	546	00	549	25
16	133	60	134	40	135	20	66	551	10	554	40	557	70
17	141	95	142	80	143	65	67	559	45	562	80	566	15
18	150	30	151	20	152	10	68	567	80	571	20	574	60
19	158	65	159	60	160	55	69	576	15	579	60	583	05
20	167	00	168	00	169	00	70	584	50	588	00	591	50
21	175	35	176	40	177	45	71	592	85	596	40	599	95
22	183	70	184	80	185	90	72	601	20	604	80	608	40
23	192	05	193	20	194	35	73	609	55	613	20	616	85
24	200	40	201	60	202	80	74	617	90	621	60	625	30
25	208	75	210	00	211	25	75	626	25	630	00	633	75
26	217	10	218	40	219	70	76	634	60	638	40	642	20
27	225	45	226	80	228	15	77	642	95	646	80	650	65
28	233	80	235	20	236	60	78	651	30	655	20	659	10
29	242	15	243	60	245	05	79	659	65	663	60	667	55
30	250	50	252	00	253	50	80	668	00	672	00	676	00
31	258	85	260	40	261	95	81	676	35	680	40	684	45
32	267	20	268	80	270	40	82	684	70	688	80	692	90
33	275	55	277	20	278	85	83	693	05	697	20	701	35
34	283	90	285	60	287	30	84	701	40	705	60	709	80
35	292	25	294	00	295	75	85	709	75	714	00	718	25
36	300	60	302	40	304	20	86	718	10	722	40	726	70
37	308	95	310	80	312	65	87	726	45	730	80	735	15
38	317	30	319	20	321	10	88	734	80	739	20	743	60
39	325	65	327	60	329	55	89	743	15	747	60	752	05
40	334	00	336	00	338	00	90	751	50	756	00	760	50
41	342	35	344	40	346	45	91	759	85	764	40	768	95
42	350	70	352	80	354	90	92	768	20	772	80	777	40
43	359	05	361	20	363	35	93	776	55	781	20	785	85
44	367	40	369	60	371	80	94	784	90	789	60	794	30
45	375	75	378	00	380	25	95	793	25	798	00	802	75
46	384	10	386	40	388	70	96	801	60	806	40	811	20
47	392	45	394	80	397	15	97	809	95	814	80	819	65
48	400	80	403	20	405	60	98	818	30	823	20	828	10
49	409	15	411	60	414	05	99	826	65	831	60	836	55
50	417	50	420	00	422	50	100	835	00	840	00	845	00
¼	2·0875		2·10		2·1125		¾	6·2625		6·30		6·3375	
½	4·175		4·20		4·2250		1¼	10·4875		10·50		10·5625	

*Dozens.

No.	£8·35 £ p	£8·40 £ p	£8·45 £ p
101	843 35	848 40	853 45
102	851 70	856 80	861 90
103	860 05	865 20	870 35
104	868 40	873 60	878 80
105	876 75	882 00	887 25
106	885 10	890 40	895 70
107	893 45	898 80	904 15
108	901 80	907 20	912 60
109	910 15	915 60	921 05
110	918 50	924 00	929 50
111	926 85	932 40	937 95
112	935 20	940 80	946 40
113	943 55	949 20	954 85
114	951 90	957 60	963 30
115	960 25	966 00	971 75
116	968 60	974 40	980 20
117	976 95	982 80	988 65
118	985 30	991 20	997 10
119	993 65	999 60	1005 55
120	1002 00	1008 00	1014 00
121	1010 35	1016 40	1022 45
122	1018 70	1024 80	1030 90
123	1027 05	1033 20	1039 35
124	1035 40	1041 60	1047 80
125	1043 75	1050 00	1056 25
126	1052 10	1058 40	1064 70
127	1060 45	1066 80	1073 15
128	1068 80	1075 20	1081 60
129	1077 15	1083 60	1090 05
130	1085 50	1092 00	1098 50
131	1093 85	1100 40	1106 95
132	1102 20	1108 80	1115 40
133	1110 55	1117 20	1123 85
134	1118 90	1125 60	1132 30
135	1127 25	1134 00	1140 75
136	1135 60	1142 40	1149 20
137	1143 95	1150 80	1157 65
138	1152 30	1159 20	1166 10
139	1160 65	1167 60	1174 55
140	1169 00	1176 00	1183 00
141	1177 35	1184 40	1191 45
142	1185 70	1192 80	1199 90
143	1194 05	1201 20	1208 35
144	1202 40	1209 60	1216 80
145	1210 75	1218 00	1225 25
146	1219 10	1226 40	1233 70
147	1227 45	1234 80	1242 15
148	1235 80	1243 20	1250 60
149	1244 15	1251 60	1259 05
150	1252 50	1260 00	1267 50
1016	8483 60	8534 40	8585 20
1296	10821 60	10886 40	10951 20

No.	£8·35 £ p	£8·40 £ p	£8·45 £ p
155 (Doz)	1294 25	1302 00	1309 75
156 (13)	1302 60	1310 40	1318 20
165	1377 75	1386 00	1394 25
168 (14)	1402 80	1411 20	1419 60
175	1461 25	1470 00	1478 75
180 (15)	1503 00	1512 00	1521 00
185	1544 75	1554 00	1563 25
192 (16)	1603 20	1612 80	1622 40
195	1628 25	1638 00	1647 75
200	1670 00	1680 00	1690 00
204 (17)	1703 40	1713 60	1723 80
205	1711 75	1722 00	1732 25
215	1795 25	1806 00	1816 75
216 (18)	1803 60	1814 40	1825 20
224	1870 40	1881 60	1892 80
225	1878 75	1890 00	1901 25
228 (19)	1903 80	1915 20	1926 60
235	1962 25	1974 00	1985 75
245	2045 75	2058 00	2070 25
250	2087 50	2100 00	2112 50
252 (21)	2104 20	2116 80	2129 40
255	2129 25	2142 00	2154 75
265	2212 75	2226 00	2239 25
272	2271 20	2284 80	2298 40
275	2296 25	2310 00	2323 75
280	2338 00	2352 00	2366 00
285 (2 gross)	2379 75	2394 00	2408 25
288	2404 80	2419 20	2433 60
295	2463 25	2478 00	2492 75
300	2505 00	2520 00	2535 00
325	2713 75	2730 00	2746 25
336	2805 60	2822 40	2839 20
365	3047 75	3066 00	3084 25
375	3131 25	3150 00	3168 75
400	3340 00	3360 00	3380 00
425	3548 75	3570 00	3591 25
432 (3 gr)	3607 20	3628 80	3650 40
475	3966 25	3990 00	4013 75
480	4008 00	4032 00	4056 00
500	4175 00	4200 00	4225 00
504 (4 gr)	4208 40	4233 60	4258 80
576	4809 60	4838 40	4867 20
600	5010 00	5040 00	5070 00
700	5845 00	5880 00	5915 00
750	6262 50	6300 00	6337 50
800	6680 00	6720 00	6760 00
900	7515 00	7560 00	7605 00
1000	8350 00	8400 00	8450 00
2500	20875 0	21000 0	21125 0
5000	41750 0	42000 0	42250 0
1728	14428 80	14515 20	14601 60
1760	14696 00	14784 00	14872 00

No.	£8·50		£8·55		£8·60		No.	£8·50		£8·55		£8·60	
	£	P	£	P	£	P		£	P	£	P	£	P
1	8	50	8	55	8	60	51	433	50	436	05	438	60
2	17	00	17	10	17	20	52	442	00	444	60	447	20
3	25	50	25	65	25	80	53	450	50	453	15	455	80
4	34	00	34	20	34	40	54	459	00	461	70	464	40
5	42	50	42	75	43	00	55	467	50	470	25	473	00
6	51	00	51	30	51	60	56	476	00	478	80	481	60
7	59	50	59	85	60	20	57	484	50	487	35	490	20
8	68	00	68	40	68	80	58	493	00	495	90	498	80
9	76	50	76	95	77	40	59	501	50	504	45	507	40
10	85	00	85	50	86	00	60	510	00	513	00	516	00
11	93	50	94	05	94	60	61	518	50	521	55	524	60
12	102	00	102	60	103	20	62	527	00	530	10	533	20
13	110	50	111	15	111	80	63	535	50	538	65	541	80
14	119	00	119	70	120	40	64	544	00	547	20	550	40
15	127	50	128	25	129	00	65	552	50	555	75	559	00
16	136	00	136	80	137	60	66	561	00	564	30	567	60
17	144	50	145	35	146	20	67	569	50	572	85	576	20
18	153	00	153	90	154	80	68	578	00	581	40	584	80
19	161	50	162	45	163	40	69	586	50	589	95	593	40
20	170	00	171	00	172	00	70	595	00	598	50	602	00
21	178	50	179	55	180	60	71	603	50	607	05	610	60
22	187	00	188	10	189	20	72	612	00	615	60	619	20
23	195	50	196	65	197	80	73	620	50	624	15	627	80
24	204	00	205	20	206	40	74	629	00	632	70	636	40
25	212	50	213	75	215	00	75	637	50	641	25	645	00
26	221	00	222	30	223	60	76	646	00	649	80	653	60
27	229	50	230	85	232	20	77	654	50	658	35	662	20
28	238	00	239	40	240	80	78	663	00	666	90	670	80
29	246	50	247	95	249	40	79	671	50	675	45	679	40
30	255	00	256	50	258	00	80	680	00	684	00	688	00
31	263	50	265	05	266	60	81	688	50	692	55	696	60
32	272	00	273	60	275	20	82	697	00	701	10	705	20
33	280	50	282	15	283	80	83	705	50	709	65	713	80
34	289	00	290	70	292	40	84	714	00	718	20	722	40
35	297	50	299	25	301	00	85	722	50	726	75	731	00
36	306	00	307	80	309	60	86	731	00	735	30	739	60
37	314	50	316	35	318	20	87	739	50	743	85	748	20
38	323	00	324	90	326	80	88	748	00	752	40	756	80
39	331	50	333	45	335	40	89	756	50	760	95	765	40
40	340	00	342	00	344	00	90	765	00	769	50	774	00
41	348	50	350	55	352	60	91	773	50	778	05	782	60
42	357	00	359	10	361	20	92	782	00	786	60	791	20
43	365	50	367	65	369	80	93	790	50	795	15	799	80
44	374	00	376	20	378	40	94	799	00	803	70	808	40
45	382	50	384	75	387	00	95	807	50	812	25	817	00
46	391	00	393	30	395	60	96	816	00	820	80	825	60
47	399	50	401	85	404	20	97	824	50	829	35	834	20
48	408	00	410	40	412	80	98	833	00	837	90	842	80
49	416	50	418	95	421	40	99	841	50	846	45	851	40
50	425	00	427	50	430	00	100	850	00	855	00	860	00
¼	2·125		2·1375		2·15		¾	6·875		6·4125		6·45	
½	4·250		4·2750		4·30		1¼	10·625		10·6875		10·75	

No.	£8.50 £ p	£8.55 £ p	£8.60 £ p
101	858 50	863 55	868 60
102	867 00	872 10	877 20
103	875 50	880 65	885 80
104	884 00	889 20	894 40
105	892 50	897 75	903 00
106	901 00	906 30	911 60
107	909 50	914 85	920 20
108	918 00	923 40	928 80
109	926 50	931 95	937 20
110	935 00	940 50	946 00
111	943 50	949 05	954 60
112	952 00	957 60	963 20
113	960 50	966 15	971 80
114	969 00	974 70	980 40
115	977 50	983 25	989 00
116	986 00	991 80	997 60
117	994 50	1000 35	1006 20
118	1003 00	1008 90	1014 80
119	1011 50	1017 45	1023 40
120	1020 00	1026 00	1032 00
121	1028 50	1034 55	1040 60
122	1037 00	1043 10	1049 20
123	1045 50	1051 65	1057 80
124	1054 00	1060 20	1066 40
125	1062 50	1068 75	1075 00
126	1071 00	1077 30	1083 60
127	1079 50	1085 85	1092 20
128	1088 00	1094 40	1100 80
129	1096 50	1102 95	1109 40
130	1105 00	1111 50	1118 00
131	1113 50	1120 05	1126 60
132	1122 00	1128 60	1135 20
133	1130 50	1137 15	1143 80
134	1139 00	1145 70	1152 40
135	1147 50	1154 25	1161 00
136	1156 00	1162 80	1169 60
137	1164 50	1171 35	1178 20
138	1173 00	1179 90	1186 80
139	1181 50	1188 45	1195 40
140	1190 00	1197 00	1204 00
141	1198 50	1205 55	1212 60
142	1207 00	1214 10	1221 20
143	1215 50	1222 65	1229 80
144	1224 00	1231 20	1238 40
145	1232 50	1239 75	1247 00
146	1241 00	1248 30	1255 60
147	1249 50	1256 85	1264 20
148	1258 00	1265 40	1272 80
149	1266 50	1273 95	1281 40
150	1275 00	1282 50	1290 00
1016	8636·00	8686·80	8737·60
1296	11016·00	11080·80	11145·60

No.	£8.50 £ p	£8.55 £ p	£8.60 £ p
155	1317 50	1325 25	1333 00
156	1326 00	1333 80	1341 60
165	1402 50	1410 75	1419 00
168	1428 00	1436 40	1444 80
175	1487 50	1496 25	1505 00
180	1530 00	1539 00	1548 00
185	1572 50	1581 75	1591 00
192	1632 00	1641 60	1651 20
195	1657 50	1667 25	1677 00
200	1700 00	1710 00	1720 00
204	1734 00	1744 20	1754 40
205	1742 50	1752 75	1763 00
215	1827 50	1838 25	1849 00
216	1836 00	1846 80	1857 60
224	1904 00	1915 20	1926 40
225	1912 50	1923 75	1935 00
228	1938 00	1949 40	1960 80
235	1997 50	2009 25	2021 00
245	2082 50	2094 75	2107 00
250	2125 00	2137 50	2150 00
252	2142 00	2154 60	2167 20
255	2167 50	2180 25	2193 00
265	2252 50	2265 75	2279 00
272	2312 00	2325 60	2339 20
275	2337 50	2351 25	2365 00
280	2380 00	2394 00	2408 00
285	2422 50	2436 75	2451 00
288	2448 00	2462 40	2476 80
295	2507 50	2522 25	2537 00
300	2550 00	2565 00	2580 00
325	2762 50	2778 75	2795 00
336	2856 00	2872 80	2889 60
365	3102 50	3120 75	3139 00
375	3187 50	3206 25	3225 00
400	3400 00	3420 00	3440 00
425	3612 50	3633 75	3655 00
432	3672 00	3693 60	3715 20
475	4037 50	4061 25	4085 00
480	4080 00	4104 00	4128 00
500	4250 00	4275 00	4300 00
504	4284 00	4309 20	4334 40
576	4896 00	4924 80	4953 60
600	5100 00	5130 00	5160 00
700	5950 00	5985 00	6020 00
750	6375 00	6412 50	6450 00
800	6800 00	6840 00	6880 00
900	7650 00	7695 00	7740 00
1000	8500 00	8550 00	8600 00
2500	21250 00	21375 ·0	21500 ·0
5000	42500 ·0	42750 ·0	43000 ·0
1728	14688·00	14774·40	14860·80
1760	14960·00	15048·00	15186·00

No.	£8·65		£8·70		£8·75		No.	£8·65		£8·70		£8·75	
	£	P	£	P	£	P		£	P	£	P	£	P
1	8	65	8	70	8	75	51	441	15	443	70	446	25
2	17	30	17	40	17	50	52	449	80	452	40	455	00
3	25	95	26	10	26	25	53	458	45	461	10	463	75
4	34	60	34	80	35	00	54	467	10	469	80	472	50
5	43	25	43	50	43	75	55	475	75	478	50	481	25
6	51	90	52	20	52	50	56	484	40	487	20	490	00
7	60	55	60	90	61	25	57	493	05	495	90	498	75
8	69	20	69	60	70	00	58	501	70	504	60	507	50
9	77	85	78	30	78	75	59	510	35	513	30	516	25
10	86	50	87	00	87	50	60	519	00	522	00	525	00
11	95	15	95	70	96	25	61	527	65	530	70	533	75
12	103	80	104	40	105	00	62	536	30	539	40	542	50
13	112	45	113	10	113	75	63	544	95	548	10	551	25
14	121	10	121	80	122	50	64	553	60	556	80	560	00
15	129	75	130	50	131	25	65	562	25	565	50	568	75
16	138	40	139	20	140	00	66	570	90	574	20	577	50
17	147	05	147	90	148	75	67	579	55	582	90	586	25
18	155	70	156	60	157	50	68	588	20	591	60	595	00
19	164	35	165	30	166	25	69	596	85	600	30	603	75
20	173	00	174	00	175	00	70	605	50	609	00	612	50
21	181	65	182	70	183	75	71	614	15	617	70	621	25
22	190	30	191	40	192	50	72	622	80	626	40	630	00
23	198	95	200	10	201	25	73	631	45	635	10	638	75
24	207	60	208	80	210	00	74	640	10	643	80	647	50
25	216	25	217	50	218	75	75	648	75	652	50	656	25
26	224	90	226	20	227	50	76	657	40	661	20	665	00
27	233	55	234	90	236	25	77	666	05	669	90	673	75
28	242	20	243	60	245	00	78	674	70	678	60	682	50
29	250	85	252	30	253	75	79	683	35	687	30	691	25
30	259	50	261	00	262	50	80	692	00	696	00	700	00
31	268	15	269	70	271	25	81	700	65	704	70	708	75
32	276	80	278	40	280	00	82	709	30	713	40	717	50
33	285	45	287	10	288	75	83	717	95	722	10	726	25
34	294	10	295	80	297	50	84	726	60	730	80	735	00
35	302	75	304	50	306	25	85	735	25	739	50	743	75
36	311	40	313	20	315	00	86	743	90	748	20	752	50
37	320	05	321	90	323	75	87	752	55	756	90	761	25
38	328	70	330	60	332	50	88	761	20	765	60	770	00
39	337	35	339	30	341	25	89	769	85	774	30	778	75
40	346	00	348	00	350	00	90	778	50	783	00	787	50
41	354	65	356	70	358	75	91	787	15	791	70	796	25
42	363	30	365	40	367	50	92	795	80	800	40	805	00
43	371	95	374	10	376	25	93	804	45	809	10	813	75
44	380	60	382	80	385	00	94	813	10	817	80	822	50
45	389	25	391	50	393	75	95	821	75	826	50	831	25
46	397	90	400	20	402	50	96	830	40	835	20	840	00
47	406	55	408	90	411	25	97	839	05	843	90	848	75
48	415	20	417	60	420	00	98	847	70	852	60	857	50
49	423	85	426	30	428	75	99	856	35	861	30	866	25
50	432	50	435	00	437	50	100	865	00	870	00	875	00
¼	2·1625		2·175		2·1875		¾	6·4875		6·525		6·5625	
½	4·8250		4·350		4·3750		1¼	10·8125		10·875		10·9875	

No.	£8·65	£8·70	£8·75	No.	£8·65	£8·70	£8·75
101	873 65	878 70	883 75	155	1340 75	1348 50	1356 25
102	882 30	887 40	892 50	13 156	1349 40	1357 20	1365 00
103	890 95	896 10	901 25	165	1427 25	1435 50	1443 75
104	899 60	904 80	910 00	14 168	1453 20	1461 60	1470 00
105	908 25	913 50	918 75	175	1513 75	1522 50	1531 25
106	916 90	922 20	927 50	15 180	1557 00	1566 00	1575 00
107	925 55	930 90	936 25	185	1600 25	1609 50	1618 75
108	934 20	939 60	945 00	16 192	1660 80	1670 40	1680 00
109	942 85	948 30	953 75	195	1686 75	1696 50	1706 25
10	951 50	957 00	962 50	200	1730 00	1740 00	1750 00
111	960 15	965 70	971 25	17 204	1764 60	1774 80	1785 00
112	968 80	974 40	980 00	205	1773 25	1783 50	1793 75
113	977 45	983 10	988 75	215	1859 50	1870 50	1881 25
114	986 10	991 80	997 50	18 216	1868 40	1879 20	1890 00
115	994 75	1000 50	1006 25	224	1937 60	1948 80	1960 00
116	1003 40	1009 20	1015 00	225	1946 25	1957 50	1968 75
117	1012 05	1017 90	1023 75	19 228	1972 20	1983 60	1995 00
118	1020 70	1026 60	1032 50	235	2032 75	2044 50	2056 25
119	1029 35	1035 30	1041 25	245	2119 25	2131 50	2143 75
120	1038 00	1044 00	1050 00	250	2162 50	2175 00	2187 50
121	1046 65	1052 70	1058 75	21 252	2179 80	2192 40	2205 00
122	1055 30	1061 40	1067 50	255	2205 75	2218 50	2231 25
123	1063 95	1070 10	1076 25	265	2292 25	2305 50	2318 75
124	1072 60	1078 80	1085 00	272	2352 80	2366 40	2380 00
125	1081 25	1087 50	1093 75	275	2378 75	2392 50	2406 25
126	1089 90	1096 20	1102 50	280	2422 00	2436 00	2450 00
127	1098 55	1104 90	1111 25	285	2465 25	2479 50	2493 75
128	1107 20	1113 60	1120 00	288	2491 20	2505 60	2520 00
129	1115 85	1122 30	1128 75	295	2551 75	2566 50	2581 25
30	1124 50	1131 00	1137 50	300	2595 00	2610 00	2625 00
131	1133 15	1139 70	1146 25	325	2811 25	2827 50	2843 75
132	1141 80	1148 40	1155 00	336	2906 40	2923 20	2940 00
133	1150 45	1157 10	1163 75	365	3157 25	3175 50	3193 75
134	1159 10	1165 80	1172 50	375	3243 75	3262 50	3281 25
135	1167 75	1174 50	1181 25	400	3460 00	3480 00	3500 00
136	1176 40	1183 20	1190 00	425	3676 25	3697 50	3718 75
137	1185 05	1191 90	1198 75	432	3736 80	3758 40	3780 00
138	1193 70	1200 60	1207 50	475	4108 75	4132 50	4156 25
139	1202 35	1209 30	1216 25	480	4152 00	4176 00	4200 00
40	1211 00	1218 00	1225 00	500	4325 00	4350 00	4375 00
141	1219 65	1226 70	1233 75	504	4359 60	4384 80	4410 00
142	1228 30	1235 40	1242 50	576	4982 40	5011 20	5040 00
143	1236 95	1244 10	1251 25	600	5190 00	5220 00	5250 00
144	1245 60	1252 80	1260 00	700	6055 00	6090 00	6125 00
145	1254 25	1261 50	1268 75	750	6487 50	6525 00	6562 50
146	1262 90	1270 20	1277 50	800	6920 00	6960 00	7000 00
147	1271 55	1278 90	1286 25	900	7785 00	7830 00	7875 00
148	1280 20	1287 60	1295 00	1000	8650 00	8700 00	8750 00
149	1288 85	1296 30	1303 75	2500	21625 ·0	21750 ·0	21875 ·0
50	1297 50	1305 00	1312 50	5000	43250 ·0	43500 ·0	43750 ·0
1016	8788·40	8839·20	8890·00	1728	14947·20	15033·60	15120·00
1296	11210·40	11275·20	11340·00	1760	15224·00	15312·00	15400·00

No.	£8·80 £	p	£8·85 £	p	£8·90 £	p	No.	£8·80 £	p	£8·85 £	p	£8·90 £	p
1	8	80	8	85	8	90	51	448	80	451	35	453	90
2	17	60	17	70	17	80	52	457	60	460	20	462	80
3	26	40	26	55	26	70	53	466	40	469	05	471	70
4	35	20	35	40	35	60	54	475	20	477	90	480	60
5	44	00	44	25	44	50	55	484	00	486	75	489	50
6	52	80	53	10	53	40	56	492	80	495	60	498	40
7	61	60	61	95	62	30	57	501	60	504	45	507	30
8	70	40	70	80	71	20	58	510	40	513	30	516	20
9	79	20	79	65	80	10	59	519	20	522	15	525	10
10	88	00	88	50	89	00	60	528	00	531	00	534	00
11	96	80	97	35	97	90	61	536	80	539	85	542	90
12	105	60	106	20	106	80	62	545	60	548	70	551	80
13	114	40	115	05	115	70	63	554	40	557	55	560	70
14	123	20	123	90	124	60	64	563	20	566	40	569	60
15	132	00	132	75	133	50	65	572	00	575	25	578	50
16	140	80	141	60	142	40	66	580	80	584	10	587	40
17	149	60	150	45	151	30	67	589	60	592	95	596	30
18	158	40	159	30	160	20	68	598	40	601	80	605	20
19	167	20	168	15	169	10	69	607	20	610	65	614	10
20	176	00	177	00	178	00	70	616	00	619	50	623	00
21	184	80	185	85	186	90	71	624	80	628	35	631	90
22	193	60	194	70	195	80	72	633	60	637	20	640	80
23	202	40	203	55	204	70	73	642	40	646	05	649	70
24	211	20	212	40	213	60	74	651	20	654	90	658	60
25	220	00	221	25	222	50	75	660	00	663	75	667	50
26	228	80	230	10	231	40	76	668	80	672	60	676	40
27	237	60	238	95	240	30	77	677	60	681	45	685	30
28	246	40	247	80	249	20	78	686	40	690	30	694	20
29	255	20	256	65	258	10	79	695	20	699	15	703	10
30	264	00	265	50	267	00	80	704	00	708	00	712	00
31	272	80	274	35	275	90	81	712	80	716	85	720	90
32	281	60	283	20	284	80	82	721	60	725	70	729	80
33	290	40	292	05	293	70	83	730	40	734	55	738	70
34	299	20	300	90	302	60	84	739	20	743	40	747	60
35	308	00	309	75	311	50	85	748	00	752	25	756	50
36	316	80	318	60	320	40	86	756	80	761	10	765	40
37	325	60	327	45	329	30	87	765	60	769	95	774	30
38	334	40	336	30	338	20	88	774	40	778	80	783	20
39	343	20	345	15	347	10	89	783	20	787	65	792	10
40	352	00	354	00	356	00	90	792	00	796	50	801	00
41	360	80	362	85	364	90	91	800	80	805	35	809	90
42	369	60	371	70	373	80	92	809	60	814	20	818	80
43	378	40	380	55	382	70	93	818	40	823	05	827	70
44	387	20	389	40	391	60	94	827	20	831	90	836	60
45	396	00	398	25	400	50	95	836	00	840	75	845	50
46	404	80	407	10	409	40	96	844	80	849	60	854	40
47	413	60	415	95	418	30	97	853	60	858	45	863	30
48	422	40	424	80	427	20	98	862	40	867	30	872	20
49	431	20	433	65	436	10	99	871	20	876	15	881	10
50	440	00	442	50	445	00	100	880	00	885	00	890	00
¼		2·20		2·2125		2·225	¾		6·60		6·6375		6·675
½		4·40		4·425		4·450	1¼		11·00		11·0625		11·125

No.	£8·80		£8·85		£8·90	
	£	P	£	P	£	P
101	888	80	893	85	898	90
102	897	60	902	70	907	80
103	906	40	911	55	916	70
104	915	20	920	40	925	60
105	924	00	929	25	934	50
106	932	80	938	10	943	40
107	941	60	946	95	952	30
108	950	40	955	80	961	20
109	959	20	964	65	970	10
10	968	00	973	50	979	00
111	976	80	982	35	987	90
112	985	60	991	20	996	80
113	994	40	1000	05	1005	70
114	1003	20	1008	90	1014	60
115	1012	00	1017	75	1023	50
116	1020	80	1026	60	1032	40
117	1029	60	1035	45	1041	30
118	1038	40	1044	30	1050	20
119	1047	20	1053	15	1059	10
120	1056	00	1062	00	1068	00
121	1064	80	1070	85	1076	90
122	1073	60	1079	70	1085	80
123	1082	40	1088	55	1094	70
124	1091	20	1097	40	1103	60
125	1100	00	1106	25	1112	50
126	1108	80	1115	10	1121	40
127	1117	60	1123	95	1130	30
128	1126	40	1132	80	1139	20
129	1135	20	1141	65	1148	10
30	1144	00	1150	50	1157	00
131	1152	80	1159	35	1165	90
132	1161	60	1168	20	1174	80
133	1170	40	1177	05	1183	70
134	1179	20	1185	90	1192	60
135	1188	00	1194	75	1201	50
136	1196	80	1203	60	1210	40
137	1205	60	1212	45	1219	30
138	1214	40	1221	30	1228	20
139	1223	20	1230	15	1237	10
40	1232	00	1239	00	1246	00
141	1240	80	1247	85	1254	90
142	1249	60	1256	70	1263	80
143	1258	40	1265	55	1272	70
144	1267	20	1274	40	1281	60
145	1276	00	1283	25	1290	50
146	1284	80	1292	10	1299	40
147	1293	60	1300	95	1308	30
148	1302	40	1309	80	1317	20
149	1311	20	1318	65	1326	10
50	1320	00	1327	50	1335	00
1016	8940	80	8991	60	9042	40
1296	11404	80	11469	60	11584	40

No.	£8·80		£8·85		£8·90	
	£	P	£	P	£	P
155	1364	00	1371	75	1379	50
156	1372	80	1380	60	1388	40
165	1452	00	1460	25	1468	50
168	1478	40	1486	80	1495	20
175	1540	00	1548	75	1557	50
180	1584	00	1593	00	1602	00
185	1628	00	1637	25	1646	50
192	1689	60	1699	20	1708	80
195	1716	00	1725	75	1735	50
200	1760	00	1770	00	1780	00
204	1795	20	1805	40	1815	60
205	1804	00	1814	25	1824	50
215	1892	00	1902	75	1913	50
216	1900	80	1911	60	1922	40
224	1971	20	1982	40	1993	60
225	1980	00	1991	25	2002	50
228	2006	40	2017	80	2029	20
235	2068	00	2079	75	2091	20
245	2156	00	2168	25	2180	50
250	2200	00	2212	50	2225	00
252	2217	60	2230	20	2242	80
255	2244	00	2256	75	2269	50
265	2332	00	2345	25	2358	50
272	2393	60	2407	20	2420	80
275	2420	00	2433	75	2447	50
280	2464	00	2478	00	2492	00
285	2508	00	2522	25	2536	50
288	2534	40	2548	80	2563	20
295	2596	00	2610	75	2625	50
300	2640	00	2655	00	2670	00
325	2860	00	2876	25	2892	50
336	2956	80	2973	60	2990	40
365	3212	00	3230	25	3248	50
375	3300	00	3318	75	3337	50
400	3520	00	3540	00	3560	00
425	3740	00	3761	25	3782	50
432	3801	60	3823	20	3844	80
475	4180	00	4203	75	4227	50
480	4224	00	4248	00	4272	00
500	4400	00	4425	00	4450	00
504	4435	20	4460	40	4485	60
576	5068	80	5097	60	5126	40
600	5280	00	5310	00	5340	00
700	6160	00	6195	00	6230	00
750	6600	00	6637	50	6675	00
800	7040	00	7080	00	7120	00
900	7920	00	7965	00	8010	00
1000	8800	00	8850	00	8900	00
2500	22000	0	22125	0	22250	0
5000	44000	0	44250	0	44500	0
1723	15206	40	15292	80	15879	20
1760	15488	00	15576	00	15664	00

No.	£8·95 £ p	£9·00 £ p	£9·05 £ p	No.	£8·95 £ p	£9·00 £ p	£9·05 £ p
1	8 95	9 00	9 05	51	456 45	459 00	461 55
2	17 90	18 00	18 10	52	465 40	468 00	470 60
3	26 85	27 00	27 15	53	474 35	477 00	479 65
4	35 80	36 00	36 20	54	483 30	486 00	488 70
5	44 75	45 00	45 25	55	492 25	495 00	497 75
6	53 70	54 00	54 30	56	501 20	504 00	506 80
7	62 65	63 00	63 35	57	510 15	513 00	515 85
8	71 60	72 00	72 40	58	519 10	522 00	524 90
9	80 55	81 00	81 45	59	528 05	531 00	533 95
10	89 50	90 00	90 50	60	537 00	540 00	543 00
11	98 45	99 00	99 55	61	545 95	549 00	552 05
12	107 40	108 00	108 60	62	554 90	558 00	561 10
13	116 35	117 00	117 65	63	563 85	567 00	570 15
14	125 30	126 00	126 70	64	572 80	576 00	579 20
15	134 25	135 00	135 75	65	581 75	585 00	588 25
16	143 20	144 00	144 80	66	590 70	594 00	597 30
17	152 15	153 00	153 85	67	599 65	603 00	606 35
18	161 10	162 00	162 90	68	608 60	612 00	615 40
19	170 05	171 00	171 95	69	617 55	621 00	624 45
20	179 00	180 00	181 00	70	626 50	630 00	633 50
21	187 95	189 00	190 05	71	635 45	639 00	642 55
22	196 90	198 00	199 10	72	644 40	648 00	651 60
23	205 85	207 00	208 15	73	653 35	657 00	660 65
24	214 80	216 00	217 20	74	662 30	666 00	669 70
25	223 75	225 00	226 25	75	671 25	675 00	678 75
26	232 70	234 00	235 30	76	680 20	684 00	687 80
27	241 65	243 00	244 35	77	689 15	693 00	696 85
28	250 60	252 00	253 40	78	698 10	702 00	705 90
29	259 55	261 00	262 45	79	707 05	711 00	714 95
30	268 50	270 00	271 50	80	716 00	720 00	724 00
31	277 45	279 00	280 55	81	724 95	729 00	733 05
32	286 40	288 00	289 60	82	733 90	738 00	742 10
33	295 35	297 00	298 65	83	742 85	747 00	751 15
34	304 30	306 00	307 70	84	751 80	756 00	760 20
35	313 25	315 00	316 75	85	760 75	765 00	769 25
36	322 20	324 00	325 80	86	769 70	774 00	778 30
37	331 15	333 00	334 85	87	778 65	783 00	787 35
38	340 10	342 00	343 90	88	787 60	792 00	796 40
39	349 05	351 00	352 95	89	796 55	801 00	805 45
40	358 00	360 00	362 00	90	805 50	810 00	814 50
41	366 95	369 00	371 05	91	814 45	819 00	823 55
42	375 90	378 00	380 10	92	823 40	828 00	832 60
43	384 85	387 00	389 15	93	832 35	837 00	841 65
44	393 80	396 00	398 20	94	841 30	846 00	850 70
45	402 75	405 00	407 25	95	850 25	855 00	859 75
46	411 70	414 00	416 30	96	859 20	864 00	868 80
47	420 65	423 00	425 35	97	868 15	873 00	877 85
48	429 60	432 00	434 40	98	877 10	882 00	886 90
49	438 55	441 00	443 45	99	886 05	891 00	895 95
50	447 50	450 00	452 50	100	895 00	900 00	905 00
¼	2·2375	2·25	2·2625	¾	6·7125	6·75	6·7875
½	4·4750	4·50	4·5250	1¼	11·1875	11·25	11·3125

Dozens.

No.	£8·95 £	p	£9·00 £	p	£9·05 £	p
101	903	95	909	00	914	05
102	912	90	918	00	923	10
103	921	85	927	00	932	15
104	930	80	936	00	941	20
105	939	75	945	00	950	25
106	948	70	954	00	959	30
107	957	65	963	00	968	35
108	966	60	972	00	977	40
109	975	55	981	00	986	45
110	984	50	990	00	995	50
111	993	45	999	00	1004	55
112	1002	40	1008	00	1013	60
113	1011	35	1017	00	1022	65
114	1020	30	1026	00	1031	70
115	1029	25	1035	00	1040	75
116	1038	20	1044	00	1049	80
117	1047	15	1053	00	1058	85
118	1056	10	1062	00	1067	90
119	1065	05	1071	00	1076	95
120	1074	00	1080	00	1086	00
121	1082	95	1089	00	1095	05
122	1091	90	1098	00	1104	10
123	1100	85	1107	00	1113	15
124	1109	80	1116	00	1122	20
125	1118	75	1125	00	1131	25
126	1127	70	1134	00	1140	30
127	1136	65	1143	00	1149	35
128	1145	60	1152	00	1158	40
129	1154	55	1161	00	1167	45
130	1163	50	1170	00	1176	50
131	1172	45	1179	00	1185	55
132	1181	40	1188	00	1194	60
133	1190	35	1197	00	1203	65
134	1199	30	1206	00	1212	70
135	1208	25	1215	00	1221	75
136	1217	20	1224	00	1230	80
137	1226	15	1233	00	1239	85
138	1235	10	1242	00	1248	90
139	1244	05	1251	00	1257	95
140	1253	00	1260	00	1267	00
141	1261	95	1269	00	1276	05
142	1270	90	1278	00	1285	10
143	1279	85	1287	00	1294	15
144	1288	80	1296	00	1303	20
145	1297	75	1305	00	1312	25
146	1306	70	1314	00	1321	30
147	1315	65	1323	00	1330	35
148	1324	60	1332	00	1339	40
149	1333	55	1341	00	1348	45
150	1342	50	1350	00	1357	50
1016	9093	20	9144	00	9194	80
1296	11599	20	11664	00	11728	80

No.	£8·95 £	p	£9·00 £	p	£9·05 £	p
Doz 155	1387	25	1395	00	1402	75
13 156	1396	20	1404	00	1411	80
165	1476	75	1485	00	1493	25
14 168	1503	60	1512	00	1520	40
175	1566	25	1575	00	1583	75
15 180	1611	00	1620	00	1629	00
185	1655	75	1665	00	1674	25
16 192	1718	40	1728	00	1737	60
195	1745	25	1755	00	1764	75
200	1790	00	1800	00	1810	00
17 204	1825	80	1836	00	1846	20
205	1834	75	1845	00	1855	25
215	1924	25	1935	00	1945	75
18 216	1933	20	1944	00	1954	80
224	2004	80	2016	00	2027	20
225	2013	75	2025	00	2036	25
19 228	2040	60	2052	00	2063	40
235	2103	25	2115	00	2126	75
245	2192	75	2205	00	2217	25
250	2237	50	2250	00	2262	50
21 252	2255	40	2268	00	2280	60
255	2282	25	2295	00	2307	75
265	2371	75	2385	00	2398	25
272	2434	40	2448	00	2461	60
275	2461	25	2475	00	2488	75
280	2506	00	2520	00	2534	00
285	2550	75	2565	00	2579	25
2 gross 288	2577	60	2592	00	2606	40
295	2640	25	2655	00	2669	75
300	2685	00	2700	00	2715	00
325	2908	75	2925	00	2941	25
336	3007	20	3024	00	3040	80
365	3266	75	3285	00	3303	25
375	3356	25	3375	00	3393	75
400	3580	00	3600	00	3620	00
3 gr 425	3803	75	3825	00	3846	25
432	3866	40	3888	00	3909	60
475	4251	25	4275	00	4298	75
480	4296	00	4320	00	4344	00
500	4475	00	4500	00	4525	00
4 gr 504	4510	80	4536	00	4561	20
576	5155	20	5184	00	5212	80
600	5370	00	5400	00	5430	00
700	6265	00	6300	00	6335	00
750	6712	50	6750	00	6787	50
800	7160	00	7200	00	7240	00
900	8055	00	8100	00	8145	00
1000	8950	00	9000	00	9050	00
2500	22375	0	22500	0	22625	0
5000	44750	0	45000	0	45250	0
1728	15465	60	15552	00	15638	40
1760	15752	00	15840	00	15928	00

SECTION II.

PERCENTAGE TABLES

The black columnar figures represent Pence and
£s on which a percentage is desired.

The Columnar Titles:

Percentage on Cost = the percentage of Pence or
£s at the rate per cent shown by the page heading.

Examples: 7% of 73 pence=5p
                7% of £85   =£5 95p

                7% of £14 73p
                7% of £14=£0 98p
                7% of 73p=   5p
                _____
                £1 3p
                ================

Profit on Returns=the required selling price which
will bring a profit of the desired percentage, as per the
page heading, on the cost of the article.

Example:
    7% Profit on Gross Returns on £5 73p
    7% on £5 =£5 37¾p
    7% on 73p=   78½p
    _____
    £6 16¼p
    ====================

ON COST

£	1/4% P	1/2% P	3/4% P	1% P	£	1/4% £ P	1/2% P	3/4% P	1% £ P
1	0¼	0½	0¾	1	51	12¾	25½	38¼	0 51
2	0½	1	1½	2	52	13	26	39	0 52
3	0¾	1½	2¼	3	53	13¼	26½	39¾	0 53
4	1	2	3	4	54	13½	27	40½	0 54
5	1¼	2½	3¾	5	55	13¾	27½	41¼	0 55
6	1½	3	4½	6	56	14	28	42	0 56
7	1¾	3½	5¼	7	57	14¼	28½	42¾	0 57
8	2	4	6	8	58	14½	29	43½	0 58
9	2¼	4½	6¾	9	59	14¾	29½	44¼	0 59
10	2½	5	7½	10	60	15	30	45	0 60
11	2¾	5½	8¼	11	61	15¼	30½	45¾	0 61
12	3	6	9	12	62	15½	31	46½	0 62
13	3¼	6½	9¾	13	63	15¾	31½	47¼	0 63
14	3½	7	10½	14	64	16	32	48	0 64
15	3¾	7½	11¼	15	65	16¼	32½	48¾	0 65
16	4	8	12	16	66	16½	33	49½	0 66
17	4¼	8½	12¾	17	67	16¾	33½	50¼	0 67
18	4½	9	13½	18	68	17	34	51	0 68
19	4¾	9½	14¼	19	69	17¼	34½	51¾	0 69
20	5	10	15	20	70	17½	35	52½	0 70
21	5¼	10½	15¾	21	71	17¾	35½	53¼	0 71
22	5½	11	16½	22	72	18	36	54	0 72
23	5¾	11½	17¼	23	73	18¼	36½	54¾	0 73
24	6	12	18	24	74	18½	37	55½	0 74
25	6¼	12½	18¾	25	75	18¾	37½	56¼	0 75
26	6½	13	19½	26	76	19	38	57	0 76
27	6¾	13½	20¼	27	77	19¼	38½	57¾	0 77
28	7	14	21	28	78	19½	39	58½	0 78
29	7¼	14½	21¾	29	79	19¾	39½	59¼	0 79
30	7½	15	22½	30	80	20	40	60	0 80
31	7¾	15½	23¼	31	81	20¼	40½	60¾	0 81
32	8	16	24	32	82	20½	41	61½	0 82
33	8¼	16½	24¾	33	83	20¾	41½	62¼	0 83
34	8½	17	25½	34	84	21	42	63	0 84
35	8¾	17½	26¼	35	85	21¼	42½	63¾	0 85
36	9	18	27	36	86	21½	43	64½	0 86
37	9¼	18½	27¾	37	87	21¾	43½	65¼	0 87
38	9½	19	28½	38	88	22	44	66	0 88
39	9¾	19½	29¼	39	89	22¼	44½	66¾	0 89
40	10	20	30	40	90	22½	45	67½	0 90
41	10¼	20½	30¾	41	91	22¾	45½	68¼	0 91
42	10½	21	31½	42	92	23	46	69	0 92
43	10¾	21½	32¼	43	93	23¼	46½	69¾	0 93
44	11	22	33	44	94	23½	47	70½	0 94
45	11¼	22½	33¾	45	95	23¾	47½	71¼	0 95
46	11½	23	34½	46	96	24	48	72	0 96
47	11¾	23½	35¼	47	97	24¼	48½	72¾	0 97
48	12	24	36	48	98	24½	49	73½	0 98
49	12¼	24½	36¾	49	99	24¾	49½	74¼	0 99
50	12½	25	37½	50	100	25	50	75	1 0

£	1/4% £ P	1/2% £ P	3/4% £ P	1% £ P	£	1/4% £ P	1/2% £ P	3/4% £ P	1% £ P
150	0 37½	0 75	1 12½	1 50	600	1 50	3 0	4 50	6 0
200	0 50	1 0	1 50	2 0	650	1 62½	3 25	4 87½	6 50
250	0 62½	1 25	1 87½	2 50	700	1 75	3 50	5 25	7 0
300	0 75	1 50	2 25	3 0	750	1 87½	3 75	5 62½	7 50
350	0 87½	1 75	2 62½	3 50	800	2 0	4 0	6 0	8 0
400	1 0	2 0	3 0	4 0	850	2 12½	4 25	6 37½	8 50
450	1 12½	2 25	3 37½	4 50	900	2 25	4 50	6 75	9 0
500	1 25	2 50	3 75	5 0	950	2 37½	4 75	7 12½	9 50
550	1 37½	2 75	4 12½	5 50	1000	2 50	5 0	7 50	10 0

	Profit on Cost	Profit on Returns		Profit on Cost	Profit on Returns		Profit on Cost	Profit on Returns			Profit on Cost		Profit on Returns	
P	P	P	P	P	P	£	P	£	P	£	£	P	£	P
1	0	1	51	0¾	51¾	1	1¼	1	1¼	51	0	63¾	51	64½
2	0	2	52	0¾	52¾	2	2½	2	2½	52	0	65	52	65¾
3	0	3	53	0¾	53¾	3	3¾	3	3¾	53	0	66¼	53	67
4	0	4	54	0¾	54¾	4	5	4	5	54	0	67½	54	68¼
5	0	5	55	0¾	55¾	5	6¼	5	6¼	55	0	68¾	55	69¾
6	0	6	56	0¾	56¾	6	7½	6	7½	56	0	70	56	71
7	0	7	57	0¾	57¾	7	8¾	7	8¾	57	0	71¼	57	72¼
8	0	8	58	0¾	58¾	8	10	8	10¼	58	0	72½	58	73½
9	0	9	59	0¾	59¾	9	11¼	9	11½	59	0	73¾	59	74¾
10	**0¼**	**10¼**	**60**	**0¾**	**60¾**	**10**	**12½**	**10**	**12¾**	**60**	**0**	**75**	**60**	**76**
11	0¼	11¼	61	0¾	61¾	11	13¾	11	14	61	0	76¼	61	77¼
12	0¼	12¼	62	0¾	62¾	12	15	12	15¼	62	0	77½	62	78½
13	0¼	13¼	63	0¾	63¾	13	16¼	13	16½	63	0	78¾	63	79¾
14	0¼	14¼	64	0¾	64¾	14	17½	14	17¾	64	0	80	64	81
15	0¼	15¼	65	0¾	65¾	15	18¾	15	19	65	0	81¼	65	82¼
16	0¼	16¼	66	0¾	66¾	16	20	16	20¼	66	0	82½	66	83½
17	0¼	17¼	67	0¾	67¾	17	21¼	17	21½	67	0	83¾	67	84¾
18	0¼	18¼	68	0¾	68¾	18	22½	18	22¾	68	0	85	68	86
19	0¼	19¼	69	0¾	69¾	19	23¾	19	24	69	0	86¼	69	87¼
20	**0¼**	**20¼**	**70**	**1**	**71**	**20**	**25**	**20**	**25¼**	**70**	**0**	**87½**	**70**	**88½**
21	0¼	21¼	71	1	72	21	26¼	21	26½	71	0	88¾	71	90
22	0¼	22¼	72	1	73	22	27½	22	27¾	72	0	90	72	91¼
23	0¼	23¼	73	1	74	23	28¾	23	29	73	0	91¼	73	92½
24	0¼	24¼	74	1	75	24	30	24	30½	74	0	92½	74	93¾
25	0¼	25¼	75	1	76	25	31¼	25	31¾	75	0	93¾	75	95
26	0¼	26¼	76	1	77	26	32½	26	33	76	0	95	76	96¼
27	0¼	27¼	77	1	78	27	33¾	27	34¼	77	0	96¼	77	97½
28	0¼	28¼	78	1	79	28	35	28	35½	78	0	97½	78	98¾
29	0¼	29¼	79	1	80	29	36¼	29	36¾	79	0	98¾	80	0
30	**0½**	**30½**	**80**	**1**	**81**	**30**	**37½**	**30**	**38**	**80**	**1**	**0**	**81**	**1¼**
31	0½	31½	81	1	82	31	38¾	31	39¼	81	1	1¼	82	2½
32	0½	32½	82	1	83	32	40	32	40½	82	1	2½	83	3¾
33	0½	33½	83	1	84	33	41¼	33	41¾	83	1	3¾	84	5
34	0½	34½	84	1	85	34	42½	34	43	84	1	5	85	6¼
35	0½	35½	85	1	86	35	43¾	35	44¼	85	1	6¼	86	7½
36	0½	36½	86	1	87	36	45	36	45½	86	1	7½	87	8¾
37	0½	37½	87	1	88	37	46¼	37	46¾	87	1	8¾	88	10¼
38	0½	38½	88	1	89	38	47½	38	48	88	1	10	89	11½
39	0½	39½	89	1	90¼	39	48¾	39	49¼	89	1	11¼	90	12¾
40	**0½**	**40½**	**90**	**1¼**	**91¼**	**40**	**50**	**40**	**50¾**	**90**	**1**	**12½**	**91**	**14**
41	0½	41½	91	1¼	92¼	41	51¼	41	52	91	1	13¾	92	15¼
42	0½	42½	92	1¼	93¼	42	52½	42	53¼	92	1	15	93	16½
43	0½	43½	93	1¼	94¼	43	53¾	43	54½	93	1	16¼	94	17¾
44	0½	44½	94	1¼	95¼	44	55	44	55¾	94	1	17½	95	19
45	0½	45½	95	1¼	96¼	45	56¼	45	57	95	1	18¾	96	20¼
46	0½	46½	96	1¼	97¼	46	57½	46	58¼	96	1	20	97	21½
47	0½	47½	97	1¼	98¼	47	58¾	47	59½	97	1	21¼	98	22¾
48	0½	48½	98	1¼	99¼	48	60	48	60¾	98	1	22½	99	24
49	0½	49½	99	1¼	100¼	49	61¼	49	62	99	1	23¾	100	25¼
50	**0¾**	**50¾**	**100**	**1¼**	**101¼**	**50**	**62½**	**50**	**63¼**	**100**	**1**	**25**	**101**	**26½**

	On Cost		Profit on Returns			On Cost		Profit on Returns			On Cost		Profit on Returns	
150	1	87½	151	90	450	5	62½	455	69¾	750	9	37½	759	49¼
200	2	50	202	53¼	500	6	25	506	33	800	10	0	810	12¾
250	3	12½	253	16½	550	6	87½	556	96¼	850	10	62½	860	76
300	3	75	303	79¾	600	7	50	607	59½	900	11	25	911	39¼
350	4	37½	354	43	650	8	12½	658	22¾	950	11	87½	962	2½
400	5	0	405	6¼	700	8	75	708	86	1000	12	50	1012	65¾

1½ Per Cent

	On Cost	Profit on Returns		On Cost	Profit on Returns			On Cost	Profit on Returns			On Cost		Profit on Returns	
P	P	P	P	P	£	P	£	P	£	P	£	£	P	£	P
1	0	1	51	0¾	0	51¾	1	1½	1	1½	51	0	76½	51	77¾
2	0	2	52	0¾	0	52¾	2	3	2	3	52	0	78	52	79¼
3	0	3	53	0¾	0	53¾	3	4½	3	4½	53	0	79½	53	80¾
4	0	4	54	0¾	0	54¾	4	6	4	6	54	0	81	54	82¼
5	0	5	55	0¾	0	55¾	5	7½	5	7½	55	0	82½	55	83¾
6	0	6	56	0¾	0	56¾	6	9	6	9¼	56	0	84	56	85¼
7	0	7	57	0¾	0	57¾	7	10½	7	10¾	57	0	85½	57	86¾
8	0	8	58	0¾	0	59	8	12	8	12¼	58	0	87	58	88¼
9	0¼	9¼	59	1	0	60	9	13½	9	13¾	59	0	88½	59	89¾
10	0¼	10¼	60	1	0	61	10	15	10	15¼	60	0	90	60	91¼
11	0¼	11¼	61	1	0	62	11	16½	11	16¾	61	0	91½	61	93
12	0¼	12¼	62	1	0	63	12	18	12	18¼	62	0	93	62	94½
13	0¼	13¼	63	1	0	64	13	19½	13	19¾	63	0	94½	63	96
14	0¼	14¼	64	1	0	65	14	21	14	21¼	64	0	96	64	97½
15	0¼	15¼	65	1	0	66	15	22½	15	22¾	65	0	97½	65	99
16	0¼	16¼	66	1	0	67	16	24	16	24¼	66	0	99	67	0½
17	0¼	17¼	67	1	0	68	17	25½	17	26	67	1	0½	68	2
18	0¼	18¼	68	1	0	69	18	27	18	27½	68	1	2	69	3½
19	0¼	19¼	69	1	0	70	19	28½	19	29	69	1	3½	70	5
20	0¼	20¼	70	1	0	71	20	30	20	30½	70	1	5	71	6½
21	0¼	21¼	71	1	0	72	21	31½	21	32	71	1	6½	72	8
22	0¼	22¼	72	1	0	73	22	33	22	33½	72	1	8	73	9¾
23	0¼	23¼	73	1	0	74	23	34½	23	35	73	1	9½	74	11¼
24	0¼	24¼	74	1	0	75¼	24	36	24	36½	74	1	11	75	12¾
25	0½	25½	75	1¼	0	76¼	25	37½	25	38	75	1	12½	76	14¼
26	0½	26½	76	1¼	0	77¼	26	39	26	39½	76	1	14	77	15¾
27	0½	27½	77	1¼	0	78¼	27	40½	27	41	77	1	15½	78	17¼
28	0½	28½	78	1¼	0	79¼	28	42	28	42¾	78	1	17	79	18¾
29	0½	29½	79	1¼	0	80¼	29	43½	29	44¼	79	1	18½	80	20¼
30	0½	30½	80	1¼	0	81¼	30	45	30	45¾	80	1	20	81	21¾
31	0½	31½	81	1¼	0	82¼	31	46½	31	47¼	81	1	21½	82	23¼
32	0½	32½	82	1¼	0	83¼	32	48	32	48¾	82	1	23	83	24¾
33	0½	33½	83	1¼	0	84¼	33	49½	33	50¼	83	1	24½	84	26½
34	0½	34½	84	1¼	0	85¼	34	51	34	51¾	84	1	26	85	28
35	0½	35½	85	1¼	0	86¼	35	52½	35	53¼	85	1	27½	86	29¼
36	0½	36½	86	1¼	0	87¼	36	54	36	54¾	86	1	29	87	31
37	0½	37½	87	1¼	0	88¼	37	55½	37	56¼	87	1	30½	88	32½
38	0½	38½	88	1¼	0	89¼	38	57	38	57¾	88	1	32	89	34
39	0½	39½	89	1¼	0	90¼	39	58½	39	59½	89	1	33½	90	35½
40	0½	40½	90	1¼	0	91¼	40	60	40	61	90	1	35	91	37
41	0½	41½	91	1¼	0	92½	41	61½	41	62¼	91	1	36½	92	38½
42	0¾	42¾	92	1½	0	93½	42	63	42	64	92	1	38	93	40
43	0¾	43¾	93	1½	0	94½	43	64½	43	65½	93	1	39½	94	41¾
44	0¾	44¾	94	1½	0	95½	44	66	44	67	94	1	41	95	43¼
45	0¾	45¾	95	1½	0	96½	45	67½	45	68½	95	1	42½	96	44¾
46	0¾	46¾	96	1½	0	97½	46	69	46	70	96	1	44	97	46¼
47	0¾	47¾	97	1½	0	98½	47	70½	47	71½	97	1	45½	98	47¾
48	0¾	48¾	98	1½	0	99½	48	72	48	73	98	1	47	99	49¼
49	0¾	49¾	99	1½	1	0½	49	73½	49	74½	99	1	48½	100	50¾
50	0¾	50¾	100	1½	1	1½	50	75	50	76¼	100	1	50	101	52¼

	On Cost		Profit on Returns			On Cost		Profit on Returns			On Cost		Profit on Returns	
150	2	25	152	28½	450	6	75	456	85¼	750	11	25	761	42¼
200	3	0	203	4½	500	7	50	507	61½	800	12	0	812	18¼
250	3	75	253	80¾	550	8	25	558	37½	850	12	75	862	94½
300	4	50	304	56¾	600	9	0	609	13¾	900	13	50	913	70½
350	5	25	355	33	650	9	75	659	89¾	950	14	25	964	46¾
400	6	0	406	9¼	700	10	50	710	66	1000	15	0	1015	22¾

2 PER CENT

	on Cost	Profit on Returns		on Cost	Profit on Returns			on Cost	Profit on Returns			on Cost		Profit on Returns	
P	P	P	P	P	£	P	£	P	£	P	£	£	P	£	P
1	0	1	51	1	0	52	1	2	1	2	51	1	2	52	4
2	0	2	52	1	0	53	2	4	2	4	52	1	4	53	6¼
3	0	3	53	1	0	54	3	6	3	6¼	53	1	6	54	8¼
4	0	4	54	1	0	55	4	8	4	8¼	54	1	8	55	10¼
5	0	5	55	1	0	56	5	10	5	10¼	55	1	10	56	12¼
6	0	6¼	56	1	0	57¼	6	12	6	12¼	56	1	12	57	14¼
7	0¼	7¼	57	1¼	0	58¼	7	14	7	14¼	57	1	14	58	16¼
8	0¼	8¼	58	1¼	0	59¼	8	16	8	16¼	58	1	16	59	18½
9	0¼	9¼	59	1¼	0	60¼	9	18	9	18½	59	1	18	60	20½
10	0¼	10¼	60	1¼	0	61¼	10	20	10	20½	60	1	20	61	22½
11	0¼	11¼	61	1¼	0	62¼	11	22	11	22½	61	1	22	62	24½
12	0¼	12¼	62	1¼	0	63¼	12	24	12	24½	62	1	24	63	26½
13	0¼	13¼	63	1¼	0	64¼	13	26	13	26½	63	1	26	64	28½
14	0¼	14¼	64	1¼	0	65¼	14	28	14	28½	64	1	28	65	30½
15	0¼	15¼	65	1¼	0	66¼	15	30	15	30½	65	1	30	66	32¾
16	0¼	16¼	66	1¼	0	67¼	16	32	16	32¾	66	1	32	67	34¾
17	0¼	17¼	67	1¼	0	68¼	17	34	17	34¾	67	1	34	68	36¾
18	0¼	18¼	68	1¼	0	69½	18	36	18	36¾	68	1	36	69	38¾
19	0½	19½	69	1½	0	70½	19	38	19	38¾	69	1	38	70	40¾
20	0½	20½	70	1½	0	71½	20	40	20	40¾	70	1	40	71	42¾
21	0½	21½	71	1½	0	72½	21	42	21	42¾	71	1	42	72	45
22	0½	22½	72	1½	0	73½	22	44	22	45	72	1	44	73	47
23	0½	23½	73	1½	0	74½	23	46	23	47	73	1	46	74	49
24	0½	24½	74	1½	0	75½	24	48	24	49	74	1	48	75	51
25	0½	25½	75	1½	0	76½	25	50	25	51	75	1	50	76	53
26	0½	26½	76	1½	0	77½	26	52	26	53	76	1	52	77	55
27	0½	27½	77	1½	0	78½	27	54	27	55	77	1	54	78	57¼
28	0½	28½	78	1½	0	79½	28	56	28	57¼	78	1	56	79	59¼
29	0½	29½	79	1½	0	80½	29	58	29	59¼	79	1	58	80	61¼
30	0½	30½	80	1½	0	81¾	30	60	30	61¼	80	1	60	81	63¼
31	0½	31¾	81	1½	0	82¾	31	62	31	63¼	81	1	62	82	65¼
32	0¾	32¾	82	1¾	0	83¾	32	64	32	65¼	82	1	64	83	67¼
33	0¾	33¾	83	1¾	0	84¾	33	66	33	67¼	83	1	66	84	69¼
34	0¾	34¾	84	1¾	0	85¾	34	68	34	69¼	84	1	68	85	71½
35	0¾	35¾	85	1¾	0	86¾	35	70	35	71½	85	1	70	86	73½
36	0¾	36¾	86	1¾	0	87¾	36	72	36	73½	86	1	72	87	75½
37	0¾	37¾	87	1¾	0	88¾	37	74	37	75½	87	1	74	88	77½
38	0¾	38¾	88	1¾	0	89¾	38	76	38	77½	88	1	76	89	79½
39	0¾	39¾	89	1¾	0	90¾	39	78	39	79½	89	1	78	90	81¾
40	0¾	40¾	90	1¾	0	91¾	40	80	40	81¾	90	1	80	91	83¾
41	0¾	41¾	91	1¾	0	92¾	41	82	41	83¾	91	1	82	92	85¾
42	0¾	42¾	92	1¾	0	94	42	84	42	85¾	92	1	84	93	87¾
43	0¾	44	93	1¾	0	95	43	86	43	87¾	93	1	86	94	89¾
44	1	45	94	2	0	96	44	88	44	89¾	94	1	88	95	91¾
45	1	46	95	2	0	97	45	90	45	91¾	95	1	90	96	94
46	1	47	96	2	0	98	46	92	46	94	96	1	92	97	96
47	1	48	97	2	0	99	47	94	47	96	97	1	94	98	98
48	1	49	98	2	1	0	48	96	48	98	98	1	96	100	0
49	1	50	99	2	1	1	49	98	50	0	99	1	98	101	2
50	1	51	100	2	1	2	50	100	51	2	100	2	0	102	4

	On Cost		Profit on Returns			On Cost		Profit on Returns			On Cost		Profit on Returns	
150	3	0	153	6¼	450	9	0	459	18½	750	15	0	765	30½
200	4	0	204	8¼	500	10	0	510	20½	800	16	0	816	32¾
250	5	0	255	10¼	550	11	0	561	22½	850	17	0	867	34¾
300	6	0	306	12¼	600	12	0	612	24½	900	18	0	918	36¾
350	7	0	357	14¼	650	13	0	663	26½	950	19	0	969	38¾
400	8	0	408	16¼	700	14	0	714	28½	1000	20	0	1020	40¾

2½ Per Cent

	on Cost	Profit on Returns		on Cost	Profit on Returns			on Cost		Profit on Returns			on Cost		Profit on Returns	
P	P	P	P	P	£	P	£	£	P	£	P	£	£	P	£	P
1	0	1	51	1¼	0	52¼	1	0	2½	1	2½	51	1	27½	52	30¾
2	0	2	52	1¼	0	53¼	2	0	5	2	5¼	52	1	30	53	33¼
3	0	3	53	1¼	0	54¼	3	0	7½	3	7¾	53	1	32½	54	36
4	0	4	54	1¼	0	55½	4	0	10	4	10¼	54	1	35	55	38½
5	0¼	5¼	55	1½	0	56½	5	0	12½	5	12¾	55	1	37½	56	41
6	0¼	6¼	56	1½	0	57½	6	0	15	6	15½	56	1	40	57	43½
7	0¼	7¼	57	1½	0	58½	7	0	17½	7	18	57	1	42½	58	46
8	0¼	8¼	58	1½	0	59½	8	0	20	8	20½	58	1	45	59	48
9	0¼	9¼	59	1½	0	60½	9	0	22½	9	23	59	1	47½	60	51
10	0¼	10¼	**60**	1½	0	61½	**10**	0	25	10	25¾	**60**	1	50	61	53
11	0¼	11¼	61	1½	0	62½	11	0	27½	11	28¼	61	1	52½	62	56
12	0¼	12¼	62	1½	0	63½	12	0	30	12	30¾	62	1	55	63	59
13	0¼	13¼	63	1½	0	64½	13	0	32½	13	33¼	63	1	57½	64	61
14	0¼	14¼	64	1½	0	65¾	14	0	35	14	36	64	1	60	65	64
15	0½	15½	65	1¾	0	66¾	15	0	37½	15	38½	65	1	62½	66	66
16	0½	16½	66	1¾	0	67¾	16	0	40	16	41	66	1	65	67	69
17	0½	17½	67	1¾	0	68¾	17	0	42½	17	43½	67	1	67½	68	71
18	0½	18½	68	1¾	0	69¾	18	0	45	18	46¼	68	1	70	69	74
19	0½	19½	69	1¾	0	70¾	19	0	47½	19	48¾	69	1	72½	70	77
20	0½	20½	**70**	1¾	0	71¾	**20**	0	50	20	51¼	**70**	1	75	71	79
21	0½	21½	71	1¾	0	72¾	21	0	52½	21	53¾	71	1	77½	72	82
22	0½	22½	72	1¾	0	73¾	22	0	55	22	56½	72	1	80	73	84
23	0½	23½	73	1¾	0	74¾	23	0	57½	23	59	73	1	82½	74	87
24	0½	24½	74	1¾	0	76	24	0	60	24	61½	74	1	85	75	89
25	0¾	25¾	75	2	0	77	25	0	62½	25	64	75	1	87½	76	92
26	0¾	26¾	76	2	0	78	26	0	65	26	66¾	76	1	90	77	94
27	0¾	27¾	77	2	0	79	27	0	67½	27	69¼	77	1	92½	78	97
28	0¾	28¾	78	2	0	80	28	0	70	28	71¾	78	1	95	80	0
29	0¾	29¾	79	2	0	81	29	0	72½	29	74¼	79	1	97½	81	2
30	0¾	30¾	**80**	2	0	82	**30**	0	75	30	77	**80**	2	0	82	5
31	0¾	31¾	81	2	0	83	31	0	77½	31	79½	81	2	2½	83	7
32	0¾	32¾	82	2	0	84	32	0	80	32	82	82	2	5	84	10
33	0¾	33¾	83	2	0	85¼	33	0	82½	33	84¾	83	2	7½	85	12
34	0¾	34¾	84	2	0	86¼	34	0	85	34	87¼	84	2	10	86	15
35	1	36	85	2¼	0	87¼	35	0	87½	35	89¾	85	2	12½	87	18
36	1	37	86	2¼	0	88¼	36	0	90	36	92¼	86	2	15	88	20
37	1	38	87	2¼	0	89¼	37	0	92½	37	94¾	87	2	17½	89	23
38	1	39	88	2¼	0	90¼	38	0	95	38	97½	88	2	20	90	25
39	1	40	89	2¼	0	91¼	39	0	97½	40	0	89	2	22½	91	28
40	1	41	**90**	2¼	0	92¼	**40**	1	00	41	2½	**90**	2	25	92	30
41	1	42	91	2¼	0	93¼	41	1	02½	42	5¼	91	2	27½	93	33
42	1	43	92	2¼	0	94¼	42	1	05	43	7¾	92	2	30	94	36
43	1	44	93	2¼	0	95½	43	1	07½	44	10¼	93	2	32½	95	38
44	1	45¼	94	2¼	0	96½	44	1	10	45	12¾	94	2	35	96	41
45	1¼	46¼	95	2½	0	97½	45	1	12½	46	15¼	95	2	37½	97	43
46	1¼	47¼	96	2½	0	98½	46	1	15	47	18	96	2	40	98	46
47	1¼	48¼	97	2½	0	99½	47	1	17½	48	20½	97	2	42½	99	48
48	1¼	49¼	98	2½	1	0½	48	1	20	49	23	98	2	45	100	51
49	1¼	50¼	99	2½	1	1½	49	1	22½	50	25¾	99	2	47½	101	53
50	1¼	51¼	**100**	2½	1	2½	**50**	1	25	51	28¼	**100**	2	50	102	56

	On Cost		Profit on Returns			On Cost		Profit on Returns			On Cost		Profit on Returns	
150	3	75	153	84½	450	11	25	461	53¾	750	18	75	769	23
200	5	0	205	12¾	500	12	50	512	82	800	20	0	820	51
250	6	25	256	41	550	13	75	564	10¼	850	21	25	871	79
300	7	50	307	69¼	600	15	0	615	38½	900	22	50	923	07
350	8	75	358	97½	650	16	25	666	66¾	950	23	75	974	36
400	10	0	410	25¾	700	17	50	717	95	1000	25	0	1025	64

3 Per Cent

3%

	on Cost	Profit on Returns		on Cost	Profit on Returns			on Cost		Profit on Returns			on Cost		Profit on Returns	
P	P	P	P	P	£	P	£	£	P	£	P	£	£	P	£	P
1	0	1	51	1½	0	52½	1	0	3	1	3	51	1	53	52	57¾
2	0	2	52	1½	0	53½	2	0	6	2	6¼	52	1	56	53	60¾
3	0	3	53	1½	0	54¾	3	0	9	3	9¼	53	1	59	54	64
4	0	4¼	54	1½	0	55¾	4	0	12	4	12½	54	1	62	55	67
5	0¼	5¼	55	1¾	0	56¾	5	0	15	5	15½	55	1	65	56	70
6	0¼	6¼	56	1¾	0	57¾	6	0	18	6	18½	56	1	68	57	73¼
7	0¼	7¼	57	1¾	0	58¾	7	0	21	7	21¾	57	1	71	58	76¼
8	0¼	8¼	58	1¾	0	59¾	8	0	24	8	24¾	58	1	74	59	79½
9	0¼	9¼	59	1¾	0	60¾	9	0	27	9	27¾	59	1	77	60	82½
10	0¼	10¼	60	1¾	0	61¾	10	0	30	10	31	60	1	80	61	85½
11	0¼	11¼	61	1¾	0	63	11	0	33	11	34	61	1	83	62	88¾
12	0¼	12½	62	1¾	0	64	12	0	36	12	37	62	1	86	63	91¾
13	0½	13½	63	2	0	65	13	0	39	13	40¼	63	1	89	64	94¾
14	0½	14½	64	2	0	66	14	0	42	14	43¼	64	1	92	65	98
15	0½	15½	65	2	0	67	15	0	45	15	46½	65	1	95	67	1
16	0½	16½	66	2	0	68	16	0	48	16	49½	66	1	98	68	4¼
17	0½	17½	67	2	0	69	17	0	51	17	52½	67	2	1	69	7¼
18	0½	18½	68	2	0	70	18	0	54	18	55¾	68	2	4	70	10¼
19	0½	19½	69	2	0	71¼	19	0	57	19	58¾	69	2	7	71	13½
20	0½	20½	70	2	0	72¼	20	0	60	20	61¾	70	2	10	72	16½
21	0¾	21¾	71	2¼	0	73¼	21	0	63	21	65	71	2	13	73	19½
22	0¾	22¾	72	2¼	0	74¼	22	0	66	22	68	72	2	16	74	22¾
23	0¾	23¾	73	2¼	0	75¼	23	0	69	23	71¼	73	2	19	75	25¾
24	0¾	24¾	74	2¼	0	76¼	24	0	72	24	74¼	74	2	22	76	29
25	0¾	25¾	75	2¼	0	77¼	25	0	75	25	77¼	75	2	25	77	32
26	0¾	26¾	76	2¼	0	78¼	26	0	78	2f	80½	76	2	28	78	35
27	0¾	27¾	77	2¼	0	79½	27	0	81	27	83½	77	2	31	79	38¼
28	0¾	28¾	78	2¼	0	80½	28	0	84	28	86½	78	2	34	80	41¼
29	0¾	30	79	2¼	0	81½	29	0	87	29	89¾	79	2	37	81	44¼
30	1	31	80	2½	0	82½	30	0	90	30	92¾	80	2	40	82	47½
31	1	32	81	2½	0	83½	31	0	93	31	96	81	2	43	83	50½
32	1	33	82	2½	0	84½	32	0	96	32	99	82	2	46	84	53½
33	1	34	83	2½	0	85½	33	0	99	34	2	83	2	49	85	56¾
34	1	35	84	2½	0	86½	34	1	2	35	5¼	84	2	52	86	59¾
35	1	36	85	2½	0	87¾	35	1	5	36	8¼	85	2	55	87	63
36	1	37	86	2½	0	88¾	36	1	8	37	11¼	86	2	58	88	66
37	1	38¼	87	2½	0	89¾	37	1	11	38	14¼	87	2	61	89	69
38	1¼	39¼	88	2¾	0	90¾	38	1	14	39	17½	88	2	64	90	72¼
39	1¼	40¼	89	2¾	0	91¾	39	1	17	40	20¾	89	2	67	91	75¼
40	1¼	41¼	90	2¾	0	92¾	40	1	20	41	23¾	90	2	70	92	78¼
41	1¼	42¼	91	2¾	0	93¾	41	1	23	42	26¾	91	2	73	93	81½
42	1¼	43¼	92	2¾	0	94¾	42	1	26	43	30	92	2	76	94	84½
43	1¼	44¼	93	2¾	0	96	43	1	29	44	33	93	2	79	95	87¾
44	1¼	45¼	94	2¾	0	97	44	1	32	45	36	94	2	82	96	90¾
45	1¼	46½	95	2¾	0	98	45	1	35	46	39¼	95	2	85	97	93¾
46	1½	47½	96	3	0	99	46	1	38	47	42¼	96	2	88	98	97
47	1½	48½	97	3	1	0	47	1	41	48	45¼	97	2	91	100	0
48	1½	49½	98	3	1	1	48	1	44	49	48½	98	2	94	101	3
49	1½	50½	99	3	1	2	49	1	47	50	51½	99	2	97	102	6¼
50	1½	51½	100	3	1	3	50	1	50	51	54¾	100	3	0	103	9¼

	On Cost		Profit on Returns			On Cost		Profit on Returns			On Cost		Profit on Returns	
150	4	50	154	64	450	13	50	463	91¾	750	22	50	773	19½
200	6	0	206	18½	500	15	0	515	46½	800	24	0	824	74¼
250	7	50	257	73¼	550	16	50	567	1	850	25	50	876	28¾
300	9	0	309	27¾	600	18	0	618	55¾	900	27	0	927	83½
350	10	50	360	82½	650	19	50	670	10¼	950	28	50	979	38¼
400	12	0	412	37	700	21	0	721	65	1000	30	0	1030	92¾

	Profit on Cost	Profit on Returns		Profit on Cost	Profit on Returns			Profit on Cost		Profit on Returns			Profit on Cost		Profit on Returns	
P	P	P	P	P		P	£	£	P	£	P	£	£	P	£	P
1	0	1	51	1¾	0	52¾	1	0	3½	1	3¾	51	1	78½	52	85
2	0	2	52	1¾	0	54	2	0	7	2	7¼	52	1	82	53	88½
3	0	3	53	1¾	0	55	3	0	10½	3	11	53	1	85½	54	92¼
4	0¼	4¼	54	2	0	56	4	0	14	4	14½	54	1	89	55	95¾
5	0¼	5¼	55	2	0	57	5	0	17½	5	18¼	55	1	92½	56	99½
6	0¼	6¼	56	2	0	58	6	0	21	6	21¾	56	1	96	58	3
7	0¼	7¼	57	2	0	59	7	0	24½	7	25½	57	1	99½	59	6¾
8	0¼	8¼	58	2	0	60	8	0	28	8	29	58	2	3	60	10½
9	0¼	9¼	59	2	0	61¼	9	0	31½	9	32¾	59	2	6½	61	14
10	0¼	10¼	60	2	0	62¼	10	0	35	10	36¼	60	2	10	62	17¾
11	0½	11½	61	2¼	0	63¼	11	0	38½	11	40	61	2	13½	63	21¼
12	0½	12½	62	2¼	0	64¼	12	0	42	12	43½	62	2	17	64	25
13	0½	13½	63	2¼	0	65¼	13	0	45½	13	47¼	63	2	20½	65	28½
14	0½	14½	64	2¼	0	66¼	14	0	49	14	50¾	64	2	24	66	32¼
15	0½	15½	65	2¼	0	67¼	15	0	52½	15	54½	65	2	27½	67	35¾
16	0½	16½	66	2¼	0	68½	16	0	56	16	58	66	2	31	68	39½
17	0½	17½	67	2¼	0	69½	17	0	59½	17	61¾	67	2	34½	69	43
18	0¾	18¾	68	2½	0	70½	18	0	63	18	65¼	68	2	38	70	46¾
19	0¾	19¾	69	2½	0	71½	19	0	66½	19	69	69	2	41½	71	50¼
20	0¾	20¾	70	2½	0	72½	20	0	70	20	72½	70	2	45	72	54
21	0¾	21¾	71	2½	0	73½	21	0	73½	21	76¼	71	2	48½	73	57½
22	0¾	22¾	72	2½	0	74½	22	0	77	22	79¾	72	2	52	74	61¼
23	0¾	23¾	73	2½	0	75¾	23	0	80½	23	83½	73	2	55½	75	64¾
24	0¾	24¾	74	2½	0	76¾	24	0	84	24	87	74	2	59	76	68½
25	1	26	75	2¾	0	77¾	25	0	87½	25	90¾	75	2	62½	77	72
26	1	27	76	2¾	0	78¾	26	0	91	26	94¼	76	2	66	78	75¾
27	1	28	77	2¾	0	79¾	27	0	94½	27	98	77	2	69½	79	79¼
28	1	29	78	2¾	0	80¾	28	0	98	29	1½	78	2	73	80	83
29	1	30	79	2¾	0	81¾	29	1	1½	30	5¼	79	2	76½	81	86½
30	1	31	80	2¾	0	83	30	1	5	31	8¾	80	2	80	82	90¼
31	1	32¼	81	2¾	0	84	31	1	8½	32	12½	81	2	83½	83	93¾
32	1	33¼	82	2¾	0	85	32	1	12	33	16	82	2	87	84	97½
33	1¼	34¼	83	3	0	86	33	1	15½	34	19¾	83	2	90½	86	1
34	1¼	35¼	84	3	0	87	34	1	19	35	23¼	84	2	94	87	4¾
35	1¼	36¼	85	3	0	88	35	1	22½	36	27	85	2	97½	88	8¼
36	1¼	37¼	86	3	0	89	36	1	26	37	30½	86	3	1	89	12
37	1¼	38¼	87	3	0	90¼	37	1	29½	38	34¼	87	3	4½	90	15½
38	1¼	39½	88	3	0	91¼	38	1	33	39	37¾	88	3	8	91	19¼
39	1¼	40½	89	3	0	92¼	39	1	36½	40	41½	89	3	11½	92	22¾
40	1½	41½	90	3¼	0	93¼	40	1	40	41	45	90	3	15	93	26½
41	1½	42½	91	3¼	0	94¼	41	1	43½	42	48¾	91	3	18½	94	30
42	1½	43½	92	3¼	0	95¼	42	1	47	43	52¼	92	3	22	95	33¾
43	1½	44½	93	3¼	0	96¼	43	1	50½	44	56	93	3	25½	96	37¼
44	1½	45½	94	3¼	0	97½	44	1	54	45	59½	94	3	29	97	41
45	1½	46¾	95	3¼	0	98½	45	1	57½	46	63¼	95	3	32½	98	44½
46	1½	47¾	96	3¼	0	99½	46	1	61	47	66¾	96	3	36	99	48¼
47	1¾	48¾	97	3½	1	0½	47	1	64½	48	70½	97	3	39½	100	51¾
48	1¾	49¾	98	3½	1	1½	48	1	68	49	74	98	3	43	101	55½
49	1¾	50¾	99	3½	1	2½	49	1	71½	50	77¾	99	3	46½	102	59
50	1¾	51¾	100	3½	1	3¾	50	1	75	51	81¼	100	3	50	103	62¾

	On Cost		Profit on Returns			On Cost		Profit on Returns			On Cost		Profit on Returns	
150	5	25	155	44	450	15	75	466	32¼	750	26	25	777	20¼
200	7	0	207	25½	500	17	50	518	13½	800	28	0	829	1½
250	8	75	259	6¾	550	19	25	569	94¾	850	29	75	880	83
300	10	50	310	88	600	21	0	621	76¼	900	31	50	932	64¼
350	12	25	362	69½	650	22	75	673	57½	950	33	25	984	45½
400	14	0	414	50¾	700	24	50	725	38¾	1000	35	0	1036	27

P	Profit on Cost P	Profit on Returns P	P	Profit on Cost P	Profit on Returns £	P	£	Profit on Cost £	P	Profit on Returns £	P	£	Profit on Cost £	P	Profit on Returns £	P
1	0	1	51	2	0	53	1	0	3¾	1	4	51	1	91¼	52	98¾
2	0	2	52	2	0	54	2	0	7½	2	7¾	52	1	95	54	2½
3	0	3	53	2	0	55	3	0	11¼	3	11¾	53	1	98¾	55	6½
4	0¼	4¼	54	2	0	56	4	0	15	4	15½	54	2	2½	56	10½
5	0¼	5¼	55	2	0	57¼	5	0	18¾	5	19½	55	2	6¼	57	14¼
6	0¼	6¼	56	2	0	58¼	6	0	22½	6	23½	56	2	10	58	18¼
7	0¼	7¼	57	2¼	0	59¼	7	0	26¼	7	27¼	57	2	13¾	59	22
8	0¼	8¼	58	2¼	0	60¼	8	0	30	8	31¼	58	2	17½	60	26
9	0¼	9¼	59	2¼	0	61¼	9	0	33¾	9	35	59	2	21¼	61	29¾
10	0½	10½	60	2¼	0	62¼	10	0	37½	10	39	60	2	25	62	33¾
11	0½	11½	61	2¼	0	63½	11	0	41¼	11	42¾	61	2	28¾	63	37¾
12	0½	12½	62	2¼	0	64½	12	0	45	12	46¾	62	2	32½	64	41½
13	0½	13½	63	2½	0	65½	13	0	48¾	13	50¾	63	2	36¼	65	45½
14	0½	14½	64	2½	0	66½	14	0	52½	14	54½	64	2	40	66	49½
15	0½	15½	65	2½	0	67½	15	0	56¼	15	58½	65	2	43¾	67	53¼
16	0½	16½	66	2½	0	68½	16	0	60	16	62¼	66	2	47½	68	57¼
17	0¾	17¾	67	2½	0	69½	17	0	63¾	17	66¼	67	2	51¼	69	61
18	0¾	18¾	68	2½	0	70¾	18	0	67½	18	70¼	68	2	55	70	65
19	0¾	19¾	69	2½	0	71¾	19	0	71¼	19	74	69	2	58¾	71	68¾
20	0¾	20¾	70	2¾	0	72¾	20	0	75	20	78	70	2	62½	72	72¾
21	0¾	21¾	71	2¾	0	73¾	21	0	78¾	21	81¾	71	2	66¼	73	76½
22	0¾	22¾	72	2¾	0	74¾	22	0	82½	22	85¾	72	2	70	74	80½
23	0¾	24	73	2¾	0	75¾	23	0	86¼	23	89½	73	2	73¾	75	84½
24	1	25	74	2¾	0	77	24	0	90	24	93½	74	2	77½	76	88¼
25	1	26	75	2¾	0	78	25	0	93¾	25	97½	75	2	81¼	77	92¼
26	1	27	76	2¾	0	79	26	0	97½	27	1¼	76	2	85	78	96
27	1	28	77	3	0	80	27	1	1¼	28	5¼	77	2	88¾	80	0
28	1	29	78	3	0	81	28	1	5	29	9	78	2	92½	81	4
29	1	30¼	79	3	0	82	29	1	8¾	30	13	79	2	96¼	82	7¾
30	1¼	31¼	80	3	0	83	30	1	12½	31	17	80	3	0	83	11¾
31	1¼	32¼	81	3	0	84¼	31	1	16¼	32	20¾	81	3	3¾	84	15½
32	1¼	33¼	82	3	0	85¼	32	1	20	33	24¾	82	3	7½	85	19½
33	1¼	34¼	83	3	0	86¼	33	1	23¾	34	28½	83	3	11¼	86	23½
34	1¼	35¼	84	3¼	0	87¼	34	1	27½	35	32½	84	3	15	87	27¼
35	1¼	36¼	85	3¼	0	88¼	35	1	31¼	36	36½	85	3	18¾	88	31¼
36	1¼	37½	86	3¼	0	89¼	36	1	35	37	40¼	86	3	22½	89	35
37	1½	38½	87	3¼	0	90½	37	1	38¾	38	44¼	87	3	26¼	90	39
38	1½	39½	88	3¼	0	91½	38	1	42½	39	48	88	3	30	91	42¾
39	1½	40½	89	3¼	0	92½	39	1	46¼	40	52	89	3	33¾	92	46¾
40	1½	41½	90	3½	0	93½	40	1	50	41	55¾	90	3	37½	93	50¾
41	1½	42½	91	3½	0	94½	41	1	53¾	42	59¾	91	3	41¼	94	54½
42	1½	43¾	92	3½	0	95½	42	1	57½	43	63¾	92	3	45	95	58½
43	1½	44¾	93	3½	0	96½	43	1	61¼	44	67½	93	3	48¾	96	62¼
44	1¾	45¾	94	3½	0	97¾	44	1	65	45	71½	94	3	52½	97	66¼
45	1¾	46¾	95	3½	0	98¾	45	1	68¾	46	75½	95	3	56¼	98	70¼
46	1¾	47¾	96	3½	0	99¾	46	1	72½	47	79½	96	3	60	99	74
47	1¾	48¾	97	3¾	1	0¾	47	1	76¼	48	83	97	3	63¾	100	78
48	1¾	49¾	98	3¾	1	1¾	48	1	80	49	87	98	3	67½	101	81¾
49	1¾	51	99	3¾	1	2¾	49	1	83¾	50	91	99	3	71¼	102	85¾
50	2	52	100	3¾	1	4	50	1	87½	51	94¾	100	3	75	103	89½

	On Cost		Profit on Returns			On Cost		Profit on Returns			On Cost		Profit on Returns	
150	5	62½	155	84½	450	16	87½	467	53¼	750	28	12½	779	22
200	7	50	207	79¼	500	18	75	519	48	800	30	0	831	17
250	9	37½	259	74	550	20	62½	571	42¾	850	31	87½	883	11¾
300	11	25	311	68¾	600	22	50	623	37¾	900	33	75	935	6½
350	13	12½	363	63¾	650	24	37½	675	32½	950	35	62½	987	1¼
400	15	0	415	58½	700	26	25	727	27¼	1000	37	50	1038	96

	Profit on Cost	Profit on Returns		Profit on Cost	Profit on Returns			Profit on Cost		Profit on Returns			Profit on Cost		Profit on Returns	
P	P	P	P	P	£	P	£	£	P	£	P	£	£	P	£	P
1	0	1	**51**	2	0	53¼	**1**	0	4	1	4¼	**51**	2	4	53	12½
2	0	2	**52**	2	0	54¼	**2**	0	8	2	8¼	**52**	2	8	54	16¾
3	0	3¼	**53**	2	0	55¼	**3**	0	12	3	12½	**53**	2	12	55	20¾
4	0¼	4¼	**54**	2¼	0	56¼	**4**	0	16	4	16¾	**54**	2	16	56	25
5	0¼	5¼	**55**	2¼	0	57¼	**5**	0	20	5	20¾	**55**	2	20	57	29¼
6	0¼	6¼	**56**	2¼	0	58¼	**6**	0	24	6	25	**56**	2	24	58	33¼
7	0¼	7¼	**57**	2¼	0	59½	**7**	0	28	7	29¼	**57**	2	28	59	37½
8	0¼	8¼	**58**	2¼	0	60½	**8**	0	32	8	33¼	**58**	2	32	60	41¾
9	0¼	9½	**59**	2¼	0	61½	**9**	0	36	9	37½	**59**	2	36	61	45¾
10	0½	10½	**60**	2½	**0**	**62½**	**10**	**0**	**40**	**10**	**41¾**	**60**	**2**	**40**	**62**	**50**
11	0½	11½	**61**	2½	0	63½	**11**	0	44	11	45¾	**61**	2	44	63	54¼
12	0½	12½	**62**	2½	0	64½	**12**	0	48	12	50	**62**	2	48	64	58¼
13	0½	13½	**63**	2½	0	65¾	**13**	0	52	13	54¼	**63**	2	52	65	62½
14	0½	14½	**64**	2½	0	66¾	**14**	0	56	14	58¼	**64**	2	56	66	66¾
15	0½	15¾	**65**	2½	0	67¾	**15**	0	60	15	62½	**65**	2	60	67	70¾
16	0¾	16¾	**66**	2¾	0	68¾	**16**	0	64	16	66¾	**66**	2	64	68	75
17	0¾	17¾	**67**	2¾	0	69¾	**17**	0	68	17	70¾	**67**	2	68	69	79¼
18	0¾	18¾	**68**	2¾	0	70¾	**18**	0	72	18	75	**68**	2	72	70	83¼
19	0¾	19¾	**69**	2¾	0	72	**19**	0	76	19	79¼	**69**	2	76	71	87½
20	**0¾**	**20¾**	**70**	**2¾**	**0**	**73**	**20**	**0**	**80**	**20**	**83¼**	**70**	**2**	**80**	**72**	**91¾**
21	0¾	22	**71**	2¾	0	74	**21**	0	84	21	87½	**71**	2	84	73	95¾
22	1	23	**72**	3	0	75	**22**	0	88	22	91¾	**72**	2	88	75	0
23	1	24	**73**	3	0	76	**23**	0	92	23	95¾	**73**	2	92	76	4¼
24	1	25	**74**	3	0	77	**24**	0	96	25	0	**74**	2	96	77	8¼
25	1	26	**75**	3	0	78¼	**25**	1	0	26	4¼	**75**	3	0	78	12½
26	1	27	**76**	3	0	79¼	**26**	1	4	27	8¼	**76**	3	4	79	16¾
27	1	28¼	**77**	3	0	80¼	**27**	1	8	28	12½	**77**	3	8	80	20¾
28	1	29¼	**78**	3	0	81¼	**28**	1	12	29	16¾	**78**	3	12	81	25
29	1¼	30¼	**79**	3¼	0	82¼	**29**	1	16	30	20¾	**79**	3	16	82	29¼
30	**1¼**	**31¼**	**80**	**3¼**	**0**	**83¼**	**30**	**1**	**20**	**31**	**25**	**80**	**3**	**20**	**83**	**33¼**
31	1¼	32¼	**81**	3¼	0	84½	**31**	1	24	32	29¼	**81**	3	24	84	37½
32	1¼	33¼	**82**	3¼	0	85½	**32**	1	28	33	33¼	**82**	3	28	85	41¾
33	1¼	34½	**83**	3¼	0	86½	**33**	1	32	34	37½	**83**	3	32	86	45¾
34	1¼	35½	**84**	3¼	0	87½	**34**	1	36	35	41¾	**84**	3	36	87	50
35	1½	36½	**85**	3½	0	88½	**35**	1	40	36	45¾	**85**	3	40	88	54¼
36	1½	37½	**86**	3½	0	89½	**36**	1	44	37	50	**86**	3	44	89	58¼
37	1½	38½	**87**	3½	0	90¾	**37**	1	48	38	54¼	**87**	3	48	90	62½
38	1½	39½	**88**	3½	0	91¾	**38**	1	52	39	58¼	**88**	3	52	91	66¾
39	1½	40¾	**89**	3½	0	92¾	**39**	1	56	40	62½	**89**	3	56	92	70¾
40	**1½**	**41¾**	**90**	**3½**	**0**	**93¾**	**40**	**1**	**60**	**41**	**66¾**	**90**	**3**	**60**	**93**	**75**
41	1¾	42¾	**91**	3¾	0	94¾	**41**	1	64	42	70¾	**91**	3	64	94	79¼
42	1¾	43¾	**92**	3¾	0	95¾	**42**	1	68	43	75	**92**	3	68	95	83¼
43	1¾	44¾	**93**	3¾	0	97	**43**	1	72	44	79¼	**93**	3	72	96	87½
44	1¾	45¾	**94**	3¾	0	98	**44**	1	76	45	83¼	**94**	3	76	97	91¾
45	1¾	47	**95**	3¾	0	99	**45**	1	80	46	87½	**95**	3	80	98	95¾
46	1¾	48	**96**	3¾	1	0	**46**	1	84	47	91¾	**96**	3	84	100	0
47	2	49	**97**	4	1	1	**47**	1	88	48	95¾	**97**	3	88	101	4¼
48	2	50	**98**	4	1	2	**48**	1	92	50	0	**98**	3	92	102	8¼
49	2	51	**99**	4	1	3¼	**49**	1	96	51	4¼	**99**	3	96	103	12½
50	**2**	**52**	**100**	**4**	**1**	**4¼**	**50**	**2**	**0**	**52**	**8¼**	**100**	**4**	**0**	**104**	**16¾**

	On Cost		Profit on Returns			On Cost		Profit on Returns			On Cost		Profit on Returns	
150	6	0	156	25	**450**	18	0	468	75	**750**	30	0	781	25
200	8	0	208	33¼	**500**	20	0	520	83¼	**800**	32	0	833	33¼
250	10	0	260	41¾	**550**	22	0	572	91¾	**850**	34	0	885	41¾
300	12	0	312	50	**600**	24	0	625	0	**900**	36	0	937	50
350	14	0	364	58¼	**650**	26	0	677	8¼	**950**	38	0	989	58¼
400	16	0	416	66¾	**700**	28	0	729	16¾	**1000**	40	0	1041	66¾

4½ Per Cent

	on Cost	Profit on Returns		on Cost	Profit on Returns			on Cost		Profit on Returns			on Cost		Profit on Returns	
P	P	P	P	P	£	P	£	£	P	£	P	£	£	P	£	P
1	0	1	51	2¼	0	53½	1	0	4½	1	4¾	51	2	29½	53	40¼
2	0	2	52	2¼	0	54½	2	0	9	2	9½	52	2	34	54	45
3	0¼	3¼	53	2½	0	55½	3	0	13½	3	14¼	53	2	38½	55	49¾
4	0¼	4¼	54	2½	0	56½	4	0	18	4	18¾	54	2	43	56	54½
5	0¼	5¼	55	2½	0	57½	5	0	22½	5	23½	55	2	47½	57	59¼
6	0¼	6¼	56	2½	0	58¾	6	0	27	6	28¼	56	2	52	58	63¾
7	0¼	7¼	57	2½	0	59¾	7	0	31½	7	33	57	2	56½	59	68½
8	0¼	8½	58	2½	0	60¾	8	0	36	8	37¾	58	2	61	60	73¼
9	0½	9½	59	2¾	0	61¾	9	0	40½	9	42½	59	2	65½	61	78
10	**0½**	**10½**	**60**	**2¾**	**0**	**62¾**	**10**	**0**	**45**	**10**	**47**	**60**	**2**	**70**	**62**	**82¾**
11	0½	11½	61	2¾	0	64	11	0	49½	11	51¾	61	2	74½	63	87½
12	0½	12½	62	2¾	0	65	12	0	54	12	56½	62	2	79	64	92¼
13	0½	13½	63	2¾	0	66	13	0	58½	13	61¼	63	2	83½	65	96¾
14	0¾	14¾	64	3	0	67	14	0	63	14	66	64	2	88	67	1½
15	0¾	15¾	65	3	0	68	15	0	67½	15	70¾	65	2	92½	68	6¼
16	0¾	16¾	66	3	0	69	16	0	72	16	75½	66	2	97	69	11
17	0¾	17¾	67	3	0	70¼	17	0	76½	17	80	67	3	1½	70	15¾
18	0¾	18¾	68	3	0	71¼	18	0	81	18	84¾	68	3	6	71	20½
19	0¾	20	69	3	0	72¼	19	0	85½	19	89½	69	3	10½	72	25¼
20	**1**	**21**	**70**	**3¼**	**0**	**73¼**	**20**	**0**	**90**	**20**	**94¼**	**70**	**3**	**15**	**73**	**29¾**
21	1	22	71	3¼	0	74¼	21	0	94½	21	99	71	3	19½	74	34½
22	1	23	72	3¼	0	75½	22	0	99	23	3¾	72	3	24	75	39¼
23	1	24	73	3¼	0	76½	23	1	3½	24	8½	73	3	28½	76	44
24	1	25¼	74	3¼	0	77½	24	1	8	25	13	74	3	33	77	48¾
25	1¼	26¼	75	3½	0	78½	25	1	12½	26	17¾	75	3	37½	78	53½
26	1¼	27¼	76	3½	0	79½	26	1	17	27	22½	76	3	42	79	58
27	1¼	28¼	77	3½	0	80¾	27	1	21½	28	27¼	77	3	46½	80	62¾
28	1¼	29¼	78	3½	0	81¾	28	1	26	29	32	78	3	51	81	67½
29	1¼	30½	79	3½	0	82¾	29	1	30½	30	36¾	79	3	55½	82	72¼
30	**1¼**	**31½**	**80**	**3½**	**0**	**83¾**	**30**	**1**	**35**	**31**	**41¼**	**80**	**3**	**60**	**83**	**77**
31	1½	32½	81	3¾	0	84¾	31	1	39½	32	46	81	3	64½	84	81¾
32	1½	33½	82	3¾	0	85¾	32	1	44	33	50¾	82	3	69	85	86½
33	1½	34½	83	3¾	0	87	33	1	48½	34	55½	83	3	73½	86	91
34	1½	35½	84	3¾	0	88	34	1	53	35	60¼	84	3	78	87	95¾
35	1½	36¾	85	3¾	0	89	35	1	57½	36	65	85	3	82½	89	0½
36	1½	37¾	86	3¾	0	90	36	1	62	37	69¾	86	3	87	90	5¼
37	1¾	38¾	87	4	0	91	37	1	66½	38	74¼	87	3	91½	91	10
38	1¾	39¾	88	4	0	92¼	38	1	71	39	79	88	3	96	92	14¾
39	1¾	40¾	89	4	0	93¼	39	1	75½	40	83¾	89	4	0½	93	19½
40	**1¾**	**42**	**90**	**4**	**0**	**94¼**	**40**	**1**	**80**	**41**	**88½**	**90**	**4**	**5**	**94**	**24**
41	1¾	43	91	4	0	95¼	41	1	84½	42	93¼	91	4	9½	95	28¾
42	2	44	92	4¼	0	96¼	42	1	89	43	98	92	4	14	96	33½
43	2	45	93	4¼	0	97½	43	1	93½	45	2¾	93	4	18½	97	38¼
44	2	46	94	4¼	0	98½	44	1	98	46	7¼	94	4	23	98	43
45	2	47¼	95	4¼	0	99½	45	2	2½	47	12	95	4	27½	99	47¾
46	2	48¼	96	4¼	1	0½	46	2	7	48	16¾	96	4	32	100	52¼
47	2	49¼	97	4¼	1	1½	47	2	11½	49	21½	97	4	36½	101	57
48	2¼	50¼	98	4½	1	2½	48	2	16	50	26¼	98	4	41	102	61¾
49	2¼	51¼	99	4½	1	3¾	49	2	20½	51	31	99	4	45½	103	66½
50	**2¼**	**52¼**	**100**	**4½**	**1**	**4¾**	**50**	**2**	**25**	**52**	**35½**	**100**	**4**	**50**	**104**	**71¼**

	On Cost		Profit on Returns			On Cost		Profit on Returns			On Cost		Profit on Returns	
150	6	75	157	6¾	450	20	25	471	20½	750	33	75	785	34
200	9	0	209	42½	500	22	50	523	56	800	36	0	837	69¾
250	11	25	261	78	550	24	75	575	91½	850	38	25	890	5¼
300	13	50	314	13½	600	27	0	628	27¼	900	40	50	942	40¾
350	15	75	366	49¼	650	29	25	680	62¾	950	42	75	994	76½
400	18	0	418	84¾	700	31	50	732	98½	1000	45	0	1047	12

	on Cost	Profit on Returns		on Cost	Profit on Returns			on Cost		Profit on Returns			on Cost		Profit on Returns	
P	P	P	P	P	£	P	£	£	P	£	P	£	£	P	£	P
1	0	1	51	2½	0	53¾	1	0	5	1	5¼	51	2	55	53	68½
2	0	2	52	2½	0	54¾	2	0	10	2	10½	52	2	60	54	73¾
3	0¼	3¼	53	2¾	0	55¾	3	0	15	3	15¾	53	2	65	55	79
4	0¼	4¼	54	2¾	0	56¾	4	0	20	4	21	54	2	70	56	84¼
5	0¼	5¼	55	2¾	0	58	5	0	25	5	26¼	55	2	75	57	89½
6	0¼	6¼	56	2¾	0	59	6	0	30	6	31½	56	2	80	58	94¾
7	0¼	7¼	57	2¾	0	60	7	0	35	7	36¾	57	2	85	60	0
8	0½	8½	58	3	0	61	8	0	40	8	42	58	2	90	61	5¼
9	0½	9½	59	3	0	62	9	0	45	9	47¼	59	2	95	62	10½
10	0½	10½	**60**	3	0	63¼	**10**	0	50	10	52¾	**60**	3	0	63	15¾
11	0½	11½	61	3	0	64¼	11	0	55	11	58	61	3	5	64	21
12	0½	12¾	62	3	0	65¼	12	0	60	12	63¼	62	3	10	65	26¼
13	0¾	13¾	63	3¼	0	66¼	13	0	65	13	68½	63	3	15	66	31½
14	0¾	14¾	64	3¼	0	67¼	14	0	70	14	73¾	64	3	20	67	36¾
15	0¾	15¾	65	3¼	0	68½	15	0	75	15	79	65	3	25	68	42
16	0¾	16¾	66	3¼	0	69½	16	0	80	16	84¼	66	3	30	69	47¼
17	0¾	18	67	3¼	0	70½	17	0	85	17	89½	67	3	35	70	52¾
18	1	19	68	3½	0	71½	18	0	90	18	94¾	68	3	40	71	58
19	1	20	69	3½	0	72¾	19	0	95	20	0	69	3	45	72	63¼
20	1	21	**70**	3½	0	73¾	**20**	1	0	21	5¼	**70**	3	50	73	68½
21	1	22	71	3½	0	74¾	21	1	5	22	10½	71	3	55	74	73¾
22	1	23¼	72	3½	0	75¾	22	1	10	23	15¾	72	3	60	75	79
23	1¼	24¼	73	3¾	0	76¾	23	1	15	24	21	73	3	65	76	84¼
24	1¼	25¼	74	3¾	0	78	24	1	20	25	26¼	74	3	70	77	89½
25	1¼	26¼	75	3¾	0	79	25	1	25	26	31½	75	3	75	78	94¾
26	1¼	27¼	76	3¾	0	80	26	1	30	27	36¾	76	3	80	80	0
27	1¼	28½	77	3¾	0	81	27	1	35	28	42	77	3	85	81	5¼
28	1½	29½	78	4	0	82	28	1	40	29	47¼	78	3	90	82	10½
29	1½	30½	79	4	0	83¼	29	1	45	30	52¾	79	3	95	83	15¾
30	1½	31½	**80**	4	0	84¼	**30**	1	50	31	58	**80**	4	0	84	21
31	1½	32¾	81	4	0	85¼	31	1	55	32	63¼	81	4	5	85	26¼
32	1½	33¾	82	4	0	86¼	32	1	60	33	68½	82	4	10	86	31½
33	1¾	34¾	83	4¼	0	87¼	33	1	65	34	73¾	83	4	15	87	36¾
34	1¾	35¾	84	4¼	0	88½	34	1	70	35	79	84	4	20	88	42
35	1¾	36¾	85	4¼	0	89½	35	1	75	36	84¼	85	4	25	89	47¼
36	1¾	38	86	4¼	0	90½	36	1	80	37	89½	86	4	30	90	52¾
37	1¾	39	87	4¼	0	91½	37	1	85	38	94¾	87	4	35	91	58
38	2	40	88	4½	0	92¾	38	1	90	40	0	88	4	40	92	63¼
39	2	41	89	4½	0	93¾	39	1	95	41	5¼	89	4	45	93	68½
40	2	42	**90**	4½	0	94¾	**40**	2	0	42	10½	**90**	4	50	94	73¾
41	2	43¼	91	4½	0	95¾	41	2	5	43	15¾	91	4	55	95	79
42	2	44¼	92	4½	0	96¾	42	2	10	44	21	92	4	60	96	84¼
43	2¼	45¼	93	4¾	0	98	43	2	15	45	26¼	93	4	65	97	89½
44	2¼	46¼	94	4¾	0	99	44	2	20	46	31½	94	4	70	98	94¾
45	2¼	47¼	95	4¾	1	0	45	2	25	47	36¾	95	4	75	100	0
46	2¼	48½	96	4¾	1	1	46	2	30	48	42	96	4	80	101	5¼
47	2¼	49½	97	4¾	1	2	47	2	35	49	47¼	97	4	85	102	10½
48	2½	50½	98	5	1	3¼	48	2	40	50	52¾	98	4	90	103	15¾
49	2½	51½	99	5	1	4¼	49	2	45	51	58	99	4	95	104	21
50	2½	52¾	**100**	5	1	5¼	**50**	2	50	52	63¼	**100**	5	0	105	26¼

	On Cost		Profit on Returns			On Cost		Profit on Returns			On Cost		Profit on Returns	
150	7	50	157	89½	450	22	50	473	68½	750	37	50	789	47¼
200	10	0	210	52¾	500	25	0	526	31½	800	40	0	842	10½
250	12	50	263	15¾	550	27	50	578	94¾	850	42	50	894	73¾
300	15	0	315	79	600	30	0	631	58	900	45	0	947	36¾
350	17	50	368	42	650	32	50	684	21	950	47	50	1000	0
400	20	0	421	5¼	700	35	0	736	84¼	1000	50	0	1052	63¼

	Profit on Cost	Profit on Returns		Profit on Cost	Profit on Returns			Profit on Cost		Profit on Returns			Profit on Cost		Profit on Returns	
P	P	P	P	P		P	£	£	P	£	P	£	£	P	£	P
1	0	1	51	3	0	54¼	1	0	6	1	6½	51	3	6	54	25½
2	0	2¼	52	3	0	55¼	2	0	12	2	12¾	52	3	12	55	32
3	0¼	3¼	53	3¼	0	56½	3	0	18	3	19¼	53	3	18	56	38¼
4	0¼	4¼	54	3¼	0	57½	4	0	24	4	25½	54	3	24	57	44¾
5	0¼	5¼	55	3¼	0	58½	5	0	30	5	32	55	3	30	58	51
6	0¼	6½	56	3¼	0	59½	6	0	36	6	38¼	56	3	36	59	57½
7	0½	7½	57	3½	0	60¾	7	0	42	7	44¾	57	3	42	60	63¾
8	0½	8½	58	3½	0	61¾	8	0	48	8	51	58	3	48	61	70¼
9	0½	9½	59	3½	0	62¾	9	0	54	9	57½	59	3	54	62	76½
10	0½	10¾	**60**	3½	0	63¾	**10**	0	60	10	63¾	**60**	3	60	63	83
11	0¾	11¾	61	3¾	0	65	11	0	66	11	70¼	61	3	66	64	89¼
12	0¾	12¾	62	3¾	0	66	12	0	72	12	76½	62	3	72	65	95¾
13	0¾	13¾	63	3¾	0	67	13	0	78	13	83	63	3	78	67	2¼
14	0¾	15	64	3¾	0	68	14	0	84	14	89¼	64	3	84	68	8½
15	1	16	65	4	0	69¼	15	0	90	15	95¾	65	3	90	69	15
16	1	17	66	4	0	70¼	16	0	96	17	2¼	66	3	96	70	21¼
17	1	18	67	4	0	71¼	17	1	2	18	8½	67	4	2	71	27¾
18	1	19¼	68	4	0	72¼	18	1	8	19	15	68	4	8	72	34
19	1¼	20¼	69	4¼	0	73½	19	1	14	20	21¼	69	4	14	73	40½
20	1¼	21¼	**70**	4¼	0	74½	**20**	1	20	21	27¾	**70**	4	20	74	46¾
21	1¼	22¼	71	4¼	0	75½	21	1	26	22	34	71	4	26	75	53¼
22	1¼	23½	72	4¼	0	76½	22	1	32	23	40½	72	4	32	76	59½
23	1½	24½	73	4½	0	77¾	23	1	38	24	46¾	73	4	38	77	66
24	1½	25½	74	4½	0	78¾	24	1	44	25	53¼	74	4	44	78	72¼
25	1½	26½	75	4½	0	79¾	25	1	50	26	59½	75	4	50	79	78¾
26	1½	27¾	76	4½	0	80¾	26	1	56	27	66	76	4	56	80	85
27	1½	28¾	77	4½	0	82	27	1	62	28	72¼	77	4	62	81	91½
28	1¾	29¾	78	4¾	0	83	28	1	68	29	78¾	78	4	68	82	97¾
29	1¾	30¾	79	4¾	0	84	29	1	74	30	85	79	4	74	84	4¼
30	1¾	32	**80**	4¾	0	85	**30**	1	80	31	91½	**80**	4	80	85	10¾
31	1¾	33	81	4¾	0	86¼	31	1	86	32	97¾	81	4	86	86	17
32	2	34	82	5	0	87¼	32	1	92	34	4¼	82	4	92	87	23½
33	2	35	83	5	0	88¼	33	1	98	35	10¾	83	4	98	88	29¾
34	2	36¼	84	5	0	89¼	34	2	4	36	17	84	5	4	89	36¼
35	2	37¼	85	5	0	90½	35	2	10	37	23½	85	5	10	90	42½
36	2¼	38¼	86	5¼	0	91½	36	2	16	38	29¾	86	5	16	91	49
37	2¼	39¼	87	5¼	0	92½	37	2	22	39	36¼	87	5	22	92	55¼
38	2¼	40½	88	5¼	0	93½	38	2	28	40	42½	88	5	28	93	61¾
39	2¼	41½	89	5¼	0	94¾	39	2	34	41	49	89	5	34	94	68
40	2½	42½	**90**	5½	0	95¾	**40**	2	40	42	55¼	**90**	5	40	95	74½
41	2½	43½	91	5½	0	96¾	41	2	46	43	61¾	91	5	46	96	80¾
42	2½	44¾	92	5½	0	97¾	42	2	52	44	68	92	5	52	97	87¼
43	2½	45¾	93	5½	0	99	43	2	58	45	74½	93	5	58	98	93½
44	2¾	46¾	94	5¾	1	0	44	2	64	46	80¾	94	5	64	100	0
45	2¾	47¾	95	5¾	1	1	45	2	70	47	87¼	95	5	70	101	6½
46	2¾	49	96	5¾	1	2¼	46	2	76	48	93½	96	5	76	102	12¾
47	2¾	50	97	5¾	1	3¼	47	2	82	50	0	97	5	82	103	19¼
48	3	51	98	6	1	4¼	48	2	88	51	6½	98	5	88	104	25½
49	3	52¼	99	6	1	5¼	49	2	94	52	12¾	99	5	94	105	32
50	3	53¼	**100**	6	1	6½	**50**	3	0	53	19¼	**100**	6	0	106	38¼

	On Cost		Profit on Returns			On Cost		Profit on Returns			On Cost		Profit on Returns	
150	9	0	159	57½	450	27	0	478	72¼	750	45	0	797	87¼
200	12	0	212	76½	500	30	0	531	91½	800	48	0	851	6½
250	15	0	265	95¾	550	33	0	585	10¾	850	51	0	904	25½
300	18	0	319	15	600	36	0	638	29¾	900	54	0	957	44¾
350	21	0	372	34	650	39	0	691	49	950	57	0	1010	63¾
400	24	0	425	53¼	700	42	0	744	68	1000	60	0	1063	83

6¼ Per Cent

	on Cost	Profit on Returns		on Cost	Profit on Returns			on Cost		Profit on Returns			on Cost		Profit on Returns	
P	P	P	P	P	£	P	£	£	P	£	P	£	£	P	£	P
1	0	1	51	3¼	0	54½	1	0	6¼	1	6¾	51	3	18¾	54	40
2	0¼	2¼	52	3¼	0	55½	2	0	12½	2	13¼	52	3	25	55	46¾
3	0¼	3¼	53	3¼	0	56½	3	0	18¾	3	20	53	3	31¼	56	53¼
4	0¼	4¼	54	3½	0	57½	4	0	25	4	26¾	54	3	37½	57	60
5	0¼	5¼	55	3½	0	58¾	5	0	31¼	5	33¼	55	3	43¾	58	66¾
6	0½	6½	56	3½	0	59¾	6	0	37½	6	40	56	3	50	59	73¼
7	0½	7½	57	3½	0	60¾	7	0	43¾	7	46¾	57	3	56¼	60	80
8	0½	8½	58	3¾	0	61¾	8	0	50	8	53¼	58	3	62½	61	86¾
9	0½	9½	59	3¾	0	63	9	0	56¼	9	60	59	3	68¾	62	93¼
10	0¾	10¾	**60**	3¾	0	64	**10**	0	62½	10	66¾	**60**	3	75	64	0
11	0¾	11¾	61	3¾	0	65	11	0	68¾	11	73¼	61	3	81¼	65	6¾
12	0¾	12¾	62	4	0	66¼	12	0	75	12	80	62	3	87½	66	13¼
13	0¾	13¾	63	4	0	67¼	13	0	81¼	13	86¾	63	3	93¾	67	20
14	1	15	64	4	0	68¼	14	0	87½	14	93¼	64	4	0	68	26¾
15	1	16	65	4	0	69¼	15	0	93¾	16	0	65	4	6¼	69	33¼
16	1	17	66	4¼	0	70½	16	1	0	17	6¾	66	4	12½	70	40
17	1	18¼	67	4¼	0	71½	17	1	6¼	18	13¼	67	4	18¾	71	46¾
18	1¼	19¼	68	4¼	0	72½	18	1	12½	19	20	68	4	25	72	53¼
19	1¼	20¼	69	4¼	0	73½	19	1	18¾	20	26¾	69	4	31¼	73	60
20	1¼	21¼	**70**	4½	0	74¾	**20**	1	25	21	33¼	**70**	4	37½	74	66¾
21	1¼	22½	71	4½	0	75¾	21	1	31¼	22	40	71	4	43¾	75	73¼
22	1½	23½	72	4½	0	76¾	22	1	37½	23	46¾	72	4	50	76	80
23	1½	24½	73	4½	0	77¾	23	1	43¾	24	53¼	73	4	56¼	77	86¾
24	1½	25½	74	4¾	0	79	24	1	50	25	60	74	4	62½	78	93¼
25	1½	26¾	75	4¾	0	80	25	1	56¼	26	66¾	75	4	68¾	80	0
26	1¾	27¾	76	4¾	0	81	26	1	62½	27	73¼	76	4	75	81	6¾
27	1¾	28¾	77	4¾	0	82¼	27	1	68¾	28	80	77	4	81¼	82	13¼
28	1¾	29¾	78	5	0	83¼	28	1	75	29	86¾	78	4	87½	83	20
29	1¾	31	79	5	0	84¼	29	1	81¼	30	93¼	79	4	93¾	84	26¾
30	2	32	**80**	5	0	85¼	**30**	1	87½	32	0	**80**	5	0	85	33¼
31	2	33	81	5	0	86½	31	1	93¾	33	6¾	81	5	6¼	86	40
32	2	34¼	82	5¼	0	87½	32	2	0	34	13¼	82	5	12½	87	46¾
33	2	35¼	83	5¼	0	88½	33	2	6¼	35	20	83	5	18¾	88	53¼
34	2¼	36¼	84	5¼	0	89½	34	2	12½	36	26¾	84	5	25	89	60
35	2¼	37¼	85	5¼	0	90¾	35	2	18¾	37	33¼	85	5	31¼	90	66¾
36	2¼	38½	86	5½	0	91¾	36	2	25	38	40	86	5	37½	91	73¼
37	2¼	39½	87	5½	0	92¾	37	2	31¼	39	46¾	87	5	43¾	92	80
38	2½	40½	88	5½	0	93¾	38	2	37½	40	53¼	88	5	50	93	86¾
39	2½	41½	89	5½	0	95	39	2	43¾	41	60	89	5	56¼	94	93¼
40	2½	42¾	**90**	5¾	0	96	**40**	2	50	42	66¾	**90**	5	62½	96	0
41	2½	43¾	91	5¾	0	97	41	2	56¼	43	73¼	91	5	68¾	97	6¾
42	2¾	44¾	92	5¾	0	98¼	42	2	62½	44	80	92	5	75	98	13¼
43	2¾	45¾	93	5¾	0	99¼	43	2	68¾	45	86¾	93	5	81¼	99	20
44	2¾	46	94	6	1	0¼	44	2	75	46	93¼	94	5	87½	100	26¾
45	2¾	48	95	6	1	1¼	45	2	81¼	48	0	95	5	93¾	101	33¼
46	3	49	96	6	1	2½	46	2	87½	49	6¾	96	6	0	102	40
47	3	50¼	97	6	1	3½	47	2	93¾	50	13¼	97	6	6¼	103	46¾
48	3	51¼	98	6¼	1	4½	48	3	0	51	20	98	6	12½	104	53¼
49	3	52¼	99	6¼	1	5½	49	3	6¼	52	26¾	99	6	18¾	105	60
50	3¼	53¼	**100**	6¼	1	6¾	**50**	3	12½	53	33¼	**100**	6	25	106	66¾

	On Cost		Profit on Returns			On Cost		Profit on Returns			On Cost		Profit on Returns	
150	9	37½	160	00	450	28	12½	480	00	750	46	87½	800	00
200	12	50	213	33¼	500	31	25	533	33¼	800	50	0	853	33¼
250	15	62½	266	66¾	550	34	37½	586	66¾	850	53	12½	906	66¾
300	18	75	320	00	600	37	50	640	00	900	56	25	960	00
350	21	87½	373	33¼	650	40	62½	693	33¼	950	59	37½	1013	33¼
400	25	0	426	66¾	700	43	75	746	66¾	1000	62	50	1066	66¾

P	on Cost P	Profit on Returns P	P	on Cost P	Profit on Returns £	P	£	on Cost £	P	Profit on Returns £	P	£	on Cost £	P	Profit on Returns £	P
1	0	1	51	3½	0	54¾	1	0	7	1	7½	51	3	57	54	83¾
2	0¼	2¼	52	3¾	0	56	2	0	14	2	15	52	3	64	55	91½
3	0¼	3¼	53	3¾	0	57	3	0	21	3	22½	53	3	71	56	99
4	0¼	4¼	54	3¾	0	58	4	0	28	4	30	54	3	78	58	6½
5	0¼	5½	55	3¾	0	59¼	5	0	35	5	37¾	55	3	85	59	14
6	0½	6½	56	4	0	60¼	6	0	42	6	45½	56	3	92	60	21½
7	0½	7½	57	4	0	61¼	7	0	49	7	52¾	57	3	99	61	29
8	0½	8½	58	4	0	62¼	8	0	56	8	60¼	58	4	6	62	36½
9	0¾	9¾	59	4¼	0	63½	9	0	63	9	67¾	59	4	13	63	44
10	0¾	10¾	**60**	4¼	0	64½	**10**	0	70	10	75¼	**60**	4	20	64	51½
11	0¾	11¾	61	4¼	0	65½	11	0	77	11	82¾	61	4	27	65	59¼
12	0¾	13	62	4¼	0	66¾	12	0	84	12	90¼	62	4	34	66	66¾
13	1	14	63	4½	0	67¾	13	0	91	13	97¾	63	4	41	67	74¼
14	1	15	64	4½	0	68¾	14	0	98	15	5½	64	4	48	68	81¾
15	1	16¼	65	4½	0	70	15	1	5	16	13	65	4	55	69	89¼
16	1	17¼	66	4½	0	71	16	1	12	17	20½	66	4	62	70	96¾
17	1¼	18¼	67	4¾	0	72	17	1	19	18	28	67	4	69	72	4¼
18	1¼	19¼	68	4¾	0	73	18	1	26	19	35½	68	4	76	73	11¾
19	1¼	20½	69	4¾	0	74¼	19	1	33	20	43	69	4	83	74	19¼
20	1½	21½	**70**	5	0	75¼	**20**	1	40	21	50½	**70**	4	90	75	27
21	1½	22½	71	5	0	76¼	21	1	47	22	58	71	4	97	76	34½
22	1½	23¾	72	5	0	77½	22	1	54	23	65½	72	5	4	77	42
23	1½	24¾	73	5	0	78½	23	1	61	24	73	73	5	11	78	49½
24	1¾	25¾	74	5¼	0	79½	24	1	68	25	80¾	74	5	18	79	57
25	1¾	27	75	5¼	0	80¾	25	1	75	26	88¼	75	5	25	80	64½
26	1¾	28	76	5¼	0	81¾	26	1	82	27	95¾	76	5	32	81	72
27	2	29	77	5½	0	82¾	27	1	89	29	3¼	77	5	39	82	79½
28	2	30	78	5½	0	83¾	28	1	96	30	10¾	78	5	46	83	87
29	2	31¼	79	5½	0	85	29	2	3	31	18¼	79	5	53	84	94½
30	2	32¼	**80**	5½	0	86	**30**	2	10	32	25¾	**80**	5	60	86	2¼
31	2¼	33¼	81	5¾	0	87	31	2	17	33	33¼	81	5	67	87	9¾
32	2¼	34½	82	5¾	0	88¼	32	2	24	34	40¾	82	5	74	88	17¼
33	2¼	35½	83	5¾	0	89¼	33	2	31	35	48½	83	5	81	89	24¾
34	2½	36½	84	6	0	90¼	34	2	38	36	56	84	5	88	90	32¼
35	2½	37¾	85	6	0	91½	35	2	45	37	63½	85	5	95	91	39¾
36	2½	38¾	86	6	0	92½	36	2	52	38	71	86	6	2	92	47¼
37	2½	39¾	87	6	0	93½	37	2	59	39	78½	87	6	9	93	54¾
38	2¾	40¾	88	6¼	0	94¾	38	2	66	40	86	88	6	16	94	62¼
39	2¾	42	89	6¼	0	95¾	39	2	73	41	93½	89	6	23	95	70
40	2¾	43	**90**	6¼	0	96¾	**40**	2	80	43	1	**90**	6	30	96	77½
41	2¾	44	91	6¼	0	97¾	41	2	87	44	8½	91	6	37	97	85
42	3	45¼	92	6½	0	99	42	2	94	45	16¼	92	6	44	98	92½
43	3	46¼	93	6½	1	0	43	3	1	46	23¾	93	6	51	100	0
44	3	47¼	94	6½	1	1	44	3	8	47	31¼	94	6	58	101	7½
45	3¼	48½	95	6¾	1	2¼	45	3	15	48	38¾	95	6	65	102	15
46	3¼	49½	96	6¾	1	3¼	46	3	22	49	46¼	96	6	72	103	22½
47	3¼	50½	97	6¾	1	4¼	47	3	29	50	53¾	97	6	79	104	30
48	3¼	51½	98	6¾	1	5½	48	3	36	51	61¼	98	6	86	105	37¾
49	3½	52¾	99	7	1	6½	49	3	43	52	68¾	99	6	93	106	45½
50	3½	53¾	**100**	7	1	7½	**50**	3	50	53	76¼	**100**	7	0	107	52¾

£	On Cost £	P	Profit on Returns £	P	£	On Cost £	P	Profit on Returns £	P	£	On Cost £	P	Profit on Returns £	P
150	10	50	161	29	450	31	50	483	87	750	52	50	806	45¼
200	14	0	215	5½	500	35	0	537	63½	800	56	0	860	21½
250	17	50	268	81¾	550	38	50	591	39¾	850	59	50	913	97¾
300	21	0	322	58	600	42	0	645	16¼	900	63	0	967	74¼
350	24	50	376	34½	650	45	50	698	92½	950	66	50	1021	50½
400	28	0	430	10¾	700	49	0	752	68¾	1000	70	0	1075	27

	Profit on Cost	Profit on Returns		Profit on Cost	Profit on Returns			Profit on Cost		Profit on Returns			Profit on Cost		Profit on Returns	
P	P	P	P	P	£	P	£	£	P	£	P	£	£	P	£	P
1	0	1	51	3¾	0	55¼	1	0	7½	1	8	51	3	82½	55	13½
2	0¼	2¼	52	4	0	56¼	2	0	15	2	16¼	52	3	90	56	21½
3	0¼	3¼	53	4	0	57¼	3	0	22½	3	24¼	53	3	97½	57	29¾
4	0¼	4¼	54	4	0	58½	4	0	30	4	32½	54	4	5	58	37¾
5	0½	5½	55	4¼	0	59½	5	0	37½	5	40½	55	4	12½	59	46
6	0½	6½	56	4¼	0	60½	6	0	45	6	48¾	56	4	20	60	54
7	0½	7½	57	4¼	0	61½	7	0	52½	7	56¾	57	4	27½	61	62¼
8	0½	8¾	58	4¼	0	62¾	8	0	60	8	64¾	58	4	35	62	70¼
9	0¾	9¾	59	4½	0	63¾	9	0	67½	9	73	59	4	42½	63	78½
10	0¾	10¾	60	4½	0	64¾	10	0	75	10	81	60	4	50	64	86½
11	0¾	12	61	4½	0	66	11	0	82½	11	89¼	61	4	57½	65	94½
12	1	13	62	4¾	0	67	12	0	90	12	97¼	62	4	65	67	2¾
13	1	14	63	4¾	0	68	13	0	97½	14	5½	63	4	72½	68	10¾
14	1	15¼	64	4¾	0	69¼	14	1	5	15	13½	64	4	80	69	19
15	1¼	16¼	65	5	0	70¼	15	1	12½	16	21½	65	4	87½	70	27
16	1¼	17¼	66	5	0	71¼	16	1	20	17	29¾	66	4	95	71	35¼
17	1¼	18½	67	5	0	72½	17	1	27½	18	37¾	67	5	2½	72	43¼
18	1¼	19½	68	5	0	73½	18	1	35	19	46	68	5	10	73	51¼
19	1½	20½	69	5¼	0	74½	19	1	42½	20	54	69	5	17½	74	59½
20	1½	21½	70	5¼	0	75¾	20	1	50	21	62¼	70	5	25	75	67½
21	1½	22¾	71	5¼	0	76¾	21	1	57½	22	70¼	71	5	32½	76	75¾
22	1¾	23¾	72	5½	0	77¾	22	1	65	23	78½	72	5	40	77	83¾
23	1¾	24¾	73	5½	0	79	23	1	72½	24	86½	73	5	47½	78	92
24	1¾	26	74	5½	0	80	24	1	80	25	94½	74	5	55	80	0
25	2	27	75	5¾	0	81	25	1	87½	27	2¾	75	5	62½	81	8
26	2	28	76	5¾	0	82¼	26	1	95	28	10¾	76	5	70	82	16¼
27	2	29¼	77	5¾	0	83¼	27	2	2½	29	19	77	5	77½	83	24¼
28	2	30¼	78	5¾	0	84¼	28	2	10	30	27	78	5	85	84	32½
29	2¼	31¼	79	6	0	85½	29	2	17½	31	35¼	79	5	92½	85	40½
30	2¼	32½	80	6	0	86½	30	2	25	32	43¼	80	6	0	86	48¾
31	2¼	33½	81	6	0	87½	31	2	32½	33	51¼	81	6	7½	87	56¾
32	2½	34½	82	6¼	0	88¾	32	2	40	34	59½	82	6	15	88	64¾
33	2½	35¾	83	6¼	0	89¾	33	2	47½	35	67½	83	6	22½	89	73
34	2½	36¾	84	6¼	0	90¾	34	2	55	36	75¾	84	6	30	90	81
35	2¾	37¾	85	6½	0	92	35	2	62½	37	83¾	85	6	37½	91	89¼
36	2¾	39	86	6½	0	93	36	2	70	38	92	86	6	45	92	97¼
37	2¾	40	87	6½	0	94	37	2	77½	40	0	87	6	52½	94	5½
38	2¾	41	88	6½	0	95¼	38	2	85	41	8	88	6	60	95	13½
39	3	42¼	89	6¾	0	96¼	39	2	92½	42	16¼	89	6	67½	96	21½
40	3	43¼	90	6¾	0	97¼	40	3	0	43	24¼	90	6	75	97	29¾
41	3	44¼	91	6¾	0	98½	41	3	7½	44	32½	91	6	82½	98	37¾
42	3¼	45½	92	7	0	99½	42	3	15	45	40½	92	6	90	99	46
43	3¼	46½	93	7	1	0½	43	3	22½	46	48¾	93	6	97½	100	54
44	3¼	47½	94	7	1	1½	44	3	30	47	56¾	94	7	5	101	62¼
45	3½	48¾	95	7¼	1	2¾	45	3	37½	48	64¾	95	7	12½	102	70¼
46	3½	49¾	96	7¼	1	3¾	46	3	45	49	73	96	7	20	103	78½
47	3½	50¾	97	7¼	1	4¾	47	3	52½	50	81	97	7	27½	104	86½
48	3½	52	98	7¼	1	6	48	3	60	51	89¼	98	7	35	105	94½
49	3¾	53	99	7½	1	7	49	3	67½	52	97¼	99	7	42½	107	2¾
50	3¾	54	100	7½	1	8	50	3	75	54	5½	100	7	50	108	10¾

	On Cost		Profit on Returns			On Cost		Profit on Returns			On Cost		Profit on Returns	
150	11	25	162	16¼	450	33	75	486	48¾	750	56	25	810	81
200	15	0	216	21½	500	37	50	540	54	800	60	0	864	86½
250	18	75	270	27	550	41	25	594	59½	850	63	75	918	92
300	22	50	324	32½	600	45	0	648	64¾	900	67	50	972	97¼
350	26	25	378	37¾	650	48	75	702	70¼	950	71	25	1027	2¾
400	30	0	432	43¼	700	52	50	756	75¾	1000	75	0	1081	8

10% — 10 Per Cent — 10%

	Profit on Cost	Profit on Returns		Profit on Cost	Profit on Returns			Profit on Cost		Profit on Returns			Profit on Cost		Profit on Returns	
p	p	p	p	p	£	p	£	£	p	£	p	£	£	p	£	p
1	0	1	51	5	0	56¾	1	0	10	1	11	51	5	10	56	66¾
2	0¼	2¼	52	5¼	0	57¾	2	0	20	2	22¼	52	5	20	57	77¾
3	0¼	3¼	53	5¼	0	59	3	0	30	3	33¼	53	5	30	58	89
4	0½	4½	54	5½	0	60	4	0	40	4	44½	54	5	40	60	0
5	0½	5½	55	5½	0	61	5	0	50	5	55½	55	5	50	61	11
6	0½	6¾	56	5½	0	62¼	6	0	60	6	66¾	56	5	60	62	22¼
7	0¾	7¾	57	5¾	0	63¼	7	0	70	7	77¾	57	5	70	63	33¼
8	0¾	9	58	5¾	0	64½	8	0	80	8	89	58	5	80	64	44½
9	1	10	59	6	0	65½	9	0	90	10	0	59	5	90	65	55½
10	1	11	**60**	6	0	66¾	**10**	1	0	11	11	**60**	6	0	66	66¾
11	1	12¼	61	6	0	67¾	11	1	10	12	22¼	61	6	10	67	77¾
12	1¼	13¼	62	6¼	0	69	12	1	20	13	33¼	62	6	20	68	89
13	1¼	14½	63	6¼	0	70	13	1	30	14	44½	63	6	30	70	0
14	1½	15½	64	6½	0	71	14	1	40	15	55½	64	6	40	71	11
15	1½	16¾	65	6½	0	72¼	15	1	50	16	66¾	65	6	50	72	22¼
16	1½	17¾	66	6½	0	73¼	16	1	60	17	77¾	66	6	60	73	33¼
17	1¾	19	67	6¾	0	74½	17	1	70	18	89	67	6	70	74	44½
18	1¾	20	68	6¾	0	75½	18	1	80	20	0	68	6	80	75	55½
19	2	21	69	7	0	76¾	19	1	90	21	11	69	6	90	76	66¾
20	2	22¼	**70**	7	0	77¾	**20**	2	0	22	22¼	**70**	7	0	77	77¾
21	2	23¼	71	7	0	79	21	2	10	23	33¼	71	7	10	78	89
22	2¼	24½	72	7¼	0	80	22	2	20	24	44½	72	7	20	80	0
23	2¼	25½	73	7¼	0	81	23	2	30	25	55½	73	7	30	81	11
24	2½	26¾	74	7½	0	82¼	24	2	40	26	66¾	74	7	40	82	22¼
25	2½	27¾	75	7½	0	83¼	25	2	50	27	77¾	75	7	50	83	33¼
26	2½	29	76	7½	0	84½	26	2	60	28	89	76	7	60	84	44½
27	2¾	30	77	7¾	0	85½	27	2	70	30	0	77	7	70	85	55½
28	2¾	31	78	7¾	0	86¾	28	2	80	31	11	78	7	80	86	66¾
29	3	32¼	79	8	0	87¾	29	2	90	32	22¼	79	7	90	87	77¾
30	3	33¼	**80**	8	0	89	**30**	3	0	33	33¼	**80**	8	0	88	89
31	3	34½	81	8	0	90	31	3	10	34	44½	81	8	10	90	0
32	3¼	35½	82	8¼	0	91	32	3	20	35	55½	82	8	20	91	11
33	3¼	36¾	83	8¼	0	92¼	33	3	30	36	66¾	83	8	30	92	22¼
34	3½	37¾	84	8½	0	93¼	34	3	40	37	77¾	84	8	40	93	33¼
35	3½	39	85	8½	0	94½	35	3	50	38	89	85	8	50	94	44½
36	3½	40	86	8½	0	95½	36	3	60	40	0	86	8	60	95	55½
37	3¾	41	87	8¾	0	96¾	37	3	70	41	11	87	8	70	96	66¾
38	3¾	42¼	88	8¾	0	97¾	38	3	80	42	22¼	88	8	80	97	77¾
39	4	43¼	89	9	0	99	39	3	90	43	33¼	89	8	90	98	89
40	4	44½	**90**	9	1	0	**40**	4	0	44	44½	**90**	9	0	100	0
41	4	45½	91	9	1	1	41	4	10	45	55½	91	9	10	101	11
42	4¼	46¾	92	9¼	1	2¼	42	4	20	46	66¾	92	9	20	102	22¼
43	4¼	47¾	93	9¼	1	3¼	43	4	30	47	77¾	93	9	30	103	33¼
44	4½	49	94	9½	1	4½	44	4	40	48	89	94	9	40	104	44½
45	4½	50	95	9½	1	5½	45	4	50	50	0	95	9	50	105	55½
46	4½	51	96	9½	1	6¾	46	4	60	51	11	96	9	60	106	66¾
47	4¾	52¼	97	9¾	1	7¾	47	4	70	52	22¼	97	9	70	107	77¾
48	4¾	53¼	98	9¾	1	9	48	4	80	53	33¼	98	9	80	108	89
49	5	54½	99	10	1	10	49	4	90	54	44½	99	9	90	110	0
50	5	55½	**100**	10	1	11	**50**	5	0	55	55½	**100**	10	0	111	11

	On Cost		Profit on Returns			On Cost		Profit on Returns			On Cost		Profit on Returns	
150	15	0	166	66¾	450	45	0	500	0	750	75	0	833	33¼
200	20	0	222	22¼	500	50	0	555	55½	800	80	0	888	89
250	25	0	277	77¾	550	55	0	611	11	850	85	0	944	44½
300	30	0	333	33¼	600	60	0	666	66¾	900	90	0	1000	0
350	35	0	388	89	650	65	0	722	22¼	950	95	0	1055	55½
400	40	0	444	44½	700	70	0	777	77¾	1000	100	0	1111	11

P	on Cost P	Profit on Returns P	P	on Cost P	Profit on Returns P	£	on Cost £ P	Profit on Returns £ P	£	on Cost £ P	Profit on Returns £ P
1	0¼	1¼	51	6½	0 58¼	1	0 12½	1 14¼	51	6 37½	58 28½
2	0¼	2¼	52	6½	0 59½	2	0 25	2 28½	52	6 50	59 42¾
3	0½	3½	53	6¾	0 60½	3	0 37½	3 42¾	53	6 62½	60 57¼
4	0½	4½	54	6¾	0 61¾	4	0 50	4 57¼	54	6 75	61 71½
5	0¾	5¾	55	7	0 62¾	5	0 62½	5 71½	55	6 87½	62 85¾
6	0¾	6¾	56	7	0 64	6	0 75	6 85¾	56	7 0	64 0
7	1	8	57	7¼	0 65¼	7	0 87½	8 0	57	7 12½	65 14¼
8	1	9¼	58	7¼	0 66¼	8	1 0	9 14¼	58	7 25	66 28½
9	1¼	10¼	59	7½	0 67½	9	1 12½	10 28½	59	7 37½	67 42¾
10	1¼	11½	**60**	7½	0 68½	**10**	1 25	11 42¾	**60**	7 50	68 57¼
11	1½	12½	61	7¾	0 69¾	11	1 37½	12 57¼	61	7 62½	69 71½
12	1½	13¾	62	7¾	0 70¾	12	1 50	13 71½	62	7 75	70 85¾
13	1¾	14¾	63	8	0 72	13	1 62½	14 85¾	63	7 87½	72 0
14	1¾	16	64	8	0 73¼	14	1 75	16 0	64	8 0	73 14¼
15	2	17¼	65	8¼	0 74¼	15	1 87½	17 14¼	65	8 12½	74 28½
16	2	18¼	66	8¼	0 75½	16	2 0	18 28½	66	8 25	75 42¾
17	2¼	19½	67	8½	0 76½	17	2 12½	19 42¾	67	8 37½	76 57¼
18	2¼	20½	68	8½	0 77¾	18	2 25	20 57¼	68	8 50	77 71½
19	2½	21¾	69	8¾	0 78¾	19	2 37½	21 71½	69	8 62½	78 85¾
20	2½	22¾	**70**	8¾	0 80	**20**	2 50	22 85¾	**70**	8 75	80 0
21	2¾	24	71	9	0 81¼	21	2 62½	24 0	71	8 87½	81 14¼
22	2¾	25¼	72	9	0 82¼	22	2 75	25 14¼	72	9 0	82 28½
23	3	26¼	73	9¼	0 83½	23	2 87½	26 28½	73	9 12½	83 42¾
24	3	27½	74	9¼	0 84½	24	3 0	27 42¾	74	9 25	84 57¼
25	3¼	28½	75	9½	0 85¾	25	3 12½	28 57¼	75	9 37½	85 71½
26	3¼	29¾	76	9½	0 86¾	26	3 25	29 71½	76	9 50	86 85¾
27	3½	30¾	77	9¾	0 88	27	3 37½	30 85¾	77	9 62½	88 0
28	3½	32	78	9¾	0 89¼	28	3 50	32 0	78	9 75	89 14¼
29	3¾	33¼	79	10	0 90¼	29	3 62½	33 14¼	79	9 87½	90 28½
30	3¾	34¼	**80**	10	0 91½	**30**	3 75	34 28½	**80**	10 0	91 42¾
31	4	35½	81	10¼	0 92½	31	3 87½	35 42¾	81	10 12½	92 57¼
32	4	36½	82	10¼	0 93¾	32	4 0	36 57¼	82	10 25	93 71½
33	4¼	37¾	83	10½	0 94¾	33	4 12½	37 71½	83	10 37½	94 85¾
34	4¼	38¾	84	10½	0 96	34	4 25	38 85¾	84	10 50	96 0
35	4½	40	85	10¾	0 97¼	35	4 37½	40 0	85	10 62½	97 14¼
36	4½	41¼	86	10¾	0 98¼	36	4 50	41 14¼	86	10 75	98 28½
37	4¾	42¼	87	11	0 99½	37	4 62½	42 28½	87	10 87½	99 42¾
38	4¾	43½	88	11	1 0½	38	4 75	43 42¾	88	11 0	100 57¼
39	5	44½	89	11¼	1 1¾	39	4 87½	44 57¼	89	11 12½	101 71½
40	5	45¾	**90**	11¼	1 2¾	**40**	5 0	45 71½	**90**	11 25	102 85¾
41	5¼	46¾	91	11½	1 4	41	5 12½	46 85¾	91	11 37½	104 0
42	5¼	48	92	11½	1 5¼	42	5 25	48 0	92	11 50	105 14¼
43	5½	49¼	93	11¾	1 6¼	43	5 37½	49 14¼	93	11 62½	106 28½
44	5½	50¼	94	11¾	1 7½	44	5 50	50 28½	94	11 75	107 42¾
45	5¾	51½	95	12	1 8½	45	5 62½	51 42¾	95	11 87½	108 57¼
46	5¾	52½	96	12	1 9¾	46	5 75	52 57¼	96	12 0	109 71½
47	6	53¾	97	12¼	1 10¾	47	5 87½	53 71½	97	12 12½	110 85¾
48	6	54¾	98	12¼	1 12	48	6 0	54 85¾	98	12 25	112 0
49	6¼	56	99	12½	1 13¼	49	6 12½	56 0	99	12 37½	113 14¼
50	6¼	57¼	**100**	12½	1 14¼	**50**	6 25	57 14¼	**100**	12 50	114 28½

	On Cost	Profit on Returns		On Cost	Profit on Returns		On Cost	Profit on Returns
150	18 75	171 42¾	450	56 25	514 28½	750	93 75	857 14¼
200	25 0	228 57¼	500	62 50	571 42¾	800	100 0	914 28½
250	31 25	285 71½	550	68 75	628 57¼	850	106 25	971 42¾
300	37 50	342 85¾	600	75 0	685 71½	900	112 50	1028 57¼
350	43 75	400 00	650	81 25	742 85¾	950	118 75	1085 71½
400	50 0	457 14¼	700	87 50	800 0	1000	125 0	1142 85¾

	on Cost	Profit on Returns		on Cost	Profit on Returns			on Cost		Profit on Returns			on Cost		Profit on Returns	
P	P	P	P	P	£	P	£	£	P	£	P	£	£	P	£	P
1	0¼	1¼	51	7¾	0	60	1	0	15	1	17¾	51	7	65	60	0
2	0¼	2¼	52	7¾	0	61¼	2	0	30	2	35¼	52	7	80	61	17¾
3	0½	3½	53	8	0	62¼	3	0	45	3	53	53	7	95	62	35¼
4	0½	4¾	54	8	0	63½	4	0	60	4	70½	54	8	10	63	53
5	0¾	6	55	8¼	0	64¾	5	0	75	5	88¼	55	8	25	64	70½
6	1	7	56	8½	0	66	6	0	90	7	6	56	8	40	65	88¼
7	1	8¼	57	8½	0	67	7	1	5	8	23½	57	8	55	67	6
8	1¼	9½	58	8¾	0	68¼	8	1	20	9	41¼	58	8	70	68	23½
9	1¼	10½	59	8¾	0	69½	9	1	35	10	58¾	59	8	85	69	41¼
10	1½	11¾	**60**	9	0	70½	**10**	1	50	11	76½	**60**	9	0	70	58¾
11	1¾	13	61	9¼	0	71¾	11	1	65	12	94	61	9	15	71	76½
12	1¾	14	62	9¼	0	73	12	1	80	14	11¾	62	9	30	72	94
13	2	15¼	63	9½	0	74	13	1	95	15	29½	63	9	45	74	11¾
14	2	16½	64	9½	0	75¼	14	2	10	16	47	64	9	60	75	29½
15	2¼	17¾	65	9¾	0	76½	15	2	25	17	64¾	65	9	75	76	47
16	2½	18¾	66	10	0	77¾	16	2	40	18	82¼	66	9	90	77	64¾
17	2½	20	67	10	0	78¾	17	2	55	20	0	67	10	5	78	82¼
18	2¾	21¼	68	10¼	0	80	18	2	70	21	17¾	68	10	20	80	0
19	2¾	22¼	69	10¼	0	81¼	19	2	85	22	35¼	69	10	35	81	17¾
20	3	23½	**70**	10½	0	82¼	**20**	3	0	23	53	**70**	10	50	82	35¼
21	3¼	24¾	71	10¾	0	83½	21	3	15	24	70½	71	10	65	83	53
22	3¼	26	72	10¾	0	84¾	22	3	30	25	88¼	72	10	80	84	70½
23	3½	27	73	11	0	86	23	3	45	27	6	73	10	95	85	88¼
24	3½	28¼	74	11	0	87	24	3	60	28	23½	74	11	10	87	6
25	3¾	29½	75	11¼	0	88¼	25	3	75	29	41¼	75	11	25	88	23½
26	4	30½	76	11½	0	89½	26	3	90	30	58¾	76	11	40	89	41¼
27	4	31¾	77	11½	0	90½	27	4	5	31	76½	77	11	55	90	58¾
28	4¼	33	78	11¾	0	91¾	28	4	20	32	94	78	11	70	91	76½
29	4¼	34	79	11¾	0	93	29	4	35	34	11¾	79	11	85	92	94
30	4½	35¼	**80**	12	0	94	**30**	4	50	35	29½	**80**	12	0	94	11¾
31	4¾	36½	81	12¼	0	95¼	31	4	65	36	47	81	12	15	95	29½
32	4¾	37¾	82	12¼	0	96½	32	4	80	37	64¾	82	12	30	96	47
33	5	38¾	83	12½	0	97¾	33	4	95	38	82¼	83	12	45	97	64¾
34	5	40	84	12½	0	98¾	34	5	10	40	0	84	12	60	98	82¼
35	5¼	41¼	85	12¾	1	0	35	5	25	41	17¾	85	12	75	100	0
36	5½	42¼	86	13	1	1¼	36	5	40	42	35¼	86	12	90	101	17¾
37	5½	43½	87	13	1	2¼	37	5	55	43	53	87	13	5	102	35¼
38	5¾	44¾	88	13¼	1	3½	38	5	70	44	70½	88	13	20	103	53
39	5¾	46	89	13¼	1	4¾	39	5	85	45	88¼	89	13	35	104	70½
40	6	47	**90**	13½	1	6	**40**	6	0	47	6	**90**	13	50	105	88¼
41	6¼	48¼	91	13¾	1	7	41	6	15	48	23½	91	13	65	107	6
42	6¼	49½	92	13¾	1	8¼	42	6	30	49	41¼	92	13	80	108	23½
43	6½	50½	93	14	1	9½	43	6	45	50	58¾	93	13	95	109	41¼
44	6½	51¾	94	14	1	10½	44	6	60	51	76½	94	14	10	110	58¾
45	6¾	53	95	14¼	1	11¾	45	6	75	52	94	95	14	25	111	76½
46	7	54	96	14½	1	13	46	6	90	54	11¾	96	14	40	112	94
47	7	55¼	97	14½	1	14	47	7	5	55	29½	97	14	55	114	11¾
48	7¼	56½	98	14¾	1	15¼	48	7	20	56	47	98	14	70	115	29½
49	7¼	57¾	99	14¾	1	16½	49	7	35	57	64¾	99	14	85	116	47
50	7½	58¾	**100**	15	1	17¾	**50**	7	50	58	82¼	**100**	15	0	117	64¾

	On Cost		Profit on Returns			On Cost		Profit on Returns			On Cost		Profit on Returns	
150	22	50	176	47	450	67	50	529	41¼	750	112	50	882	35¼
200	30	0	235	29½	500	75	0	588	23½	800	120	0	941	17¾
250	37	50	294	11¾	550	82	50	647	6	850	127	50	1000	0
300	45	0	352	94	600	90	0	705	88¼	900	135	0	1058	82¼
350	52	50	411	76½	650	97	50	764	70½	950	142	50	1117	64¾
400	60	0	470	58¾	700	105	0	823	53	1000	150	0	1176	47

	on Cost	Profit on Returns		on Cost	Profit on Returns			on Cost		Profit on Returns			on Cost		Profit on Returns	
P	P	P	P	P	£	P	£	£	P	£	P	£	£	P	£	P
1	0¼	1¼	51	8½	0	61¼	1	0	17	1	20	51	8	50	61	20
2	0¼	2½	52	8¾	0	62½	2	0	33	2	40	52	8	67	62	40
3	0½	3½	53	8¾	0	63½	3	0	50	3	60	53	8	83	63	60
4	0¾	4¾	54	9	0	64¾	4	0	67	4	80	54	9	0	64	80
5	0¾	6	55	9¼	0	66	5	0	83	6	0	55	9	17	66	0
6	1	7¼	56	9¼	0	67¼	6	1	0	7	20	56	9	33	67	20
7	1¼	8½	57	9½	0	68½	7	1	17	8	40	57	9	50	68	40
8	1¼	9½	58	9¾	0	69½	8	1	33	9	60	58	9	67	69	60
9	1½	10¾	59	9¾	0	70¾	9	1	50	10	80	59	9	83	70	80
10	1¾	12	60	10	0	72	10	1	67	12	0	60	10	0	72	0
11	1¾	13¼	61	10¼	0	73¼	11	1	83	13	20	61	10	17	73	20
12	2	14½	62	10¼	0	74½	12	2	0	14	40	62	10	33	74	40
13	2¼	15½	63	10½	0	75½	13	2	17	15	60	63	10	50	75	60
14	2¼	16¾	64	10¾	0	76¾	14	2	33	16	80	64	10	67	76	80
15	2½	18	65	10¾	0	78	15	2	50	18	0	65	10	83	78	0
16	2¾	19¼	66	11	0	79¼	16	2	67	19	20	66	11	0	79	20
17	2¾	20½	67	11¼	0	80½	17	2	83	20	40	67	11	17	80	40
18	3	21½	68	11¼	0	81½	18	3	0	21	60	68	11	33	81	60
19	3¼	22¾	69	11½	0	82¾	19	3	17	22	80	69	11	50	82	80
20	3¼	24	70	11¾	0	84	20	3	33	24	0	70	11	67	84	0
21	3½	25¼	71	11¾	0	85¼	21	3	50	25	20	71	11	83	85	20
22	3¾	26½	72	12	0	86½	22	3	67	26	40	72	12	0	86	40
23	3¾	27½	73	12¼	0	87½	23	3	83	27	60	73	12	17	87	60
24	4	28¾	74	12¼	0	88¾	24	4	0	28	80	74	12	33	88	80
25	4¼	30	75	12½	0	90	25	4	17	30	0	75	12	50	90	0
26	4¼	31¼	76	12¾	0	91¼	26	4	33	31	20	76	12	67	91	20
27	4½	32½	77	12¾	0	92½	27	4	50	32	40	77	12	83	92	40
28	4¾	33½	78	13	0	93½	28	4	67	33	60	78	13	0	93	60
29	4¾	34¾	79	13¼	0	94¾	29	4	83	34	80	79	13	17	94	80
30	5	36	80	13¼	0	96	30	5	0	36	0	80	13	33	96	0
31	5¼	37¼	81	13½	0	97¼	31	5	17	37	20	81	13	50	97	20
32	5¼	38½	82	13¾	0	98½	32	5	33	38	40	82	13	67	98	40
33	5½	39½	83	13¾	0	99½	33	5	50	39	60	83	13	83	99	60
34	5¾	40¾	84	14	1	0¾	34	5	67	40	80	84	14	0	100	80
35	5¾	42	85	14¼	1	2	35	5	83	42	0	85	14	17	102	0
36	6	43¼	86	14¼	1	3¼	36	6	0	43	20	86	14	33	103	20
37	6¼	44½	87	14½	1	4½	37	6	17	44	40	87	14	50	104	40
38	6¼	45½	88	14¾	1	5½	38	6	33	45	60	88	14	67	105	60
39	6½	46¾	89	14¾	1	6¾	39	6	50	46	80	89	14	83	106	80
40	6¾	48	90	15	1	8	40	6	67	48	0	90	15	0	108	0
41	6¾	49¼	91	15¼	1	9¼	41	6	83	49	20	91	15	17	109	20
42	7	50½	92	15¼	1	10½	42	7	0	50	40	92	15	33	110	40
43	7¼	51½	93	15½	1	11½	43	7	17	51	60	93	15	50	111	60
44	7¼	52¾	94	15¾	1	12¾	44	7	33	52	80	94	15	67	112	80
45	7½	54	95	15¾	1	14	45	7	50	54	0	95	15	83	114	0
46	7¾	55¼	96	16	1	15¼	46	7	67	55	20	96	16	0	115	20
47	7¾	56½	97	16¼	1	16½	47	7	83	56	40	97	16	17	116	40
48	8	57½	98	16¼	1	17½	48	8	0	57	60	98	16	33	117	60
49	8¼	58¾	99	16½	1	18¾	49	8	17	58	80	99	16	50	118	80
50	8¼	60	100	16¾	1	20	50	8	33	60	0	100	16	67	120	0

	On Cost		Profit on Returns			On Cost		Profit on Returns			On Cost		Profit on Returns	
150	25	0	180	0	450	75	0	540	0	750	125	0	900	0
200	33	33	240	0	500	83	33	600	0	800	133	33	960	0
250	41	67	300	0	550	91	67	660	0	850	141	67	1020	0
300	50	0	360	0	600	100	0	720	0	900	150	0	1080	0
350	58	33	420	0	650	108	33	780	0	950	158	33	1140	0
400	66	67	480	0	700	116	67	840	0	1000	166	67	1200	0

P	Profit on Cost P	Profit on Returns P	P	Profit on Cost P	Profit on Returns £	P	£	Profit on Cost £	P	Profit on Returns £	P	£	Profit on Cost £	P	Profit on Returns £	P
1	0¼	1¼	51	9	0	61¾	1	0	17½	1	21¼	51	8	92½	61	81¾
2	0¼	2½	52	9	0	63	2	0	35	2	42½	52	9	10	63	3
3	0½	3¾	53	9¼	0	64¼	3	0	52½	3	63¾	53	9	27½	64	24¼
4	0¾	4¾	54	9½	0	65½	4	0	70	4	84¾	54	9	45	65	45½
5	1	6	55	9¾	0	66¾	5	0	87½	6	6	55	9	62½	66	66¾
6	1	7¼	56	9¾	0	68	6	1	5	7	27¼	56	9	80	67	88
7	1¼	8½	57	10	0	69	7	1	22½	8	48½	57	9	97½	69	9
8	1½	9¾	58	10¼	0	70¼	8	1	40	9	69¾	58	10	15	70	30¼
9	1½	11	59	10¼	0	71½	9	1	57½	10	91	59	10	32½	71	51½
10	1¾	12	60	10½	0	72¾	10	1	75	12	12	60	10	50	72	72¾
11	2	13¼	61	10¾	0	74	11	1	92½	13	33¼	61	10	67½	73	94
12	2	14½	62	10¾	0	75¼	12	2	10	14	54½	62	10	85	75	15
13	2¼	15¾	63	11	0	76¼	13	2	27½	15	75¾	63	11	2½	76	36¼
14	2½	17	64	11¼	0	77½	14	2	45	16	97	64	11	20	77	57½
15	2¾	18¼	65	11¼	0	78¾	15	2	62½	18	18¼	65	11	37½	78	78¾
16	2¾	19½	66	11½	0	80	16	2	80	19	39½	66	11	55	80	0
17	3	20½	67	11¾	0	81¼	17	2	97½	20	60¾	67	11	72½	81	21¼
18	3¼	21¾	68	12	0	82½	18	3	15	21	81¾	68	11	90	82	42½
19	3¼	23	69	12	0	83¾	19	3	32½	23	3	69	12	7½	83	63¾
20	3½	24¼	70	12¼	0	84¾	20	3	50	24	24¼	70	12	25	84	84¾
21	3¾	25½	71	12½	0	86	21	3	67½	25	45½	71	12	42½	86	6
22	3¾	26¾	72	12½	0	87¼	22	3	85	26	66¾	72	12	60	87	27¼
23	4	28	73	12¾	0	88½	23	4	2½	27	88	73	12	77½	88	48½
24	4¼	29	74	13	0	89¾	24	4	20	29	9	74	12	95	89	69¾
25	4¼	30¼	75	13¼	0	91	25	4	37½	30	30¼	75	13	12½	90	91
26	4½	31½	76	13¼	0	92	26	4	55	31	51½	76	13	30	92	12
27	4¾	32¾	77	13½	0	93¼	27	4	72½	32	72¾	77	13	47½	93	33¼
28	5	34	78	13¾	0	94½	28	4	90	33	94	78	13	65	94	54½
29	5	35¼	79	13¾	0	95¾	29	5	7½	35	15	79	13	82½	95	75¾
30	5¼	36¼	80	14	0	97	30	5	25	36	36¼	80	14	0	96	97
31	5½	37½	81	14¼	0	98¼	31	5	42½	37	57½	81	14	17½	98	18¼
32	5½	38¾	82	14¼	0	99½	32	5	60	38	78¾	82	14	35	99	39½
33	5¾	40	83	14½	1	0½	33	5	77½	40	0	83	14	52½	100	60¾
34	6	41¼	84	14¾	1	1¾	34	5	95	41	21¼	84	14	70	101	81¾
35	6¼	42½	85	15	1	3	35	6	12½	42	42½	85	14	87½	103	3
36	6¼	43¾	86	15	1	4¼	36	6	30	43	63¾	86	15	5	104	24¼
37	6½	44¾	87	15¼	1	5½	37	6	47½	44	84¾	87	15	22½	105	45½
38	6¾	46	88	15½	1	6¾	38	6	65	46	6	88	15	40	106	66¾
39	6¾	47¼	89	15½	1	8	39	6	82½	47	27¼	89	15	57½	107	88
40	7	48½	90	15¾	1	9	40	7	0	48	48½	90	15	75	109	9
41	7¼	49¾	91	16	1	10¼	41	7	17½	49	69¾	91	15	92½	110	30¼
42	7¼	51	92	16	1	11½	42	7	35	50	91	92	16	10	111	51½
43	7½	52	93	16¼	1	12¾	43	7	52½	52	12	93	16	27½	112	72¾
44	7¾	53¼	94	16½	1	14	44	7	70	53	33¼	94	16	45	113	94
45	8	54½	95	16¾	1	15¼	45	7	87½	54	54½	95	16	62½	115	15
46	8	55¾	96	16¾	1	16¼	46	8	5	55	75¾	96	16	80	116	36¼
47	8¼	57	97	17	1	17½	47	8	22½	56	97	97	16	97½	117	57½
48	8½	58¼	98	17¼	1	18¾	48	8	40	58	18¼	98	17	15	118	78¾
49	8½	59½	99	17¼	1	20	49	8	57½	59	39½	99	17	32½	120	0
50	8¾	60½	100	17½	1	21¼	50	8	75	60	60¾	100	17	50	121	21¼

	On Cost		Profit on Returns			On Cost		Profit on Returns			On Cost		Profit on Returns	
150	26	25	181	81¾	450	78	75	545	45½	750	131	25	909	9
200	35	0	242	42½	500	87	50	606	6	800	140	0	969	69¾
250	43	75	303	03	550	96	25	666	66¾	850	148	75	1030	30¼
300	52	50	363	63¾	600	105	0	727	27¼	900	157	50	1090	91
350	61	25	424	24¼	650	113	75	787	88	950	166	25	1151	51½
400	70	0	484	84¾	700	122	50	848	48½	1000	175	0	1212	12¼

P	Profit on Cost P	Profit on Returns £ P	P	Profit on Cost P	Profit on Returns £ P	£	Profit on Cost £ P	Profit on Returns £ P	£	Profit on Cost £ P	Profit on Returns £ P
1	0¼	1¼	51	10¼	0 63¾	1	0 20	1 25	51	10 20	63 75
2	0½	2½	52	10½	0 65	2	0 40	2 50	52	10 40	65 0
3	0½	3¾	53	10½	0 66¼	3	0 60	3 75	53	10 60	66 25
4	0¾	5	54	10¾	0 67½	4	0 80	5 0	54	10 80	67 50
5	1	6¼	55	11	0 68¾	5	1 0	6 25	55	11 0	68 75
6	1¼	7½	56	11¼	0 70	6	1 20	7 50	56	11 20	70 0
7	1½	8¾	57	11½	0 71¼	7	1 40	8 75	57	11 40	71 25
8	1½	10	58	11½	0 72½	8	1 60	10 0	58	11 60	72 50
9	1¾	11¼	59	11¾	0 73¾	9	1 80	11 25	59	11 80	73 75
10	2	12½	60	12	0 75	10	2 0	12 50	60	12 0	75 0
11	2¼	13¾	61	12¼	0 76¼	11	2 20	13 75	61	12 20	76 25
12	2½	15	62	12½	0 77½	12	2 40	15 0	62	12 40	77 50
13	2½	16¼	63	12½	0 78¾	13	2 60	16 25	63	12 60	78 75
14	2¾	17½	64	12¾	0 80	14	2 80	17 50	64	12 80	80 0
15	3	18¾	65	13	0 81¼	15	3 0	18 75	65	13 0	81 25
16	3¼	20	66	13¼	0 82½	16	3 20	20 0	66	13 20	82 50
17	3½	21¼	67	13½	0 83¾	17	3 40	21 25	67	13 40	83 75
18	3½	22½	68	13½	0 85	18	3 60	22 50	68	13 60	85 0
19	3¾	23¾	69	13¾	0 86¼	19	3 80	23 75	69	13 80	86 25
20	4	25	70	14	0 87½	20	4 0	25 0	70	14 0	87 50
21	4¼	26¼	71	14¼	0 88¾	21	4 20	26 25	71	14 20	88 75
22	4½	27½	72	14½	0 90	22	4 40	27 50	72	14 40	90 0
23	4½	28¾	73	14½	0 91¼	23	4 60	28 75	73	14 60	91 25
24	4¾	30	74	14¾	0 92½	24	4 80	30 0	74	14 80	92 50
25	5	31¼	75	15	0 93¾	25	5 0	31 25	75	15 0	93 75
26	5¼	32½	76	15¼	0 95	26	5 20	32 50	76	15 20	95 0
27	5½	33¾	77	15½	0 96¼	27	5 40	33 75	77	15 40	96 25
28	5½	35	78	15½	0 97½	28	5 60	35 0	78	15 60	97 50
29	5¾	36¼	79	15¾	0 98¾	29	5 80	36 25	79	15 80	98 75
30	6	37½	80	16	1 0	30	6 0	37 50	80	16 0	100 0
31	6¼	38¾	81	16¼	1 1¼	31	6 20	38 75	81	16 20	101 25
32	6½	40	82	16½	1 2½	32	6 40	40 0	82	16 40	102 50
33	6½	41¼	83	16½	1 3¾	33	6 60	41 25	83	16 60	103 75
34	6¾	42½	84	16¾	1 5	34	6 80	42 50	84	16 80	105 0
35	7	43¾	85	17	1 6¼	35	7 0	43 75	85	17 0	106 25
36	7¼	45	86	17¼	1 7½	36	7 20	45 0	86	17 20	107 50
37	7½	46¼	87	17½	1 8¾	37	7 40	46 25	87	17 40	108 75
38	7½	47½	88	17½	1 10	38	7 60	47 50	88	17 60	110 0
39	7¾	48¾	89	17¾	1 11¼	39	7 80	48 75	89	17 80	111 25
40	8	50	90	18	1 12½	40	8 0	50 0	90	18 0	112 50
41	8¼	51¼	91	18¼	1 13¾	41	8 20	51 25	91	18 20	113 75
42	8½	52½	92	18½	1 15	42	8 40	52 50	92	18 40	115 0
43	8½	53¾	93	18½	1 16¼	43	8 60	53 75	93	18 60	116 25
44	8¾	55	94	18¾	1 17½	44	8 80	55 0	94	18 80	117 50
45	9	56¼	95	19	1 18¾	45	9 0	56 25	95	19 0	118 75
46	9¼	57½	96	19¼	1 20	46	9 20	57 50	96	19 20	120 0
47	9½	58¾	97	19½	1 21¼	47	9 40	58 75	97	19 40	121 25
48	9½	60	98	19½	1 22½	48	9 60	60 0	98	19 60	122 50
49	9¾	61¼	99	19¾	1 23¾	49	9 80	61 25	99	19 80	123 75
50	10	62½	100	20	1 25	50	10 0	62 50	100	20 0	125 0

	On Cost	Profit on Returns		On Cost	Profit on Returns		On Cost	Profit on Returns
150	30 0	187 50	450	90 0	562 50	750	150 0	937 50
200	40 0	250 0	500	100 0	625 0	800	160 0	1000 0
250	50 0	312 50	550	110 0	687 50	850	170 0	1062 50
300	60 0	375 0	600	120 0	750 0	900	180 0	1125 0
350	70 0	437 50	650	130 0	812 50	950	190 0	1187 50
400	80 0	500 0	700	140 0	875 0	1000	200 0	1250 0

22½ Per Cent

22½%

P	on Cost P	Profit on Returns P	P	on Cost P	Profit on Returns P
1	0¼	1¼	51	11½	0 65¾
2	0½	2½	52	11¾	0 67
3	0¾	3¾	53	12	0 68½
4	1	5¼	54	12¼	0 69¾
5	1¼	6½	55	12½	0 71
6	1¼	7¾	56	12½	0 72¼
7	1½	9	57	12¾	0 73½
8	1¾	10¼	58	13	0 74¾
9	2	11½	59	13¼	0 76¼
10	2¼	13	**60**	13½	0 77½
11	2½	14¼	61	13¾	0 78¾
12	2¾	15½	62	14	0 80
13	3	16¾	63	14¼	0 81¼
14	3¼	18	64	14½	0 82½
15	3½	19¼	65	14¾	0 83¾
16	3½	20¾	66	14¾	0 85¼
17	3¾	22	67	15	0 86½
18	4	23¼	68	15¼	0 87¾
19	4¼	24½	69	15½	0 89
20	4½	25¾	**70**	15¾	0 90¼
21	4¾	27	71	16	0 91½
22	5	28½	72	16¼	0 93
23	5¼	29¾	73	16½	0 94¼
24	5½	31	74	16¾	0 95½
25	5¾	32¼	75	17	0 96¾
26	5¾	33½	76	17	0 98
27	6	34¾	77	17¼	0 99¼
28	6¼	36¼	78	17½	1 0¾
29	6½	37½	79	17¾	1 2
30	6¾	38¾	**80**	18	1 3¼
31	7	40	81	18¼	1 4½
32	7¼	41¼	82	18½	1 5¾
33	7½	42½	83	18¾	1 7
34	7¾	43¾	84	19	1 8½
35	8	45¼	85	19¼	1 9¾
36	8	46½	86	19¼	1 11
37	8¼	47¾	87	19½	1 12¼
38	8½	49	88	19¾	1 13½
39	8¾	50¼	89	20	1 14¾
40	9	51½	**90**	20¼	1 15¼
41	9¼	53	91	20½	1 17½
42	9½	54¼	92	20¾	1 18¾
43	9¾	55½	93	21	1 20
44	10	56¾	94	21¼	1 21¼
45	10¼	58	95	21½	1 22½
46	10¼	59¼	96	21½	1 23¾
47	10½	60¾	97	21¾	1 25¼
48	10¾	62	98	22	1 26½
49	11	63¼	99	22¼	1 27¾
50	11¼	64½	**100**	22½	1 29

£	on Cost £ P	Profit on Returns £ P	£	on Cost £ P	Profit on Returns £ P
1	0 22½	1 29	51	11 47½	65 80¾
2	0 45	2 58	52	11 70	67 9¾
3	0 67½	3 87	53	11 92½	68 38¾
4	0 90	5 16½	54	12 15	69 67¾
5	1 12½	6 45¼	55	12 37½	70 96¾
6	1 35	7 74¼	56	12 60	72 25¾
7	1 57½	9 3¼	57	12 82½	73 54¾
8	1 80	10 32¼	58	13 5	74 83¾
9	2 2½	11 61¼	59	13 27½	76 13
10	2 25	12 90¼	**60**	13 50	77 42
11	2 47½	14 19½	61	13 72½	78 71
12	2 70	15 48½	62	13 95	80 0
13	2 92½	16 77½	63	14 17½	81 29
14	3 15	18 6½	64	14 40	82 58
15	3 37½	19 35½	65	14 62½	83 87
16	3 60	20 64½	66	14 85	85 16¼
17	3 82½	21 93½	67	15 7½	86 45¼
18	4 5	23 22½	68	15 30	87 74¼
19	4 27½	24 51½	69	15 52½	89 3¼
20	4 50	25 80¾	**70**	15 75	90 32¼
21	4 72½	27 9¾	71	15 97½	91 61¼
22	4 95	28 38¾	72	16 20	92 90¼
23	5 17½	29 67¾	73	16 42½	94 19½
24	5 40	30 96¾	74	16 65	95 48½
25	5 62½	32 25¾	75	16 87½	96 77½
26	5 85	33 54¾	76	17 10	98 6½
27	6 7½	34 83¾	77	17 32½	99 35½
28	6 30	36 13	78	17 55	100 64½
29	6 52½	37 42	79	17 77½	101 93½
30	6 75	38 71	**80**	18 0	103 22½
31	6 97½	40 0	81	18 22½	104 51½
32	7 20	41 29	82	18 45	105 80¾
33	7 42½	42 58	83	18 67½	107 9¾
34	7 65	43 87	84	18 90	108 38¾
35	7 87½	45 16¼	85	19 12½	109 67¾
36	8 10	46 45¼	86	19 35	110 96¾
37	8 32½	47 74¼	87	19 57½	112 25¾
38	8 55	49 3¼	88	19 80	113 54¾
39	8 77½	50 32¼	89	20 2½	114 83¾
40	9 0	51 61¼	**90**	20 25	116 13
41	9 22½	52 90¼	91	20 47½	117 42
42	9 45	54 19½	92	20 70	118 71
43	9 67½	55 48½	93	20 92½	120 0
44	9 90	56 77½	94	21 15	121 29
45	10 12½	58 6½	95	21 37½	122 58
46	10 35	59 35½	96	21 60	123 87
47	10 57½	60 64½	97	21 82½	125 16¼
48	10 80	61 93½	98	22 5	126 45¼
49	11 2½	63 22½	99	22 27½	127 74¼
50	11 25	64 51½	**100**	22 50	129 3¼

	On Cost	Profit on Returns		On Cost	Profit on Returns		On Cost	Profit on Returns
150	33 75	193 54¾	450	101 25	580 64½	750	168 75	967 74¼
200	45 0	258 6¼	500	112 50	645 16½	800	180 0	1032 25¾
250	56 25	322 58	550	123 75	709 67¾	850	191 25	1096 77½
300	67 50	387 9¾	600	135 0	774 19¼	900	202 50	1161 29
350	78 75	451 61¼	650	146 25	838 71	950	213 75	1225 80¾
400	90 0	516 13	700	157 50	903 22½	1000	225 0	1290 32¼

	on Cost	Profit on Returns		on Cost	Profit on Returns			on Cost		Profit on Returns			on Cost		Profit on Returns	
P	P	P	P	P	£	P	£	£	P	£	P	£	£	P	£	P
1	0¼	1⅓	51	12¾	0	68	1	0	25	1	33⅓	51	12	75	68	0
2	0½	2⅔	52	13	0	69⅓	2	0	50	2	66⅔	52	13	0	69	33⅓
3	0¾	4	53	13¼	0	70⅔	3	0	75	4	0	53	13	25	70	66⅔
4	1	5⅓	54	13½	0	72	4	1	0	5	33⅓	54	13	50	72	0
5	1¼	6⅔	55	13¾	0	73⅓	5	1	25	6	66⅔	55	13	75	73	33⅓
6	1½	8	56	14	0	74⅔	6	1	50	8	0	56	14	0	74	66⅔
7	1¾	9⅓	57	14¼	0	76	7	1	75	9	33⅓	57	14	25	76	0
8	2	10⅔	58	14½	0	77⅓	8	2	0	10	66⅔	58	14	50	77	33⅓
9	2¼	12	59	14¾	0	78⅔	9	2	25	12	0	59	14	75	78	66⅔
10	2½	13⅓	**60**	15	0	80	**10**	2	50	13	33⅓	**60**	15	0	80	0
11	2¾	14⅔	61	15¼	0	81⅓	11	2	75	14	66⅔	61	15	25	81	33⅓
12	3	16	62	15½	0	82⅔	12	3	0	16	0	62	15	50	82	66⅔
13	3¼	17⅓	63	15¾	0	84	13	3	25	17	33⅓	63	15	75	84	0
14	3½	18⅔	64	16	0	85⅓	14	3	50	18	66⅔	64	16	0	85	33⅓
15	3¾	20	65	16¼	0	86⅔	15	3	75	20	0	65	16	25	86	66⅔
16	4	21⅓	66	16½	0	88	16	4	0	21	33⅓	66	16	50	88	0
17	4¼	22⅔	67	16¾	0	89⅓	17	4	25	22	66⅔	67	16	75	89	33⅓
18	4½	24	68	17	0	90⅔	18	4	50	24	0	68	17	0	90	66⅔
19	4¾	25⅓	69	17¼	0	92	19	4	75	25	33⅓	69	17	25	92	0
20	5	26⅔	**70**	17½	0	93⅓	**20**	5	0	26	66⅔	**70**	17	50	93	33⅓
21	5¼	28	71	17¾	0	94⅔	21	5	25	28	0	71	17	75	94	66⅔
22	5½	29⅓	72	18	0	96	22	5	50	29	33⅓	72	18	0	96	0
23	5¾	30⅔	73	18¼	0	97⅓	23	5	75	30	66⅔	73	18	25	97	33⅓
24	6	32	74	18½	0	98⅔	24	6	0	32	0	74	18	50	98	66⅔
25	6¼	33⅓	75	18¾	1	0	25	6	25	33	33⅓	75	18	75	100	0
26	6½	34⅔	76	19	1	1⅓	26	6	50	34	66⅔	76	19	0	101	33⅓
27	6¾	36	77	19¼	1	2⅔	27	6	75	36	0	77	19	25	102	66⅔
28	7	37⅓	78	19½	1	4	28	7	0	37	33⅓	78	19	50	104	0
29	7¼	38⅔	79	19¾	1	5⅓	29	7	25	38	66⅔	79	19	75	105	33⅓
30	7½	40	**80**	20	1	6⅔	**30**	7	50	40	0	**80**	20	0	106	66⅔
31	7¾	41⅓	81	20¼	1	8	31	7	75	41	33⅓	81	20	25	108	0
32	8	42⅔	82	20½	1	9⅓	32	8	0	42	66⅔	82	20	50	109	33⅓
33	8¼	44	83	20¾	1	10⅔	33	8	25	44	0	83	20	75	110	66⅔
34	8½	45⅓	84	21	1	12	34	8	50	45	33⅓	84	21	0	112	0
35	8¾	46⅔	85	21¼	1	13⅓	35	8	75	46	66⅔	85	21	25	113	33⅓
36	9	48	86	21½	1	14⅔	36	9	0	48	0	86	21	50	114	66⅔
37	9¼	49⅓	87	21¾	1	16	37	9	25	49	33⅓	87	21	75	116	0
38	9½	50⅔	88	22	1	17⅓	38	9	50	50	66⅔	88	22	0	117	33⅓
39	9¾	52	89	22¼	1	18⅔	39	9	75	52	0	89	22	25	118	66⅔
40	10	53⅓	**90**	22½	1	20	**40**	10	0	53	33⅓	**90**	22	50	120	0
41	10¼	54⅔	91	22¾	1	21⅓	41	10	25	54	66⅔	91	22	75	121	33⅓
42	10½	56	92	23	1	22⅔	42	10	50	56	0	92	23	0	122	66⅔
43	10¾	57⅓	93	23¼	1	24	43	10	75	57	33⅓	93	23	25	124	0
44	11	58⅔	94	23½	1	25⅓	44	11	0	58	66⅔	94	23	50	125	33⅓
45	11¼	60	95	23¾	1	26⅔	45	11	25	60	0	95	23	75	126	66⅔
46	11½	61⅓	96	24	1	28	46	11	50	61	33⅓	96	24	0	128	0
47	11¾	62⅔	97	24¼	1	29⅓	47	11	75	62	66⅔	97	24	25	129	33⅓
48	12	64	98	24½	1	30⅔	48	12	0	64	0	98	24	50	130	66⅔
49	12¼	65⅓	99	24¾	1	32	49	12	25	65	33⅓	99	24	75	132	0
50	12½	66⅔	**100**	25	1	33⅓	**50**	12	50	66	66⅔	**100**	25	0	133	33⅓

	On Cost		Profit on Returns			On Cost		Profit on Returns			On Cost		Profit on Returns	
150	37	50	200	00	450	112	50	600	00	750	187	50	1000	00
200	50	0	266	66⅔	500	125	0	666	66⅔	800	200	0	1066	66⅔
250	62	50	333	33⅓	550	137	50	733	33⅓	850	212	50	1133	33⅓
300	75	0	400	00	600	150	0	800	00	900	225	0	1200	00
350	87	50	466	66⅔	650	162	50	866	66⅔	950	237	50	1266	66⅔
400	100	0	533	33⅓	700	175	0	933	33⅓	1000	250	0	1333	33⅓

	on Cost	Profit on Returns		on Cost	Profit on Returns	
P	P	P	P	P	£	P
1	0¼	1½	51	14	0	70¼
2	0½	2¾	52	14¼	0	71¾
3	0¾	4¼	53	14½	0	73
4	1	5½	54	14¾	0	74½
5	1½	7	55	15¼	0	75¾
6	1¾	8¼	56	15½	0	77¼
7	2	9¾	57	15¾	0	78½
8	2¼	11	58	16	0	80
9	2½	12½	59	16¼	0	81½
10	2¾	13¾	60	16½	0	82¾
11	3	15¼	61	16¾	0	84¼
12	3¼	16½	62	17	0	85½
13	3½	18	63	17¼	0	87
14	3¾	19¼	64	17½	0	88¼
15	4¼	20¾	65	18	0	89¾
16	4½	22	66	18¼	0	91
17	4¾	23½	67	18½	0	92½
18	5	24¾	68	18¾	0	93¾
19	5¼	26¼	69	19	0	95¼
20	5½	27½	70	19¼	0	96½
21	5¾	29	71	19½	0	98
22	6	30¼	72	19¾	0	99¼
23	6¼	31¾	73	20	1	0¾
24	6½	33	74	20¼	1	2
25	7	34½	75	20¾	1	3½
26	7¼	35¾	76	21	1	4¾
27	7½	37¼	77	21¼	1	6¼
28	7¾	38½	78	21½	1	7½
29	8	40	79	21¾	1	9
30	8¼	41½	80	22	1	10¼
31	8½	42¾	81	22¼	1	11¾
32	8¾	44¼	82	22½	1	13
33	9	45½	83	22¾	1	14½
34	9¼	47	84	23	1	15¾
35	9¾	48¼	85	23½	1	17¼
36	10	49¾	86	23¾	1	18½
37	10¼	51	87	24	1	20
38	10½	52½	88	24¼	1	21½
39	10¾	53¾	89	24½	1	22¾
40	11	55¼	90	24¾	1	24¼
41	11¼	56½	91	25	1	25½
42	11½	58	92	25¼	1	27
43	11¾	59¼	93	25½	1	28¼
44	12	60¾	94	25¾	1	29¾
45	12½	62	95	26¼	1	31
46	12¾	63½	96	26½	1	32½
47	13	64¾	97	26¾	1	33¾
48	13¼	66¼	98	27	1	35¼
49	13½	67½	99	27¼	1	36½
50	13¾	69	100	27½	1	38

	on Cost		Profit on Returns			on Cost		Profit on Returns	
£	£	P	£	P	£	£	P	£	P
1	0	27½	1	38	51	14	2½	70	34½
2	0	55	2	75¾	52	14	30	71	72½
3	0	82½	4	13¾	53	14	57½	73	10¼
4	1	10	5	51¾	54	14	85	74	48¼
5	1	37½	6	89¾	55	15	12½	75	86¼
6	1	65	8	27½	56	15	40	77	24¼
7	1	92½	9	65½	57	15	67½	78	62
8	2	20	11	3½	58	15	95	80	0
9	2	47½	12	41½	59	16	22½	81	38
10	2	75	13	79¼	60	16	50	82	75¾
11	3	2½	15	17¼	61	16	77½	84	13¾
12	3	30	16	55¼	62	17	5	85	51¾
13	3	57½	17	93	63	17	32½	86	89¾
14	3	85	19	31	64	17	60	88	27¾
15	4	12½	20	69	65	17	87½	89	65½
16	4	40	22	7	66	18	15	91	3½
17	4	67½	23	44¾	67	18	42½	92	41½
18	4	95	24	82¾	68	18	70	93	79¼
19	5	22½	26	20¾	69	18	97½	95	17¼
20	5	50	27	58½	70	19	25	96	55¼
21	5	77½	28	96½	71	19	52½	97	93
22	6	5	30	34½	72	19	80	99	31
23	6	32½	31	72½	73	20	7½	100	69
24	6	60	33	10¼	74	20	35	102	7
25	6	87½	34	48¼	75	20	62½	103	44¾
26	7	15	35	86¼	76	20	90	104	82¾
27	7	42½	37	24¼	77	21	17½	106	20¾
28	7	70	38	62	78	21	45	107	58½
29	7	97½	40	0	79	21	72½	108	96½
30	8	25	41	38	80	22	0	110	34½
31	8	52½	42	75¾	81	22	27½	111	72½
32	8	80	44	13¾	82	22	55	113	10¼
33	9	7½	45	51¾	83	22	82½	114	48¼
34	9	35	46	89¾	84	23	10	115	86¼
35	9	62½	48	27½	85	23	37½	117	24¼
36	9	90	49	65½	86	23	65	118	62
37	10	17½	51	3½	87	23	92½	120	0
38	10	45	52	41½	88	24	20	121	38
39	10	72½	53	79¼	89	24	47½	122	75¾
40	11	0	55	17¼	90	24	75	124	13¾
41	11	27½	56	55¼	91	25	2½	125	51¾
42	11	55	57	93	92	25	30	126	89¾
43	11	82½	59	31	93	25	57½	128	27½
44	12	10	60	69	94	25	85	129	65½
45	12	37½	62	7	95	26	12½	131	3½
46	12	65	63	44¾	96	26	40	132	41½
47	12	92½	64	82¾	97	26	67½	133	79¼
48	13	20	66	20¾	98	26	95	135	17¼
49	13	47½	67	58½	99	27	22½	136	55¼
50	13	75	68	96½	100	27	50	137	93

	On Cost		Profit on Returns			On Cost		Profit on Returns			On Cost		Profit on Returns	
150	41	25	206	89¾	450	123	75	620	69	750	206	25	1034	48¼
200	55	0	275	86¼	500	137	50	689	65½	800	220	0	1103	44¾
250	68	75	344	82¾	550	151	25	758	62	850	233	75	1172	41½
300	82	50	413	79¼	600	165	0	827	58½	900	247	50	1241	38
350	96	25	482	75¾	650	178	75	896	55¼	950	261	25	1310	34½
400	110	0	551	72½	700	192	50	965	51¾	1000	275	0	1379	31

30 Per Cent

	Profit on Cost	Profit on Returns		Profit on Cost	Profit on Returns			Profit on Cost		Profit on Returns			Profit on Cost		Profit on Returns	
P	P	P	P	P	£	P	£	£	P	£	P	£	£	P	£	P
1	0¼	1½	51	15¼	0	72¾	1	0	30	1	42¾	51	15	30	72	85¾
2	0½	2¾	52	15½	0	74¼	2	0	60	2	85¾	52	15	60	74	28½
3	1	4¼	53	16	0	75¾	3	0	90	4	28½	53	15	90	75	71½
4	1¼	5¾	54	16¼	0	77¼	4	1	20	5	71½	54	16	20	77	14¼
5	1½	7¼	55	16½	0	78½	5	1	50	7	14¼	55	16	50	78	57¼
6	1¾	8½	56	16¾	0	80	6	1	80	8	57¼	56	16	80	80	0
7	2	10	57	17	0	81½	7	2	10	10	0	57	17	10	81	42¾
8	2½	11½	58	17½	0	82¾	8	2	40	11	42¾	58	17	40	82	85¾
9	2¾	12¾	59	17¾	0	84¼	9	2	70	12	85¾	59	17	70	84	28½
10	3	14¼	**60**	18	0	85¾	**10**	3	0	14	28½	**60**	18	0	85	71½
11	3¼	15¾	61	18¼	0	87¼	11	3	30	15	71½	61	18	30	87	14¼
12	3½	17¼	62	18½	0	88½	12	3	60	17	14¼	62	18	60	88	57¼
13	4	18½	63	19	0	90	13	3	90	18	57¼	63	18	90	90	0
14	4¼	20	64	19¼	0	91½	14	4	20	20	0	64	19	20	91	42¾
15	4½	21½	65	19½	0	92¾	15	4	50	21	42¾	65	19	50	92	85¾
16	4¾	22¾	66	19¾	0	94¼	16	4	80	22	85¾	66	19	80	94	28½
17	5	24¼	67	20	0	95¾	17	5	10	24	28½	67	20	10	95	71½
18	5½	25¾	68	20½	0	97¼	18	5	40	25	71½	68	20	40	97	14¼
19	5¾	27¼	69	20¾	0	98½	19	5	70	27	14¼	69	20	70	98	57¼
20	6	28½	**70**	21	1	0	**20**	6	0	28	57¼	**70**	21	0	100	0
21	6¼	30	71	21¼	1	1½	21	6	30	30	0	71	21	30	101	42¾
22	6½	31½	72	21½	1	2¾	22	6	60	31	42¾	72	21	60	102	85¾
23	7	32¾	73	22	1	4¼	23	6	90	32	85¾	73	21	90	104	28½
24	7¼	34¼	74	22¼	1	5¾	24	7	20	34	28½	74	22	20	105	71½
25	7½	35¾	75	22½	1	7¼	25	7	50	35	71½	75	22	50	107	14¼
26	7¾	37¼	76	22¾	1	8½	26	7	80	37	14¼	76	22	80	108	57¼
27	8	38½	77	23	1	10	27	8	10	38	57¼	77	23	10	110	0
28	8½	40	78	23½	1	11½	28	8	40	40	0	78	23	40	111	42¾
29	8¾	41½	79	23¾	1	12¾	29	8	70	41	42¾	79	23	70	112	85¾
30	9	42¾	**80**	24	1	14¼	**30**	9	0	42	85¾	**80**	24	0	114	28½
31	9¼	44¼	81	24¼	1	15¾	31	9	30	44	28½	81	24	30	115	71½
32	9½	45¾	82	24½	1	17¼	32	9	60	45	71½	82	24	60	117	14¼
33	10	47¼	83	25	1	18½	33	9	90	47	14¼	83	24	90	118	57¼
34	10¼	48½	84	25¼	1	20	34	10	20	48	57¼	84	25	20	120	0
35	10½	50	85	25½	1	21½	35	10	50	50	0	85	25	50	121	42¾
36	10¾	51½	86	25¾	1	22¾	36	10	80	51	42¾	86	25	80	122	85¾
37	11	52¾	87	26	1	24¼	37	11	10	52	85¾	87	26	10	124	28½
38	11½	54¼	88	26½	1	25¾	38	11	40	54	28½	88	26	40	125	71½
39	11¾	55¾	89	26¾	1	27¼	39	11	70	55	71½	89	26	70	127	14¼
40	12	57¼	**90**	27	1	28½	**40**	12	0	57	14¼	**90**	27	0	128	57¼
41	12¼	58½	91	27¼	1	30	41	12	30	58	57¼	91	27	30	130	0
42	12½	60	92	27½	1	31½	42	12	60	60	0	92	27	60	131	42¾
43	13	61½	93	28	1	32¾	43	12	90	61	42¾	93	27	90	132	85¾
44	13¼	62¾	94	28¼	1	34¼	44	13	20	62	85¾	94	28	20	134	28½
45	13½	64¼	95	28½	1	35¾	45	13	50	64	28½	95	28	50	135	71½
46	13¾	65¾	96	28¾	1	37¼	46	13	80	65	71½	96	28	80	137	14¼
47	14	67¼	97	29	1	38½	47	14	10	67	14¼	97	29	10	138	57¼
48	14½	68½	98	29½	1	40	48	14	40	68	57¼	98	29	40	140	0
49	14¾	70	99	29¾	1	41½	49	14	70	70	0	99	29	70	141	42¾
50	15	71½	**100**	30	1	42¾	**50**	15	0	71	42¾	**100**	30	0	142	85¾

	On Cost		Profit on Returns			On Cost		Profit on Returns			On Cost		Profit on Returns	
150	45	0	214	28½	450	135	0	642	85¾	750	225	0	1071	42¾
200	60	0	285	71½	500	150	0	714	28½	800	240	0	1142	85¾
250	75	0	357	14¼	550	165	0	785	71½	850	255	0	1214	28½
300	90	0	428	57¼	600	180	0	857	14¼	900	270	0	1285	71½
350	105	0	500	0	650	195	0	928	57¼	950	285	0	1357	14¼
400	120	0	571	42¾	700	210	0	1000	0	1000	300	0	1428	57¼

32½ Per Cent

	on Cost	Profit on Returns		on Cost	Profit on Returns	
P	P	P	P	P	£	P
1	0¼	1½	51	16½	0	75½
2	0¾	3	52	17	0	77
3	1	4½	53	17¼	0	78½
4	1¼	6	54	17½	0	80
5	1¾	7½	55	18	0	81½
6	2	9	56	18¼	0	83
7	2¼	10¼	57	18½	0	84½
8	2½	11¾	58	18¾	0	86
9	3	13¼	59	19¼	0	87½
10	3¼	14¾	60	19½	0	89
11	3½	16¼	61	19¾	0	90½
12	4	17¾	62	20¼	0	91¾
13	4¼	19¼	63	20½	0	93¼
14	4½	20¾	64	20¾	0	94¾
15	5	22¼	65	21¼	0	96¼
16	5¼	23¾	66	21½	0	97¾
17	5½	25¼	67	21¾	0	99¼
18	5¾	26¾	68	22	1	0¾
19	6¼	28¼	69	22½	1	2¼
20	6½	29¾	70	22¾	1	3¾
21	6¾	31	71	23	1	5¼
22	7¼	32½	72	23½	1	6¾
23	7½	34	73	23¾	1	8¼
24	7¾	35½	74	24	1	9¾
25	8¼	37	75	24¼	1	11
26	8½	38½	76	24¾	1	12½
27	8¾	40	77	25	1	14
28	9	41½	78	25¼	1	15½
29	9½	43	79	25¾	1	17
30	9¾	44½	80	26	1	18½
31	10	46	81	26¼	1	20
32	10½	47½	82	26¾	1	21½
33	10¾	49	83	27	1	23
34	11	50¼	84	27¼	1	24½
35	11¼	51¾	85	27¾	1	26
36	11¾	53¼	86	28	1	27½
37	12	54¾	87	28¼	1	29
38	12¼	56¼	88	28½	1	30¼
39	12¾	57¾	89	29	1	31¾
40	13	59¼	90	29¼	1	33¼
41	13¼	60¾	91	29½	1	34¾
42	13¾	62¼	92	30	1	36¼
43	14	63¾	93	30¼	1	37¾
44	14¼	65¼	94	30½	1	39¼
45	14¾	66¾	95	31	1	40¾
46	15	68¼	96	31¼	1	42¼
47	15¼	69¾	97	31½	1	43¾
48	15½	71	98	31¾	1	45¼
49	16	72½	99	32¼	1	46¾
50	16¼	74	100	32½	1	48¼

	on Cost		Profit on Returns			on Cost		Profit on Returns	
£	£	P	£	P	£	£	P	£	P
1	0	32½	1	48¼	51	16	57½	75	55½
2	0	65	2	96¼	52	16	90	77	3¾
3	0	97½	4	44½	53	17	22½	78	51¾
4	1	30	5	92½	54	17	55	80	0
5	1	62½	7	40¾	55	17	87½	81	48¼
6	1	95	8	89	56	18	20	82	96¼
7	2	27½	10	37	57	18	52½	84	44½
8	2	60	11	85¼	58	18	85	85	92½
9	2	92½	13	33¼	59	19	17½	87	40¾
10	3	25	14	81½	60	19	50	88	89
11	3	57½	16	29¾	61	19	82½	90	37
12	3	90	17	77¾	62	20	15	91	85¼
13	4	22½	19	26	63	20	47½	93	33¼
14	4	55	20	74	64	20	80	94	81½
15	4	87½	22	22¼	65	21	12½	96	29¾
16	5	20	23	70¼	66	21	45	97	77¾
17	5	52½	25	18½	67	21	77½	99	26
18	5	85	26	66¾	68	22	10	100	74
19	6	17½	28	14¾	69	22	42½	102	22¼
20	6	50	29	63	70	22	75	103	70¼
21	6	82½	31	11	71	23	7½	105	18½
22	7	15	32	59¼	72	23	40	106	66¾
23	7	47½	34	7½	73	23	72½	108	14¾
24	7	80	35	55½	74	24	5	109	63
25	8	12½	37	3¾	75	24	37½	111	11
26	8	45	38	51¾	76	24	70	112	59¼
27	8	77½	40	0	77	25	2½	114	7½
28	9	10	41	48¼	78	25	35	115	55½
29	9	42½	42	96¼	79	25	67½	117	3¾
30	9	75	44	44½	80	26	0	118	51¾
31	10	7½	45	92½	81	26	32½	120	0
32	10	40	47	40¾	82	26	65	121	48¼
33	10	72½	48	89	83	26	97½	122	96¼
34	11	5	50	37	84	27	30	124	44½
35	11	37½	51	85¼	85	27	62½	125	92½
36	11	70	53	33¼	86	27	95	127	40¾
37	12	2½	54	81½	87	28	27½	128	89
38	12	35	56	29¾	88	28	60	130	37
39	12	67½	57	77¾	89	28	92½	131	85¼
40	13	0	59	26	90	29	25	133	33¼
41	13	32½	60	74	91	29	57½	134	81½
42	13	65	62	22¼	92	29	90	136	29¾
43	13	97½	63	70¼	93	30	22½	137	77¾
44	14	30	65	18½	94	30	55	139	26
45	14	62½	66	66¾	95	30	87½	140	74
46	14	95	68	14¾	96	31	20	142	22¼
47	15	27½	69	63	97	31	52½	143	70¼
48	15	60	71	11	98	31	85	145	18½
49	15	92½	72	59¼	99	32	17½	146	66¾
50	16	25	74	7½	100	32	50	148	14¾

	On Cost		Profit on Returns			On Cost		Profit on Returns			On Cost		Profit on Returns	
150	48	75	222	22¼	450	146	25	666	66¾	750	243	75	1111	11
200	65	0	296	29¾	500	162	50	740	74	800	260	0	1185	18½
250	81	25	370	37	550	178	75	814	81½	850	276	25	1259	26
300	97	50	444	44½	600	195	0	888	89	900	292	50	1333	33¼
350	113	75	518	51¾	650	211	25	962	96¼	950	308	75	1407	40¾
400	130	0	592	59¼	700	227	50	1037	3¾	1000	325	0	1481	48¼

P	Profit on Cost P	Profit on Returns P	P	Profit on Cost P	Profit on Returns £	P	£	Profit on Cost £	P	Profit on Returns £	P	£	Profit on Cost £	P	Profit on Returns £	P
1	0⅓	1½	51	17	0	76½	1	0	33	1	50	51	17	0	76	50
2	0⅔	3	52	17⅓	0	78	2	0	67	3	0	52	17	33	78	0
3	1	4½	53	17⅔	0	79½	3	1	0	4	50	53	17	67	79	50
4	1⅓	6	54	18	0	81	4	1	33	6	0	54	18	0	81	0
5	1⅔	7½	55	18⅓	0	82½	5	1	67	7	50	55	18	33	82	50
6	2	9	56	18⅔	0	84	6	2	0	9	0	56	18	67	84	0
7	2⅓	10½	57	19	0	85½	7	2	33	10	50	57	19	0	85	50
8	2⅔	12	58	19⅓	0	87	8	2	67	12	0	58	19	33	87	0
9	3	13½	59	19⅔	0	88½	9	3	0	13	50	59	19	67	88	50
10	3⅓	15	**60**	20	0	90	**10**	3	33	15	0	**60**	20	0	90	0
11	3⅔	16½	61	20⅓	0	91½	11	3	67	16	50	61	20	33	91	50
12	4	18	62	20⅔	0	93	12	4	0	18	0	62	20	67	93	0
13	4⅓	19½	63	21	0	94½	13	4	33	19	50	63	21	0	94	50
14	4⅔	21	64	21⅓	0	96	14	4	67	21	0	64	21	33	96	0
15	5	22½	65	21⅔	0	97½	15	5	0	22	50	65	21	67	97	50
16	5⅓	24	66	22	0	99	16	5	33	24	0	66	22	0	99	0
17	5⅔	25½	67	22⅓	1	0½	17	5	67	25	50	67	22	33	100	50
18	6	27	68	22⅔	1	2	18	6	0	27	0	68	22	67	102	0
19	6⅓	28½	69	23	1	3½	19	6	33	28	50	69	23	0	103	50
20	6⅔	30	**70**	23⅓	1	5	**20**	6	67	30	0	**70**	23	33	105	0
21	7	31½	71	23⅔	1	6½	21	7	0	31	50	71	23	67	106	50
22	7⅓	33	72	24	1	8	22	7	33	33	0	72	24	0	108	0
23	7⅔	34½	73	24⅓	1	9½	23	7	67	34	50	73	24	33	109	50
24	8	36	74	24⅔	1	11	24	8	0	36	0	74	24	67	111	0
25	8⅓	37½	75	25	1	12½	25	8	33	37	50	75	25	0	112	50
26	8⅔	39	76	25⅓	1	14	26	8	67	39	0	76	25	33	114	0
27	9	40½	77	25⅔	1	15½	27	9	0	40	50	77	25	67	115	50
28	9⅓	42	78	26	1	17	28	9	33	42	0	78	26	0	117	0
29	9⅔	43½	79	26⅓	1	18½	29	9	67	43	50	79	26	33	118	50
30	10	45	**80**	26⅔	1	20	**30**	10	0	45	0	**80**	26	67	120	0
31	10⅓	46½	81	27	1	21½	31	10	33	46	50	81	27	0	121	50
32	10⅔	48	82	27⅓	1	23	32	10	67	48	0	82	27	33	123	0
33	11	49½	83	27⅔	1	24½	33	11	0	49	50	83	27	67	124	50
34	11⅓	51	84	28	1	26	34	11	33	51	0	84	28	0	126	0
35	11⅔	52½	85	28⅓	1	27½	35	11	67	52	50	85	28	33	127	50
36	12	54	86	28⅔	1	29	36	12	0	54	0	86	28	67	129	0
37	12⅓	55½	87	29	1	30½	37	12	33	55	50	87	29	0	130	50
38	12⅔	57	88	29⅓	1	32	38	12	67	57	0	88	29	33	132	0
39	13	58½	89	29⅔	1	33½	39	13	0	58	50	89	29	67	133	50
40	13⅓	60	**90**	30	1	35	**40**	13	33	60	0	**90**	30	0	135	0
41	13⅔	61½	91	30⅓	1	36½	41	13	67	61	50	91	30	33	136	50
42	14	63	92	30⅔	1	38	42	14	0	63	0	92	30	67	138	0
43	14⅓	64½	93	31	1	39½	43	14	33	64	50	93	31	0	139	50
44	14⅔	66	94	31⅓	1	41	44	14	67	66	0	94	31	33	141	0
45	15	67½	95	31⅔	1	42½	45	15	0	67	50	95	31	67	142	50
46	15⅓	69	96	32	1	44	46	15	33	69	0	96	32	0	144	0
47	15⅔	70½	97	32⅓	1	45½	47	15	67	70	50	97	32	33	145	50
48	16	72	98	32⅔	1	47	48	16	0	72	0	98	32	67	147	0
49	16⅓	73½	99	33	1	48½	49	16	33	73	50	99	33	0	148	50
50	16⅔	75	**100**	33⅓	1	50	**50**	16	67	75	0	**100**	33	33	150	0

£	On Cost £	P	Profit on Returns £	P	£	On Cost £	P	Profit on Returns £	P	£	On Cost £	P	Profit on Returns £	P
150	50	0	225	0	450	150	0	675	0	750	250	0	1125	0
200	66	67	300	0	500	166	67	750	0	800	266	67	1200	0
250	83	33	375	0	550	183	33	825	0	850	283	33	1275	0
300	100	0	450	0	600	200	0	900	0	900	300	0	1350	0
350	116	67	525	0	650	216	67	975	0	950	316	67	1425	0
400	133	33	600	0	700	233	33	1050	0	1000	333	33	1500	0

P	on Cost P	Profit on Returns P	P	on Cost P	Profit on Returns £	Profit on Returns P
1	0¼	1½	51	17¾	0	78½
2	0¾	3	52	18¼	0	80
3	1	4½	53	18½	0	81½
4	1½	6¼	54	19	0	83
5	1¾	7¾	55	19¼	0	84½
6	2	9¼	56	19½	0	86¼
7	2½	10¾	57	20	0	87¾
8	2¾	12¼	58	20¼	0	89¼
9	3¼	13¾	59	20¾	0	90¾
10	3½	15½	**60**	21	0	92¼
11	3¾	17	61	21¼	0	93¾
12	4¼	18½	62	21¾	0	95½
13	4½	20	63	22	0	97
14	5	21½	64	22½	0	98½
15	5¼	23	65	22¾	1	0
16	5½	24½	66	23	1	1½
17	6	26¼	67	23½	1	3
18	6¼	27¾	68	23¾	1	4½
19	6¾	29¼	69	24¼	1	6¼
20	7	30¾	**70**	24½	1	7¾
21	7¼	32¼	71	24¾	1	9¼
22	7¾	33¾	72	25¼	1	10¾
23	8	35½	73	25½	1	12¼
24	8½	37	74	26	1	13¾
25	8¾	38½	75	26¼	1	15½
26	9	40	76	26½	1	17
27	9½	41½	77	27	1	18½
28	9¾	43	78	27¼	1	20
29	10¼	44½	79	27¾	1	21½
30	10½	46¼	**80**	28	1	23
31	10¾	47¾	81	28¼	1	24½
32	11¼	49¼	82	28¾	1	26¼
33	11½	50¾	83	29	1	27¾
34	12	52¼	84	29½	1	29¼
35	12¼	53¾	85	29¾	1	30¾
36	12½	55½	86	30	1	32¼
37	13	57	87	30½	1	33¾
38	13¼	58½	88	30¾	1	35½
39	13¾	60	89	31¼	1	37
40	14	61½	**90**	31½	1	38½
41	14¼	63	91	31¾	1	40
42	14¾	64½	92	32¼	1	41½
43	15	66¼	93	32½	1	43
44	15½	67¾	94	33	1	44½
45	15¾	69¼	95	33¼	1	46¼
46	16	70¾	96	33½	1	47¾
47	16½	72¼	97	34	1	49¼
48	16¾	73¾	98	34¼	1	50¾
49	17¼	75½	99	34¾	1	52¼
50	17½	77	**100**	35	1	53¾

£	on Cost £	on Cost P	Profit on Returns £	Profit on Returns P	£	on Cost £	on Cost P	Profit on Returns £	Profit on Returns P
1	0	35	1	53¾	51	17	85	78	46¼
2	0	70	3	7¾	52	18	20	80	0
3	1	5	4	61½	53	18	55	81	53¾
4	1	40	6	15	54	18	90	83	7¾
5	1	75	7	69¼	55	19	25	84	61½
6	2	10	9	23	56	19	60	86	15
7	2	45	10	77	57	19	95	87	69¼
8	2	80	12	30¾	58	20	30	89	23
9	3	15	13	84½	59	20	65	90	77
10	3	50	15	38½	**60**	21	0	92	30¾
11	3	85	16	92¼	61	21	35	93	84½
12	4	20	18	46¼	62	21	70	95	38½
13	4	55	20	0	63	22	5	96	92¼
14	4	90	21	53¾	64	22	40	98	46¼
15	5	25	23	7¾	65	22	75	100	0
16	5	60	24	61½	66	23	10	101	53¾
17	5	95	26	15	67	23	45	103	7¾
18	6	30	27	69¼	68	23	80	104	61½
19	6	65	29	23	69	24	15	106	15
20	7	0	30	77	**70**	24	50	107	69¼
21	7	35	32	30¾	71	24	85	109	23
22	7	70	33	84½	72	25	20	110	77
23	8	5	35	38½	73	25	55	112	30¾
24	8	40	36	92¼	74	25	90	113	84½
25	8	75	38	46¼	75	26	25	115	38½
26	9	10	40	0	76	26	60	116	92¼
27	9	45	41	53¾	77	26	95	118	46¼
28	9	80	43	7¾	78	27	30	120	0
29	10	15	44	61½	79	27	65	121	53¾
30	10	50	46	15	**80**	28	0	123	7¾
31	10	85	47	69¼	81	28	35	124	61½
32	11	20	49	23	82	28	70	126	15
33	11	55	50	77	83	29	5	127	69¼
34	11	90	52	30¾	84	29	40	129	23
35	12	25	53	84½	85	29	75	130	77
36	12	60	55	38½	86	30	10	132	30¾
37	12	95	56	92¼	87	30	45	133	84½
38	13	30	58	46¼	88	30	80	135	38½
39	13	65	60	0	89	31	15	136	92¼
40	14	0	61	53¾	**90**	31	50	138	46¼
41	14	35	63	7¾	91	31	85	140	0
42	14	70	64	61½	92	32	20	141	53¾
43	15	5	66	15	93	32	55	143	7¾
44	15	40	67	69¼	94	32	90	144	61½
45	15	75	69	23	95	33	25	146	15
46	16	10	70	77	96	33	60	147	69¼
47	16	45	72	30¾	97	33	95	149	23
48	16	80	73	84½	98	34	30	150	77
49	17	15	75	38½	99	34	65	152	30¾
50	17	50	76	92¼	**100**	35	0	153	84½

£	On Cost £	On Cost P	Profit on Returns £	Profit on Returns P	£	On Cost £	On Cost P	Profit on Returns £	Profit on Returns P	£	On Cost £	On Cost P	Profit on Returns £	Profit on Returns P
150	52	50	230	77	450	157	50	692	30¾	750	262	50	1153	84½
200	70	0	307	69¼	500	175	0	769	23	800	280	0	1230	77
250	87	50	384	61½	550	192	50	846	15½	850	297	50	1307	69¼
300	105	0	461	53¾	600	210	0	923	7¾	900	315	0	1384	61½
350	122	50	538	46¼	650	227	50	1000	0	950	332	50	1461	53¾
400	140	0	615	38½	700	245	0	1076	92¼	1000	350	0	1538	46¼

36⅔ Per Cent

P	on Cost P	Profit on Returns P	P	on Cost P	Profit on Returns £	Profit on Returns P
1	0¼	1½	51	18¾	0	80½
2	0¾	3¼	52	19	0	82
3	1	4¾	53	19½	0	83¾
4	1½	6¼	54	19¾	0	85¼
5	1¾	8	55	20¼	0	86¾
6	2¼	9½	56	20½	0	88½
7	2½	11	57	21	0	90
8	3	12¾	58	21¼	0	91½
9	3¼	14¼	59	21¾	0	93¼
10	3¾	15¾	60	22	0	94¾
11	4	17¼	61	22¼	0	96¼
12	4½	19	62	22¾	0	98
13	4¾	20½	63	23	0	99½
14	5¼	22	64	23½	1	1
15	5½	23¾	65	23¾	1	2¾
16	5¾	25¼	66	24¼	1	4¼
17	6¼	26¾	67	24½	1	5¾
18	6½	28½	68	25	1	7¼
19	7	30	69	25¼	1	9
20	7¼	31½	70	25¾	1	10½
21	7¾	33¼	71	26	1	12
22	8	34¾	72	26½	1	13¾
23	8½	36¼	73	26¾	1	15¼
24	8¾	38	74	27¼	1	16¾
25	9¼	39½	75	27½	1	18½
26	9½	41	76	27¾	1	20
27	10	42¾	77	28¼	1	21½
28	10¼	44¼	78	28½	1	23¼
29	10¾	45¾	79	29	1	24¾
30	11	47¼	80	29¼	1	26¼
31	11¼	49	81	29¾	1	28
32	11¾	50½	82	30	1	29½
33	12	52	83	30½	1	31
34	12½	53¾	84	30¾	1	32¾
35	12¾	55¼	85	31¼	1	34¼
36	13¼	56¾	86	31½	1	35¾
37	13½	58½	87	32	1	37¼
38	14	60	88	32¼	1	39
39	14¼	61½	89	32¾	1	40½
40	14¾	63¼	90	33	1	42
41	15	64¾	91	33¼	1	43¾
42	15½	66¼	92	33¾	1	45¼
43	15¾	68	93	34	1	46¾
44	16¼	69½	94	34½	1	48½
45	16½	71	95	34¾	1	50
46	16¾	72¾	96	35¼	1	51½
47	17¼	74¼	97	35½	1	53¼
48	17½	75¾	98	36	1	54¾
49	18	77¼	99	36¼	1	56¼
50	18¼	79	100	36¾	1	58

£	on Cost £	on Cost P	Profit on Returns £	Profit on Returns P	£	on Cost £	on Cost P	Profit on Returns £	Profit on Returns P
1	0	36¾	1	58	51	18	70	80	52¾
2	0	73¼	3	15¾	52	19	6¾	82	10½
3	1	10	4	73¾	53	19	43¼	83	68½
4	1	46¾	6	31½	54	19	80	85	26¼
5	1	83¼	7	89½	55	20	16¾	86	84¼
6	2	20	9	47¼	56	20	53¼	88	42
7	2	56¾	11	5¼	57	20	90	90	0
8	2	93¼	12	63¼	58	21	26¾	91	58
9	3	30	14	21	59	21	63¼	93	15¾
10	3	66¾	15	79	60	22	0	94	73¾
11	4	3¼	17	36¾	61	22	36¾	96	31½
12	4	40	18	94¾	62	22	73¼	97	89½
13	4	76¾	20	52¾	63	23	10	99	47¼
14	5	13¼	22	10½	64	23	46¾	101	5¼
15	5	50	23	68½	65	23	83¼	102	63¼
16	5	86¾	25	26¼	66	24	20	104	21
17	6	23¼	26	84¼	67	24	56¾	105	79
18	6	60	28	42	68	24	93¼	107	36¾
19	6	96¾	30	0	69	25	30	108	94¾
20	7	33¼	31	58	70	25	66¾	110	52¾
21	7	70	33	15¾	71	26	3¼	112	10½
22	8	6¾	34	73¾	72	26	40	113	68½
23	8	43¼	36	31½	73	26	76¾	115	26¼
24	8	80	37	89½	74	27	13¼	116	84¼
25	9	16¾	39	47¼	75	27	50	118	42
26	9	53¼	41	5¼	76	27	86¾	120	0
27	9	90	42	63¼	77	28	23¼	121	58
28	10	26¾	44	21	78	28	60	123	15¾
29	10	63¼	45	79	79	28	96¾	124	73¾
30	11	0	47	36¾	80	29	33¼	126	31½
31	11	36¾	48	94¾	81	29	70	127	89½
32	11	73¼	50	52¾	82	30	6¾	129	47¼
33	12	10	52	10½	83	30	43¼	131	5¼
34	12	46¾	53	68½	84	30	80	132	63¼
35	12	83¼	55	26¼	85	31	16¾	134	21
36	13	20	56	84¼	86	31	53¼	135	79
37	13	56¾	58	42	87	31	90	137	36¾
38	13	93¼	60	0	88	32	26¾	138	94¾
39	14	30	61	58	89	32	63¼	140	52¾
40	14	66¾	63	15¾	90	33	0	142	10½
41	15	3¼	64	73¾	91	33	36¾	143	68½
42	15	40	66	31½	92	33	73¼	145	26¼
43	15	76¾	67	89½	93	34	10	146	84¼
44	16	13¼	69	47¼	94	34	46¾	148	42
45	16	50	71	5¼	95	34	83¼	150	0
46	16	86¾	72	63¼	96	35	20	151	58
47	17	23¼	74	21	97	35	56¾	153	15¾
48	17	60	75	79	98	35	93¼	154	73¾
49	17	96¾	77	36¾	99	36	30	156	31½
50	18	33¼	78	94¾	100	36	66¾	157	89½

	On Cost		Profit on Returns			On Cost		Profit on Returns			On Cost		Profit on Returns	
150	55	0	236	84¼	450	165	0	710	52¾	750	275	0	1184	21
200	73	33¼	315	79	500	183	33¼	789	47¼	800	293	33¼	1263	15¾
250	91	66¾	394	73¾	550	201	66¾	868	42	850	311	66¾	1342	10½
300	110	0	473	68½	600	220	0	947	36¾	900	330	0	1421	5¼
350	128	33¼	552	63½	650	238	33¼	1026	31½	950	348	33¼	1500	0
400	146	66¾	631	58	700	256	66¾	1105	26¼	1000	366	66¾	1578	94¾

37½ Per Cent

	on Cost	Profit on Returns		on Cost	Profit on Returns			on Cost		Profit on Returns			on Cost		Profit on Returns	
P	P	P	P	P	£	P	£	£	P	£	P	£	£	P	£	P
1	0¼	1½	51	19¼	0	81½	1	0	37½	1	60	51	19	12½	81	60
2	0¾	3¼	52	19½	0	83¼	2	0	75	3	20	52	19	50	83	20
3	1¼	4¾	53	20	0	84¾	3	1	12½	4	80	53	19	87½	84	80
4	1½	6½	54	20¼	0	86½	4	1	50	6	40	54	20	25	86	40
5	2	8	55	20¾	0	88	5	1	87½	8	0	55	20	62½	88	0
6	2¼	9½	56	21	0	89½	6	2	25	9	60	56	21	0	89	60
7	2¾	11¼	57	21¼	0	91¼	7	2	62½	11	20	57	21	37½	91	20
8	3	12¾	58	21¾	0	92¾	8	3	0	12	80	58	21	75	92	80
9	3¼	14½	59	22¼	0	94½	9	3	37½	14	40	59	22	12½	94	40
10	**3¾**	**16**	**60**	**22½**	**0**	**96**	**10**	**3**	**75**	**16**	**0**	**60**	**22**	**50**	**96**	**0**
11	4¼	17½	61	23	0	97½	11	4	12½	17	60	61	22	87½	97	60
12	4½	19¼	62	23¼	0	99¼	12	4	50	19	20	62	23	25	99	20
13	5	20¾	63	23¾	1	0¾	13	4	87½	20	80	63	23	62½	100	80
14	5¼	22½	64	24	1	2½	14	5	25	22	40	64	24	0	102	40
15	5¾	24	65	24¼	1	4	15	5	62½	24	0	65	24	37½	104	0
16	6	25½	66	24¾	1	5½	16	6	0	25	60	66	24	75	105	60
17	6¼	27¼	67	25¼	1	7¼	17	6	37½	27	20	67	25	12½	107	20
18	6¾	28¾	68	25½	1	8¾	18	6	75	28	80	68	25	50	108	80
19	7¼	30½	69	26	1	10½	19	7	12½	30	40	69	25	87½	110	40
20	**7½**	**32**	**70**	**26¼**	**1**	**12**	**20**	**7**	**50**	**32**	**0**	**70**	**26**	**25**	**112**	**0**
21	8	33½	71	26¾	1	13½	21	7	87½	33	60	71	26	62½	113	60
22	8¼	35¼	72	27	1	15¼	22	8	25	35	20	72	27	0	115	20
23	8¾	36¾	73	27¼	1	16¾	23	8	62½	36	80	73	27	37½	116	80
24	9	38½	74	27¾	1	18½	24	9	0	38	40	74	27	75	118	40
25	9¼	40	75	28¼	1	20	25	9	37½	40	0	75	28	12½	120	0
26	9¾	41½	76	28½	1	21½	26	9	75	41	60	76	28	50	121	60
27	10¼	43¼	77	29	1	23¼	27	10	12½	43	20	77	28	87½	123	20
28	10½	44¾	78	29¼	1	24¾	28	10	50	44	80	78	29	25	124	80
29	11	46½	79	29¾	1	26½	29	10	87½	46	40	79	29	62½	126	40
30	**11¼**	**48**	**80**	**30**	**1**	**28**	**30**	**11**	**25**	**48**	**0**	**80**	**30**	**0**	**128**	**0**
31	11¾	49½	81	30¼	1	29½	31	11	62½	49	60	81	30	37½	129	60
32	12	51¼	82	30¾	1	31¼	32	12	0	51	20	82	30	75	131	20
33	12¼	52¾	83	31¼	1	32¾	33	12	37½	52	80	83	31	12½	132	80
34	12¾	54½	84	31½	1	34½	34	12	75	54	40	84	31	50	134	40
35	13¼	56	85	32	1	36	35	13	12½	56	0	85	31	87½	136	0
36	13½	57½	86	32¼	1	37½	36	13	50	57	60	86	32	25	137	60
37	14	59¼	87	32¾	1	39¼	37	13	87½	59	20	87	32	62½	139	20
38	14¼	60¾	88	33	1	40¾	38	14	25	60	80	88	33	0	140	80
39	14¾	62½	89	33¼	1	42½	39	14	62½	62	40	89	33	37½	142	40
40	**15**	**64**	**90**	**33¾**	**1**	**44**	**40**	**15**	**0**	**64**	**0**	**90**	**33**	**75**	**144**	**0**
41	15¼	65½	91	34¼	1	45½	41	15	37½	65	60	91	34	12½	145	60
42	15¾	67¼	92	34½	1	47¼	42	15	75	67	20	92	34	50	147	20
43	16¼	68¾	93	35	1	48¾	43	16	12½	68	80	93	34	87½	148	80
44	16½	70½	94	35¼	1	50½	44	16	50	70	40	94	35	25	150	40
45	17	72	95	35¾	1	52	45	16	87½	72	0	95	35	62½	152	0
46	17¼	73½	96	36	1	53½	46	17	25	73	60	96	36	0	153	60
47	17¾	75¼	97	36¼	1	55¼	47	17	62½	75	20	97	36	37½	155	20
48	18	76¾	98	36¾	1	56¾	48	18	0	76	80	98	36	75	156	80
49	18¼	78½	99	37¼	1	58½	49	18	37½	78	40	99	37	12½	158	40
50	**18¾**	**80**	**100**	**37½**	**1**	**60**	**50**	**18**	**75**	**80**	**0**	**100**	**37**	**50**	**160**	**0**

	On Cost		Profit on Returns			On Cost		Profit on Returns			On Cost		Profit on Returns	
150	56	25	240	0	450	168	75	720	0	750	281	25	1200	0
200	75	0	320	0	500	187	50	800	0	800	300	0	1280	0
250	93	75	400	0	550	206	25	880	0	850	318	75	1360	0
300	112	50	480	0	600	225	0	960	0	900	337	50	1440	0
350	131	25	560	0	650	243	75	1040	0	950	356	25	1520	0
400	150	0	640	0	700	262	50	1120	0	1000	375	0	1600	0

	Profit on Cost	Profit on Returns		Profit on Cost	Profit on Returns			Profit on Cost		Profit on Returns			Profit on Cost		Profit on Returns	
P	P	P	P	P	£	P	£	£	P	£	P	£	£	P	£	P
1	0½	1⅔	51	20½	0	85	1	0	40	1	66⅔	51	20	40	85	0
2	0¾	3⅓	52	20¾	0	86⅔	2	0	80	3	33⅓	52	20	80	86	66⅔
3	1¼	5	53	21¼	0	88⅓	3	1	20	5	0	53	21	20	88	33⅓
4	1½	6⅔	54	21½	0	90	4	1	60	6	66⅔	54	21	60	90	0
5	2	8⅓	55	22	0	91⅔	5	2	0	8	33⅓	55	22	0	91	66⅔
6	2½	10	56	22½	0	93⅓	6	2	40	10	0	56	22	40	93	33⅓
7	2¾	11⅔	57	22¾	0	95	7	2	80	11	66⅔	57	22	80	95	0
8	3¼	13⅓	58	23¼	0	96⅔	8	3	20	13	33⅓	58	23	20	96	66⅔
9	3½	15	59	23½	0	98⅓	9	3	60	15	0	59	23	60	98	33⅓
10	4	16⅔	60	24	1	0	10	4	0	16	66⅔	60	24	0	100	0
11	4½	18⅓	61	24½	1	1⅔	11	4	40	18	33⅓	61	24	40	101	66⅔
12	4¾	20	62	24¾	1	3⅓	12	4	80	20	0	62	24	80	103	33⅓
13	5¼	21⅔	63	25¼	1	5	13	5	20	21	66⅔	63	25	20	105	0
14	5½	23⅓	64	25½	1	6⅔	14	5	60	23	33⅓	64	25	60	106	66⅔
15	6	25	65	26	1	8⅓	15	6	0	25	0	65	26	0	108	33⅓
16	6½	26⅔	66	26½	1	10	16	6	40	26	66⅔	66	26	40	110	0
17	6¾	28⅓	67	26¾	1	11⅔	17	6	80	28	33⅓	67	26	80	111	66⅔
18	7¼	30	68	27¼	1	13⅓	18	7	20	30	0	68	27	20	113	33⅓
19	7½	31⅔	69	27½	1	15	19	7	60	31	66⅔	69	27	60	115	0
20	8	33⅓	70	28	1	16⅔	20	8	0	33	33⅓	70	28	0	116	66⅔
21	8½	35	71	28½	1	18⅓	21	8	40	35	0	71	28	40	118	33⅓
22	8¾	36⅔	72	28¾	1	20	22	8	80	36	66⅔	72	28	80	120	0
23	9¼	38⅓	73	29¼	1	21⅔	23	9	20	38	33⅓	73	29	20	121	66⅔
24	9½	40	74	29½	1	23⅓	24	9	60	40	0	74	29	60	123	33⅓
25	10	41⅔	75	30	1	25	25	10	0	41	66⅔	75	30	0	125	0
26	10½	43⅓	76	30½	1	26⅔	26	10	40	43	33⅓	76	30	40	126	66⅔
27	10¾	45	77	30¾	1	28⅓	27	10	80	45	0	77	30	80	128	33⅓
28	11¼	46⅔	78	31¼	1	30	28	11	20	46	66⅔	78	31	20	130	0
29	11½	48⅓	79	31½	1	31⅔	29	11	60	48	33⅓	79	31	60	131	66⅔
30	12	50	80	32	1	33⅓	30	12	0	50	0	80	32	0	133	33⅓
31	12½	51⅔	81	32½	1	35	31	12	40	51	66⅔	81	32	40	135	0
32	12¾	53⅓	82	32¾	1	36⅔	32	12	80	53	33⅓	82	32	80	136	66⅔
33	13¼	55	83	33¼	1	38⅓	33	13	20	55	0	83	33	20	138	33⅓
34	13½	56⅔	84	33½	1	40	34	13	60	56	66⅔	84	33	60	140	0
35	14	58⅓	85	34	1	41⅔	35	14	0	58	33⅓	85	34	0	141	66⅔
36	14½	60	86	34½	1	43⅓	36	14	40	60	0	86	34	40	143	33⅓
37	14¾	61⅔	87	34¾	1	45	37	14	80	61	66⅔	87	34	80	145	0
38	15¼	63⅓	88	35¼	1	46⅔	38	15	20	63	33⅓	88	35	20	146	66⅔
39	15½	65	89	35½	1	48⅓	39	15	60	65	0	89	35	60	148	33⅓
40	16	66⅔	90	36	1	50	40	16	0	66	66⅔	90	36	0	150	0
41	16½	68⅓	91	36½	1	51⅔	41	16	40	68	33⅓	91	36	40	151	66⅔
42	16¾	70	92	36¾	1	53⅓	42	16	80	70	0	92	36	80	153	33⅓
43	17¼	71⅔	93	37¼	1	55	43	17	20	71	66⅔	93	37	20	155	0
44	17½	73⅓	94	37½	1	56⅔	44	17	60	73	33⅓	94	37	60	156	66⅔
45	18	75	95	38	1	58⅓	45	18	0	75	0	95	38	0	158	33⅓
46	18½	76⅔	96	38½	1	60	46	18	40	76	66⅔	96	38	40	160	0
47	18¾	78⅓	97	38¾	1	61⅔	47	18	80	78	33⅓	97	38	80	161	66⅔
48	19¼	80	98	39¼	1	63⅓	48	19	20	80	0	98	39	20	163	33⅓
49	19½	81⅔	99	39½	1	65	49	19	60	81	66⅔	99	39	60	165	0
50	20	83⅓	100	40	1	66⅔	50	20	0	83	33⅓	100	40	0	166	66⅔

	On Cost		Profit on Returns			On Cost		Profit on Returns			On Cost		Profit on Returns	
150	60	0	250	0	450	180	0	750	0	750	300	0	1250	0
200	80	0	333	33⅓	500	200	0	833	33⅓	800	320	0	1333	33⅓
250	100	0	416	66⅔	550	220	0	916	66⅔	850	340	0	1416	66⅔
300	120	0	500	0	600	240	0	1000	0	900	360	0	1500	0
350	140	0	583	33⅓	650	260	0	1083	33⅓	950	380	0	1583	33⅓
400	160	0	666	66⅔	700	280	0	1166	66⅔	1000	400	0	1666	66⅔

P	on Cost P	Profit on Returns P	P	on Cost P	Profit on Returns £	Profit on Returns P	£	on Cost £	on Cost P	Profit on Returns £	Profit on Returns P	£	on Cost £	on Cost P	Profit on Returns £	Profit on Returns P
1	0½	1¾	51	21¾	0	88¾	1	0	42½	1	74	51	21	67½	88	69½
2	0¾	3½	52	22	0	90½	2	0	85	3	47¾	52	22	10	90	43½
3	1¼	5¼	53	22½	0	92¼	3	1	27½	5	21¾	53	22	52½	92	17½
4	1¾	7	54	23	0	94	4	1	70	6	95¾	54	22	95	93	91¼
5	2¼	8¾	55	23½	0	95¾	5	2	12½	8	69½	55	23	37½	95	65¼
6	2½	10½	56	23¾	0	97½	6	2	55	10	43½	56	23	80	97	39¼
7	3	12¼	57	24¼	0	99¼	7	2	97½	12	17½	57	24	22½	99	13
8	3½	14	58	24¾	1	0¾	8	3	40	13	91¼	58	24	65	100	87
9	3¾	15¾	59	25	1	2½	9	3	82½	15	65¼	59	25	7½	102	60¾
10	4¼	17½	**60**	25½	1	4¼	**10**	4	25	17	39¼	**60**	25	50	104	34¾
11	4¾	19¼	61	26	1	6	11	4	67½	19	13	61	25	92½	106	8¾
12	5	21	62	26¼	1	7¾	12	5	10	20	87	62	26	35	107	82½
13	5½	22½	63	26¾	1	9½	13	5	52½	22	60¾	63	26	77½	109	56½
14	6	24¼	64	27¼	1	11¼	14	5	95	24	34¾	64	27	20	111	30½
15	6½	26	65	27¾	1	13	15	6	37½	26	8¾	65	27	62½	113	4¼
16	6¾	27¾	66	28	1	14¾	16	6	80	27	82½	66	28	5	114	78¼
17	7¼	29½	67	28½	1	16½	17	7	22½	29	56½	67	28	47½	116	52¼
18	7¾	31¼	68	29	1	18¼	18	7	65	31	30½	68	28	90	118	26
19	8	33	69	29¼	1	20	19	8	7½	33	4¼	69	29	32½	120	0
20	8½	34¾	**70**	29¾	1	21¾	**20**	8	50	34	78¼	**70**	29	75	121	74
21	9	36½	71	30¼	1	23½	21	8	92½	36	52¼	71	30	17½	123	47¾
22	9¼	38¼	72	30½	1	25¼	22	9	35	38	26	72	30	60	125	21¾
23	9¾	40	73	31	1	27	23	9	77½	40	0	73	31	2½	126	95¾
24	10¼	41¾	74	31½	1	28¾	24	10	20	41	74	74	31	45	128	69½
25	10¾	43½	75	32	1	30½	25	10	62½	43	47¾	75	31	87½	130	43½
26	11	45¼	76	32¼	1	32¼	26	11	5	45	21¾	76	32	30	132	17½
27	11½	47	77	32¾	1	34	27	11	47½	46	95¾	77	32	72½	133	91¼
28	12	48¾	78	33¼	1	35¾	28	11	90	48	69½	78	33	15	135	65¼
29	12¼	50½	79	33½	1	37½	29	12	32½	50	43½	79	33	57½	137	39¼
30	12¾	52¼	**80**	34	1	39¼	**30**	12	75	52	17½	**80**	34	0	139	13
31	13¼	54	81	34½	1	40¾	31	13	17½	53	91¼	81	34	42½	140	87
32	13½	55¾	82	34¾	1	42½	32	13	60	55	65¼	82	34	85	142	60¾
33	14	57½	83	35¼	1	44¼	33	14	2½	57	39¼	83	35	27½	144	34¾
34	14½	59¼	84	35¾	1	46	34	14	45	59	13	84	35	70	146	8¾
35	15	60¾	85	36¼	1	47¾	35	14	87½	60	87	85	36	12½	147	82½
36	15¼	62½	86	36½	1	49½	36	15	30	62	60¾	86	36	55	149	56½
37	15¾	64¼	87	37	1	51¼	37	15	72½	64	34¾	87	36	97½	151	30½
38	16¼	66	88	37½	1	53	38	16	15	66	8¾	88	37	40	153	4¼
39	16½	67¾	89	37¾	1	54¾	39	16	57½	67	82½	89	37	82½	154	78¼
40	17	69½	**90**	38¼	1	56½	**40**	17	0	69	56½	**90**	38	25	156	52¼
41	17½	71¼	91	38¾	1	58¼	41	17	42½	71	30½	91	38	67½	158	26
42	17¾	73	92	39	1	60	42	17	85	73	4¼	92	39	10	160	0
43	18¼	74¾	93	39½	1	61¾	43	18	27½	74	78¼	93	39	52½	161	74
44	18¾	76½	94	40	1	63½	44	18	70	76	52¼	94	39	95	163	47¾
45	19¼	78¼	95	40¼	1	65¼	45	19	12½	78	26	95	40	37½	165	21¾
46	19½	80	96	40¾	1	67	46	19	55	80	0	96	40	80	166	95¾
47	20	81¾	97	41¼	1	68¾	47	19	97½	81	74	97	41	22½	168	69½
48	20½	83½	98	41¾	1	70½	48	20	40	83	47¾	98	41	65	170	43½
49	20¾	85¼	99	42	1	72¼	49	20	82½	85	21¾	99	42	7½	172	17½
50	21¼	87	**100**	42½	1	74	**50**	21	25	86	95¾	**100**	42	50	173	91¼

£	On Cost £	On Cost P	Profit on Returns £	Profit on Returns P	£	On Cost £	On Cost P	Profit on Returns £	Profit on Returns P	£	On Cost £	On Cost P	Profit on Returns £	Profit on Returns P
150	63	75	260	87	450	191	25	782	60¾	750	318	75	1304	34¾
200	85	0	347	82½	500	212	50	869	56½	800	340	0	1391	30½
250	106	25	434	78¼	550	233	75	956	52¼	850	361	25	1478	26
300	127	50	521	74	600	255	0	1043	47¾	900	382	50	1565	21¾
350	148	75	608	69½	650	276	25	1130	43½	950	403	75	1652	17½
400	170	0	695	65¼	700	297	50	1217	39¼	1000	425	0	1739	13

45 Per Cent

	on Cost	Profit on Returns		on Cost	Profit on Returns			on Cost		Profit on Returns			on Cost		Profit on Returns	
P	P	P	P	P	£	P	£	£	P	£	P	£	£	P	£	P
1	0½	1¾	51	23	0	92¾	1	0	45	1	81¾	51	22	95	92	72¾
2	1	3¾	52	23½	0	94½	2	0	90	3	63¾	52	23	40	94	54½
3	1¼	5½	53	23¾	0	96¼	3	1	35	5	45½	53	23	85	96	36¼
4	1¾	7¼	54	24¼	0	98¼	4	1	80	7	27¼	54	24	30	98	18¼
5	2¼	9	55	24¾	1	0	5	2	25	9	9	55	24	75	100	0
6	2¾	11	56	25¼	1	1¾	6	2	70	10	91	56	25	20	101	81¾
7	3¼	12¾	57	25¾	1	3¾	7	3	15	12	72¾	57	25	65	103	63¾
8	3½	14½	58	26	1	5½	8	3	60	14	54½	58	26	10	105	45½
9	4	16¼	59	26½	1	7¼	9	4	5	16	36¼	59	26	55	107	27¼
10	**4½**	**18¼**	**60**	**27**	**1**	**9**	**10**	**4**	**50**	**18**	**18¼**	**60**	**27**	**0**	**109**	**9**
11	5	20	61	27½	1	11	11	4	95	20	0	61	27	45	110	91
12	5½	21¾	62	28	1	12¾	12	5	40	21	81¾	62	27	90	112	72¾
13	5¾	23¾	63	28¼	1	14½	13	5	85	23	63¾	63	28	35	114	54½
14	6¼	25½	64	28¾	1	16¼	14	6	30	25	45½	64	28	80	116	36¼
15	6¾	27¼	65	29¼	1	18¼	15	6	75	27	27¼	65	29	25	118	18¼
16	7¼	29	66	29¾	1	20	16	7	20	29	9	66	29	70	120	0
17	7¾	31	67	30¼	1	21¾	17	7	65	30	91	67	30	15	121	81¾
18	8	32¾	68	30½	1	23¾	18	8	10	32	72¾	68	30	60	123	63¾
19	8½	34½	69	31	1	25½	19	8	55	34	54½	69	31	5	125	45½
20	**9**	**36¼**	**70**	**31½**	**1**	**27¼**	**20**	**9**	**0**	**36**	**36¼**	**70**	**31**	**50**	**127**	**27¼**
21	9½	38¼	71	32	1	29	21	9	45	38	18¼	71	31	95	129	9
22	10	40	72	32½	1	31	22	9	90	40	0	72	32	40	130	91
23	10¼	41¾	73	32¾	1	32¾	23	10	35	41	81¾	73	32	85	132	72¾
24	10¾	43¾	74	33¼	1	34½	24	10	80	43	63¾	74	33	30	134	54½
25	11¼	45½	75	33¾	1	36¼	25	11	25	45	45½	75	33	75	136	36¼
26	11¾	47¼	76	34¼	1	38¼	26	11	70	47	27¼	76	34	20	138	18¼
27	12¼	49	77	34¾	1	40	27	12	15	49	9	77	34	65	140	0
28	12½	51	78	35	1	41¾	28	12	60	50	91	78	35	10	141	81¾
29	13	52¾	79	35½	1	43¾	29	13	5	52	72¾	79	35	55	143	63¾
30	**13½**	**54½**	**80**	**36**	**1**	**45½**	**30**	**13**	**50**	**54**	**54½**	**80**	**36**	**0**	**145**	**45½**
31	14	56¼	81	36½	1	47¼	31	13	95	56	36¼	81	36	45	147	27¼
32	14½	58¼	82	37	1	49	32	14	40	58	18¼	82	36	90	149	9
33	14¾	60	83	37¼	1	51	33	14	85	60	0	83	37	35	150	91
34	15¼	61¾	84	37¾	1	52¾	34	15	30	61	81¾	84	37	80	152	72¾
35	15¾	63¾	85	38¼	1	54½	35	15	75	63	63¾	85	38	25	154	54½
36	16¼	65½	86	38¾	1	56¼	36	16	20	65	45½	86	38	70	156	36¼
37	16¾	67¼	87	39¼	1	58¼	37	16	65	67	27¼	87	39	15	158	18¼
38	17	69	88	39½	1	60	38	17	10	69	9	88	39	60	160	0¾
39	17½	71	89	40	1	61¾	39	17	55	70	91	89	40	5	161	81½
40	**18**	**72¾**	**90**	**40½**	**1**	**63¾**	**40**	**18**	**0**	**72**	**72¾**	**90**	**40**	**50**	**163**	**63¾**
41	18½	74½	91	41	1	65½	41	18	45	74	54½	91	40	95	165	45½
42	19	76¼	92	41½	1	67¼	42	18	90	76	36¼	92	41	40	167	27¼
43	19¼	78	93	41¾	1	69	43	19	35	78	18¼	93	41	85	169	9
44	19¾	80	94	42¼	1	71	44	19	80	80	0	94	42	30	170	91
45	20¼	81¾	95	42¾	1	72¾	45	20	25	81	81¾	95	42	75	172	72¾
46	20¾	83¾	96	43¼	1	74½	46	20	70	83	63¾	96	43	20	174	54½
47	21	85½	97	43¾	1	76¼	47	21	15	85	45½	97	43	65	176	36¼
48	21½	87¼	98	44	1	78	48	21	60	87	27¼	98	44	10	178	18¼
49	22	89	99	44½	1	80	49	22	5	89	9	99	44	55	180	0
50	**22½**	**91**	**100**	**45**	**1**	**81¾**	**50**	**22**	**50**	**90**	**91**	**100**	**45**	**0**	**181**	**81¾**

	On Cost		Profit on Returns			On Cost		Profit on Returns			On Cost		Profit on Returns	
150	67	50	272	72¾	450	202	50	818	18¼	750	337	50	1363	63¾
200	90	0	363	63¾	500	225	0	909	9	800	360	0	1454	54½
250	112	50	454	54½	550	247	50	1000	0	850	382	50	1545	45½
300	135	0	545	45½	600	270	0	1090	91	900	405	0	1636	36¼
350	157	50	636	36¼	650	292	50	1181	81¾	950	427	50	1727	27¼
400	180	0	727	27¼	700	315	0	1272	72¾	1000	450	0	1818	18¼

P	Profit on Cost P	Profit on Returns P	P	Profit on Cost P	Profit on Returns £	Profit on Returns P
1	0½	2	51	24¼	0	97¼
2	1	3¾	52	24¾	0	99
3	1½	5¾	53	25¼	1	1
4	2	7½	54	25¾	1	2¾
5	2½	9½	55	26¼	1	4¾
6	2¾	11½	56	26½	1	6¾
7	3¼	13¼	57	27	1	8½
8	3¾	15¼	58	27½	1	10½
9	4¼	17¼	59	28	1	12½
10	4¾	19	60	28½	1	14¼
11	5¼	21	61	29	1	16¼
12	5¾	22¾	62	29½	1	18
13	6¼	24¾	63	30	1	20
14	6¾	26¾	64	30½	1	22
15	7¼	28½	65	31	1	23¾
16	7½	30½	66	31¼	1	25¾
17	8	32½	67	31¾	1	27½
18	8½	34¼	68	32¼	1	29½
19	9	36¼	69	32¾	1	31½
20	9½	38	70	33¼	1	33¼
21	10	40	71	33¾	1	35¼
22	10½	42	72	34¼	1	37¼
23	11	43¾	73	34¾	1	39
24	11½	45¾	74	35¼	1	41
25	12	47½	75	35¾	1	42¾
26	12¼	49½	76	36	1	44¾
27	12¾	51½	77	36½	1	46¾
28	13¼	53¼	78	37	1	48½
29	13¾	55¼	79	37½	1	50½
30	14¼	57¼	80	38	1	52½
31	14¾	59	81	38½	1	54¼
32	15¼	61	82	39	1	56¼
33	15¾	62¾	83	39½	1	58
34	16¼	64¾	84	40	1	60
35	16¾	66¾	85	40¼	1	62
36	17	68½	86	40¾	1	63¾
37	17½	70½	87	41¼	1	65¾
38	18	72½	88	41¾	1	67½
39	18½	74¼	89	42¼	1	69½
40	19	76¼	90	42¾	1	71½
41	19½	78	91	43¼	1	73¼
42	20	80	92	43¾	1	75¼
43	20½	82	93	44¼	1	77¼
44	21	83¾	94	44¾	1	79
45	21¼	85¾	95	45¼	1	81
46	21¾	87½	96	45½	1	82¾
47	22¼	89½	97	46	1	84¾
48	22¾	91½	98	46½	1	86¾
49	23¼	93¼	99	47	1	88½
50	23¾	95¼	100	47½	1	90½

£	Profit on Cost £	Profit on Cost P	Profit on Returns £	Profit on Returns P	£	Profit on Cost £	Profit on Cost P	Profit on Returns £	Profit on Returns P
1	0	47½	1	90½	51	24	22½	97	14¼
2	0	95	3	81	52	24	70	99	4¾
3	1	42½	5	71½	53	25	17½	100	95¼
4	1	90	7	62	54	25	65	102	85¾
5	2	37½	9	52½	55	26	12½	104	76¼
6	2	85	11	42¾	56	26	60	106	66¾
7	3	32½	13	33¼	57	27	7½	108	57¼
8	3	80	15	23¾	58	27	55	110	47¾
9	4	27½	17	14¼	59	28	2½	112	38
10	4	75	19	4¾	60	28	50	114	28½
11	5	22½	20	95¼	61	28	97½	116	19
12	5	70	22	85¾	62	29	45	118	9½
13	6	17½	24	76¼	63	29	92½	120	0
14	6	65	26	66¾	64	30	40	121	90½
15	7	12½	28	57¼	65	30	87½	123	81
16	7	60	30	47¾	66	31	35	125	71½
17	8	7½	32	38	67	31	82½	127	62
18	8	55	34	28½	68	32	30	129	52½
19	9	2½	36	19	69	32	77½	131	42¾
20	9	50	38	9½	70	33	25	133	33¼
21	9	97½	40	0	71	33	72½	135	23¾
22	10	45	41	90½	72	34	20	137	14¼
23	10	92½	43	81	73	34	67½	135	4¾
24	11	40	45	71½	74	35	15	140	95¼
25	11	87½	47	62	75	35	62½	142	85¾
26	12	35	49	52½	76	36	10	144	76¼
27	12	82½	51	42¾	77	36	57½	146	66¾
28	13	30	53	33¼	78	37	5	148	57¼
29	13	77½	55	23¾	79	37	52½	150	47¾
30	14	25	57	14¼	80	38	0	152	38
31	14	72½	59	4¾	81	38	47½	154	28½
32	15	20	60	95¼	82	38	95	156	19
33	15	67½	62	85¾	83	39	42½	158	9½
34	16	15	64	76¼	84	39	90	160	0
35	16	62½	66	66¾	85	40	37½	161	90½
36	17	10	68	57¼	86	40	85	163	81
37	17	57½	70	47¾	87	41	32½	165	71½
38	18	5	72	38	88	41	80	167	62
39	18	52½	74	28½	89	42	27½	169	52½
40	19	0	76	19	90	42	75	171	42¾
41	19	47½	78	9½	91	43	22½	173	33¼
42	19	95	80	0	92	43	70	175	23¾
43	20	42½	81	90½	93	44	17½	177	14¼
44	20	90	83	81	94	44	65	179	4¾
45	21	37½	85	71½	95	45	12½	180	95¼
46	21	85	87	62	96	45	60	182	85¾
47	22	32½	89	52½	97	46	7½	184	76¼
48	22	80	91	42¾	98	46	55	186	66¾
49	23	27½	93	33¼	99	47	2½	188	57¼
50	23	75	95	23¾	100	47	50	190	47¾

£	On Cost £	On Cost P	Profit on Returns £	Profit on Returns P	£	On Cost £	On Cost P	Profit on Returns £	Profit on Returns P	£	On Cost £	On Cost P	Profit on Returns £	Profit on Returns P
150	71	25	285	71½	450	213	75	857	14¼	750	356	25	1428	57¼
200	95	0	380	95¼	500	237	50	952	38	800	380	0	1523	81
250	118	75	476	19	550	261	25	1047	62	850	403	75	1619	4¾
300	142	50	571	42¾	600	285	0	1142	85¾	900	427	50	1714	28½
350	166	25	666	66¾	650	308	75	1238	9½	950	451	25	1809	52½
400	190	0	761	90½	700	332	50	1333	33¼	1000	475	0	1904	76¼

50% ON COST 52½%

	P	£ P		P	£ P		P	£ P		P	£ P
1	0½	0 50	51	25½	25 50	1	0½	0 52½	51	26¾	26 77½
2	1	1 0	52	26	26 0	2	1	1 5	52	27¼	27 30
3	1½	1 50	53	26½	26 50	3	1½	1 57½	53	27¾	27 82½
4	2	2 0	54	27	27 0	4	2	2 10	54	28¼	28 35
5	2½	2 50	55	27½	27 50	5	2¾	2 62½	55	29	28 87½
6	3	3 0	56	28	28 0	6	3	3 15	56	29½	29 40
7	3½	3 50	57	28½	28 50	7	3¾	3 67½	57	30	29 92½
8	4	4 0	58	29	29 0	8	4¼	4 20	58	30½	30 45
9	4½	4 50	59	29½	29 50	9	4¾	4 72½	59	31	30 97½
10	**5**	**5 0**	**60**	**30**	**30 0**	**10**	**5¼**	**5 25**	**60**	**31½**	**31 50**
11	5½	5 50	61	30½	30 50	11	5¾	5 77½	61	32	32 2½
12	6	6 0	62	31	31 0	12	6¼	6 30	62	32½	32 55
13	6½	6 50	63	31½	31 50	13	6¾	6 82½	63	33	33 7½
14	7	7 0	64	32	32 0	14	7¼	7 35	64	33½	33 60
15	7½	7 50	65	32½	32 50	15	8	7 87½	65	34¼	34 12½
16	8	8 0	66	33	33 0	16	8½	8 40	66	34¾	34 65
17	8½	8 50	67	33½	33 50	17	9	8 92½	67	35	35 17½
18	9	9 0	68	34	34 0	18	9½	9 45	68	35¾	35 70
19	9½	9 50	69	34½	34 50	19	10	9 97½	69	36¼	36 22½
20	**10**	**10 0**	**70**	**35**	**35 0**	**20**	**10½**	**10 50**	**70**	**36¾**	**36 75**
21	10½	10 50	71	35½	35 50	21	11	11 2½	71	37¼	37 27½
22	11	11 0	72	36	36 0	22	11½	11 55	72	37¾	37 80
23	11½	11 50	73	36½	36 50	23	12	12 7½	73	38¼	38 32½
24	12	12 0	74	37	37 0	24	12½	12 60	74	38¾	38 85
25	12½	12 50	75	37½	37 50	25	13¼	13 12½	75	39½	39 37½
26	13	13 0	76	38	38 0	26	13¾	13 65	76	40	39 90
27	13½	13 50	77	38½	38 50	27	14¼	14 17½	77	40½	40 42½
28	14	14 0	78	39	39 0	28	14¾	14 70	78	41	40 95
29	14½	14 50	79	39½	39 50	29	15¼	15 22½	79	41½	41 47½
30	**15**	**15 0**	**80**	**40**	**40 0**	**30**	**15¾**	**15 75**	**80**	**42**	**42 0**
31	15½	15 50	81	40½	40 50	31	16¼	16 27½	81	42½	42 52½
32	16	16 0	82	41	41 0	32	16¾	16 80	82	43	43 5
33	16½	16 50	83	41½	41 50	33	17¼	17 32½	83	43½	43 57½
34	17	17 0	84	42	42 0	34	17¾	17 85	84	44	44 10
35	17½	17 50	85	42½	42 50	35	18½	18 37½	85	44¾	44 62½
36	18	18 0	86	43	43 0	36	19	18 90	86	45¼	45 15
37	18½	18 50	87	43½	43 50	37	19½	19 42½	87	45¾	45 67½
38	19	19 0	88	44	44 0	38	20	19 95	88	46¼	46 20
39	19½	19 50	89	44½	44 50	39	20½	20 47½	89	46¾	46 72½
40	**20**	**20 0**	**90**	**45**	**45 0**	**40**	**21**	**21 0**	**90**	**47¼**	**47 25**
41	20½	20 50	91	45½	45 50	41	21½	21 52½	91	47¾	47 77½
42	21	21 0	92	46	46 0	42	22	22 5	92	48¼	48 30
43	21½	21 50	93	46½	46 50	43	22½	22 57½	93	48¾	48 82½
44	22	22 0	94	47	47 0	44	23	23 10	94	49¼	49 35
45	22½	22 50	95	47½	47 50	45	23¾	23 62½	95	50	49 87½
46	23	23 0	96	48	48 0	46	24¼	24 15	96	50½	50 40
47	23½	23 50	97	48½	48 50	47	24¾	24 67½	97	51	50 92½
48	24	24 0	98	49	49 0	48	25¼	25 20	98	51½	51 45
49	24½	24 50	99	49½	49 50	49	25¾	25 72½	99	52	51 97½
50	**25**	**25 0**	**100**	**50**	**50 0**	**50**	**26¼**	**26 25**	**100**	**52½**	**52 50**

150	75	0	600	300	0	150	78	75	600	315	0
200	100	0	650	325	0	200	105	0	650	341	25
250	125	0	700	350	0	250	131	25	700	367	50
300	150	0	750	375	0	300	157	50	750	393	75
350	175	0	800	400	0	350	183	75	800	420	0
400	200	0	850	425	0	400	210	0	850	446	25
450	225	0	900	450	0	450	236	25	900	472	50
500	250	0	950	475	0	500	262	50	950	498	75
550	275	0	1000	500	0	550	288	75	1000	525	0

55% ON COST 57½%

55%

	P	£	P		P	£	P
1	0½	0	55	51	28	28	5
2	1	1	10	52	28½	28	60
3	1¾	1	65	53	29¼	29	15
4	2¼	2	20	54	29¾	29	70
5	2¾	2	75	55	30¼	30	25
6	3¼	3	30	56	30¾	30	80
7	4	3	85	57	31¼	31	35
8	4½	4	40	58	32	31	90
9	5	4	95	59	32½	32	45
10	**5½**	**5**	**50**	**60**	**33**	**33**	**0**
11	6	6	5	61	33½	33	55
12	6½	6	60	62	34	34	10
13	7	7	15	63	34¾	34	65
14	7¾	7	70	64	35¼	35	20
15	8¼	8	25	65	35¾	35	75
16	9	8	80	66	36¼	36	30
17	9¼	9	35	67	36¾	36	85
18	10	9	90	68	37½	37	40
19	10½	10	45	69	38	37	95
20	**11**	**11**	**0**	**70**	**38½**	**38**	**50**
21	11½	11	55	71	39	39	5
22	12	12	10	72	39½	39	60
23	12¾	12	65	73	40¼	40	15
24	13¼	13	20	74	40¾	40	70
25	13¾	13	75	75	41¼	41	25
26	14¼	14	30	76	41¾	41	80
27	14¾	14	85	77	42¼	42	35
28	15½	15	40	78	43	42	90
29	16	15	95	79	43½	43	45
30	**16½**	**16**	**50**	**80**	**44**	**44**	**0**
31	17	17	5	81	44½	44	55
32	17½	17	60	82	45	45	10
33	18	18	15	83	45¾	45	65
34	18¾	18	70	84	46¼	46	20
35	19¼	19	25	85	46¾	46	75
36	20	19	80	86	47¼	47	30
37	20¼	20	35	87	47¾	47	85
38	21	20	90	88	48½	48	40
39	21½	21	45	89	49	48	95
40	**22**	**22**	**0**	**90**	**49½**	**49**	**50**
41	22½	22	55	91	50	50	5
42	23	23	10	92	50½	50	60
43	23¾	23	65	93	51¼	51	15
44	24¼	24	20	94	51¾	51	70
45	24¾	24	75	95	52¼	52	25
46	25¼	25	30	96	52¾	52	80
47	25¾	25	85	97	53¼	53	35
48	26½	26	40	98	54	53	90
49	27	26	95	99	54½	54	45
50	**27½**	**27**	**50**	**100**	**55**	**55**	**0**

150	82	50	600	330	0
200	110	0	650	357	50
250	137	50	700	385	0
300	165	0	750	412	50
350	192	50	800	440	0
400	220	0	850	467	50
450	247	50	900	495	0
500	275	0	950	522	50
550	302	50	1000	550	0

57½%

	P	£	P		P	£	P
1	0½	0	57½	51	29¼	29	32½
2	1	1	15	52	30	29	90
3	1¾	1	72½	53	30½	30	47½
4	2¼	2	30	54	31	31	5
5	3	2	87½	55	31¾	31	62½
6	3½	3	45	56	32¼	32	20
7	4	4	2½	57	32¾	32	77½
8	4½	4	60	58	33¼	33	35
9	5¼	5	17½	59	34	33	92½
10	**5¾**	**5**	**75**	**60**	**34½**	**34**	**50**
11	6¼	6	32½	61	35	35	7½
12	7	6	90	62	35¾	35	65
13	7½	7	47½	63	36¼	36	22½
14	8	8	5	64	36¾	36	80
15	8¾	8	62½	65	37¼	37	37½
16	9¼	9	20	66	38	37	95
17	9¾	9	77½	67	38½	38	52½
18	10¼	10	35	68	39	39	10
19	11	10	92½	69	39¾	39	67½
20	**11½**	**11**	**50**	**70**	**40¼**	**40**	**25**
21	12	12	7½	71	40¾	40	82½
22	12¾	12	65	72	41½	41	40
23	13¼	13	22½	73	42	41	97½
24	13¾	13	80	74	42½	42	55
25	14¼	14	37½	75	43¼	43	12½
26	15	14	95	76	43¾	43	70
27	15½	15	52½	77	44¼	44	27½
28	16	16	10	78	44¾	44	85
29	16¾	16	67½	79	45½	45	42½
30	**17**	**17**	**25**	**80**	**46**	**46**	**0**
31	17¾	17	82½	81	46½	46	57½
32	18½	18	40	82	47¼	47	15
33	19	18	97½	83	47¾	47	72½
34	19½	19	55	84	48¼	48	30
35	20¼	20	12½	85	49	48	87½
36	20¾	20	70	86	49½	49	45
37	21¼	21	27½	87	50	50	2½
38	21¾	21	85	88	50½	50	60
39	22½	22	42½	89	51¼	51	17½
40	**23**	**23**	**0**	**90**	**51¾**	**51**	**75**
41	23½	23	57½	91	52¼	52	32½
42	24¼	24	15	92	53	52	90
43	24¾	24	72½	93	53½	53	47½
44	25¼	25	30	94	54	54	5
45	26	25	87½	95	54¾	54	62½
46	26½	26	45	96	55¼	55	20
47	27	27	2½	97	55¾	55	77½
48	27½	27	60	98	56¼	56	35
49	28¼	28	17½	99	57	56	92½
50	**28¾**	**28**	**75**	**100**	**57½**	**57**	**50**

150	86	25	600	345	0
200	115	0	650	373	75
250	143	75	700	402	50
300	172	50	750	431	25
350	201	25	800	460	0
400	230	0	850	488	75
450	258	75	900	517	50
500	287	50	950	546	25
550	316	25	1000	575	0

60% On Cost 62½%

	P	£	P		P	£	P		P	£	P		P	£	P
1	0½	0	60	51	30½	30	60	1	0¾	0	62½	51	32	31	87½
2	1¼	1	20	52	31¼	31	20	2	1¼	1	25	52	32½	32	50
3	1¾	1	80	53	31¾	31	80	3	2	1	87½	53	33¼	33	12½
4	2½	2	40	54	32½	32	40	4	2½	2	50	54	33¾	33	75
5	3	3	0	55	33	33	0	5	3¼	3	12½	55	34¼	34	37½
6	3½	3	60	56	33½	33	60	6	3¾	3	75	56	35	35	0
7	4¼	4	20	57	34¼	34	20	7	4½	4	37½	57	35¾	35	62½
8	4¾	4	80	58	34¾	34	80	8	5	5	0	58	36¼	36	25
9	5½	5	40	59	35½	35	40	9	5¾	5	62½	59	37	36	87½
10	**6**	**6**	**0**	**60**	**36**	**36**	**0**	**10**	**6¼**	**6**	**25**	**60**	**37½**	**37**	**50**
11	6½	6	60	61	36½	36	60	11	7	6	87½	61	38¼	38	12½
12	7¼	7	20	62	37¼	37	20	12	7½	7	50	62	38¾	38	75
13	7¾	7	80	63	37¾	37	80	13	8¼	8	12½	63	39½	39	37½
14	8½	8	40	64	38½	38	40	14	8¾	8	75	64	40	40	0
15	9	9	0	65	39	39	0	15	9½	9	37½	65	40¾	40	62½
16	9½	9	60	66	39½	39	60	16	10	10	0	66	41¼	41	25
17	10¼	10	20	67	40¼	40	20	17	10¾	10	62½	67	42	41	87½
18	10¾	10	80	68	40¾	40	80	18	11¼	11	25	68	42½	42	50
19	11½	11	40	69	41½	41	40	19	12	11	87½	69	43¼	43	12½
20	**12**	**12**	**0**	**70**	**42**	**42**	**0**	**20**	**12½**	**12**	**50**	**70**	**43¾**	**43**	**75**
21	12½	12	60	71	42½	42	60	21	13¼	13	12½	71	44½	44	37½
22	13¼	13	20	72	43¼	43	20	22	13¾	13	75	72	45	45	0
23	13¾	13	80	73	43¾	43	80	23	14½	14	37½	73	45¾	45	62½
24	14½	14	40	74	44½	44	40	24	15	15	0	74	46¼	46	25
25	15	15	0	75	45	45	0	25	15¾	15	62½	75	47	46	87½
26	15½	15	60	76	45½	45	60	26	16¼	16	25	76	47½	47	50
27	16¼	16	20	77	46¼	46	20	27	17	16	87½	77	48¼	48	12½
28	16¾	16	80	78	46¾	46	80	28	17½	17	50	78	48¾	48	75
29	17½	17	40	79	47½	47	40	29	18	18	12½	79	49½	49	37½
30	**18**	**18**	**0**	**80**	**48**	**48**	**0**	**30**	**18¾**	**18**	**75**	**80**	**50**	**50**	**0**
31	18½	18	60	81	48½	48	60	31	19½	19	37½	81	50¾	50	62½
32	19¼	19	20	82	49¼	49	20	32	20	20	0	82	51¼	51	25
33	19¾	19	80	83	49¾	49	80	33	20¾	20	62½	83	52	51	87½
34	20½	20	40	84	50½	50	40	34	21¼	21	25	84	52½	52	50
35	21	21	0	85	51	51	0	35	22	21	87½	85	53¼	53	12½
36	21½	21	60	86	51½	51	60	36	22½	22	50	86	53¾	53	75
37	22¼	22	20	87	52¼	52	20	37	23¼	23	12½	87	54½	54	37½
38	22¾	22	80	88	52¾	52	80	38	23¾	23	75	88	55	55	0
39	23½	23	40	89	53½	53	40	39	24½	24	37½	89	55¾	55	62½
40	**24**	**24**	**0**	**90**	**54**	**54**	**0**	**40**	**25**	**25**	**0**	**90**	**56¼**	**56**	**25**
41	24½	24	60	91	54½	54	60	41	25¾	25	62½	91	57	56	87½
42	25¼	25	20	92	55¼	55	20	42	26¼	26	25	92	57½	57	50
43	25¾	25	80	93	55¾	55	80	43	27	26	87½	93	58¼	58	12½
44	26½	26	40	94	56½	56	40	44	27½	27	50	94	58¾	58	75
45	27	27	0	95	57	57	0	45	28¼	28	12½	95	59½	59	37½
46	27½	27	60	96	57½	57	60	46	28¾	28	75	96	60	60	0
47	28¼	28	20	97	58¼	58	20	47	29½	29	37½	97	60¾	60	62½
48	28¾	28	80	98	58¾	58	80	48	30	30	0	98	61¼	61	25
49	29½	29	40	99	59½	59	40	49	30¾	30	62½	99	62	61	87½
50	**30**	**30**	**0**	**100**	**60**	**60**	**0**	**50**	**31¼**	**31**	**25**	**100**	**62½**	**62**	**50**

150	90	0	600	360	0	150	93	75	600	375	0
200	120	0	650	390	0	200	125	0	650	406	25
250	150	0	700	420	0	250	156	25	700	437	50
300	180	0	750	450	0	300	187	50	750	468	75
350	210	0	800	480	0	350	218	75	800	500	0
400	240	0	850	510	0	400	250	0	850	531	25
450	270	0	900	540	0	450	281	25	900	562	50
500	300	0	950	570	0	500	312	50	950	593	75
550	330	0	1000	600	0	550	343	75	1000	625	0

On Cost

65%

	P	£	P		P	£	P
1	0¾	0	65	51	33¼	33	15
2	1¼	1	30	52	33¾	33	80
3	2	1	95	53	34½	34	45
4	2½	2	60	54	35	35	10
5	3¼	3	25	55	35¾	35	75
6	4	3	90	56	36½	36	40
7	4½	4	55	57	37	37	5
8	5¼	5	20	58	37¾	37	70
9	5¾	5	85	59	38¼	38	35
10	**6½**	**6**	**50**	**60**	**39**	**39**	**0**
11	7¼	7	15	61	39¾	39	65
12	7¾	7	80	62	40¼	40	30
13	8½	8	45	63	41	40	95
14	9	9	10	64	41½	41	60
15	9¾	9	75	65	42¼	42	25
16	10½	10	40	66	43	42	90
17	11	11	5	67	43½	43	55
18	11¾	11	70	68	44¼	44	20
19	12¼	12	35	69	44¾	44	85
20	**13**	**13**	**0**	**70**	**45½**	**45**	**50**
21	13¾	13	65	71	46¼	46	15
22	14¼	14	30	72	46¾	46	80
23	15	14	95	73	47½	47	45
24	15½	15	60	74	48	48	10
25	16¼	16	25	75	48¾	48	75
26	17	16	90	76	49½	49	40
27	17½	17	55	77	50	50	5
28	18¼	18	20	78	50¾	50	70
29	18¾	18	85	79	51¼	51	35
30	**19½**	**19**	**50**	**80**	**52**	**52**	**0**
31	20¼	20	15	81	52¾	52	65
32	20¾	20	80	82	53¼	53	30
33	21½	21	45	83	54	53	95
34	22	22	10	84	54½	54	60
35	22¾	22	75	85	55¼	55	25
36	23½	23	40	86	56	55	90
37	24	24	5	87	56½	56	55
38	24¾	24	70	88	57¼	57	20
39	25¼	25	35	89	58	57	85
40	**26**	**26**	**0**	**90**	**58½**	**58**	**50**
41	26¾	26	65	91	59¼	59	15
42	27¼	27	30	92	59¾	59	80
43	28	27	95	93	60½	60	45
44	28½	28	60	94	61	61	10
45	29¼	29	25	95	61¾	61	75
46	30	29	90	96	62½	62	40
47	30½	30	55	97	63	63	5
48	31¼	31	20	98	63¾	63	70
49	31¾	31	85	99	64¼	64	35
50	**32½**	**32**	**50**	**100**	**65**	**65**	**0**

	£	P		£	P
150	97	50	600	390	0
200	130	0	650	422	50
250	162	50	700	455	0
300	195	0	750	487	50
350	227	50	800	520	0
400	260	0	850	552	50
450	292	50	900	585	0
500	325	0	950	617	50
550	357	50	1000	650	0

67½%

	P	£	P		P	£	P
1	0¾	0	67½	51	34½	34	42½
2	1¼	1	35	52	35	35	10
3	2	2	2½	53	35¾	35	77½
4	2¾	2	70	54	36½	36	45
5	3¼	3	37½	55	37¼	37	12½
6	4	4	5	56	37¾	37	80
7	4¾	4	72½	57	38½	38	47½
8	5½	5	40	58	39¼	39	15
9	6	6	7½	59	39¾	39	82½
10	**6¾**	**6**	**75**	**60**	**40½**	**40**	**50**
11	7½	7	42½	61	41¼	41	17½
12	8	8	10	62	41¾	41	85
13	8¾	8	77½	63	42½	42	52½
14	9½	9	45	64	43¼	43	20
15	10¼	10	12½	65	44	43	87½
16	10¾	10	80	66	44½	44	55
17	11½	11	47½	67	45¼	45	22½
18	12¼	12	15	68	46	45	90
19	12¾	12	82½	69	46½	46	57½
20	**13½**	**13**	**50**	**70**	**47¼**	**47**	**25**
21	14¼	14	17½	71	48	47	92½
22	14¾	14	85	72	48½	48	60
23	15½	15	52½	73	49¼	49	27½
24	16¼	16	20	74	50	49	95
25	17	16	87½	75	50¾	50	62½
26	17½	17	55	76	51¼	51	30
27	18¼	18	22½	77	52	51	97½
28	19	18	90	78	52¾	52	65
29	19½	19	57½	79	53¼	53	32½
30	**20¼**	**20**	**25**	**80**	**54**	**54**	**0**
31	21	20	92½	81	54¾	54	67½
32	21½	21	60	82	55¼	55	35
33	22¼	22	27½	83	56	56	2½
34	23	22	95	84	56¾	56	70
35	23¾	23	62½	85	57½	57	37½
36	24¼	24	30	86	58	58	5
37	25	24	97½	87	58¾	58	72½
38	25¾	25	65	88	59½	59	40
39	26¼	26	32½	89	60	60	7½
40	**27**	**27**	**0**	**90**	**60¾**	**60**	**75**
41	27¾	27	67½	91	61½	61	42½
42	28¼	28	35	92	62	62	10
43	29	29	2½	93	62¾	62	77½
44	29¾	29	70	94	63½	63	45
45	30½	30	37½	95	64¼	64	12½
46	31	31	5	96	64¾	64	80
47	31¾	31	72½	97	65½	65	47½
48	32½	32	40	98	66¼	66	15
49	33	33	7½	99	66¾	66	82½
50	**33¾**	**33**	**75**	**100**	**67½**	**67**	**50**

	£	P		£	P
150	101	25	600	405	0
200	135	0	650	438	75
250	168	75	700	472	50
300	202	50	750	506	25
350	236	25	800	540	0
400	270	0	850	573	75
450	303	75	900	607	50
500	337	50	950	641	25
550	371	25	1000	675	0

70% ON COST 72½%

70%

	P	£	P		P	£	P
1	0¾	0	70	51	35¾	35	70
2	1½	1	40	52	36½	36	40
3	2	2	10	53	37	37	10
4	2¾	2	80	54	37¾	37	80
5	3½	3	50	55	38½	38	50
6	4¼	4	20	56	39¼	39	20
7	5	4	90	57	40	39	90
8	5½	5	60	58	40½	40	60
9	6¼	6	30	59	41¼	41	30
10	**7**	**7**	**0**	**60**	**42**	**42**	**0**
11	7¾	7	70	61	42¾	42	70
12	8½	8	40	62	43½	43	40
13	9	9	10	63	44	44	10
14	9¾	9	80	64	44¾	44	80
15	10½	10	50	65	45½	45	50
16	11¼	11	20	66	46¼	46	20
17	12	11	90	67	47	46	90
18	12½	12	60	68	47½	47	60
19	13¼	13	30	69	48¼	48	30
20	**14**	**14**	**0**	**70**	**49**	**49**	**0**
21	14¾	14	70	71	49¾	49	70
22	15½	15	40	72	50½	50	40
23	16	16	10	73	51	51	10
24	16¾	16	80	74	51¾	51	80
25	17½	17	50	75	52½	52	50
26	18¼	18	20	76	53¼	53	20
27	19	18	90	77	54	53	90
28	19½	19	60	78	54½	54	60
29	20¼	20	30	79	55¼	55	30
30	**21**	**21**	**0**	**80**	**56**	**56**	**0**
31	21¾	21	70	81	56¾	56	70
32	22½	22	40	82	57½	57	40
33	23	23	10	83	58	58	10
34	23¾	23	80	84	58¾	58	80
35	24½	24	50	85	59½	59	50
36	25¼	25	20	86	60¼	60	20
37	26	25	90	87	61	60	90
38	26½	26	60	88	61½	61	60
39	27¼	27	30	89	62¼	62	30
40	**28**	**28**	**0**	**90**	**63**	**63**	**0**
41	28¾	28	70	91	63¾	63	70
42	29½	29	40	92	64½	64	40
43	30	30	10	93	65	65	10
44	30¾	30	80	94	65¾	65	80
45	31½	31	50	95	66½	66	50
46	32¼	32	20	96	67¼	67	20
47	33	32	90	97	68	67	90
48	33½	33	60	98	68½	68	60
49	34¼	34	30	99	69¼	69	30
50	**35**	**35**	**0**	**100**	**70**	**70**	**0**

	£	P		£	P
150	105	0	600	420	0
200	140	0	650	455	0
250	175	0	700	490	0
300	210	0	750	525	0
350	245	0	800	560	0
400	280	0	850	595	0
450	315	0	900	630	0
500	350	0	950	665	0
550	385	0	1000	700	0

72½%

	P	£	P		P	£	P
1	0¾	0	72½	51	37	36	97½
2	1½	1	45	52	37¾	37	70
3	2¼	2	17½	53	38½	38	42½
4	3	2	90	54	39¼	39	15
5	3¾	3	62½	55	40	39	87½
6	4¼	4	35	56	40½	40	60
7	5	5	7½	57	41¼	41	32½
8	5¾	5	80	58	42	42	5
9	6½	6	52½	59	42¾	42	77½
10	**7¼**	**7**	**25**	**60**	**43½**	**43**	**50**
11	8	7	97½	61	44¼	44	22½
12	8¾	8	70	62	45	44	95
13	9½	9	42½	63	45¾	45	67½
14	10¼	10	15	64	46½	46	40
15	11	10	87½	65	47¼	47	12½
16	11½	11	60	66	47¾	47	85
17	12¼	12	32½	67	48¾	48	57½
18	13	13	5	68	49¼	49	30
19	13¾	13	77½	69	50	50	2½
20	**14½**	**14**	**50**	**70**	**50¾**	**50**	**75**
21	15¼	15	22½	71	51½	51	47½
22	16	15	95	72	52¼	52	20
23	16¾	16	67½	73	53	52	92½
24	17½	17	40	74	53¾	53	65
25	18¼	18	12½	75	54¼	54	37½
26	18¾	18	85	76	55	55	10
27	19½	19	57½	77	55¾	55	82½
28	20¼	20	30	78	56½	56	55
29	21	21	2½	79	57¼	57	27½
30	**21¾**	**21**	**75**	**80**	**58**	**58**	**0**
31	22½	22	47½	81	58¾	58	72½
32	23¼	23	20	82	59½	59	45
33	24	23	92½	83	60¼	60	17½
34	24¾	24	65	84	61	60	90
35	25¼	25	37½	85	61¾	61	62½
36	26	26	10	86	62¼	62	35
37	26¾	26	82½	87	63	63	7½
38	27½	27	55	88	63¾	63	80
39	28¼	28	27½	89	64½	64	52½
40	**29**	**29**	**0**	**90**	**65¼**	**65**	**25**
41	29¾	29	72½	91	66	65	97½
42	30½	30	45	92	66¾	66	70
43	31¼	31	17½	93	67½	67	42½
44	32	31	90	94	68¼	68	15
45	32¾	32	62½	95	69	68	87½
46	33¼	33	35	96	69½	69	60
47	34	34	7½	97	70¼	70	32½
48	34¾	34	80	98	71	71	5
49	35½	35	52½	99	71¾	71	77½
50	**36¼**	**36**	**25**	**100**	**72½**	**72**	**50**

	£	P		£	P
150	108	75	600	435	0
200	145	0	650	471	25
250	181	25	700	507	50
300	217	50	750	543	75
350	253	75	800	580	0
400	290	0	850	616	25
450	326	25	900	652	50
500	362	50	950	688	75
550	398	75	1000	725	0

75% ON COST 77½%

	P	£	P		P	£	P		P	£	P		P	£	P
1	0¾	0	75	51	38¼	38	25	1	0¾	0	77½	51	39½	39	52½
2	1½	1	50	52	39	39	0	2	1½	1	55	52	40¼	40	30
3	2¼	2	25	53	39¾	39	75	3	2¼	2	32½	53	41	41	7½
4	3	3	0	54	40½	40	50	4	3	3	10	54	41¾	41	85
5	3¾	3	75	55	41¼	41	25	5	4	3	87½	55	42¾	42	62½
6	4½	4	50	56	42	42	0	6	4¾	4	65	56	43½	43	40
7	5¼	5	25	57	42¾	42	75	7	5½	5	42½	57	44¼	44	17½
8	6	6	0	58	43½	43	50	8	6¼	6	20	58	45	44	95
9	6¾	6	75	59	44¼	44	25	9	7	6	97½	59	45¾	45	72½
10	**7½**	**7**	**50**	**60**	**45**	**45**	**0**	**10**	**7¾**	**7**	**75**	**60**	**46½**	**43**	**50**
11	8¼	8	25	61	45¾	45	75	11	8½	8	52½	61	47¼	47	27½
12	9	9	0	62	46½	46	50	12	9¼	9	30	62	48	48	5
13	9¾	9	75	63	47¼	47	25	13	10	10	7½	63	48¾	48	82½
14	10½	10	50	64	48	48	0	14	10¾	10	85	64	49½	49	60
15	11¼	11	25	65	48¾	48	75	15	11¾	11	62½	65	50¼	50	37½
16	12	12	0	66	49½	49	50	16	12½	12	40	66	51¼	51	15
17	12¾	12	75	67	50¼	50	25	17	13¼	13	17½	67	52	51	92½
18	13½	13	50	68	51	51	0	18	14	13	95	68	52¾	52	70
19	14¼	14	25	69	51¾	51	75	19	14¾	14	72½	69	53½	53	47½
20	**15**	**15**	**0**	**70**	**52½**	**52**	**50**	**20**	**15½**	**15**	**50**	**70**	**54¼**	**54**	**25**
21	15¾	15	75	71	53¼	53	25	21	16¼	16	27½	71	55	55	2½
22	16½	16	50	72	54	54	0	22	17	17	5	72	55¾	55	80
23	17¼	17	25	73	54¾	54	75	23	17¾	17	82½	73	56½	56	57½
24	18	18	0	74	55½	55	50	24	18½	18	60	74	57¼	57	35
25	18¾	18	75	75	56¼	56	25	25	19¼	19	37½	75	58¼	58	12½
26	19½	19	50	76	57	57	0	26	20¼	20	15	76	59	58	90
27	20¼	20	25	77	57¾	57	75	27	21	20	92½	77	59¾	59	67½
28	21	21	0	78	58½	58	50	28	21¾	21	70	78	60½	60	45
29	21¾	21	75	79	59¼	59	25	29	22½	22	47½	79	61¼	61	22½
30	**22½**	**22**	**50**	**80**	**60**	**60**	**0**	**30**	**23¼**	**23**	**25**	**80**	**62**	**62**	**0**
31	23¼	23	25	81	60¾	60	75	31	24	24	2½	81	62¾	62	77½
32	24	24	0	82	61½	61	50	32	24¾	24	80	82	63½	63	55
33	24¾	24	75	83	62¼	62	25	33	25½	25	57½	83	64¼	64	32½
34	25½	25	50	84	63	63	0	34	26¼	26	35	84	65	65	10
35	26¼	26	25	85	63¾	63	75	35	27¼	27	12½	85	66	65	87½
36	27	27	0	86	64½	64	50	36	28	27	90	86	66¾	66	65
37	27¾	27	75	87	65¼	65	25	37	28¾	28	67½	87	67½	67	42½
38	28½	28	50	88	66	66	0	38	29½	29	45	88	68¼	68	20
39	29¼	29	25	89	66¾	66	75	39	30¼	30	22½	89	69	68	97½
40	**30**	**30**	**0**	**90**	**67½**	**67**	**50**	**40**	**31**	**31**	**0**	**90**	**69¾**	**69**	**75**
41	30¾	30	75	91	68¼	68	25	41	31¾	31	77½	91	70½	70	52½
42	31½	31	50	92	69	69	0	42	32½	32	55	92	71¼	71	30
43	32¼	32	25	93	69¾	69	75	43	33¼	33	32½	93	72	72	7½
44	33	33	0	94	70½	70	50	44	34	34	10	94	72¾	72	85
45	33¾	33	75	95	71¼	71	25	45	35	34	87½	95	73¾	73	62½
46	34½	34	50	96	72	72	0	[illegible]	[illegible]	35	65	96	74½	74	40
47	35¼	35	25	97	72¾	72	75	47	36½	36	42½	97	75¼	75	17½
48	36	36	0	98	73½	73	50	48	37¼	37	20	98	76	75	95
49	36¾	36	75	99	74¼	74	25	49	38	37	97½	99	76¾	76	72½
50	**37½**	**37**	**50**	**100**	**75**	**75**	**0**	**50**	**38¾**	**38**	**75**	**100**	**77½**	**77**	**50**

	£	P		£	P		£	P		£	P
150	112	50	600	450	0	150	116	25	600	465	0
200	150	0	650	487	50	200	155	0	650	503	75
250	187	50	700	525	0	250	193	75	700	542	50
300	225	0	750	562	50	300	232	50	750	581	25
350	262	50	800	600	0	350	271	25	800	620	0
400	300	0	850	637	50	400	310	0	850	658	75
450	337	50	900	675	0	450	348	75	900	697	50
500	375	0	950	712	50	500	387	50	950	736	25
550	412	50	1000	750	0	550	426	25	1000	775	0

80% On Cost 82½%

80%

	P	£	P		P	£	P
1	0¾	0	80	51	40¾	40	80
2	1½	1	60	52	41½	41	60
3	2½	2	40	53	42½	42	40
4	3¼	3	20	54	43¼	43	20
5	4	4	0	55	44	44	0
6	4¾	4	80	56	44¾	44	80
7	5½	5	60	57	45½	45	60
8	6½	6	40	58	46½	46	40
9	7¼	7	20	59	47¼	47	20
10	**8**	**8**	**0**	**60**	**48**	**48**	**0**
11	8¾	8	80	61	48¾	48	80
12	9½	9	60	62	49½	49	60
13	10½	10	40	63	50½	50	40
14	11¼	11	20	64	51¼	51	20
15	12	12	0	65	52	52	0
16	12¾	12	80	66	52¾	52	80
17	13½	13	60	67	53½	53	60
18	14½	14	40	68	54½	54	40
19	15¼	15	20	69	55¼	55	20
20	**16**	**16**	**0**	**70**	**56**	**56**	**0**
21	16¾	16	80	71	56¾	56	80
22	17½	17	60	72	57½	57	60
23	18½	18	40	73	58½	58	40
24	19¼	19	20	74	59¼	59	20
25	20	20	0	75	60	60	0
26	20¾	20	80	76	60¾	60	80
27	21½	21	60	77	61½	61	60
28	22½	22	40	78	62½	62	40
29	23¼	23	20	79	63¼	63	20
30	**24**	**24**	**0**	**80**	**64**	**64**	**0**
31	24¾	24	80	81	64¾	64	80
32	25½	25	60	82	65½	65	60
33	26½	26	40	83	66½	66	40
34	27¼	27	20	84	67¼	67	20
35	28	28	0	85	68	68	0
36	28¾	28	80	86	68¾	68	80
37	29½	29	60	87	69½	69	60
38	30½	30	40	88	70½	70	40
39	31¼	31	20	89	71¼	71	20
40	**32**	**32**	**0**	**90**	**72**	**72**	**0**
41	32¾	32	80	91	72¾	72	80
42	33½	33	60	92	73½	73	60
43	34½	34	40	93	74½	74	40
44	35¼	35	20	94	75¼	75	20
45	36	36	0	95	76	76	0
46	36¾	36	80	96	76¾	76	80
47	37½	37	60	97	77½	77	60
48	38½	38	40	98	78½	78	40
49	39¼	39	20	99	79¼	79	20
50	**40**	**40**	**0**	**100**	**80**	**80**	**0**

	£	P		£	P
150	120	0	600	480	0
200	160	0	650	520	0
250	200	0	700	560	0
300	240	0	750	600	0
350	280	0	800	640	0
400	320	0	850	680	0
450	360	0	900	720	0
500	400	0	950	760	0
550	440	0	1000	800	0

82½%

	P	£	P		P	£	P
1	0¾	0	82½	51	42	42	7½
2	1¾	1	65	52	43	42	90
3	2½	2	47½	53	43¾	43	72½
4	3¼	3	30	54	44½	44	55
5	4¼	4	12½	55	45¼	45	37½
6	5	4	95	56	46¼	46	20
7	5¾	5	77½	57	47	47	2½
8	6½	6	60	58	47¾	47	85
9	7½	7	42½	59	48¾	48	67½
10	**8¼**	**8**	**25**	**60**	**49½**	**49**	**50**
11	9	9	7½	61	50¼	50	32½
12	10	9	90	62	51¼	51	15
13	10¾	10	72½	63	52	51	97½
14	11½	11	55	64	52¾	52	80
15	12¼	12	37½	65	53¾	53	62½
16	13¼	13	20	66	54½	54	45
17	14	14	2½	67	55¼	55	27½
18	14¾	14	85	68	56	56	10
19	15¾	15	67½	69	57	56	92½
20	**16½**	**16**	**50**	**70**	**57¾**	**57**	**75**
21	17¼	17	32½	71	58½	58	57½
22	18¼	18	15	72	59½	59	40
23	19	18	97½	73	60¼	60	22½
24	19¾	19	80	74	61	61	5
25	20½	20	62½	75	62	61	87½
26	21½	21	45	76	62¾	62	70
27	22¼	22	27½	77	63½	63	52½
28	23	23	10	78	64¼	64	35
29	24	23	92½	79	65¼	65	17½
30	**24¾**	**24**	**75**	**80**	**66**	**66**	**0**
31	25½	25	57½	81	66¾	66	82½
32	26½	26	40	82	67¾	67	65
33	27¼	27	22½	83	68½	68	47½
34	28	28	5	84	69¼	69	30
35	29	28	87½	85	70¼	70	12½
36	29¾	29	70	86	71	70	95
37	30½	30	52½	87	71¾	71	77½
38	31¼	31	35	88	72½	72	60
39	32¼	32	17½	89	73½	73	42½
40	**33**	**33**	**0**	**90**	**74¼**	**74**	**25**
41	33¾	33	82½	91	75	75	7½
42	34¾	34	65	92	76	75	90
43	35½	35	47½	93	76¾	76	72½
44	36¼	36	30	94	77½	77	55
45	37¼	37	12½	95	78¼	78	37½
46	38	37	95	96	79¼	79	20
47	38¾	38	77½	97	80	80	2½
48	39½	39	60	98	80¾	80	85
49	40½	40	42½	99	81¾	81	67½
50	**41¼**	**41**	**25**	**100**	**82½**	**82**	**50**

	£	P		£	P
150	123	75	600	495	0
200	165	0	650	536	25
250	206	25	700	577	50
300	247	50	750	618	75
350	288	75	800	660	0
400	330	0	850	701	25
450	371	25	900	742	50
500	412	50	950	783	75
550	453	75	1000	825	0

85%						ON COST				87½%	
	P	£ P		P	£ P		P	£ P		P	£ P
1	0¾	0 85	**51**	43¼	43 35	**1**	1	0 87½	**51**	44¾	44 62½
2	1¾	1 70	**52**	44¼	44 20	**2**	1¾	1 75	**52**	45½	45 50
3	2½	2 55	**53**	45	45 5	**3**	2¾	2 62½	**53**	46½	46 37½
4	3½	3 40	**54**	46	45 90	**4**	3½	3 50	**54**	47¼	47 25
5	4¼	4 25	**55**	46¾	46 75	**5**	4½	4 37½	**55**	48¼	48 12½
6	5	5 10	**56**	47½	47 60	**6**	5¼	5 25	**56**	49	49 0
7	6	5 95	**57**	48½	48 45	**7**	6¼	6 12½	**57**	50	49 87½
8	6¾	6 80	**58**	49¼	49 30	**8**	7	7 0	**58**	50¾	50 75
9	7¾	7 65	**59**	50¼	50 15	**9**	8	7 87½	**59**	51¾	51 62½
10	**8½**	**8 50**	**60**	**51**	**51 0**	**10**	**8¾**	**8 75**	**60**	**52½**	**52 50**
11	9¼	9 35	**61**	51¾	51 85	**11**	9¾	9 62½	**61**	53½	53 37½
12	10¼	10 20	**62**	52¾	52 70	**12**	10½	10 50	**62**	54¼	54 25
13	11	11 5	**63**	53½	53 55	**13**	11½	11 37½	**63**	55¼	55 12½
14	12	11 90	**64**	54½	54 40	**14**	12¼	12 25	**64**	56	56 0
15	12¾	12 75	**65**	55¼	55 25	**15**	13¼	13 12½	**65**	57	56 87½
16	13½	13 60	**66**	56	56 10	**16**	14	14 0	**66**	57¾	57 75
17	14½	14 45	**67**	57	56 95	**17**	15	14 87½	**67**	58¾	58 62½
18	15¼	15 30	**68**	57¾	57 80	**18**	15¾	15 75	**68**	59½	59 50
19	16¼	16 15	**69**	58¾	58 65	**19**	16¾	16 62½	**69**	60½	60 37½
20	**17**	**17 0**	**70**	**59½**	**59 50**	**20**	**17½**	**17 50**	**70**	**61¼**	**61 25**
21	17¾	17 85	**71**	60¼	60 35	**21**	18½	18 37½	**71**	62¼	62 12½
22	18¾	18 70	**72**	61¼	61 20	**22**	19¼	19 25	**72**	63	63 0
23	19½	19 55	**73**	62	62 5	**23**	20¼	20 12½	**73**	64	63 87½
24	20½	20 40	**74**	63	62 90	**24**	21¼	21 0	**74**	64¾	64 75
25	21¼	21 25	**75**	63¾	63 75	**25**	22	21 87½	**75**	65¾	65 62½
26	22	22 10	**76**	64½	64 60	**26**	22¾	22 75	**76**	66½	66 50
27	23	22 95	**77**	65½	65 45	**27**	23¾	23 62½	**77**	67½	67 37½
28	23¾	23 80	**78**	66¼	66 30	**28**	24½	24 50	**78**	68¼	68 25
29	24¾	24 65	**79**	67¼	67 15	**29**	25½	25 37½	**79**	69¼	69 12½
30	**25½**	**25 50**	**80**	**68**	**68 0**	**30**	**26¼**	**26 25**	**80**	**70**	**70 0**
31	26¼	26 35	**81**	68¾	68 85	**31**	27¼	27 12½	**81**	71	70 87½
32	27¼	27 20	**82**	69¾	69 70	**32**	28	28 0	**82**	71¾	71 75
33	28	28 5	**83**	70½	70 55	**33**	29	28 87½	**83**	72¾	72 62½
34	29	28 90	**84**	71½	71 40	**34**	29¾	29 75	**84**	73½	73 50
35	29¾	29 75	**85**	72¼	72 25	**35**	30¾	30 62½	**85**	74½	74 37½
36	30½	30 60	**86**	73	73 10	**36**	31½	31 50	**86**	75¼	75 25
37	31½	31 45	**87**	74	73 95	**37**	32½	32 37½	**87**	76¼	76 12½
38	32¼	32 30	**88**	74¾	74 80	**38**	33¼	33 25	**88**	77	77 0
39	33¼	33 15	**89**	75¾	75 65	**39**	34¼	34 12½	**89**	78	77 87½
40	**34**	**34 0**	**90**	**76½**	**76 50**	**40**	**35**	**35 0**	**90**	**78¾**	**78 75**
41	34¾	34 85	**91**	77¼	77 35	**41**	36	35 87½	**91**	79¾	79 62½
42	35¾	35 70	**92**	78¼	78 20	**42**	36¾	36 75	**92**	80½	80 50
43	36½	36 55	**93**	79	79 5	**43**	37¾	37 62½	**93**	81½	81 37½
44	37½	37 40	**94**	80	79 90	**44**	38½	38 50	**94**	82¼	82 25
45	38¼	38 25	**95**	80¾	80 75	**45**	39½	39 37½	**95**	83¼	83 12½
46	39	39 10	**96**	81½	81 60	**46**	40¼	40 25	**96**	84	84 0
47	40	39 95	**97**	82½	82 45	**47**	41¼	41 12½	**97**	85	84 87½
48	40¾	40 80	**98**	83¼	83 30	**48**	42	42 0	**98**	85¾	85 75
49	41¾	41 65	**99**	84¼	84 15	**49**	43	42 87½	**99**	86¾	86 62½
50	**42½**	**42 50**	**100**	**85**	**85 0**	**50**	**43¾**	**43 75**	**100**	**87½**	**87 50**

150	127	50	**600**	510	0	**150**	131	25	**600**	525	0
200	170	0	**650**	552	50	**200**	175	0	**650**	568	75
250	212	50	**700**	595	0	**250**	218	75	**700**	612	50
300	255	0	**750**	637	50	**300**	262	50	**750**	656	25
350	297	50	**800**	680	0	**350**	306	25	**800**	700	0
400	340	0	**850**	722	50	**400**	350	0	**850**	743	75
450	382	50	**900**	765	0	**450**	393	75	**900**	787	50
500	425	0	**950**	807	50	**500**	437	50	**950**	831	25
550	467	50	**1000**	850	0	**550**	481	25	**1000**	875	0

90% ON COST 95%

n	P	£ P	n	P	£ P	n	P	£ P	n	P	£ P
1	1	0 90	51	46	45 90	1	1	0 95	51	48½	48 45
2	1¾	1 80	52	46¾	46 80	2	2	1 90	52	49½	49 40
3	2¾	2 70	53	47¾	47 70	3	2¾	2 85	53	50¼	50 35
4	3½	3 60	54	48½	48 60	4	3¾	3 80	54	51¼	51 30
5	4½	4 50	55	49½	49 50	5	4¾	4 75	55	52¼	52 25
6	5½	5 40	56	50½	50 40	6	5¾	5 70	56	53¼	53 20
7	6¼	6 30	57	51¼	51 30	7	6¾	6 65	57	54¼	54 15
8	7¼	7 20	58	52¼	52 20	8	7½	7 60	58	55	55 10
9	8	8 10	59	53	53 10	9	8½	8 55	59	56	56 5
10	9	9 0	60	54	54 0	10	9½	9 50	60	57	57 0
11	10	9 90	61	55	54 90	11	10½	10 45	61	58	57 95
12	10¾	10 80	62	55¾	55 80	12	11½	11 40	62	59	58 90
13	11¾	11 70	63	56¾	56 70	13	12¼	12 35	63	59¾	59 85
14	12½	12 60	64	57½	57 60	14	13¼	13 30	64	60¾	60 80
15	13½	13 50	65	58½	58 50	15	14¼	14 25	65	61¾	61 75
16	14½	14 40	66	59½	59 40	16	15¼	15 20	66	62¾	62 70
17	15¼	15 30	67	60¼	60 30	17	16¼	16 15	67	63¾	63 65
18	16¼	16 20	68	61¼	61 20	18	17	17 10	68	64½	64 60
19	17	17 10	69	62	62 10	19	18	18 5	69	65½	65 55
20	18	18 0	70	63	63 0	20	19	19 0	70	66½	66 50
21	19	18 90	71	64	63 90	21	20	19 95	71	67½	67 45
22	19¾	19 80	72	64¾	64 80	22	21	20 90	72	68½	68 40
23	20¾	20 70	73	65¾	65 70	23	21¾	21 85	73	69¼	69 35
24	21½	21 60	74	66½	66 60	24	22¾	22 80	74	70¼	70 30
25	22½	22 50	75	67½	67 50	25	23¾	23 75	75	71¼	71 25
26	23½	23 40	76	68½	68 40	26	24¾	24 70	76	72¼	72 20
27	24¼	24 30	77	69¼	69 30	27	25¾	25 65	77	73¼	73 15
28	25¼	25 20	78	70¼	70 20	28	26½	26 60	78	74	74 10
29	26	26 10	79	71	71 10	29	27½	27 55	79	75	75 5
30	27	27 0	80	72	72 0	30	28½	28 50	80	76	76 0
31	28	27 90	81	73	72 90	31	29½	29 45	81	77	76 95
32	28¾	28 80	82	73¾	73 80	32	30½	30 40	82	78	77 90
33	29¾	29 70	83	74¾	74 70	33	31¼	31 35	83	78¾	78 85
34	30½	30 60	84	75½	75 60	34	32¼	32 30	84	79¾	79 80
35	31½	31 50	85	76½	76 50	35	33¼	33 25	85	80¾	80 75
36	32½	32 40	86	77½	77 40	36	34¼	34 20	86	81¾	81 70
37	33¼	33 30	87	78¼	78 30	37	35¼	35 15	87	82¾	82 65
38	34¼	34 20	88	79¼	79 20	38	36	36 10	88	83½	83 60
39	35	35 10	89	80	80 10	39	37	37 5	89	84½	84 55
40	36	36 0	90	81	81 0	40	38	38 0	90	85½	85 50
41	37	36 90	91	82	81 90	41	39	38 95	91	86½	86 45
42	37¾	37 80	92	82¾	82 80	42	40	39 90	92	87½	87 40
43	38¾	38 70	93	83¾	83 70	43	40¾	40 85	93	88¼	88 35
44	39½	39 60	94	84½	84 60	44	41¾	41 80	94	89¼	89 30
45	40½	40 50	95	85½	85 50	45	42¾	42 75	95	90¼	90 25
46	41½	41 40	96	86½	86 40	46	43¾	43 70	96	91¼	91 20
47	42¼	42 30	97	87¼	87 30	47	44¾	44 65	97	92¼	92 15
48	43¼	43 20	98	88¼	88 20	48	45½	45 60	98	93	93 10
49	44	44 10	99	89	89 10	49	46½	46 55	99	94	94 5
50	45	45 0	100	90	90 0	50	47½	47 50	100	95	95 0

90%

n	£ P	n	£ P
150	135 0	600	540 0
200	180 0	650	585 0
250	225 0	700	630 0
300	270 0	750	675 0
350	315 0	800	720 0
400	360 0	850	765 0
450	405 0	900	810 0
500	450 0	950	855 0
550	495 0	1000	900 0

95%

n	£ P	n	£ P
150	142 50	600	570 0
200	190 0	650	617 50
250	237 50	700	665 0
300	285 0	750	712 50
350	332 50	800	760 0
400	380 0	850	807 50
450	427 50	900	855 0
500	475 0	950	902 50
550	522 50	1000	950 0

SECTION III.

INTEREST TABLES

These Tables show the Interest at various rates percent on any given unit.

It is important to note that 'Interest' and 'Percentage' are two totally different bases of calculation.

The Tables, as they stand, enable Interest on any number of £s up to 1000 to be calculated.

Examples:
    Interest on £70 for 27 days @ 3%=£0 16p
    Interest on £340 for 19 days @ 2½%
        "   "   £300 for 19 days=£0 39p
        "   "   £40 for 19 days=£0 5p
        ───────────
                                      £0 44p
        ═══════════

To obtain Interest in thousands of £s above 1000, shift the decimal point of the *hundreds* figure one place to the *right*.

Example:
Interest on £7000 for 27 days @ 3%
Take the figure for £700 for 27 days at 3%
                =£1·553

Shift the decimal point one place to the right
                =£15 53p

the required answer.

	1Day	2	3	4	5	6	7	8	9	10	11	12
1	·000	·000	·000	·000	·000	·000	·000	·000	·000	·000	·000	·000
2	·000	·000	·000	·000	·000	·000	·000	·000	·001	·001	·001	·001
3	·000	·000	·000	·000	·000	·001	·001	·001	·001	·001	·001	·001
4	·000	·000	·000	·000	·001	·001	·001	·001	·001	·001	·001	·001
5	·000	·000	·000	·001	·001	·001	·001	·001	·001	·001	·002	·002
6	·000	·000	·001	·001	·001	·001	·001	·001	·002	·002	·002	·002
7	·000	·001	·001	·001	·001	·001	·001	·002	·002	·002	·002	·002
8	·000	·001	·001	·001	·001	·001	·002	·002	·002	·002	·002	·003
9	·000	·001	·001	·001	·001	·001	·002	·002	·002	·002	·003	·003
10	·000	·001	·001	·001	·001	·002	·002	·002	·002	·003	·003	·003
20	·001	·001	·002	·002	·003	·003	·004	·004	·005	·006	·006	·007
30	·001	·002	·003	·003	·004	·005	·006	·007	·007	·008	·009	·010
40	·001	·002	·003	·004	·005	·007	·008	·009	·010	·011	·012	·013
50	·001	·003	·004	·005	·007	·008	·010	·011	·012	·014	·015	·016
60	·002	·003	·005	·007	·008	·010	·012	·013	·015	·016	·018	·020
70	·002	·004	·006	·008	·010	·012	·013	·015	·017	·019	·021	·023
80	·002	·004	·007	·009	·011	·013	·015	·018	·020	·022	·024	·026
90	·002	·005	·007	·010	·012	·015	·017	·020	·022	·025	·027	·030
100	·003	·005	·008	·011	·014	·016	·019	·022	·025	·027	·030	·033
200	·005	·011	·016	·022	·027	·033	·038	·044	·049	·055	·060	·066
300	·008	·016	·025	·033	·041	·049	·058	·066	·074	·082	·090	·099
400	·011	·022	·033	·044	·055	·066	·077	·088	·099	·110	·121	·132
500	·014	·027	·041	·055	·068	·082	·096	·110	·123	·137	·151	·164
600	·016	·033	·049	·066	·082	·099	·115	·132	·148	·164	·181	·197
700	·019	·038	·058	·077	·096	·115	·134	·153	·173	·192	·211	·230
800	·022	·044	·066	·088	·110	·132	·153	·175	·197	·219	·241	·263
900	·025	·049	·074	·099	·123	·148	·173	·197	·222	·247	·271	·296
1000	·027	·055	·082	·110	·137	·164	·192	·219	·247	·274	·301	·329

	13	14	15	16	17	18	19	20	21	22	23	24
1	·000	·000	·000	·000	·001	·001	·001	·001	·001	·001	·001	·001
2	·001	·001	·001	·001	·001	·001	·001	·001	·001	·001	·001	·001
3	·001	·001	·001	·001	·001	·002	·002	·002	·002	·002	·002	·002
4	·001	·002	·002	·002	·002	·002	·002	·002	·002	·002	·003	·003
5	·002	·002	·002	·002	·002	·003	·003	·003	·003	·003	·003	·003
6	·002	·002	·003	·003	·003	·003	·003	·003	·004	·004	·004	·004
7	·003	·003	·003	·003	·003	·004	·004	·004	·004	·004	·004	·005
8	·003	·003	·003	·004	·004	·004	·004	·004	·005	·005	·005	·005
9	·003	·003	·004	·004	·004	·004	·005	·005	·005	·005	·006	·006
10	·004	·004	·004	·004	·005	·005	·005	·006	·006	·006	·006	·007
20	·007	·008	·008	·009	·009	·010	·010	·011	·012	·012	·013	·013
30	·011	·012	·012	·013	·014	·015	·016	·017	·017	·018	·019	·020
40	·014	·015	·016	·018	·019	·020	·021	·022	·023	·024	·025	·026
50	·018	·019	·021	·022	·023	·025	·026	·027	·029	·030	·032	·033
60	·021	·023	·025	·026	·028	·030	·031	·033	·035	·036	·038	·039
70	·025	·027	·029	·031	·033	·035	·036	·038	·040	·042	·044	·046
80	·029	·031	·033	·035	·037	·040	·042	·044	·046	·048	·050	·053
90	·032	·035	·037	·040	·042	·044	·047	·049	·052	·054	·057	·059
100	·036	·038	·041	·044	·047	·049	·052	·055	·058	·060	·063	·066
200	·071	·077	·082	·088	·093	·099	·104	·110	·115	·121	·126	·132
300	·107	·115	·123	·132	·140	·148	·156	·164	·173	·181	·189	·197
400	·143	·153	·164	·175	·186	·197	·208	·219	·230	·241	·252	·263
500	·178	·192	·206	·219	·233	·247	·260	·274	·288	·301	·315	·329
600	·214	·230	·247	·263	·280	·296	·312	·329	·345	·362	·378	·395
700	·249	·269	·288	·307	·326	·345	·364	·384	·403	·422	·441	·460
800	·285	·307	·329	·351	·373	·395	·416	·438	·460	·482	·504	·526
900	·321	·345	·370	·395	·419	·444	·469	·493	·518	·543	·567	·592
1000	·356	·384	·411	·438	·466	·493	·521	·548	·575	·603	·630	·658

25 Days	26	27	28	29	30	40	50	60	100	200	300
·001	·001	·001	·001	·001	·001	0·001	0·001	0·002	0·003	0·006	0·008
·001	·001	·002	·002	·002	·002	0·002	0·003	0·003	0·006	0·011	0·016
·002	·002	·002	·002	·002	·003	0·003	0·004	0·005	0·008	0·016	0·025
·003	·003	·003	·003	·003	·003	0·004	0·005	0·007	0·011	0·022	0·033
·003	·004	·004	·004	·004	·004	0·006	0·007	0·008	0·014	0·027	0·041
·004	·004	·004	·005	·005	·005	0·007	0·008	0·010	0·016	0·033	0·049
·005	·005	·005	·005	·006	·006	0·008	0·010	0·012	0·019	0·038	0·058
·006	·006	·006	·006	·006	·007	0·009	0·011	0·013	0·022	0·044	0·066
·006	·006	·007	·007	·007	·007	0·010	0·012	0·015	0·025	0·049	0·074
10 ·007	·007	·007	·008	·008	·008	0·011	0·014	0·016	0·027	0·055	0·082
20 ·014	·014	·015	·015	·016	·016	0·022	0·027	0·033	0·055	0·110	0·164
30 ·021	·021	·022	·024	·024	·023	0·033	0·041	0·049	0·082	0·164	0·247
40 ·027	·029	·030	·031	·032	·033	0·044	0·055	0·066	0·110	0·219	0·329
50 ·034	·036	·037	·038	·040	·041	0·055	0·069	0·082	0·137	0·274	0·411
60 ·041	·043	·044	·046	·048	·049	0·066	0·082	0·099	0·164	0·329	0·493
70 ·048	·050	·052	·054	·056	·058	0·077	0·096	0·115	0·192	0·384	0·575
80 ·055	·057	·059	·061	·064	·066	0·088	0·110	0·132	0·219	0·438	0·658
90 ·062	·064	·067	·069	·072	·074	0·099	0·123	0·148	0·247	0·493	0·740
100 ·069	·071	·074	·077	·080	·082	0·110	0·137	0·164	0·274	0·548	0·822
200 ·137	·143	·148	·153	·159	·164	0·219	0·274	0·329	0·548	1·096	1·644
300 ·206	·214	·222	·230	·238	·247	0·329	0·411	0·493	0·822	1·644	2·466
400 ·274	·285	·296	·307	·318	·329	0·438	0·548	0·658	1·096	2·192	3·288
500 ·343	·356	·370	·384	·397	·411	0·548	0·685	0·822	1·370	2·740	4·110
600 ·411	·427	·444	·460	·477	·493	0·658	0·822	0·986	1·644	3·288	4·932
700 ·480	·499	·518	·537	·556	·575	0·767	0·959	1·151	1·918	3·836	5·753
800 ·548	·570	·592	·614	·636	·658	0·877	1·096	1·315	2·192	4·384	6·575
900 ·616	·641	·666	·690	·715	·740	0·986	1·233	1·479	2·466	4·932	7·397
1000 ·685	·712	·740	·767	·795	·822	1·096	1·370	1·644	2·740	5·480	8·219

1 Mth	2	3	4	5	6	7	8	9	10	11	12
1 ·001	0·002	0·003	0·003	0·004	0·005	0·006	0·007	0·008	0·008	0·009	0·01
2 ·002	0·003	0·005	0·007	0·008	0·010	0·012	0·013	0·015	0·017	0·018	0·02
3 ·003	0·005	0·008	0·010	0·013	0·015	0·018	0·020	0·023	0·025	0·028	0·03
4 ·003	0·007	0·010	0·013	0·017	0·020	0·023	0·027	0·030	0·033	0·037	0·04
5 ·004	0·008	0·013	0·017	0·021	0·025	0·029	0·033	0·038	0·042	0·046	0·05
6 ·005	0·010	0·015	0·020	0·025	0·030	0·035	0·040	0·045	0·050	0·055	0·06
7 ·006	0·012	0·018	0·023	0·029	0·035	0·041	0·047	0·053	0·058	0·064	0·07
8 ·007	0·013	0·020	0·027	0·033	0·040	0·047	0·053	0·060	0·067	0·073	0·08
9 ·008	0·015	0·023	0·030	0·038	0·045	0·053	0·060	0·068	0·075	0·083	0·09
10 ·008	0·017	0·025	0·033	0·042	0·050	0·058	0·067	0·075	0·083	0·092	0·10
20 ·017	0·033	0·050	0·067	0·083	0·100	0·117	0·133	0·150	0·167	0·183	0·20
30 ·025	0·050	0·075	0·100	0·125	0·150	0·175	0·200	0·225	0·250	0·275	0·30
40 ·033	0·067	0·100	0·133	0·167	0·200	0·233	0·267	0·300	0·333	0·367	0·40
50 ·042	0·083	0·125	0·167	0·208	0·250	0·292	0·333	0·375	0·417	0·458	0·50
60 ·050	0·100	0·150	0·200	0·250	0·300	0·350	0·400	0·450	0·500	0·550	0·60
70 ·058	0·117	0·175	0·233	0·292	0·350	0·408	0·467	0·525	0·583	0·642	0·70
80 ·067	0·133	0·200	0·267	0·333	0·400	0·467	0·533	0·600	0·667	0·733	0·80
90 ·075	0·150	0·225	0·300	0·375	0·450	0·525	0·600	0·675	0·750	0·825	0·90
100 ·083	0·167	0·250	0·333	0·417	0·500	0·583	0·667	0·750	0·833	0·917	1·00
200 ·167	0·333	0·500	0·667	0·833	1·000	1·167	1·333	1·500	1·667	1·833	2·00
300 ·250	0·500	0·750	1·000	1·250	1·500	1·750	2·000	2·250	2·500	2·750	3·00
400 ·333	0·667	1·000	1·333	1·667	2·000	2·333	2·667	3·000	3·333	3·667	4·00
500 ·417	0·833	1·250	1·667	2·083	2·500	2·917	3·333	3·750	4·167	4·583	5·00
600 ·500	1·000	1·500	2·000	2·500	3·000	3·500	4·000	4·500	5·000	5·500	6·00
700 ·583	1·167	1·750	2·333	2·917	3·500	4·083	4·667	5·250	5·833	6·417	7·00
800 ·667	1·333	2·000	2·667	3·333	4·000	4·667	5·333	6·000	6·667	7·333	8·00
900 ·750	1·500	2·250	3·000	3·750	4·500	5·250	6·000	6·750	7·500	8·250	9·00
1000 ·833	1·667	2·500	3·333	4·167	5·000	5·833	6·667	7·500	8·333	9·167	10·00

	1Day	2	3	4	5	6	7	8	9	10	11	12
1	·000	·000	·000	·000	·000	·000	·000	·000	·001	·001	·001	·001
2	·000	·000	·000	·000	·001	·001	·001	·001	·001	·001	·001	·001
3	·000	·000	·001	·001	·001	·001	·001	·001	·002	·002	·002	·002
4	·000	·000	·001	·001	·001	·001	·002	·002	·002	·002	·002	·003
5	·000	·001	·001	·001	·001	·002	·002	·002	·003	·003	·003	·003
6	·000	·001	·001	·001	·002	·002	·002	·003	·003	·003	·004	·004
7	·000	·001	·001	·002	·002	·002	·003	·003	·004	·004	·004	·005
8	·000	·001	·001	·002	·002	·003	·003	·004	·004	·004	·005	·005
9	·001	·001	·001	·002	·002	·003	·003	·004	·004	·005	·005	·006
10	·001	·001	·002	·002	·003	·003	·004	·004	·005	·006	·006	·007
20	·001	·002	·003	·004	·006	·007	·008	·009	·010	·011	·012	·013
30	·002	·003	·005	·007	·008	·010	·012	·013	·015	·017	·018	·020
40	·002	·004	·007	·009	·011	·013	·015	·018	·020	·022	·024	·026
50	·003	·005	·008	·011	·014	·016	·019	·022	·025	·027	·030	·033
60	·003	·007	·010	·013	·016	·020	·023	·026	·030	·033	·036	·039
70	·004	·008	·012	·015	·019	·023	·027	·031	·035	·038	·042	·046
80	·004	·009	·013	·018	·022	·026	·031	·035	·040	·044	·048	·053
90	·005	·010	·015	·020	·025	·030	·035	·040	·044	·049	·054	·059
100	·005	·011	·016	·022	·027	·033	·038	·044	·049	·055	·060	·066
200	·011	·022	·033	·044	·055	·066	·077	·088	·099	·110	·121	·132
300	·016	·033	·049	·066	·082	·099	·115	·132	·148	·164	·181	·197
400	·022	·044	·066	·088	·110	·132	·153	·175	·197	·219	·241	·263
500	·027	·055	·082	·110	·137	·164	·192	·219	·247	·274	·301	·329
600	·033	·066	·099	·132	·164	·197	·230	·263	·296	·329	·362	·395
700	·038	·077	·115	·153	·192	·230	·269	·307	·345	·384	·422	·460
800	·044	·088	·132	·175	·219	·263	·307	·351	·395	·438	·482	·526
900	·049	·099	·148	·197	·247	·296	·345	·395	·444	·493	·543	·592
1000	·055	·110	·164	·219	·274	·329	·384	·438	·493	·548	·603	·658

	13	14	15	16	17	18	19	20	21	22	23	24
1	·001	·001	·001	·001	·001	·001	0·001	0·001	0·001	0·001	0·001	0·001
2	·001	·002	·002	·002	·002	·002	0·002	0·002	0·002	0·002	0·003	0·003
3	·002	·002	·003	·003	·003	·003	0·003	0·003	0·003	0·004	0·004	0·004
4	·003	·003	·003	·004	·004	·004	0·004	0·004	0·005	0·005	0·005	0·005
5	·004	·004	·004	·004	·005	·005	0·005	0·006	0·006	0·006	0·006	0·007
6	·004	·005	·005	·005	·006	·006	0·006	0·007	0·007	0·007	0·008	0·008
7	·005	·005	·006	·006	·007	·007	0·007	0·008	0·008	0·008	0·009	0·009
8	·006	·006	·007	·007	·007	·008	0·008	0·009	0·009	0·010	0·010	0·011
9	·006	·007	·007	·008	·008	·009	0·009	0·010	0·010	0·011	0·011	0·012
10	·007	·008	·008	·009	·009	·010	0·010	0·011	0·012	0·012	0·013	0·013
20	·014	·015	·016	·018	·019	·020	0·021	0·022	0·023	0·024	0·025	0·026
30	·021	·024	·023	·026	·028	·030	0·031	0·033	0·035	0·036	0·038	0·039
40	·029	·031	·033	·035	·037	·040	0·042	0·044	0·046	0·048	0·050	0·053
50	·036	·038	·041	·044	·047	·049	0·052	0·055	0·058	0·060	0·063	0·066
60	·043	·046	·049	·053	·056	·059	0·062	0·066	0·069	0·072	0·076	0·079
70	·050	·054	·058	·061	·065	·069	0·073	0·077	0·081	0·084	0·088	0·092
80	·057	·061	·066	·070	·075	·079	0·083	0·088	0·092	0·096	0·101	0·105
90	·064	·069	·074	·079	·084	·089	0·094	0·099	0·104	0·109	0·113	0·118
100	·071	·077	·082	·088	·093	·099	0·104	0·110	0·115	0·121	0·126	0·132
200	·143	·153	·164	·175	·186	·197	0·208	0·219	0·230	0·241	0·252	0·263
300	·214	·230	·247	·263	·279	·296	0·312	0·329	0·345	0·362	0·378	0·395
400	·285	·307	·329	·351	·373	·395	0·416	0·438	0·460	0·482	0·504	0·526
500	·356	·384	·411	·438	·466	·493	0·521	0·548	0·575	0·603	0·630	0·658
600	·427	·460	·493	·526	·559	·592	0·625	0·658	0·690	0·723	0·756	0·789
700	·499	·537	·575	·614	·652	·690	0·729	0·767	0·806	0·844	0·882	0·921
800	·570	·614	·658	·701	·745	·789	0·833	0·877	0·921	0·964	1·008	1·052
900	·641	·690	·740	·789	·838	·888	0·937	0·986	1·036	1·084	1·134	1·184
1000	·712	·767	·822	·877	·932	·986	1·041	1·096	1·151	1·206	1·260	1·315

25 Days	26	27	28	29	30	40	50	60	100	200	300
1	0·001	0·001	0·002	0·002	0·002	0·002	0·002	0·003	0·003	0·006	0·011	0·016
2	0·003	0·003	0·003	0·003	0·003	0·003	0·004	0·006	0·007	0·011	0·022	0·033
3	0·004	0·004	0·004	0·005	0·005	0·005	0·007	0·008	0·010	0·016	0·033	0·049
4	0·005	0·006	0·006	0·006	0·006	0·007	0·009	0·011	0·013	0·022	0·044	0·066
5	0·007	0·007	0·007	0·008	0·008	0·008	0·011	0·014	0·016	0·027	0·055	0·082
6	0·008	0·009	0·009	0·009	0·010	0·010	0·013	0·016	0·020	0·033	0·066	0·099
7	0·010	0·010	0·010	0·011	0·011	0·012	0·015	0·019	0·023	0·038	0·077	0·115
8	0·011	0·011	0·012	0·012	0·013	0·013	0·018	0·022	0·026	0·044	0·088	0·132
9	0·012	0·013	0·013	0·014	0·014	0·015	0·020	0·025	0·030	0·049	0·099	0·148
10	0·014	0·014	0·015	0·015	0·016	0·016	0·022	0·027	0·033	0·055	0·110	0·164
20	0·027	0·028	0·030	0·031	0·032	0·033	0·044	0·055	0·066	0·110	0·219	0·329
30	0·041	0·043	0·044	0·046	0·048	0·049	0·066	0·082	0·099	0·164	0·329	0·493
40	0·055	0·057	0·059	0·061	0·064	0·066	0·088	0·110	0·132	0·219	0·438	0·658
50	0·069	0·071	0·074	0·077	0·079	0·082	0·110	0·137	0·164	0·274	0·548	0·822
60	0·082	0·086	0·089	0·092	0·095	0·099	0·132	0·164	0·197	0·329	0·658	0·986
70	0·096	0·100	0·104	0·107	0·111	0·115	0·153	0·192	0·230	0·384	0·767	1·151
80	0·110	0·114	0·118	0·123	0·127	0·132	0·175	0·219	0·263	0·438	0·877	1·315
90	0·123	0·128	0·133	0·138	0·143	0·148	0·197	0·247	0·296	0·493	0·986	1·479
100	0·137	0·143	0·148	0·153	0·159	0·164	0·219	0·274	0·329	0·548	1·096	1·644
200	0·274	0·285	0·296	0·307	0·318	0·329	0·438	0·548	0·658	1·096	2·192	3·288
300	0·411	0·427	0·444	0·460	0·477	0·493	0·658	0·822	0·986	1·644	3·288	4·932
400	0·548	0·570	0·592	0·614	0·636	0·658	0·877	1·096	1·315	2·192	4·384	6·575
500	0·685	0·712	0·740	0·767	0·795	0·822	1·096	1·370	1·644	2·740	5·479	8·219
600	0·822	0·855	0·888	0·921	0·954	0·986	1·315	1·644	1·973	3·288	6·575	9·863
700	0·959	0·997	1·036	1·074	1·112	1·151	1·534	1·918	2·301	3·836	7·671	11·507
800	1·096	1·140	1·184	1·227	1·271	1·315	1·753	2·192	2·630	4·384	8·767	13·151
900	1·233	1·282	1·332	1·381	1·430	1·479	1·973	2·466	2·959	4·932	9·863	14·795
1000	1·370	1·425	1·480	1·534	1·589	1·644	2·192	2·740	3·288	5·480	10·959	16·438

1 Mth	2	3	4	5	6	7	8	9	10	11	12
1	0·002	0·003	0·005	0·007	0·008	0·01	0·012	0·013	0·015	0·017	0·018	0·02
2	0·003	0·007	0·010	0·013	0·017	0·02	0·023	0·027	0·030	0·033	0·037	0·04
3	0·005	0·010	0·015	0·020	0·025	0·03	0·035	0·040	0·045	0·050	0·055	0·06
4	0·007	0·013	0·020	0·027	0·033	0·04	0·047	0·053	0·060	0·067	0·073	0·08
5	0·008	0·017	0·025	0·033	0·042	0·05	0·058	0·067	0·075	0·083	0·092	0·10
6	0·010	0·020	0·030	0·040	0·050	0·06	0·070	0·080	0·090	0·100	0·110	0·12
7	0·012	0·023	0·035	0·047	0·058	0·07	0·082	0·093	0·105	0·117	0·128	0·14
8	0·013	0·027	0·040	0·053	0·067	0·08	0·093	0·107	0·120	0·133	0·147	0·16
9	0·015	0·030	0·045	0·060	0·075	0·09	0·105	0·120	0·135	0·150	0·165	0·18
10	0·017	0·033	0·050	0·067	0·083	0·10	0·117	0·133	0·150	0·167	0·183	0·20
20	0·033	0·067	0·100	0·133	0·167	0·20	0·233	0·267	0·300	0·333	0·367	0·40
30	0·050	0·100	0·150	0·200	0·250	0·30	0·350	0·400	0·450	0·500	0·550	0·60
40	0·067	0·133	0·200	0·267	0·333	0·40	0·467	0·533	0·600	0·667	0·733	0·80
50	0·083	0·167	0·250	0·333	0·417	0·50	0·583	0·667	0·750	0·833	0·917	1·00
60	0·100	0·200	0·300	0·400	0·500	0·60	0·700	0·800	0·900	1·000	1·100	1·20
70	0·117	0·233	0·350	0·467	0·583	0·70	0·817	0·933	1·050	1·167	1·283	1·40
80	0·133	0·267	0·400	0·533	0·667	0·80	0·933	1·067	1·200	1·333	1·467	1·60
90	0·150	0·300	0·450	0·600	0·750	0·90	1·050	1·200	1·350	1·500	1·650	1·80
100	0·167	0·333	0·500	0·667	0·833	1·00	1·167	1·333	1·500	1·667	1·833	2·00
200	0·333	0·667	1·000	1·333	1·667	2·00	2·333	2·667	3·000	3·333	3·667	4·00
300	0·500	1·000	1·500	2·000	2·500	3·00	3·500	4·000	4·500	5·000	5·500	6·00
400	0·667	1·333	2·000	2·667	3·333	4·00	4·667	5·333	6·000	6·667	7·333	8·00
500	1·833	1·667	2·500	3·333	4·167	5·00	5·833	6·667	7·500	8·333	9·167	10·00
600	1·000	2·000	3·000	4·000	5·000	6·00	7·000	8·000	9·000	10·000	11·000	12·00
700	1·167	2·333	3·500	4·667	5·833	7·00	8·167	9·333	10·500	11·667	12·833	14·00
800	1·333	2·667	4·000	5·333	6·667	8·00	9·333	10·667	12·000	13·333	14·667	16·00
900	1·500	3·000	4·500	6·000	7·500	9·00	10·500	12·000	13·500	15·000	16·500	18·00
1000	1·667	3·333	5·000	6·667	8·333	10·00	11·667	13·333	15·000	16·667	18·333	20·00

	1Day	2	3	4	5	6	7	8	9	10	11	12
1	·000	·000	·000	·000	·000	·000	·000	·001	·001	·001	·001	·001
2	·000	·000	·000	·001	·001	·001	·001	·001	·001	·001	·002	·002
3	·000	·000	·001	·001	·001	·001	·001	·002	·002	·002	·002	·003
4	·000	·001	·001	·001	·001	·002	·002	·002	·003	·003	·003	·003
5	·000	·001	·001	·001	·002	·002	·002	·003	·003	·003	·004	·004
6	·000	·001	·001	·002	·002	·003	·003	·003	·004	·004	·005	·005
7	·001	·001	·001	·002	·002	·003	·003	·004	·004	·005	·005	·006
8	·001	·001	·002	·002	·003	·003	·004	·004	·005	·006	·006	·007
9	·001	·001	·002	·002	·003	·004	·004	·005	·006	·006	·007	·007
10	·001	·001	·002	·003	·003	·004	·005	·006	·006	·007	·008	·008
20	·001	·003	·004	·006	·007	·008	·010	·011	·012	·014	·015	·016
30	·002	·004	·006	·008	·010	·012	·014	·017	·019	·021	·023	·025
40	·003	·005	·008	·011	·014	·016	·019	·022	·025	·027	·030	·033
50	·003	·007	·010	·014	·017	·021	·024	·027	·031	·034	·038	·041
60	·004	·008	·012	·016	·021	·025	·029	·033	·037	·041	·045	·049
70	·005	·010	·014	·019	·024	·029	·034	·038	·043	·048	·053	·058
80	·006	·011	·016	·022	·027	·033	·038	·044	·049	·055	·060	·066
90	·006	·012	·019	·025	·031	·037	·043	·049	·056	·062	·068	·074
100	·007	·014	·021	·027	·034	·041	·048	·055	·062	·069	·075	·082
200	·014	·027	·041	·055	·069	·082	·096	·110	·123	·137	·151	·164
300	·021	·041	·062	·082	·103	·123	·144	·164	·185	·206	·226	·247
400	·027	·055	·082	·110	·137	·164	·192	·219	·247	·274	·301	·329
500	·034	·068	·103	·137	·171	·206	·240	·274	·308	·343	·377	·411
600	·041	·082	·123	·164	·206	·247	·288	·329	·370	·411	·452	·493
700	·048	·096	·144	·192	·240	·288	·336	·384	·432	·480	·527	·575
800	·055	·110	·164	·219	·274	·329	·384	·438	·493	·548	·603	·658
900	·062	·123	·185	·247	·308	·370	·432	·493	·555	·616	·678	·740
1000	·069	·137	·206	·274	·342	·411	·479	·548	·616	·685	·753	·822

	13	14	15	16	17	18	19	20	21	22	23	24
1	·001	·001	0·001	0·001	0·001	0·001	0·001	0·001	0·001	0·002	0·002	0·002
2	·002	·002	0·002	0·002	0·002	0·003	0·003	0·003	0·003	0·003	0·003	0·003
3	·003	·003	0·003	0·003	0·004	0·004	0·004	0·004	0·004	0·005	0·005	0·005
4	·004	·004	0·004	0·004	0·005	0·005	0·005	0·005	0·006	0·006	0·006	0·007
5	·004	·005	0·005	0·006	0·006	0·006	0·007	0·007	0·007	0·008	0·008	0·008
6	·005	·006	0·006	0·007	0·007	0·007	0·008	0·008	0·009	0·009	0·009	0·010
7	·006	·007	0·007	0·008	0·008	0·009	0·009	0·010	0·010	0·011	0·011	0·012
8	·007	·008	0·008	0·009	0·009	0·010	0·010	0·011	0·012	0·012	0·013	0·013
9	·008	·009	0·009	0·010	0·011	0·011	0·012	0·012	0·013	0·014	0·014	0·015
10	·009	·010	0·010	0·011	0·012	0·012	0·013	0·014	0·014	0·015	0·016	0·016
20	·018	·019	0·021	0·022	0·023	0·025	0·026	0·027	0·029	0·030	0·032	0·033
30	·027	·029	0·031	0·033	0·035	0·037	0·039	0·041	0·043	0·045	0·047	0·049
40	·036	·038	0·041	0·044	0·047	0·049	0·052	0·055	0·058	0·060	0·063	0·066
50	·045	·048	0·051	0·055	0·058	0·062	0·065	0·069	0·072	0·075	0·079	0·082
60	·053	·058	0·062	0·066	0·070	0·074	0·078	0·082	0·086	0·090	0·095	0·099
70	·062	·067	0·072	0·077	0·082	0·086	0·091	0·096	0·101	0·106	0·110	0·115
80	·071	·077	0·082	0·088	0·093	0·099	0·104	0·110	0·115	0·121	0·126	0·132
90	·080	·086	0·092	0·099	0·105	0·111	0·117	0·123	0·129	0·136	0·142	0·148
100	·089	·096	0·103	0·110	0·116	0·123	0·130	0·137	0·144	0·151	0·158	0·164
200	·178	·192	0·206	0·219	0·233	0·247	0·260	0·274	0·288	0·301	0·315	0·329
300	·267	·288	0·308	0·329	0·349	0·370	0·390	0·411	0·432	0·452	0·473	0·493
400	·356	·384	0·411	0·438	0·466	0·493	0·521	0·548	0·575	0·603	0·630	0·658
500	·445	·479	0·514	0·548	0·582	0·616	0·651	0·685	0·719	0·753	0·788	0·822
600	·534	·575	0·616	0·658	0·699	0·740	0·781	0·822	0·863	0·904	0·945	0·986
700	·623	·671	0·719	0·767	0·815	0·863	0·911	0·959	1·007	1·055	1·103	1·151
800	·712	·767	0·822	0·877	0·932	0·986	1·041	1·096	1·151	1·206	1·260	1·315
900	·801	·863	0·925	0·986	1·048	1·110	1·171	1·233	1·295	1·356	1·418	1·479
1000	·890	·959	1·027	1·096	1·164	1·233	1·301	1·370	1·438	1·507	1·575	1·644

	25 Days	26	27	28	29	30	40	50	60	100	200	300
1	0·002	0·002	0·002	0·002	0·002	0·002	0·003	0·003	0·004	0·007	0·014	0·020
2	0·003	0·004	0·004	0·004	0·004	0·004	0·006	0·007	0·008	0·014	0·027	0·041
3	0·005	0·005	0·006	0·006	0·006	0·006	0·008	0·010	0·012	0·021	0·041	0·062
4	0·007	0·007	0·007	0·008	0·008	0·008	0·011	0·014	0·016	0·027	0·055	0·082
5	0·009	0·009	0·009	0·010	0·010	0·010	0·014	0·017	0·021	0·034	0·069	0·103
6	0·010	0·011	0·011	0·012	0·012	0·012	0·016	0·021	0·025	0·041	0·082	0·123
7	0·012	0·012	0·013	0·013	0·014	0·014	0·019	0·024	0·029	0·048	0·096	0·144
8	0·014	0·014	0·015	0·015	0·016	0·016	0·022	0·027	0·033	0·055	0·110	0·164
9	0·015	0·016	0·017	0·017	0·018	0·019	0·025	0·031	0·037	0·062	0·123	0·185
10	0·017	0·018	0·019	0·019	0·020	0·021	0·027	0·034	0·041	0·069	0·137	0·206
20	0·034	0·036	0·037	0·038	0·040	0·041	0·055	0·069	0·082	0·137	0·274	0·411
30	0·051	0·053	0·056	0·058	0·060	0·060	0·082	0·103	0·123	0·206	0·411	0·616
40	0·069	0·071	0·074	0·077	0·079	0·082	0·110	0·137	0·164	0·274	0·548	0·822
50	0·086	0·089	0·092	0·096	0·099	0·103	0·137	0·171	0·206	0·342	0·685	1·027
60	0·103	0·107	0·111	0·115	0·119	0·123	0·164	0·206	0·247	0·411	0·822	1·233
70	0·120	0·125	0·129	0·134	0·139	0·144	0·192	0·240	0·288	0·479	0·959	1·438
80	0·137	0·142	0·148	0·153	0·159	0·164	0·219	0·274	0·329	0·548	1·096	1·644
90	0·154	0·160	0·166	0·172	0·179	0·185	0·247	0·308	0·370	0·616	1·233	1·849
100	0·171	0·178	0·185	0·192	0·199	0·206	0·274	0·342	0·411	0·685	1·370	2·055
200	0·342	0·356	0·370	0·384	0·397	0·411	0·548	0·685	0·822	1·370	2·740	4·110
300	0·514	0·534	0·555	0·575	0·596	0·616	0·822	1·027	1·233	2·055	4·110	6·164
400	0·685	0·712	0·740	0·767	0·795	0·822	1·096	1·370	1·644	2·740	5·479	8·219
500	0·856	0·890	0·925	0·959	0·993	1·027	1·370	1·712	2·055	3·425	6·849	10·274
600	1·027	1·069	1·110	1·151	1·192	1·233	1·644	2·055	2·466	4·110	8·219	12·329
700	1·199	1·247	1·295	1·342	1·390	1·438	1·918	2·397	2·877	4·795	9·589	14·384
800	1·370	1·425	1·480	1·534	1·589	1·644	2·192	2·740	3·288	5·479	10·959	16·438
900	1·541	1·603	1·664	1·726	1·788	1·849	2·466	3·082	3·699	6·164	12·329	18·493
1000	1·712	1·781	1·849	1·918	1·986	2·055	2·740	3·425	4·110	6·849	13·699	20·548

	1 Mth	2	3	4	5	6	7	8	9	10	11	12
1	0·002	0·004	0·006	0·008	0·010	0·013	0·015	0·017	0·019	0·021	0·023	0·025
2	0·004	0·008	0·013	0·017	0·021	0·025	0·029	0·033	0·038	0·042	0·046	0·050
3	0·006	0·013	0·019	0·025	0·031	0·038	0·044	0·050	0·056	0·063	0·069	0·075
4	0·008	0·017	0·025	0·033	0·042	0·050	0·058	0·067	0·075	0·083	0·092	0·100
5	0·010	0·021	0·031	0·042	0·052	0·063	0·073	0·083	0·094	0·104	0·115	0·125
6	0·013	0·025	0·038	0·050	0·063	0·075	0·088	0·100	0·113	0·125	0·138	0·150
7	0·015	0·029	0·044	0·058	0·073	0·088	0·102	0·117	0·131	0·146	0·160	0·175
8	0·017	0·033	0·050	0·067	0·083	0·100	0·117	0·133	0·150	0·167	0·183	0·200
9	0·019	0·038	0·056	0·075	0·094	0·113	0·131	0·150	0·169	0·188	0·206	0·225
10	0·021	0·042	0·063	0·083	0·104	0·125	0·146	0·167	0·188	0·208	0·229	0·250
20	0·042	0·083	0·125	0·167	0·208	0·250	0·292	0·333	0·375	0·417	0·458	0·500
30	0·063	0·125	0·188	0·250	0·313	0·375	0·438	0·500	0·563	0·625	0·688	0·750
40	0·083	0·167	0·250	0·333	0·417	0·500	0·583	0·667	0·750	0·833	0·917	1·000
50	0·104	0·208	0·313	0·417	0·521	0·625	0·729	0·833	0·938	1·042	1·146	1·250
60	0·125	0·250	0·375	0·500	0·625	0·750	0·875	1·000	1·125	1·250	1·375	1·500
70	0·146	0·292	0·438	0·583	0·729	0·875	1·021	1·167	1·313	1·458	1·604	1·750
80	0·167	0·333	0·500	0·667	0·833	1·000	1·167	1·333	1·500	1·666	1·833	2·000
90	0·188	0·375	0·563	0·750	0·938	1·125	1·313	1·500	1·688	1·875	2·063	2·250
100	0·208	0·417	0·625	0·833	1·042	1·250	1·458	1·667	1·875	2·083	2·292	2·500
200	0·417	0·833	1·250	1·667	2·083	2·500	2·916	3·333	3·750	4·167	4·583	5·000
300	0·625	1·250	1·875	2·500	3·125	3·750	4·375	5·000	5·625	6·250	6·875	7·500
400	0·833	1·667	2·500	3·333	4·167	5·000	5·833	6·667	7·500	8·333	9·167	10·000
500	1·042	2·083	3·125	4·167	5·208	6·250	7·292	8·333	9·375	10·417	11·458	12·500
600	1·250	2·500	3·750	5·000	6·250	7·500	8·750	10·000	11·250	12·500	13·750	15·000
700	1·458	2·917	4·375	5·833	7·292	8·750	10·208	11·667	13·125	14·583	16·042	17·500
800	1·667	3·333	5·000	6·667	8·333	10·000	11·667	13·333	15·000	16·667	18·333	20·000
900	1·875	3·750	5·625	7·500	9·375	11·250	13·125	15·000	16·875	18·750	20·625	22·500
1000	2·083	4·167	6·250	8·333	10·417	12·500	14·583	16·667	18·750	20·833	22·917	25·000

	1Day	2	3	4	5	6	7	8	9	10	11	12
1	·000	·000	·000	·000	·000	·001	·001	·001	·001	·001	·001	·001
2	·000	·000	·001	·001	·001	·001	·001	·001	·001	·002	·002	·002
3	·000	·001	·001	·001	·001	·002	·002	·002	·002	·002	·003	·003
4	·000	·001	·001	·001	·002	·002	·002	·003	·003	·003	·004	·004
5	·000	·001	·001	·002	·002	·003	·003	·003	·004	·004	·005	·005
6	·001	·001	·002	·002	·003	·003	·004	·004	·004	·005	·005	·006
7	·001	·001	·002	·002	·003	·004	·004	·005	·005	·006	·006	·007
8	·001	·001	·002	·003	·003	·004	·005	·005	·006	·007	·007	·008
9	·001	·001	·002	·003	·004	·004	·005	·006	·007	·007	·008	·009
10	·001	·002	·002	·003	·004	·005	·006	·007	·007	·008	·009	·010
20	·002	·003	·005	·007	·008	·010	·012	·013	·015	·016	·018	·020
30	·002	·005	·007	·010	·012	·015	·017	·020	·022	·025	·027	·030
40	·003	·007	·010	·013	·016	·020	·023	·026	·030	·033	·036	·040
50	·004	·008	·012	·016	·021	·025	·029	·033	·037	·041	·045	·049
60	·005	·010	·015	·020	·025	·030	·035	·040	·044	·049	·054	·059
70	·006	·012	·017	·023	·029	·035	·040	·046	·052	·058	·063	·069
80	·007	·013	·020	·026	·033	·040	·046	·053	·059	·066	·072	·079
90	·007	·015	·022	·030	·037	·044	·052	·059	·067	·074	·081	·089
100	·008	·016	·025	·033	·041	·049	·058	·066	·074	·082	·090	·099
200	·016	·033	·049	·066	·082	·099	·115	·132	·148	·164	·181	·197
300	·025	·049	·074	·099	·123	·148	·173	·197	·222	·247	·271	·296
400	·032	·066	·099	·132	·164	·197	·230	·263	·296	·329	·362	·395
500	·041	·082	·123	·164	·206	·247	·288	·329	·370	·411	·452	·493
600	·049	·099	·148	·197	·247	·296	·345	·395	·444	·493	·542	·592
700	·058	·115	·173	·230	·288	·345	·403	·460	·518	·575	·633	·690
800	·066	·132	·197	·263	·329	·395	·460	·526	·592	·658	·723	·789
900	·074	·148	·222	·296	·370	·444	·518	·592	·666	·740	·814	·888
1000	·082	·164	·247	·329	·411	·493	·575	·658	·740	·822	·904	·986

	13	14	15	16	17	18	19	20	21	22	23	24
1	0·001	0·001	0·001	0·001	0·001	0·002	0·002	0·002	0·002	0·002	0·002	0·002
2	0·002	0·002	0·003	0·003	0·003	0·003	0·003	0·003	0·004	0·004	0·004	0·004
3	0·003	0·003	0·004	0·004	0·004	0·004	0·005	0·005	0·005	0·005	0·006	0·006
4	0·004	0·005	0·005	0·005	0·006	0·006	0·006	0·007	0·007	0·007	0·008	0·008
5	0·005	0·006	0·006	0·007	0·007	0·007	0·008	0·008	0·009	0·009	0·009	0·010
6	0·006	0·007	0·007	0·008	0·008	0·009	0·009	0·010	0·010	0·011	0·011	0·012
7	0·008	0·008	0·009	0·009	0·010	0·010	0·011	0·012	0·012	0·013	0·013	0·014
8	0·009	0·009	0·010	0·011	0·011	0·012	0·013	0·013	0·014	0·014	0·015	0·016
9	0·010	0·010	0·011	0·012	0·013	0·013	0·014	0·015	0·016	0·016	0·017	0·018
10	0·011	0·012	0·012	0·013	0·014	0·015	0·016	0·016	0·017	0·018	0·019	0·020
20	0·021	0·023	0·025	0·026	0·028	0·030	0·031	0·033	0·035	0·036	0·038	0·040
30	0·032	0·035	0·037	0·039	0·042	0·044	0·047	0·049	0·052	0·054	0·057	0·059
40	0·043	0·046	0·049	0·053	0·056	0·059	0·062	0·066	0·069	0·072	0·076	0·079
50	0·053	0·058	0·062	0·066	0·070	0·074	0·078	0·082	0·086	0·090	0·095	0·099
60	0·064	0·069	0·074	0·079	0·084	0·089	0·094	0·099	0·104	0·109	0·113	0·118
70	0·075	0·081	0·086	0·092	0·098	0·104	0·109	0·115	0·121	0·127	0·132	0·138
80	0·086	0·092	0·099	0·105	0·112	0·118	0·125	0·132	0·138	0·145	0·151	0·158
90	0·096	0·104	0·111	0·118	0·126	0·133	0·141	0·148	0·155	0·163	0·170	0·178
100	0·107	0·115	0·123	0·132	0·140	0·148	0·156	0·164	0·173	0·181	0·189	0·197
200	0·214	0·230	0·247	0·263	0·279	0·296	0·312	0·329	0·345	0·362	0·378	0·395
300	0·321	0·345	0·370	0·395	0·419	0·444	0·469	0·493	0·518	0·542	0·567	0·592
400	0·427	0·460	0·493	0·526	0·559	0·592	0·625	0·658	0·690	0·723	0·756	0·789
500	0·534	0·575	0·616	0·658	0·699	0·740	0·781	0·822	0·863	0·904	0·945	0·986
600	0·641	0·690	0·740	0·789	0·838	0·888	0·937	0·986	1·036	1·085	1·134	1·184
700	0·748	0·806	0·863	0·921	0·978	1·036	1·093	1·151	1·208	1·266	1·323	1·381
800	0·855	0·921	0·986	1·052	1·118	1·184	1·249	1·315	1·381	1·447	1·512	1·578
900	0·962	1·036	1·110	1·184	1·258	1·332	1·406	1·479	1·553	1·627	1·701	1·775
1000	1·069	1·151	1·233	1·315	1·397	1·480	1·562	1·644	1·726	1·808	1·890	1·973

25 Days	26	27	28	29	30	40	50	60	100	200	300
1 0·002	0·002	0·002	0·002	0·002	0·003	0·003	0·004	0·005	0·008	0·016	0·025
2 0·004	0·004	0·004	0·005	0·005	0·005	0·007	0·008	0·010	0·016	0·033	0·049
3 0·006	0·006	0·007	0·007	0·007	0·007	0·010	0·012	0·015	0·025	0·049	0·074
4 0·008	0·009	0·009	0·009	0·010	0·010	0·013	0·016	0·020	0·033	0·066	0·099
5 0·010	0·011	0·011	0·012	0·012	0·012	0·016	0·021	0·025	0·041	0·082	0·123
6 0·012	0·013	0·013	0·014	0·014	0·015	0·020	0·025	0·030	0·049	0·099	0·148
7 0·014	0·015	0·016	0·016	0·017	0·017	0·023	0·029	0·035	0·058	0·115	0·173
8 0·016	0·017	0·018	0·018	0·019	0·020	0·026	0·033	0·040	0·066	0·132	0·197
9 0·019	0·019	0·020	0·021	0·022	0·022	0·030	0·037	0·044	0·074	0·148	0·222
10 0·021	0·021	0·022	0·023	0·024	0·025	0·033	0·041	0·049	0·082	0·164	0·247
20 0·041	0·043	0·044	0·046	0·048	0·049	0·066	0·082	0·099	0·164	0·329	0·493
30 0·062	0·064	0·067	0·069	0·072	0·074	0·099	0·123	0·148	0·247	0·493	0·740
40 0·082	0·086	0·089	0·092	0·095	0·099	0·132	0·164	0·197	0·329	0·658	0·986
50 0·103	0·107	0·111	0·115	0·119	0·123	0·164	0·206	0·247	0·411	0·822	1·233
60 0·123	0·128	0·133	0·138	0·143	0·148	0·197	0·247	0·296	0·493	0·986	1·479
70 0·144	0·150	0·155	0·161	0·167	0·173	0·230	0·288	0·345	0·575	1·151	1·726
80 0·164	0·171	0·178	0·184	0·191	0·197	0·263	0·329	0·395	0·658	1·315	1·973
90 0·185	0·192	0·200	0·207	0·215	0·222	0·296	0·370	0·444	0·740	1·479	2·219
100 0·206	0·214	0·222	0·230	0·238	0·247	0·329	0·411	0·493	0·822	1·644	2·466
200 0·411	0·427	0·444	0·460	0·477	0·493	0·658	0·822	0·986	1·644	3·288	4·932
300 0·616	0·641	0·666	0·690	0·715	0·740	0·986	1·233	1·480	2·466	4·932	7·397
400 0·822	0·855	0·888	0·921	0·953	0·986	1·315	1·644	1·973	3·288	6·575	9·863
500 1·027	1·069	1·110	1·151	1·192	1·233	1·644	2·055	2·466	4·110	8·219	12·329
600 1·233	1·282	1·332	1·381	1·430	1·480	1·973	2·466	2·959	4·932	9·863	14·795
700 1·438	1·496	1·553	1·611	1·669	1·726	2·301	2·877	3·452	5·753	11·507	17·261
800 1·644	1·710	1·775	1·841	1·907	1·973	2·630	3·288	3·945	6·575	13·151	19·726
900 1·849	1·923	1·997	2·071	2·145	2·219	2·959	3·699	4·438	7·397	14·795	22·192
1000 2·055	2·137	2·219	2·301	2·384	2·466	3·288	4·110	4·932	8·219	16·438	24·658

1Mth	2	3	4	5	6	7	8	9	10	11	12
1 0·003	0·005	0·008	0·01	0·013	0·015	0·018	0·02	0·023	0·025	0·028	0·03
2 0·005	0·010	0·015	0·02	0·025	0·030	0·035	0·04	0·045	0·050	0·055	0·06
3 0·008	0·015	0·023	0·03	0·038	0·045	0·053	0·06	0·068	0·075	0·083	0·09
4 0·010	0·020	0·030	0·04	0·050	0·060	0·070	0·08	0·090	0·100	0·110	0·12
5 0·013	0·025	0·038	0·05	0·063	0·075	0·088	0·10	0·113	0·150	0·138	0·15
6 0·015	0·030	0·045	0·06	0·075	0·090	0·105	0·12	0·135	0·150	0·165	0·18
7 0·018	0·035	0·053	0·07	0·088	0·105	0·123	0·14	0·158	0·175	0·193	0·21
8 0·020	0·040	0·060	0·08	0·100	0·120	0·140	0·16	0·180	0·200	0·220	0·24
9 0·023	0·045	0·068	0·09	0·113	0·135	0·158	0·18	0·203	0·225	0·248	0·27
10 0·025	0·050	0·075	0·10	0·125	0·150	0·175	0·20	0·225	0·250	0·275	0·30
20 0·050	0·100	0·150	0·20	0·250	0·300	0·350	0·40	0·450	0·500	0·550	0·60
30 0·075	0·150	0·225	0·30	0·375	0·450	0·525	0·60	0·675	0·750	0·825	0·90
40 0·100	0·200	0·300	0·40	0·500	0·600	0·700	0·80	0·900	1·000	1·100	1·20
50 0·125	0·250	0·375	0·50	0·625	0·750	0·875	1·00	1·125	1·250	1·375	1·50
60 0·150	0·300	0·450	0·60	0·750	0·900	1·050	1·20	1·350	1·500	1·650	1·80
70 0·175	0·350	0·525	0·70	0·875	1·050	1·225	1·40	1·575	1·750	1·925	2·10
80 0·200	0·400	0·600	0·80	1·000	1·200	1·400	1·60	1·800	2·000	2·200	2·40
90 0·225	0·450	0·675	0·90	1·125	1·350	1·575	1·80	2·025	2·250	2·475	2·70
100 0·250	0·500	0·750	1·00	1·250	1·500	1·750	2·00	2·250	2·500	2·750	3·00
200 0·500	1·000	1·500	2·00	2·500	3·000	3·500	4·00	4·500	5·000	5·500	6·00
300 0·750	1·500	2·250	3·00	3·750	4·500	5·250	6·00	6·750	7·500	8·250	9·00
400 1·000	2·000	3·000	4·00	5·000	6·000	7·000	8·00	9·000	10·000	11·000	12·00
500 1·250	2·500	3·750	5·00	6·250	7·500	8·750	10·00	11·250	12·500	13·750	15·00
600 1·500	3·000	4·500	6·00	7·500	9·000	10·500	12·00	13·500	15·000	16·500	18·00
700 1·750	3·500	5·250	7·00	8·750	10·500	12·250	14·00	15·750	17·500	19·250	21·00
800 2·000	4·000	6·000	8·00	10·000	12·000	14·000	16·00	18·000	20·000	22·000	24·00
900 2·250	4·500	6·750	9·00	11·250	13·500	15·750	18·00	20·250	22·500	24·750	27·00
1000 2·500	5·000	7·500	10·00	12·500	15·000	17·500	20·00	22·500	25·000	27·500	30·00

	1Day	2	3	4	5	6	7	8	9	10	11	12
1	·000	·000	·000	·000	·001	·001	·001	·001	·001	0·001	0·001	0·001
2	·000	·000	·001	·001	·001	·001	·002	·002	·002	0·002	0·002	0·003
3	·000	·001	·001	·001	·002	·002	·002	·003	·003	0·003	0·004	0·004
4	·000	·001	·001	·002	·002	·003	·003	·004	·004	0·004	0·005	0·005
5	·001	·001	·002	·002	·003	·003	·004	·004	·005	0·006	0·006	0·007
6	·001	·001	·002	·003	·003	·004	·005	·005	·006	0·007	0·007	0·008
7	·001	·002	·002	·003	·004	·005	·005	·006	·007	0·008	0·008	0·009
8	·001	·002	·003	·004	·004	·005	·006	·007	·008	0·009	0·010	0·011
9	·001	·002	·003	·004	·005	·006	·007	·008	·009	0·010	0·011	0·012
10	·001	·002	·003	·004	·006	·007	·008	·009	·010	0·011	0·012	0·013
20	·002	·004	·007	·009	·011	·013	·015	·018	·020	0·022	0·024	0·026
30	·003	·007	·010	·013	·017	·020	·023	·026	·030	0·033	0·036	0·039
40	·004	·009	·013	·018	·022	·026	·031	·035	·040	0·044	0·048	0·053
50	·005	·011	·016	·022	·027	·033	·038	·044	·049	0·055	0·060	0·066
60	·007	·013	·020	·026	·033	·039	·046	·053	·059	0·066	0·072	0·079
70	·008	·015	·023	·031	·038	·046	·054	·061	·069	0·077	0·084	0·092
80	·009	·018	·026	·035	·044	·053	·061	·070	·079	0·088	0·096	0·105
90	·010	·020	·030	·040	·049	·059	·069	·079	·089	0·099	0·109	0·118
100	·011	·022	·033	·044	·055	·066	·077	·088	·099	0·110	0·121	0·132
200	·022	·044	·066	·088	·110	·132	·153	·175	·197	0·219	0·241	0·263
300	·033	·066	·099	·132	·164	·197	·230	·263	·296	0·329	0·362	0·395
400	·044	·088	·132	·175	·219	·263	·307	·351	·395	0·438	0·482	0·526
500	·055	·110	·164	·219	·274	·329	·384	·438	·493	0·548	0·603	0·658
600	·066	·132	·197	·263	·329	·395	·460	·526	·592	0·658	0·723	0·789
700	·077	·153	·230	·307	·384	·460	·537	·614	·690	0·767	0·844	0·921
800	·088	·175	·263	·351	·438	·526	·614	·701	·789	0·877	0·964	1·052
900	·099	·197	·296	·395	·493	·592	·690	·789	·888	0·986	1·084	1·184
1000	·110	·219	·329	·438	·548	·658	·767	·877	·986	1·096	1·206	1·315

	13	14	15	16	17	18	19	20	21	22	23	24
1	0·001	0·002	0·002	0·002	0·002	0·002	0·002	0·002	0·002	0·002	0·003	0·003
2	0·003	0·003	0·003	0·004	0·004	0·004	0·004	0·004	0·005	0·005	0·005	0·005
3	0·004	0·005	0·005	0·005	0·006	0·006	0·006	0·007	0·007	0·007	0·008	0·008
4	0·006	0·006	0·007	0·007	0·007	0·008	0·008	0·009	0·009	0·010	0·010	0·011
5	0·007	0·008	0·008	0·009	0·009	0·010	0·010	0·011	0·012	0·012	0·013	0·013
6	0·009	0·009	0·010	0·011	0·011	0·012	0·013	0·013	0·014	0·014	0·015	0·016
7	0·010	0·011	0·012	0·012	0·013	0·014	0·015	0·015	0·016	0·017	0·018	0·018
8	0·011	0·012	0·013	0·014	0·015	0·016	0·017	0·018	0·018	0·019	0·020	0·021
9	0·013	0·014	0·015	0·016	0·017	0·018	0·019	0·020	0·021	0·022	0·023	0·024
10	0·014	0·015	0·016	0·018	0·019	0·020	0·021	0·022	0·023	0·024	0·025	0·026
20	0·028	0·031	0·033	0·035	0·037	0·040	0·042	0·044	0·046	0·048	0·050	0·053
30	0·043	0·046	0·049	0·053	0·056	0·059	0·063	0·066	0·069	0·072	0·076	0·079
40	0·057	0·061	0·066	0·070	0·075	0·079	0·083	0·088	0·092	0·096	0·101	0·105
50	0·071	0·077	0·082	0·088	0·093	0·099	0·104	0·110	0·115	0·121	0·126	0·132
60	0·086	0·092	0·099	0·105	0·112	0·118	0·125	0·132	0·138	0·145	0·151	0·158
70	0·100	0·107	0·115	0·123	0·130	0·138	0·146	0·153	0·161	0·169	0·176	0·184
80	0·114	0·123	0·132	0·140	0·149	0·158	0·167	0·175	0·184	0·193	0·202	0·210
90	0·128	0·138	0·148	0·158	0·168	0·178	0·187	0·197	0·207	0·217	0·227	0·237
100	0·143	0·153	0·164	0·175	0·186	0·197	0·208	0·219	0·230	0·241	0·252	0·263
200	0·285	0·307	0·329	0·351	0·373	0·395	0·416	0·438	0·460	0·482	0·504	0·526
300	0·427	0·460	0·493	0·526	0·559	0·592	0·625	0·658	0·690	0·723	0·756	0·789
400	0·570	0·614	0·658	0·701	0·745	0·789	0·833	0·877	0·921	0·964	1·008	1·052
500	0·712	0·767	0·822	0·877	0·932	0·986	1·041	1·096	1·151	1·206	1·260	1·315
600	0·855	0·921	0·986	1·052	1·118	1·184	1·249	1·315	1·381	1·447	1·512	1·578
700	0·997	1·074	1·151	1·227	1·304	1·381	1·458	1·534	1·611	1·688	1·764	1·841
800	1·140	1·227	1·315	1·403	1·490	1·578	1·666	1·753	1·841	1·929	2·016	2·104
900	1·282	1·381	1·479	1·578	1·677	1·775	1·874	1·973	2·071	2·170	2·268	2·367
1000	1·425	1·534	1·644	1·753	1·863	1·973	2·082	2·192	2·301	2·411	2·520	2·630

25 Days	26	27	28	29	30	40	50	60	100	200	300
1	0·003	0·003	0·003	0·003	0·003	0·003	0·004	0·006	0·007	0·011	0·022	0·033
2	0·006	0·006	0·006	0·006	0·006	0·007	0·009	0·011	0·013	0·022	0·044	0·066
3	0·008	0·009	0·009	0·009	0·010	0·010	0·013	0·016	0·020	0·033	0·066	0·099
4	0·011	0·011	0·012	0·012	0·013	0·013	0·018	0·022	0·026	0·044	0·088	0·132
5	0·014	0·014	0·015	0·015	0·016	0·016	0·022	0·027	0·033	0·055	0·110	0·164
6	0·016	0·017	0·018	0·018	0·019	0·019	0·026	0·033	0·039	0·066	0·132	0·197
7	0·019	0·020	0·021	0·022	0·022	0·023	0·031	0·038	0·046	0·077	0·153	0·230
8	0·022	0·023	0·024	0·025	0·025	0·026	0·035	0·044	0·053	0·088	0·175	0·263
9	0·025	0·026	0·027	0·028	0·029	0·030	0·039	0·049	0·059	0·099	0·197	0·296
10	0·027	0·029	0·030	0·031	0·032	0·033	0·044	0·055	0·066	0·110	0·219	0·329
20	0·055	0·057	0·059	0·061	0·064	0·066	0·088	0·110	0·132	0·219	0·438	0·658
30	0·082	0·086	0·089	0·092	0·095	0·099	0·132	0·164	0·197	0·329	0·658	0·986
40	0·110	0·114	0·118	0·123	0·127	0·132	0·175	0·219	0·263	0·438	0·877	1·315
50	0·137	0·143	0·148	0·153	0·159	0·164	0·219	0·274	0·329	0·548	1·096	1·644
60	0·164	0·171	0·178	0·184	0·191	0·197	0·263	0·329	0·395	0·658	1·315	1·973
70	0·192	0·200	0·207	0·215	0·223	0·230	0·307	0·384	0·460	0·767	1·534	2·301
80	0·219	0·228	0·237	0·246	0·254	0·263	0·351	0·438	0·526	0·877	1·753	2·630
90	0·247	0·256	0·266	0·276	0·286	0·296	0·395	0·493	0·592	0·986	1·973	2·959
100	0·274	0·285	0·296	0·307	0·318	0·329	0·438	0·548	0·658	1·096	2·192	3·288
200	0·548	0·570	0·592	0·614	0·636	0·658	0·877	1·096	1·315	2·192	4·384	6·575
300	0·822	0·855	0·888	0·920	0·953	0·986	1·315	1·644	1·973	3·288	6·575	9·863
400	1·096	1·140	1·184	1·227	1·271	1·315	1·753	2·192	2·630	4·384	8·767	13·151
500	1·370	1·425	1·480	1·534	1·589	1·644	2·192	2·740	3·288	5·479	10·959	16·438
600	1·644	1·710	1·775	1·841	1·907	1·973	2·630	3·288	3·945	6·575	13·151	19·726
700	1·918	1·995	2·071	2·148	2·225	2·301	3·069	3·836	4·603	7·671	15·342	23·014
800	2·192	2·280	2·367	2·455	2·542	2·630	3·507	4·384	5·260	8·767	17·534	26·301
900	2·466	2·564	2·663	2·762	2·860	2·959	3·945	4·932	5·918	9·863	19·726	29·589
1000	2·740	2·849	2·959	3·069	3·178	3·288	4·384	5·480	6·575	10·959	21·917	32·877

1 Mth	2	3	4	5	6	7	8	9	10	11	12
1	0·003	0·007	0·01	0·013	0·017	0·02	0·023	0·027	0·03	0·033	0·037	0·04
2	0·007	0·013	0·02	0·027	0·033	0·04	0·047	0·053	0·06	0·067	0·073	0·08
3	0·010	0·020	0·03	0·040	0·050	0·06	0·070	0·080	0·09	0·100	0·110	0·12
4	0·013	0·027	0·04	0·053	0·067	0·08	0·093	0·107	0·12	0·133	0·147	0·16
5	0·017	0·033	0·05	0·067	0·083	0·10	0·117	0·133	0·15	0·167	0·183	0·20
6	0·020	0·040	0·06	0·080	0·100	0·12	0·140	0·160	0·18	0·200	0·220	0·24
7	0·023	0·047	0·07	0·093	0·117	0·14	0·163	0·187	0·21	0·233	0·257	0·28
8	0·027	0·053	0·08	0·107	0·133	0·16	0·187	0·213	0·24	0·267	0·293	0·32
9	0·030	0·060	0·09	0·120	0·150	0·18	0·210	0·240	0·27	0·300	0·330	0·36
10	0·033	0·067	0·10	0·133	0·167	0·20	0·233	0·267	0·30	0·333	0·367	0·40
20	0·067	0·133	0·20	0·267	0·333	0·40	0·467	0·533	0·60	0·667	0·733	0·80
30	0·100	0·200	0·30	0·400	0·500	0·60	0·700	0·800	0·90	1·000	1·100	1·20
40	0·133	0·267	0·40	0·533	0·667	0·80	0·933	1·067	1·20	1·333	1·467	1·60
50	0·167	0·333	0·50	0·667	0·833	1·00	1·167	1·333	1·50	1·667	1·833	2·00
60	0·200	0·400	0·60	0·800	1·000	1·20	1·400	1·600	1·80	2·000	2·200	2·40
70	0·233	0·467	0·70	0·933	1·167	1·40	1·633	1·867	2·10	2·333	2·567	2·80
80	0·267	0·533	0·80	1·067	1·333	1·60	1·867	2·133	2·40	2·667	2·933	3·20
90	0·300	0·600	0·90	1·200	1·500	1·80	2·100	2·400	2·70	3·000	3·300	3·60
100	0·333	0·667	1·00	1·333	1·667	2·00	2·333	2·667	3·00	3·333	3·667	4·00
200	0·667	1·333	2·00	2·667	3·333	4·00	4·667	5·333	6·00	6·667	7·333	8·00
300	1·000	2·000	3·00	4·000	5·000	6·00	7·000	8·000	9·00	10·000	11·000	12·00
400	1·333	2·667	4·00	5·333	6·667	8·00	9·333	10·667	12·00	13·333	14·667	16·00
500	1·667	3·333	5·00	6·667	8·333	10·00	11·667	13·333	15·00	16·667	18·333	20·00
600	2·000	4·000	6·00	8·000	10·000	12·00	14·000	16·000	18·00	20·000	22·000	24·00
700	2·333	4·667	7·00	9·333	11·667	14·00	16·333	18·667	21·00	23·333	25·667	28·00
800	2·667	5·333	8·00	10·667	13·333	16·00	18·667	21·333	24·00	26·667	29·333	32·00
900	3·000	6·000	9·00	12·000	15·000	18·00	21·000	24·000	27·00	30·000	33·000	36·00
1000	3·333	6·667	10·00	13·333	16·667	20·00	23·333	26·666	30·00	33·333	36·667	40·00

	1Day	2	3	4	5	6	7	8	9	10	11	12
1	·000	·000	·000	·001	·001	·001	·001	·001	0·001	0·001	0·002	0·002
2	·000	·001	·001	·001	·001	·002	·002	0·002	0·003	0·003	0·003	0·003
3	·000	·001	·001	·002	·002	·003	·003	0·003	0·004	0·004	0·005	0·005
4	·001	·001	·002	·002	·003	·003	·004	0·004	0·005	0·005	0·006	0·007
5	·001	·001	·002	·003	·003	·004	·005	0·006	0·006	0·007	0·008	0·008
6	·001	·002	·003	·003	·004	·005	·006	0·007	0·007	0·008	0·009	0·010
7	·001	·002	·003	·004	·005	·006	·007	0·008	0·009	0·010	0·011	0·012
8	·001	·002	·003	·004	·006	·007	·008	0·009	0·010	0·011	0·012	0·013
9	·001	·002	·004	·005	·006	·007	·009	0·010	0·011	0·012	0·014	0·015
10	·001	·003	·004	·006	·007	·008	·010	0·011	0·012	0·014	0·015	0·016
20	·003	·006	·008	·011	·014	·016	·019	0·022	0·025	0·027	0·030	0·033
30	·004	·008	·012	·017	·021	·025	·029	0·033	0·037	0·041	0·045	0·049
40	·005	·011	·016	·022	·027	·033	·038	0·044	0·049	0·055	0·060	0·066
50	·007	·014	·021	·027	·034	·041	·048	0·055	0·062	0·069	0·075	0·082
60	·008	·016	·025	·033	·041	·049	·058	0·066	0·074	0·082	0·090	0·099
70	·010	·019	·029	·038	·048	·058	·067	0·077	0·086	0·096	0·106	0·115
80	·011	·022	·033	·044	·055	·066	·077	0·088	0·099	0·110	0·121	0·132
90	·012	·025	·037	·049	·062	·074	·086	0·099	0·111	0·123	0·136	0·148
100	·014	·027	·041	·055	·069	·082	·096	0·110	0·123	0·137	0·151	0·164
200	·027	·055	·082	·110	·137	·164	·192	0·219	0·247	0·274	0·301	0·329
300	·041	·082	·123	·164	·206	·247	·288	0·329	0·370	0·411	0·452	0·493
400	·055	·110	·164	·219	·274	·329	·384	0·438	0·493	0·548	0·603	0·658
500	·068	·137	·206	·274	·343	·411	·479	0·548	0·616	0·685	0·753	0·822
600	·082	·164	·247	·329	·411	·493	·575	0·658	0·740	0·822	0·904	0·986
700	·096	·192	·288	·384	·480	·575	·671	0·767	0·863	0·959	1·055	1·151
800	·110	·219	·329	·438	·548	·658	·767	0·877	0·986	1·096	1·206	1·315
900	·123	·247	·370	·493	·616	·740	·863	0·986	1·110	1·233	1·356	1·479
1000	·137	·274	·411	·548	·685	·822	·959	1·096	1·233	1·370	1·507	1·644

	13	14	15	16	17	18	19	20	21	22	23	24
1	0·002	0·002	0·002	0·002	0·002	0·003	0·003	0·003	0·003	0·003	0·003	0·003
2	0·004	0·004	0·004	0·004	0·005	0·005	0·005	0·005	0·006	0·006	0·006	0·007
3	0·005	0·006	0·006	0·007	0·007	0·007	0·008	0·008	0·009	0·009	0·009	0·010
4	0·007	0·008	0·008	0·009	0·009	0·010	0·010	0·011	0·012	0·012	0·013	0·013
5	0·009	0·010	0·010	0·011	0·012	0·012	0·013	0·014	0·014	0·015	0·016	0·016
6	0·011	0·012	0·012	0·013	0·014	0·015	0·016	0·016	0·017	0·018	0·019	0·020
7	0·012	0·013	0·014	0·015	0·016	0·017	0·018	0·019	0·020	0·021	0·022	0·023
8	0·014	0·015	0·016	0·018	0·019	0·020	0·021	0·022	0·023	0·024	0·025	0·026
9	0·016	0·017	0·019	0·020	0·021	0·022	0·023	0·025	0·026	0·027	0·028	0·030
10	0·018	0·019	0·021	0·022	0·023	0·025	0·026	0·027	0·029	0·030	0·032	0·033
20	0·036	0·038	0·041	0·044	0·047	0·049	0·052	0·055	0·058	0·060	0·063	0·066
30	0·053	0·058	0·062	0·066	0·070	0·074	0·078	0·082	0·086	0·090	0·095	0·099
40	0·071	0·077	0·082	0·088	0·093	0·099	0·104	0·110	0·115	0·121	0·126	0·132
50	0·089	0·096	0·103	0·110	0·116	0·123	0·130	0·137	0·144	0·151	0·158	0·164
60	0·107	0·115	0·123	0·132	0·140	0·148	0·156	0·164	0·173	0·181	0·189	0·197
70	0·125	0·134	0·144	0·153	0·163	0·173	0·182	0·192	0·201	0·211	0·221	0·230
80	0·142	0·153	0·164	0·175	0·186	0·197	0·208	0·219	0·230	0·241	0·252	0·263
90	0·160	0·173	0·185	0·197	0·210	0·222	0·234	0·247	0·259	0·271	0·284	0·296
100	0·178	0·192	0·206	0·219	0·233	0·247	0·260	0·274	0·288	0·301	0·315	0·329
200	0·356	0·384	0·411	0·438	0·466	0·493	0·521	0·548	0·575	0·603	0·630	0·658
300	0·534	0·575	0·616	0·658	0·699	0·740	0·781	0·822	0·863	0·904	0·945	0·986
400	0·712	0·767	0·822	0·877	0·932	0·986	1·041	1·096	1·151	1·206	1·260	1·315
500	0·890	0·959	1·027	1·096	1·164	1·233	1·301	1·370	1·438	1·507	1·575	1·644
600	1·069	1·151	1·233	1·315	1·397	1·480	1·562	1·644	1·726	1·808	1·890	1·973
700	1·247	1·342	1·438	1·534	1·630	1·726	1·822	1·918	2·014	2·110	2·206	2·301
800	1·425	1·534	1·644	1·753	1·863	1·973	2·082	2·192	2·301	2·411	2·521	2·630
900	1·603	1·726	1·849	1·973	2·096	2·219	2·342	2·466	2·589	2·712	2·836	2·959
1000	1·781	1·918	2·055	2·192	2·329	2·466	2·603	2·740	2·877	3·014	3·151	3·288

	25 Days	26	27	28	29	30	40	50	60	100	200	300
1	0.003	0.004	0.004	0.004	0.004	0.004	0.006	0.007	0.008	0.014	0.027	0.041
2	0.007	0.007	0.007	0.008	0.008	0.008	0.011	0.014	0.016	0.027	0.055	0.082
3	0.010	0.011	0.011	0.012	0.012	0.012	0.016	0.021	0.025	0.041	0.082	0.123
4	0.014	0.014	0.015	0.015	0.016	0.016	0.022	0.027	0.033	0.055	0.110	0.164
5	0.017	0.018	0.019	0.019	0.020	0.021	0.027	0.034	0.041	0.069	0.137	0.206
6	0.021	0.021	0.022	0.023	0.024	0.025	0.033	0.041	0.049	0.082	0.164	0.247
7	0.024	0.025	0.026	0.027	0.028	0.029	0.038	0.048	0.058	0.096	0.192	0.288
8	0.027	0.029	0.030	0.031	0.032	0.033	0.044	0.055	0.066	0.110	0.219	0.329
9	0.031	0.032	0.033	0.035	0.036	0.037	0.049	0.062	0.074	0.123	0.247	0.370
10	0.034	0.036	0.037	0.038	0.040	0.041	0.055	0.069	0.082	0.137	0.274	0.411
20	0.069	0.071	0.074	0.077	0.079	0.082	0.110	0.137	0.164	0.274	0.548	0.822
30	0.103	0.107	0.111	0.115	0.119	0.123	0.164	0.206	0.247	0.411	0.822	1.233
40	0.137	0.142	0.148	0.153	0.159	0.164	0.219	0.274	0.329	0.548	1.096	1.644
50	0.171	0.178	0.185	0.192	0.199	0.206	0.274	0.342	0.411	0.685	1.370	2.055
60	0.206	0.214	0.222	0.230	0.238	0.247	0.329	0.411	0.493	0.822	1.644	2.466
70	0.240	0.249	0.259	0.269	0.278	0.288	0.384	0.479	0.575	0.959	1.918	2.877
80	0.274	0.285	0.296	0.307	0.318	0.329	0.438	0.548	0.658	1.096	2.192	3.288
90	0.308	0.321	0.333	0.345	0.358	0.370	0.493	0.616	0.740	1.233	2.466	3.699
100	0.342	0.356	0.370	0.384	0.397	0.411	0.548	0.685	0.822	1.370	2.740	4.110
200	0.685	0.712	0.740	0.767	0.795	0.822	1.096	1.370	1.644	2.740	5.479	8.219
300	1.027	1.069	1.110	1.151	1.192	1.233	1.644	2.055	2.466	4.110	8.219	12.328
400	1.370	1.424	1.480	1.534	1.589	1.644	2.192	2.740	3.288	5.479	10.959	16.438
500	1.712	1.781	1.849	1.918	1.986	2.055	2.740	3.425	4.110	6.849	13.699	20.548
600	2.055	2.137	2.219	2.301	2.384	2.466	3.288	4.110	4.932	8.219	16.438	24.658
700	2.397	2.493	2.589	2.685	2.781	2.877	3.836	4.795	5.753	9.589	19.178	28.767
800	2.740	2.849	2.959	3.069	3.178	3.288	4.384	5.479	6.575	10.959	21.918	32.877
900	3.082	3.206	3.329	3.452	3.575	3.699	4.932	6.164	7.397	12.329	24.658	36.986
1000	3.425	3.561	3.699	3.836	3.973	4.110	5.480	6.849	8.219	13.699	27.397	41.096

	1 Mth	2	3	4	5	6	7	8	9	10	11	12
1	0.004	0.008	0.013	0.017	0.021	0.025	0.029	0.033	0.038	0.042	0.046	0.05
2	0.008	0.017	0.025	0.033	0.042	0.050	0.058	0.067	0.075	0.083	0.092	0.10
3	0.013	0.025	0.038	0.050	0.063	0.075	0.088	0.100	0.113	0.125	0.138	0.15
4	0.017	0.033	0.050	0.067	0.083	0.100	0.117	0.133	0.150	0.167	0.183	0.20
5	0.021	0.042	0.063	0.083	0.104	0.125	0.146	0.167	0.188	0.208	0.229	0.25
6	0.025	0.050	0.075	0.100	0.125	0.150	0.175	0.200	0.225	0.250	0.275	0.30
7	0.029	0.058	0.088	0.117	0.146	0.175	0.204	0.233	0.263	0.292	0.321	0.35
8	0.033	0.067	0.100	0.133	0.167	0.200	0.233	0.267	0.300	0.333	0.367	0.40
9	0.038	0.075	0.113	0.150	0.188	0.225	0.263	0.300	0.338	0.375	0.413	0.45
10	0.042	0.083	0.125	0.167	0.208	0.250	0.292	0.333	0.375	0.417	0.458	0.50
20	0.083	0.167	0.250	0.333	0.417	0.500	0.583	0.667	0.750	0.833	0.917	1.00
30	0.125	0.250	0.375	0.500	0.625	0.750	0.875	1.000	1.125	1.250	1.375	1.50
40	0.167	0.333	0.500	0.667	0.833	1.000	1.167	1.333	1.500	1.667	1.833	2.00
50	0.208	0.417	0.625	0.833	1.042	1.250	1.458	1.667	1.875	2.083	2.292	2.50
60	0.250	0.500	0.750	1.000	1.250	1.500	1.750	2.000	2.250	2.500	2.750	3.00
70	0.292	0.583	0.875	1.167	1.458	1.750	2.042	2.333	2.625	2.917	3.208	3.50
80	0.333	0.667	1.000	1.333	1.666	2.000	2.333	2.667	3.000	3.333	3.666	4.00
90	0.375	0.750	1.125	1.500	1.875	2.250	2.625	3.000	3.375	3.750	4.125	4.50
100	0.417	0.833	1.250	1.667	2.083	2.500	2.917	3.333	3.750	4.167	4.583	5.00
200	0.833	1.667	2.500	3.333	4.167	5.000	5.833	6.667	7.500	8.333	9.167	10.00
300	1.250	2.500	3.750	5.000	6.250	7.500	8.750	10.000	11.250	12.500	13.750	15.00
400	1.667	3.333	5.000	6.667	8.333	10.000	11.667	13.333	15.000	16.667	18.333	20.00
500	2.083	4.167	6.250	8.333	10.417	12.500	14.583	16.667	18.750	20.833	22.917	25.00
600	2.500	5.000	7.500	10.000	12.500	15.000	17.500	20.000	22.500	25.000	27.500	30.00
700	2.917	5.833	8.750	11.667	14.583	17.500	20.417	23.333	26.250	29.167	32.083	35.00
800	3.333	6.667	10.000	13.333	16.667	20.000	23.333	26.667	30.000	33.333	36.667	40.00
900	3.750	7.500	11.250	15.000	18.750	22.500	26.250	30.000	33.750	37.500	41.250	45.00
1000	4.167	8.333	12.500	16.667	20.833	25.000	29.167	33.333	37.500	41.667	45.833	50.00

	1Day	2	3	4	5	6	7	8	9	10	11	12
1	·000	·000	·001	·001	·001	·001	0·001	0·001	0·002	0·002	0·002	0·002
2	·000	·001	·001	·001	·002	·002	0·002	0·003	0·003	0·003	0·004	0·004
3	·001	·001	·002	·002	·003	·003	0·003	0·004	0·004	0·005	0·005	0·006
4	·001	·001	·002	·003	·003	·004	0·005	0·005	0·006	0·007	0·007	0·008
5	·001	·002	·003	·003	·004	·005	0·006	0·007	0·007	0·008	0·009	0·010
6	·001	·002	·003	·004	·005	·006	0·007	0·008	0·009	0·010	0·011	0·012
7	·001	·002	·004	·005	·006	·007	0·008	0·009	0·010	0·012	0·013	0·014
8	·001	·003	·004	·005	·007	·008	0·009	0·011	0·012	0·013	0·014	0·016
9	·001	·003	·004	·006	·007	·009	0·010	0·012	0·013	0·015	0·016	0·018
10	·002	·003	·005	·007	·008	·010	0·012	0·013	0·015	0·016	0·018	0·020
20	·003	·007	·010	·013	·016	·020	0·023	0·026	0·030	0·033	0·036	0·040
30	·005	·010	·015	·020	·025	·030	0·035	0·039	0·044	0·049	0·054	0·059
40	·007	·013	·020	·026	·033	·040	0·046	0·053	0·059	0·066	0·072	0·079
50	·008	·016	·025	·033	·041	·049	0·058	0·066	0·074	0·082	0·090	0·099
60	·010	·020	·030	·039	·049	·059	0·069	0·079	0·089	0·099	0·109	0·118
70	·012	·023	·035	·046	·058	·069	0·081	0·092	0·104	0·115	0·127	0·138
80	·013	·026	·040	·053	·066	·079	0·092	0·105	0·118	0·132	0·145	0·158
90	·015	·030	·044	·059	·074	·089	0·104	0·118	0·133	0·148	0·163	0·178
100	·016	·033	·049	·066	·082	·099	0·115	0·132	0·148	0·164	0·181	0·197
200	·033	·066	·099	·132	·164	·197	0·230	0·263	0·296	0·329	0·362	0·395
300	·049	·099	·148	·197	·247	·296	0·345	0·395	0·444	0·493	0·542	0·592
400	·066	·132	·197	·263	·329	·395	0·460	0·526	0·592	0·658	0·723	0·789
500	·082	·164	·247	·329	·411	·493	0·575	0·658	0·740	0·822	0·904	0·986
600	·099	·197	·296	·395	·492	·592	0·690	0·690	0·888	0·986	1·085	1·184
700	·115	·230	·345	·460	·575	·690	0·806	0·921	1·036	1·151	1·266	1·381
800	·132	·263	·395	·526	·658	·789	0·921	1·052	1·184	1·315	1·447	1·578
900	·148	·296	·444	·592	·740	·888	1·036	1·184	1·332	1·479	1·627	1·775
1000	·164	·329	·493	·658	·822	·986	1·151	1·315	1·480	1·644	1·808	1·973

	13	14	15	16	17	18	19	20	21	22	23	24
1	0·002	0·002	0·003	0·003	0·003	0·003	0·003	0·003	0·004	0·004	0·004	0·004
2	0·004	0·005	0·005	0·005	0·006	0·006	0·006	0·006	0·007	0·007	0·008	0·008
3	0·006	0·007	0·007	0·008	0·008	0·009	0·009	0·010	0·010	0·011	0·011	0·012
4	0·009	0·009	0·010	0·011	0·011	0·012	0·013	0·013	0·014	0·014	0·015	0·016
5	0·011	0·012	0·012	0·013	0·014	0·015	0·016	0·016	0·017	0·018	0·019	0·020
6	0·013	0·014	0·015	0·016	0·017	0·018	0·019	0·020	0·021	0·022	0·023	0·024
7	0·015	0·016	0·017	0·018	0·020	0·021	0·022	0·023	0·024	0·025	0·026	0·028
8	0·017	0·018	0·020	0·021	0·022	0·024	0·025	0·026	0·028	0·029	0·030	0·032
9	0·019	0·021	0·022	0·024	0·025	0·027	0·028	0·030	0·031	0·033	0·034	0·036
10	0·021	0·023	0·025	0·026	0·028	0·030	0·031	0·033	0·035	0·036	0·038	0·040
20	0·043	0·046	0·049	0·053	0·056	0·059	0·062	0·066	0·069	0·072	0·076	0·079
30	0·064	0·069	0·074	0·079	0·084	0·089	0·094	0·099	0·104	0·109	0·113	0·118
40	0·086	0·092	0·099	0·105	0·112	0·118	0·125	0·132	0·138	0·145	0·151	0·158
50	0·107	0·115	0·123	0·132	0·140	0·148	0·156	0·164	0·173	0·181	0·189	0·197
60	0·128	0·138	0·148	0·158	0·168	0·178	0·187	0·197	0·207	0·217	0·227	0·237
70	0·150	0·161	0·173	0·184	0·196	0·207	0·219	0·230	0·242	0·253	0·265	0·276
80	0·171	0·184	0·197	0·210	0·224	0·237	0·250	0·263	0·276	0·289	0·302	0·316
90	0·192	0·207	0·222	0·237	0·252	0·266	0·281	0·296	0·311	0·326	0·340	0·355
100	0·214	0·230	0·247	0·263	0·279	0·296	0·312	0·329	0·345	0·362	0·378	0·395
200	0·427	0·460	0·493	0·526	0·559	0·592	0·625	0·658	0·690	0·723	0·756	0·789
300	0·641	0·690	0·740	0·789	0·838	0·888	0·937	0·986	1·036	1·085	1·134	1·184
400	0·855	0·921	0·986	1·052	1·118	1·184	1·249	1·315	1·381	1·447	1·512	1·578
500	1·069	1·151	1·233	1·315	1·397	1·480	1·562	1·644	1·726	1·808	1·890	1·973
600	1·282	1·381	1·480	1·578	1·677	1·775	1·874	1·973	2·071	2·170	2·269	2·367
700	1·496	1·611	1·726	1·841	1·956	2·071	2·186	2·301	2·416	2·532	2·647	2·762
800	1·710	1·841	1·973	2·104	2·236	2·367	2·499	2·630	2·762	2·893	3·025	3·156
900	1·923	2·071	2·219	2·367	2·515	2·663	2·811	2·959	3·107	3·255	3·403	3·551
1000	2·137	2·301	2·466	2·630	2·795	2·959	3·123	3·288	3·452	3·616	3·781	3·945

25 Days	26	27	28	29	30	40	50	60	100	200	300
1	0.004	0.004	0.004	0.005	0.005	0.005	0.007	0.008	0.010	0.016	0.033	0.049
2	0.008	0.009	0.009	0.009	0.010	0.010	0.013	0.016	0.020	0.033	0.066	0.099
3	0.012	0.013	0.013	0.014	0.014	0.015	0.020	0.025	0.030	0.049	0.099	0.148
4	0.016	0.017	0.018	0.018	0.019	0.020	0.026	0.033	0.040	0.066	0.132	0.197
5	0.021	0.021	0.022	0.023	0.024	0.025	0.033	0.041	0.049	0.082	0.164	0.247
6	0.025	0.026	0.027	0.028	0.029	0.030	0.040	0.049	0.059	0.099	0.197	0.296
7	0.029	0.030	0.031	0.032	0.033	0.035	0.046	0.058	0.069	0.115	0.230	0.345
8	0.033	0.034	0.036	0.037	0.038	0.040	0.053	0.066	0.079	0.132	0.263	0.395
9	0.037	0.038	0.040	0.041	0.043	0.044	0.059	0.074	0.089	0.148	0.296	0.444
10	0.041	0.043	0.044	0.046	0.048	0.049	0.066	0.082	0.099	0.164	0.329	0.493
20	0.082	0.086	0.089	0.092	0.095	0.099	0.132	0.164	0.197	0.329	0.658	0.986
30	0.123	0.128	0.133	0.138	0.143	0.148	0.197	0.247	0.296	0.493	0.986	1.480
40	0.164	0.171	0.178	0.184	0.191	0.197	0.263	0.329	0.395	0.658	1.315	1.973
50	0.206	0.214	0.222	0.230	0.238	0.247	0.329	0.411	0.493	0.822	1.644	2.466
60	0.247	0.256	0.266	0.276	0.286	0.296	0.395	0.493	0.592	0.986	1.973	2.959
70	0.288	0.299	0.311	0.322	0.334	0.345	0.460	0.575	0.690	1.151	2.301	3.452
80	0.329	0.342	0.355	0.368	0.381	0.395	0.526	0.658	0.789	1.315	2.630	3.945
90	0.370	0.385	0.400	0.414	0.429	0.444	0.592	0.740	0.888	1.479	2.959	4.438
100	0.411	0.427	0.444	0.460	0.477	0.493	0.658	0.822	0.986	1.644	3.288	4.932
200	0.822	0.855	0.888	0.921	0.953	0.986	1.315	1.644	1.973	3.288	6.575	9.863
300	1.233	1.282	1.332	1.381	1.430	1.480	1.973	2.466	2.959	4.932	9.863	14.795
400	1.644	1.710	1.775	1.841	1.907	1.973	2.630	3.288	3.945	6.575	13.151	19.726
500	2.055	2.137	2.219	2.301	2.384	2.466	3.288	4.110	4.932	8.219	16.438	24.658
600	2.466	2.564	2.663	2.762	2.860	2.959	3.945	4.932	5.918	9.863	19.726	29.589
700	2.877	2.992	3.107	3.222	3.337	3.452	4.603	5.753	6.904	11.507	23.014	34.521
800	3.288	3.419	3.551	3.682	3.814	3.945	5.260	6.575	7.890	13.151	26.301	39.452
900	3.699	3.847	3.995	4.142	4.290	4.438	5.918	7.397	8.877	14.795	29.589	44.384
1000	4.110	4.274	4.435	4.603	4.767	4.932	6.575	8.219	9.863	16.438	32.877	49.315

1 Mth.	2	3	4	5	6	7	8	9	10	11	12
1	0.005	0.01	0.015	0.02	0.025	0.03	0.035	0.04	0.045	0.05	0.055	0.06
2	0.010	0.02	0.030	0.04	0.050	0.06	0.070	0.08	0.090	0.10	0.110	0.12
3	0.015	0.03	0.045	0.06	0.075	0.09	0.105	0.12	0.135	0.15	0.165	0.18
4	0.020	0.04	0.060	0.08	0.100	0.12	0.140	0.16	0.180	0.20	0.220	0.24
5	0.025	0.05	0.075	0.10	0.125	0.15	0.175	0.20	0.225	0.25	0.275	0.30
6	0.030	0.06	0.090	0.12	0.150	0.18	0.210	0.24	0.270	0.30	0.330	0.36
7	0.035	0.07	0.105	0.14	0.175	0.21	0.245	0.28	0.315	0.35	0.385	0.42
8	0.040	0.08	0.120	0.16	0.200	0.24	0.280	0.32	0.360	0.40	0.440	0.48
9	0.045	0.09	0.135	0.18	0.225	0.27	0.315	0.36	0.405	0.45	0.495	0.54
10	0.050	0.10	0.150	0.20	0.250	0.30	0.350	0.40	0.450	0.50	0.550	0.60
20	0.100	0.20	0.300	0.40	0.500	0.60	0.700	0.80	0.900	1.00	1.100	1.20
30	0.150	0.30	0.450	0.60	0.750	0.90	1.050	1.20	1.350	1.50	1.650	1.80
40	0.200	0.40	0.600	0.80	1.000	1.20	1.400	1.60	1.800	2.00	2.200	2.40
50	0.250	0.50	0.750	1.00	1.250	1.50	1.750	2.00	2.250	2.50	2.750	3.00
60	0.300	0.60	0.900	1.20	1.500	1.80	2.100	2.40	2.700	3.00	3.300	3.60
70	0.350	0.70	1.050	1.40	1.750	2.10	2.450	2.80	3.150	3.50	3.850	4.20
80	0.400	0.80	1.200	1.60	2.000	2.40	2.800	3.20	3.600	4.00	4.400	4.80
90	0.450	0.90	1.350	1.80	2.250	2.70	3.150	3.60	4.050	4.50	4.950	5.40
100	0.500	1.00	1.500	2.00	2.500	3.00	3.500	4.00	4.500	5.00	5.500	6.00
200	1.000	2.00	3.000	4.00	5.000	6.00	7.000	8.00	9.000	10.00	11.000	12.00
300	1.500	3.00	4.500	6.00	7.500	9.00	10.500	12.00	13.500	15.00	16.500	18.00
400	2.000	4.00	6.000	8.00	10.000	12.00	14.000	16.00	18.000	20.00	22.000	24.00
500	2.500	5.00	7.500	10.00	12.500	15.00	17.500	20.00	22.500	25.00	27.500	30.00
600	3.000	6.00	9.000	12.00	15.000	18.00	21.000	24.00	27.000	30.00	33.000	36.00
700	3.500	7.00	10.500	14.00	17.500	21.00	24.500	28.00	31.500	35.00	38.500	42.00
800	4.000	8.00	12.000	16.00	20.000	24.00	28.000	32.00	36.000	40.00	44.000	48.00
900	4.500	9.00	13.500	18.00	22.500	27.00	31.500	36.00	40.500	45.00	49.500	54.00
1000	5.000	10.00	15.000	20.00	25.000	30.00	35.000	40.00	45.000	50.00	55.000	60.00

	1Day	2	3	4	5	6	7	8	9	10	11	12
1	·000	·000	·001	·001	·001	0·001	0·001	0·002	0·002	0·002	0·002	0·002
2	·000	·001	·001	·002	·002	0·002	0·003	0·003	0·004	0·004	0·004	0·005
3	·001	·001	·002	·002	·003	0·003	0·004	0·005	0·005	0·006	0·006	0·007
4	·001	·002	·002	·003	·004	0·005	0·005	0·006	0·007	0·008	0·008	0·009
5	·001	·002	·003	·004	·005	0·006	0·007	0·008	0·009	0·010	0·011	0·012
6	·001	·002	·004	·005	·006	0·007	0·008	0·009	0·010	0·012	0·013	0·014
7	·001	·003	·004	·005	·007	0·008	0·009	0·011	0·012	0·013	0·015	0·016
8	·002	·003	·005	·006	·008	0·009	0·011	0·012	0·014	0·015	0·017	0·018
9	·002	·003	·005	·007	·009	0·010	0·012	0·014	0·016	0·017	0·019	0·021
10	·002	·004	·006	·008	·010	0·012	0·013	0·015	0·017	0·019	0·021	0·023
20	·004	·008	·012	·015	·019	0·023	0·027	0·031	0·035	0·038	0·042	0·046
30	·006	·012	·017	·023	·029	0·035	0·040	0·046	0·052	0·058	0·063	0·069
40	·008	·015	·023	·031	·038	0·046	0·054	0·061	0·069	0·077	0·084	0·092
50	·010	·019	·029	·038	·048	0·058	0·067	0·077	0·086	0·096	0·106	0·115
60	·012	·023	·035	·046	·058	0·069	0·081	0·092	0·104	0·115	0·127	0·138
70	·013	·027	·040	·054	·067	0·081	0·094	0·107	0·121	0·134	0·148	0·161
80	·015	·031	·046	·061	·077	0·092	0·107	0·123	0·138	0·153	0·169	0·184
90	·017	·035	·052	·069	·086	0·104	0·121	0·138	0·155	0·173	0·190	0·207
100	·019	·038	·058	·077	·096	0·115	0·134	0·153	0·173	0·192	0·211	0·230
200	·038	·077	·115	·153	·192	0·230	0·269	0·307	0·345	0·384	0·422	0·460
300	·058	·115	·173	·230	·288	0·345	0·403	0·460	0·518	0·575	0·633	0·690
400	·077	·153	·230	·307	·384	0·460	0·537	0·614	0·690	0·767	0·844	0·921
500	·096	·192	·288	·384	·479	0·575	0·671	0·767	0·863	0·959	1·055	1·151
600	·115	·230	·345	·460	·575	0·690	0·806	0·921	1·036	1·151	1·266	1·381
700	·134	·269	·403	·537	·671	0·806	0·940	1·074	1·208	1·342	1·477	1·611
800	·153	·307	·460	·614	·767	0·921	1·074	1·227	1·381	1·534	1·688	1·841
900	·173	·345	·518	·690	·863	1·036	1·208	1·381	1·553	1·726	1·899	2·071
1000	·192	·384	·575	·767	·959	1·151	1·343	1·534	1·726	1·918	2·110	2·301

	13	14	15	16	17	18	19	20	21	22	23	24
1	0·003	0·003	0·003	0·003	0·003	0·004	0·004	0·004	0·004	0·004	0·004	0·005
2	0·005	0·005	0·006	0·006	0·007	0·007	0·007	0·008	0·008	0·008	0·009	0·009
3	0·008	0·008	0·009	0·009	0·010	0·010	0·011	0·012	0·012	0·013	0·013	0·014
4	0·010	0·011	0·012	0·012	0·013	0·014	0·015	0·015	0·016	0·017	0·018	0·018
5	0·012	0·013	0·014	0·015	0·016	0·017	0·018	0·019	0·020	0·021	0·022	0·023
6	0·015	0·016	0·017	0·018	0·020	0·021	0·022	0·023	0·024	0·025	0·026	0·028
7	0·017	0·019	0·020	0·022	0·023	0·024	0·026	0·027	0·028	0·030	0·031	0·032
8	0·020	0·022	0·023	0·025	0·026	0·028	0·029	0·031	0·032	0·034	0·035	0·037
9	0·022	0·024	0·026	0·028	0·029	0·031	0·033	0·035	0·036	0·038	0·040	0·041
10	0·025	0·027	0·029	0·031	0·033	0·035	0·036	0·038	0·040	0·042	0·044	0·046
20	0·050	0·054	0·058	0·061	0·065	0·069	0·073	0·077	0·081	0·084	0·088	0·092
30	0·075	0·081	0·086	0·092	0·098	0·104	0·109	0·115	0·121	0·127	0·132	0·138
40	0·100	0·107	0·115	0·123	0·130	0·138	0·146	0·153	0·161	0·169	0·176	0·184
50	0·125	0·134	0·144	0·153	0·163	0·173	0·182	0·192	0·201	0·211	0·221	0·230
60	0·150	0·161	0·173	0·184	0·196	0·207	0·219	0·230	0·242	0·253	0·265	0·276
70	0·175	0·188	0·201	0·215	0·228	0·242	0·255	0·269	0·282	0·295	0·309	0·322
80	0·199	0·215	0·230	0·246	0·261	0·276	0·292	0·307	0·322	0·338	0·353	0·368
90	0·224	0·242	0·259	0·276	0·293	0·311	0·328	0·345	0·362	0·380	0·397	0·414
100	0·249	0·269	0·288	0·307	0·326	0·345	0·364	0·384	0·403	0·422	0·441	0·460
200	0·499	0·537	0·575	0·614	0·652	0·690	0·729	0·767	0·806	0·844	0·882	0·921
300	0·748	0·806	0·863	0·920	0·978	1·036	1·093	1·151	1·208	1·266	1·323	1·381
400	0·997	1·074	1·151	1·227	1·304	1·381	1·458	1·534	1·611	1·688	1·764	1·841
500	1·247	1·342	1·438	1·534	1·630	1·726	1·822	1·918	2·014	2·110	2·206	2·301
600	1·496	1·611	1·726	1·841	1·956	2·071	2·186	2·301	2·416	2·532	2·647	2·762
700	1·745	1·879	2·014	2·148	2·282	2·416	2·551	2·685	2·819	2·953	3·088	3·222
800	1·995	2·148	2·301	2·455	2·608	2·762	2·915	3·069	3·222	3·375	3·529	3·682
900	2·244	2·416	2·589	2·762	2·934	3·107	3·279	3·452	3·625	3·797	3·970	4·142
1000	2·493	2·685	2·877	3·069	3·260	3·452	3·644	3·836	4·027	4·219	4·411	4·603

25Days	26	27	28	29	30	40	50	60	100	200	300
1	0·005	0·005	0·005	0·005	0·006	0·006	0·008	0·010	0·012	0·019	0·038	0·058
2	0·01C	0·010	0·010	0·011	0·011	0·012	0·015	0·019	0·023	0·038	0·077	0·115
3	0·014	0·015	0·016	0·016	0·017	0·017	0·023	0·029	0·035	0·058	0·115	0·173
4	0·019	0·020	0·021	0·021	0·022	0·023	0·031	0·038	0·046	0·077	0·153	0·230
5	0·024	0·025	0·026	0·027	0·028	0·029	0·038	0·048	0·058	0·096	0·192	0·288
6	0·029	0·030	0·031	0·032	0·033	0·035	0·046	0·058	0·069	0·115	0·230	0·345
7	0·034	0·035	0·036	0·038	0·039	0·040	0·054	0·067	0·081	0·134	0·269	0·403
8	0·038	0·040	0·041	0·043	0·045	0·046	0·061	0·077	0·092	0·153	0·307	0·460
9	0·043	0·045	0·047	0·048	0·050	0·052	0·069	0·086	0·104	0·173	0·345	0·518
10	0·048	0·050	0·052	0·054	0·056	0·058	0·077	0·096	0·115	0·192	0·384	0·575
20	0·096	0·100	0·104	0·107	0·111	0·115	0·153	0·192	0·230	0·384	0·767	1·151
30	0·144	0·150	0·155	0·161	0·167	0·173	0·230	0·288	0·345	0·575	1·151	1·726
40	0·192	0·199	0·207	0·215	0·222	0·230	0·307	0·384	0·460	0·767	1·534	2·301
50	0·240	0·249	0·259	0·269	0·278	0·288	0·384	0·480	0·575	0·959	1·918	2·877
60	0·288	0·299	0·311	0·322	0·334	0·345	0·460	0·575	0·690	1·151	2·301	3·452
70	0·336	0·349	0·363	0·376	0·389	0·403	0·537	0·671	0·806	1·342	2·685	4·027
80	0·384	0·399	0·414	0·430	0·445	0·460	0·614	0·767	0·921	1·534	3·069	4·603
90	0·432	0·449	0·466	0·483	0·506	0·518	0·690	0·863	1·036	1·726	3·452	5·178
.00	0·479	0·499	0·518	0·537	0·556	0·575	0·767	0·959	1·151	1·918	3·836	5·753
200	0·959	0·997	1·036	1·074	1·112	1·151	1·534	1·918	2·301	3·836	7·671	11·507
300	1·438	1·496	1·553	1·611	1·669	1·726	2·301	2·877	3·452	5·753	11·507	17·260
400	1·918	1·995	2·071	2·148	2·225	2·301	3·069	3·836	4·603	7·671	15·342	23·014
500	2·397	2·493	2·589	2·685	2·781	2·877	3·836	4·795	5·753	9·589	19·178	28·767
600	2·877	2·992	3·107	3·222	3·337	3·452	4·603	5·753	6·904	11·507	23·014	34·521
700	3·356	3·490	3·625	3·759	3·893	4·027	5·370	6·712	8·055	13·425	26·849	40·274
800	3·836	3·989	4·143	4·296	4·449	4·603	6·137	7·671	9·206	15·343	30·685	46·027
900	4·315	4·488	4·660	4·833	5·006	5·178	6·904	8·630	10·356	17·260	34·521	51·781
1000	4·795	4·986	5·178	5·370	5·562	5·753	7·671	9·589	11·507	19·178	38·356	57·534

1Mth.	2	3	4	5	6	7	8	9	10	11	12
1	0·006	0·012	0·018	0·023	0·029	0·035	0·041	0·047	0·053	0·058	0·064	0·07
2	0·012	0·023	0·035	0·047	0·058	0·070	0·082	0·093	0·105	0·117	0·128	0·14
3	0·018	0·035	0·053	0·070	0·088	0·105	0·123	0·140	0·158	0·175	0·193	0·21
4	0·023	0·047	0·070	0·093	0·117	0·140	0·163	0·187	0·210	0·233	0·257	0·28
5	0·029	0·058	0·088	0·117	0·146	0·175	0·204	0·233	0·263	0·292	0·321	0·35
6	0·035	0·070	0·105	0·140	0·175	0·210	0·245	0·280	0·315	0·350	0·385	0·42
7	0·041	0·082	0·123	0·163	0·204	0·245	0·286	0·327	0·368	0·408	0·449	0·49
8	0·047	0·093	0·140	0·187	0·233	0·280	0·327	0·373	0·420	0·467	0·513	0·56
9	0·053	0·105	0·158	0·210	0·263	0·315	0·368	0·420	0·473	0·525	0·578	0·63
10	0·058	0·117	0·175	0·233	0·292	0·350	0·408	0·467	0·525	0·583	0·642	0·70
20	0·117	0·233	0·350	0·467	0·583	0·700	0·817	0·933	1·050	1·167	1·283	1·40
30	0·175	0·350	0·525	0·700	0·875	1·050	1·225	1·400	1·575	1·175	1·925	2·10
40	0·233	0·467	0·700	0·933	1·167	1·400	1·633	1·867	2·100	2·333	2·567	2·80
50	0·292	0·583	0·875	1·167	1·458	1·750	2·042	2·333	2·625	2·917	3·208	3·50
60	0·350	0·700	1·050	1·400	1·750	2·100	2·450	2·800	3·150	3·500	3·850	4·20
70	0·408	0·817	1·225	1·633	2·042	2·450	2·858	3·267	3·675	4·083	4·492	4·90
80	0·467	0·933	1·400	1·867	2·333	2·800	3·267	3·733	4·200	4·667	5·133	5·60
90	0·525	1·050	1·575	2·100	2·625	3·150	3·675	4·200	4·725	5·250	5·775	6·30
.00	0·583	1·167	1·750	2·333	2·917	3·500	4·083	4·667	5·250	5·833	6·417	7·00
200	1·167	2·333	3·500	4·667	5·833	7·000	8·167	9·333	10·500	11·667	12·833	14·00
300	1·750	3·500	5·250	7·000	8·750	10·500	12·250	14·000	15·750	17·500	19·250	21·00
400	2·333	4·667	7·000	9·333	11·667	14·000	16·333	18·667	21·000	23·333	25·667	28·00
500	2·917	5·833	8·750	11·667	14·583	17·500	20·417	23·333	26·250	29·167	32·083	35·00
600	3·500	7·000	10·500	14·000	17·500	21·000	24·500	28·000	31·500	35·000	38·500	42·00
700	4·083	8·167	12·250	16·333	20·417	24·500	28·583	32·667	36·750	40·833	44·917	49·00
800	4·667	9·333	14·000	18·667	23·333	28·000	32·667	37·333	42·000	46·667	51·333	56·00
900	5·250	10·500	15·750	21·000	26·250	31·500	36·750	42·000	47·250	52·500	57·750	63·00
1000	5·833	11·667	17·500	23·333	29·167	35·000	40·833	46·667	52·500	58·333	64·167	70·00

	1Day	2	3	4	5	6	7	8	9	10	11	12
1	·000	·000	·001	·001	0·001	0·001	0·002	0·002	0·002	0·002	0·002	0·003
2	·000	·001	·001	·002	0·002	0·003	0·003	0·004	0·004	0·004	0·005	0·005
3	·001	·001	·002	·003	0·003	0·004	0·005	0·005	0·006	0·007	0·007	0·008
4	·001	·002	·003	·004	0·004	0·005	0·006	0·007	0·008	0·009	0·010	0·011
5	·001	·002	·003	·004	0·006	0·007	0·008	0·019	0·010	0·011	0·012	0·013
6	·001	·003	·004	·005	0·007	0·008	0·009	0·011	0·012	0·013	0·014	0·016
7	·002	·003	·005	·006	0·008	0·009	0·011	0·012	0·014	0·015	0·017	0·018
8	·002	·004	·005	·007	0·009	0·011	0·012	0·014	0·016	0·018	0·019	0·021
9	·002	·004	·006	·008	0·010	0·012	0·014	0·016	0·018	0·020	0·022	0·024
10	·002	·004	·007	·009	0·011	0·013	0·015	0·018	0·020	0·022	0·024	0·026
20	·004	·009	·013	·018	0·022	0·026	0·031	0·035	0·040	0·044	0·048	0·053
30	·007	·013	·020	·026	0·033	0·039	0·046	0·053	0·059	0·066	0·072	0·079
40	·009	·018	·026	·035	0·044	0·053	0·061	0·070	0·079	0·088	0·096	0·105
50	·011	·022	·033	·044	0·055	0·066	0·077	0·088	0·099	0·110	0·121	0·132
60	·013	·026	·039	·053	0·066	0·079	0·092	0·105	0·118	0·132	0·145	0·158
70	·015	·031	·046	·061	0·077	0·092	0·107	0·123	0·138	0·153	0·169	0·184
80	·018	·035	·053	·070	0·088	0·105	0·123	0·140	0·158	0·175	0·193	0·210
90	·020	·040	·059	·079	0·099	0·118	0·138	0·158	0·178	0·197	0·217	0·237
100	·022	·044	·066	·088	0·110	0·132	0·153	0·175	0·197	0·219	0·241	0·263
200	·044	·088	·132	·175	0·219	0·263	0·307	0·351	0·395	0·438	0·482	0·526
300	·066	·131	·197	·263	0·329	0·395	0·460	0·526	0·592	0·656	0·723	0·789
400	·088	·175	·263	·351	0·438	0·526	0·614	0·701	0·789	0·877	0·964	1·052
500	·110	·219	·329	·438	0·548	0·658	0·767	0·877	0·986	1·096	1·206	1·315
600	·132	·263	·395	·526	0·658	0·789	0·921	1·052	1·184	1·315	1·447	1·578
700	·153	·307	·460	·614	0·767	0·920	1·074	1·227	1·381	1·534	1·688	1·841
800	·175	·351	·526	·701	0·877	1·052	1·227	1·403	1·578	1·753	1·929	2·104
900	·197	·395	·592	·789	0·986	1·184	1·381	1·578	1·775	1·973	2·170	2·367
1000	·219	·438	·658	·877	1·096	1·315	1·534	1·753	1·973	2·192	2·411	2·630

	13	14	15	16	17	18	19	20	21	22	23	24
1	0·003	0·003	0·003	0·004	0·004	0·004	0·004	0·004	0·004	0·005	0·005	0·005
2	0·006	0·006	0·007	0·007	0·007	0·008	0·008	0·009	0·009	0·010	0·010	0·011
3	0·009	0·009	0·010	0·011	0·011	0·012	0·013	0·013	0·014	0·015	0·015	0·016
4	0·011	0·012	0·013	0·014	0·015	0·016	0·017	0·018	0·018	0·019	0·020	0·021
5	0·014	0·015	0·016	0·018	0·019	0·020	0·021	0·022	0·023	0·024	0·025	0·026
6	0·017	0·018	0·020	0·021	0·022	0·024	0·025	0·026	0·028	0·029	0·030	0·032
7	0·020	0·022	0·023	0·025	0·026	0·028	0·029	0·031	0·032	0·034	0·035	0·037
8	0·023	0·025	0·026	0·028	0·030	0·032	0·033	0·035	0·037	0·039	0·040	0·042
9	0·026	0·028	0·030	0·032	0·034	0·036	0·037	0·039	0·041	0·043	0·045	0·047
10	0·029	0·031	0·033	0·035	0·037	0·039	0·040	0·042	0·044	0·046	0·048	0·050
20	0·057	0·061	0·066	0·070	0·075	0·079	0·083	0·088	0·092	0·096	0·101	0·105
30	0·086	0·092	0·099	0·105	0·112	0·118	0·125	0·132	0·138	0·145	0·151	0·158
40	0·114	0·123	0·132	0·140	0·149	0·158	0·167	0·175	0·184	0·193	0·202	0·210
50	0·143	0·153	0·164	0·175	0·186	0·197	0·208	0·219	0·230	0·241	0·252	0·263
60	0·171	0·184	0·197	0·210	0·224	0·237	0·250	0·263	0·276	0·289	0·302	0·316
70	0·200	0·215	0·230	0·246	0·261	0·276	0·292	0·307	0·322	0·338	0·353	0·368
80	0·228	0·246	0·263	0·281	0·298	0·316	0·333	0·351	0·368	0·386	0·403	0·421
90	0·256	0·276	0·296	0·316	0·335	0·355	0·375	0·395	0·414	0·434	0·454	0·473
100	0·285	0·307	0·329	0·351	0·373	0·395	0·416	0·438	0·460	0·482	0·504	0·526
200	0·570	0·614	0·658	0·701	0·745	0·789	0·833	0·877	0·921	0·964	1·008	1·052
300	0·855	0·920	0·986	1·052	1·118	1·184	1·249	1·315	1·381	1·447	1·512	1·578
400	1·140	1·227	1·315	1·403	1·490	1·578	1·666	1·753	1·841	1·929	2·016	2·104
500	1·425	1·534	1·644	1·753	1·863	1·973	2·082	2·192	2·301	2·411	2·521	2·630
600	1·710	1·841	1·973	2·104	2·236	2·367	2·499	2·630	2·762	2·893	3·025	3·156
700	1·995	2·148	2·301	2·455	2·608	2·762	2·915	3·069	3·222	3·375	3·528	3·682
800	2·280	2·455	2·630	2·806	2·981	3·156	3·332	3·507	3·682	3·858	4·033	4·208
900	2·564	2·762	2·959	3·156	3·353	3·551	3·748	3·945	4·142	4·340	4·537	4·734
1000	2·849	3·069	3·288	3·507	3·726	3·945	4·164	4·384	4·603	4·822	5·041	5·260

25 Days	26	27	28	29	30	40	50	60	100	200	300
1	0·006	0·006	0·006	0·006	0·007	0·009	0·011	0·013	0·022	0·044	0·066
2	0·011	0·011	0·012	0·012	0·013	0·013	0·018	0·022	0·026	0·044	0·088	0·132
3	0·016	0·017	0·018	0·018	0·019	0·020	0·026	0·033	0·039	0·066	0·132	0·197
4	0·022	0·023	0·024	0·025	0·025	0·026	0·035	0·044	0·053	0·088	0·175	0·263
5	0·027	0·029	0·030	0·031	0·032	0·033	0·044	0·055	0·066	0·110	0·219	0·329
6	0·033	0·034	0·036	0·037	0·038	0·039	0·053	0·066	0·079	0·132	0·263	0·395
7	0·038	0·040	0·041	0·043	0·045	0·046	0·061	0·077	0·092	0·153	0·307	0·460
8	0·044	0·046	0·047	0·049	0·051	0·053	0·070	0·088	0·105	0·175	0·351	0·526
9	0·049	0·051	0·053	0·055	0·057	0·059	0·079	0·099	0·118	0·197	0·395	0·592
10	0·055	0·057	0·059	0·061	0·064	0·066	0·088	0·110	0·132	0·219	0·438	0·658
20	0·110	0·114	0·118	0·123	0·127	0·132	0·175	0·219	0·263	0·438	0·877	1·315
30	0·164	0·171	0·178	0·184	0·191	0·197	0·263	0·329	0·395	0·658	1·315	1·973
40	0·219	0·228	0·237	0·246	0·254	0·263	0·351	0·438	0·526	0·877	1·753	2·630
50	0·274	0·285	0·296	0·307	0·318	0·329	0·438	0·547	0·658	1·096	2·192	3·288
60	0·329	0·342	0·355	0·368	0·381	0·365	0·526	0·658	0·789	1·315	2·630	3·945
70	0·384	0·399	0·414	0·430	0·445	0·460	0·614	0·767	0·921	1·534	3·069	4·603
80	0·438	0·456	0·473	0·491	0·509	0·526	0·701	0·877	1·052	1·753	3·507	5·260
90	0·493	0·513	0·533	0·552	0·572	0·592	0·789	0·986	1·184	1·973	3·945	5·918
100	0·548	0·570	0·592	0·614	0·636	0·658	0·877	1·096	1·315	2·192	4·384	6·575
200	1·096	1·140	1·184	1·227	1·271	1·315	1·753	2·192	2·630	4·384	8·767	13·151
300	1·644	1·710	1·775	1·841	1·907	1·973	2·630	3·288	3·945	6·575	13·151	19·726
400	2·192	2·279	2·367	2·455	2·542	2·630	3·507	4·384	5·260	8·767	17·534	26·301
500	2·740	3·849	2·959	3·069	3·178	3·288	4·384	5·479	6·575	10·959	21·918	32·877
600	3·288	3·419	3·551	3·682	3·814	3·945	5·260	6·575	7·890	13·151	26·301	39·452
700	3·836	3·989	4·143	4·296	4·449	4·603	6·137	7·671	9·206	15·342	30·685	46·027
800	4·384	4·559	4·734	4·910	5·085	5·260	7·014	8·767	10·521	17·534	35·069	52·603
900	4·932	5·129	5·326	5·523	5·721	5·918	7·890	9·863	11·836	19·726	39·452	59·178
1000	5·480	5·699	5·918	6·137	6·356	6·575	8·767	10·959	13·151	21·917	43·836	65·753

1 Mth.	2	3	4	5	6	7	8	9	10	11	12
1	0·007	0·013	0·02	0·027	0·033	0·04	0·047	0·053	0·06	0·066	0·073	0·080
2	0·013	0·027	0·04	0·053	0·067	0·08	0·093	0·107	0·12	0·133	0·147	0·160
3	0·020	0·040	0·06	0·080	0·100	0·12	0·140	0·160	0·18	0·200	0·220	0·240
4	0·027	0·053	0·08	0·107	0·133	0·16	0·187	0·213	0·24	0·267	0·293	0·320
5	0·033	0·067	0·10	0·133	0·167	0·20	0·233	0·267	0·30	0·333	0·367	0·400
6	0·040	0·080	0·12	0·160	0·200	0·24	0·280	0·320	0·36	0·400	0·440	0·480
7	0·047	0·093	0·14	0·187	0·233	0·28	0·327	0·373	0·42	0·467	0·513	0·560
8	0·053	0·107	0·16	0·213	0·267	0·32	0·373	0·427	0·48	0·533	0·587	0·640
9	0·060	0·120	0·18	0·240	0·300	0·36	0·420	0·480	0·54	0·600	0·660	0·720
10	0·067	0·133	0·20	0·267	0·333	0·40	0·467	0·533	0·60	0·667	0·733	0·800
20	0·133	0·267	0·40	0·533	0·667	0·80	0·933	1·067	1·20	1·333	1·467	1·600
30	0·200	0·400	0·60	0·800	1·000	1·20	1·400	1·600	1·80	2·000	2·200	2·400
40	0·267	0·533	0·80	1·067	1·333	1·60	1·867	2·133	2·40	2·667	2·933	3·200
50	0·333	0·667	1·00	1·333	1·667	2·00	2·333	2·666	3·00	3·333	3·667	4·000
60	0·400	0·800	1·20	1·600	2·000	2·40	2·800	3·200	3·60	4·000	4·400	4·800
70	0·467	0·933	1·40	1·867	2·333	2·80	3·267	3·733	4·20	4·666	5·133	5·600
80	0·533	1·067	1·60	2·133	2·667	3·20	3·733	4·266	4·80	5·333	5·867	6·400
90	0·600	1·200	1·80	2·400	3·000	3·60	4·200	4·800	5·40	6·000	6·600	7·200
100	0·667	1·333	2·00	2·667	3·333	4·00	4·667	5·333	6·00	6·667	7·333	8·000
200	1·333	2·667	4·00	5·333	6·667	8·00	9·333	10·667	12·00	13·333	14·667	16·000
300	2·000	4·000	6·00	8·000	10·000	12·00	14·000	16·000	18·00	20·000	22·000	24·000
400	2·667	5·333	8·00	10·667	13·333	16·00	18·667	21·333	24·00	26·667	29·333	32·000
500	3·333	6·667	10·00	13·333	16·667	20·00	23·333	26·667	30·00	33·333	36·667	40·000
600	4·000	8·000	12·00	16·000	20·000	24·00	28·000	32·000	36·00	40·000	44·000	48·000
700	4·667	9·333	14·00	18·667	23·333	28·00	32·667	37·333	42·00	46·667	51·333	56·000
800	5·333	10·667	16·00	21·333	26·667	32·00	37·333	42·667	48·00	53·333	58·667	64·000
900	6·000	12·000	18·00	24·000	30·000	36·00	42·000	48·000	54·00	60·000	66·000	72·000
1000	6·667	13·333	20·00	26·667	33·333	40·00	46·667	53·333	60·00	66·667	73·333	80·000

	1Day	2	3	4	5	6	7	8	9	10	11	12
1	·000	·001	·001	·001	0·001	0·002	0·002	0·002	0·002	0.003	0·003	0·003
2	·001	·001	·002	·002	0·003	0·003	0·004	0·004	0·004	0.005	0·005	0·006
3	·001	·002	·002	·003	0·004	0·004	0·005	0·006	0·007	0.007	0·008	0·009
4	·001	·002	·003	·004	0·005	0·006	0·007	0·008	0·009	0.010	0·011	0·012
5	·001	·003	·004	·005	0·006	0·007	0·009	0·010	0·011	0.012	0·014	0·015
6	·002	·003	·004	·006	0·007	0·009	0·010	0·012	0·013	0.015	0·016	0·018
7	·002	·004	·005	·007	0·009	0·010	0·012	0·014	0·016	0.017	0·019	0·021
8	·002	·004	·006	·008	0·010	0·012	0·014	0·016	0·018	0.020	0·022	0·024
9	·002	·004	·007	·009	0·011	0·013	0·016	0·018	0·020	0.022	0·024	0·027
10	·002	·005	·007	·010	0·012	0·015	0 017	0·020	0·022	0.025	0·027	0·030
20	·005	·010	·015	·020	0·025	0·030	0·035	0·040	0·044	0.049	0·054	0·059
30	·007	·015	·022	·030	0·037	0·044	0·052	0·059	0·067	0.074	0·081	0·089
40	·010	·020	·030	·040	0·049	0·059	0·069	0·079	0·089	0.099	0·109	0·118
50	·012	·025	·037	·049	0·062	0·074	0·086	0·099	0·111	0.123	0·136	0·148
60	·015	·030	·044	·059	0·074	0·089	0·104	0·118	0·133	0.148	0·163	0·178
70	·017	·035	·052	·069	0·086	0·104	0·121	0·138	0·155	0.173	0·190	0·207
80	·020	·040	·059	·079	0·099	0·118	0·138	0·158	0·178	0.197	0·217	0·237
90	·022	·044	·067	·089	0·111	0·133	0·155	0·178	0·200	0.222	0·244	0·266
100	·025	·049	·074	·099	0·123	0·148	0·173	0·197	0·222	0.247	0·271	0·296
200	·049	·099	·148	·197	0·247	0·296	0·345	0·394	0·444	0·493	0·543	0·592
300	·074	·148	·222	·296	0·370	0·444	0·518	0·592	0·666	0·740	0·814	0·888
400	·099	·197	·296	·395	0·493	0·592	0·690	0·789	0·888	0·986	1·085	1·184
500	·123	·247	·370	·493	0·616	0·740	0·863	0·986	1·110	1·233	1·356	1·480
600	·148	·296	·444	·592	0·740	0·888	1·036	1·184	1·332	1·480	1·627	1·775
700	·173	·345	·518	·690	0·863	1·036	1·208	1·381	1·553	1·726	1·899	2·071
800	·197	·395	·592	·789	0·986	1·184	1·381	1·578	1·775	1·973	2·170	2·367
900	·222	·444	·666	·888	1·110	1·332	1·553	1·775	1·997	2·219	2·441	2·663
1000	·247	·493	·740	·986	1·233	1·480	1·726	1·973	2·219	2·466	2·712	2·959

	13	14	15	16	17	18	19	20	21	22	23	24
1	0·003	0·004	0·004	0·004	0·004	0·004	0·005	0·005	0·005	0·005	0·006	0·006
2	0·006	0·007	0·007	0·008	0·008	0·009	0·009	0·010	0·010	0·011	0·011	0·012
3	0·010	0·010	0·011	0·012	0·013	0·013	0·014	0·015	0·016	0·016	0·017	0·018
4	0·013	0·014	0·015	0·016	0·017	0·018	0·019	0·020	0·021	0·022	0·023	0·024
5	0·016	0·017	0·019	0·020	0·021	0·022	0·023	0·025	0·026	0·027	0·028	0·030
6	0·019	0·021	0·022	0·024	0·025	0·027	0·028	0·030	0·031	0·033	0·034	0·036
7	0·022	0·024	0·026	0·028	0·029	0·031	0·033	0·035	0·036	0·038	0·040	0·041
8	0·026	0·028	0·030	0·032	0·034	0·036	0·038	0·040	0·041	0·043	0·045	0·047
9	0·029	0·031	0·033	0·036	0·038	0·040	0·042	0·044	0·047	0·049	0·051	0·053
10	0·032	0·035	0·037	0·040	0·042	0·044	0·047	0·049	0·052	0·054	0·057	0·059
20	0·064	0·069	0·074	0·079	0·084	0·089	0·094	0·099	0·104	0·109	0·113	0.118
30	0·096	0·104	0·111	0·118	0·126	0·133	0·141	0·148	0·155	0·163	0·170	0·178
40	0·128	0·138	0·148	0·158	0·168	0·178	0·187	0·197	0·207	0·217	0·227	0.237
50	0·160	0·173	0·185	0·197	0·210	0·222	0·234	0·247	0·259	0·271	0·284	0·296
60	0·192	0·207	0·222	0·237	0·252	0·266	0·281	0·296	0·311	0·326	0·340	0·355
70	0·224	0·242	0·259	0·276	0·293	0·311	0·328	0·345	0·363	0·380	0·397	0·414
80	0·256	0·276	0·296	0·316	0·335	0·355	0·375	0·395	0·414	0·434	0·454	0·473
90	0·289	0·311	0·333	0·355	0·377	0·400	0·422	0·444	0·466	0·488	0·510	0·533
100	0·321	0·345	0·370	0·395	0·419	0·444	0·469	0·493	0·518	0·543	0·567	0·592
200	0·641	0·690	0·740	0·789	0·838	0·888	0·937	0·986	1·036	1·085	1·134	1·184
300	0·962	1·036	1·110	1·184	1·258	1·332	1·406	1·480	1·553	1·627	1·701	1·775
400	1·282	1·381	1·480	1·578	1·677	1·775	1·874	1·973	2·071	2·170	2·269	2·367
500	1·603	1·726	1·849	1·973	2·096	2·219	2·343	2·466	2·589	2·712	2·836	2·959
600	1·923	2·071	2·219	2·367	2·515	2·663	2·811	2·959	3·107	3·255	3·403	3·551
700	2·244	2·416	2·589	2·762	2·934	3·107	3·280	3·452	3·625	3·797	3·970	4·143
800	2·564	2·762	2·959	3·156	3·353	3·551	3·748	3·945	4·143	4·340	4·537	4·734
900	2·885	3·107	3·329	3·551	3·773	3·995	4·216	4·438	4·660	4·882	5·104	5·326
1000	3·206	3·452	3·699	3·945	4·192	4·438	4·685	4·932	5·178	5·425	5·671	5·918

	25 Days	26	27	28	29	30	40	50	60	100	200	300
1	0·006	0·006	0·007	0·007	0·007	0·007	0·010	0·012	0·015	0·025	0·049	0·074
2	0·012	0·013	0·013	0·014	0·014	0·015	0·020	0·025	0·030	0·049	0·099	0·148
3	0·019	0·019	0·020	0·021	0·022	0·022	0·030	0·037	0·044	0·074	0·148	0·222
4	0·025	0·026	0·027	0·028	0·029	0·030	0·040	0·049	0·059	0·099	0·197	0·296
5	0·031	0·032	0·033	0·035	0·036	0·037	0·049	0·062	0·074	0·123	0·247	0·370
6	0·037	0·039	0·040	0·041	0·043	0·044	0·059	0·074	0·089	0·148	0·296	0·444
7	0·043	0·045	0·047	0·048	0·050	0·052	0·069	0·086	0·104	0·173	0·345	0·518
8	0·049	0·051	0·053	0·055	0·057	0·059	0·079	0·099	0·118	0·197	0·395	0·592
9	0·056	0·058	0·060	0·062	0·064	0·067	0·089	0·111	0·133	0·222	0·444	0·666
10	0·062	0·064	0·067	0·069	0·072	0·074	0·099	0·123	0·148	0·247	0·493	0·740
20	0·123	0·128	0·133	0·138	0·143	0·148	0·197	0·247	0·296	0·493	0·986	1·480
30	0·185	0·192	0·200	0·207	0·215	0·222	0·296	0·370	0·444	0·740	1·480	2·219
40	0·247	0·256	0·266	0·276	0·286	0·296	0·395	0·493	0·592	0·986	1·973	2·959
50	0·308	0·321	0·333	0·345	0·358	0·370	0·493	0·616	0·740	1·233	2·466	3·699
60	0·370	0·385	0·400	0·414	0·429	0·444	0·592	0·740	0·888	1·480	2·959	4·438
70	0·432	0·449	0·466	0·483	0·501	0·518	0·690	0·863	1·036	1·726	3·452	5·178
80	0·493	0·513	0·533	0·552	0·572	0·592	0·789	0·986	1·184	1·973	3·945	5·918
90	0·555	0·577	0·599	0·621	0·644	0·666	0·888	1·110	1·332	2·219	4·438	6·658
100	0·616	0·641	0·666	0·690	0·715	0·740	0·986	1·233	1·480	2·466	4·932	7·397
200	1·233	1·282	1·332	1·381	1·430	1·480	1·973	2·466	2·959	4·932	9·863	14·795
300	1·849	1·923	1·997	2·071	2·145	2·219	2·959	3·699	4·438	7·397	14·795	22·192
400	2·466	2·564	2·663	2·762	2·860	2·959	3·945	4·932	5·918	9·863	19·726	29·589
500	3·082	3·206	3·329	3·452	3·575	3·699	4·932	6·164	7·397	12·329	24·658	36·986
600	3·699	3·847	3·995	4·143	4·290	4·438	5·918	7·397	8·877	14·795	29·589	44·384
700	4·315	4·488	4·660	4·833	5·006	5·178	6·904	8·630	10·356	17·260	34·521	51·780
800	4·932	5·129	5·326	5·523	5·721	5·918	7·890	9·863	11·836	19·726	39·452	59·178
900	5·548	5·770	5·992	6·214	6·436	6·658	8·877	11·096	13·315	22·192	44·384	66·575
1000	6·164	6·411	6·658	6·904	7·151	7·397	9·863	12·329	14·795	24·658	49·315	73·973

	1 Mth.	2	3	4	5	6	7	8	9	10	11	12
1	0·008	0·015	0·023	0·03	0·038	0·045	0·053	0·06	0·068	0·075	0·083	0·09
2	0·015	0·030	0·045	0·06	0·075	0·090	0·105	0·12	0·135	0·150	0·165	0·18
3	0·023	0·045	0·068	0·09	0·113	0·135	0·158	0·18	0·203	0·225	0·248	0·27
4	0·030	0·060	0·090	0·12	0·150	0·180	0·210	0·24	0·270	0·300	0·330	0·36
5	0·038	0·075	0·113	0·15	0·188	0·225	0·263	0·30	0·338	0·375	0·413	0·45
6	0·045	0·090	0·135	0·18	0·225	0·270	0·315	0·36	0·405	0·450	0·495	0·54
7	0·053	0·105	0·158	0·21	0·263	0·315	0·368	0·42	0·473	0·525	0·578	0·63
8	0·060	0·120	0·180	0·24	0·300	0·360	0·420	0·48	0·540	0·600	0·660	0·72
9	0·068	0·135	0·203	0·27	0·338	0·405	0·473	0·54	0·608	0·675	0·743	0·81
10	0·075	0·150	0·225	0·30	0·375	0·450	0·525	0·60	0·675	0·750	0·825	0·90
20	0·150	0·300	0·450	0·60	0·750	0·900	1·050	1·20	1·350	1·500	1·650	1·80
30	0·225	0·450	0·675	0·90	1·125	1·350	1·575	1·80	2·025	2·250	2·475	2·70
40	0·300	0·600	0·900	1·20	1·500	1·800	2·100	2·40	2·700	3·000	3·300	3·60
50	0·375	0·750	1·125	1·50	1·875	2·250	2·625	3·00	3·375	3·750	4·125	4·50
60	0·450	0·900	1·350	1·80	2·250	2·700	3·150	3·60	4·050	4·500	4·950	5·40
70	0·525	1·050	1·575	2·10	2·625	3·150	3·675	4·20	4·725	5·250	5·775	6·30
80	0·600	1·200	1·800	2·40	3·000	3·600	4·200	4·80	5·400	6·000	6·600	7·20
90	0·675	1·350	2·025	2·70	3·375	4·050	4·725	5·40	6·075	6·750	7·425	8·10
100	0·750	1·500	2·250	3·00	3·750	4·500	5·250	6·00	6·750	7·500	8·250	9·00
200	1·500	3·000	4·500	6·00	7·500	9·000	10·500	12·00	13·500	15·000	16·500	18·00
300	2·250	4·500	6·750	9·00	11·250	13·500	15·750	18·00	20·250	22·500	24·750	27·00
400	3·000	6·000	9·000	12·00	15·000	18·000	21·000	24·00	27·000	30·000	33·000	36·00
500	3·750	7·500	11·250	15·00	18·750	22·500	26·250	30·00	33·750	37·500	41·250	45·00
600	4·500	9·000	13·500	18·00	22·500	27·000	31·500	36·00	40·500	45·000	49·500	54·00
700	5·250	10·500	15·750	21·00	26·250	31·500	36·750	42·00	47·250	52·500	57·750	63·00
800	6·000	12·000	18·000	24·00	30·000	36·000	42·000	48·00	54·000	60·000	66·000	72·00
900	6·750	13·500	20·250	27·00	33·750	40·500	47·250	54·00	60·750	67·500	74·250	81·00
1000	7·500	15·000	22·500	30·00	37·500	45·000	52·500	60·00	67·500	75·000	82·500	90·00

SECTION IV.

1. Per Cwt.
2. Per Ton.
3. Per Kilo.
4. Miscellaneous Tables :
   Lbs. expressed in Cwts., Qrs. and Lbs.
   Equivalents per Lb., Kilo, Cwt. and Ton.
   Metric Conversion Tables.
   Multiplication Tables.
   Salary per Annum, Month, Week and Day.
   40 hr. Week Wage Tables.

PER CWT. AND PER TON.

The value of every Lb. at every Penny from 1–99 pence and every £ from £1–£99 per Cwt., and from 1p–£900 per Ton, is obtained by adding the required number of Lbs., Qrs., or Cwts. from two component rates on the facing pages. The small figures represent tenths of a penny, and are necessary for addition purposes to give accurate valuation.

Examples :

    47 lbs. @ 53 pence per Cwt.
    47 lbs. @ 50p per Cwt. $=21^8$p
    47 lbs. @ 3p per Cwt. $= 1^3$p

                            22^3p$=22$p

    33 lbs. @ £47 per Cwt.
    33 lbs. @ £40 per Cwt. $=$£11 78^6p
    33 lbs. @ £7 per Cwt. $=$ £2 6^3p

                    $=$£13 84^9p$=$£13 85p

    25 lbs. @ £94 per Ton.
    25 lbs. @ £90 per ton $=$£1 0^4p
    25 lbs. @ £4 per ton $=$£0 4^5p

                        £1 4^9p$=$£1 5p

    14 Cwts. at £423 per Ton.
    14 cwts. @ £400 per ton $=$£280 0p
    14 cwts. @ £20 per ton $=$ 14 0p
    14 cwts. @   £3 per ton $=$ 2 10p

                            £296 10p

PER KILO.

The value of every lb. at every penny per kilo from 1p–£1 per kilo, is obtained by adding the required number of lbs. from two or more component rates on the facing pages. The small figures represent tenths of a penny, and are necessary for addition purposes to give accurate valuation.

Example :

    73 lbs. @ 93p per Kilo.
    73 lbs. @ 90p per kilo $=$£29 80 p
    73 lbs. @ 3p per kilo $=$ £0 99^2p

                        £30 79^4p$=$£30 79p

LBS. EXPRESSED IN CWTS. AND QRS.

lbs.	c. q. lb.	lbs.	c. q. lb.	lbs.	c. q. lb.	lbs.	c. q. lb.	lbs.	c. q. lb.	lbs.	c. q. lb.
63	0 2 7	427	3 3 7	791	7 0 7	1155	10 1 7	1519	13 2 7	1883	16 3 7
70	0 2 14	434	3 3 14	798	7 0 14	1162	10 1 14	1526	13 2 14	1890	16 3 14
77	0 2 21	441	3 3 21	805	7 0 21	1169	10 1 21	1533	13 2 21	1897	16 3 21
84	0 3 0	448	4 0 0	812	7 1 0	1176	10 2 0	1540	13 3 0	1904	17 0 0
91	0 3 7	455	4 0 7	819	7 1 7	1183	10 2 7	1547	13 3 7	1911	17 0 7
98	0 3 14	462	4 0 14	826	7 1 14	1190	10 2 14	1554	13 3 14	1918	17 0 14
105	0 3 21	469	4 0 21	833	7 1 21	1197	10 2 21	1561	13 3 21	1925	17 0 21
112	1 0 0	476	4 1 0	840	7 2 0	1204	10 3 0	1568	14 0 0	1932	17 1 0
119	1 0 7	483	4 1 7	847	7 2 7	1211	10 3 7	1575	14 0 7	1939	17 1 7
126	1 0 14	490	4 1 14	854	7 2 14	1218	10 3 14	1582	14 0 14	1946	17 1 14
133	1 0 21	497	4 1 21	861	7 2 21	1225	10 3 21	1589	14 0 21	1953	17 1 21
140	1 1 0	504	4 2 0	868	7 3 0	1232	11 0 0	1596	14 1 0	1960	17 2 0
147	1 1 7	511	4 2 7	875	7 3 7	1239	11 0 7	1603	14 1 7	1967	17 2 7
154	1 1 14	518	4 2 14	882	7 3 14	1246	11 0 14	1610	14 1 14	1974	17 2 14
161	1 1 21	525	4 2 21	889	7 3 21	1253	11 0 21	1617	14 1 21	1981	17 2 21
168	1 2 0	532	4 3 0	896	8 0 0	1260	11 1 0	1624	14 2 0	1988	17 3 0
175	1 2 7	539	4 3 7	903	8 0 7	1267	11 1 7	1631	14 2 7	1995	17 3 7
182	1 2 14	546	4 3 14	910	8 0 14	1274	11 1 14	1638	14 2 14	2002	17 3 14
189	1 2 21	553	4 3 21	917	8 0 21	1281	11 1 21	1645	14 2 21	2009	17 3 21
196	1 3 0	560	5 0 0	924	8 1 0	1288	11 2 0	1652	14 3 0	2016	18 0 0
203	1 3 7	567	5 0 7	931	8 1 7	1295	11 2 7	1659	14 3 7	2023	18 0 7
210	1 3 14	574	5 0 14	938	8 1 14	1302	11 2 14	1666	14 3 14	2030	18 0 14
217	1 3 21	581	5 0 21	945	8 1 21	1309	11 2 21	1673	14 3 21	2037	18 0 21
224	2 0 0	588	5 1 0	952	8 2 0	1316	11 3 0	1680	15 0 0	2044	18 1 0
231	2 0 7	595	5 1 7	959	8 2 7	1323	11 3 7	1687	15 0 7	2051	18 1 7
238	2 0 14	602	5 1 14	966	8 2 14	1330	11 3 14	1694	15 0 14	2058	18 1 14
245	2 0 21	609	5 1 21	973	8 2 21	1337	11 3 21	1701	15 0 21	2065	18 1 21
252	2 1 0	616	5 2 0	980	8 3 0	1344	12 0 0	1708	15 1 0	2072	18 2 0
259	2 1 7	623	5 2 7	987	8 3 7	1351	12 0 7	1715	15 1 7	2079	18 2 7
266	2 1 14	630	5 2 14	994	8 3 14	1358	12 0 14	1722	15 1 14	2086	18 2 14
273	2 1 21	637	5 2 21	1001	8 3 21	1365	12 0 21	1729	15 1 21	2093	18 2 21
280	2 2 0	644	5 3 0	1008	9 0 0	1372	12 1 0	1736	15 2 0	2100	18 3 0
287	2 2 7	651	5 3 7	1015	9 0 7	1379	12 1 7	1743	15 2 7	2107	18 3 7
294	2 2 14	658	5 3 14	1022	9 0 14	1386	12 1 14	1750	15 2 14	2114	18 3 14
301	2 2 21	665	5 3 21	1029	9 0 21	1393	12 1 21	1757	15 2 21	2121	18 3 21
308	2 3 0	672	6 0 0	1036	9 1 0	1400	12 2 0	1764	15 3 0	2128	19 0 0
315	2 3 7	679	6 0 7	1043	9 1 7	1407	12 2 7	1771	15 3 7	2135	19 0 7
322	2 3 14	686	6 0 14	1050	9 1 14	1414	12 2 14	1778	15 3 14	2142	19 0 14
329	2 3 21	693	6 0 21	1057	9 1 21	1421	12 2 21	1785	15 3 21	2149	19 0 21
336	3 0 0	700	6 1 0	1064	9 2 0	1428	12 3 0	1792	16 0 0	2156	19 1 0
343	3 0 7	707	6 1 7	1071	9 2 7	1435	12 3 7	1799	16 0 7	2163	19 1 7
350	3 0 14	714	6 1 14	1078	9 2 14	1442	12 3 14	1806	16 0 14	2170	19 1 14
357	3 0 21	721	6 1 21	1085	9 2 21	1449	12 3 21	1813	16 0 21	2177	19 1 21
364	3 1 0	728	6 2 0	1092	9 3 0	1456	13 0 0	1820	16 1 0	2184	19 2 0
371	3 1 7	735	6 2 7	1099	9 3 7	1463	13 0 7	1827	16 1 7	2191	19 2 7
378	3 1 14	742	6 2 14	1106	9 3 14	1470	13 0 14	1834	16 1 14	2198	19 2 14
385	3 1 21	749	6 2 21	1113	9 3 21	1477	13 0 21	1841	16 1 21	2205	19 2 21
392	3 2 0	756	6 3 0	1120	10 0 0	1484	13 1 0	1848	16 2 0	2212	19 3 0
399	3 2 7	763	6 3 7	1127	10 0 7	1491	13 1 7	1855	16 2 7	2219	19 3 7
406	3 2 14	770	6 3 14	1134	10 0 14	1498	13 1 14	1862	16 2 14	2226	19 3 14
413	3 2 21	777	6 3 21	1141	10 0 21	1505	13 1 21	1869	16 2 21	2233	19 3 21
420	3 3 0	784	7 0 0	1148	10 1 0	1512	13 2 0	1876	16 3 0	2240	20 0 0

2000 lb.	T.0 17c. 3q. 12lb	5000 lb.	T.2 4c. 2q 16lb	8000 lb.	T.3 11c. 1q. 20lb
3000 ,,	1 6 3 4	6000 ,,	2 13 2 8	9000 ,,	4 0 1 12
4000 ,,	1 15 2 24	7000 ,,	3 2 2 0	10,000	4 9 1 4

Per Cwt. Lbs.	1p	2p	2½p	3p	4p	5p	6p	7p	7½p	8p	9p
	P	P	P	P	P	P	P	P	P	P	P
1	–	–	–	–	–	–	0^1	0^1	0^1	0^1	0^1
2	–	–	0^1	0^1	0^1	0^1	0^1	0^1	0^1	0^1	0^2
3	–	0^1	0^1	0^1	0^1	0^1	0^2	0^2	0^2	0^2	0^2
4	–	0^1	0^1	0^1	0^1	0^2	0^2	0^3	0^3	0^3	0^3
5	–	0^1	0^1	0^1	0^2	0^2	0^2	0^3	0^3	0^4	0^4
6	0^1	0^1	0^1	0^2	0^2	0^3	0^3	0^4	0^4	0^4	0^5
7	0^1	0^1	0^2	0^2	0^3	0^3	0^4	0^4	0^5	0^5	0^6
8	0^1	0^1	0^2	0^2	0^3	0^4	0^4	0^5	0^5	0^6	0^6
9	0^1	0^2	0^2	0^2	0^3	0^4	0^5	0^6	0^6	0^6	0^7
10	0^1	0^2	0^2	0^2	0^3	0^4	0^5	0^6	0^6	0^7	0^8
11	0^1	0^2	0^2	0^3	0^4	0^5	0^5	0^6	0^7	0^8	0^9
12	0^1	0^2	0^3	0^3	0^4	0^5	0^6	0^7	0^8	0^9	1^0
13	0^1	0^2	0^3	0^3	0^5	0^6	0^6	0^7	0^8	0^9	1^0
14	0^1	0^2	0^3	0^4	0^5	0^6	0^8	0^9	0^9	1^0	1^1
15	0^1	0^3	0^3	0^4	0^5	0^7	0^8	0^9	1^0	1^1	1^2
16	0^1	0^3	0^4	0^4	0^6	0^7	0^9	1^0	1^1	1^1	1^3
17	0^2	0^3	0^4	0^5	0^6	0^8	0^9	1^1	1^1	1^2	1^4
18	0^2	0^3	0^4	0^5	0^6	0^8	1^0	1^1	1^2	1^3	1^4
19	0^2	0^3	0^4	0^5	0^7	0^8	1^0	1^2	1^3	1^4	1^5
20	0^2	0^4	0^4	0^5	0^7	0^9	1^1	1^3	1^3	1^4	1^6
21	0^2	0^4	0^5	0^6	0^8	0^9	1^1	1^3	1^4	1^5	1^7
22	0^2	0^4	0^5	0^6	0^8	1^0	1^2	1^4	1^5	1^6	1^8
23	0^2	0^4	0^5	0^6	0^8	1^0	1^2	1^4	1^5	1^6	1^8
24	0^2	0^4	0^5	0^6	0^9	1^1	1^3	1^5	1^6	1^7	1^9
25	0^2	0^4	0^6	0^7	0^9	1^1	1^3	1^6	1^7	1^8	2^0
26	0^2	0^5	0^6	0^7	0^9	1^2	1^4	1^6	1^7	1^9	2^1
27	0^2	0^5	0^6	0^7	1^0	1^2	1^5	1^7	1^8	1^9	2^2
28	0^2	0^5	0^6	0^8	1^0	1^3	1^5	1^8	1^9	2^0	2^3
29	0^3	0^5	0^6	0^8	1^0	1^3	1^6	1^8	1^9	2^1	2^4
30	0^3	0^5	0^7	0^8	1^1	1^3	1^6	1^9	2^0	2^1	2^4
31	0^3	0^6	0^7	0^8	1^1	1^4	1^7	1^9	2^0	2^2	2^5
32	0^3	0^6	0^7	0^9	1^1	1^4	1^7	2^0	2^1	2^3	2^6
33	0^3	0^6	0^7	0^9	1^2	1^5	1^8	2^1	2^2	2^4	2^7
34	0^3	0^6	0^8	0^9	1^2	1^5	1^8	2^1	2^2	2^4	2^7
35	0^3	0^6	0^8	0^9	1^3	1^6	1^9	2^2	2^3	2^5	2^8
36	0^3	0^6	0^8	1^0	1^3	1^6	1^9	2^3	2^4	2^6	2^9
37	0^3	0^7	0^8	1^0	1^3	1^7	2^0	2^3	2^5	2^6	3^0
38	0^3	0^7	0^8	1^0	1^4	1^7	2^0	2^4	2^5	2^7	3^1
39	0^3	0^7	0^9	1^0	1^4	1^7	2^1	2^4	2^6	2^8	3^2
40	0^4	0^7	0^9	1^1	1^4	1^8	2^1	2^5	2^7	2^9	3^2
41	0^4	0^7	0^9	1^1	1^5	1^8	2^2	2^6	2^7	2^9	3^3
42	0^4	0^8	0^9	1^1	1^5	1^9	2^3	2^6	2^8	3^0	3^4
43	0^4	0^8	1^0	1^2	1^5	1^9	2^3	2^7	2^9	3^1	3^5
44	0^4	0^8	1^0	1^2	1^6	2^0	2^4	2^8	2^9	3^1	3^5
45	0^4	0^8	1^0	1^2	1^6	2^0	2^4	2^8	3^0	3^2	3^6
46	0^4	0^8	1^0	1^2	1^6	2^1	2^5	2^9	3^1	3^3	3^7
47	0^4	0^8	1^1	1^3	1^7	2^1	2^5	2^9	3^1	3^3	3^7
48	0^4	0^9	1^1	1^3	1^7	2^1	2^6	3^0	3^2	3^4	3^8
49	0^4	0^9	1^1	1^3	1^8	2^2	2^6	3^1	3^3	3^5	3^9
50	0^4	0^9	1^1	1^3	1^8	2^2	2^7	3^1	3^3	3^6	4^0
51	0^5	0^9	1^1	1^4	1^8	2^3	2^7	3^2	3^4	3^6	4^0
52	0^5	0^9	1^2	1^4	1^9	2^3	2^8	3^3	3^5	3^7	4^1
53	0^5	0^9	1^2	1^4	1^9	2^4	2^8	3^3	3^6	3^8	4^3
54	0^5	1^0	1^2	1^4	1^9	2^4	2^9	3^4	3^6	3^9	4^3
55	0^5	1^0	1^2	1^5	2^0	2^5	3^0	3^4	3^7	3^9	4^4
56	0^5	1^0	1^2	1^5	2^0	2^5	3^0	3^5	3^7	4^0	4^5

Per Cwt. Lbs.	1p	2p	2½p	3p	4p	5p	6p	7p	7½p	8p	9p
	P	P	P	P	P	P	P	P	P	P	P
57	0^5	1^0	1^3	1^5	2^0	2^5	3^0	3^6	3^8	4^1	4^6
58	0^5	1^0	1^3	1^6	2^1	2^6	3^1	3^6	3^8	4^1	4^7
59	0^5	1^1	1^3	1^6	2^1	2^6	3^2	3^7	3^9	4^2	4^7
60	0^5	1^1	1^3	1^6	2^1	2^7	3^2	3^8	4^0	4^3	4^8
61	0^5	1^1	1^4	1^6	2^2	2^7	3^3	3^8	4^0	4^4	4^9
62	0^6	1^1	1^4	1^7	2^2	2^8	3^3	3^9	4^1	4^4	5^0
63	0^6	1^1	1^4	1^7	2^3	2^8	3^4	3^9	4^2	4^5	5^1
64	0^6	1^1	1^4	1^7	2^3	2^9	3^4	4^0	4^2	4^6	5^1
65	0^6	1^2	1^5	1^7	2^3	2^9	3^5	4^1	4^3	4^6	5^2
66	0^6	1^2	1^5	1^8	2^4	2^9	3^5	4^1	4^4	4^7	5^3
67	0^6	1^2	1^5	1^8	2^4	3^0	3^6	4^2	4^4	4^8	5^4
68	0^6	1^2	1^5	1^8	2^4	3^0	3^6	4^3	4^5	4^9	5^5
69	0^6	1^2	1^5	1^9	2^5	3^1	3^7	4^3	4^6	4^9	5^5
70	0^6	1^3	1^6	1^9	2^5	3^1	3^8	4^4	4^6	5^0	5^6
71	0^6	1^3	1^6	1^9	2^5	3^2	3^8	4^4	4^7	5^1	5^7
72	0^6	1^3	1^6	1^9	2^6	3^2	3^9	4^5	4^8	5^1	5^8
73	0^7	1^3	1^6	2^0	2^6	3^3	3^9	4^6	4^8	5^2	5^8
74	0^7	1^3	1^7	2^0	2^6	3^3	4^0	4^6	4^9	5^3	5^9
75	0^7	1^3	1^7	2^0	2^7	3^4	4^0	4^7	5^0	5^4	6^0
76	0^7	1^4	1^7	2^0	2^7	3^4	4^1	4^8	5^0	5^4	6^1
77	0^7	1^4	1^7	2^1	2^8	3^4	4^1	4^8	5^1	5^5	6^2
78	0^7	1^4	1^7	2^1	2^8	3^5	4^2	4^9	5^2	5^6	6^3
79	0^7	1^4	1^8	2^1	2^8	3^5	4^2	4^9	5^2	5^6	6^3
80	0^7	1^4	1^8	2^1	2^9	3^6	4^3	5^0	5^3	5^7	6^4
81	0^7	1^4	1^8	2^2	2^9	3^6	4^3	5^1	5^4	5^8	6^5
82	0^7	1^5	1^8	2^2	2^9	3^7	4^4	5^1	5^4	5^9	6^6
83	0^7	1^5	1^9	2^2	3^0	3^7	4^4	5^2	5^5	5^9	6^7
84	0^8	1^5	1^9	2^3	3^0	3^8	4^5	5^3	5^6	6^0	6^8
85	0^8	1^5	1^9	2^3	3^0	3^8	4^6	5^3	5^6	6^1	6^8
86	0^8	1^5	1^9	2^3	3^1	3^8	4^6	5^4	5^7	6^1	6^9
87	0^8	1^6	1^9	2^3	3^1	3^9	4^7	5^4	5^8	6^2	7^0
88	0^8	1^6	2^0	2^4	3^1	3^9	4^7	5^5	5^8	6^3	7^1
89	0^8	1^6	2^0	2^4	3^2	4^0	4^8	5^6	5^9	6^4	7^2
90	0^8	1^6	2^0	2^4	3^2	4^0	4^8	5^6	6^0	6^4	7^2
91	0^8	1^6	2^0	2^4	3^3	4^1	4^9	5^7	6^0	6^5	7^3
92	0^8	1^6	2^1	2^5	3^3	4^1	4^9	5^8	6^1	6^6	7^4
93	0^8	1^7	2^1	2^5	3^3	4^2	5^0	5^8	6^2	6^6	7^5
94	0^8	1^7	2^1	2^5	3^4	4^2	5^0	5^9	6^2	6^7	7^6
95	0^9	1^7	2^1	2^5	3^4	4^2	5^1	5^9	6^3	6^8	7^6
96	0^9	1^7	2^1	2^6	3^4	4^3	5^1	6^0	6^4	6^9	7^7
97	0^9	1^7	2^2	2^6	3^5	4^3	5^2	6^1	6^4	6^9	7^8
98	0^9	1^8	2^2	2^6	3^5	4^4	5^3	6^1	6^5	7^0	7^9
99	0^9	1^8	2^2	2^7	3^5	4^4	5^3	6^2	6^6	7^1	8^0
100	0^9	1^8	2^2	2^7	3^6	4^5	5^4	6^3	6^6	7^1	8^0
101	0^9	1^8	2^3	2^7	3^6	4^5	5^4	6^3	6^7	7^2	8^1
102	0^9	1^8	2^3	2^7	3^6	4^6	5^4	6^4	6^8	7^3	8^2
103	0^9	1^8	2^3	2^8	3^7	4^6	5^5	6^4	6^8	7^4	8^3
104	0^9	1^9	2^3	2^8	3^7	4^6	5^6	6^5	6^9	7^4	8^4
105	0^9	1^9	2^3	2^8	3^8	4^7	5^6	6^6	7^0	7^5	8^4
106	0^9	1^9	2^4	2^8	3^8	4^7	5^7	6^6	7^0	7^6	8^5
107	1^0	1^9	2^4	2^9	3^8	4^8	5^7	6^7	7^1	7^6	8^6
108	1^0	1^9	2^4	2^9	3^9	4^8	5^8	6^8	7^2	7^7	8^7
109	1^0	1^9	2^4	2^9	3^9	4^9	5^8	6^8	7^2	7^8	8^7
110	1^0	2^0	2^5	2^9	3^9	4^9	5^9	6^9	7^3	7^9	8^8
111	1^0	2^0	2^5	3^0	4^0	5^0	5^9	6^9	7^4	7^9	8^9
112	1^0	2^0	2^5	3^0	4^0	5^0	6^0	7^0	7^5	8^0	9^0

Per Cwt. Lbs.	10p	20p	30p	40p	50p	60p	70p	80p	90p
	P	P	P	P	P	P	P	P	P
1	0^1	0^2	0^3	0^4	0^5	0^5	0^6	0^7	0^8
2	0^2	0^4	0^5	0^7	0^9	1^1	1^3	1^4	1^6
3	0^3	0^5	0^8	1^1	1^3	1^6	1^9	2^1	2^4
4	0^4	0^7	1^1	1^4	1^8	2^1	2^5	2^9	3^2
5	0^5	0^9	1^3	1^8	2^2	2^7	3^1	3^6	4^0
6	0^5	1^1	1^6	2^1	2^7	3^2	3^8	4^3	4^8
7	0^6	1^3	1^9	2^5	3^1	3^8	4^4	5^0	5^6
8	0^7	1^4	2^1	2^9	3^6	4^3	5^0	5^7	6^4
9	0^8	1^6	2^4	3^2	4^0	4^8	5^6	6^4	7^2
10	0^9	1^8	2^7	3^6	4^5	5^4	6^3	7^1	8^0
11	1^0	2^0	2^9	3^9	4^9	5^9	6^9	7^9	8^8
12	1^1	2^1	3^2	4^3	5^4	6^4	7^5	8^6	9^6
13	1^2	2^3	3^5	4^6	5^8	7^0	8^1	9^3	10^4
14	1^3	2^5	3^8	5^0	6^3	7^5	8^8	10^0	11^3
15	1^3	2^7	4^0	5^4	6^7	8^0	9^4	10^7	12^1
16	1^4	2^9	4^3	5^7	7^1	8^6	10^0	11^4	12^9
17	1^5	3^0	4^6	6^1	7^6	9^1	10^6	12^1	13^7
18	1^6	3^2	4^8	6^4	8^0	9^6	11^3	12^9	14^5
19	1^7	3^4	5^1	6^8	8^5	10^2	11^9	13^6	15^3
20	1^8	3^6	5^4	7^1	8^9	10^7	12^5	14^3	16^1
21	1^9	3^8	5^6	7^5	9^4	11^3	13^1	15^0	16^9
22	2^0	3^9	5^9	7^9	9^8	11^8	13^8	15^7	17^7
23	2^1	4^1	6^2	8^2	10^3	12^3	14^4	16^4	18^5
24	2^1	4^3	6^4	8^6	10^7	12^9	15^0	17^1	19^3
25	2^2	4^5	6^7	8^9	11^2	13^4	15^6	17^9	20^1
26	2^3	4^6	7^0	9^3	11^6	13^9	16^3	18^6	20^9
27	2^4	4^8	7^2	9^6	12^1	14^5	16^9	19^3	21^7
28	2^5	5^0	7^5	10^0	12^5	15^0	17^5	20^0	22^5
29	2^6	5^2	7^8	10^4	12^9	15^5	18^1	20^7	23^3
30	2^7	5^4	8^0	10^7	13^4	16^1	18^8	21^4	24^1
31	2^8	5^5	8^3	11^1	13^8	16^6	19^4	22^1	24^9
32	2^9	5^7	8^6	11^4	14^3	17^1	20^0	22^9	25^7
33	2^9	5^9	8^8	11^8	14^7	17^7	20^6	23^6	26^5
34	3^0	6^1	9^1	12^1	15^2	18^2	21^3	24^3	27^3
35	3^1	6^3	9^4	12^5	15^6	18^8	21^9	25^0	28^1
36	3^2	6^4	9^6	12^9	16^1	19^3	22^5	25^7	28^9
37	3^3	6^6	9^9	13^2	16^5	19^8	23^1	26^4	29^7
38	3^4	6^8	10^2	13^6	17^0	20^4	23^8	27^1	30^5
39	3^5	7^0	10^4	13^9	17^4	20^9	24^4	27^9	31^3
40	3^6	7^1	10^7	14^3	17^9	21^4	25^0	28^6	32^1
41	3^7	7^3	11^0	14^6	18^3	22^0	25^6	29^3	32^9
42	3^8	7^5	11^3	15^0	18^8	22^5	26^3	30^0	33^8
43	3^8	7^7	11^5	15^4	19^2	23^0	26^9	30^7	34^6
44	3^9	7^9	11^8	15^7	19^6	23^6	27^5	31^4	35^4
45	4^0	8^0	12^1	16^1	20^1	24^1	28^1	32^1	36^2
46	4^1	8^2	12^3	16^4	20^5	24^6	28^8	32^9	37^0
47	4^2	8^4	12^6	16^8	21^0	25^2	29^4	33^6	37^8
48	4^3	8^6	12^9	17^1	21^4	25^7	30^0	34^3	38^6
49	4^4	8^8	13^1	17^5	21^9	26^3	30^6	35^0	39^4
50	4^5	8^9	13^4	17^9	22^3	26^8	31^3	35^7	40^2
51	4^6	9^1	13^7	18^2	22^8	27^3	31^9	36^4	41^0
52	4^6	9^3	13^9	18^6	23^2	27^9	32^5	37^1	41^8
53	4^7	9^5	14^2	18^9	23^7	28^4	33^1	37^9	42^6
54	4^8	9^6	14^5	19^3	24^1	28^9	33^8	38^6	43^4
55	4^9	9^8	14^7	19^6	24^6	29^5	34^4	39^3	44^2
56	5^0	10^0	15^0	20^0	25^0	30^0	35^0	40^0	45^0

RATES PER CWT.

Per Cwt. Lbs.	10p	20p	30p	40p	50p	60p	70p	80p	90p
	P	P	P	P	P	P	P	P	P
57	5^1	10^2	15^3	20^4	25^5	30^5	35^6	40^7	45^8
58	5^2	10^4	15^5	20^7	25^9	31^1	36^3	41^4	46^6
59	5^3	10^5	15^8	21^1	26^3	31^6	36^9	42^1	47^4
60	5^4	10^7	16^1	21^4	26^8	32^1	37^5	42^9	48^2
61	5^4	10^9	16^3	21^8	27^2	32^7	38^1	43^6	49^0
62	5^5	11^1	16^6	22^1	27^7	33^2	38^8	44^3	49^5
63	5^6	11^3	16^9	22^5	28^1	33^8	39^4	45^0	50^6
64	5^7	11^4	17^1	22^9	28^6	34^3	40^0	45^7	51^4
65	5^8	11^6	17^4	23^2	29^0	34^8	40^6	46^4	52^2
66	5^9	11^8	17^7	23^6	29^5	35^4	41^3	47^1	53^0
67	6^0	12^0	17^9	23^9	29^9	35^9	41^9	47^9	53^8
68	6^1	12^1	18^2	24^3	30^4	36^4	42^5	48^6	54^6
69	6^2	12^3	18^5	24^6	30^8	37^0	43^1	49^3	55^4
70	6^3	12^5	18^8	25^0	31^3	37^5	43^8	50^0	56^3
71	6^3	12^7	19^0	25^4	31^7	38^0	44^4	50^7	57^1
72	6^4	12^9	19^3	25^7	32^1	38^6	45^0	51^4	57^9
73	6^5	13^0	19^6	26^1	32^6	39^1	45^6	52^1	58^7
74	6^6	13^2	19^8	26^4	33^0	39^6	46^3	52^9	59^5
75	6^7	13^4	20^1	26^8	33^5	40^2	46^9	53^6	60^3
76	6^8	13^6	20^4	27^1	33^9	40^7	47^5	54^3	61^1
77	6^9	13^8	20^6	27^5	34^4	41^3	48^1	55^0	61^9
78	7^0	13^9	20^9	27^9	34^8	41^8	48^8	55^7	62^7
79	7^1	14^1	21^2	28^2	35^3	42^3	49^4	56^4	63^5
80	7^1	14^3	21^4	28^6	35^7	42^9	50^0	57^1	64^3
81	7^2	14^5	21^7	28^9	36^2	43^4	50^6	57^9	65^1
82	7^3	14^6	22^0	29^3	36^6	43^9	51^3	58^6	65^9
83	7^4	14^8	22^2	29^6	37^1	44^5	51^9	59^3	66^7
84	7^5	15^0	22^5	30^0	37^5	45^0	52^5	60^0	67^5
85	7^6	15^2	22^8	30^4	37^9	45^5	53^1	60^7	68^3
86	7^7	15^4	23^0	30^7	38^4	46^1	53^8	61^4	69^1
87	7^8	15^5	23^3	31^1	38^8	46^6	54^4	62^1	69^9
88	7^9	15^7	23^6	31^4	39^3	47^1	55^0	62^9	70^7
89	7^9	15^9	23^8	31^8	39^7	47^7	55^6	63^6	71^5
90	8^0	16^1	24^1	32^1	40^2	48^2	56^3	64^3	72^3
91	8^1	16^3	24^4	32^5	40^6	48^8	56^9	65^0	73^1
92	8^2	16^4	24^6	32^9	41^1	49^3	57^5	65^7	73^9
93	8^3	16^6	24^9	33^2	41^5	49^8	58^1	66^4	74^7
94	8^4	16^8	25^2	33^6	42^0	50^4	58^8	67^1	75^5
95	8^5	17^0	25^4	33^9	42^4	50^9	59^4	67^9	76^3
96	8^6	17^1	25^7	34^3	42^9	51^4	60^0	68^6	77^1
97	8^7	17^3	26^0	34^6	43^3	52^0	60^6	69^3	77^9
98	8^8	17^5	26^3	35^0	43^8	52^5	61^3	70^0	78^8
99	8^8	17^7	26^5	35^4	44^2	53^0	61^9	70^7	79^6
100	8^9	17^9	26^8	35^7	44^6	53^6	62^5	71^4	80^4
101	9^0	18^0	27^1	36^1	45^1	54^1	63^1	72^1	81^2
102	9^1	18^2	27^3	36^4	45^5	54^6	63^8	72^9	82^0
103	9^2	18^4	27^6	36^8	46^0	55^2	64^4	73^6	82^8
104	9^3	18^6	27^9	37^1	46^4	55^7	65^0	74^3	83^6
105	9^4	18^8	28^1	37^5	46^9	56^3	65^6	75^0	84^4
106	9^5	18^9	28^4	37^9	47^3	56^8	66^3	75^7	85^2
107	9^6	19^1	28^7	38^2	47^8	57^3	66^9	76^4	86^0
108	9^6	19^3	28^9	38^6	48^2	57^9	67^5	77^1	86^8
109	9^7	19^5	29^2	38^9	48^7	58^4	68^1	77^9	87^6
110	9^8	19^6	29^5	39^3	49^1	58^9	68^8	78^6	88^4
111	9^9	19^8	29^7	39^6	49^6	59^5	69^4	79^3	89^2
112	10^0	20^0	30^0	40^0	50^0	60^0	70^0	80^0	90^0

RATES PER CWT.

Per Cwt. Lbs.	£1		£2		£3		£4		£5		£6		£7		£8		£9		£10	
	£	P	£	P	£	P	£	P	£	P	£	P	£	P	£	P	£	P	£	P
1		0^9		1^8		2^7		3^6		4^5		5^4		6^3		7^1		8^0		8^9
2		1^8		3^6		5^4		7^1		8^9		10^7		12^5		14^3		16^1		17^9
3		2^7		5^4		8^0		10^7		13^4		16^1		18^8		21^4		24^1		26^8
4		3^6		7^1		10^7		14^3		17^9		21^4		25^0		28^6		32^1		35^7
5		4^5		8^9		13^4		17^9		22^3		26^8		31^3		35^7		40^2		44^6
6		5^4		10^7		16^1		21^4		26^8		32^1		37^5		42^9		48^2		53^6
7		6^3		12^5		18^8		25^0		31^3		37^5		43^8		50^0		56^3		62^5
8		7^1		14^3		21^4		28^6		35^7		42^9		50^0		57^1		64^3		71^4
9		8^0		16^1		24^1		32^1		40^2		48^2		56^2		64^3		72^3		80^4
10		8^9		17^9		26^8		35^7		44^6		53^6		62^5		71^4		80^4		89^3
11		9^8		19^6		29^5		39^3		49^1		58^9		68^8		78^6		88^4		98^2
12		10^7		21^4		32^1		42^9		53^6		64^3		75^0		85^7		96^4	1	7^1
13		11^6		23^2		34^8		46^4		58^0		69^6		81^3		92^9	1	4^5	1	16^1
14		12^5		25^0		37^5		50^0		62^5		75^0		87^5	1	0^0	1	12^5	1	25^0
15		13^4		26^8		40^2		53^6		67^0		80^4		93^8	1	7^1	1	20^5	1	33^9
16		14^3		28^6		42^9		57^1		71^4		85^7	1	0^0	1	14^3	1	28^6	1	42^9
17		15^2		30^4		45^5		60^7		76^0		91^1	1	6^3	1	21^4	1	36^6	1	51^8
18		16^1		32^1		48^2		64^3		80^4		96^4	1	12^5	1	28^6	1	44^6	1	60^7
19		17^0		33^9		50^9		67^9		84^8	1	1^8	1	18^8	1	35^7	1	52^7	1	69^6
20		17^9		35^7		53^6		71^4		89^3	1	7^1	1	25^0	1	42^9	1	60^7	1	78^6
21		18^8		37^5		56^3		75^0		93^8	1	12^5	1	31^3	1	50^0	1	68^8	1	87^5
22		19^6		39^3		58^9		78^6		98^2	1	17^9	1	37^5	1	57^1	1	76^8	1	96^4
23		20^5		41^1		61^6		82^1	1	2^7	1	23^2	1	43^8	1	64^3	1	84^8	2	5^4
24		21^4		42^9		64^3		85^7	1	7^1	1	28^6	1	50^0	1	71^4	1	92^9	2	14^3
25		22^3		44^6		67^0		89^3	1	11^6	1	33^9	1	56^3	1	78^6	2	0^9	2	23^2
26		23^2		46^4		69^6		92^9	1	16^1	1	39^3	1	62^5	1	85^7	2	8^9	2	32^1
27		24^1		48^2		72^3		96^4	1	20^5	1	44^6	1	68^8	1	92^9	2	17^0	2	41^1
28		25^0		50^0		75^0	1	0^0	1	25^0	1	50^0	1	75^0	2	0^0	2	25^0	2	50^0
29		25^9		51^8		77^7	1	3^6	1	29^5	1	55^4	1	81^3	2	7^1	2	33^0	2	58^9
30		26^8		53^6		80^4	1	7^1	1	33^9	1	60^7	1	87^5	2	14^3	2	41^1	2	67^9
31		27^7		55^4		83^0	1	10^7	1	38^4	1	66^1	1	93^8	2	21^4	2	49^1	2	76^8
32		28^6		57^1		85^7	1	14^3	1	42^9	1	71^4	2	0^0	2	28^6	2	57^1	2	85^7
33		29^5		58^9		88^4	1	17^9	1	47^3	1	76^8	2	6^3	2	35^7	2	65^2	2	94^6
34		30^4		60^7		91^1	1	21^4	1	51^8	1	82^1	2	12^5	2	42^9	2	73^2	3	3^6
35		31^3		62^5		93^8	1	25^0	1	56^3	1	87^5	2	18^8	2	50^0	2	81^3	3	12^5
36		32^1		64^3		96^4	1	28^6	1	60^7	1	92^9	2	25^0	2	57^1	2	89^3	3	21^4
37		33^0		66^1		99^1	1	32^1	1	65^2	1	98^2	2	31^3	2	64^3	2	97^3	3	30^4
38		33^9		67^9	1	1^8	1	35^7	1	69^6	2	3^6	2	37^5	2	71^4	3	5^4	3	39^3
39		34^8		69^6	1	4^5	1	39^3	1	74^1	2	8^9	2	43^8	2	78^6	3	13^4	3	48^2
40		35^7		71^4	1	7^1	1	42^9	1	78^6	2	14^3	2	50^0	2	85^7	3	21^4	3	57^1
41		36^6		73^2	1	9^8	1	46^4	1	83^0	2	19^6	2	56^3	2	92^9	3	29^5	3	66^1
42		37^5		75^0	1	12^5	1	50^0	1	87^5	2	25^0	2	62^5	3	0^0	3	37^5	3	75^0
43		38^4		76^8	1	15^2	1	53^6	1	92^0	2	30^4	2	68^8	3	7^1	3	45^5	3	83^9
44		39^3		78^6	1	17^9	1	57^1	1	96^4	2	35^7	2	75^0	3	14^3	3	53^6	3	92^9
45		40^2		80^4	1	20^5	1	60^7	2	0^9	2	41^1	2	81^3	3	21^4	3	61^6	4	1^8
46		41^1		82^1	1	23^2	1	64^3	2	5^4	2	46^4	2	87^5	3	28^6	3	69^6	4	10^7
47		42^0		83^9	1	25^9	1	67^9	2	9^8	2	51^8	2	93^8	3	35^7	3	77^7	4	19^6
48		42^9		85^7	1	28^6	1	71^4	2	14^3	2	57^1	3	0^0	3	42^9	3	85^7	4	28^6
49		43^8		87^5	1	31^3	1	75^0	2	18^8	2	62^5	3	6^3	3	50^0	3	93^8	4	37^5
50		44^6		89^3	1	33^9	1	78^6	2	23^2	2	67^9	3	12^5	3	57^1	4	1^8	4	46^4
51		45^5		91^1	1	36^6	1	82^1	2	27^7	2	73^2	3	18^8	3	64^3	4	9^8	4	55^4
52		46^4		92^9	1	39^3	1	85^7	2	32^1	2	78^6	3	25^0	3	71^4	4	17^9	4	64^3
53		47^3		94^6	1	42^0	1	89^3	2	36^6	2	83^9	3	31^3	3	78^6	4	25^9	4	73^2
54		48^2		96^4	1	44^6	1	92^9	2	41^1	2	89^3	3	37^5	3	85^7	4	33^9	4	82^1
55		49^1		98^2	1	47^3	1	96^4	2	45^5	2	94^6	3	43^8	3	92^9	4	42^0	4	91^1
56		50^0	1	0^0	1	50^0	2	0^0	2	50^0	3	0^0	3	50^0	4	0^0	4	50^0	5	0^0

RATES PER CWT.

Per Cwt. Lbs.	£1	£2	£3	£4	£5	£6	£7	£8	£9	£10
57	50^{9}	$1\ 01^{8}$	$1\ 52^{7}$	$2\ 03^{6}$	$2\ 54^{5}$	$3\ 05^{4}$	$3\ 56^{3}$	$4\ 07^{1}$	$4\ 58^{0}$	$5\ 08^{9}$
58	51^{8}	$1\ 03^{6}$	$1\ 55^{4}$	$2\ 07^{1}$	$2\ 58^{9}$	$3\ 10^{7}$	$3\ 62^{5}$	$4\ 14^{3}$	$4\ 66^{1}$	$5\ 17^{9}$
59	52^{7}	$1\ 05^{4}$	$1\ 58^{0}$	$2\ 10^{7}$	$2\ 63^{4}$	$3\ 16^{1}$	$3\ 68^{8}$	$4\ 21^{4}$	$4\ 74^{1}$	$5\ 26^{8}$
60	53^{6}	$1\ 07^{1}$	$1\ 60^{7}$	$2\ 14^{3}$	$2\ 67^{9}$	$3\ 21^{4}$	$3\ 75^{0}$	$4\ 28^{6}$	$4\ 82^{1}$	$5\ 35^{7}$
61	54^{5}	$1\ 08^{9}$	$1\ 63^{4}$	$2\ 17^{9}$	$2\ 72^{3}$	$3\ 26^{8}$	$3\ 81^{3}$	$4\ 35^{7}$	$4\ 90^{2}$	$5\ 44^{6}$
62	55^{4}	$1\ 10^{7}$	$1\ 66^{1}$	$2\ 21^{4}$	$2\ 76^{8}$	$3\ 32^{1}$	$3\ 87^{5}$	$4\ 42^{9}$	$4\ 98^{2}$	$5\ 53^{6}$
63	56^{3}	$1\ 12^{5}$	$1\ 68^{8}$	$2\ 25^{0}$	$2\ 81^{3}$	$3\ 37^{5}$	$3\ 93^{8}$	$4\ 50^{0}$	$5\ 06^{3}$	$5\ 62^{5}$
64	57^{1}	$1\ 14^{3}$	$1\ 71^{4}$	$2\ 28^{6}$	$2\ 85^{7}$	$3\ 42^{9}$	$4\ 00^{0}$	$4\ 57^{1}$	$5\ 14^{3}$	$5\ 71^{4}$
65	58^{0}	$1\ 16^{1}$	$1\ 74^{1}$	$2\ 32^{1}$	$2\ 90^{2}$	$3\ 48^{2}$	$4\ 06^{3}$	$4\ 64^{3}$	$5\ 22^{3}$	$5\ 80^{4}$
66	58^{9}	$1\ 17^{9}$	$1\ 76^{8}$	$2\ 35^{7}$	$2\ 94^{6}$	$3\ 53^{6}$	$4\ 12^{5}$	$4\ 71^{4}$	$5\ 30^{4}$	$5\ 89^{3}$
67	59^{8}	$1\ 19^{6}$	$1\ 79^{5}$	$2\ 39^{3}$	$2\ 99^{1}$	$3\ 58^{9}$	$4\ 18^{8}$	$4\ 78^{6}$	$5\ 38^{4}$	$5\ 98^{2}$
68	60^{7}	$1\ 21^{4}$	$1\ 82^{1}$	$2\ 42^{9}$	$3\ 03^{6}$	$3\ 64^{3}$	$4\ 25^{0}$	$4\ 85^{7}$	$5\ 46^{4}$	$6\ 07^{1}$
69	61^{6}	$1\ 23^{2}$	$1\ 84^{8}$	$2\ 46^{4}$	$3\ 08^{0}$	$3\ 69^{6}$	$4\ 31^{3}$	$4\ 92^{9}$	$5\ 54^{5}$	$6\ 16^{1}$
70	62^{5}	$1\ 25^{0}$	$1\ 87^{5}$	$2\ 50^{0}$	$3\ 12^{5}$	$3\ 75^{0}$	$4\ 37^{5}$	$5\ 00^{0}$	$5\ 62^{5}$	$6\ 25^{0}$
71	63^{4}	$1\ 26^{8}$	$1\ 90^{2}$	$2\ 53^{6}$	$3\ 17^{0}$	$3\ 80^{4}$	$4\ 43^{8}$	$5\ 07^{1}$	$5\ 70^{5}$	$6\ 33^{9}$
72	64^{3}	$1\ 28^{6}$	$1\ 92^{9}$	$2\ 57^{1}$	$3\ 21^{4}$	$3\ 85^{7}$	$4\ 50^{0}$	$5\ 14^{3}$	$5\ 78^{6}$	$6\ 42^{9}$
73	65^{2}	$1\ 30^{4}$	$1\ 95^{5}$	$2\ 60^{7}$	$3\ 25^{9}$	$3\ 91^{1}$	$4\ 56^{3}$	$5\ 21^{4}$	$5\ 86^{6}$	$6\ 51^{8}$
74	66^{1}	$1\ 32^{1}$	$1\ 98^{2}$	$2\ 64^{3}$	$3\ 30^{4}$	$3\ 96^{4}$	$4\ 62^{5}$	$5\ 28^{6}$	$5\ 94^{6}$	$6\ 60^{7}$
75	67^{0}	$1\ 33^{9}$	$2\ 00^{9}$	$2\ 67^{9}$	$3\ 34^{8}$	$4\ 01^{8}$	$4\ 68^{8}$	$5\ 35^{7}$	$6\ 02^{7}$	$6\ 69^{6}$
76	67^{9}	$1\ 35^{7}$	$2\ 03^{6}$	$2\ 71^{4}$	$3\ 39^{3}$	$4\ 07^{1}$	$4\ 75^{0}$	$5\ 42^{9}$	$6\ 10^{7}$	$6\ 78^{6}$
77	68^{8}	$1\ 37^{5}$	$2\ 06^{3}$	$2\ 75^{0}$	$3\ 43^{8}$	$4\ 12^{5}$	$4\ 81^{3}$	$5\ 50^{0}$	$6\ 18^{8}$	$6\ 87^{5}$
78	69^{6}	$1\ 39^{3}$	$2\ 08^{9}$	$2\ 78^{6}$	$3\ 48^{2}$	$4\ 17^{9}$	$4\ 87^{5}$	$5\ 57^{1}$	$6\ 26^{8}$	$6\ 96^{4}$
79	70^{5}	$1\ 41^{1}$	$2\ 11^{6}$	$2\ 82^{1}$	$3\ 52^{7}$	$4\ 23^{2}$	$4\ 93^{8}$	$5\ 64^{3}$	$6\ 34^{8}$	$7\ 05^{4}$
80	71^{4}	$1\ 42^{9}$	$2\ 14^{3}$	$2\ 85^{7}$	$3\ 57^{1}$	$4\ 28^{6}$	$5\ 00^{0}$	$5\ 71^{4}$	$6\ 42^{9}$	$7\ 14^{3}$
81	72^{3}	$1\ 44^{6}$	$2\ 17^{0}$	$2\ 89^{3}$	$3\ 61^{6}$	$4\ 33^{9}$	$5\ 06^{3}$	$5\ 78^{6}$	$6\ 50^{9}$	$7\ 23^{2}$
82	73^{2}	$1\ 46^{4}$	$2\ 19^{6}$	$2\ 92^{9}$	$3\ 66^{1}$	$4\ 39^{3}$	$5\ 12^{5}$	$5\ 85^{7}$	$6\ 58^{9}$	$7\ 32^{1}$
83	74^{1}	$1\ 48^{2}$	$2\ 22^{3}$	$2\ 96^{4}$	$3\ 70^{5}$	$4\ 44^{6}$	$5\ 18^{8}$	$5\ 92^{9}$	$6\ 67^{0}$	$7\ 41^{1}$
84	75^{0}	$1\ 50^{0}$	$2\ 25^{0}$	$3\ 00^{0}$	$3\ 75^{0}$	$4\ 50^{0}$	$5\ 25^{0}$	$6\ 00^{0}$	$6\ 75^{0}$	$7\ 50^{0}$
85	75^{9}	$1\ 51^{8}$	$2\ 27^{7}$	$3\ 03^{6}$	$3\ 79^{5}$	$4\ 55^{4}$	$5\ 31^{3}$	$6\ 07^{1}$	$6\ 83^{0}$	$7\ 58^{9}$
86	76^{8}	$1\ 53^{6}$	$2\ 30^{4}$	$3\ 07^{1}$	$3\ 83^{9}$	$4\ 60^{7}$	$5\ 37^{5}$	$6\ 14^{3}$	$6\ 91^{1}$	$7\ 67^{9}$
87	77^{7}	$1\ 55^{4}$	$2\ 33^{0}$	$3\ 10^{7}$	$3\ 88^{4}$	$4\ 66^{1}$	$5\ 43^{8}$	$6\ 21^{4}$	$6\ 99^{1}$	$7\ 76^{8}$
88	78^{6}	$1\ 57^{1}$	$2\ 35^{7}$	$3\ 14^{3}$	$3\ 92^{9}$	$4\ 71^{4}$	$5\ 50^{0}$	$6\ 28^{6}$	$7\ 07^{1}$	$7\ 85^{7}$
89	79^{5}	$1\ 58^{9}$	$2\ 38^{4}$	$3\ 17^{9}$	$3\ 97^{3}$	$4\ 76^{8}$	$5\ 56^{3}$	$6\ 35^{7}$	$7\ 15^{2}$	$7\ 94^{6}$
90	80^{4}	$1\ 60^{7}$	$2\ 41^{1}$	$3\ 21^{4}$	$4\ 01^{8}$	$4\ 82^{1}$	$5\ 62^{5}$	$6\ 42^{9}$	$7\ 23^{2}$	$8\ 03^{6}$
91	81^{3}	$1\ 62^{5}$	$2\ 43^{8}$	$3\ 25^{0}$	$4\ 06^{3}$	$4\ 87^{5}$	$5\ 68^{8}$	$6\ 50^{0}$	$7\ 31^{3}$	$8\ 12^{5}$
92	82^{1}	$1\ 64^{3}$	$2\ 46^{4}$	$3\ 28^{6}$	$4\ 10^{7}$	$4\ 92^{9}$	$5\ 75^{0}$	$6\ 57^{1}$	$7\ 39^{3}$	$8\ 21^{4}$
93	83^{0}	$1\ 66^{1}$	$2\ 49^{1}$	$3\ 32^{1}$	$4\ 15^{2}$	$4\ 98^{2}$	$5\ 81^{3}$	$6\ 64^{3}$	$7\ 47^{3}$	$8\ 30^{4}$
94	83^{9}	$1\ 67^{9}$	$2\ 51^{8}$	$3\ 35^{7}$	$4\ 19^{6}$	$5\ 03^{6}$	$5\ 87^{5}$	$6\ 71^{4}$	$7\ 55^{4}$	$8\ 39^{3}$
95	84^{8}	$1\ 69^{6}$	$2\ 54^{5}$	$3\ 39^{3}$	$4\ 24^{1}$	$5\ 08^{9}$	$5\ 93^{8}$	$6\ 78^{6}$	$7\ 63^{4}$	$8\ 48^{2}$
96	85^{7}	$1\ 71^{4}$	$2\ 57^{1}$	$3\ 42^{9}$	$4\ 28^{6}$	$5\ 14^{3}$	$6\ 00^{0}$	$6\ 85^{7}$	$7\ 71^{4}$	$8\ 57^{1}$
97	86^{6}	$1\ 73^{2}$	$2\ 59^{8}$	$3\ 46^{4}$	$4\ 33^{0}$	$5\ 19^{6}$	$6\ 06^{3}$	$6\ 92^{9}$	$7\ 79^{5}$	$8\ 66^{1}$
98	87^{5}	$1\ 75^{0}$	$2\ 62^{5}$	$3\ 50^{0}$	$4\ 37^{5}$	$5\ 25^{0}$	$6\ 12^{5}$	$7\ 00^{0}$	$7\ 87^{5}$	$8\ 75^{0}$
99	88^{4}	$1\ 76^{8}$	$2\ 65^{2}$	$3\ 53^{6}$	$4\ 42^{0}$	$5\ 30^{4}$	$6\ 18^{8}$	$7\ 07^{1}$	$7\ 95^{5}$	$8\ 83^{9}$
100	89^{3}	$1\ 78^{6}$	$2\ 67^{9}$	$3\ 57^{1}$	$4\ 46^{4}$	$5\ 35^{7}$	$6\ 25^{0}$	$7\ 14^{3}$	$8\ 03^{6}$	$8\ 92^{9}$
101	90^{2}	$1\ 80^{4}$	$2\ 70^{5}$	$3\ 60^{7}$	$4\ 50^{9}$	$5\ 41^{1}$	$6\ 31^{3}$	$7\ 21^{4}$	$8\ 11^{6}$	$9\ 01^{8}$
102	91^{1}	$1\ 82^{1}$	$2\ 73^{2}$	$3\ 64^{3}$	$4\ 55^{4}$	$5\ 46^{4}$	$6\ 37^{5}$	$7\ 28^{6}$	$8\ 19^{6}$	$9\ 10^{7}$
103	92^{0}	$1\ 83^{9}$	$2\ 75^{9}$	$3\ 67^{9}$	$4\ 59^{8}$	$5\ 51^{8}$	$6\ 43^{8}$	$7\ 35^{7}$	$8\ 27^{7}$	$9\ 19^{6}$
104	92^{9}	$1\ 85^{7}$	$2\ 78^{6}$	$3\ 71^{4}$	$4\ 64^{3}$	$5\ 57^{1}$	$6\ 50^{0}$	$7\ 42^{9}$	$8\ 35^{7}$	$9\ 28^{6}$
105	93^{8}	$1\ 87^{5}$	$2\ 81^{3}$	$3\ 75^{0}$	$4\ 68^{8}$	$5\ 62^{5}$	$6\ 56^{3}$	$7\ 50^{0}$	$8\ 43^{8}$	$9\ 37^{5}$
106	94^{6}	$1\ 89^{3}$	$2\ 83^{9}$	$3\ 78^{6}$	$4\ 73^{2}$	$5\ 67^{9}$	$6\ 62^{5}$	$7\ 57^{1}$	$8\ 51^{8}$	$9\ 46^{4}$
107	95^{5}	$1\ 91^{1}$	$2\ 86^{6}$	$3\ 82^{1}$	$4\ 77^{7}$	$5\ 73^{2}$	$6\ 68^{8}$	$7\ 64^{3}$	$8\ 59^{8}$	$9\ 55^{4}$
108	96^{4}	$1\ 92^{9}$	$2\ 89^{3}$	$3\ 85^{7}$	$4\ 82^{1}$	$5\ 78^{6}$	$6\ 75^{0}$	$7\ 71^{4}$	$8\ 67^{9}$	$9\ 64^{3}$
109	97^{3}	$1\ 94^{6}$	$2\ 92^{0}$	$3\ 89^{3}$	$4\ 86^{6}$	$5\ 83^{9}$	$6\ 81^{3}$	$7\ 78^{6}$	$8\ 75^{9}$	$9\ 73^{2}$
110	98^{2}	$1\ 96^{4}$	$2\ 94^{6}$	$3\ 92^{9}$	$4\ 91^{1}$	$5\ 89^{3}$	$6\ 87^{5}$	$7\ 85^{7}$	$8\ 83^{9}$	$9\ 82^{1}$
111	99^{1}	$1\ 98^{2}$	$2\ 97^{3}$	$3\ 96^{4}$	$4\ 95^{5}$	$5\ 94^{6}$	$6\ 93^{8}$	$7\ 92^{9}$	$8\ 92^{0}$	$9\ 91^{1}$
112	$1\ 00^{0}$	$2\ 00^{0}$	$3\ 00^{0}$	$4\ 00^{0}$	$5\ 00^{0}$	$6\ 00^{0}$	$7\ 00^{0}$	$8\ 00^{0}$	$9\ 00^{0}$	$10\ 00^{0}$

Per Cwt. Lbs.	£20 £ P	£30 £ P	£40 £ P	£50 £ P	£60 £ P	£70 £ P	£80 £ P	£90 £ P
1	0 17^9	0 26^8	0 35^7	0 44^6	0 53^6	0 62^5	0 71^4	0 80^4
2	0 35^7	0 53^6	0 71^4	0 89^3	1 7^1	1 25^0	1 42^9	1 60^7
3	0 53^6	0 80^4	1 7^1	1 33^9	1 60^7	1 87^5	2 14^3	2 41^1
4	0 71^4	1 7^1	1 42^9	1 78^6	2 14^3	2 50^0	2 85^7	3 21^4
5	0 89^3	1 33^9	1 78^6	2 23^2	2 67^9	3 12^5	3 57^1	4 1^8
6	1 7^1	1 60^7	2 14^3	2 67^9	3 21^4	3 75^0	4 28^6	4 82^1
7	1 25^0	1 87^5	2 50^0	3 12^5	3 75^0	4 37^5	5 0^0	5 62^5
8	1 42^9	2 14^3	2 85^7	3 57^1	4 28^6	5 0^0	5 71^4	6 42^9
9	1 60^7	2 41^1	3 21^4	4 1^8	4 82^1	5 62^5	6 42^9	7 23^2
10	1 78^6	2 67^9	3 57^1	4 46^4	5 35^7	6 25^0	7 14^3	8 3^6
11	1 96^4	2 94^6	3 92^9	4 91^1	5 89^3	6 87^5	7 85^7	8 83^9
12	2 14^3	3 21^4	4 28^6	5 35^7	6 42^9	7 50^0	8 57^1	9 64^3
13	2 32^1	3 48^2	4 64^3	5 80^4	6 96^4	8 12^5	9 28^6	10 44^6
14	2 50^0	3 75^0	5 0^0	6 25^0	7 50^0	8 75^0	10 0^0	11 25^0
15	2 67^9	4 1^8	5 35^7	6 69^6	8 3^6	9 37^5	10 71^4	12 5^4
16	2 85^7	4 28^6	5 71^4	7 14^3	8 57^1	10 0^0	11 42^9	12 85^7
17	3 3^6	4 55^4	6 7^1	7 58^9	9 10^7	10 62^5	12 14^3	13 66^1
18	3 21^4	4 82^1	6 42^9	8 3^6	9 64^2	11 25^0	12 85^7	14 46^4
19	3 39^3	5 8^9	6 78^6	8 48^2	10 17^9	11 87^5	13 57^1	15 26^8
20	3 57^1	5 35^7	7 14^3	8 92^9	10 71^4	12 50^0	14 28^6	16 7^1
21	3 75^0	5 62^5	7 50^0	9 37^5	11 25^0	13 12^5	15 0^0	16 87^5
22	3 92^9	5 89^3	7 85^7	9 82^1	11 78^6	13 75^0	15 71^4	17 67^9
23	4 10^7	6 16^1	8 21^4	10 26^8	12 32^1	14 37^5	16 42^9	18 48^2
24	4 28^6	6 42^9	8 57^1	10 71^4	12 85^7	15 0^0	17 14^3	19 28^6
25	4 46^4	6 69^6	8 92^9	11 16^1	13 39^3	15 62^5	17 85^7	20 8^9
26	4 64^3	6 96^4	9 28^6	11 60^7	13 92^9	16 25^0	18 57^1	20 89^3
27	4 82^1	7 23^2	9 64^3	12 5^4	14 46^4	16 87^5	19 28^6	21 69^6
28	5 0^0	7 50^0	10 0^0	12 50^0	15 0^0	17 50^0	20 0^0	22 50^0
29	5 17^9	7 76^8	10 35^7	12 94^6	15 53^6	18 12^5	20 71^4	23 30^4
30	5 35^7	8 3^6	10 71^4	13 39^3	16 7^1	18 75^0	21 42^9	24 10^7
31	5 53^6	8 30^4	11 7^1	13 83^9	16 60^7	19 37^5	22 14^3	24 91^1
32	5 71^4	8 57^1	11 42^9	14 28^6	17 14^3	20 0^0	22 85^7	25 71^4
33	5 89^3	8 83^9	11 78^6	14 73^2	17 67^9	20 62^5	23 57^1	26 51^8
34	6 7^1	9 10^7	12 14^3	15 17^9	18 21^4	21 25^0	24 28^6	27 32^1
35	6 25^0	9 37^5	12 50^0	15 62^5	18 75^0	21 87^5	25 0^0	28 12^5
36	6 42^9	9 64^3	12 85^7	16 7^1	19 28^6	22 50^0	25 71^4	28 92^9
37	6 60^7	9 91^1	13 21^4	16 51^8	19 82^1	23 12^5	26 42^9	29 73^2
38	6 78^6	10 17^9	13 57^1	16 96^4	20 35^7	23 75^0	27 14^3	30 53^6
39	6 96^4	10 44^6	13 92^9	17 41^1	20 89^3	24 37^5	27 85^7	31 33^9
40	7 14^3	10 71^4	14 28^6	17 85^7	21 42^9	25 0^0	28 57^1	32 14^3
41	7 32^1	10 98^2	14 64^3	18 30^4	21 96^4	25 62^5	29 28^6	32 94^6
42	7 50^0	11 25^0	15 0^0	18 75^0	22 50^0	26 25^0	30 0^0	33 75^0
43	7 67^9	11 51^8	15 35^7	19 19^6	23 3^6	26 87^5	30 71^4	34 55^4
44	7 85^7	11 78^6	15 71^4	19 64^3	23 57^1	27 50^0	31 42^9	35 35^7
45	8 3^6	12 5^4	16 7^1	20 8^9	24 10^7	28 12^5	32 14^3	36 16^1
46	8 21^4	12 32^1	16 42^9	20 53^8	24 64^3	28 75^0	32 85^7	36 96^4
47	8 39^3	12 58^9	16 78^6	20 98^2	25 17^9	29 37^5	33 57^1	37 76^8
48	8 57^1	12 85^7	17 14^3	21 42^9	25 71^4	30 0^0	34 28^6	38 57^1
49	8 75^0	13 12^5	17 50^0	21 87^5	26 25^0	30 62^5	35 0^0	39 37^5
50	8 92^9	13 39^3	17 85^7	22 32^1	26 78^6	31 25^0	35 71^4	40 17^9
51	9 10^7	13 66^1	18 21^4	22 76^8	27 32^1	31 87^5	36 42^9	40 98^2
52	9 28^6	13 92^9	18 57^1	23 21^4	27 85^7	32 50^0	37 14^3	41 78^6
53	9 46^4	14 19^6	18 92^9	23 66^1	28 39^3	33 12^5	37 85^7	42 58^9
54	9 64^3	14 46^4	19 28^6	24 10^7	28 92^9	33 75^0	38 57^1	43 39^8
55	9 82^1	14 73^2	19 64^3	24 55^4	29 46^4	34 37^5	39 28^6	44 19^6
56	10 0^0	15 0^0	20 0^0	25 0^0	30 0^0	35 0^0	40 0^0	45 0^0

Per Cwt. Lbs.	£20 £ P	£30 £ P	£40 £ P	£50 £ P	£60 £ P	£70 £ P	£80 £ P	£90 £ P
57	10 17^9	15 26^8	20 35^7	25 44^6	30 53^6	35 62^5	40 71^4	45 80^4
58	10 35^7	15 53^6	20 71^4	25 89^3	31 7^1	36 25^0	41 42^9	46 60^7
59	10 53^6	15 80^4	21 7^1	26 33^9	31 60^7	36 87^5	42 14^3	47 41^1
60	10 71^4	16 7^1	21 42^9	26 78^6	32 14^3	37 50^0	42 85^7	48 21^4
61	10 89^3	16 33^9	21 78^6	27 23^2	32 67^9	38 12^5	43 57^1	49 1^8
62	11 7^1	16 60^7	22 14^3	27 67^9	33 21^4	38 75^0	44 28^6	49 82^1
63	11 25^0	16 87^5	22 50^0	28 12^5	33 75^0	39 37^5	45 0^0	50 62^5
64	11 42^9	17 14^3	22 85^7	28 57^1	34 28^6	40 0^0	45 71^4	51 42^9
65	11 60^7	17 41^1	23 21^4	29 1^8	34 82^1	40 62^5	46 42^9	52 23^2
66	11 78^6	17 67^9	23 57^1	29 46^4	35 35^7	41 25^0	47 14^3	53 3^6
67	11 96^4	17 94^6	23 92^9	29 91^1	35 89^3	41 87^5	47 85^7	53 83^9
68	12 14^3	18 21^4	24 28^6	30 35^7	36 42^9	42 50^0	48 57^1	54 64^3
69	12 32^1	18 48^2	24 64^3	30 80^4	36 96^4	43 12^5	49 28^6	55 44^6
70	12 50^0	18 75^0	25 0^0	31 25^0	37 50^0	43 75^0	50 0^0	56 25^0
71	12 67^9	19 1^8	25 35^7	31 69^6	38 3^6	44 37^5	50 71^4	57 5^4
72	12 85^7	19 28^6	25 71^4	32 14^3	38 57^1	45 0^0	51 42^9	57 85^7
73	13 3^6	19 55^4	26 7^1	32 58^9	39 10^7	45 62^5	52 14^3	58 66^1
74	13 21^4	19 82^1	26 42^9	33 3^6	39 64^3	46 25^0	52 85^7	59 46^4
75	13 39^3	20 8^9	26 78^6	33 48^2	40 17^9	46 87^5	53 57^1	60 26^3
76	13 57^1	20 35^7	27 14^3	33 92^9	40 71^4	47 50^0	54 28^6	61 7^1
77	13 75^0	20 62^5	27 50^0	34 37^5	41 25^0	48 12^5	55 0^0	61 87^5
78	13 92^9	20 89^3	27 85^7	34 82^1	41 78^6	48 75^0	55 71^4	62 67^9
79	14 10^7	21 16^1	28 21^4	35 26^8	42 32^1	49 37^5	56 42^9	63 48^2
80	14 28^6	21 42^9	28 57^1	35 71^4	42 85^7	50 0^0	57 14^3	64 28^6
81	14 46^4	21 69^6	28 92^9	36 16^1	43 39^3	50 62^5	57 85^7	65 8^9
82	14 64^3	21 96^4	29 28^6	36 60^7	43 92^9	51 25^0	58 57^1	65 89^3
83	14 82^1	22 23^2	29 64^3	37 5^4	44 46^4	51 87^5	59 28^6	66 69^6
84	15 0^0	22 50^0	30 0^0	37 50^0	45 0^0	52 50^0	60 0^0	67 50^0
85	15 17^9	22 76^8	30 35^7	37 94^6	45 53^6	53 12^5	60 71^4	68 30^4
86	15 35^7	23 3^6	30 71^4	38 39^3	46 7^1	53 75^0	61 42^9	69 10^7
87	15 53^6	23 30^4	31 7^1	38 83^9	46 60^7	54 37^5	62 14^3	69 91^1
88	15 71^4	23 57^1	31 42^9	39 28^6	47 14^3	55 0^0	62 85^7	70 71^4
89	15 89^3	23 83^9	31 78^6	39 73^2	47 67^9	55 62^5	63 57^1	71 51^8
90	16 7^1	24 10^7	32 14^3	40 17^9	48 21^4	56 25^0	64 28^6	72 32^1
91	16 25^0	24 37^5	32 50^0	40 62^5	48 75^0	56 87^5	65 0^0	73 12^5
92	16 42^9	24 64^3	32 85^7	41 7^1	49 28^6	57 50^0	65 71^4	73 92^9
93	16 60^7	24 91^1	33 21^4	41 51^8	49 82^1	58 12^5	66 42^9	74 73^2
94	16 78^6	25 17^9	33 57^1	41 96^4	50 35^7	58 75^0	67 14^3	75 53^6
95	16 96^4	25 44^6	33 92^9	42 41^1	50 89^3	59 37^5	67 85^7	76 33^9
96	17 14^3	25 71^4	34 28^6	42 85^7	51 42^9	60 0^0	68 57^1	77 14^3
97	17 32^1	25 98^2	34 64^3	43 30^4	51 96^4	60 62^5	69 28^6	77 94^6
98	17 50^0	26 25^0	35 0^0	43 75^0	52 50^0	61 25^0	70 0^0	78 75^0
99	17 67^9	26 51^8	35 35^7	44 19^6	53 3^6	61 87^5	70 71^4	79 55^4
100	17 85^7	26 78^6	35 71^4	44 64^3	53 57^1	62 50^0	71 42^9	80 35^7
101	18 3^6	27 5^4	36 7^1	45 8^9	54 10^7	63 12^5	72 14^3	81 16^1
102	18 21^4	27 32^1	36 42^9	45 53^6	54 64^3	63 75^0	72 85^7	81 96^4
103	18 39^3	27 58^9	36 78^6	45 98^2	55 17^9	64 37^5	73 57^1	82 76^8
104	18 57^1	27 85^7	37 14^3	46 42^9	55 71^4	65 0^0	74 28^6	83 57^1
105	18 75^0	28 12^5	37 50^0	46 87^5	56 25^0	65 62^5	75 0^0	84 37^5
106	18 92^9	28 39^3	37 85^7	47 32^1	56 78^6	66 25^0	75 71^4	85 17^9
107	19 10^7	28 66^1	38 21^4	47 76^8	57 32^1	66 87^5	76 42^9	85 98^2
108	19 28^6	28 92^9	38 57^1	48 21^4	57 85^7	67 50^0	77 14^3	86 78^6
109	19 46^4	29 19^6	38 92^9	48 66^1	58 39^3	68 12^5	77 85^7	87 58^9
110	19 64^3	29 46^4	39 28^6	49 10^7	58 92^9	68 75^0	78 57^1	88 39^3
111	19 82^1	29 73^2	39 64^3	49 55^4	59 46^4	69 37^5	79 28^6	89 19^6
112	20 0^0	30 0^0	40 0^0	50 0^0	60 0^0	70 0^0	80 0^0	90 0^0

RATES PER TON OR CWT.

Per Ton	1p	2p	3p	4p	5p	6p	7p	8p	9p	10	20	30	40	50	60	70	80	90
	P	P	P	P	P	P	P	P	P	P	P	P	P	P	P	P	P	P
Lbs. 1	—	—	—	—	—	—	—	—	—	—	0^0	0^0	0^0	0^0	0^0	0^0	0^0	0^0
2	—	—	—	—	—	—	—	—	—	—	0^0	0^0	0^0	0^1	0^1	0^1	0^1	0^1
3	—	—	—	—	—	—	—	—	—	—	0^0	0^0	0^1	0^1	0^1	0^1	0^1	0^1
4	—	—	—	—	—	—	—	—	—	—	0^0	0^1	0^1	0^1	0^1	0^1	0^1	0^2
5	—	—	—	—	—	—	—	—	—	—	0^0	0^1	0^1	0^1	0^1	0^2	0^2	0^2
6	—	—	—	—	—	—	—	—	—	—	0^1	0^1	0^1	0^1	0^2	0^2	0^2	0^2
7	—	—	—	—	—	—	—	—	—	—	0^1	0^1	0^1	0^2	0^2	0^2	0^3	0^3
8	—	—	—	—	—	—	—	—	—	—	0^1	0^1	0^1	0^2	0^2	0^3	0^3	0^3
9	—	—	—	—	—	—	—	—	—	—	0^1	0^1	0^2	0^2	0^2	0^3	0^3	0^4
10	—	—	—	—	—	—	—	—	—	—	0^1	0^1	0^2	0^2	0^3	0^3	0^3	0^4
11	—	—	—	—	—	—	—	—	—	0^0	0^1	0^2	0^2	0^3	0^3	0^3	0^4	0^4
12	—	—	—	—	—	—	—	—	—	0^0	0^1	0^2	0^2	0^3	0^3	0^4	0^4	0^4
13	—	—	—	—	—	—	—	0^0	0^1	0^1	0^1	0^2	0^2	0^3	0^4	0^4	0^5	0^5
14	—	—	—	—	—	—	—	—	0^1	0^1	0^1	0^2	0^2	0^3	0^4	0^4	0^5	0^6
15	—	—	—	—	—	0^0	0^1	0^1	0^1	0^1	0^2	0^2	0^3	0^3	0^4	0^5	0^5	0^6
16	—	—	—	—	—	0^1	0^1	0^1	0^1	0^1	0^2	0^2	0^3	0^4	0^4	0^5	0^6	0^6
17	—	—	—	—	—	0^1	0^1	0^1	0^1	0^2	0^2	0^2	0^3	0^4	0^5	0^5	0^6	0^7
18	—	—	—	—	0^0	0^1	0^1	0^1	0^1	0^1	0^2	0^3	0^3	0^4	0^5	0^6	0^6	0^7
19	—	—	—	—	0^1	0^1	0^1	0^1	0^1	0^1	0^2	0^3	0^3	0^4	0^5	0^6	0^7	0^8
20	—	—	—	—	0^1	0^1	0^1	0^1	0^1	0^1	0^2	0^3	0^4	0^5	0^6	0^7	0^8	0^8
21	—	—	—	—	0^1	0^1	0^1	0^1	0^1	0^1	0^2	0^3	0^4	0^5	0^6	0^7	0^8	0^8
22	—	—	—	—	0^0	0^1	0^1	0^1	0^1	0^1	0^2	0^4	0^4	0^5	0^6	0^7	0^8	0^9
23	—	—	—	—	0^1	0^1	0^1	0^1	0^1	0^1	0^2	0^3	0^4	0^5	0^6	0^7	0^8	0^9
24	—	—	—	—	0^1	0^1	0^1	0^1	0^1	0^1	0^4	0^3	0^4	0^5	0^6	0^8	0^9	1^0
25	—	—	—	—	0^1	0^1	0^1	0^1	0^1	0^1	0^2	0^3	0^5	0^6	0^7	0^8	0^9	1^0
26	—	—	—	—	0^1	0^1	0^1	0^1	0^1	0^1	0^2	0^3	0^5	0^6	0^7	0^8	0^9	1^0
27	—	—	—	—	0^0	0^1	0^1	0^1	0^1	0^1	0^2	0^4	0^5	0^6	0^7	0^8	1^0	1^1
Qrs. 1	—	0^0	0^0	0^1	0^1	0^1	0^1	0^1	0^1	0^1	0^3	0^4	0^5	0^6	0^8	0^9	1^0	1^1
2	—	0^1	0^1	0^1	0^1	0^2	0^2	0^2	0^2	0^3	0^5	0^8	1^0	1^3	1^5	1^8	2^0	2^3
3	0^0	0^1	0^1	0^2	0^2	0^3	0^3	0^3	0^3	0^4	0^8	1^1	1^5	1^9	2^3	2^6	3^0	3^4
Cwts. 1	0^1	0^1	0^2	0^2	0^3	0^3	0^4	0^4	0^5	0^5	1^0	1^5	2^0	2^5	3^0	3^5	4^0	4^5
2	0^1	0^2	0^3	0^4	0^5	0^6	0^7	0^8	0^9	1^0	2^0	3^0	4^0	5^0	6^0	7^0	8^0	9^0
3	0^2	0^3	0^5	0^6	0^8	0^9	1^1	1^2	1^4	1^5	3^0	4^5	6^0	7^5	9^0	10^5	12^0	13^5
4	0^2	0^4	0^6	0^8	1^0	1^2	1^4	1^6	1^8	2^0	4^0	6^0	8^0	10^0	12^0	14^0	16^0	18^0
5	0^3	0^5	0^8	1^0	1^3	1^5	1^8	2^0	2^3	2^5	5^0	7^5	10^0	12^5	15^0	17^5	20^0	22^5
6	0^3	0^6	0^9	1^2	1^5	1^8	2^1	2^4	2^7	3^0	6^0	9^0	12^0	15^0	18^0	21^0	24^0	27^0
7	0^4	0^7	1^1	1^4	1^8	2^1	2^5	2^8	3^2	3^5	7^0	10^5	14^0	17^5	21^0	24^5	28^0	31^5
8	0^4	0^8	1^2	1^6	2^0	2^4	2^8	3^2	3^6	4^0	8^0	12^0	16^0	20^0	24^0	28^0	32^0	36^0
9	0^5	0^9	1^4	1^8	2^3	2^7	3^2	3^6	4^1	4^5	9^0	13^5	18^0	22^5	27^0	31^5	36^0	40^5
10	0^5	1^0	1^5	2^0	2^5	3^0	3^5	4^0	4^5	5^0	10^0	15^0	20^0	25^0	30^0	35^0	40^0	45^0
11	0^6	1^1	1^7	2^2	2^8	3^3	3^9	4^4	5^0	5^5	11^0	16^5	22^0	27^5	33^0	38^5	44^0	49^5
12	0^6	1^2	1^8	2^4	3^0	3^6	4^2	4^8	5^4	6^0	12^0	18^0	24^0	30^0	36^0	42^0	48^0	54^0
13	0^7	1^3	2^0	2^6	3^3	3^9	4^6	5^2	5^9	6^5	13^0	19^5	26^0	32^5	39^0	45^5	52^0	58^5
14	0^7	1^4	2^1	2^8	3^5	4^2	4^9	5^6	6^3	7^0	14^0	21^0	28^0	35^0	42^0	49^0	56^0	63^0
15	0^8	1^5	2^3	3^0	3^8	4^5	5^3	6^0	6^8	7^5	15^0	22^5	30^0	37^5	45^0	52^5	60^0	67^5
16	0^8	1^6	2^4	3^2	4^0	4^8	5^6	6^4	7^2	8^0	16^0	24^0	32^0	40^0	48^0	56^0	64^0	72^0
17	0^9	1^7	2^6	3^4	4^3	5^1	6^0	6^8	7^7	8^5	17^0	25^5	34^0	42^5	51^0	59^5	68^0	76^5
18	0^9	1^8	2^7	3^6	4^5	5^4	6^3	7^2	8^1	9^0	18^0	27^0	36^0	45^0	54^0	63^0	72^0	81^0
19	1^0	1^9	2^9	3^8	4^8	5^7	6^7	7^6	8^6	9^5	19^0	28^5	38^0	47^5	57^0	66^5	76^0	85^5
20	1^0	2^0	3^0	4^0	5^0	6^0	7^0	8^0	9^0	10^0	20^0	30^0	40^0	50^0	60^0	70^0	80^0	90^0
Price per ℔ Cwt.	0^1p	0^1p	0^2p	0^2p	0^3p	0^3p	0^4p	0^4p	0^5p	0^5p	1^0p	1^5p	2^0p	2^5p	3^0p	3^5p	4^0p	4^5p

RATES PER TON OR CWT.

Per Ton	£1	£2	£3	£4	£5	£6	£7	£8	£9	£10	£20	£30	£40
Lbs.	P	P	P	P	P	P	P	P	P	P	P	£ P	£ P
1	0^0	0^1	0^1	0^2	0^2	0^3	0^3	0^4	0^4	0^4	0^8	1^3	1^8
2	0^1	0^2	0^3	0^4	0^5	0^5	0^6	0^7	0^8	0^9	1^8	2^7	3^6
3	0^1	0^3	0^4	0^5	0^7	0^8	0^9	1^1	1^2	1^3	2^7	4^0	5^4
4	0^2	0^4	0^5	0^7	0^9	1^1	1^3	1^4	1^6	1^8	3^6	5^4	7^1
5	0^2	0^4	0^7	0^9	1^1	1^3	1^6	1^8	2^0	2^2	4^5	6^7	8^9
6	0^3	0^5	0^8	1^1	1^3	1^6	1^9	2^1	2^4	2^7	5^4	8^0	10^7
7	0^3	0^6	0^9	1^3	1^6	1^9	2^2	2^5	2^8	3^1	6^3	9^4	12^5
8	0^4	0^7	1^1	1^4	1^8	2^1	2^5	2^9	3^2	3^6	7^1	10^7	14^3
9	0^4	0^8	1^2	1^6	2^0	2^4	2^8	3^2	3^6	4^0	8^0	12^1	16^1
10	0^5	0^9	1^3	1^8	2^2	2^7	3^1	3^6	4^0	4^5	8^9	13^1	17^9
11	0^5	1^0	1^5	2^0	2^5	2^9	3^4	3^9	4^4	4^9	9^8	14^7	19^6
12	0^5	1^1	1^6	2^1	2^7	3^2	3^8	4^3	4^8	5^4	10^7	16^1	21^4
13	0^6	1^2	1^7	2^3	2^9	3^5	4^1	4^6	5^2	5^8	11^6	17^4	23^2
14	0^6	1^3	1^9	2^5	3^1	3^8	4^4	5^0	5^6	6^3	12^6	18^8	25^0
15	0^7	1^3	2^0	2^7	3^4	4^0	4^7	5^4	6^0	6^7	13^4	20^1	26^8
16	0^7	1^4	2^1	2^9	3^6	4^3	5^0	5^7	6^4	7^1	14^3	21^4	28^6
17	0^8	1^5	2^3	3^0	3^8	4^6	5^3	6^1	6^8	7^6	15^2	22^8	30^4
18	0^8	1^6	2^4	3^2	4^0	4^8	5^6	6^4	7^2	8^0	16^1	24^1	32^1
19	0^9	1^7	2^5	3^4	4^2	5^1	5^9	6^8	7^6	8^5	17^0	25^4	33^9
20	0^9	1^8	2^7	3^6	4^5	5^4	6^3	7^1	8^0	8^9	17^9	26^8	35^7
21	0^9	1^9	2^8	3^8	4^7	5^6	6^6	7^5	8^4	9^4	18^8	28^1	37^5
22	1^0	2^0	2^9	3^9	4^9	5^9	6^9	7^9	8^8	9^8	19^6	29^5	39^3
23	1^0	2^1	3^1	4^1	5^1	6^2	7^2	8^2	9^2	10^3	20^5	30^8	41^1
24	1^1	2^1	3^2	4^3	5^3	6^4	7^5	8^6	9^6	10^7	21^4	32^1	42^9
25	1^1	2^2	3^4	4^5	5^6	6^7	7^8	8^9	10^0	11^2	22^3	33^5	44^6
26	1^2	2^3	3^5	4^6	5^8	7^0	8^1	9^3	10^4	11^6	23^2	34^8	46^4
27	1^2	2^4	3^6	4^8	6^0	7^2	8^4	9^6	10^9	12^1	24^1	36^2	48^2
Qrs.													
1	1^3	2^5	3^8	5^0	6^3	7^5	8^8	10^0	11^3	12^5	25^0	37^5	50^0
2	2^5	5^0	7^5	10^0	12^5	15^0	17^5	20^0	22^5	25^0	50^0	75^0	1 0^0
3	3^8	7^5	11^3	15^0	18^8	22^5	26^3	30^0	33^8	37^5	75^0	1 12^5	1 50^0
Cwts.											£ P	£ P	£ P
1	5	10	15	20	25	30	35	40	45	50	1 0	1 50	2 0
2	10	20	30	40	50	60	70	80	90	1 0	2 0	3 0	4 0
3	15	30	45	60	75	90	1 5	1 20	1 35	1 50	3 0	4 50	6 0
4	20	40	60	80	1 0	1 20	1 40	1 60	1 80	2 0	4 0	6 0	8 0
5	25	50	75	1 0	1 25	1 50	1 75	2 0	2 25	2 50	5 0	7 50	10 0
6	30	60	90	1 20	1 50	1 80	2 10	2 40	2 70	3 0	6 0	9 0	12 0
7	35	70	1 5	1 40	1 75	2 10	2 45	2 80	3 15	3 50	7 0	10 50	14 0
8	40	80	1 20	1 60	2 0	2 40	2 80	3 20	3 60	4 0	8 0	12 0	16 0
9	45	90	1 35	1 80	2 25	2 70	3 15	3 60	4 05	4 50	9 0	13 50	18 0
10	50	1 0	1 50	2 0	2 50	3 0	3 50	4 0	4 50	5 0	10 0	15 0	20 0
11	55	1 10	1 65	2 20	2 75	3 30	3 85	4 40	4 95	5 50	11 0	16 50	22 0
12	60	1 20	1 80	2 40	3 0	3 60	4 20	4 80	5 40	6 0	12 0	18 0	24 0
13	65	1 30	1 95	2 60	3 25	3 90	4 55	5 20	5 85	6 50	13 0	19 50	26 0
14	70	1 40	2 10	2 80	3 50	4 20	4 90	5 60	6 30	7 0	14 0	21 0	28 0
15	75	1 50	2 25	3 0	3 75	4 50	5 25	6 0	6 75	7 50	15 0	22 50	30 0
16	80	1 60	2 40	3 20	4 0	4 80	5 60	6 40	7 20	8 0	16 0	24 0	32 0
17	85	1 70	2 55	3 40	4 25	5 10	5 95	6 80	7 65	8 50	17 0	25 50	34 0
18	90	1 80	2 70	3 60	4 50	5 40	6 30	7 20	8 10	9 0	18 0	27 0	36 0
19	95	1 90	2 85	3 80	4 75	5 70	6 65	7 60	8 55	9 50	19 0	28 50	38 0
20	1 0	2 0	3 0	4 0	5 0	6 0	7 0	8 0	9 0	10 0	20 0	30 0	40 0
Price ⅌ Cwt.	5p	10p	15p	20p	25p	30p	35p	40p	45p	50p	£1	£1 50p	£2

RATES PER TON OR CWT.

Per Ton	£1	£2	£3	£4	£5	£6	£7	£8	£9	£50	£60	£70	£80
	P	P	P	P	P	P	P	P	P	£ P	£ P	£ P	£ P
Lbs													
1	0^0	0^1	0^1	0^1	0^2	0^2	0^3	0^3	0^4	2^2	2^7	3^1	3^6
2	0^1	0^2	0^3	0^4	0^5	0^5	0^6	0^7	0^8	4^5	5^4	6^3	7^1
3	0^1	0^3	0^4	0^5	0^7	0^8	0^9	1^1	1^2	6^7	8^0	9^4	10^7
4	0^2	0^4	0^5	0^7	0^9	1^1	1^3	1^4	1^6	8^9	10^7	12^5	14^3
5	0^2	0^4	0^7	0^9	1^1	1^3	1^6	1^8	2^0	11^2	13^4	15^6	17^9
6	0^3	0^5	0^8	1^1	1^3	1^6	1^9	2^1	2^4	13^4	16^1	18^8	21^4
7	0^3	0^6	0^9	1^3	1^6	1^9	2^2	2^5	2^8	15^6	18^8	21^9	25^0
8	0^4	0^7	1^1	1^4	1^8	2^1	2^5	2^9	3^2	17^9	21^4	25^0	28^6
9	0^4	0^8	1^2	1^6	2^0	2^4	2^8	3^2	3^6	20^1	24^1	28^1	32^1
10	0^5	0^9	1^3	1^8	2^2	2^7	3^1	3^6	4^0	22^3	26^8	31^3	35^7
11	0^5	1^0	1^5	2^0	2^5	2^9	3^4	3^9	4^4	24^6	29^5	34^4	39^3
12	0^5	1^1	1^6	2^1	2^7	3^2	3^8	4^3	4^8	26^8	32^1	37^5	42^9
13	0^6	1^2	1^7	2^3	2^9	3^5	4^1	4^6	5^2	29^0	34^8	40^6	46^4
14	0^6	1^3	1^9	2^5	3^1	3^8	4^4	5^0	5^6	31^3	37^5	43^8	50^0
15	0^7	1^3	2^0	2^7	3^4	4^0	4^7	5^4	6^0	33^5	40^2	46^9	53^6
16	0^7	1^4	2^1	2^9	3^6	4^3	5^0	5^7	6^4	35^7	42^9	50^0	57^1
17	0^8	1^5	2^3	3^0	3^8	4^6	5^3	6^1	6^8	37^2	45^5	53^1	60^7
18	0^8	1^6	2^4	3^2	4^0	4^8	5^6	6^4	7^2	40^2	48^2	56^3	64^3
19	0^9	1^7	2^5	3^4	4^2	5^1	5^9	6^8	7^6	42^4	50^9	59^4	67^9
20	0^9	1^8	2^7	3^6	4^5	5^4	6^3	7^1	8^0	44^6	53^6	62^5	71^4
21	0^9	1^9	2^8	3^8	4^7	5^6	6^6	7^5	8^4	46^9	56^3	65^6	75^0
22	1^0	2^0	2^9	3^9	4^9	5^9	6^9	7^9	8^8	49^1	58^9	68^8	78^6
23	1^0	2^1	3^1	4^1	5^1	6^2	7^2	8^2	9^2	51^3	61^6	71^9	82^1
24	1^1	2^1	3^2	4^3	5^4	6^4	7^5	8^6	9^6	53^6	64^3	75^0	85^7
25	1^1	2^2	3^4	4^5	5^6	6^7	7^8	8^9	10^0	55^8	67^0	78^1	89^3
26	1^2	2^3	3^5	4^6	5^8	7^0	8^1	9^3	10^4	58^0	69^6	81^3	92^9
27	1^2	2^4	3^6	4^8	6^0	7^2	8^4	9^6	10^9	60^3	72^3	84^4	96^4
Qrs													
¼	1^3	2^5	3^8	5^0	6^3	7^5	8^8	10^0	11^3	62^5	75^0	87^5	1 00
½	2^5	5^0	7^5	10^0	12^5	15^0	17^5	20^0	22^5	1 25^0	1 50^0	1 75^0	2 00
¾	3^8	7^5	11^3	15^0	18^8	22^5	26^3	30^0	33^8	1 87^5	2 25^0	2 62^5	3 00
Cwts													
1	5	10	15	20	25	30	35	40	45	2 50	3 0	3 50	4 0
2	10	20	30	40	50	60	70	80	90	5 0	6 0	7 0	8 0
3	15	30	45	60	75	90	1 5	1 20	1 35	7 50	9 0	10 50	12 0
4	20	40	60	80	1 0	1 20	1 40	1 60	1 80	10 0	12 0	14 0	16 0
5	25	50	75	1 0	1 25	1 50	1 75	2 0	2 25	12 50	15 0	17 50	20 0
6	30	60	90	1 20	1 50	1 80	2 10	2 40	2 70	15 0	18 0	21 0	24 0
7	35	70	1 5	1 40	1 75	2 10	2 45	2 80	3 15	17 50	21 0	24 50	28 0
8	40	80	1 20	1 60	2 0	2 40	2 80	3 20	3 60	20 0	24 0	28 0	32 0
9	45	90	1 35	1 80	2 25	2 70	3 15	3 60	4 05	22 50	27 0	31 50	36 0
10	50	1 0	1 50	2 0	2 50	3 0	3 50	4 0	4 50	25 0	30 0	35 0	40 0
11	55	1 10	1 65	2 20	2 75	3 30	3 85	4 40	4 95	27 50	33 0	38 50	44 0
12	60	1 20	1 80	2 40	3 0	3 60	4 20	4 80	5 40	30 0	36 0	42 0	48 0
13	65	1 30	1 95	2 60	3 25	3 90	4 55	5 20	5 85	32 50	39 0	45 50	52 0
14	70	1 40	2 10	2 80	3 50	4 20	4 90	5 60	6 30	35 0	42 0	49 0	56 0
15	75	1 50	2 25	3 0	3 75	4 50	5 25	6 0	6 75	37 50	45 0	52 50	60 0
16	80	1 60	2 40	3 20	4 0	4 80	5 60	6 40	7 20	47 0	48 0	56 0	64 0
17	85	1 70	2 55	3 40	4 25	5 10	5 95	6 80	7 65	40 50	51 0	59 50	68 0
18	90	1 80	2 70	3 60	4 50	5 40	6 30	7 20	8 10	42 0	54 0	63 0	72 0
19	95	1 90	2 85	3 75	4 75	5 65	6 65	7 55	8 55	45 50	57 0	66 50	76 0
20	1 0	2 0	3 0	4 0	5 0	6 0	7 0	8 0	9 0	50 0	60 0	70 0	80 0
Price per Cwt.	5p	10p	15p	20p	25p	30p	35p	40p	45p	£2 50p	£3	£3 50p	£4

RATES PER TON OR CWT.

Lbs.

Per Ton	£90	£100	£200	£300	£400	£500	£600	£700	£800	£900
	£ P	£ P	£ P	£ P	£ P	£ P	£ P	£ P	£ P	£ P
1	$0\ 4^{0}$	$0\ 4^{5}$	$0\ 8^{9}$	$0\ 13^{4}$	$0\ 17^{9}$	$0\ 22^{3}$	$0\ 26^{8}$	$0\ 31^{3}$	$0\ 35^{7}$	$0\ 40^{2}$
2	$0\ 8^{0}$	$0\ 8^{9}$	$0\ 17^{9}$	$0\ 26^{8}$	$0\ 35^{7}$	$0\ 44^{6}$	$0\ 53^{6}$	$0\ 62^{5}$	$0\ 71^{4}$	$0\ 80^{4}$
3	$0\ 12^{1}$	$0\ 13^{4}$	$0\ 26^{8}$	$0\ 40^{2}$	$0\ 53^{6}$	$0\ 67^{0}$	$0\ 80^{4}$	$0\ 93^{8}$	$1\ 7^{1}$	$1\ 20^{5}$
4	$0\ 16^{1}$	$0\ 17^{9}$	$0\ 35^{7}$	$0\ 53^{6}$	$0\ 71^{4}$	$0\ 89^{3}$	$1\ 7^{1}$	$1\ 25^{0}$	$1\ 42^{9}$	$1\ 60^{7}$
5	$0\ 20^{1}$	$0\ 22^{3}$	$0\ 44^{6}$	$0\ 67^{0}$	$0\ 89^{3}$	$1\ 11^{6}$	$1\ 33^{9}$	$1\ 56^{3}$	$1\ 78^{6}$	$2\ 0^{9}$
6	$0\ 24^{1}$	$0\ 26^{8}$	$0\ 53^{6}$	$0\ 80^{4}$	$1\ 7^{1}$	$1\ 33^{9}$	$1\ 60^{7}$	$1\ 87^{5}$	$2\ 14^{3}$	$2\ 41^{1}$
7	$0\ 28^{1}$	$0\ 31^{3}$	$0\ 62^{5}$	$0\ 93^{8}$	$1\ 25^{0}$	$1\ 56^{3}$	$1\ 87^{5}$	$2\ 18^{8}$	$2\ 50^{0}$	$2\ 81^{3}$
8	$0\ 32^{1}$	$0\ 35^{7}$	$0\ 71^{4}$	$1\ 7^{1}$	$1\ 42^{9}$	$1\ 78^{6}$	$2\ 14^{3}$	$2\ 50^{0}$	$2\ 85^{7}$	$3\ 21^{4}$
9	$0\ 36^{2}$	$0\ 40^{2}$	$0\ 80^{4}$	$1\ 20^{5}$	$1\ 60^{7}$	$2\ 0^{9}$	$2\ 41^{1}$	$2\ 81^{3}$	$3\ 21^{4}$	$3\ 61^{6}$
10	$0\ 40^{2}$	$0\ 44^{6}$	$0\ 89^{3}$	$1\ 33^{9}$	$1\ 78^{6}$	$2\ 23^{2}$	$2\ 67^{9}$	$3\ 12^{5}$	$3\ 57^{1}$	$4\ 1^{8}$
11	$0\ 44^{2}$	$0\ 49^{1}$	$0\ 98^{2}$	$1\ 47^{3}$	$1\ 96^{4}$	$2\ 45^{5}$	$2\ 94^{6}$	$3\ 43^{8}$	$3\ 92^{9}$	$4\ 42^{0}$
12	$0\ 48^{2}$	$0\ 53^{6}$	$1\ 7^{1}$	$1\ 60^{7}$	$2\ 14^{3}$	$2\ 67^{9}$	$3\ 21^{4}$	$3\ 75^{0}$	$4\ 28^{6}$	$4\ 82^{1}$
13	$0\ 52^{2}$	$0\ 58^{0}$	$1\ 16^{1}$	$1\ 74^{1}$	$2\ 32^{1}$	$2\ 90^{2}$	$3\ 48^{2}$	$4\ 6^{3}$	$4\ 64^{3}$	$5\ 22^{3}$
14	$0\ 56^{3}$	$0\ 62^{5}$	$1\ 25^{0}$	$1\ 87^{5}$	$2\ 50^{0}$	$3\ 12^{5}$	$3\ 75^{0}$	$4\ 37^{5}$	$5\ 0^{0}$	$5\ 62^{5}$
15	$0\ 60^{3}$	$0\ 67^{0}$	$1\ 33^{9}$	$2\ 0^{9}$	$2\ 67^{9}$	$3\ 34^{8}$	$4\ 1^{8}$	$4\ 68^{8}$	$5\ 35^{7}$	$6\ 2^{7}$
16	$0\ 64^{3}$	$0\ 71^{4}$	$1\ 42^{9}$	$2\ 14^{3}$	$2\ 85^{7}$	$3\ 57^{1}$	$4\ 28^{6}$	$5\ 0^{0}$	$5\ 71^{4}$	$6\ 42^{9}$
17	$0\ 68^{3}$	$0\ 75^{9}$	$1\ 51^{8}$	$2\ 27^{7}$	$3\ 3^{6}$	$3\ 79^{5}$	$4\ 55^{4}$	$5\ 31^{3}$	$6\ 7^{1}$	$6\ 83^{0}$
18	$0\ 72^{3}$	$0\ 80^{4}$	$1\ 60^{7}$	$2\ 41^{1}$	$3\ 21^{4}$	$4\ 1^{8}$	$4\ 82^{1}$	$5\ 62^{5}$	$6\ 42^{9}$	$7\ 23^{2}$
19	$0\ 76^{3}$	$0\ 84^{8}$	$1\ 69^{6}$	$2\ 54^{5}$	$3\ 39^{3}$	$4\ 24^{1}$	$5\ 8^{9}$	$5\ 93^{8}$	$6\ 78^{6}$	$7\ 63^{4}$
20	$0\ 80^{4}$	$0\ 89^{3}$	$1\ 78^{6}$	$2\ 67^{9}$	$3\ 57^{1}$	$4\ 46^{4}$	$5\ 35^{7}$	$6\ 25^{0}$	$7\ 14^{3}$	$8\ 3^{6}$
21	$0\ 84^{4}$	$0\ 93^{8}$	$1\ 87^{5}$	$2\ 81^{3}$	$3\ 75^{0}$	$4\ 68^{8}$	$5\ 62^{5}$	$6\ 56^{3}$	$7\ 50^{0}$	$8\ 43^{8}$
22	$0\ 88^{4}$	$0\ 98^{2}$	$1\ 96^{4}$	$2\ 94^{6}$	$3\ 92^{9}$	$4\ 91^{1}$	$5\ 89^{3}$	$6\ 87^{5}$	$7\ 85^{7}$	$8\ 83^{9}$
23	$0\ 92^{4}$	$1\ 2^{7}$	$2\ 5^{4}$	$3\ 8^{0}$	$4\ 10^{7}$	$5\ 13^{4}$	$6\ 16^{1}$	$7\ 18^{8}$	$8\ 21^{4}$	$9\ 24^{1}$
24	$0\ 96^{4}$	$1\ 7^{1}$	$2\ 14^{3}$	$3\ 21^{4}$	$4\ 28^{6}$	$5\ 35^{7}$	$6\ 42^{9}$	$7\ 50^{0}$	$8\ 57^{1}$	$9\ 64^{3}$
25	$1\ 0^{4}$	$1\ 11^{6}$	$2\ 23^{2}$	$3\ 34^{8}$	$4\ 46^{4}$	$5\ 58^{0}$	$6\ 69^{6}$	$7\ 81^{3}$	$8\ 92^{9}$	$10\ 4^{5}$
26	$1\ 4^{5}$	$1\ 16^{1}$	$2\ 32^{1}$	$3\ 48^{2}$	$4\ 64^{3}$	$5\ 80^{4}$	$6\ 96^{4}$	$8\ 12^{5}$	$9\ 28^{6}$	$10\ 44^{6}$
27	$1\ 8^{5}$	$1\ 20^{5}$	$2\ 41^{1}$	$3\ 61^{6}$	$4\ 82^{1}$	$6\ 2^{7}$	$7\ 23^{2}$	$8\ 43^{8}$	$9\ 64^{3}$	$10\ 84^{8}$

Qrs.

Per Ton	£90	£100	£200	£300	£400	£500	£600	£700	£800	£900
1	$1\ 12^{5}$	$1\ 25^{0}$	$2\ 50^{0}$	$3\ 75^{0}$	$5\ 0^{0}$	$6\ 25^{0}$	$7\ 50^{0}$	$8\ 75^{0}$	$10\ 0^{0}$	$11\ 25^{0}$
2	$2\ 25^{0}$	$2\ 50^{0}$	$5\ 0^{0}$	$7\ 50^{0}$	$10\ 0^{0}$	$12\ 50^{0}$	$15\ 0^{0}$	$17\ 50^{0}$	$20\ 0^{0}$	$22\ 50^{0}$
3	$3\ 37^{5}$	$3\ 75^{0}$	$7\ 50^{0}$	$11\ 25^{0}$	$15\ 0^{0}$	$18\ 75^{0}$	$22\ 50^{0}$	$26\ 25^{0}$	$30\ 0^{0}$	$33\ 75^{0}$

Cwts.

Per Ton	£90	£100	£200	£300	£400	£500	£600	£700	£800	£900
1	4 50	5 0	10 0	15 0	20 0	25 0	30 0	35 0	40 0	45 0
2	9 0	10 0	20 0	30 0	40 0	50 0	60 0	70 0	80 0	90 0
3	13 50	15 0	30 0	45 0	60 0	75 0	90 0	105 0	120 0	135 0
4	18 0	20 0	40 0	60 0	80 0	100 0	120 0	140 0	160 0	180 0
5	22 50	25 0	50 0	75 0	100 0	125 0	150 0	175 0	200 0	225 0
6	27 0	30 0	60 0	90 0	120 0	150 0	180 0	210 0	240 0	270 0
7	31 50	35 0	70 0	105 0	140 0	175 0	210 0	245 0	280 0	315 0
8	36 0	40 0	80 0	120 0	160 0	200 0	240 0	280 0	320 0	360 0
9	40 50	45 0	90 0	135 0	180 0	225 0	270 0	315 0	360 0	405 0
10	45 0	50 0	100 0	150 0	200 0	250 0	300 0	350 0	400 0	450 0
11	49 50	55 0	110 0	165 0	220 0	275 0	330 0	385 0	440 0	495 0
12	54 0	60 0	120 0	180 0	240 0	300 0	360 0	420 0	480 0	540 0
13	58 50	65 0	130 0	195 0	260 0	325 0	390 0	455 0	520 0	585 0
14	63 0	70 0	140 0	210 0	280 0	350 0	420 0	490 0	560 0	630 0
15	67 50	75 0	150 0	225 0	300 0	375 0	450 0	525 0	600 0	675 0
16	72 0	80 0	160 0	240 0	320 0	400 0	480 0	560 0	640 0	720 0
17	76 50	85 0	170 0	255 0	340 0	425 0	510 0	595 0	680 0	765 0
18	81 0	90 0	180 0	270 0	360 0	450 0	540 0	630 0	720 0	810 0
19	85 50	95 0	190 0	285 0	380 0	475 0	570 0	665 0	760 0	855 0
20	90 0	100 0	200 0	300 0	400 0	500 0	600 0	700 0	800 0	900 0

Price ⅌ Cwt.	£4 50p	£5	£10	£15	£20	£25	£30	£35	£40	£45

RATES PER KILO

Per Kilo Lbs.	1p (P)	2p (P)	3p (P)	4p (£ P)	5p (£ P)	6p (£ P)	7p (£ P)	8p (£ P)	9p (£ P)	10p (£ P)
1	0^5	0^9	1^4	0 1^8	0 2^3	0 2^7	0 3^2	0 3^6	0 4^1	0 4^5
2	0^9	1^8	2^7	0 3^6	0 4^5	0 5^4	0 6^4	0 7^3	0 8^2	0 9^1
3	1^4	2^7	4^1	0 5^4	0 6^8	0 8^2	0 9^5	0 10^9	0 12^3	0 13^6
4	1^8	3^6	5^4	0 7^3	0 9^1	0 10^9	0 12^7	0 14^5	0 16^3	0 18^1
5	2^3	4^5	6^8	0 9^1	0 11^3	0 13^6	0 15^9	0 18^1	0 20^4	0 22^7
6	2^7	5^4	8^2	0 10^9	0 13^6	0 16^3	0 19^1	0 21^8	0 24^5	0 27^2
7	3^2	6^4	9^5	0 12^7	0 15^9	0 19^1	0 22^2	0 25^4	0 28^6	0 31^8
8	3^6	7^3	10^9	0 14^5	0 18^1	0 21^8	0 25^4	0 29^0	0 32^7	0 36^3
9	4^1	8^2	12^2	0 16^3	0 20^4	0 24^5	0 28^6	0 32^7	0 36^7	0 40^8
10	4^5	9^1	13^6	0 18^1	0 22^7	0 27^2	0 31^8	0 36^3	0 40^8	0 45^4
11	5^0	10^0	15^0	0 20^0	0 25^0	0 29^9	0 34^9	0 39^9	0 44^9	0 49^9
12	5^4	10^9	16^3	0 21^8	0 27^2	0 32^7	0 38^1	0 43^5	0 49^0	0 54^4
13	5^9	11^8	17^7	0 23^6	0 29^5	0 35^4	0 41^3	0 47^2	0 53^1	0 59^0
14	6^3	12^7	19^1	0 25^4	0 31^8	0 38^1	0 44^5	0 50^8	0 57^2	0 63^5
15	6^8	13^6	20^4	0 27^2	0 34^0	0 40^8	0 47^6	0 54^4	0 61^2	0 68^0
16	7^3	14^5	21^8	0 29^0	0 36^3	0 43^5	0 50^8	0 58^1	0 65^3	0 72^6
17	7^7	15^4	23^1	0 30^8	0 38^6	0 46^3	0 54^0	0 61^7	0 69^4	0 77^1
18	8^2	16^3	24^5	0 32^7	0 40^8	0 49^0	0 57^2	0 65^3	0 73^5	0 81^6
19	8^6	17^2	25^9	0 34^5	0 43^1	0 51^7	0 60^3	0 68^9	0 77^6	0 86^2
20	9^1	18^1	27^2	0 36^3	0 45^4	0 54^4	0 63^5	0 72^6	0 81^6	0 90^7
21	9^5	19^1	28^6	0 38^1	0 47^6	0 57^2	0 66^7	0 76^2	0 85^7	0 95^3
22	10^0	20^0	29^9	0 39^9	0 49^9	0 59^9	0 69^9	0 79^8	0 89^8	0 99^8
23	10^4	20^9	31^3	0 41^7	0 52^2	0 62^6	0 73^0	0 83^5	0 93^9	1 4^3
24	10^9	21^8	32^7	0 43^5	0 54^4	0 65^3	0 76^2	0 87^1	0 98^0	1 8^9
25	11^3	22^7	34^0	0 45^4	0 56^7	0 68^0	0 79^4	0 90^7	1 2^1	1 13^4
26	11^8	23^6	35^4	0 47^2	0 59^0	0 70^8	0 82^6	0 94^3	1 6^1	1 17^9
27	12^3	24^5	36^7	0 49^0	0 61^2	0 73^5	0 85^7	0 98^0	1 10^2	1 22^5
28	12^7	25^4	38^1	0 50^8	0 63^5	0 76^2	0 88^9	1 1^6	1 14^3	1 27^0
29	13^2	26^3	39^5	0 52^6	0 65^8	0 78^9	0 92^1	1 5^2	1 18^4	1 31^5
30	13^6	27^2	40^8	0 54^4	0 68^0	0 81^7	0 95^3	1 8^9	1 22^5	1 36^1
31	14^1	28^1	42^2	0 56^2	0 70^3	0 84^4	0 98^4	1 12^5	1 26^6	1 40^6
32	14^5	29^0	43^5	0 58^1	0 72^6	0 87^1	1 1^6	1 16^1	1 30^6	1 45^2
33	15^0	29^9	44^9	0 59^9	0 74^8	0 89^8	1 4^8	1 19^8	1 34^7	1 49^7
34	15^4	30^8	46^3	0 61^7	0 77^1	0 92^5	1 8^0	1 23^4	1 38^8	1 54^2
35	15^9	31^8	47^6	0 63^5	0 79^4	0 95^3	1 11^1	1 27^0	1 42^9	1 58^8
36	16^3	32^7	49^0	0 65^3	0 81^6	0 98^0	1 14^3	1 30^6	1 47^0	1 63^3
37	16^8	33^6	50^3	0 67^1	0 83^9	1 0^7	1 17^5	1 34^3	1 51^0	1 67^8
38	17^2	34^5	51^7	0 68^9	0 86^2	1 3^4	1 20^7	1 37^9	1 55^1	1 72^4
39	17^7	35^4	53^1	0 70^8	0 88^5	1 6^1	1 23^8	1 41^5	1 59^2	1 76^9
40	18^1	36^3	54^4	0 72^6	0 90^7	1 8^9	1 27^0	1 45^2	1 63^3	1 81^4
41	18^6	37^2	55^8	0 74^4	0 93^0	1 11^6	1 30^2	1 48^8	1 67^4	1 86^0
42	19^1	38^1	57^2	0 76^2	0 95^3	1 14^3	1 33^4	1 52^4	1 71^5	1 90^5
43	19^5	39^0	58^5	0 78^0	0 97^5	1 17^0	1 36^5	1 56^0	1 75^5	1 95^0
44	20^0	39^9	59^9	0 79^8	0 99^8	1 19^8	1 39^7	1 59^7	1 79^6	1 99^6
45	20^4	40^8	61^2	0 81^6	1 2^1	1 22^5	1 42^9	1 63^3	1 83^7	2 4^1
46	20^9	41^7	62^6	0 83^5	1 4^3	1 25^2	1 46^1	1 66^9	1 87^8	2 8^7
47	21^3	42^6	64^0	0 85^3	1 6^6	1 27^9	1 49^2	1 70^6	1 91^9	2 13^2
48	21^8	43^5	65^3	0 87^1	1 8^9	1 30^6	1 52^4	1 74^2	1 96^0	2 17^7
49	22^2	44^5	66^7	0 88^9	1 11^1	1 33^4	1 55^6	1 77^8	2 0^0	2 22^3
50	22^7	45^4	68^0	0 90^7	1 13^4	1 36^1	1 58^8	1 81^4	2 4^1	2 26^8
51	23^1	46^3	69^4	0 92^5	1 15^7	1 38^8	1 61^9	1 85^1	2 8^2	2 31^3
52	23^6	47^2	70^8	0 94^3	1 17^9	1 41^5	1 65^1	1 88^7	2 12^3	2 35^9
53	24^0	48^1	72^1	0 96^2	1 20^2	1 44^2	1 68^3	1 92^3	2 16^4	2 40^4
54	24^5	49^0	73^5	0 98^0	1 22^5	1 47^0	1 71^5	1 96^0	2 20^4	2 44^9
55	25^0	49^9	74^8	0 99^8	1 24^7	1 49^7	1 74^6	1 99^6	2 24^5	2 49^5
56	25^4	50^8	76^2	1 1^6	1 27^0	1 52^4	1 77^8	2 3^2	2 28^6	2 54^0

Per Kilo Lbs.	1p P	2p £ P	3p £ P	4p £ P	5p £ P	6p £ P	7p £ P	8p £ P	9p £ P	10p £ P
57	25^9	$0\ 51^7$	$0\ 77^6$	$1\ 3^4$	$1\ 29^3$	$1\ 55^1$	$1\ 81^0$	$2\ 6^8$	$2\ 32^7$	$2\ 58^5$
58	26^3	$0\ 52^6$	$0\ 78^9$	$1\ 5^2$	$1\ 31^5$	$1\ 57^9$	$1\ 84^2$	$2\ 10^5$	$2\ 36^8$	$2\ 63^1$
59	26^8	$0\ 53^5$	$0\ 80^3$	$1\ 7^0$	$1\ 33^8$	$1\ 60^6$	$1\ 87^3$	$2\ 14^1$	$2\ 40^9$	$2\ 67^6$
60	27^2	$0\ 54^4$	$0\ 81^6$	$1\ 8^9$	$1\ 36^1$	$1\ 63^3$	$1\ 90^5$	$2\ 17^7$	$2\ 44^9$	$2\ 72^2$
61	27^7	$0\ 55^3$	$0\ 83^0$	$1\ 10^7$	$1\ 38^4$	$1\ 66^0$	$1\ 93^7$	$2\ 21^4$	$2\ 49^0$	$2\ 76^7$
62	28^1	$0\ 56^2$	$0\ 84^4$	$1\ 12^5$	$1\ 40^6$	$1\ 68^7$	$1\ 96^9$	$2\ 25^0$	$2\ 53^1$	$2\ 81^2$
63	28^6	$0\ 57^2$	$0\ 85^7$	$1\ 14^3$	$1\ 42^9$	$1\ 71^5$	$2\ 0^0$	$2\ 28^6$	$2\ 57^2$	$2\ 85^8$
64	29^0	$0\ 58^1$	$0\ 87^1$	$1\ 16^1$	$1\ 45^2$	$1\ 74^2$	$2\ 3^2$	$2\ 32^2$	$2\ 61^3$	$2\ 90^3$
65	29^5	$0\ 59^0$	$0\ 88^5$	$1\ 17^9$	$1\ 47^4$	$1\ 76^9$	$2\ 6^4$	$2\ 35^9$	$2\ 65^4$	$2\ 94^8$
66	29^9	$0\ 59^9$	$0\ 89^8$	$1\ 19^7$	$1\ 49^7$	$1\ 79^6$	$2\ 9^6$	$2\ 39^5$	$2\ 69^4$	$2\ 99^4$
67	30^4	$0\ 60^8$	$0\ 91^2$	$1\ 21^6$	$1\ 52^0$	$1\ 82^8$	$2\ 12^7$	$2\ 43^1$	$2\ 73^5$	$3\ 3^9$
68	30^8	$0\ 61^7$	$0\ 92^5$	$1\ 23^4$	$1\ 54^2$	$1\ 85^1$	$2\ 15^9$	$2\ 46^8$	$2\ 77^6$	$3\ 8^4$
69	31^3	$0\ 62^6$	$0\ 93^9$	$1\ 25^2$	$1\ 56^5$	$1\ 87^8$	$2\ 19^1$	$2\ 50^4$	$2\ 81^7$	$3\ 13^0$
70	31^8	$0\ 63^5$	$0\ 95^3$	$1\ 27^0$	$1\ 58^8$	$1\ 90^5$	$2\ 22^3$	$2\ 54^0$	$2\ 85^8$	$3\ 17^5$
71	32^3	$0\ 64^4$	$0\ 96^6$	$1\ 28^6$	$1\ 61^0$	$1\ 93^2$	$2\ 25^4$	$2\ 57^6$	$2\ 89^8$	$3\ 22^1$
72	32^7	$0\ 65^3$	$0\ 98^0$	$1\ 30^6$	$1\ 63^3$	$1\ 96^0$	$2\ 28^6$	$2\ 61^3$	$2\ 93^9$	$3\ 26^6$
73	33^1	$0\ 66^2$	$0\ 99^3$	$1\ 32^4$	$1\ 65^5$	$1\ 98^7$	$2\ 31^8$	$2\ 64^9$	$2\ 98^0$	$3\ 31^1$
74	33^6	$0\ 67^1$	$1\ 0^7$	$1\ 34^5$	$1\ 67^8$	$2\ 1^4$	$2\ 35^0$	$2\ 68^5$	$3\ 2^1$	$3\ 35^7$
75	34^0	$0\ 68^0$	$1\ 2^1$	$1\ 36^1$	$1\ 70^1$	$2\ 4^1$	$2\ 38^1$	$2\ 72^2$	$3\ 6^2$	$3\ 40^2$
76	34^5	$0\ 69^0$	$1\ 3^4$	$1\ 37^9$	$1\ 72^4$	$2\ 6^8$	$2\ 41^3$	$2\ 75^8$	$3\ 10^3$	$3\ 44^7$
77	34^9	$0\ 69^9$	$1\ 4^8$	$1\ 39^7$	$1\ 74^6$	$2\ 9^6$	$2\ 44^5$	$2\ 79^4$	$3\ 14^3$	$3\ 49^3$
78	35^4	$0\ 70^8$	$1\ 6^1$	$1\ 41^5$	$1\ 76^9$	$2\ 12^3$	$2\ 47^7$	$2\ 83^0$	$3\ 18^4$	$3\ 53^8$
79	35^8	$0\ 71^7$	$1\ 7^5$	$1\ 43^3$	$1\ 79^2$	$2\ 15^0$	$2\ 50^8$	$2\ 86^7$	$3\ 22^5$	$3\ 58^3$
80	36^3	$0\ 72^6$	$1\ 8^9$	$1\ 45^1$	$1\ 81^4$	$2\ 17^7$	$2\ 54^0$	$2\ 90^3$	$3\ 26^5$	$3\ 62^9$
81	36^7	$0\ 73^5$	$1\ 10^2$	$1\ 47^0$	$1\ 83^7$	$2\ 20^4$	$2\ 57^2$	$2\ 93^9$	$3\ 30^7$	$3\ 67^4$
82	37^2	$0\ 74^4$	$1\ 11^6$	$1\ 48^8$	$1\ 86^0$	$2\ 23^2$	$2\ 60^4$	$2\ 97^6$	$3\ 34^8$	$3\ 71^9$
83	37^7	$0\ 75^3$	$1\ 12^9$	$1\ 50^6$	$1\ 88^2$	$2\ 25^9$	$2\ 63^5$	$3\ 1^2$	$3\ 38^8$	$3\ 76^5$
84	38^1	$0\ 76^2$	$1\ 14^3$	$1\ 52^4$	$1\ 90^5$	$2\ 28^6$	$2\ 66^7$	$3\ 4^8$	$3\ 42^9$	$3\ 81^0$
85	38^6	$0\ 77^1$	$1\ 15^7$	$1\ 54^2$	$1\ 92^8$	$2\ 31^3$	$2\ 69^9$	$3\ 8^4$	$3\ 47^0$	$3\ 85^6$
86	39^0	$0\ 78^0$	$1\ 17^0$	$1\ 56^0$	$1\ 95^0$	$2\ 34^1$	$2\ 73^1$	$3\ 12^1$	$3\ 51^2$	$3\ 90^1$
87	39^5	$0\ 78^9$	$1\ 18^4$	$1\ 57^9$	$1\ 97^3$	$2\ 36^8$	$2\ 76^2$	$3\ 15^7$	$3\ 55^2$	$3\ 94^6$
88	39^9	$0\ 79^8$	$1\ 19^7$	$1\ 59^7$	$1\ 99^6$	$2\ 39^5$	$2\ 79^4$	$3\ 19^3$	$3\ 59^2$	$3\ 99^2$
89	40^4	$0\ 80^7$	$1\ 21^1$	$1\ 61^5$	$2\ 1^9$	$2\ 42^2$	$2\ 82^6$	$3\ 23^0$	$3\ 63^3$	$4\ 3^7$
90	40^8	$0\ 81^7$	$1\ 22^5$	$1\ 63^3$	$2\ 4^1$	$2\ 44^9$	$2\ 85^8$	$3\ 26^6$	$3\ 67^4$	$4\ 8^0$
91	41^3	$0\ 82^6$	$1\ 23^8$	$1\ 65^1$	$2\ 6^4$	$2\ 47^7$	$2\ 88^9$	$3\ 30^2$	$3\ 71^5$	$4\ 12^8$
92	41^7	$0\ 83^5$	$1\ 25^2$	$1\ 66^9$	$2\ 8^7$	$2\ 50^4$	$2\ 92^1$	$3\ 33^8$	$3\ 75^6$	$4\ 17^3$
93	42^2	$0\ 84^4$	$1\ 26^6$	$1\ 68^7$	$2\ 10^9$	$2\ 53^1$	$2\ 95^3$	$3\ 37^5$	$3\ 79^7$	$4\ 21^8$
94	42^6	$0\ 85^3$	$1\ 27^9$	$1\ 70^6$	$2\ 13^2$	$2\ 55^8$	$2\ 98^5$	$3\ 41^1$	$3\ 83^7$	$4\ 26^4$
95	43^1	$0\ 86^2$	$1\ 29^3$	$1\ 72^4$	$2\ 15^5$	$2\ 58^6$	$3\ 1^6$	$3\ 44^7$	$3\ 87^8$	$4\ 30^9$
96	43^5	$0\ 87^1$	$1\ 30^6$	$1\ 74^2$	$2\ 17^7$	$2\ 61^3$	$3\ 4^8$	$3\ 48^4$	$3\ 91^9$	$4\ 35^4$
97	44^0	$0\ 88^0$	$1\ 32^0$	$1\ 76^0$	$2\ 20^0$	$2\ 64^0$	$3\ 8^0$	$3\ 52^0$	$3\ 96^0$	$4\ 40^0$
98	44^5	$0\ 88^9$	$1\ 33^4$	$1\ 77^8$	$2\ 22^3$	$2\ 66^7$	$3\ 11^2$	$3\ 55^6$	$4\ 0^1$	$4\ 44^5$
99	44^9	$0\ 89^8$	$1\ 34^7$	$1\ 79^6$	$2\ 24^5$	$2\ 69^4$	$3\ 14^3$	$3\ 59^3$	$4\ 4^2$	$4\ 49^1$
100	45^4	$0\ 90^7$	$1\ 36^1$	$1\ 81^4$	$2\ 26^8$	$2\ 72^2$	$3\ 17^5$	$3\ 62^9$	$4\ 8^2$	$4\ 53^6$
101	45^8	$0\ 91^6$	$1\ 37^4$	$1\ 83^3$	$2\ 29^1$	$2\ 74^9$	$3\ 20^7$	$3\ 66^5$	$4\ 12^3$	$4\ 58^1$
102	46^3	$0\ 92^5$	$1\ 38^8$	$1\ 85^1$	$2\ 31^3$	$2\ 77^6$	$3\ 23^9$	$3\ 70^1$	$4\ 16^4$	$4\ 62^7$
103	46^7	$0\ 93^4$	$1\ 40^2$	$1\ 86^9$	$2\ 33^6$	$2\ 80^3$	$3\ 27^0$	$3\ 73^8$	$4\ 20^5$	$4\ 67^2$
104	47^2	$0\ 94^4$	$1\ 41^5$	$1\ 88^7$	$2\ 35^9$	$2\ 83^0$	$3\ 30^2$	$3\ 77^4$	$4\ 24^6$	$4\ 71^7$
105	47^6	$0\ 95^3$	$1\ 42^9$	$1\ 90^5$	$2\ 38^1$	$2\ 85^8$	$3\ 33^4$	$3\ 81^0$	$4\ 28^6$	$4\ 76^3$
106	48^1	$0\ 96^2$	$1\ 44^2$	$1\ 92^3$	$2\ 40^4$	$2\ 88^5$	$3\ 36^6$	$3\ 84^7$	$4\ 32^7$	$4\ 80^8$
107	48^5	$0\ 97^1$	$1\ 45^6$	$1\ 94^1$	$2\ 42^7$	$2\ 91^2$	$3\ 39^7$	$3\ 88^3$	$4\ 36^8$	$4\ 85^3$
108	49^0	$0\ 98^0$	$1\ 47^0$	$1\ 96^0$	$2\ 44^9$	$2\ 93^9$	$3\ 42^9$	$3\ 91^9$	$4\ 40^9$	$4\ 89^9$
109	49^4	$0\ 98^9$	$1\ 48^3$	$1\ 97^8$	$2\ 47^2$	$2\ 96^7$	$3\ 46^1$	$3\ 95^5$	$4\ 45^0$	$4\ 94^4$
110	49^9	$0\ 99^8$	$1\ 49^7$	$1\ 99^6$	$2\ 49^5$	$2\ 99^4$	$3\ 49^3$	$3\ 99^2$	$4\ 49^1$	$4\ 99^0$
111	50^3	$1\ 0^7$	$1\ 51^0$	$2\ 1^4$	$2\ 51^7$	$3\ 2^1$	$3\ 52^4$	$4\ 2^8$	$4\ 53^1$	$5\ 3^5$
112	50^8	$1\ 1^6$	$1\ 52^4$	$2\ 3^2$	$2\ 54^0$	$3\ 4^8$	$3\ 55^6$	$4\ 6^4$	$4\ 57^2$	$5\ 8^0$

Per Kilo Lbs.	20p £ P	30p £ P	40p £ P	50p £ P	60p £ P	70p £ P	80p £ P	90p £ P
1	0 9^1	0 13^6	0 18^1	0 22^7	0 27^2	0 31^8	0 36^3	0 40^8
2	0 18^1	0 27^2	0 36^3	0 45^4	0 54^4	0 63^5	0 72^6	0 81^6
3	0 27^2	0 40^8	0 54^4	0 68^0	0 81^6	0 95^3	1 8^9	1 22^5
4	0 36^3	0 54^4	0 72^6	0 90^7	1 8^9	1 27^0	1 45^2	1 63^3
5	0 45^4	0 68^0	0 90^7	1 13^4	1 36^1	1 58^8	1 81^4	2 4^1
6	0 54^4	0 81^6	1 8^9	1 36^1	1 63^2	1 90^5	2 17^7	2 44^9
7	0 63^5	0 95^3	1 27^0	1 58^8	1 90^5	2 22^3	2 54^0	2 85^8
8	0 72^6	1 8^9	1 45^2	1 81^4	2 17^7	2 54^0	2 90^8	3 26^6
9	0 81^6	1 22^5	1 63^3	2 4^1	2 44^9	2 85^8	3 26^6	3 67^4
10	0 90^7	1 36^1	1 81^4	2 26^8	2 72^2	3 17^5	3 62^9	4 8^2
11	0 99^8	1 49^7	1 99^6	2 49^5	2 99^4	3 49^8	3 99^2	4 49^1
12	1 8^9	1 63^3	2 17^7	2 72^2	3 26^6	3 81^0	4 35^5	4 89^9
13	1 17^9	1 76^9	2 35^9	2 94^8	3 53^8	4 12^8	4 71^7	5 30^7
14	1 27^0	1 90^5	2 54^0	3 17^5	3 81^0	4 44^5	5 8^0	5 71^5
15	1 36^1	2 4^1	2 72^2	3 40^2	4 8^2	4 76^3	5 44^3	6 12^4
16	1 45^2	2 17^7	2 90^3	3 62^9	4 35^4	5 8^0	5 80^6	6 53^2
17	1 54^2	2 31^8	3 8^4	3 85^6	4 62^7	5 39^8	6 16^9	6 94^0
18	1 63^3	2 44^9	3 26^6	4 8^2	4 89^9	5 71^5	6 53^2	7 34^8
19	1 72^4	2 58^5	3 44^7	4 30^9	5 17^1	6 3^3	6 89^5	7 75^6
20	1 81^4	2 72^2	3 62^9	4 53^6	5 44^3	6 35^0	7 25^8	8 16^5
21	1 90^5	2 85^8	3 81^0	4 76^3	5 71^5	6 66^8	7 62^0	8 57^3
22	1 99^6	2 99^4	3 99^2	4 99^0	5 98^7	6 98^5	7 98^3	8 98^1
23	2 8^7	3 13^0	4 17^3	5 21^6	6 26^0	7 30^3	8 34^6	9 38^9
24	2 17^7	3 26^6	4 35^5	5 44^3	6 53^2	7 62^0	8 70^9	9 79^8
25	2 26^8	3 40^2	4 53^6	5 67^0	6 80^4	7 93^8	9 7^2	10 20^6
26	2 35^9	3 53^8	4 71^7	5 89^7	7 7^6	8 25^5	9 43^5	10 61^4
27	2 44^9	3 67^4	4 89^9	6 12^4	7 34^8	8 57^3	9 79^8	11 2^2
28	2 54^0	3 81^0	5 8^0	6 35^0	7 62^0	8 89^0	10 16^1	11 43^1
29	2 63^1	3 94^7	5 26^2	6 57^7	7 89^3	9 20^8	10 52^3	11 83^9
30	2 72^2	4 8^2	5 44^3	6 80^4	8 16^5	9 52^5	10 88^6	12 24^7
31	2 81^2	4 21^8	5 62^5	7 3^1	8 43^7	9 84^3	11 24^9	12 65^5
32	2 90^3	4 35^4	5 80^6	7 25^8	8 70^9	10 16^0	11 61^2	13 6^3
33	2 99^4	4 49^1	5 98^7	7 48^4	8 98^1	10 47^8	11 97^5	13 47^2
34	3 8^4	4 62^7	6 16^9	7 71^1	9 25^3	10 79^5	12 33^8	13 88^0
35	3 17^5	4 76^3	6 35^0	7 93^8	9 52^5	11 11^3	12 70^1	14 28^8
36	3 26^6	4 89^9	6 53^2	8 16^5	9 79^8	11 43^1	13 6^3	14 69^6
37	3 35^7	5 3^5	6 71^3	8 39^1	10 7^0	11 74^8	13 42^6	15 10^5
38	3 44^7	5 17^1	6 89^5	8 61^8	10 34^2	12 6^6	13 78^9	15 51^3
39	3 53^8	5 30^7	7 7^6	8 84^5	10 61^4	12 38^3	14 15^2	15 92^1
40	3 62^9	5 44^3	7 25^8	9 7^2	10 88^6	12 70^1	14 51^5	16 32^9
41	3 71^9	5 57^9	7 43^9	9 29^9	11 15^8	13 1^8	14 87^8	16 73^8
42	3 81^0	5 71^5	7 62^0	9 52^5	11 43^1	13 33^6	15 24^1	17 14^6
43	3 90^1	5 85^1	7 80^2	9 75^2	11 70^3	13 65^3	15 60^4	17 55^4
44	3 99^2	5 98^7	7 98^3	9 97^9	11 97^5	13 97^1	15 96^6	17 96^2
45	4 8^2	6 12^4	8 16^5	10 20^6	12 24^7	14 28^8	16 32^9	18 37^1
46	4 17^3	6 26^0	8 34^6	10 43^3	12 51^9	14 60^6	16 69^2	18 77^9
47	4 26^4	6 39^6	8 52^8	10 65^9	12 79^1	14 92^3	17 5^5	19 18^7
48	4 35^4	6 53^2	8 70^9	10 88^6	13 6^3	15 24^1	17 41^8	19 59^5
49	4 44^5	6 66^8	8 89^0	11 11^3	13 33^6	15 55^8	17 78^1	20 0^3
50	4 53^6	6 80^4	9 7^2	11 34^0	13 60^8	15 87^6	18 14^4	20 41^2
51	4 62^6	6 94^0	9 25^3	11 56^7	13 88^0	16 19^3	18 50^7	20 82^0
52	4 71^7	7 7^6	9 43^5	11 79^3	14 15^2	16 51^1	18 86^9	21 22^8
53	4 80^8	7 21^2	9 61^6	12 2^0	14 42^4	16 82^8	19 23^2	21 63^6
54	4 89^9	7 34^8	9 79^8	12 24^7	14 69^6	17 14^6	19 59^5	22 4^5
55	4 99^0	7 48^4	9 97^9	12 47^4	14 96^9	17 46^3	19 95^8	22 45^3
56	5 8^0	7 62^0	10 16^1	12 70^1	15 24^1	17 78^1	20 32^1	22 86$_1$

RATES PER KILO

Per Kilo Lbs.	20p £ P	30p £ P	40p £ P	50p £ P	60p £ P	70p £ P	80p £ P	90p £ P
57	5 17^1	7 75^6	10 34^2	12 92^7	15 51^8	18 9^8	20 68^4	23 26^9
58	5 26^2	7 89^3	10 52^3	13 15^4	15 78^5	18 41^6	21 4^7	23 67^8
59	5 35^2	8 2^9	10 70^5	13 38^1	16 5^7	18 73^8	21 41^0	24 8^6
60	5 44^3	8 16^5	10 88^6	13 60^8	16 32^9	19 5^1	21 77^2	24 49^4
61	5 53^4	8 30^1	11 6^8	13 83^5	16 60^2	19 36^8	22 13^5	24 90^2
62	5 62^5	8 43^7	11 24^9	14 6^1	16 87^4	19 68^6	22 49^8	25 31^0
63	5 71^5	8 57^3	11 43^1	14 28^8	17 14^6	20 0^3	22 86^1	25 71^9
64	5 80^6	8 70^9	11 61^2	14 51^5	17 41^8	20 32^1	23 22^4	26 12^7
65	5 89^7	8 84^5	11 79^3	14 74^2	17 69^0	20 63^8	23 58^7	26 53^5
66	5 98^7	8 98^1	11 97^5	14 96^9	17 96^2	20 95^6	23 95^0	26 94^3
67	6 7^8	9 11^7	12 15^6	15 19^5	18 23^4	21 27^4	24 31^3	27 35^2
68	6 16^9	9 25^3	12 33^8	15 42^2	18 50^7	21 59^1	24 67^5	27 76^0
69	6 26^0	9 38^9	12 51^9	15 64^9	18 77^9	21 90^9	25 3^8	28 16^8
70	6 35^0	9 52^5	12 70^1	15 87^6	19 5^1	22 22^6	25 40^1	28 57^6
71	6 44^1	9 66^2	12 88^2	16 10^3	19 32^3	22 54^4	25 76^4	28 98^5
72	6 53^2	9 79^8	13 6^4	16 32^9	19 59^5	22 86^1	26 12^7	29 39^3
73	6 62^2	9 93^4	13 24^5	16 55^6	19 86^7	23 17^9	26 49^0	29 80^1
74	6 71^3	10 7^0	13 42^6	16 78^3	20 14^0	23 49^6	26 85^3	30 20^9
75	6 80^4	10 20^6	13 60^8	17 1^0	20 41^2	23 81^4	27 21^6	30 61^8
76	6 89^5	10 34^2	13 78^9	17 23^7	20 68^4	24 13^1	27 57^8	31 2^6
77	6 98^5	10 47^8	13 97^1	17 46^3	20 95^6	24 44^9	27 94^1	31 43^4
78	7 7^6	10 61^4	14 15^2	17 69^0	21 22^8	24 76^6	28 30^4	31 84^2
79	7 16^7	10 75^0	14 33^3	17 91^7	21 50^0	25 8^4	28 66^7	32 25^0
80	7 25^7	10 88^6	14 51^5	18 14^4	21 77^2	25 40^1	29 3^0	32 65^9
81	7 34^8	11 2^2	14 69^6	18 37^0	22 4^5	25 71^9	29 39^3	33 6^7
82	7 43^9	11 15^8	14 87^8	18 59^7	22 31^7	26 3^6	29 75^6	33 47^5
83	7 53^0	11 29^4	15 5^9	18 82^4	22 58^9	26 35^4	30 11^9	33 88^3
84	7 62^0	11 43^1	15 24^1	19 5^1	22 86^1	26 67^1	30 48^1	34 29^2
85	7 71^1	11 56^6	15 42^2	19 27^8	23 13^3	26 98^9	30 84^4	34 70^0
86	7 80^2	11 70^3	15 60^4	19 50^4	23 40^5	27 30^6	31 20^7	35 10^8
87	7 89^3	11 83^9	15 78^5	19 73^1	23 67^8	27 62^4	31 57^0	35 51^6
88	7 98^3	11 97^5	15 96^6	19 95^8	23 95^0	27 94^1	31 93^3	35 92^5
89	8 7^4	12 11^1	16 14^8	20 18^5	24 22^2	28 25^9	32 29^6	36 33^3
90	8 16^5	12 24^7	16 32^9	20 41^2	24 49^4	28 57^6	32 65^9	36 74^1
91	8 25^5	12 38^3	16 51^1	20 63^8	24 76^6	28 89^4	33 2^2	37 14^9
92	8 34^6	12 51^9	16 69^2	20 86^5	25 3^8	29 21^1	33 38^4	37 55^7
93	8 43^7	12 65^5	16 87^4	21 9^2	25 31^0	29 52^9	33 74^7	37 96^6
94	8 52^8	12 79^1	17 5^5	21 31^9	25 58^2	29 84^6	34 11^0	38 37^4
95	8 61^8	12 92^7	17 23^7	21 54^6	25 85^5	30 16^4	34 47^3	38 78^2
96	8 70^9	13 6^3	17 41^8	21 77^2	26 12^7	30 48^1	34 83^6	39 19^0
97	8 80^0	13 20^0	17 59^0	21 99^9	26 39^9	30 79^9	35 19^9	39 59^9
98	8 89^0	13 33^6	17 78^1	22 22^6	26 67^1	31 11^6	35 56^2	40 0^7
99	8 98^1	13 47^2	17 96^2	22 45^3	26 94^3	31 43^4	35 92^5	40 41^5
100	9 7^2	13 60^8	18 14^4	22 68^0	27 21^6	31 75^1	36 28^7	40 82^3
101	9 16^3	13 74^4	18 32^5	22 90^6	27 48^8	32 6^9	36 65^0	41 23^2
102	9 25^3	13 88^0	18 50^7	23 13^3	27 76^0	32 38^7	37 1^8	41 64^0
103	9 34^4	14 1^6	18 68^8	23 36^0	28 3^2	32 70^4	37 37^6	42 4^8
104	9 43^5	14 15^2	18 86^9	23 58^7	28 30^4	33 2^2	37 73^9	42 45^6
105	9 52^5	14 28^8	19 5^1	23 81^4	28 57^6	33 33^9	38 10^2	42 86^4
106	9 61^6	14 42^4	19 23^2	24 4^0	28 84^9	33 65^7	38 46^5	43 27^3
107	9 70^7	14 56^0	19 41^4	24 26^7	29 12^1	33 97^4	38 82^8	43 68^1
108	9 79^8	14 69^6	19 59^5	24 49^4	29 39^3	34 29^2	39 19^0	44 8^9
109	9 88^8	14 83^3	19 77^7	24 72^1	29 66^5	34 60^9	39 55^3	44 49^7
110	9 97^9	14 96^9	19 95^8	24 94^8	29 93^7	34 92^7	39 91^6	44 90^6
111	10 7^0	15 10^5	20 14^0	25 17^4	30 20^9	35 24^4	40 27^9	45 31^4
112	10 16^0	15 24^1	20 32^1	25 40^1	30 48^1	35 56^2	40 64^2	45 72^2

RATES PER KILO

Per Kilo	1p	2p	3p	4p	5p	6p	7p	8p	9p	10p
Cwts.	£ P	£ P	£ P	£ P	£ P	£ P	£ P	£ P	£ P	£ P
1	0 50^8	1 1^6	1 52^4	2 3^2	2 54^0	3 4^8	3 55^6	4 6^4	4 57^2	5 8^0
2	1 1^6	2 3^2	3 4^8	4 6^4	5 8^0	6 9^6	7 11^2	8 12^8	9 14^4	10 16^0
3	1 52^4	3 4^8	4 57^2	6 9^6	7 62^0	9 14^4	10 66^9	12 19^3	13 71^7	15 24^1
4	2 3^2	4 6^4	6 9^6	8 12^8	10 16^0	12 19^3	14 22^4	16 25^7	18 28^9	20 32^1
5	2 54^0	5 8^0	7 62^0	10 16^0	12 70^1	15 24^1	17 78^0	20 32^1	22 86^1	25 40^1
6	3 4^8	6 9^6	9 14^4	12 19^3	15 24^1	18 28^9	21 33^7	24 38^5	27 43^3	30 48^1
7	3 55^6	7 11^2	10 66^9	14 22^5	17 78^1	21 33^7	24 89^3	28 44^9	32 0^5	35 56^2
8	4 6^4	8 12^8	12 19^3	16 25^7	20 32^1	24 38^5	28 44^9	32 51^4	36 57^8	40 64^2
9	4 57^2	9 14^4	13 71^7	18 28^9	22 86^1	27 43^3	32 0^5	36 57^8	41 15^0	45 72^2
10	5 8^0	10 16^1	15 24^1	20 32^1	25 40^1	30 48^1	35 56^2	40 64^2	45 72^2	50 80^2
11	5 58^8	11 17^7	16 76^5	22 35^3	27 94^1	33 53^0	39 11^8	44 70^6	50 29^4	55 88^3
12	6 9^6	12 19^3	18 28^9	24 38^5	30 48^1	36 57^8	42 67^4	48 77^0	54 86^6	60 96^3
13	6 60^4	13 20^9	19 81^3	26 41^7	33 2^2	39 62^6	46 23^0	52 83^4	59 43^9	66 4^3
14	7 11^2	14 22^4	21 33^7	28 44^9	35 56^2	42 67^4	49 78^6	56 89^9	64 1^1	71 12^3
15	7 62^0	15 24^1	22 86^1	30 48^1	38 10^2	45 72^2	53 34^2	60 96^2	68 58^2	76 20^4
16	8 12^8	16 25^7	24 38^5	32 51^4	40 64^2	48 77^0	56 89^9	65 2^7	73 15^5	81 28^4
17	8 63^6	17 27^3	25 90^9	34 54^6	43 18^2	51 81^8	60 45^5	69 9^1	77 72^8	86 36^4
18	9 14^4	18 28^9	27 43^3	36 57^8	45 72^2	54 86^7	64 1^1	73 15^5	82 30^0	91 44^4
19	9 65^2	19 30^5	28 95^7	38 61^0	48 26^2	57 91^5	67 56^7	77 21^9	86 87^2	96 52^4
20	10 16^1	20 32^1	30 48^1	40 64^2	50 80^2	60 96^3	71 12^3	81 28^4	91 44^4	101 60^5
21	10 66^9	21 33^7	32 0^5	42 67^4	53 34^2	64 1^1	74 67^9	85 34^8	96 1^6	106 68^5
22	11 17^7	22 35^3	33 53^0	44 70^6	55 88^3	67 5^9	78 23^6	89 41^2	100 58^9	111 76^5
23	11 68^5	23 36^9	35 5^4	46 73^8	58 42^3	70 10^7	81 79^2	93 47^6	105 16^1	116 84^5
24	12 19^3	24 39^5	36 57^8	48 77^0	60 96^3	73 15^5	85 34^8	97 54^1	109 73^3	121 92^6
25	12 70^1	25 40^1	38 10^2	50 80^2	63 50^3	76 20^4	88 90^4	101 60^5	114 30^5	127 0^6
26	13 20^9	26 41^7	39 62^6	52 83^4	66 4^3	79 25^2	92 46^0	105 66^9	118 87^8	132 8^6
27	13 71^7	27 43^3	41 15^0	54 86^6	68 58^3	82 30^0	96 1^6	109 73^3	123 45^0	137 16^6
28	14 22^5	28 44^9	42 67^4	56 89^9	71 12^3	85 34^8	99 57^3	113 79^7	128 2^2	142 24^7

Per Kilo	20p	30p	40p	50p	60p	70p	80p	90p
Cwts.	£ P	£ P	£ P	£ P	£ P	£ P	£ P	£ P
1	10 16^0	15 24^1	20 32^1	25 40^1	30 48^1	35 56^2	40 64^2	45 72^2
2	20 32^1	30 48^1	40 64^2	50 80^2	60 96^3	71 12^3	81 28^4	91 44^4
3	30 48^1	45 72^2	60 96^3	76 20^4	91 44^4	106 68^5	121 92^6	137 16^6
4	40 64^2	60 96^3	81 28^4	101 60^5	121 92^6	142 24^7	162 56^8	182 88^8
5	50 80^2	76 20^4	101 60^5	127 0^6	152 40^7	177 80^8	203 20^9	228 61^1
6	60 96^3	91 44^4	121 92^6	152 40^7	182 88^8	213 37^0	243 85^1	274 33^3
7	71 12^3	106 68^5	142 24^7	177 80^8	213 37^0	248 93^2	284 49^3	320 05^5
8	81 28^4	121 92^6	162 56^8	203 20^9	243 85^1	284 49^3	325 13^5	365 77^7
9	91 44^4	137 16^7	182 88^8	228 61^1	274 33^3	320 5^5	365 77^7	411 49^9
10	101 60^5	152 40^7	203 20^9	254 1^2	304 81^4	355 61^6	406 41^9	457 22^1
11	111 76^5	167 64^8	223 53^0	279 41^3	335 29^6	391 17^8	447 6^1	502 94^3
12	121 92^6	182 88^8	243 85^1	304 81^4	365 77^7	426 74^0	487 70^3	548 66^5
13	132 8^6	198 12^9	264 17^2	330 21^5	396 25^8	462 30^1	528 34^4	594 38^8
14	142 24^7	213 37^0	284 49^3	355 61^6	426 74^0	497 86^3	568 98^6	640 11^0
15	152 40^7	228 61^1	304 81^4	381 1^8	457 22^1	533 42^5	609 62^8	685 83^2
16	162 56^8	243 85^1	325 13^5	406 41^9	487 70^3	568 98^6	650 27^0	731 55^4
17	172 72^8	259 9^2	345 45^6	431 82^0	518 18^4	604 54^8	690 91^2	777 27^6
18	182 88^8	274 33^3	365 77^7	457 22^1	548 66^5	640 11^0	731 55^4	822 99^8
19	193 4^9	289 57^3	386 9^8	482 62^3	579 14^7	675 67^1	772 19^6	868 72^0
20	203 20^9	304 81^4	406 41^9	508 2^4	609 62^8	711 23^3	812 83^8	914 44^2
21	213 37^0	320 5^5	426 74^0	533 42^5	640 11^0	746 79^5	853 48^0	960 16^4
22	223 53^0	335 29^6	447 6^1	558 82^6	670 59^1	782 35^6	894 12^1	1005 88^7
23	233 69^1	350 53^6	467 38^2	584 22^7	701 7^2	817 91^8	934 76^3	1051 66^9
24	243 85^1	365 77^7	487 70^3	609 62^8	731 55^4	853 48^0	975 40^5	1097 33^1
25	254 1^1	381 1^8	508 2^4	635 2^9	762 3^5	889 4^1	1016 4^7	1143 5^3
26	264 17^2	396 25^8	528 34^4	660 43^1	792 51^7	924 60^3	1056 68^9	1188 77^5
27	274 33^3	411 49^9	548 66^5	685 83^2	822 99^8	960 16^4	1097 33^1	1234 49^9
28	284 49^3	426 74^0	568 98^6	711 23^3	835 48^9	995 72^6	1137 97^3	1280 21^7

Left panel

℔Oz. P	℔Lb. P	℔Kilo. £	℔Cwt. £	℔Ton. £	P
0	0⁵	1	0	51	10 16
0	0⁹	2⁰	1	0	20 0
0	1	2²	1	12	22 40
0	1⁸	3⁹	2	0	40 0
0¼	2	4⁴	2	24	44 80
0¼	2²	4⁹	2	50	50 0
0¼	2⁷	5⁹	3	0	60 0
0¼	3	6⁶	3	36	67 20
0¼	3⁶	7⁹	4	0	80 0
0¼	4	8⁸	4	48	89 60
0¼	4⁴	9⁸	5	0	100 0
0¼	5	11⁰	5	60	112 0
0¼	5⁴	11⁹	6	0	120 0
0¼	6	13²	6	72	134 40
0¼	6³	13⁸	7	0	140 0
0¼	6⁷	14⁸	7	50	150 0
0½	7	15⁴	7	84	156 80
0½	7¹	15⁷	8	0	160 0
0½	8	17⁶	8	96	179 20
0½	8⁰	17⁷	9	0	180 0
0½	8⁹	19⁷	10	0	200 0
0½	9	19⁸	10	8	201 60
0½	9⁸	21⁷	11	0	220 0
0¾	10	22⁰	11	20	224 0
0¾	10⁷	23⁶	12	0	240 0
0¾	11	24²	12	32	246 40
0¾	11²	24⁶	12	50	250 0
0¾	11⁶	25⁶	13	0	260 0
0¾	12	26⁵	13	44	268 80
0¾	12⁵	27⁶	14	0	280 0
0¾	13	28⁷	14	56	291 20
0¾	13⁴	29⁵	15	0	300 0
1	14	30⁹	15	68	313 60
1	14³	31⁵	16	0	320 0
1	15	33¹	16	80	336 0
1	15²	33⁵	17	0	340 0
1	15⁶	34⁵	17	50	350 0
1	16	35³	17	92	358 40
1	16¹	35⁴	18	0	360 0
1	17⁰	37⁴	19	0	380 0
1	17	37⁵	19	4	380 80
1	17⁹	39⁴	20	0	400 0
1¼	18	39⁷	20	16	403 20
1¼	19	41⁹	21	28	425 60
1¼	20	44¹	22	40	448 0
1¼	20¹	44³	22	50	450 0
1¼	21	46³	23	52	470 40
1¼	22	48⁵	24	64	492 80
1½	22³	49²	25	0	500 0
1½	23	50⁷	25	76	515 20
1½	24	52⁹	26	88	537 60
1½	25	55¹	28	0	560 0
1½	26	57³	29	12	582 40
1¾	26⁸	59¹	30	0	600 0
1¾	27	59⁵	30	24	604 80

Right panel

℔Oz. P	℔Lb. £	℔Kilo. £	℔Cwt. £	P	℔Ton. £	P
1¾	– 28	– 61⁷	31	36	627	20
1½	– 29	– 63⁹	32	48	649	60
2	– 30	– 66¹	33	60	672	0
2	– 31	– 68³	34	72	694	40
2	– 31³	– 68⁹	35	0	700	0
2	– 32	– 70⁶	35	84	716	80
2	– 33	– 72⁸	36	96	739	20
2¼	– 34	– 75⁰	38	8	761	60
2¼	– 35	– 77²	39	20	784	0
2¼	– 35⁷	– 78⁷	40	0	800	0
2¼	– 36	– 79⁴	40	32	806	40
2¼	– 37	– 81⁶	41	44	828	80
2½	– 38	– 83⁸	42	56	851	20
2½	– 39	– 86⁰	43	68	873	60
2½	– 40	– 88²	44	80	896	0
2½	– 40²	– 88⁶	45	0	900	0
2½	– 41	– 90⁴	45	92	918	40
2¾	– 42	– 92⁶	47	4	940	80
2¾	– 43	– 94⁸	48	16	963	20
2¾	– 44	– 97⁰	49	28	985	60
2¾	– 44⁶	– 98⁴	50	0	1000	0
2¾	– 45	– 99²	50	40	1008	0
3	– 46	1 1⁴	51	52	1030	40
3	– 47	1 3⁶	52	64	1052	80
3	– 48	1 5⁸	53	76	1075	20
3	– 49	1 8⁰	54	88	1097	60
3½	– 50	1 10²	56	0	1120	0
3½	– 51	1 12⁴	57	12	1142	40
3½	– 52	1 14⁶	58	24	1164	80
3½	– 53	1 16⁵	59	36	1187	20
3½	– 54	1 19¹	60	48	1209	60
3½	– 56	1 23⁵	62	72	1254	40
3¾	– 58	1 27⁹	64	96	1299	20
3¾	– 60	1 32³	67	20	1344	0
4	– 62	1 36⁷	69	44	1388	80
4	– 64	1 41¹	71	68	1433	60
4½	– 66	1 45⁵	73	92	1478	0
4½	– 68	1 49⁹	76	16	1523	20
4½	– 70	1 54³	78	40	1568	0
4½	– 72	1 58⁷	80	64	1612	80
4¾	– 74	1 63¹	82	88	1657	60
4¾	– 75	1 65³	84	0	1680	0
4¾	– 76	1 67⁶	85	12	1702	40
5	– 78	1 72⁰	87	36	1747	20
5	– 80	1 76⁴	89	60	1792	0
5½	– 82	1 80⁸	91	84	1836	80
5½	– 84	1 85²	94	8	1881	60
5½	– 86	1 89⁶	96	32	1926	0
5½	– 88	1 94⁰	98	56	1971	20
5¾	– 90	1 98⁴	100	80	2016	0
5¾	– 92	2 2⁸	103	4	2060	80
5¾	– 94	2 7²	105	28	2105	60
6	– 96	2 11⁶	107	52	2150	40
6½	– 98	2 16¹	109	76	2195	20
6½	1 0	2 20⁵	112	0	2240	0

British into Metric Measures. By shifting the point one place to right, 1 to 100 become 10, 20, 30, &c. to 1000; or, two places to the right, 100, 200, &c. to 10,000. Thus 800 lbs. = the figures for 80 lbs. with point shifted 1 place to right = 362·9 kg.

Contractions :—*gms.*=grams ; *grs.*=grains ; *hectol.*=hectolitres ; *km.*=kilometres ; *kilos., kg.*=kilograms ; *mm.*=millimetres ; *met.*=metres ; *Tnns.*=Tonnes, or Metric Tons.

Ins. =mm.	Feet =met.	Yards =met.	Miles =km.	Bush.= hectol.	Brit. Meas.	Tons= tonnes	Cwts. =kilos.	Lbs. =kilos.	Ozs. (av.) =gms.	Grs. gms
25·4	0·30	0·91	1·61	0·36	1	1·02	50·8	0·45	28·35	0·06
50·8	0·61	1·83	3·22	0·73	2	2·03	101·6	0·91	56·70	0·13
76·2	0·91	2·74	4·83	1·09	3	3·05	152·4	1·36	85·05	0·19
101·6	1·22	3·66	6·44	1·45	4	4·06	203·2	1·81	113·40	0·26
127·0	1·52	4·57	8·05	1·82	5	5·08	254·0	2·27	141·75	0·32
152·4	1·83	5·49	9·66	2·18	6	6·10	304·8	2·72	170·10	0·39
177·8	2·13	6·40	11·26	2·55	7	7·11	355·6	3·18	198·45	0·45
203·2	2·44	7·31	12·87	2·91	8	8·13	406·4	3·63	226·80	0·52
228·6	2·74	8·23	14·48	3·27	9	9·14	457·2	4·08	255·15	0·58
254·0	3·05	9·14	16·09	3·64	10	10·16	508·0	4·54	283·50	0·65
279·4	3·35	10·06	17·70	4·00	11	11·18	558·8	4·99	311·85	0·71
304·8	3·66	10·97	19·31	4·36	12	12·19	609·6	5·44	340·20	0·78
330·2	3·96	11·89	20·92	4·73	13	13·21	660·4	5·90	368·55	0·84
355·6	4·27	12·80	22·53	5·09	14	14·22	711·2	6·35	396·90	0·91
381·0	4·57	13·72	24·14	5·46	15	15·24	762·0	6·80	425·25	0·97
406·4	4·88	14·63	25·75	5·82	16	16·26	812·8	7·26	453·60	1·04
431·8	5·18	15·54	27·36	6·18	17	17·27	863·6	7·71	481·95	1·10
457·2	5·49	16·46	28·97	6·55	18	18·29	914·4	8·16	510·30	1·17
482·6	5·79	17·37	30·58	6·91	19	19·30	965·2	8·62	538·65	1·23
508·0	6·10	18·29	32·19	7·27	20	20·32	1016·0	9·07	567·00	1·30
533·4	6·40	19·20	33·80	7·64	21	21·34	1066·8	9·53	595·35	1·36
558·8	6·71	20·12	35·40	8·00	22	22·35	1117·7	9·98	623·70	1·43
584·2	7·01	21·03	37·01	8·36	23	23·37	1168·5	10·43	652·05	1·49
609·6	7·31	21·95	38·62	8·73	24	24·39	1219·3	10·89	680·40	1·55
635·0	7·62	22·86	40·23	9·09	25	25·40	1270·1	11·34	708·75	1·62
660·4	7·92	23·77	41·84	9·46	26	26·42	1320·9	11·79	737·10	1·68
685·8	8·23	24·69	43·45	9·82	27	27·43	1371·7	12·25	765·45	1·75
711·2	8·53	25·60	45·06	10·18	28	28·45	1422·5	12·70	793·80	1·81
736·6	8·84	26·52	46·67	10·55	29	29·47	1473·3	13·15	822·15	1·88
762·0	9·14	27·43	48·28	10·91	30	30·48	1524·1	13·61	850·50	1·94
787·4	9·45	28·35	49·89	11·27	31	31·50	1574·9	14·06	878·85	2·01
812·8	9·75	29·26	51·50	11·64	32	32·51	1625·7	14·51	907·20	2·07
838·2	10·06	30·17	53·11	12·00	33	33·53	1676·5	14·97	935·55	2·14
863·6	10·36	31·09	54·72	12·36	34	34·55	1727·3	15·42	963·90	2·20
889·0	10·67	32·00	56·33	12·73	35	35·56	1778·1	15·88	992·25	2·27
914·4	10·97	32·92	57·94	13·09	36	36·58	1828·9	16·33	1020·6	2·33
939·8	11·28	33·83	59·55	13·46	37	37·59	1879·7	16·78	1048·9	2·40
965·2	11·58	34·75	61·15	13·82	38	38·61	1930·5	17·24	1077·3	2·46
990·6	11·89	35·66	62·76	14·18	39	39·63	1981·3	17·69	1105·6	2·53
1016·0	12·19	36·58	64·37	14·55	40	40·64	2032·1	18·14	1134·0	2·59
1041·4	12·50	37·49	65·98	14·91	41	41·66	2082·9	18·60	1162·3	2·66
1066·8	12·80	38·40	67·59	15·27	42	42·67	2133·7	19·05	1190·7	2·72
1092·2	13·11	39·32	69·20	15·64	43	43·69	2184·5	19·50	1219·0	2·79
1117·6	13·41	40·23	70·81	16·00	44	44·71	2235·3	19·96	1247·4	2·85
1143·0	13·72	41·15	72·42	16·37	45	45·72	2286·1	20·41	1275·7	2·92
1168·4	14·02	42·06	74·03	16·73	46	46·74	2336·9	20·86	1304·1	2·98
1193·8	14·33	42·98	75·64	17·09	47	47·75	2387·7	21·32	1332·4	3·05
1219·2	14·63	43·89	77·25	17·46	48	48·77	2438·5	21·77	1360·8	3·11
1244·6	14·93	44·81	78·86	17·82	49	49·79	2489·3	22·23	1389·1	3·17
1270·0	15·24	45·72	80·47	18·18	50	50·80	2540·1	22·68	1417·5	3·24
1524·0	18·29	54·86	96·56	21·82	60	60·96	3048·1	27·21	1701·0	3·89
2032·0	24·38	73·15	128·7	29·09	80	81·28	4064·2	36·29	2268·0	5·18
2540·0	30·48	91·44	160·9	36·37	100	101·6	5080·2	45·36	2835·0	6·48

British into Metric Measures. By shifting the point one place to right, 1 to 100 become 10, 20, 30, &c. to 1000; or, two places to the right, 100, 200, &c. to 10,000. Thus 90 acres = the figs. for 9 ac. with point shifted 1 place to right = 36·4 h'ares.

Contractions:—*c.*=cube; *cc.*=cube centimetres; *cm.*=centimetres; *m., met.*=metres; *km.*=kilometres; *h'are, hecta.*=hectare.

Acres =hecta.	Sq. Ins. =sq. cm	Sq. Ft. =sq.m.	Sq. Yds. =sq. met	Gallons =litres	Brit. Meas.	Pints =litres	Fl. Ozs. =cc.	Cb. Ins =cc.	Cub.Ft. =c.met	Cub.Yd. =c. m.
0·40	6·45	0·093	0·836	4·55	1	0·57	28	16	0·028	0·76
0·81	12·90	0·186	1·672	9·09	2	1·14	57	33	0·057	1·53
1·21	19·35	0·279	2·508	13·64	3	1·70	85	49	0·085	2·29
1·62	25·81	0·372	3·345	18·18	4	2·27	114	65	0·113	3·06
2·02	32·26	0·465	4·181	22·73	5	2·84	142	82	0·142	3·82
2·43	38·71	0·557	5·017	27·28	6	3·41	170	98	0·170	4·59
2·83	45·16	0·650	5·853	31·82	7	3·98	199	115	0·198	5·35
3·24	51·61	0·743	6·689	36·37	8	4·55	227	131	0·227	6·12
3·64	58·06	0·836	7·525	40·91	9	5·11	256	147	0·255	6·88
4·05	64·52	0·929	8·361	45·46	10	5·68	284	164	0·283	7·65
4·45	70·97	1·022	9·197	50·01	11	6·25	312	180	0·311	8·41
4·86	77·42	1·115	10·034	54·55	12	6·82	341	197	0·340	9·17
5·26	83·87	1·208	10·870	59·10	13	7·39	369	213	0·368	9·94
5·67	90·32	1·301	11·706	63·64	14	7·95	398	229	0·396	10·70
6·07	96·77	1·394	12·542	68·19	15	8·52	426	246	0·425	11·47
6·47	103·2	1·486	13·378	72·73	16	9·09	455	262	0·453	12·23
6·88	109·7	1·579	14·214	77·28	17	9·66	483	279	0·481	13·00
7·28	116·1	1·672	15·050	81·83	18	10·23	511	295	0·510	13·76
7·69	122·6	1·765	15·886	86·37	19	10·80	540	311	0·538	14·53
8·09	129·0	1·858	16·723	90·92	20	11·36	568	328	0·566	15·29
8·50	135·5	1·951	17·559	95·46	21	11·93	597	344	0·595	16·06
8·90	141·9	2·044	18·395	100·01	22	12·50	625	360	0·623	16·82
9·31	148·4	2·137	19·231	104·56	23	13·07	653	377	0·651	17·58
9·71	154·8	2·230	20·067	109·10	24	13·64	682	393	0·680	18·35
10·12	161·3	2·323	20·903	113·65	25	14·21	710	410	0·708	19·11
10·52	167·7	2·415	21·739	118·19	26	14·77	739	426	0·736	19·88
10·93	174·2	2·508	22·575	122·74	27	15·34	767	442	0·765	20·64
11·33	180·6	2·601	23·412	127·29	28	15·91	796	459	0·793	21·41
11·74	187·1	2·694	24·248	131·83	29	16·48	824	475	0·821	22·17
12·14	193·6	2·787	25·084	136·38	30	17·05	852	492	0·850	22·94
12·55	200·0	2·880	25·920	140·92	31	17·62	881	508	0·878	23·70
12·95	206·4	2·973	26·756	145·47	32	18·18	909	524	0·906	24·47
13·35	212·9	3·066	27·592	150·02	33	18·75	938	541	0·934	25·23
13·76	219·3	3·159	28·428	154·56	34	19·32	966	557	0·963	25·99
14·16	225·8	3·252	29·264	159·11	35	19·89	994	573	0·991	26·76
14·57	232·3	3·345	30·101	163·65	36	20·46	1023	590	1·019	27·52
14·97	238·7	3·437	30·937	168·20	37	21·02	1051	606	1·048	28·29
15·38	245·2	3·530	31·773	172·75	38	21·59	1080	623	1·076	29·05
15·78	251·6	3·623	32·609	177·29	39	22·16	1108	639	1·104	29·82
16·19	258·1	3·716	33·445	181·84	40	22·73	1136	655	1·133	30·58
16·59	264·5	3·809	34·281	186·38	41	23·30	1165	672	1·161	31·35
17·00	271·0	3·902	35·117	190·93	42	23·87	1193	688	1·189	32·11
17·40	277·4	3·995	35·953	195·48	43	24·43	1222	705	1·218	32·88
17·81	283·9	4·088	36·790	200·02	44	25·00	1250	721	1·246	33·64
18·21	290·3	4·181	37·626	204·57	45	25·57	1279	737	1·274	34·40
18·62	296·8	4·274	38·462	209·11	46	26·14	1307	754	1·303	35·17
19·02	303·2	4·366	39·298	213·66	47	26·71	1335	770	1·331	35·93
19·42	309·7	4·459	40·134	218·21	48	27·28	1364	787	1·359	36·70
19·83	316·1	4·552	40·970	222·75	49	27·84	1392	803	1·388	37·46
20·23	322·6	4·645	41·806	227·30	50	28·41	1421	819	1·416	38·23
24·28	387·1	5·574	50·168	272·76	60	34·09	1705	983	1·699	45·87
32·37	516·1	7·432	66·890	363·68	80	45·46	2273	1311	2·265	61·16
40·47	645·2	9·290	83·613	454·60	100	56·82	2841	1639	2·832	76·45

MULTIPLICATION TABLE [Look for larger

..	11	12	13	14	15	16	17	18	19	20	21	22	23	24	..
1	11	12	13	14	15	16	17	18	19	20	21	22	23	24	1
2	22	24	26	28	30	32	34	36	38	40	42	44	46	48	2
3	33	36	39	42	45	48	51	54	57	60	63	66	69	72	3
4	44	48	52	56	60	64	68	72	76	80	84	88	92	96	4
5	55	60	65	70	75	80	85	90	95	100	105	110	115	120	5
6	66	72	78	84	90	96	102	108	114	120	126	132	138	144	6
7	77	84	91	98	105	112	119	126	133	140	147	154	161	168	7
8	88	96	104	112	120	128	136	144	152	160	168	176	184	192	8
9	99	108	117	126	135	144	153	162	171	180	189	198	207	216	9
10	110	120	130	140	150	160	170	180	190	200	210	220	230	240	10
11	121	132	143	154	165	176	187	198	209	220	231	242	253	264	11
12	..	144	156	168	180	192	204	216	228	240	252	264	276	288	12
13	..	..	169	182	195	208	221	234	247	260	273	286	299	312	13
14	..	..	..	196	210	224	238	252	266	280	294	308	322	336	14
15	..	..	..	..	225	240	255	270	285	300	315	330	345	360	15
..	..	..	..	..	..	256	272	288	304	320	336	352	368	384	16
..	..	..	..	..	..	..	289	306	323	340	357	374	391	408	17
								324	342	360	378	396	414	432	18
									361	380	399	418	437	456	19
										400	420	440	460	480	20
											441	462	483	504	21
												484	506	528	22
													529	552	23
														576	24

Fractional Mult. Table

	1¼	1½	1¾	2	2¼	2½	2¾	3	3¼	3½	3¾	4	4¼	4½	
¾	1	1⅛	1¼	1½	1¾	1⅞	2								
1	1¼	1½	1¾	2	2¼	2½	2¾	3							
¼	1½	1⅞	2¼	2½	2¾	3⅛	3½	3¾	4						
1½	1⅞	2¼	2⅝	3	3⅜	3¾	4⅛	4½	4⅞	5¼					
¾	2¼	2⅝	3	3½	4	4⅜	4¾	5¼	5¾	6⅛	6½				
2	2½	3	3½	4	4½	5	5½	6	6½	7	7½	8			
¼	2¾	3⅜	4	4½	5	5⅝	6¼	6¾	7¼	7⅞	8½	9	9½		
2½	3⅛	3¾	4⅜	5	5⅝	6¼	6⅞	7½	8⅛	8¾	9⅜	10	10⅝	11¼	2½
¾	3½	4⅛	4¾	5½	6¼	6⅞	7½	8¼	9	9⅝	10¼	11	11¾	12⅜	¾
3	3¾	4½	5¼	6	6¾	7½	8¼	9	9¾	10½	11¼	12	12¾	13½	3
¼	4	4⅞	5¾	6½	7¼	8⅛	9	9¾	10½	11⅜	12¼	13	13¾	14⅝	¼
3½	4⅜	5¼	6⅛	7	7⅞	8¾	9⅝	10½	11⅜	12¼	13⅛	14	14⅞	15¾	3½
¾	4¾	5⅝	6½	7½	8½	9⅜	10¼	11¼	12¼	13⅛	14	15	16	16⅞	¾
4	5	6	7	8	9	10	11	12	13	14	15	16	17	18	4
¼	5¼	6⅜	7½	8½	9½	10⅝	11¾	12¾	13¾	14⅞	16	17	18	19⅛	¼
4½	5⅝	6¾	7⅞	9	10⅛	11¼	12⅜	13½	14⅝	15¾	16⅞	18	19⅛	20¼	4½
¾	6	7⅛	8¼	9½	10¾	11⅞	13	14¼	15½	16⅝	17¾	19	20¼	21⅜	¾
5	6¼	7½	8¾	10	11¼	12½	13¾	15	16¼	17½	18¾	20	21¼	22½	5
¼	6½	7⅞	9¼	10½	11¾	13⅛	14½	15¾	17	18⅜	19¾	21	22¼	23⅝	¼
5½	6⅞	8¼	9⅝	11	12⅜	13¾	15⅛	16½	17⅞	19¼	20⅝	22	23⅜	24¾	5½
¾	7¼	8⅝	10	11½	13	14⅜	15¾	17¼	18¾	20⅛	21½	23	24½	25⅞	¾
6	7½	9	10½	12	13½	15	16½	18	19½	21	22½	24	25½	27	6
¼	7¾	9⅜	11	12½	14	15⅝	17¼	18¾	20¼	21⅞	23½	25	26½	28⅛	¼
6½	8⅛	9¾	11⅜	13	14⅝	16¼	17⅞	19½	21⅛	22¾	24⅜	26	27⅝	29¼	6½
¾	8½	10⅛	11¾	13½	15¼	16⅞	18½	20¼	22	23⅝	25¼	27	28¾	30⅜	¾
7	8¾	10½	12¼	14	15¾	17½	19¼	21	22¾	24½	26¼	28	29¾	31½	7
¼	9	10⅞	12¾	14½	16¼	18⅛	20	21¾	23½	25⅜	27¼	29	30¾	32⅝	¼
7½	9⅜	11¼	13⅛	15	16⅞	18¾	20⅝	22½	24⅜	26¼	28⅛	30	31⅞	33¾	7½
¾	9¾	11⅝	13½	15½	17½	19⅜	21¼	23¼	25¼	27⅛	29	31	33	34⅞	¾
8	10	12	14	16	18	20	22	24	26	28	30	32	34	36	8
¼	10¼	12⅜	14½	16½	18½	20⅝	22¾	24¾	26¾	28⅞	31	33	35	37⅛	¼
8½	10⅝	12¾	14⅞	17	19⅛	21¼	23⅜	25½	27⅝	29¾	31⅞	34	36⅛	38¼	8½
¾	11	13⅛	15¼	17½	19¾	21⅞	24	26¼	28½	30⅝	32¾	35	37¼	39⅜	¾
9	11¼	13½	15¾	18	20¼	22½	24¾	27	29¼	31½	33¾	36	38¼	40½	9
¼	11½	13⅞	16¼	18½	20¾	23⅛	25½	27¾	30	32⅜	34¾	37	39¼	41⅝	¼
9½	11⅞	14¼	16⅝	19	21⅜	23¾	26⅛	28½	30⅞	33¼	35⅝	38	40⅜	42¾	9½
¾	12¼	14⅝	17	19½	22	24⅜	26¾	29¼	31¾	34⅛	36½	39	41½	43⅞	¾
10	12½	15	17½	20	22½	25	27½	30	32½	35	37½	40	42½	45	10

No. at top of page).

MULTIPLICATION TABLE.

..	25	26	27	28	29	30	31	32	33	34	35	36	..
1	25	26	27	28	29	30	31	32	33	34	35	36	1
2	50	52	54	56	58	60	62	64	66	68	70	72	2
3	75	78	81	84	87	90	93	96	99	102	105	108	3
4	100	104	108	112	116	120	124	128	132	136	140	144	4
5	125	130	135	140	145	150	155	160	165	170	175	180	5
6	150	156	162	168	174	180	186	192	198	204	210	216	6
7	175	182	189	196	203	210	217	224	231	238	245	252	7
8	200	208	216	224	232	240	248	256	264	272	280	288	8
9	225	234	243	252	261	270	279	288	297	306	315	324	9
10	250	260	270	280	290	300	310	320	330	340	350	360	10
11	275	286	297	308	319	330	341	352	363	374	385	396	11
12	300	312	324	336	348	360	372	384	396	408	420	432	12
13	325	338	351	364	377	390	403	416	429	442	455	468	13
14	350	364	378	392	406	420	434	448	462	476	490	504	14
15	375	390	405	420	435	450	465	480	495	510	525	540	15
16	400	416	432	448	464	480	496	512	528	544	560	576	16
17	425	442	459	476	493	510	527	544	561	578	595	612	17
18	450	468	486	504	522	540	558	576	594	612	630	648	18
19	475	494	513	532	551	570	589	608	627	646	665	684	19
20	500	520	540	560	580	600	620	640	660	680	700	720	20
21	525	546	567	588	609	630	651	672	693	714	735	756	21
22	550	572	594	616	638	660	682	704	726	748	770	792	22
23	575	598	621	644	667	690	713	736	759	782	805	828	23
24	600	624	648	672	696	720	744	768	792	816	840	864	24
25	625	650	675	700	725	750	775	800	825	850	875	900	25
		676	702	728	754	780	806	832	858	884	910	936	26
			729	756	783	810	837	864	891	918	945	972	27
				784	812	840	868	896	924	952	980	1008	28
					841	870	899	928	957	986	1015	1044	29
						900	930	960	990	1020	1050	1080	30
							961	992	1023	1054	1085	1116	31
								1024	1056	1088	1120	1152	32
									1089	1122	1155	1188	33
										1156	1190	1224	34
											1225	1260	35
												1296	36

..	4¾	5	5¼	5½	5¾	6	6¼	6½	6¾	7	7¼	7½	
2¾	13												
3	14¼	15											
¼	15½	16¼	17										
3½	16⅝	17½	18⅜	19¼									
¾	17¾	18¾	19¾	20⅝	21½								
4	19	20	21	22	23	24							
¼	20¼	21¼	22¼	23⅜	24½	25½	26½						
4½	21⅜	22½	23⅝	24¾	25⅞	27	28⅛	29¼					
¾	22½	23¾	25	26⅛	27¼	28½	29¾	30⅞	32				
5	23¾	25	26¼	27½	28¾	30	31¼	32½	33¾	35			..
¼	25	26¼	27½	28⅞	30¼	31½	32¾	34⅛	35½	36¾	38		5¼
5½	26⅛	27½	28⅞	30¼	31⅝	33	34⅜	35¾	37⅛	38½	39⅞	41¼	5½
¾	27¼	28¾	30¼	31⅝	33	34½	36	37⅜	38¾	40¼	41¾	43⅛	¾
6	28½	30	31½	33	34½	36	37½	39	40½	42	43½	45	6
¼	29¾	31¼	32¾	34⅜	36	37½	39	40⅝	42¼	43¾	45¼	46⅞	¼
6½	30⅞	32½	34⅛	35¾	37⅜	39	40⅝	42¼	43⅞	45½	47⅛	48¾	6½
¾	32	33¾	35½	37⅛	38¾	40½	42¼	43⅞	45½	47¼	49	50⅝	¾
7	33¼	35	36¾	38½	40¼	42	43¾	45½	47¼	49	50¾	52½	7
¼	34½	36¼	38	39⅞	41¾	43½	45¼	47⅛	49	50¾	52½	54⅜	¼
7½	35⅝	37½	39⅜	41¼	43⅛	45	46⅞	48¾	50⅝	52½	54⅜	56¼	7½
¾	36¾	38¾	40¾	42⅝	44½	46½	48½	50⅜	52¼	54¼	56¼	58⅛	¾
8	38	40	42	44	46	48	50	52	54	56	58	60	8
¼	39¼	41¼	43¼	45⅜	47½	49½	51½	53⅝	55¾	57¾	59¾	61⅞	¼
8½	40⅜	42½	44⅝	46¾	48⅞	51	53⅛	55¼	57⅜	59½	61⅝	63¾	8½
¾	41½	43¾	46	48⅛	50¼	52½	54¾	56⅞	59	61¼	63½	65⅝	¾
9	42¾	45	47¼	49½	51¾	54	56¼	58½	60¾	63	65¼	67½	9
¼	44	46¼	48½	50⅞	53¼	55½	57¾	60⅛	62½	64¾	67	69⅜	¼
9½	45⅛	47½	49⅞	52¼	54⅝	57	59⅜	61¾	64⅛	66½	68⅞	71¼	9½
¾	46¼	48¾	51¼	53⅝	56	58½	61	63⅜	65¾	68¼	70¾	73⅛	¾
10	47½	50	52½	55	57½	60	62½	65	67½	70	72½	75	10

MULTIPLICATION TABLE.

..	37	38	39	40	41	42	43	44	45	46	47	48	..
1	37	38	39	40	41	42	43	44	45	46	47	48	1
2	74	76	78	80	82	84	86	88	90	92	94	96	2
3	111	114	117	120	123	126	129	132	135	138	141	144	3
4	148	152	156	160	164	168	172	176	180	184	188	192	4
5	185	190	195	200	205	210	215	220	225	230	235	240	5
6	222	228	234	240	246	252	258	264	270	276	282	288	6
7	259	266	273	280	287	294	301	308	315	322	329	336	7
8	296	304	312	320	328	336	344	352	360	368	376	384	8
9	333	342	351	360	369	378	387	396	405	414	423	432	9
10	370	380	390	400	410	420	430	440	450	460	470	480	10
11	407	418	429	440	451	462	473	484	495	506	517	528	11
12	444	456	468	480	492	504	516	528	540	552	564	576	12
13	481	494	507	520	533	546	559	572	585	598	611	624	13
14	518	532	546	560	574	588	602	616	630	644	658	672	14
15	555	570	585	600	615	630	645	660	675	690	705	720	15
16	592	608	624	640	656	672	688	704	720	736	752	768	16
17	629	646	663	680	697	714	731	748	765	782	799	816	17
18	666	684	702	720	738	756	774	792	810	828	846	864	18
19	703	722	741	760	779	798	817	836	855	874	893	912	19
20	740	760	780	800	820	840	860	880	900	920	940	960	20
21	777	798	819	840	861	882	903	924	945	966	987	1008	21
22	814	836	858	880	902	924	946	968	990	1012	1034	1056	22
23	851	874	897	920	943	966	989	1012	1035	1058	1081	1104	23
24	888	912	936	960	984	1008	1032	1056	1080	1104	1128	1152	24
25	925	950	975	1000	1025	1050	1075	1100	1125	1150	1175	1200	25
26	962	988	1014	1040	1066	1092	1118	1144	1170	1196	1222	1248	26
27	999	1026	1053	1080	1107	1134	1161	1188	1215	1242	1269	1296	27
28	1036	1064	1092	1120	1148	1176	1204	1232	1260	1288	1316	1344	28
29	1073	1102	1131	1160	1189	1218	1247	1276	1305	1334	1363	1392	29
30	1110	1140	1170	1200	1230	1260	1290	1320	1350	1380	1410	1440	30
31	1147	1178	1209	1240	1271	1302	1333	1364	1395	1426	1457	1488	31
32	1184	1216	1248	1280	1312	1344	1376	1408	1440	1472	1504	1536	32
33	1221	1254	1287	1320	1353	1386	1419	1452	1485	1518	1551	1584	33
34	1258	1292	1326	1360	1394	1428	1462	1496	1530	1564	1598	1632	34
35	1295	1330	1365	1400	1435	1470	1505	1540	1575	1610	1645	1680	35
36	1332	1368	1404	1440	1476	1512	1548	1584	1620	1656	1692	1728	36
37	1369	1406	1443	1480	1517	1554	1591	1628	1665	1702	1739	1776	37
38	1406	1444	1482	1520	1558	1596	1634	1672	1710	1748	1786	1824	38
39	1443	1482	1521	1560	1599	1638	1677	1716	1755	1794	1833	1872	39
40	1480	1520	1560	1600	1640	1680	1720	1760	1800	1840	1880	1920	40
41	1517	1558	1599	1640	1681	1722	1763	1804	1845	1886	1927	1968	41
42	1554	1596	1638	1680	1722	1764	1806	1848	1890	1932	1974	2016	42
43	1591	1634	1677	1720	1763	1806	1849	1892	1935	1978	2021	2064	43
44	1628	1672	1716	1760	1804	1848	1892	1936	1980	2024	2068	2112	44
45	1665	1710	1755	1800	1845	1890	1935	1980	2025	2070	2115	2160	45
46	1702	1748	1794	1840	1886	1932	1978	2024	2070	2116	2162	2208	46
47	1739	1786	1833	1880	1927	1974	2021	2068	2115	2162	2209	2256	47
48	1776	1824	1872	1920	1968	2016	2064	2112	2160	2208	2256	2304	48
49	1813	1862	1911	1960	2009	2058	2107	2156	2205	2254	2303	2352	49
50	1850	1900	1950	2000	2050	2100	2150	2200	2250	2300	2350	2400	50
51	1887	1938	1989	2040	2091	2142	2193	2244	2295	2346	2397	2448	51
52	1924	1976	2028	2080	2132	2184	2236	2288	2340	2392	2444	2496	52
53	1961	2014	2067	2120	2173	2226	2279	2332	2385	2438	2491	2544	53
54	1998	2052	2106	2160	2214	2268	2322	2376	2430	2484	2538	2592	54
55	2035	2090	2145	2200	2255	2310	2365	2420	2475	2530	2585	2640	55
56	2072	2128	2184	2240	2296	2352	2408	2464	2520	2576	2632	2688	56
57	2109	2166	2223	2280	2337	2394	2451	2508	2565	2622	2679	2736	57
58	2146	2204	2262	2320	2378	2436	2494	2552	2610	2668	2726	2784	58

x by	112	120	144	165	168	*224	280	336	480	504	516	1760
¼	28	30	36	41¼	42	56	70	84	120	126	129	440
½	56	60	72	82½	84	112	140	168	240	252	258	880
¾	84	90	108	123¾	126	168	210	252	360	378	387	1320
1	112	120	144	165	168	224	280	336	480	504	516	1760
1½	168	180	216	247½	252	336	420	504	720	756	774	2640
2	224	240	288	330	336	448	560	672	960	1008	1032	3520
2½	280	300	360	412½	420	560	700	840	1200	1260	1290	4400
3	336	360	432	495	504	672	840	1008	1440	1512	1548	5280
3½	392	420	504	577½	588	784	980	1176	1680	1764	1806	6160
4	448	480	576	660	672	896	1120	1344	1920	2016	2064	7040
4½	504	540	648	742½	756	1008	1260	1512	2160	2268	2322	7920
5	560	600	720	825	840	1120	1400	1680	2400	2520	2580	8800
6	672	720	864	990	1008	1344	1680	2016	2880	3024	3096	10560
7	784	840	1008	1155	1176	1568	1960	2352	3360	3528	3612	12320
8	896	960	1152	1320	1344	1792	2240	2688	3840	4032	4128	14080
9	1008	1080	1296	1485	1512	2016	2520	3024	4320	4536	4644	15840
10	1120	1200	1440	1650	1680	2240	2800	3360	4800	5040	5160	17600
11	1232	1320	1584	1815	1848	2464	3080	3696	5280	5544	5676	19360
12	1344	1440	1728	1980	2016	2688	3360	4032	5760	6048	6192	21120
13	1456	1560	1872	2145	2184	2912	3640	4368	6240	6552	6708	22880
14	1568	1680	2016	2310	2352	3136	3920	4704	6720	7056	7224	24640
15	1680	1800	2160	2475	2520	3360	4200	5040	7200	7560	7740	26400
16	1792	1920	2304	2640	2688	3584	4480	5376	7680	8064	8256	28160
17	1904	2040	2448	2805	2856	3808	4760	5712	8160	8568	8772	29920
18	2016	2160	2592	2970	3024	4032	5040	6048	8640	9072	9288	31680
19	2128	2280	2736	3135	3192	4256	5320	6384	9120	9576	9804	33440
20	2240	2400	2880	3300	3360	4480	5600	6720	9600	10080	10320	35200
21	2352	2520	3024	3465	3528	4704	5880	7056	10080	10584	10836	36960
22	2464	2640	3168	3630	3696	4928	6160	7392	10560	11088	11352	38720
23	2576	2760	3312	3795	3864	5152	6440	7728	11040	11592	11868	40480
24	2688	2880	3456	3960	4032	5376	6720	8064	11520	12096	12384	42240
25	2800	3000	3600	4125	4200	5600	7000	8400	12000	12600	12900	44000
26	2912	3120	3744	4290	4368	5824	7280	8736	12480	13104	13416	45760
27	3024	3240	3888	4455	4536	6048	7560	9072	12960	13608	13932	47520
28	3136	3360	4032	4620	4704	6272	7840	9408	13440	14112	14448	49280
29	3248	3480	4176	4785	4872	6496	8120	9744	13920	14616	14964	51040
30	3360	3600	4320	4950	5040	6720	8400	10080	14400	15120	15480	52800
31	3472	3720	4464	5115	5208	6944	8680	10416	14880	15624	15996	54560
32	3584	3840	4608	5280	5376	7168	8960	10752	15360	16128	16512	56320
33	3696	3960	4752	5445	5544	7392	9240	11088	15840	16632	17028	58080
34	3808	4080	4896	5610	5712	7616	9520	11424	16320	17136	17544	59840
35	3920	4200	5040	5775	5880	7840	9800	11760	16800	17640	18060	61600
36	4032	4320	5184	5940	6048	8064	10080	12096	17280	18144	18576	63360
37	4144	4440	5328	6105	6216	8288	10360	12432	17760	18648	19092	65120
38	4256	4560	5472	6270	6384	8512	10640	12768	18240	19152	19608	66880
39	4368	4680	5616	6435	6552	8736	10920	13104	18720	19656	20124	68640
40	4480	4800	5760	6600	6720	8960	11200	13440	19200	20160	20640	70400
41	4592	4920	5904	6765	6888	9184	11480	13776	19680	20664	21156	72160
42	4704	5040	6048	6930	7056	9408	11760	14112	20160	21168	21672	73920
43	4816	5160	6192	7095	7224	9632	12040	14448	20640	21672	22188	75680
44	4928	5280	6336	7260	7392	9856	12320	14784	21120	22176	22704	77440
45	5040	5400	6480	7425	7560	10080	12600	15120	21600	22680	23220	79200
46	5152	5520	6624	7590	7728	10304	12880	15456	22080	23184	23736	80960
47	5264	5640	6768	7755	7896	10528	13160	15792	22560	23688	24252	82720
48	5376	5760	6912	7920	8064	10752	13440	16128	23040	24192	24768	84480
49	5488	5880	7056	8085	8232	10976	13720	16464	23520	24696	25284	86240
50	5600	6000	7200	8250	8400	11200	14000	16800	24000	25200	25800	88000

* For 2240, add "0" at right side of 224 figures.

WAGES PER YEAR, MONTH, WEEK, DAY

PER YR. £	₱MTH. 1/12 Yr. £	P	₱WK. 1/52 Yr. P	PER DAY 7-D P	6-D P	5-D P	PER YR. £	₱MTH. 1/12 Yr. £	P	₱WEEK 1/52 Yr. £	P	PER DAY 7-D P	6-D P	5-D P
1	0	8^3	1^9	0^2	0^3	0^4	51	4	25^0	0	98^1	14^0	16^3	19^6
2	0	16^7	3^8	0^5	0^6	0^8	52	4	33^3	1	0^0	14^2	16^7	20^0
3	0	25^0	5^8	0^8	1^0	1^2	53	4	41^7	1	1^9	14^5	17^0	20^4
4	0	33^3	7^7	1^1	1^3	1^5	54	4	50^0	1	3^8	14^8	17^3	20^8
5	0	41^7	9^6	1^4	1^6	1^9	55	4	58^3	1	5^8	15^1	17^6	21^2
6	0	50^0	11^5	1^6	1^9	2^3	56	4	66^7	1	7^7	15^3	17^9	21^5
7	0	58^3	13^5	1^9	2^2	2^7	57	4	75^0	1	9^6	15^6	18^3	21^9
8	0	66^7	15^4	2^2	2^6	3^1	58	4	83^3	1	11^5	15^9	18^6	22^3
9	0	75^0	17^3	2^5	2^9	3^5	59	4	91^7	1	13^5	16^2	18^9	22^7
10	0	83^3	19^2	2^7	3^2	3^8	60	5	0^0	1	15^4	16^4	19^2	23^1
11	0	91^7	21^2	3^0	3^5	4^2	61	5	8^3	1	17^3	16^7	19^6	23^5
12	1	0^0	23^1	3^3	3^8	4^6	62	5	16^7	1	19^2	17^0	19^9	23^8
13	1	8^3	25^0	3^6	4^2	5^0	63	5	25^0	1	21^2	17^3	20^2	24^2
14	1	16^7	26^9	3^8	4^5	5^4	64	5	33^3	1	23^1	17^5	20^5	24^6
15	1	25^0	28^8	4^1	4^8	5^8	65	5	41^7	1	25^0	17^8	20^8	25^0
16	1	33^3	30^8	4^4	5^1	6^2	66	5	50^0	1	26^9	18^1	21^2	25^4
17	1	41^7	32^7	4^7	5^4	6^5	67	5	58^3	1	28^8	18^4	21^5	25^8
18	1	50^0	34^6	4^9	5^8	6^9	68	5	66^7	1	30^8	18^6	21^8	26^2
19	1	58^3	36^5	5^2	6^1	7^3	69	5	75^0	1	32^7	18^9	22^1	26^5
20	1	66^7	38^5	5^5	6^4	7^7	70	5	83^3	1	34^6	19^2	22^4	26^9
21	1	75^0	40^4	5^8	6^7	8^1	71	5	91^7	1	37^5	19^5	22^8	27^3
22	1	83^3	42^3	6^0	7^1	8^5	72	6	0^0	1	38^5	19^7	23^1	27^7
23	1	91^7	44^2	6^3	7^4	8^8	73	6	8^3	1	40^4	20^0	23^4	28^1
24	2	0^0	46^2	6^6	7^7	9^2	74	6	16^7	1	42^3	20^3	23^7	28^5
25	2	8^3	48^1	6^8	8^0	9^6	75	6	25^0	1	44^2	20^5	24^0	28^8
26	2	16^7	50^0	7^1	8^3	10^0	76	6	33^3	1	46^2	20^8	24^4	29^2
27	2	25^0	51^9	7^4	8^7	10^4	77	6	41^7	1	48^1	21^1	24^7	29^6
28	2	33^3	53^8	7^7	9^0	10^8	78	6	50^0	1	50^0	21^4	25^0	30^0
29	2	41^7	55^8	7^9	9^3	11^2	79	6	58^3	1	51^9	21^6	25^3	30^4
30	2	50^0	57^7	8^2	9^6	11^5	80	6	66^7	1	53^8	21^9	25^6	30^8
31	2	58^3	59^6	8^5	9^9	11^9	81	6	75^0	1	55^8	22^2	26^0	31^2
32	2	66^7	61^5	8^8	10^3	12^3	82	6	83^3	1	57^7	22^5	26^3	31^5
33	2	75^0	63^5	9^0	10^6	12^7	83	6	91^7	1	59^6	22^7	26^6	31^9
34	2	83^3	65^4	9^3	10^9	13^1	84	7	0^0	1	61^5	23^0	26^9	32^3
35	2	91^7	67^3	9^6	11^2	13^5	85	7	8^3	1	63^5	23^3	27^2	32^7
36	3	0^0	69^2	9^9	11^5	13^8	86	7	16^7	1	65^4	23^6	27^6	33^1
37	3	8^3	71^2	10^1	11^9	14^2	87	7	25^0	1	67^3	23^8	27^9	33^5
38	3	16^7	73^1	10^4	12^2	14^6	88	7	33^3	1	69^2	24^1	28^2	33^8
39	3	25^0	75^0	10^7	12^5	15^0	89	7	41^7	1	71^2	24^4	28^5	34^2
40	3	33^3	76^9	11^0	12^8	15^4	90	7	50^0	1	73^1	24^7	28^8	34^6
41	3	41^7	78^8	11^2	13^1	15^8	91	7	58^3	1	75^0	24^9	29^2	35^0
42	3	50^0	80^8	11^5	13^5	16^2	92	7	66^7	1	76^9	25^2	29^5	35^4
43	3	58^3	82^7	11^8	13^8	16^5	93	7	75^0	1	78^8	25^5	29^8	35^8
44	3	66^7	84^6	12^1	14^1	16^9	94	7	83^3	1	80^8	25^7	30^1	36^2
45	3	75^0	86^5	12^3	14^4	17^3	95	7	91^7	1	82^7	26^0	30^4	36^5
46	3	83^3	88^5	12^6	14^7	17^7	96	8	0^0	1	84^6	26^3	30^8	36^9
47	3	91^7	90^4	12^9	15^1	18^1	97	8	8^3	1	86^5	26^6	31^1	37^3
48	4	0^0	92^3	13^2	15^4	18^5	98	8	16^7	1	88^5	26^8	31^4	37^7
49	4	8^3	94^2	13^4	15^7	18^8	99	8	25^0	1	90^4	27^1	31^7	38^1
50	4	16^7	96^2	13^7	16^0	19^2	100	8	33^3	1	92^3	27^4	32^1	38^5

PER YR. £	PER MTH. $\frac{1}{12}$ Yr. £ p	PER WK. $\frac{1}{52}$ Yr. £ p	PER DAY 7-D. £ p	6-D. £ p	5-D. £ p
110	9 16^7	2 11^5	0 30^1	0 35^8	0 42^8
120	10 0^0	2 30^8	0 32^9	0 38^5	0 46^2
125	10 41^7	2 40^4	0 34^2	0 40^1	0 48^1
130	10 83^3	2 50^0	0 35^6	0 41^7	0 50^0
140	11 66^7	2 69^2	0 38^4	0 44^9	0 53^8
150	12 50^0	2 88^5	0 41^1	0 48^1	0 57^7
160	13 33^3	3 7^7	0 43^8	0 51^3	0 61^5
170	14 16^7	3 26^9	0 46^6	0 54^5	0 65^4
175	14 58^3	3 36^5	0 47^9	0 56^1	0 67^3
180	15 0^0	3 46^2	0 49^3	0 57^7	0 69^2
190	15 83^3	3 65^4	0 52^0	0 60^9	0 73^1
200	16 66^7	3 84^6	0 54^8	0 64^1	0 76^9
210	17 50^0	4 3^8	0 57^5	0 67^3	0 80^8
220	18 33^3	4 23^1	0 60^8	0 70^5	0 84^6
225	18 75^0	4 32^7	0 61^6	0 72^1	0 86^5
230	19 16^7	4 42^3	0 63^0	0 73^7	0 88^5
240	20 0^0	4 61^5	0 65^8	0 76^9	0 92^3
250	20 83^3	4 80^8	0 68^5	0 80^1	0 96^2
260	21 66^7	5 0^0	0 71^2	0 83^3	1 0^0
270	22 50^0	5 19^2	0 74^0	0 86^5	1 3^8
275	22 91^7	5 28^8	0 75^3	0 88^1	1 5^8
280	23 33^3	5 38^5	0 76^7	0 89^7	1 7^7
290	24 16^7	5 57^7	0 79^5	0 92^9	1 11^5
300	25 0^0	5 76^9	0 82^2	0 96^2	1 15^4
310	25 83^3	5 96^2	0 84^9	0 99^4	1 19^2
320	26 66^7	6 15^4	0 87^7	1 2^6	1 23^1
325	27 8^3	6 25^0	0 89^0	1 4^2	1 25^0
330	27 50^0	6 34^6	0 90^4	1 5^8	1 26^9
340	28 33^3	6 53^8	0 93^2	1 9^0	1 30^8
350	29 16^7	6 73^1	0 95^9	1 12^2	1 34^6
360	30 0^0	6 92^3	0 98^6	1 15^4	1 38^5
370	30 83^3	7 11^5	1 1^4	1 18^6	1 42^4
375	31 25^0	7 21^2	1 2^7	1 20^2	1 44^4
380	31 66^7	7 30^8	1 4^1	1 21^8	1 46^2
390	32 50^0	7 50^0	1 6^8	1 25^0	1 50^0
400	33 33^3	7 69^2	1 9^6	1 28^2	1 53^8
425	35 41^7	8 17^3	1 16^4	1 36^2	1 63^5
450	37 50^0	8 65^4	1 23^3	1 44^2	1 73^1
475	39 58^3	9 13^5	1 30^1	1 52^2	1 82^7
500	41 66^7	9 61^5	1 37^0	1 60^3	1 92^3
550	45 83^3	10 57^7	1 50^7	1 76^2	2 11^5
600	50 0^0	11 53^8	1 64^4	1 92^3	2 30^8
650	54 16^7	12 50^0	1 78^1	2 8^3	2 50^0
700	58 33^3	13 46^2	1 91^8	2 24^4	2 69^2
750	62 50^0	14 42^3	2 5^5	2 40^4	2 88^5
800	66 66^7	15 38^5	2 19^2	2 56^4	3 7^7
850	70 83^3	16 34^6	2 32^9	2 72^4	3 26^9
900	75 0^0	17 30^8	2 46^6	2 88^5	3 46^2
950	79 16^7	18 26^9	2 60^3	3 4^5	3 65^4
1000	83 33^3	19 23^1	2 74^0	3 20^5	3 84^6

PER YR. £	PER MTH. $\frac{1}{12}$ Yr. £ p	PER WEEK $\frac{1}{52}$ Yr. £ p	PER DAY 7-D. £ p	6-D. £ p	5-D. £ p
1100	91 66^7	21 15^3	3 1^4	3 52^6	4 23^1
1200	100 0^0	23 7^7	3 28^8	3 84^6	4 61^5
1250	104 16^7	24 3^8	3 42^5	4 0^6	4 80^8
1300	108 33^3	25 0^0	3 56^2	4 16^7	5 0^0
1400	116 66^7	26 92^3	3 83^6	4 48^7	5 38^5
1500	125 0^0	28 84^6	4 11^0	4 80^8	5 76^9
1600	133 33^3	30 76^9	4 38^4	5 12^8	6 15^4
1700	141 66^7	32 69^2	4 65^8	5 44^9	6 53^8
1750	145 83^3	33 65^4	4 79^5	5 60^9	6 73^1
1800	150 0^0	34 61^5	4 93^2	5 76^9	6 92^3
1900	158 33^3	36 53^8	5 20^5	6 9^0	7 30^8
2000	166 66^7	38 46^2	5 48^0	6 41^0	7 69^2
2100	175 0^0	40 38^5	5 75^3	6 73^1	8 7^7
2200	183 33^3	42 30^8	6 2^7	7 5^1	8 46^2
2250	187 50^0	43 26^9	6 16^4	7 21^2	8 65^4
2300	191 66^7	44 23^1	6 30^1	7 37^2	8 84^6
2400	200 0^0	46 15^4	6 57^5	7 69^2	9 23^1
2500	208 33^3	48 7^7	6 84^9	8 1^3	9 61^5
2600	216 66^7	50 0^0	7 12^3	8 33^3	10 0^0
2700	225 0^0	51 92^3	7 39^7	8 65^4	10 38^5
2750	229 16^7	52 88^5	7 53^4	8 81^4	10 57^7
2800	233 33^3	53 84^6	7 67^1	8 97^4	10 76^9
2900	241 66^7	55 76^9	7 94^5	9 29^5	11 15^4
3000	250 0^0	57 69^2	8 21^9	9 61^5	11 53^8
3100	258 33^3	59 61^5	8 49^3	9 93^6	11 92^3
3200	266 66^7	61 53^8	8 76^7	10 25^6	12 30^8
3250	270 83^3	62 50^0	8 90^4	10 41^7	12 50^0
3300	275 0^0	63 46^2	9 4^1	10 57^7	12 69^2
3400	283 33^3	65 38^5	9 31^5	10 89^7	13 7^7
3500	291 66^7	67 30^8	9 58^9	11 21^8	13 46^2
3600	300 0^0	69 23^1	9 86^3	11 53^8	13 84^6
3700	308 33^3	71 15^4	10 13^7	11 85^9	14 23^1
3800	316 66^7	73 07^7	10 41^1	12 17^9	14 61^5
3900	325 0^0	75 00^0	10 68^5	12 50^0	15 0^0
4000	333 33^3	76 92^3	10 95^9	12 82^1	15 38^5
4100	341 66^7	78 84^6	11 23^3	13 14^1	15 76^9
4200	350 0^0	80 76^9	11 50^7	13 46^2	16 15^4
4300	358 33^3	82 69^2	11 78^1	13 78^2	16 53^8
4400	366 66^7	84 61^5	12 05^5	14 10^3	16 92^3
4500	375 0^7	86 53^8	12 32^9	14 42^3	17 30^8
4600	383 33^3	88 46^2	12 60^0	14 74^4	17 69^2
4700	391 66^7	90 38^5	12 87^7	15 6^4	18 7^7
4800	400 0^0	92 30^8	13 15^1	15 38^5	18 46^2
4900	408 33^3	94 23^1	13 42^5	15 70^5	18 84^6
5000	416 66^7	96 15^4	13 69^9	16 2^6	19 23^1
6000	500 0^0	115 38^5	16 43^8	19 23^1	23 7^7
7000	583 33^3	134 61^5	19 17^8	22 43^6	26 92^3
8000	666 66^7	153 84^6	21 91^8	25 64^1	30 76^9
9000	750 0^0	173 07^7	24 65^8	28 84^6	34 61^5
10,000	833 33^3	192 30^8	27 39^7	32 5^1	38 46^2

WAGES PER 40-HOUR WEEK

Hrs.	£1	£2	£3	£4	£5	£6	£7	£8	£9	£10
¼	0 0^6	0 1^3	0 1^9	0 2^5	0 3^1	0 3^8	0 4^4	0 5^0	0 5^6	0 6^3
½	0 1^3	0 2^5	0 3^8	0 5^0	0 6^2	0 7^5	0 8^8	0 10	0 11^3	0 12^5
¾	0 1^9	0 3^8	0 5^6	0 7^5	0 9^4	0 11^3	0 13^1	0 15	0 16^9	0 18^8
1	0 2^5	0 5^0	0 7^5	0 10	0 12^5	0 15^0	0 17^5	0 20	0 22^5	0 25^0
2	0 5^0	0 10	0 15^0	0 20	0 25^0	0 30	0 35^0	0 40	0 45^0	0 50
3	0 7^5	0 15	0 22^5	0 30	0 37^5	0 45	0 52^5	0 60	0 67^5	0 75
4	0 10^0	0 20	0 30^0	0 40	0 50^0	0 60	0 70^0	0 80	0 90^0	1 0
5	0 12^5	0 25	0 37^5	0 50	0 62^5	0 75	0 87^5	1 0	1 12^5	1 25
6	0 15^0	0 30	0 45^0	0 60	0 75^0	0 90	1 5^0	1 20	1 35^0	1 50
7	0 17^5	0 35	0 52^5	0 70	0 87^5	1 5	1 22^5	1 40	1 57^5	1 75
8	0 20^0	0 40	0 60^0	0 80	1 0^0	1 20	1 40^0	1 60	1 80^0	2 0
9	0 22^5	0 45	0 67^5	0 90	1 12^5	1 35	1 57^5	1 80	2 2^5	2 25
10	0 25^0	0 50	0 75^0	1 0	1 25^0	1 50	1 75^0	2 0	2 25^0	2 50
11	0 27^5	0 55	0 82^5	1 10	1 37^5	1 65	1 92^5	2 20	2 47^5	2 75
12	0 30^0	0 60	0 90^0	1 20	1 50^0	1 80	2 10^0	2 40	2 70^0	3 0
13	0 32^5	0 65	0 97^5	1 30	1 62^5	1 95	2 27^5	2 60	2 92^5	3 25
14	0 35^0	0 70	1 5^0	1 40	1 75^0	2 10	2 45^0	2 80	3 15^0	3 50
15	0 37^5	0 75	1 12^5	1 50	1 87^5	2 25	2 62^5	3 0	3 37^5	3 75
16	0 40^0	0 80	1 20^0	1 60	2 0^0	2 40	2 80^0	3 20	3 60^0	4 0
17	0 42^5	0 85	1 27^5	1 70	2 12^5	2 55	2 97^5	3 40	3 82^5	4 25
18	0 45^0	0 90	1 35^0	1 80	2 25^0	2 70	3 15^0	3 60	4 5^0	4 50
19	0 47^5	0 95	1 42^5	1 90	2 37^5	2 85	·3 32^5	3 80	4 27^5	4 75
20	0 50^0	1 0	1 50^0	2 0	2 50^0	3 0	3 50^0	4 0	4 50^0	5 0
21	0 52^5	1 5	1 57^5	2 10	2 62^5	3 15	3 67^5	4 20	4 72^5	5 25
22	0 55^0	1 10	1 65^0	2 20	2 75^0	3 30	3 85^0	4 40	4 95^0	5 50
23	0 57^5	1 15	1 72^5	2 30	2 87^5	3 45	4 2^5	4 60	5 17^5	5 75
24	0 60^0	1 20	1 80^0	2 40	3 0^0	3 60	4 20^0	4 80	5 40^0	6 0
25	0 62^5	1 25	1 87^5	2 50	3 12^5	3 75	4 37^5	5 0	5 62^5	6 25
26	0 65^0	1 30	1 95^0	2 60	3 25^0	3 90	4 55^0	5 20	5 85^0	6 50
27	0 67^5	1 35	2 2^5	2 70	3 37^5	4 5	4 72^5	5 40	6 7^5	6 75
28	0 70^0	1 40	2 10^0	2 80	3 50^0	4 20	4 90^0	5 60	6 30^0	7 0
29	0 72^5	1 45	2 17^5	2 90	3 62^5	4 35	5 7^5	5 80	6 52^5	7 25
30	0 75^0	1 50	2 25^0	3 0	3 75^0	4 50	5 25^0	6 0	6 75^0	7 50
31	0 77^5	1 55	2 32^5	3 10	3 87^5	4 65	5 42^5	6 20	6 97^5	7 75
32	0 80^0	1 60	2 40^0	3 20	4 0^0	4 80	5 60^0	6 40	7 20^0	8 0
33	0 82^5	1 65	2 47^5	3 30	4 12^5	4 95	5 77^5	6 60	7 42^5	8 25
34	0 85^0	1 70	2 55^0	3 40	4 25^0	5 10	5 95^0	6 80	7 65^0	8 50
35	0 87^5	1 75	2 62^5	3 50	4 37^5	5 25	6 12^5	7 0	7 87^5	8 75
36	0 90^0	1 80	2 70^0	3 60	4 50^0	5 40	6 30^0	7 20	8 10^0	9 0
37	0 92^5	1 85	2 77^5	3 70	4 62^5	5 55	6 47^5	7 40	8 32^5	9 25
38	0 95^0	1 90	2 85^0	3 80	4 75^0	5 70	6 65^0	7 60	8 55^0	9 50
39	0 97^5	1 95	2 92^5	3 90	4 87^5	5 85	6 82^5	7 80	8 77^5	9 75
40	1 0^0	2 0	3 0^0	4 0	5 0^0	6 0	7 0^0	8 0	9 0^0	10 0

Mins.	£1	£2	£3	£4	£5	£6	£7	£8	£9	£10
5	0^2	0^4	0^6	0^8	1^0	1^3	1^5	1^7	1^9	2^1
10	0^4	0^8	1^3	1^7	2^1	2^5	2^9	3^3	3^8	4^2
15	0^6	1^3	1^9	2^5	3^1	3^8	4^4	5^0	5^6	6^3
20	0^8	1^7	2^5	3^3	4^2	5^0	5^8	6^7	7^5	8^3
25	1^0	2^1	3^1	4^2	5^2	6^3	7^3	8^3	9^4	10^4
30	1^3	2^5	3^8	5^0	6^3	7^5	8^8	10^0	11^3	12^5
35	1^5	2^9	4^3	5^8	7^3	8^8	10^2	11^7	13^1	14^6
40	1^7	3^3	5^0	6^7	8^3	10^0	11^7	13^3	15^0	16^7
45	1^9	3^8	5^6	7^5	9^4	11^3	13^1	15^0	16^9	18^8
50	2^1	4^2	6^3	8^3	10^4	12^5	14^6	16^7	18^8	20^8
55	2^3	4^6	6^9	9^1	11^5	13^8	16^0	18^3	20^6	22^9

WAGES PER 40-HOUR WEEK

Hrs.	£20 £ P	£30 £ P	£40 £ P	£50 £ P	£60 £ P	£70 £ P	£80 £ P	£90 £ P	£100 £ P	£200 £ P
¼	0 12^5	0 18^8	0 25	0 31^3	0 37^5	0 43^8	0 50	0 56^3	0 62^5	1 25
½	0 25^0	0 37^5	0 50	0 62^5	0 75^0	0 87^5	1 0	1 12^5	1 25^0	2 50
¾	0 37^5	0 56^3	0 75	0 93^8	1 12^5	1 31^3	1 50	1 68^8	1 87^5	3 75
1	0 50	0 75	1 0	1 25	1 50	1 75	2 0	2 25	2 50	5 0
2	1 0	1 50	2 0	2 50	3 0	3 50	4 0	4 50	5 0	10 0
3	1 50	2 25	3 0	3 75	4 50	5 25	6 0	6 75	7 50	15 0
4	2 0	3 0	4 0	5 0	6 0	7 0	8 0	9 0	10 0	20 0
5	2 50	3 75	5 0	6 25	7 50	8 75	10 0	11 25	12 50	25 0
6	3 0	4 50	6 0	7 50	9 0	10 50	12 0	13 50	15 0	30 0
7	3 50	5 25	7 0	8 75	10 50	12 25	14 0	15 75	17 50	35 0
8	4 0	6 0	8 0	10 0	12 0	14 0	16 0	18 0	20 0	40 0
9	4 50	6 75	9 0	11 25	13 50	15 75	18 0	20 25	22 50	45 0
10	5 0	7 50	10 0	12 50	15 0	17 50	20 0	22 50	25 0	50 0
11	5 50	8 25	11 0	13 75	16 50	19 25	22 0	24 75	27 50	55 0
12	6 0	9 0	12 0	15 0	18 0	21 0	24 0	27 0	30 0	60 0
13	6 50	9 75	13 0	16 25	19 50	22 75	26 0	29 25	32 50	65 0
14	7 0	10 50	14 0	17 50	21 0	24 50	28 0	31 50	35 0	70 0
15	7 50	11 25	15 0	18 75	22 50	26 25	30 0	33 75	37 50	75 0
16	8 0	12 0	16 0	20 0	24 0	28 0	32 0	36 0	40 0	80 0
17	8 50	12 75	17 0	21 25	25 50	29 75	34 0	38 25	42 50	85 0
18	9 0	13 50	18 0	22 50	27 0	31 50	36 0	40 50	45 0	90 0
19	9 50	14 25	19 0	23 75	28 50	33 25	38 0	42 75	47 50	95 0
20	10 0	15 0	20 0	25 0	30 0	35 0	40 0	45 0	50 0	100 0
21	10 50	15 75	21 0	26 25	31 50	36 75	42 0	47 25	52 50	105 0
22	11 0	16 50	22 0	27 50	33 0	38 50	44 0	49 50	55 0	110 0
23	11 50	17 25	23 0	28 75	34 50	40 25	46 0	51 75	57 50	115 0
24	12 0	18 0	24 0	30 0	36 0	42 0	48 0	54 0	60 0	120 0
25	12 50	18 75	25 0	31 25	37 50	43 75	50 0	56 25	62 50	125 0
26	13 0	19 50	26 0	32 50	39 0	45 50	52 0	58 50	65 0	130 0
27	13 50	20 25	27 0	33 75	40 50	47 25	54 0	60 75	67 50	135 0
28	14 0	21 0	28 0	35 0	42 0	49 0	56 0	63 0	70 0	140 0
29	14 50	21 75	29 0	36 25	43 50	50 75	58 0	65 25	72 50	145 0
30	15 0	22 50	30 0	37 50	45 0	52 50	60 0	67 50	75 0	150 0
31	15 50	23 25	31 0	38 75	46 50	54 25	62 0	69 75	77 50	155 0
32	16 0	24 0	32 0	40 0	48 0	56 0	64 0	72 0	80 0	160 0
33	16 50	24 75	33 0	41 25	49 50	57 75	66 0	74 25	82 50	165 0
34	17 0	25 50	34 0	42 50	51 0	59 50	68 0	76 50	85 0	170 0
35	17 50	26 25	35 0	43 75	52 50	61 25	70 0	78 75	87 50	175 0
36	18 0	27 0	36 0	45 0	54 0	63 0	72 0	81 0	90 0	180 0
37	18 50	27 75	37 0	46 25	55 50	64 75	74 0	83 25	92 50	185 0
38	19 0	28 50	38 0	47 50	57 0	66 50	76 0	85 50	95 0	190 0
39	19 50	29 25	39 0	48 75	58 50	68 25	78 0	87 75	97 50	195 0
40	20 0	30 0	40 0	50 0	60 0	70 0	80 0	90 0	100 0	200 0

Mins.	£20	£30	£40	£50	£60	£70	£80	£90	£100	£200
5	4^2	6^3	8^3	0 10^4	0 12^5	0 14^6	0 16^7	0 18^8	0 20^8	0 41^7
10	8^3	12^5	16^7	0 20^8	0 25^0	0 29^1	0 33^3	0 37^5	0 41^7	0 83^3
15	12^5	18^8	25^0	0 31^3	0 37^5	0 43^8	0 50^0	0 56^3	0 62^5	1 25^0
20	16^7	25^0	33^3	0 41^7	0 50^0	0 58^3	0 66^7	0 75^0	0 83^3	1 66^7
25	20^8	31^3	41^7	0 52^1	0 62^5	0 72^9	0 83^3	1 93^8	1 4^2	2 8^3
30	25^0	37^5	50^0	0 62^5	0 75^0	0 87^5	1 0^0	1 12^5	1 25^0	2 50^0
35	29^2	43^8	58^3	0 72^9	0 87^5	1 2^1	1 16^7	1 31^3	1 45^8	2 91^7
40	33^3	50^0	66^7	0 83^3	1 0^0	1 16^7	1 33^3	1 50^0	1 66^7	3 33^3
45	37^5	56^3	75^0	0 93^8	1 12^5	1 31^3	1 50^0	1 68^8	1 87^5	3 75^0
50	41^7	62^5	83^3	1 4^2	1 25^0	1 45^8	1 66^7	1 87^5	2 8^3	4 16^7
55	45^8	68^8	91^7	1 14^6	1 37^5	1 60^4	1 83^3	2 6^3	2 29^2	4 58^3

WAGES PER 40-HOUR WEEK

Hrs.	£300 £ P	£400 £ P	£500 £ P	£600 £ P	£700 £ P	£800 £ P	£900 £ P	£1000 £ P
¼	1 87^5	2 50	3 12^5	3 75	4 37^5	5 0	5 62^5	6 25
½	3 75^0	5 00	6 25^0	7 50	8 75^0	10 0	11 25^0	12 50
¾	5 62^5	7 50	9 37^5	11 25	13 12^5	15 0	16 87^5	18 75
1	7 50	10 0	12 50	15 0	17 50	20 0	22 50	25 0
2	15 0	20 0	25 0	30 0	35 0	40 0	45 0	50 0
3	22 50	30 0	37 50	45 0	52 50	60 0	67 50	75 0
4	30 0	40 0	50 0	60 0	70 0	80 0	90 0	100 0
5	37 50	50 0	62 50	75 0	87 50	100 0	112 50	125 0
6	45 0	60 0	75 0	90 0	105 0	120 0	135 0	150 0
7	52 50	70 0	87 50	105 0	122 50	140 0	157 50	175 0
8	60 0	80 0	100 0	120 0	140 0	160 0	180 0	200 0
9	67 50	90 0	112 50	135 0	157 50	180 0	202 50	225 0
10	75 0	100 0	125 0	150 0	175 0	200 0	225 0	250 0
11	82 50	110 0	137 50	165 0	192 50	220 0	247 50	275 0
12	90 0	120 0	150 0	180 0	210 0	240 0	270 0	300 0
13	97 50	130 0	162 50	195 0	227 50	260 0	292 50	325 0
14	105 0	140 0	175 0	210 0	245 0	280 0	315 0	350 0
15	112 50	150 0	187 50	225 0	262 50	300 0	337 50	375 0
16	120 0	160 0	200 0	240 0	280 0	320 0	360 0	400 0
17	127 50	170 0	212 50	255 0	297 50	340 0	382 50	425 0
18	135 0	180 0	225 0	270 0	315 0	360 0	405 0	450 0
19	142 50	190 0	237 50	285 0	332 50	380 0	427 50	475 0
20	150 0	200 0	250 0	300 0	350 0	400 0	450 0	500 0
21	157 50	210 0	262 50	315 0	367 50	420 0	472 50	525 0
22	165 0	220 0	275 0	330 0	385 0	440 0	495 0	550 0
23	172 50	230 0	287 50	345 0	402 50	460 0	517 50	575 0
24	180 0	240 0	300 0	360 0	420 0	480 0	540 0	600 0
25	187 50	250 0	312 50	375 0	437 50	500 0	562 50	625 0
26	195 0	260 0	325 0	390 0	455 0	520 0	585 0	650 0
27	202 50	270 0	337 50	405 0	472 50	540 0	607 50	675 0
28	210 0	280 0	350 0	420 0	490 0	560 0	630 0	700 0
29	217 50	290 0	362 50	435 0	507 50	580 0	652 50	725 0
30	225 0	300 0	375 0	450 0	525 0	600 0	675 0	750 0
31	232 50	310 0	387 50	465 0	542 50	620 0	697 50	775 0
32	240 0	320 0	400 0	480 0	560 0	640 0	720 0	800 0
33	247 50	330 0	412 50	495 0	577 50	660 0	742 50	825 0
34	255 0	340 0	425 0	510 0	595 0	680 0	765 0	850 0
35	262 50	350 0	437 50	525 0	612 50	700 0	787 50	875 0
36	270 0	360 0	450 0	540 0	630 0	720 0	810 0	900 0
37	277 50	370 0	462 50	555 0	647 50	740 0	832 50	925 0
38	285 0	380 0	475 0	570 0	665 0	760 0	855 0	950 0
39	292 50	390 0	487 50	585 0	682 50	780 0	877 50	975 0
40	300 0	400 0	500 0	600 0	700 0	800 0	900 0	1000 0

Mins.	£300 £ P	£400 £ P	£500 £ P	£600 £ P	£700 £ P	£800 £ P	£900 £ P	£1000 £ P
5	0 62^5	0 83^3	1 4^1	1 25	1 45^8	1 66^7	1 87^5	2 8^3
10	1 25^0	1 66^7	2 8^3	2 50	2 91^7	3 33^3	3 75^0	4 16^7
15	1 87^5	2 50^0	3 12^5	3 75	4 37^5	5 0	5 62^5	6 25^0
20	2 50^0	3 33^3	4 16^7	5 0	5 83^3	6 66^7	7 50^0	8 33^3
25	3 12^5	4 16^7	5 20^8	6 25	7 29^2	8 33^3	9 37^5	10 41^7
30	3 75^0	5 0^0	6 25^0	7 50	8 75^0	10 0^0	11 25^0	12 50^0
35	4 37^5	5 83^3	7 29^2	8 75	10 20^8	11 66^7	13 12^5	14 58^3
40	5 0^0	6 66^7	8 33^3	10 0	11 66^7	13 33^3	15 0^0	16 66^7
45	5 62^5	7 50^0	9 37^5	11 25	13 12^5	15 0^0	16 87^5	18 75^0
50	6 25^0	8 33^3	10 41^7	12 50	14 58^3	16 66^7	18 75^0	20 83^3
55	6 87^5	9 16^7	11 45^8	13 75	16 4^2	18 33^3	20 62^5	22 91^7

COMPOUND INTEREST
TABLES

Table A:— £1 accumulated at yearly Compound Interest.

yrs	5%	4½%	4%	3½%	3%	2½%	2%	1½%	1%
1	1·0500	1·0450	1·0400	1·0350	1·0300	1·0250	1·0200	1·0150	1·0100
2	1·1025	1·0920	1·0816	1·0712	1·0609	1·0506	1·0404	1·0302	1·0201
3	1·1576	1·1412	1·1248	1·1087	1·0927	1·0769	1·0612	1·0457	1·0303
4	1·2155	1·1925	1·1698	1·1475	1·1255	1·1038	1·0824	1·0613	1·0406
5	1·2763	1·2462	1·2166	1·1877	1·1593	1·1314	1·1041	1·0773	1·0510
6	1·3401	1·3022	1·2653	1·2292	1·1940	1·1597	1·1261	1·0934	1·0615
7	1·4071	1·3608	1·3159	1·2723	1·2299	1·1887	1·1487	1·1098	1·0721
8	1·4774	1·4221	1·3686	1·3168	1·2668	1·2184	1·1716	1·1265	1·0828
9	1·5513	1·4861	1·4233	1·3629	1·3048	1·2488	1·1951	1·1434	1·0937
10	1·6289	1·5530	1·4802	1·4106	1·3439	1·2801	1·2190	1·1605	1·1046
11	1·7103	1·6228	1·5394	1·4600	1·3842	1·3121	1·2434	1·1779	1·1157
12	1·7958	1·6959	1·6010	1·5111	1·4257	1·3449	1·2682	1·1956	1·1268
13	1·8856	1·7722	1·6651	1·5639	1·4685	1·3785	1·2936	1·2135	1·1381
14	1·9799	1·8519	1·7317	1·6187	1·5126	1·4130	1·3195	1·2317	1·1495
15	2·0789	1·9353	1·8009	1·6753	1·5580	1·4483	1·3459	1·2502	1·1610
16	2·1829	2·0224	1·8730	1·7340	1·6047	1·4845	1·3728	1·2690	1·1726
17	2·2920	2·1134	1·9479	1·7947	1·6528	1·5216	1·4002	1·2880	1·1843
18	2·4066	2·2085	2·0258	1·8575	1·7024	1·5596	1·4282	1·3073	1·1961
19	2·5269	2·3078	2·1068	1·9225	1·7535	1·5986	1·4568	1·3269	1·2081
20	2·6533	2·4117	2·1911	1·9898	1·8061	1·6386	1·4859	1·3468	1·2202
21	2·7859	2·5202	2·2788	2·0594	1·8603	1·6796	1·5157	1·3670	1·2324
22	2·9252	2·6336	2·3699	2·1315	1·9161	1·7216	1·5460	1·3875	1·2447
23	3·0715	2·7522	2·4647	2·2061	1·9736	1·7646	1·5769	1·4084	1·2571
24	3·2251	2·8760	2·5633	2·2833	2·0328	1·8087	1·6084	1·4295	1·2697
25	3·3863	3·0054	2·6658	2·3632	2·0938	1·8539	1·6406	1·4509	1·2824
26	3·5557	3·1407	2·7725	2·4459	2·1566	1·9003	1·6734	1·4727	1·2952
27	3·7334	3·2820	2·8834	2·5316	2·2213	1·9478	1·7069	1·4948	1·3082
28	3·9201	3·4297	2·9987	2·6202	2·2879	1·9965	1·7410	1·5172	1·3213
29	4·1161	3·5840	3·1186	2·7119	2·3566	2·0464	1·7758	1·5400	1·3345
30	4·3219	3·7453	3·2434	2·8068	2·4272	2·0976	1·8113	1·5631	1·3478
31	4·5380	3·9139	3·3731	2·9050	2·5001	2·1500	1·8476	1·5865	1·3613
32	4·7649	4·0900	3·5081	3·0067	2·5751	2·2038	1·8845	1·6103	1·3749
33	5·0032	4·2740	3·6484	3·1119	2·6523	2·2589	1·9222	1·6345	1·3887
34	5·2534	4·4664	3·7943	3·2209	2·7319	2·3153	1·9607	1·6590	1·4026
35	5·5160	4·6674	3·9461	3·3336	2·8139	2·3732	1·9999	1·6839	1·4166
36	5·7918	4·8774	4·1039	3·4503	2·8983	2·4325	2·0399	1·7091	1·4308
37	6·0814	5·0969	4·2681	3·5710	2·9852	2·4934	2·0807	1·7348	1·4451
38	6·3855	5·3262	4·4388	3·6960	3·0748	2·5557	2·1223	1·7608	1·4595
39	6·7048	5·5659	4·6164	3·8254	3·1670	2·6196	2·1647	1·7872	1·4741
40	7·0400	5·8164	4·8010	3·9593	3·2620	2·6851	2·2080	1·8140	1·4889
41	7·3920	6·0781	4·9931	4·0978	3·3599	2·7522	2·2522	1·8412	1·5038
42	7·7616	6·3516	5·1928	4·2413	3·4607	2·8210	2·2972	1·8689	1·5188
43	8·1497	6·6374	5·4005	4·3897	3·5645	2·8915	2·3432	1·8969	1·5340
44	8·5572	6·9361	5·6165	4·5433	3·6715	2·9638	2·3901	1·9253	1·5493
45	8·9850	7·2483	5·8412	4·7023	3·7816	3·0379	2·4379	1·9542	1·5648
46	9·4343	7·5744	6·0748	4·8669	3·8950	3·1139	2·4866	1·9835	1·5805
47	9·9060	7·9153	6·3178	5·0373	4·0119	3·1917	2·5363	2·0133	1·5963
48	10·4013	8·2715	6·5705	5·2136	4·1323	3·2715	2·5871	2·0435	1·6122
49	10·9213	8·6437	6·8334	5·3961	4·2562	3·3533	2·6388	2·0741	1·6284
50	11·4674	9·0326	7·1067	5·5849	4·3839	3·4371	2·6916	2·1052	1·6446

yrs	5%	4½%	4%	3½%	3%	2½%	2%	1½%	1%
51	12·0408	9·4391	7·3910	5·7804	4·5154	3·5230	2·7454	2·1368	1·6611
52	12·6428	9·8639	7·6866	5·9827	4·6509	3·6111	2·8003	2·1689	1·6777
53	13·2750	10·3077	7·9941	6·1921	4·7904	3·7014	2·8563	2·2014	1·6945
54	13·9387	10·7716	8·3138	6·4088	4·9341	3·7939	2·9135	2·2344	1·7114
55	14·6356	11·2563	8·6464	6·6331	5·0822	3·8888	2·9717	2·2679	1·7285
56	15·3674	11·7628	8·9922	6·8653	5·2346	3·9860	3·0312	2·3020	1·7458
57	16·1358	12·2922	9·3519	7·1056	5·3917	4·0856	3·0918	2·3365	1·7633
58	16·9426	12·8453	9·7260	7·3543	5·5534	4·1878	3·1536	2·3715	1·7810
59	17·7897	13·4234	10·1150	7·6117	5·7200	4·2925	3·2167	2·4071	1·7987
60	18·6791	14·0274	10·5196	7·8781	5·8916	4·3998	3·2810	2·4432	1·8167
61	19·6131	14·6586	10·9404	8·1538	6·0684	4·5098	3·3467	2·4799	1·8349
62	20·5938	15·3182	11·3780	8·4392	6·2504	4·6225	3·4136	2·5171	1·8532
63	21·6235	16·0076	11·8332	8·7346	6·4379	4·7381	3·4819	2·5548	1·8717
64	22·7047	16·7279	12·3065	9·0403	6·6311	4·8565	3·5515	2·5931	1·8905
65	23·8399	17·4807	12·7987	9·3567	6·8300	4·9780	3·6225	2·6320	1·9094
66	25·0319	18·2673	13·3107	9·6842	7·0349	5·1024	3·6950	2·6715	1·9285
67	26·2835	19·0894	13·8431	10·0231	7·2459	5·2300	3·7689	2·7116	1·9477
68	27·5977	19·9484	14·3968	10·3739	7·4633	5·3607	3·8443	2·7523	1·9672
69	28·9775	20·8461	14·9727	10·7370	7·6872	5·4947	3·9211	2·7936	1·9869
70	30·4264	21·7841	15·5716	11·1128	7·9178	5·6321	3·9996	2·8355	2·0068
71	31·9477	22·7644	16·1945	11·5018	8·1554	5·7729	4·0796	2·8780	2·0268
72	33·5451	23·7888	16·8423	11·9043	8·4000	5·9172	4·1611	2·9212	2·0471
73	35·2224	24·8593	17·5160	12·3210	8·6520	6·0652	4·2444	2·9650	2·0676
74	36·9835	25·9780	18·2166	12·7522	8·9116	6·2168	4·3293	3·0095	2·0882
75	38·8327	27·1470	18·9453	13·1986	9·1789	6·3722	4·4158	3·0546	2·1091
76	40·7743	28·3686	19·7031	13·6605	9·4543	6·5315	4·5042	3·1004	2·1302
77	42·8130	29·6452	20·4912	14·1386	9·7379	6·6948	4·5942	3·1469	2·1515
78	44·9537	30·9792	21·3108	14·6334	10·0301	6·8622	4·6861	3·1941	2·1730
79	47·2014	32·3733	22·1633	15·1456	10·3310	7·0337	4·7798	3·2420	2·1948
80	49·5614	33·8301	23·0498	15·6757	10·6409	7·2096	4·8754	3·2907	2·2167
81	52·0395	35·3525	23·9918	16·2244	10·9601	7·3898	4·9730	3·3400	2·2389
82	54·6415	36·9433	24·9307	16·7922	11·2889	7·5746	5·0724	3·3901	2·2613
83	57·3736	38·6058	25·9279	17·3800	11·6276	7·7639	5·1739	3·4410	2·2839
84	60·2422	40·3430	26·9650	17·9883	11·9764	7·9580	5·2773	3·4926	2·3067
85	63·2544	42·1585	28·0436	18·6179	12·3357	8·1570	5·3829	3·5450	2·3298
86	66·4171	44·0556	29·1654	19·2695	12·7058	8·3609	5·4905	3·5982	2·3531
87	69·7379	46·0381	30·3320	19·9439	13·0870	8·5699	5·6004	3·6521	2·3766
88	73·2248	48·1098	31·5452	20·6420	13·4796	8·7842	5·7124	3·7069	2·4004
89	76·8861	50·2747	32·8071	21·3644	13·8839	9·0038	5·8266	3·7625	2·4244
90	80·7304	52·5371	34·1193	22·1122	14·3005	9·2289	5·9431	3·8189	2·4486
91	84·7669	54·9013	35·4841	22·8861	14·7295	9·4596	6·0620	3·8762	2·4731
92	89·0052	57·3718	36·9035	23·6871	15·1714	9·6961	6·1832	3·9344	2·4979
93	93·4555	59·9536	38·3796	24·5162	15·6265	9·9385	6·3069	3·9934	2·5228
94	98·1283	62·6515	39·9148	25·3742	16·0953	10·1869	6·4330	4·0533	2·5481
95	103·0347	65·4708	41·5114	26·2623	16·5782	10·4416	6·5617	4·1141	2·5735
96	108·1864	68·4170	43·1718	27·1815	17·0755	10·7026	6·6929	4·1758	2·5993
97	113·5957	71·4957	44·8987	28·1329	17·5878	10·9702	6·8268	4·2384	2·6253
98	119·2755	74·7131	46·6947	29·1175	18·1154	11·2445	6·9633	4·3020	2·6515
99	125·2393	78·0751	48·5625	30·1366	18·6589	11·5256	7·1026	4·3665	2·6780
100	131·5013	81·5885	50·5050	31·1914	19·2186	11·8137	7·2446	4·4320	2·7048

Table B:— Present value of £1.

yrs	5%	4½%	4%	3½%	3%	2½%	2%	1½%	1%
1	·95238	·95694	·96154	·96618	·97087	·97561	·98039	·98522	·99010
2	·90703	·91573	·92456	·93351	·94260	·95181	·96117	·97066	·98030
3	·86384	·87630	·88900	·90194	·91514	·92860	·94232	·95632	·97059
4	·82270	·83856	·85480	·87144	·88849	·90595	·92385	·94218	·96098
5	·78353	·80245	·82193	·84197	·86261	·88385	·90573	·92826	·95147
6	·74622	·76790	·79031	·81350	·83748	·86230	·88797	·91454	·94205
7	·71068	·73483	·75992	·78599	·81309	·84127	·87056	·90103	·93272
8	·67684	·70319	·73069	·75941	·78941	·82075	·85349	·88771	·92348
9	·64461	·67290	·70259	·73373	·76642	·80073	·83676	·87459	·91434
10	·61391	·64393	·67556	·70892	·74409	·78120	·82035	·86167	·90529
11	·58468	·61620	·64958	·68495	·72242	·76214	·80426	·84893	·89632
12	·55684	·58966	·62460	·66178	·70138	·74356	·78849	·83639	·88745
13	·53032	·56427	·60057	·63940	·68095	·72542	·77303	·82403	·87866
14	·50507	·53997	·57748	·61778	·66112	·70773	·75788	·81185	·86996
15	·48102	·51672	·55526	·59689	·64186	·69047	·74301	·79985	·86135
16	·45811	·49447	·53391	·57671	·62317	·67362	·72845	·78803	·85282
17	·43630	·47318	·51337	·55720	·60502	·65720	·71416	·77639	·84438
18	·41552	·45280	·49363	·53836	·58739	·64117	·70016	·76491	·83602
19	·39573	·43330	·47464	·52016	·57029	·62553	·68643	·75361	·82774
20	·37689	·41464	·45639	·50257	·55368	·61027	·67297	·74247	·81954
21	·35894	·39679	·43883	·48557	·53755	·59539	·65978	·73150	·81143
22	·34185	·37970	·42196	·46915	·52189	·58086	·64684	·72069	·80340
23	·32557	·36335	·40573	·45329	·50669	·56670	·63416	·71004	·79544
24	·31007	·34770	·39012	·43796	·49193	·55288	·62172	·69954	·78757
25	·29530	·33273	·37512	·42315	·47761	·53939	·60953	·68921	·77977
26	·28124	·31840	·36069	·40884	·46369	·52623	·59758	·67902	·77205
27	·26785	·30469	·34682	·39501	·45019	·51340	·58586	·66899	·76440
28	·25509	·29157	·33348	·38165	·43708	·50088	·57437	·65910	·75684
29	·24295	·27902	·32065	·36875	·42435	·48866	·56311	·64936	·74934
30	·23138	·26700	·30832	·35628	·41199	·47674	·55207	·63976	·74192
31	·22036	·25550	·29646	·34423	·39999	·46511	·54125	·63031	·73458
32	·20987	·24450	·28506	·33259	·38834	·45377	·53063	·62099	·72730
33	·19987	·23397	·27409	·32134	·37703	·44270	·52023	·61182	·72010
34	·19035	·22390	·26355	·31048	·36605	·43191	·51003	·60277	·71297
35	·18129	·21425	·25342	·29998	·35538	·42137	·50003	·59387	·70591
36	·17266	·20503	·24367	·28983	·34503	·41109	·49022	·58509	·69892
37	·16444	·19620	·23430	·28003	·33498	·40107	·48061	·57644	·69200
38	·15661	·18775	·22529	·27056	·32523	·39128	·47119	·56792	·68515
39	·14915	·17967	·21662	·26141	·31575	·38174	·46195	·55953	·67837
40	·14205	·17193	·20829	·25257	·30656	·37243	·45289	·55126	·67165
41	·13528	·16453	·20028	·24403	·29763	·36335	·44401	·54312	·66500
42	·12884	·15744	·19258	·23578	·28896	·35448	·43530	·53509	·65842
43	·12270	·15067	·18517	·22781	·28054	·34584	·42677	·52718	·65190
44	·11686	·14417	·17805	·22010	·27237	·33740	·41840	·51939	·64545
45	·11130	·13796	·17120	·21266	·26444	·32917	·41020	·51172	·63906
46	·10600	·13202	·16461	·20547	·25674	·32115	·40215	·50415	·63273
47	·10095	·12634	·15828	·19852	·24926	·31331	·39427	·49670	·62646
48	·09614	·12090	·15219	·19181	·24200	·30567	·38654	·48936	·62026
49	·09156	·11569	·14634	·18532	·23495	·29822	·37896	·48213	·61412
50	·08720	·11071	·14071	·17905	·22811	·29094	·37153	·47500	·60804

yrs	5%	4½%	4%	3½%	3%	2½%	2%	1½%	1%
51	·08305	·10594	·13530	·17300	·22146	·28385	·36424	·46799	·60202
52	·07910	·10138	·13010	·16715	·21501	·27692	·35710	·46107	·59606
53	·07533	·09701	·12509	·16150	·20875	·27017	·35010	·45426	·59016
54	·07174	·09284	·12028	·15604	·20267	·26358	·34323	·44754	·58431
55	·06833	·08884	·11566	·15076	·19677	·25715	·33650	·44093	·57853
56	·06507	·08501	·11121	·14566	·19104	·25088	·32991	·43441	·57280
57	·06197	·08135	·10693	·14073	·18547	·24476	·32344	·42799	·56713
58	·05902	·07785	·10282	·13598	·18007	·23879	·31710	·42167	·56151
59	·05621	·07450	·09886	·13138	·17483	·23297	·31088	·41544	·55595
60	·05354	·07129	·09506	·12693	·16973	·22728	·30478	·40930	·55045
61	·05099	·06822	·09140	·12264	·16479	·22174	·29881	·40325	·54500
62	·04856	·06528	·08789	·11849	·15999	·21633	·29295	·39729	·53960
63	·04625	·06247	·08451	·11449	·15533	·21106	·28720	·39142	·53426
64	·04404	·05978	·08126	·11032	·15081	·20591	·28157	·38563	·52897
65	·04195	·05721	·07813	·10688	·14641	·20089	·27605	·37993	·52373
66	·03995	·05474	·07513	·10326	·14215	·19599	·27064	·37432	·51855
67	·03805	·05239	·07224	·09977	·13801	·19121	·26533	·36879	·51341
68	·03624	·05013	·06946	·09640	·13399	·18654	·26013	·36334	·50833
69	·03451	·04797	·06679	·09314	·13009	·18199	·25503	·35797	·50330
70	·03287	·04591	·06422	·08999	·12630	·17755	·25003	·35268	·49831
71	·03130	·04393	·06175	·08694	·12262	·17322	·24513	·34747	·49338
72	·02981	·04204	·05937	·08400	·11905	·16900	·24032	·34233	·48850
73	·02839	·04023	·05709	·08116	·11558	·16488	·23561	·33727	·48366
74	·02704	·03849	·05490	·07842	·11221	·16085	·23099	·33229	·47887
75	·02575	·03684	·05278	·07577	·10895	·15693	·22646	·32738	·47413
76	·02453	·03525	·05075	·07320	·10577	·15310	·22202	·32254	·46944
77	·02336	·03373	·04880	·07073	·10269	·14937	·21766	·31778	·46479
78	·02225	·03228	·04692	·06834	·09970	·14573	·21340	·31308	·46019
79	·02119	·03089	·04512	·06603	·09680	·14217	·20921	·30845	·45563
80	·02018	·02956	·04338	·06379	·09398	·13870	·20511	·30389	·45112
81	·01922	·02829	·04172	·06164	·09124	·13532	·20109	·29940	·44665
82	·01830	·02707	·04011	·05955	·08858	·13202	·19715	·29497	·44223
83	·01743	·02590	·03857	·05754	·08600	·12880	·19328	·29062	·43785
84	·01660	·02479	·03709	·05559	·08350	·12566	·18949	·28632	·43352
85	·01581	·02372	·03566	·05371	·08107	·12259	·18577	·28209	·42922
86	·01506	·02270	·03429	·05190	·07870	·11960	·18213	·27792	·42497
87	·01434	·02172	·03297	·05014	·07641	·11668	·17856	·27381	·42077
88	·01366	·02079	·03170	·04845	·07419	·11384	·17506	·26977	·41660
89	·01301	·01989	·03048	·04681	·07203	·11106	·17163	·26578	·41248
90	·01239	·01903	·02931	·04522	·06993	·10836	·16826	·26185	·40839
91	·01180	·01821	·02818	·04369	·06789	·10571	·16496	·25798	·40435
92	·01124	·01743	·02710	·04222	·06591	·10313	·16173	·25417	·40034
93	·01070	·01668	·02606	·04079	·06399	·10062	·15856	·25041	·39638
94	·01019	·01596	·02505	·03941	·06213	·09817	·15545	·24671	·39246
95	·00971	·01527	·02409	·03808	·06032	·09577	·15240	·24307	·38857
96	·00924	·01462	·02316	·03679	·05856	·09344	·14941	·23948	·38472
97	·00880	·01399	·02272	·03555	·05686	·09116	·14648	·23594	·38091
98	·00838	·01338	·02142	·03434	·05520	·08893	·14361	·23245	·37714
99	·00798	·01281	·02059	·03318	·05359	·08676	·14079	·22901	·37341
100	·00760	·01226	·01980	·03206	·05203	·08465	·13803	·22563	·36971

Table C:— £1 per annum, accumulated at Compound Interest.

yrs	5%	4½%	4%	3½%	3%	2½%	2%	1½%	1%
1	1·000	1·000	1·000	1·000	1·000	1·000	1·000	1·000	1·000
2	2·050	2·045	2·040	2·035	2·030	2·025	2·020	2·015	2·010
3	3·152	3·137	3·121	3·106	3·091	3·075	3·060	3·045	3·030
4	4·310	4·278	4·246	4·215	4·183	4·152	4·122	4·091	4·060
5	5·525	5·471	5·416	5·362	5·309	5·256	5·204	5·152	5·101
6	6·802	6·717	6·633	6·550	6·468	6·388	6·308	6·230	6·152
7	8·142	8·019	7·898	7·779	7·662	7·547	7·434	7·323	7·214
8	9·549	9·380	9·214	9·052	8·892	8·736	8·583	8·433	8·286
9	11·026	10·802	10·583	10·368	10·159	9·954	9·755	9·559	9·369
10	12·578	12·288	12·006	11·731	11·464	11·203	10·949	10·703	10·462
11	14·207	13·841	13·486	13·142	12·808	12·483	12·169	11·863	11·567
12	15·917	15·464	15·026	14·602	14·192	13·795	13·412	13·041	12·683
13	17·713	17·160	16·627	16·113	15·618	15·140	14·680	14·237	13·809
14	19·598	18·932	18·292	17·677	17·086	16·519	15·974	15·450	14·947
15	21·578	20·784	20·023	19·296	18·599	17·932	17·293	16·682	16·097
16	23·657	22·719	21·824	20·971	20·157	19·380	18·639	17·932	17·258
17	25·840	24·742	23·697	22·705	21·761	20·865	20·012	19·201	18·430
18	28·132	26·855	25·645	24·500	23·414	22·386	21·412	20·489	19·615
19	30·539	29·063	27·671	26·357	25·117	23·946	22·841	21·797	20·811
20	33·066	31·371	29·778	28·280	26·870	25·545	24·297	23·124	22·019
21	35·719	33·783	31·969	30·269	28·676	27·183	25·783	24·471	23·239
22	38·505	36·303	34·248	32·329	30·537	28·863	27·299	25·838	24·472
23	41·430	38·937	36·618	34·460	32·453	30·584	28·845	27·225	25·716
24	44·502	41·689	39·083	36·667	34·426	32·349	30·422	28·634	26·973
25	47·727	44·565	41·646	38·950	36·459	34·158	32·030	30·063	28·243

Present value of £1 per Annum

yrs	5%	4½%	4%	3½%	3%	2½%	2%	1½%	1%
1	0·952	0·957	0·961	0·966	0·971	0·976	0·980	0·985	0·990
2	1·859	1·873	1·886	1·900	1·913	1·927	1·942	1·956	1·970
3	2·723	2·749	2·775	2·802	2·828	2·856	2·884	2·912	2·941
4	3·546	3·588	3·630	3·673	3·717	3·762	3·808	3·854	3·902
5	4·329	4·390	4·452	4·515	4·580	4·646	4·713	4·783	4·853
6	5·076	5·158	5·242	5·329	5·417	5·508	5·601	5·697	5·795
7	5·786	5·893	6·002	6·115	6·230	6·349	6·472	6·598	6·728
8	6·463	6·596	6·733	6·874	7·020	7·170	7·325	7·486	7·652
9	7·108	7·269	7·435	7·608	7·786	7·971	8·162	8·361	8·566
10	7·722	7·913	8·111	8·317	8·530	8·752	8·983	9·222	9·471
11	8·306	8·529	8·760	9·002	9·252	9·514	9·787	10·071	10·368
12	8·863	9·119	9·385	9·663	9·954	10·258	10·575	10·908	11·255
13	9·393	9·683	9·985	10·303	10·635	10·983	11·348	11·732	12·134
14	9·898	10·223	10·563	10·921	11·296	11·691	12·106	12·543	13·004
15	10·380	10·740	11·118	11·517	11·938	12·381	12·849	13·343	13·865
16	10·838	11·234	11·652	12·094	12·561	13·055	13·578	14·131	14·718
17	11·274	11·707	12·166	12·651	13·166	13·712	14·292	14·908	15·562
18	11·689	12·160	12·659	13·190	13·753	14·353	14·992	15·673	16·398
19	12·085	12·593	13·134	13·710	14·324	14·979	15·678	16·426	17·226
20	12·462	13·008	13·590	14·212	14·877	15·589	16·351	17·169	18·046
21	12·821	13·405	14·029	14·698	15·415	16·185	17·011	17·900	18·857
22	13·163	13·784	14·451	15·167	15·937	16·765	17·658	18·621	19·660
23	13·489	14·148	14·857	15·620	16·443	17·332	18·292	19·331	20·456
24	13·798	14·495	15·247	16·058	16·935	17·885	18·914	20·030	21·243
25	14·094	14·828	15·622	16·482	17·413	18·424	19·523	20·720	22·023

yrs	5%	4½%	4%	3½%	3%	2½%	2%	1½%	1%
1	1·05000	1·04500	1·04000	1·03500	1·03000	1·02500	1·02000	1·01500	1·01000
2	·53781	·53400	·53020	·52640	·52261	·51883	·51505	·51128	·50751
3	·36721	·36377	·36035	·35693	·35353	·35014	·34675	·34338	·34003
4	·28201	·27874	·27549	·27225	·26903	·26582	·26262	·25945	·25628
5	·23098	·22779	·22463	·22148	·21835	·21525	·21216	·20909	·20604
6	·19702	·19388	·19076	·18767	·18460	·18155	·17853	·17553	·17255
7	·17282	·16970	·16661	·16354	·16051	·15750	·15451	·15156	·14863
8	·15472	·15161	·14853	·14548	·14246	·13947	·13651	·13358	·13069
9	·14069	·13757	·13449	·13145	·12843	·12546	·12252	·11961	·11674
10	·12951	·12638	·12329	·12024	·11723	·11426	·11133	·10843	·10558
11	·12039	·11725	·11415	·11109	·10808	·10511	·10218	·09929	·09645
12	·11283	·10967	·10655	·10348	·10046	·09749	·09456	·09168	·08885
13	·10646	·10327	·10014	·09706	·09403	·09105	·08812	·08524	·08241
14	·10103	·09782	·09467	·09157	·08853	·08553	·08260	·07972	·07690
15	·09634	·09311	·08994	·08683	·08377	·08077	·07783	·07494	·07212
16	·09227	·08902	·08582	·08268	·07961	·07660	·07365	·07077	·06794
17	·08870	·08542	·08220	·07904	·07595	·07293	·06997	·06708	·06426
18	·08555	·08224	·07899	·07582	·07271	·06967	·06670	·06381	·06098
19	·08275	·07941	·07614	·07294	·06981	·06676	·06378	·06088	·05805
20	·08024	·07688	·07358	·07036	·06722	·06415	·06116	·05825	·05542
21	·07800	·07460	·07128	·06804	·06487	·06179	·05878	·05587	·05303
22	·07597	·07255	·06920	·06593	·06275	·05965	·05663	·05370	·05086
23	·07414	·07068	·06731	·06402	·06081	·05770	·05467	·05173	·04889
24	·07247	·06899	·06559	·06227	·05905	·05591	·05287	·04992	·04707
25	·07095	·06744	·06401	·06067	·05743	·05427	·05122	·04826	·04541
26	·06956	·06602	·06257	·05921	·05594	·05277	·04970	·04673	·04387
27	·06829	·06472	·06124	·05785	·05456	·05138	·04829	·04532	·04245
28	·06712	·06352	·06001	·05660	·05329	·05009	·04699	·04400	·04112
29	·06605	·06242	·05888	·05544	·05211	·04891	·04578	·04278	·03990
30	·06505	·06139	·05783	·05437	·05102	·04778	·04465	·04164	·03875
31	·06413	·06044	·05686	·05337	·05000	·04674	·04360	·04057	·03768
32	·06328	·05956	·05595	·05244	·04905	·04577	·04261	·03958	·03667
33	·06249	·05875	·05510	·05157	·04816	·04486	·04169	·03864	·03573
34	·06176	·05798	·05432	·05076	·04732	·04401	·04082	·03776	·03484
35	·06107	·05727	·05358	·05000	·04654	·04321	·04000	·03693	·03400
36	·06043	·05661	·05289	·04928	·04580	·04245	·03923	·03615	·03321
37	·05984	·05598	·05224	·04861	·04511	·04174	·03851	·03541	·03247
38	·05928	·05540	·05163	·04798	·04446	·04107	·03782	·03472	·03176
39	·05877	·05486	·05106	·04739	·04384	·04044	·03717	·03405	·03109
40	·05828	·05434	·05052	·04683	·04326	·03984	·03656	·03343	·03046
41	·05782	·05386	·05002	·04630	·04272	·03927	·03597	·03283	·02985
42	·05740	·05341	·04954	·04580	·04219	·03873	·03542	·03226	·02928
43	·05699	·05298	·04909	·04533	·04170	·03822	·03489	·03172	·02873
44	·05662	·05258	·04866	·04488	·04123	·03773	·03439	·03121	·02820
45	·05626	·05220	·04826	·04445	·04079	·03726	·03391	·03072	·02771
46	·05593	·05185	·04788	·04405	·04036	·03683	·03345	·03025	·02723
47	·05561	·05151	·04752	·04367	·03996	·03641	·03302	·02980	·02677
48	·05532	·05119	·04718	·04331	·03958	·03601	·03260	·02938	·02633
49	·05504	·05089	·04686	·04296	·03921	·03562	·03220	·02897	·02592
50	·05478	·05060	·04655	·04263	·03887	·03526	·03182	·02857	·02551

REPAYMENT BY EQUAL INSTALMENTS.

The required Instalment (also the Income or Pension purchasable per £1 expended) is obtained by multiplying the sum lent (after converting *s. d.* into decimals of £1) by the appropriate figures in Tables D or E.

Thus @ 4%, £200 is cleared off in 7 years by 7 annual payments of £200 × ·16661 = £33·322 ; or 14 half-yearly of £200 × ·08260 = £16·520 ; or 28 quarterly of £200 × ·04112 = £8·224.

Principal and Interest in an Instalment. This is given by Table B for every yearly payment ; or for half-yearly payments, every *second* half-year.

Rule—Multiply the amount of the instalment by the Present Value of £1 for the No. of INSTALMENTS (inclusive) unpaid ; the answer is **the Principal** repaid in the Instalment, and the balance the Interest.

Thus in the examples above, the 6th annual or 11th half-yearly instalment—5 and 10 respectively already paid, leaving 2 and 4 (=2 years) due—pays off capital £33·332 × ·92456, and £16·520 × ·92385. The Interest is the balance of the instal't.

Table D:—Weekly, Fortnightly, Monthly, and Quarterly Payments.

Weekly		Fortnightly		Monthly		Quarterly (4 Instal'ts per year)				
Wk.	5%	Fort.	5%	Mos	5%	Yrs. 5%	4½%	4%	3½%	3%
4	·25060	2	·50144	3	·33611	1 ·25786	·25707	·25628	·25549	·25471
8	·12554	4	·25120	4	·25261	2 ·13213	·13141	·13069	·12997	·12926
10	·10053	6	·16779	5	·20251	3 ·09026	·08955	·08885	·08815	·08745
12	·08385	8	·12608	6	·16911	4 ·06935	·06864	·06794	·06725	·06656
13	·07744	10	·10106	7	·14525	5 ·05682	·05612	·05542	·05472	·05403
16	·06301	12	·08438	8	·12736	6 ·04849	·04778	·04707	·04638	·04568
20	·05050	13	·07796	9	·11344	7 ·04255	·04183	·04112	·04042	·03973
24	·04217	14	·07246	10	·10231	8 ·03811	·03739	·03667	·03596	·03527
26	·03896	16	·06352	11	·09320	9 ·03467	·03394	·03321	·03250	·03180
30	·03383	18	·05657	12	·08561	10 ·03192	·03118	·03046	·02974	·02903

Table E:—Yearly and Half-yearly Payments, for £1.

	Yearly Instalments (1 per yr.)						Half-yearly Instal'ts (2 ♥ yr.)			
Yrs.	5%	4½%	4%	3½%	3%	2½%	5%	4½%	4%	3½%
1	1·0500	1·0450	1·0400	1·0350	1·0300	1·0250	·51883	·51694	·51505	·51316
2	·53780	·53400	·53020	·52640	·52261	·51883	·26592	·26422	·26262	·26103
3	·36721	·36377	·36035	·35693	·35353	·35014	·18155	·18004	·17853	·17702
4	·28201	·27874	·27549	·27225	·26903	·26582	·13947	·13798	·13651	·13504
5	·23097	·22779	·22463	·22148	·21835	·21525	·11426	·11279	·11133	·10988
6	·19702	·19388	·19076	·18767	·18460	·18155	·09749	·09602	·09456	·09311
7	·17282	·16970	·16661	·16354	·16051	·15750	·08554	·08406	·08260	·08116
8	·15472	·15161	·14853	·14548	·14246	·13947	·07660	·07512	·07365	·07220
9	·14069	·13757	·13449	·13145	·12843	·12546	·06967	·06818	·06670	·06524
10	·12950	·12638	·12329	·12024	·11723	·11426	·06415	·06264	·06116	·05969
11	·12039	·11725	·11415	·11109	·10808	·10511	·05965	·05813	·05663	·05516
12	·11283	·10967	·10655	·10348	·10046	·09749	·05591	·05438	·05287	·05139
13	·10646	·10328	·10014	·09706	·09403	·09105	·05277	·05122	·04970	·04820
14	·10102	·09782	·09467	·09157	·08853	·08554	·05009	·04853	·04699	·04548
15	·09634	·09311	·08994	·08688	·08377	·08077	·04778	·04620	·04465	·04313
16	·09227	·08902	·08582	·08268	·07961	·07660	·04577	·04417	·04261	·04108
17	·08870	·08542	·08220	·07904	·07595	·07293	·04401	·04240	·04082	·03927
18	·08555	·08224	·07899	·07582	·07271	·06967	·04245	·04083	·03923	·03768
19	·08275	·07941	·07614	·07294	·06981	·06676	·04107	·03943	·03782	·03625
20	·08024	·07688	·07358	·07036	·06722	·06415	·03984	·03818	·03656	·03497
21	·07800	·07460	·07128	·06804	·06487	·06179	·03873	·03705	·03542	·03382
22	·07597	·07255	·06920	·06593	·06275	·05965	·03773	·03604	·03439	·03278
23	·07414	·07068	·06731	·06402	·06081	·05770	·03683	·03512	·03345	·03183
24	·07247	·06899	·06559	·06227	·05905	·05591	·03601	·03428	·03260	·03097
25	·07095	·06744	·06401	·06067	·05743	·05428	·03526	·03352	·03182	·03017